C000302479

The Technical and Legal Guide to the UK Oil and Gas Industry

The Technical and Legal Guide to the UK Oil and Gas Industry

Editors:

John Wils and Ewan C. Neilson

ABERLOUR
PRESS

First published in 2007 by
Aberlour Press Limited
34 Albyn Place
Aberdeen AB10 1FW

www.aberlour-press.com

ISBN 978-0-9556223-0-4

The law is stated as at 1 May 2007.

To avoid distraction to the reader, Aberlour Press house style invokes the Interpretation Act 1978, so that the masculine forms 'he', 'him' and 'his' are used throughout: all such references are intended to be read as gender neutral.

British Library Cataloguing-in-Publication Data
A catalogue record for this book is available on request from the British Library

Typeset by Waverley Typesetters, Fakenham
Manufactured in Slovenia
Cover design by Artech Visual Communication

This book is dedicated to
Pamela, Robbie, Calum, Rory

CONTENTS

CONTRIBUTORS

Editors

DR JOHN WILS
Technical Consultant (Oil and Gas) Stronachs; formerly Aberdeen Director, UKOOA

EWAN C NEILSON
Partner and Head of Corporate/Commercial Department, Stronachs

Contributors

DEREK BLAIKLEY
Consultant, Gas and Energy

RICHARD CONWAY
Manager: Special Projects, Expro

CHRIS DUDGEON
Managing Director, OTM Consulting

PAUL DYMOND
Operations Director, Oil & Gas UK

KEITH EASTWOOD
Associate, OTM Consulting

JOHN EVANS
Retired Assistant Director, HMRC; Head of North Sea oil taxation policy team, HMRC, 2001 to 2005

DR C J FREEMAN
Managing Director, Prosperous Energy Ltd

MARTIN FREEMAN
Head of Engineering, BG-Group

KEITH GORDON
Operations Manager, Petrofac at Dubai Petroleum

AUSTIN HAND
General Manager, EP Projects, Shell Exploration and Production, Shell UK Ltd

RICHARD HEARD
Subsea Director, Xodus Group Limited

JOHN KEARNS
Managing Director, Kearns & Associates Ltd

PROFESSOR ALEX KEMP
Professor of Petroleum Economics, University of Aberdeen

CHRIS LINSKAILL
Formerly Goldeneye Asset Manager, now co-leads Weisenborn-Linskaill Associates

PROFESSOR C PAUL MITCHELL
Director of Institute of Energy Technologies, University of Aberdeen

DR JOYCE NEILSON
Consultant Geologist, Carbonate Reservoirs Ltd; also at Department of Geology and Petroleum Geology, University of Aberdeen

ROBERT PATERSON
Safety Issues Manager, Oil & Gas UK; previously with HSE

ALISTAIR PORTER
Process Engineering Manager, Xodus Group Ltd

MIKE PORTER
Managing Director, SBS Logistics Ltd

STEVE REDGRAVE
Director, Drillers.com Inc

PETER ROWE
Formerly Senior Geoscientist: DTI

DR ANNE M SCHWAB
Senior Lecturer in Geophysics, Department of Geology and Petroleum Geology, University of Aberdeen; currently at GeoSismique Consulting

LINDA STEPHEN
Research Fellow in Petroleum Economics, University of Aberdeen

SVEN TIEFENTHAL
Senior Partner, TRACS International

WILLIE TONER
Commercial Specialist, Petrofac Resources

NICOL WEBSTER
Director, Rowanhill Consultants Ltd

STRONACHS

Production Team

DR CAROLE DALGLEISH · LAWRIE LAW · GRAHAM LUMSDEN
KAREN HOWATSON · CHRISTINE GANE · WENDY PRINGLE

FOREWORD

The UK oil and gas industry is one of this country's best kept secrets. Its contribution to the national economy has been, and continues to be, immense yet its activities are generally not well known – or understood – by the public at large.

This is not entirely surprising, because most of the industry's activities take place over the horizon, in the sometimes hostile offshore environment. Its infrastructure of over 300 installations is accessible mainly by helicopter – and only to those who work around the clock to supply this country with an uninterrupted flow of oil and gas, which currently meets around 70% of our primary energy needs.

Oil and gas from the UK's seabed reserves have provided security of supply for much of the past three decades and will continue to meet a significant proportion of future demand. There is, however, scant knowledge of the tremendous engineering achievement and technical expertise employed by the 36,000 people working offshore and the 350,000 people who work onshore throughout the oil and gas industry supply chain, from one end of the country to the other.

Today the industry faces mounting challenges. To date, just over 36 billion barrels of oil and gas have been recovered, with an estimated 25 billion barrels still to be extracted. Yet, the now mature UK sector has to compete more than ever to attract the investment and resources it will need to recover these reserves, and this in the face of sharply rising exploration, development and production costs.

Maximising recovery of our indigenous reserves in the years to come makes great economic sense. The government's Energy White Paper, published in spring 2007, confirms that oil and gas will remain our dominant source of primary energy for many decades. The Department for Business, Enterprise and Regulatory Reform predicts that by 2020, 79% of primary energy will come from hydrocarbons (up from 74% today). What is not produced domestically will have to be imported, at a cost.

A significant part of the solution will lie in new offshore exploration and smaller field developments led, increasingly, by new entrant companies, utilising innovative technologies, and linking in with existing infrastructure. If we are to maintain current production rates, however, we will need one new development to come on-stream every three weeks, requiring a sharper, more focused industry which can turn around opportunities with far greater speed than in the past.

There is a perception that the complexities of doing business in the North Sea involve a degree of technical, commercial and legal risk, which can lead to missed opportunities – opportunities that could have been seized, had there been a wider understanding of the issues involved and an ability to address them at an early stage.

For many, this lack of understanding presents a barrier to negotiating successfully around the challenges faced in the UK Continental Shelf today. This book has been compiled to address this problem. It has been set out chapter by chapter in a sequence that reflects the typical order of activities followed by new field developments, supported by chapters on, for example, hydrocarbon export and transportation, health and safety, working in the oil and gas industry and on the renewable energy industry. Each chapter has been written as a stand-alone topic by experts in their particular discipline as an introductory guide to the subject.

Whilst there have been many books written on technical matters relating to this industry, I believe this is the first book that addresses both legal and technical concerns and, as such, provides a unique perspective of the issues that are central to the future success of our truly magnificent industry.

MALCOLM WEBB
Chief Executive, Oil and Gas UK
August 2007

PREFACE

The creation, writing and production of this book has been a joint industry project involving 44 authors, 22 companies and institutions, a six-person production team and, by the time of publication, three years of hard work. It is also a unique publication in that it has been produced by a small publishing company, Aberlour Press Limited, based in the North East of Scotland. This acknowledgement of all the people who have helped to make this book possible would extend to several pages if I named all the individuals who have been involved. The book itself highlights what can be achieved within the UK oil and gas industry. So many people can, and have, worked with a common end and community spirit for so long with limited reward to produce such an end product. I take the opportunity to thank everyone involved.

This book would not have been possible without the leadership, industry understanding and sheer tenacity of Dr John Wils and the support, expertise and aptitude of Dr Joyce Neilson throughout. John and I created the vision but John and Joyce delivered on it. There is also a special thanks to Simon Toole, Director, Licensing, Exploration and Development of the Department for Business, Enterprise and Regulatory Reform (formerly the DTI) and Paul Dymond of UK Oil & Gas who have given us much help and encouragement during the project. I would also like to thank Chris Linskaill for endorsing the project, giving us guidance and giving us great support throughout. The concept was borne out of a common desire to provide a holistic and introductory guide to a number of technical subjects; there was no other technical and legal guide to the UK oil and gas industry. In fact, it started as a series of lectures on various subjects within Stronachs. It was a bold step to write a book which joined science, engineering and law and which relied on the support of so many companies and people. It was also a substantial risk for the production team to undertake this task and the unique challenges this book created.

Without the unswerving support and enormous drive of our publishing consultant, Dr Carole Dalgleish who, along with Graham Lumsden, our typesetter, worked for several weeks without any break, the book would not have been published. Carole's assistance in educating us all as to how to become a publishing company, through to managing the editorial process to organising and proof reading the whole book was a remarkable achievement. Lawrie Law, as production manager, provided essential commercial and technical advice to get the book into print. Christine Gane worked ceaselessly over the three years to organise and arrange different aspects of the book's production and was a common link with all authors. Christine also obtained permissions for over 200 diagrams and photographs, indexed the book and was involved in all aspects of the production of the book. I would also like to thank Wendy Pringle of Stronachs who organised so many of the events and meetings as well as arranging the marketing of the book and Karen Howatson who did a sterling job correcting first proofs. Thank you to River Design, Artech and Niki Photography who provided some of the designs, illustrations, photographs and art work for the book and for Aberlour Press Limited.

Books are also produced because someone risks capital and provides the manpower to make it possible. Stronachs have provided all the capital for this book and for Aberlour Press Limited and provided the manpower without which, this book could not have been written. Eighteen lawyers in Stronachs wrote the legal sections to the chapters and contributed to some of the organigrams, giving up substantial amounts of their free time. I would like to especially thank David Sheach, Managing Partner for providing the support to make this happen and also for contributing a number of chapters. James Downie, Gillian Donald and Jim Merson, who are partners in Stronachs, also wrote parts of the book and did so whilst under pressure to fulfil other commitments; to them I would like to extend my enduring thanks. I would also like to thank individually Tom Mullen (partner in Stronachs), David Forfar, Ingrid McKay, Anna Strong, James Muir, Natalie Stevenson and Emma Wakeford for writing parts of sections, proof reading and their support in the whole project. Further thanks to Malcolm Donald, Sonia Love, Johanna Rae, Laura Petrie and Alan Clark for helping with writing and proof reading. There were a number of external contributors who helped on the legal side by providing advice, writing some parts and reviewing our work and they include Willie Tonner, Dick Pearce, John Gregory, Jeb Tyrie and June Gemmell. I would also like to thank Richard Gravenstede for quietly managing the finance of the project and ensuring its liquidity.

The contributors on the technical parts to the chapters provided not only written material but also their unwavering support in what became an ambitious project. When John and I explained the concept to those contributors there was never any question from any of them as to whether the project was possible and I am truly surprised that, in an industry where companies compete, there was so much co-operation and community spirit. I would like to take the opportunity of thanking all those authors and contributors as we appreciate that writing a chapter does not take just a few days, it often takes a number of weeks with substantial revising, editing and proof reading. I would also like to thank the organisations that have provided encouragement in the process and these include the Department for Business, Enterprise and Regulatory Reform (formerly the Department of Trade and Industry), Oil & Gas UK, different schools of the University of Aberdeen, different departments within Shell and BP, BG-Group, Expro Group, OTM Consulting, Petrofac, Bristow Helicopters, TRACKS, SBS Logistics Limited, Schlumberger, Xodus Group Limited, Health and Safety Executive and Drilling Research Institute.

Finally, I would like to thank family and friends of the editors, production team, contributors and support staff as their quiet help and encouragement in the background provided the opportunity for this book to be produced.

EWAN C. NEILSON
Stronachs, Aberdeen
29 June 2007

— 1 —

UK OIL AND GAS INDUSTRY OVERVIEW

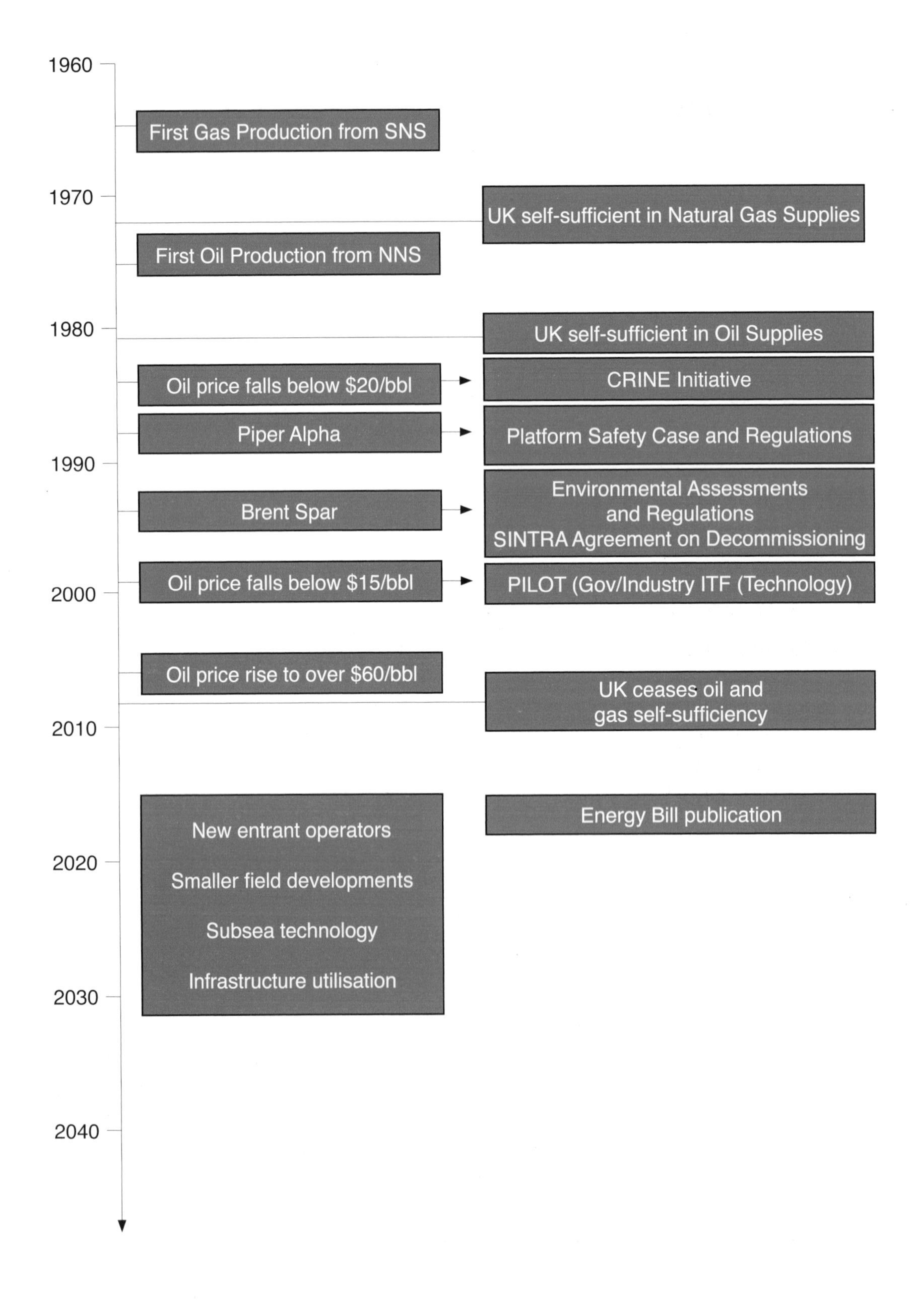

1960
1970
1980
1990
2000
2010
2020
2030
2040
First Gas Production from SNS
UK self-sufficient in Natural Gas Supplies
First Oil Production from NNS
UK self-sufficient in Oil Supplies
Oil price falls below $20/bbl
CRINE Initiative
Piper Alpha
Platform Safety Case and Regulations
Brent Spar
Environmental Assessments and Regulations SINTRA Agreement on Decommissioning
Oil price falls below $15/bbl
PILOT (Gov/Industry ITF (Technology)
Oil price rise to over $60/bbl
UK ceases oil and gas self-sufficiency
Energy Bill publication
New entrant operators
Smaller field developments
Subsea technology
Infrastructure utilisation

UK OIL AND GAS INDUSTRY OVERVIEW

1.1 The UK oil and gas industry

The UK oil and gas industry has been described as the UK's greatest industrial success story since the Second World War. It arrived at a time when the UK was facing an energy crisis and one of the darkest periods in its economic history. Shortage of energy resulted in a three-day working week in the 1970s, and a country reliant on dwindling 'town' gas and imported oil. If we had not had the good fortune to discover oil and gas offshore in the North Sea, the UK would have undoubtedly remained on course to become a nation with a significantly weakened economy.

Over the last 40 years, the oil companies have invested in excess of £220 billion in the discovery of oil and gas from UK offshore locations and the building of the huge offshore infrastructure for the supply of approximately 75% of our primary energy needs. Such investment is equivalent to building more than 12 Channel Tunnels.

The results of this investment have made the UK self-sufficient in both oil and gas since the early 1980s. Today, we are still just balancing our supply versus demand for oil consumption but will shortly cease to be self-sufficient. With continued investment by the oil companies, our indigenous supplies could still meet more than 90% of oil demand and 60% of gas demand in 2010.

Petroleum revenue taxes paid to the Treasury by the oil companies have amounted, by 2007, to some £215 billion which would have been sufficient to fund the National Health Service for over 10 years.

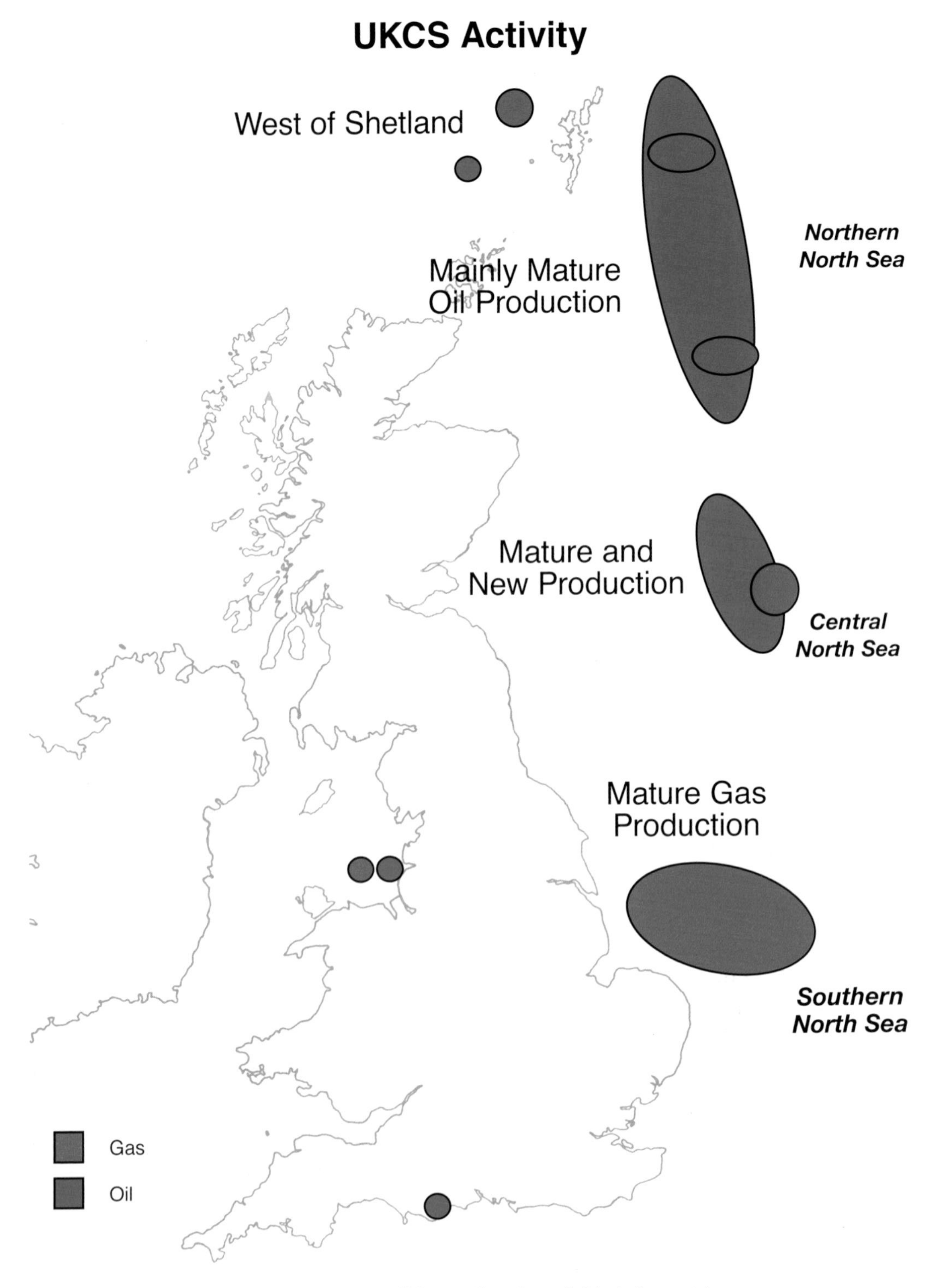

Figure 1–1 UK offshore oil and gas fields (schematic)

The international oil and gas industry had been developing for over 100 years before making its impact in the UK North Sea, and therefore the technical and logistical needs for exploration, drilling and production were well understood by the oil companies. It was actually due to the discovery of a huge onshore gas field in Schlochteren in Holland that the oil companies started to speculate that similar gas-bearing geology might exist under the North Sea. The hunt for gas started in the Southern sector of the North Sea in the early 1960s (Fig. 1–1).

The techniques for exploration and production of oil and gas will be described in more detail in subsequent chapters. The purpose of this chapter is to map out the significant milestones and events that have shaped the industry to make it such a significant contributor to the UK economy. The more detailed explanations of each stage, from exploration to production, will follow in later chapters written by various experts.

1.2 Southern North Sea activities

To determine the presence of oil and gas trapped and under pressure in porous rock some 2 miles down in the ground is a challenging and costly business in even the most benign onshore environment. It requires transporting a large drilling rig, equipment and teams of people to a remote location with the objective of keeping the operation running 24 hours a day and 7 days a week, with minimum downtime. The daily rate for such a venture is costly and paid by the oil company. There is no guarantee of a successful find, thus it is always a high financial risk venture.

Achieving the same objective by exploratory drilling in the hostile offshore environment of the Southern North Sea added considerably more challenges for the oil companies in the early 1960s. Offshore drilling involves the same deployment of people, materials and a jack-up drilling rig that is towed to the defined location. The rig is then lifted above the maximum anticipated wave height by ratcheting its legs to the sea bed to allow a stable platform for drilling to be undertaken.

This technique had been used successfully in other parts of the world since the 1950s, especially in the shallow waters of the Gulf of Mexico. More and more rigs were being built for this service when it became clear that more oil and gas fields would be found offshore.

Fleets of specially converted vessels, designed to transport materials needed to drill and construct the well safely, were also coming out of shipyards around the world. Moving people between the shore and rig by helicopter was also commonly used in offshore locations, but necessitated increased helicopter activities and procedures, including survival training for everyone working offshore.

Water depths in the Southern North Sea are about 30 m (100 ft), and this was well within the range of these jack-up rigs. Suddenly, a new industry had emerged in the 1960s, with Great Yarmouth as the major centre for this new activity.

Unfortunately, the rigs imported from other areas of the world were found to be insufficient in strength for the hostile conditions of the North Sea. With the Ocean Gem broken up in a severe gale and the Sea Gem toppled due to metal fatigue, both with considerable fatalities, a new, upgraded generation of jack-up rig emerged to withstand such conditions.

The first successful commercial gas find in the UK sector of the North Sea was made by BP, others followed, made by Shell, Amoco, Phillips, Arco and Conoco.

The next step for all these companies was to negotiate the sale of this energy from the North Sea. The British Gas Council had a monopoly to purchase this 'natural' gas for onward transportation to the customers. Long-term contracts involving daily delivery volumes and specification, measured at their new gas terminals at Bacton, Easington and Dimlington, were drawn up after exhaustive legal negotiations.

Only on successful conclusion of each of the long-term agreements were the oil companies able to commit to the capital cost of building the facilities to produce and process the gas offshore, deliver it through a subsea pipeline to an onshore terminal for final processing and measurement prior to arrival at the British Gas receiving terminal.

A new offshore construction industry emerged, led by international engineering design houses. The legs of the platforms were constructed as one steel unit known as the jacket and transported offshore by barge and secured into the seabed.

The living quarters, helideck and gas processing facilities were built as separate modules in construction yards around the world and each positioned on its jacket to make up the offshore platform facility. A second steel jacket was also normally positioned close to the platform to accommodate the gas wells as they were drilled to various separate locations in the gas reservoir some 2 miles beneath the seabed.

A jack-up rig could then be brought alongside the wellhead platform and the drilling derrick cantilevered over the wellhead jacket to drill the wells for the production of gas. The two platform structures are linked by a steel bridge supporting the flowlines transporting the gas from the wellheads to the platform processing facilities.

The purpose of the processing systems is to remove the water from the gas to avoid the formation of hydrates, which is a chemical reaction that takes place when wet gas under pressure cools to form an ice-like substance which prevent the gas from flowing through pipelines and flowlines.

The rest of these platforms were designed to include the life-supporting systems such as power generation, crew accommodation, and the numerous safety and life-saving systems similar to any vessel at sea.

Large-diameter pipelines from the various fields were laid to transport the gas to the onshore terminals. As additional platforms were built, they were linked into their respective operated pipelines.

As platforms came on stream, and the gas from the North Sea was delivered to the British Gas Council, the UK was slowly converted from the dwindling supplies of 'town' gas to the new and cleaner energy known as the 'friendly flame' from the North Sea. By the mid-1970s, the UK started to become self-sufficient in its own natural gas supplies.

1.3 Central and Northern North Sea activities

As the major oil companies began to gain more experience of the harsh environment of the North Sea, their exploration programmes included the more northern areas in the East Shetland Basin. Here, a water depth of about 200 metres and a distance from shore in excess of 100 miles provided significantly greater challenges.

A new breed of drilling rigs was mobilised for this task. Unlike the ability to utilise jack-up rigs in the shallower waters of the Southern North Sea, deep-water drilling needs floating rigs known as semi-submersibles which use ballasted pontoons to remain stable. These units are kept accurately on location by a number of anchors or dynamic positioning systems, and are capable of working in relatively stormy conditions.

The remoteness of such locations also requires a high level of logistical planning to ensure all skills, equipment, and supplies are continuously available to avoid costly periods of downtime. At costs of around £100,000 per day to hire such units, communications and support continues 24 hours per day to maintain a constant update on the status of the well-drilling programme and to anticipate any potential problems that may arise.

As the UK continued to suffer a major economic crisis, and with heavy reliance on importing highly priced oil for fuel supplies, the news of the discovery of BP's Forties field in 1970 and Shell's Brent field in 1971, both with reserves of over 1 billion barrels of oil, could not have come at a better time for the UK.

Continued exploration in the deeper northern waters of the North Sea resulted in many more discoveries being made. The UK North Sea was fast becoming a significantly sized oil province, but was also fortuitously making the UK self-sufficient in oil supplies. It remained in this position until 2005.

At this point it is worth noting that, in the business of exploration and production of oil and gas, we are dealing with the same components, known collectively as hydrocarbons. The differing depth, pressure and temperature of the source rock type will dictate the composition of the product in the well bore.

In the Southern North Sea, the product is gas with a light oil known as 'condensate'. In the northern areas of the North Sea, oil varies in composition from light to more heavily viscous types. Oil is transported up the well bore by the associated gas under the initial reservoir pressure. Various gas/liquid phase changes take place as the oil and gas proceed on their journey up the well bore. It is the work of the geologists and petroleum engineers to understand and predict such information.

A further product of the reservoir is water which can cause well performance problems but, more critically, can create serious corrosive problems both in the well bore and in the surface production facilities or pipelines. It is, therefore, important that steps are taken to treat or remove the produced water at the earliest opportunity in the process.

It follows that the technical problems in locating and producing oil or gas are similar, but the differences can lie in the environment and locations where such activities may take place.

Prior to exporting the oil to an onshore terminal, the water and gas need to be removed, and this requires the positioning of production process platforms. Unlike those in the shallower waters of the Southern North Sea, structures over 200 metres tall needed to be towed out to location. Some of the early structures were built of concrete legs with oil storage cells, whilst others were built of larger steel jackets than those of the southern gas platforms.

The processing facilities are designed to separate the oil, gas and water. The produced water is cleaned to European standards before being discharged to the sea. The gas is either treated and compressed for gas export sales to a pipeline or re-injected to aid reservoir recovery. Strict regulations apply to any volumes of gas that are flared. Whilst the objectives of separation of the oil, gas and water are the same as oil production facilities anywhere in the world, the actual design will always depend on the field characteristics.

Permanent drilling facilities were also incorporated to continue to drill the production wells to be connected to the platform production facilities.

Typical North Sea oil production platforms built in the 1970s could accommodate up to 250 persons to drill, produce, process and export the oil via pipeline or remote tanker loading. If further increases were required in the labour force, they were accommodated on converted drilling rigs moored alongside and known as flotels.

Platform construction and start-up activities continued throughout the 1970s and 1980s, leading to an infrastructure of over 200 such installations. At its peak of activity, there were around 20,000 persons per week working in the UK sector of the North Sea.

By the beginning of the 1980s the UK was not only self-sufficient in its 77 million tons per year oil consumption needs, it also had a net surplus of 50 million tons per year available for export. The UK was producing 4% of the world's oil.

The price of crude oil remained at around $35 a barrel. This was due to deliberate cutbacks by OPEC members and tensions between Iraq and Iran.

1.4 Events that shaped the culture of the UK industry

From the mid-1980s, three events occurred which were to put the North Sea under world spotlight in its response.

During the early 1980s, OPEC started to experience difficulties in aligning its members on maintaining agreed production quotas and the price of crude oil fell to $14 per barrel by 1986. Projects waiting to be approved were simply not economic at this level. Drilling activities stopped and there were prospects of earlier abandonment of existing North Sea fields.

OPEC's resolve to maintain discipline on production quotas stabilised the oil price at $18 per barrel the following year. This stability, together with the UK's resolve to find ways of reducing the excessive capital spending through an initiative known as CRINE (Cost Reduction in a New Era), eventually proved that most projects could proceed. This set world standards in co-operation between operators and contractors to improve efficiencies in capital and operating costs.

Since then, this culture has continued, with contractors progressively taking more leadership roles in managing the engineering, construction and operations of offshore facilities, leaving the oil companies to concentrate on the business of exploration and reservoir management and, of course, financing the projects.

The second major event happened in 1988 when 167 lives were lost on Piper Alpha in the world's worse offshore disaster. A number of communication problems between various groups both on the platform and on a nearby platform linked by pipeline created a series of escalating incidents which led to such a tragic loss of lives.

A far-reaching Public Inquiry followed, under the leadership of Lord Cullen. His recommendations resulted in the development of the platform 'Safety Case' which now underpins design, construction, operations and management of UK offshore facilities. Without approval for each of these phases, which is given by the Offshore Safety Division of the Health and Safety Executive, there is no legal approval to proceed.

The Safety Case for an installation is documented evidence that a rigorous hazard and operability study has been carried out on every part of the facility to ensure that all potential hazards have been identified and reasonable steps have been taken to mitigate such hazards. This technical study is underpinned by a

'Safety Management System' which provides clear statements by the platform operators of accountability for the whole management of projects and operations which take place within their organisation.

The Inquiry and actions taken in the aftermath of Piper Alpha changed the whole safety culture in the North Sea, from regulations imposed upon the industry to a situation with the need for individual companies to demonstrate to the satisfaction of the law their ability to operate safely.

The third major event occurred in 1995 when Greenpeace challenged Shell on its decision to dispose of Brent Spar. This unit had been in use for oil export via tanker loading during the early days of production from the Brent field. When the Brent pipeline to Sullom Voe came into service, Brent Spar was now rendered redundant. Shell had, therefore, intended to tow it out to deep waters and dump it.

In spite of all precautions taken over removal of all oil and the approvals in place from the appropriate government authorities, Shell was caught unawares by a very public demonstration by Greenpeace attempting to board the unit illegally, to prevent such plans. All of this took place under the eyes of the world's press.

Whilst Shell methodically proved that the dumping of Brent Spar would have no adverse effect on the environment, Greenpeace had taken the opportunity to cast doubts in the minds of the general public as to the offshore oil industry's stewardship of the environment and the whole issue of decommissioning of offshore facilities.

Furthermore, there was a realisation, not only by Shell, but by the whole offshore industry, that there needed to be greater transparency in their offshore activities if they were to gain the support of the general public.

At the time of Brent Spar there was no UK legislation in place for prosecution of oil companies for pollution of the seas. There were only recommendations and guidelines applicable to all users of the sea. Over the following years, regulations have been introduced by which prosecutions can be brought against oil companies operating offshore in UK waters. This will be dealt with in more detail in later chapters.

Furthermore, oil companies operating in UK waters are obliged to submit an environmental impact assessment for each step of the development of offshore activities from exploration drilling through production to decommissioning. Some 10 years after the submission of the first platform Safety Case and subsequent world standards set in offshore safety, a similar process has been adopted for demonstration of mitigation of environmental risk.

Environmental Impact Assessments again became prominent as activities for exploration and development started to gather pace in the deeper waters west of Shetland. Further challenges by Greenpeace prompted the debate as to whether such environmental approvals were legal under European legislation, in spite of evidence that the standards required by the UK regulatory system were in fact more rigid than European requirements. To justify this, it was necessary to go through the European parliamentary approvals before resuming activities. This cost the industry a further two years to steer its way through the bureaucracy.

The culture of cost control following the oil price collapse in 1986, safety awareness following the disaster of Piper Alpha and environmental awareness following Brent Spar have demonstrated how oil companies and contractors can respond quickly and positively alongside external regulators to sustain the industry for the foreseeable future. The response to these events has also shown that a win–win culture between operators and contractors can develop.

1.5 West of Shetland

In the early 1990s, exploration was being conducted in even deeper waters, approximately 1500 ft, in an area west of Shetland, and has resulted in the production of the Schiehallion and Foinaven field developments by BP.

This was a significant development in a new area which required the subsea installation of all the wellheads and associated facilities to be connected back to a floating production facility with offshore tanker loading. Needless to say, this development required significant co-operation with the local environmental groups concerned as to the possibilities of potential oil pollution. Until this time, all environmental approvals were carried out by the DTI. As described in the previous section, Greenpeace and other non-governmental organisations campaigned once again to have such developments regulated by the European Union. The process resulted in approximately two years' delay to the project with, arguably, no improvements to environmental standards.

A further phased development known as the Clair field is taking place in the area and will use the exiting infrastructure.

1.6 The English Channel

Concurrent with activities in the North Sea, British Gas were active in developing an oilfield, known as Wytch Farm, comprising of three separate oil reservoirs under Poole Harbour and Poole Bay in Dorset. The asset was transferred to BP as operator in the mid-1980s.

The initial development plans proposed an artificial island in the bay. However, by pursuing advances in drilling technology, and with considerable environmental and economic benefits, the wells were drilled from an onshore site. The oil-gathering station and development is Western Europe's largest onshore oil field in one of the most environmentally sensitive areas of the UK.

1.7 The Irish Sea

Other gas fields were also being developed by British Gas in the mid-1980s in much shallower waters of the Irish Sea, 25 miles west of Blackpool. South Morecambe gas field started supplying gas in 1985 and North Morecambe came on line in 1994. Both fields produce to a terminal in Barrow-in-Furness and today still supply approximately 8% of the UK's peak gas demand.

In 2004, the Rivers fields owned by Burlington Resources came on line and also produce to Barrow terminal.

Further activity in the Irish Sea continued in Liverpool Bay in the mid-1990s with the development of BHP Billiton Petroleum's largest operated asset which comprised the integrated development of five offshore oil and gas fields. The gas terminal at the Point of Ayr in North Wales processes the gas for fuel for E.ON UK's combined cycle gas turbine power station at Connah's Quay in North Wales. The oil is exported by offshore storage and tanker-loading facility.

1.8 Positioning for the next 40 years

At the turn of the century, North Sea oil production had peaked at over 2 million barrels per day, but it was clear that production rates were declining faster than new fields were coming on stream. This was in spite of the fact that only half of known reserves had been produced, but the remaining 50% will present much more of a challenge. The oil companies are also coming to the conclusion that there is little chance of any more major finds that will result in sizable projects. The industry has now entered into an era of smaller field development which involves different problems and different players.

The larger oil companies are now in a more harvesting mode whilst seeking larger reserves in other areas of the world. This has made room for smaller, entrepreneurial companies to enter the game, acquiring assets that are no longer economic for the larger companies. It has also presented opportunities for small UK independent operators to take interests in small fields that had not seemed viable to produce as stand-alone projects. The large infrastructure of existing platforms have now made it possible to become hosts to receiving production from single subsea well fields. Nowhere in the UK sector of the North Sea is more than 50 km from an existing platform.

Advances in new technology are now being driven by the need to find smaller reserves, locate these reserves through more accurate drilling techniques, and to provide subsea engineering solutions to produce these small reserves. These will be described in later chapters.

Fixed platforms will remain in production providing that the revenue gained from the oil and gas produced exceeds the operating costs plus petroleum revenue taxes. Once the point is reached when the operation is no longer economic, the platform is shut down and decommissioned. Additional production from smaller subsea fields owned by the platform operators or third parties and tied back to the host platform will extend the life of the platform before it becomes uneconomic.

Alongside the use of existing infrastructure by new entrant operators, there is a geographical rationalisation process ongoing whereby operators are attempting to secure their fields in geographical clusters. Ownership of the host platform and subsea satellites provides much greater control on operations and capital budgets and for forward planning processes.

Where the platform infrastructure is not easily accessible, floating production facilities are now being used to access production from subsea wells. These are either purpose-built, or tankers or drilling rigs converted for this purpose. Suited for small-field or deep-water development, such units have the advantage of mobility from field to field with lower deep-water development costs, and ultimately low decommissioning costs. Shuttle tankers are deployed to have produced oil transferred for shipment to a chosen refinery.

Looking ahead to the next 40 years, there are many uncertainties and challenges. Skills required to sustain the industry are in competition with different work aspirations and patterns of young people today. Competition with other emerging oil-producing areas will increasingly influence investment by the oil companies. The attitude by the Government to encouragement of continued investment by taxation changes will continue to dominate the political agenda. The policy on decommissioning may have already been decided but there are concerns that it may not provide the most pragmatic solutions.

Whatever the outcome of these issues, oil and gas production from the North Sea will continue to remain critical to the economy of the UK, especially as we cease to become self-sufficient and more reliant on the uncertainties of the importation of our energy supplies.

APPENDIX

Key events that have shaped the past, present and future of the UK oil and gas industry

1965	First commercial gas find in the Southern North Sea (BP West Sole)
1969	Gas production for sales to Gas Council
1970	First major oil discovery in the Northern North Sea (BP Forties)
1973	Oil price rises to $35 per barrel
1975	First oil production from the North Sea (Hamilton Brothers' Argyll)
1985	UK self-sufficient in both gas and oil supplies
1986	Oil price collapses to below $20 per barrel
1988	Piper Alpha incident
1990	First commercial oil discovery west of Shetland (BP Foinaven) Safety regulatory body set up under the HSE following Lord Cullen's Inquiry
1992	First platform Safety Case
1994	CRINE initiative launched (Cost Reduction in a New Era)
1995	Brent Spar incident
1998	Sintra Agreement sets regulations on decommissioning
1999	Introduction of DTI Environmental Regulations and Environmental Case for all new offshore developments.
2001	PILOT initiative for Government Industry co-operation
2004	UK ceases to be self-sufficient in gas supplies
2005	Oil price increases to above $60 per barrel
2007	UK ceases to be self-sufficient in oil supplies

— 2 —

LICENSING

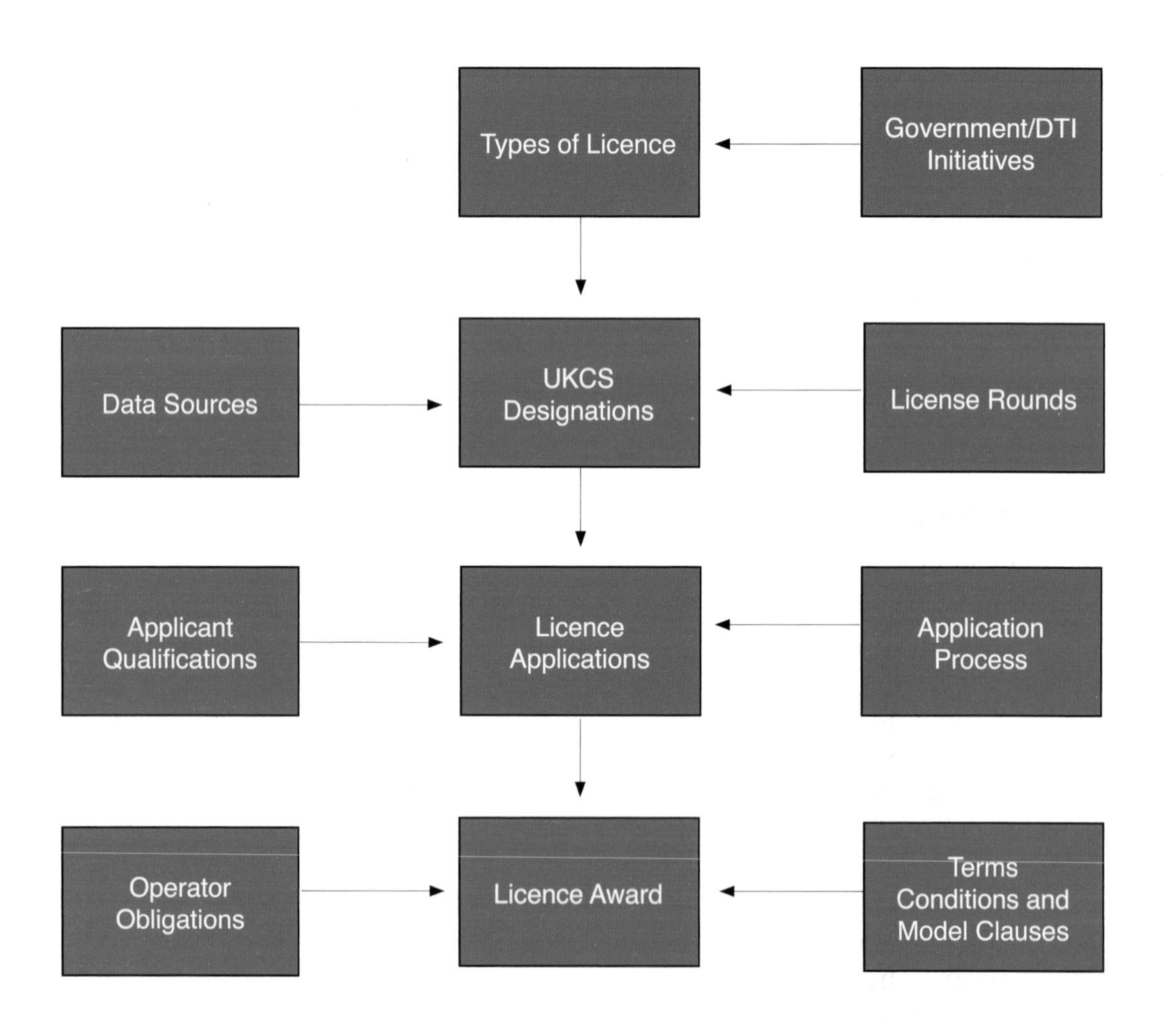
Types of Licence
Government/DTI Initiatives
Data Sources
UKCS Designations
License Rounds
Applicant Qualifications
Licence Applications
Application Process
Operator Obligations
Licence Award
Terms Conditions and Model Clauses

LICENSING

2.1 Introduction

The pattern of offshore oil and gas was set by the discovery of the 'world class' Groningen gas field in 1959. This led to the realisation by the Dutch that plentiful natural gas could supplant costly (and 'dirty') coal as a fuel both in the home and for industry.

At that time, however, the oil companies were considerably more interested in oil than in gas. Nevertheless, further wells were drilled and other (but much smaller) gas discoveries were made. One turning point was the drilling of a well on the Friesian Islands which showed that gas-bearing 'Rotliegendes Sandstone' extended towards the North Sea. The 'Yellow Sands' of Durham were known to be of the same age and origin as the Rotliegendes and the inference was drawn that similar rocks could exist, at depth, below the North Sea.

At that time, there was no international agreement covering the sovereignty of areas beyond the concept of 'territorial waters'. However, the NW Europe littoral nations had reached a series of bilateral agreements by 1958, although these were not to come into force until 1964 under the Continental Shelf Convention in Geneva.

Thereafter, progress was rapid, with exploration wells being drilled in the offshore sectors of the Netherlands and the UK. Successes followed, initially in the Southern North Sea on both sides of the Dutch–UK median line. After the gas discoveries of the 1960s, the Dutch and UK gas markets were believed to be amply supplied by current discoveries and developments.

In the UK, the focus shifted to exploration for oil. The discovery of the Ekofisk field in Norway (in chalk) and of the Forties field in the UK (in sands even younger than the chalk) confirmed the Central North Sea as an oil-productive province.

At the same time, incredible advances were being made in seismic acquisition and processing and in downhole petrophysical logging. These were enabling technologies.

The licensing authorities followed the clamour for awards to be made in ever-deeper waters of the Central and Northern North Seas which were postulated to be oil-prospective. So, by the early 1970s, with the advent of large 'semi-submersible' drilling units capable of operating in water depths of 600 ft or more, and the development of diving bells and appropriate breathing mixtures for divers, the UK had licensed numerous blocks in the North Viking Graben (north of latitude 60°N) within which seismic reflection records indicated the presence of large structures. Discoveries followed rapidly at what we now call Brent, Cormorant, Thistle, Dunlin, Hutton, Ninian, Heather and others. The Norwegians followed with a giant discovery at Nansen (renamed Statfjord), thus establishing what the British call the Northern North Sea as a prolific petroleum province.

The North Viking Graben fields are essentially contained within simple structures (by today's standards) although difficult enough to evaluate with the technology (particularly the seismic) of the day.

In the UK, the gas price for the producers was still extremely low and the oil companies continued to clamour for more acreage in the Central and Northern North Sea areas where ever more complex structures were being drilled and interpreted. So, UK licensing rounds were focused on these areas.

By the end of the 1970s, the British Geological Survey (BGS) was nearing the end of its offshore mapping projects of the UKCS and the oil companies were sufficiently encouraged by BGS findings to request acreage in the SW Approaches, the Bristol Channel and to the west of Shetland. In general, these areas have proved disappointing but west of Shetland is now recognised as both an oil (eg Clair field) and gas province and the first gas evacuation route (to Sullom Voe in Shetland) is now operational.

During the mid-1980s, deepening of a few wells beyond the Rotliegendes Sandstones of the Southern North Sea had resulted in the discovery of gas in Carboniferous-aged sandstones. So, the UK authorities were asked for additional acreage in this new play.

More recently, the oil companies have been forced into the exploitation of ever-smaller discoveries, closer and closer to existing infrastructure – so-called satellite developments – throughout the North Sea (and in Morecambe Bay). To the west of Shetland, however, deep and hostile waters and the paucity of infrastructure mean that projects have to be economic as stand-alones (ie with their own dedicated evacuation method or route).

With the large number of discoveries, whether producing or not, and the licence requirements of obligatory 50% relinquishment at the end of the initial term, the contiguous areas remaining unlicensed continue to diminish, creating numerous problems for government administrators and for oil companies trying to evaluate these small areas with items of infrastructure all around them. With such high prices for produced hydrocarbons, however, there is plenty of incentive for high levels of activity throughout the UKCS.

Geological mapping of much of the area had been completed, with the result that these data are now readily available to any prospective oil company to examine for the possibility of a potential application for a licence and to take steps to determine the potential development of an oil- or gas-producing field.

Licence applications can be made in two ways: (i) in Licensing Rounds in which the DTI invite applications; and (ii) through Out-of-Round applications in which a company must state their position as to why the DTI should invite such Out-of-Round applications. A rigorous process is then adopted by the DTI to ensure that not only is the applicant fully competent and committed to move forward with such plans, but also has the relevant plans and finance available to proceed under the terms of the licence.

The North Sea has seen many changes in investment decisions from the oil companies and today the emphasis is on the development of the remaining potential 40% of the total estimated reserves. These are understood to be small fields which may no longer be economic to the major oil companies. The DTI are therefore keen to encourage new smaller companies to make applications to exploit such reserves and are introducing new initiatives to encourage such activities.

2.2 UK offshore boundaries and designations

Boundaries and the median line principle

Until the 1940s, national boundaries of many littoral nations had been extended offshore under the concept of 'territorial waters'. For the UK and some nations, this was 3 miles (~5 km) but, for others, it was up to 12 miles (~20 km). These limits were essentially to define inshore fishing stocks and mineral (eg coal) deposits. From about 1950, some littoral nations laid claim to fishing and mineral rights (including potential oil) out to the edge of their continental shelf, largely accepted as being the 200 m (~ 650 ft) isobath.

In a confined sea space (such as the Caspian or North Sea) bordered by several littoral nations, a different approach was required to allow equable partition of

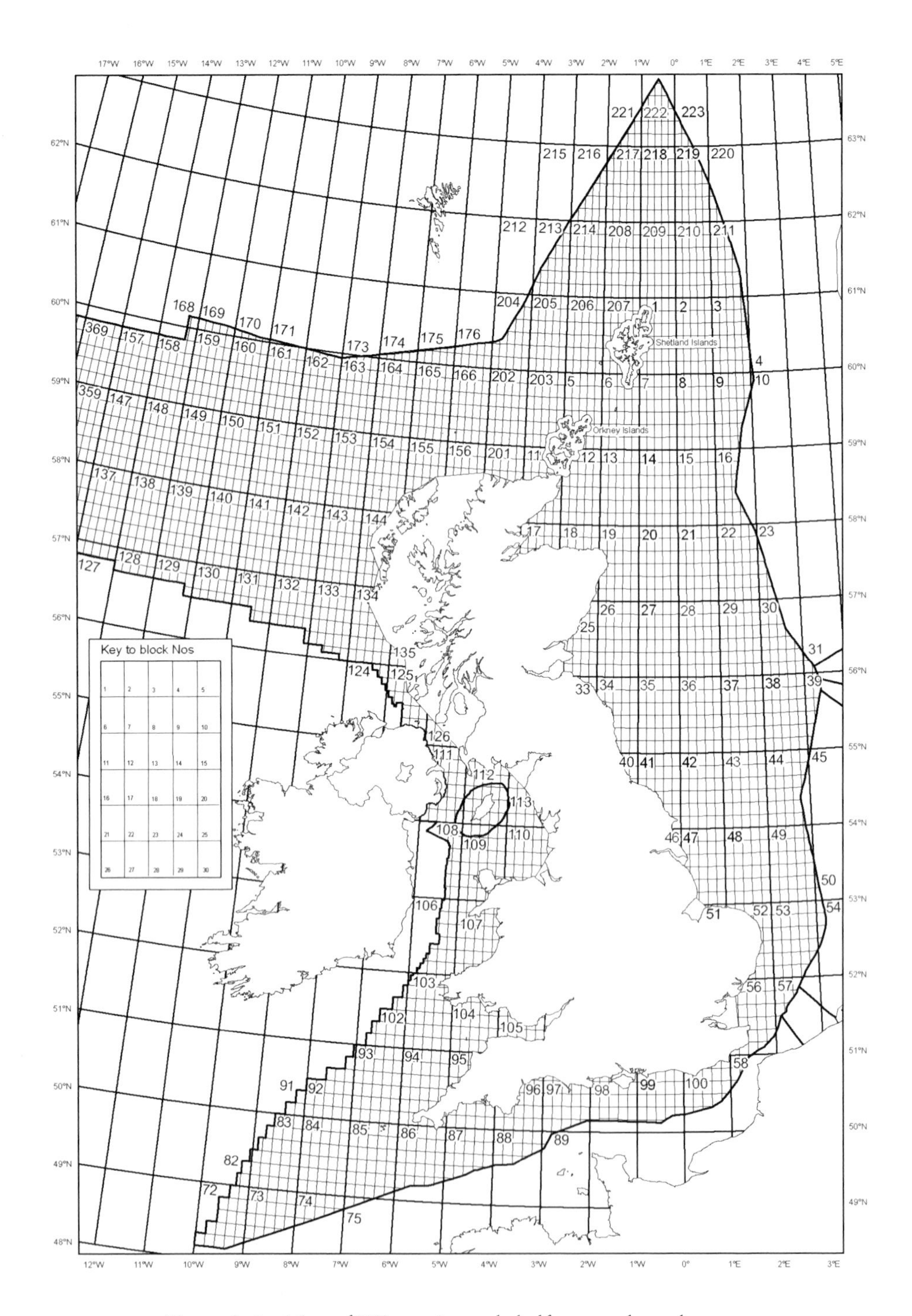

Figure 2–1 Map of UK continental shelf seaward quadrants

potential resources. In NW Europe, bilateral agreements between Denmark, the Netherlands, Norway and the UK were reached using the median line principle. This was enshrined in the Continental Shelf Convention of 1958. However, Germany continued to dispute the claims of Denmark and the Netherlands, only reaching a settlement in 1970, following a ruling from the International Court of Justice.

Later still, the UK reached agreements with Faeroe, France (except for the area around the Channel Islands) and Ireland. Hence, the final delineation of UK-controlled waters came about very considerably later to the south and to the west/north-west of the UK than it was to the east.

Continental shelf offshore quadrants

Within the UK offshore, the first quadrants to be designated were those for which there were no contentious issues with adjoining jurisdictions. Once the median line had been established within the North Sea, those nations with a North Sea jurisdiction immediately designated their quadrants. In the UK, quadrants are essentially numbered clockwise, beginning with Quadrant 1 off the east coast of Shetland – see Fig. 2–1 (www.og.dti.gov.uk/regulations/pons/pan_12sea.htm).

However, once a settlement was reached with Faeroe and Ireland, it was possible to designate further quadrants to the SW, W, NW and N of the UK with northernmost quadrants bearing the numbers 212 to 223.

In Norway, initial quadrant designations (Quadrants 1–36) were all to the south of latitude 62°N. Later designations used the same 4-digit system as in Denmark (and subsequently Faeroe). Each quadrant is numbered according to the location of its SW corner. So, (Norwegian) quadrant 6202 has its southern boundary on latitude 62°N and its western boundary along longitude 2°E – whereas the Faeroese quadrant 6202 has it southern boundary on latitude 62°N and its eastern boundary long longitude 2°W.

Offshore blocks

With the exception of France, the littoral nations of NW Europe have divided their offshore sectors into 2D quadrants (each approximately 111 km N–S by 50–60 km E–W, widening southwards). Each designated quadrant or part-quadrant is numbered (Denmark, Faeroe, Ireland, Norway and the UK) or is designated by a capital letter (Germany and the Netherlands).

Subdivision of designated quadrants differs quite markedly within the various jurisdictions. In Faeroe, Ireland and the UK, each quadrant is further divided into 30 blocks (5 E–W by 6 N–S), giving each offshore block an area of approximately 200 km^2 at the latitude of the Central North Sea. In Norway, however, each quadrant is divided into 12 blocks (3 E–W by 4 N–S), giving a block area of approximately 550 km^2 in the southern part of its jurisdiction. In

Germany and the Netherlands, quadrants are divided into 18 blocks (3 E–W by 6 N–S), giving a block area of approximately 400 km^2. Finally, in Denmark, quadrants are divided into 32 blocks (4 E–W by 8 N–S), giving a block area of approximately 200 km^2.

Onshore quadrants (UK only)

The identification of areas and spot locations onshore obviously came about long before the offshore situation came to be addressed. Most nations used their own national grid – the French used Paris as 0° meridian (whereas the rest of the world tended to use London (Greenwich) as the 0° meridian).

In the UK, a 'false origin' is used as the south-westernmost point for the national grid; this false origin lies to the SW of the Scilly Islands, some hundreds of kilometres WSW from London. In the UK, the national grid is based upon 100-km squares, measured northwards and eastwards from the false origin. However, although national grid references are the standard positioning and reference system for onshore Ordnance Survey maps, it was decided that the (offshore) quadrant system would be more appropriate and potentially less confusing than national grid reference numbers and letters.

This relatively new reference system thus tends to be shown alongside the older systems, with quadrants being preceded by the letter 'L' for 'Landward' (as opposed to 'seaward' in the offshore situation). Hence, in southern England, Quadrants 97, 98 and 99 are partly onshore and partly offshore, with the landward parts being identified as 'L97', 'L98', 'L99' etc. Landward quadrants which are wholly onshore are identified by letters. So, Landward Quadrant 'A' is strictly identified as Quadrant 'LA'.

The block and well numbering system for the onshore part of the UKCS follows the same rules as for the offshore part. (See http://www.og.dti.gov.uk. regulations/pons/pon_12htm).

Well numbering system in the UK

Well numbering in the UK can be quite complicated but the position can be summarised briefly as set out below and with reference to Fig. 2–1. In the UK, wells are numbered according to the quadrant and block within which a given well penetrated the seabed regardless of where that well finally terminated (which may be in a different block or event quadrant). If a block has been subdivided into two or more sub-blocks, the sub-block will be represented by a lower case. Hence, sub-block '22/6b' refers to the 'b' part Block in Quadrant 22. (A summary explanation of well numbering is available at the following link – www.og.dti.gov.uk/pans/pon_12htm#maps).

As the exploration phase began to yield discoveries of hydrocarbons, licensees began to appraise and then develop the economic discoveries. In the offshore environment, development is almost invariably from one or more platforms (Wytch Farm field beneath Poole Harbour in Dorset is a notable exception). The closest analogy onshore to the platform, is a well 'pad' or 'site', where numerous wellheads are in a very close proximity (eg at Singleton field in the Weald Basin of Hampshire) for environmental or economic reasons. Offshore is no different except that an offshore platform may have 30 or more wellheads from which the boreholes radiate outwards and downwards to their target location.

In the UK, platforms tend to be identified by a single letter, although there are exceptions such as the Forties field which has five platforms and the Brent field with four platforms. Hence, the Forties Alpha platform is identified as '21/10-FA' since it is situated in Block 10 of Quadrant 21 and the Brent Bravo platform is identified as '211/29-BB' since it is situated in Block 29 of Quadrant 211. As explained above, UK wells are numbered according to the location at which they penetrate the seabed so, for example, the 14th well to be drilled from the Brent Bravo platform would be 211/29-B14.

Sometimes, perhaps due to encountering a shallow obstruction (eg a large boulder) or strong seabed current, it may be necessary to restart (or 're-spud') a well. If no meaningful data have been acquired from the initial well, the first re-spud, which must be from essentially the same location, receives the postscript 'A', a second re-spud would receive the postscript 'B' and so on. So, if fictional well 99/11–1 encountered a very shallow problem, it would be re-spudded as '99/11–1A'.

Occasionally, in the exploration or appraisal phases of activity, a borehole may be partially re-drilled (or 'side-tracked'). In the UK, the first side-track receives the postscript 'Z', the second side-track 'Y', the third 'X' and so on. So, the re-spudded English Channel (fictional) well 99/11–1A would be side-tracked as Well '99/11–1AZ'.

2.3 Sources of data in the UK

Any organisation which is considering investing in an area outwith its current range of operations needs information. This might include some knowledge of the fiscal regime, employment law and so on. For hydrocarbon exploration, development and production, the requirement for geoscientific data is paramount.

In the UK, a wealth of data is now available from government, learned societies (such as the Geological Society of London), national institutions (such as the British Geological Survey) and innumerable service companies, amongst others.

Primary data sources within the UK include the seismic acquisition companies who publish regular updates of data availability in journals such as the *Petroleum Exploration Society of Great Britain ('PESGB') Newsletter*, *First Break* and other technical journals. Most of the offshore basins proven to be hydrocarbon-productive are now covered by one or more generations of 3D seismic. Some of the seismic acquisition companies have merged data over many quadrants, thus covering several thousands of square kilometres with a single merged data set. These are available both raw and as interpreted data.

Primary well data is placed in the public domain, and is available for consultation – once the period of confidentiality (five years) has expired. The British Geological Survey acts as the custodian of all core and cuttings samples which are lodged with the British Government, through the DTI. These samples, together with all hard-copy and scanned documents, are held by the BGS in Edinburgh.

Interpreted data, in the form of geological maps, are produced at a variety of scales by the BGS; these range from 1:50 000 to 1:500 000 and cover the full spectrum of geological knowledge.

The DTI (1 Victoria Street, London and 86–88 Guild Street, Aberdeen), as well as BGS in Edinburgh, hold complete sets of microfiche (only) of all wells drilled in the UKCS, both onshore and offshore, whose period of confidentiality has expired. These microfiche are available for consultation during standard office hours.

Onshore seismic data are curated by Lynx Information Systems but much of the data are analogue and reproduction quality is not always to the highest calibre.

Numerous service companies are heavily focused on the North Sea and are valuable sources of data, interpretations and advice/management services.

Numerous books, pamphlets and technical articles have been published on various aspects of the UKCS geology, geophysics, field development and management, well log interpretation and so on. (See References and Further Reading.)

2.4 Types of licence

Essentially, there are two main types of offshore licence: exploration licences and production licences.

Exploration Licences

Companies which wish to investigate broader areas of the Continental Shelf and carry out geoscientific surveys offshore may apply for an Exploration Licence which allows companies the opportunity to evaluate areas below the seabed before possibly applying for a Production Licence at a later time. An Exploration Licence prohibits any drilling to depths in excess of 350 metres. Such licences are less costly and more easily acquired. They do not require to be applied for during competitive Licensing Rounds and tend to be used by seismic acquisition companies. Exploration Licences have a life of three years and allow companies to explore any areas on the UKCS which are not already covered by a Production Licence.

Production Licences

Companies which wish to exploit the oil and gas resources in the UK require a Production Licence. The main type of offshore licence is the Seaward Production Licence. These licences cover initial exploration all the way through to eventual decommissioning. There are four kinds of Production Licence.

(i) Traditional licences

The duration of the 'Traditional' Seaward Production Licence is divided into three terms. The initial term lasts for four years and is the period during which an Agreed Work Programme of exploration must be completed. Generally, 50% of the initially licensed area has to be relinquished at the end of the initial term. The second term also lasts for a four-year period, during which a minimum of one Field Development Plan must be put together and approved by the DTI. The final term lasts for 18 years and is the period in which production takes place.

(ii) Promote licences

A modified version of the 'Traditional' Licence takes the form of the 'Promote' Seaward Production Licence, the idea being to enable small and start-up companies to obtain a Production Licence. The annual rental rate for the initial two-year period of a 'Promote' Seaward Production Licence is reduced by 90%. The way in which the 'Promote' licences are drafted ensures that companies obtaining such licences are required to have the requisite financial, technical and environmental aptitude, in addition to a definite drilling commitment, by the end of the second year. Essentially, this type of licence gives companies a two-year time frame to achieve exploration operatorship and funding to allow them to proceed. If a licence is to be relinquished, a report outlining the research and analysis undertaken has to be submitted to the DTI. For the DTI to allow a company to enter the third and fourth year, deferred financial and environmental checks need to be satisfied.

(iii) Frontier licences

A further form of licence is the 'Frontier' Seaward Production Licence which is principally designed to enable companies to examine large areas of the UKCS with a view to future production. Under this type of licence the exploration and development periods are extended. This, coupled with a 90% reduction in the annual rental rate, offers companies an added incentive to find oil and gas in those areas. After the initial 'screening' phase, companies are normally required to surrender three-quarters of the acreage under the licence. This type of licence is available only for difficult or unexplored areas, such as to the north or west of the Shetlands, in deep water.

(iv) Landward licences

Another type of production licence is the 'Landward' Production Licence, otherwise known as a Petroleum Exploration and Development Licence. As with the 'Traditional' Seaward Production Licence, these licences are split into three terms, with a six-year initial term in which an Agreed Work Programme has to be carried out before entry is granted into the second term. The second term lasts for five years and companies must obtain DTI approval of any development plan within this time before entry into the third term is granted. The third and final term is the production phase and lasts for 20 years.

Historical licences

The earliest offshore licences on the UKCS were so-called 'Mining Licences' (or MLs) to allow legislation for coal and evaporite (eg 'salt') exploitation beneath the seabed in close proximity to the shore. Until very recently, a few of these MLs were still in force on the Norfolk coast and off Scarborough (Yorkshire). There are also two MLs still extant in the East Midlands oil province in central England.

Other licence types were also awarded onshore, including XLs (Exploration Licences) but these have been supplanted totally by PEDLs (Petroleum Exploration and Development Licences).

2.5 Licensing Rounds

The first offshore licence was granted in 1964 and, generally, applications for a licence are made in Licensing Rounds during which the DTI officially invites applications from prospective licensees. The notice inviting applications is posted in the *Official Journal of the European Communities* and is also advertised on the DTI website.[1] Licensing Rounds in recent years have occurred annually, with the DTI stating that they 'are committed to a regular timetable of one onshore and one offshore Licensing Round each year'.[2] There have been 24 offshore Licensing Rounds thus far to 2007. Each of the licences on offer during a Licensing Round must include 'model clauses'. The model clauses applicable to each licence are contained in the Petroleum Licensing (Exploration and Production) (Seaward and Landward Areas) Regulations Order 2004 (SI 2004 No 352) as amended by the Petroleum Licensing (Exploration and Production) (Seaward and Landward Areas) (Amendment) Regulations Order 2006 (SI 2006 No 784). A licence will also be subject to other restrictions and conditions.

Very occasionally, the DTI will accept a request from a company for an Out-of-Round application. Unlike the system of Licensing Rounds, Out-of-Round applications are instigated by a company making a request to the DTI Exploration Unit. The onus is on the company to prove that an Out-of-Round licence should be granted and present reasons to the DTI as to why there is a pressing need to grant a licence rather than waiting for the next Licensing Round. Once the DTI has decided that there is such a need to grant a licence, they will invite applications in the same manner as they do in Licensing Rounds. Only Traditional Licences and Landward Licences can be applied for Out-of-Round as they are targeted at situations where there is a pending opportunity and time is of the essence.

2.6 The application process

Once a company has decided its strategy and the type of licence that it wishes to apply for, an application must be submitted to the DTI. For many companies, being the sole licensee in an area would be excessively onerous and so a decision is normally made to make a joint application with a number of other companies. There are, however, minimum residence requirements for companies seeking to obtain a licence which will be discussed in more detail below. The DTI outline two matters that require to be considered in determining what can be put into a single application. The list of all the proposed parties to each licence and their respective percentage interests in that licence must remain consistent throughout the entire application. Further, each application can be for only one particular type of licence: Traditional, Landward, Promote or Frontier. The DTI guidelines contain a useful example to outline this point:

> 'Suppose Company A and Company B want to make a joint application, each proposing to take a 50% interest in any licences awarded; and they seek a Traditional Licence over one block in the Northern North Sea and another over a block in the Southern Basin. They can combine the two blocks in a single application (because both licences would be of the same type and the companies would have the same equity interests in both). However, if they wanted a third Traditional Licence but with a 70:30 equity split, they would have to make a separate application; as they would if they also wanted to apply for a Promote Licence.'[3]

In order to hold a Production Licence, prospective licensees must demonstrate to the DTI that they have the requisite technical and environmental competence and the financial capability (although not for Promote Licences or PEDLs). Likewise, any party wishing to become a party to a licence by virtue of a Deed of Assignment must also meet these criteria. Applicants for Traditional, Landward and Frontier Licences must provide evidence to the DTI both of their financial capacity to perform the Agreed Work Programme, their technical ability to carry out the operation safely, and their environmental competence with respect to seaward Traditional and Frontier Licences.

Licences are currently issued under the Petroleum Act 1998 ('the Act'). All rights to the UK's petroleum resources remain vested in the Crown by virtue of the Act and the Secretary of State for Trade and Industry is empowered to grant licences to exploit these resources. Under the licensing regime no one, other than the Crown, actually owns the rights to petroleum in the UKCS, although it is generally acknowledged that the producing licensee owns it when it has passed the wellhead. Instead, certain rights are created by the licence, thus creating a contractual position with ownership still vested in the Crown.

Under the Act, the Secretary of State may grant 'to such persons as he thinks fit licences to search and bore for and get petroleum'.[4] Once approved, a licence grants rights over a defined area of the UKCS for an established period of time and takes the form of a deed, obliging the licensee to abide by the conditions imposed by the licence at all times. The Act states that 'Any such licence shall be granted for such consideration (whether by way of royalty or otherwise) as the Secretary of State with the consent of the Treasury may determine, and upon such other terms and conditions as the Secretary of State thinks fit'.[5] Companies wishing to obtain a licence are, therefore, very much bound by the terms imposed by the licence. The Secretary of State for Trade and Industry has discretion in granting licences and must be satisfied that those who are granted a licence are in a position to be able to maximise the exploitation of oil and gas in the UK. It is absolutely fundamental that those who are granted licences have the ability to exploit the resources and have the requisite technical and financial and environmental capability. The DTI is eager to avoid companies purchasing licence interests merely with a view to selling them on and want those who apply for a licence to exploit the resources themselves.

So, what are the criteria for a new operator wishing to exploit the petroleum resources in the UK and how does it obtain a licence?

Application form

Every application needs to be made on the approved application form which must be completed in full. There are also three appendices dealing with financial capability, technical information and environmental competence respectively. Appendix A is required in support of applications for Landward Production Licences, Traditional Seaward Production Licences and Frontier Seaward Production Licences. However, applicants for a Promote Production Licence do not require to submit Appendix A. The Appendix A should be signed on paper and submitted to the DTI, together with any supporting documentation which can be either on paper or in CD-ROM format.

Every application must contain Sections 1, 2 and 3 of Appendix B, which relates to geotechnical information and the means by which the applicant plans to exploit the acreage in the licence. Further, all applicants except those applying for Promote Seaward Production Licences must complete Section 4 of Appendix B, demonstrating the prospective operator's technical competence. It is important to note that at least one of the two required copies of Appendix B must be on CD-ROM.

Information relating to the environmental competence of the prospective operator is contained in Appendix C and is required in applications for Traditional Seaward Production Licences and Frontier Seaward Production Licences. Again, at least one of the two required copies of Appendix C must be on CD-ROM.

Once the applicant has gathered the information the application is submitted, together with the application fee, to the DTI. At present, the application fee for a Seaward Production Licence is currently (in 2007) £2,820 and for a Landward Petroleum Exploration and Development Licence it is £1,000 (as set out in the Petroleum (Production) (Seaward Areas) Regulations 1988 (SI 1988 No 1213) and the Petroleum (Production) (Landward Areas) Regulations 1995 (SI 1995 No 1436)). Each invitation in a Licensing Round specifies clearly the closing date by which all applications must be submitted and any applications submitted after the closing date will not be accepted.

Interviews

Following receipt of the applications, it is normal practice for the DTI to interview every applicant (or consortium) for each block or part-block being applied for. Hence, applicants may be called to interview on several occasions if they have applied for several blocks or part-blocks. The geoscientific interviews are carried out by the Licensing, Exploration and Development Branch of the DTI in London. The DTI Guidelines state: 'We will hold the first interview within two weeks of the application date, but we cannot predict when the last one will occur – that depends on the number of applications.'[6] The main purpose of the interview process is to allow the applicant an opportunity to present the technical aspects of their application, not the financial or environmental aspects, and for the DTI to discuss any aspect of the application that requires to be clarified. In the case of Promote Licence applications, the DTI will probe into the financial and environmental information and the applicant's intentions with regard to potential operatorship of the licence. However, after the initial two-year licence period, Promote Licencees would be required to fulfil the same obligations as a Traditional or Frontier Licence applicant. It is often easier to explain technical ideas and concepts in a face-to-face meeting rather than by correspondence, hence the interview has become part of the application process.

In many cases, a subsequent interview may be required in order to tie up any loose ends on the technical side of the application. In addition, the Offshore Environment and Decommissioning Branch of the DTI may ask applicants for Frontier and Traditional Seaward Production Licences to attend a further interview in Aberdeen to discuss their environmental competence.

Financial capability/capacity

For each type of licence, apart from a Promote Licence, the DTI requires prospective licensees to demonstrate their financial capability to complete the proposed Work Programme. In order to be permitted to exploit any hydrocarbon discoveries, prospective licensees must prove to the DTI that they have the financial capacity to develop the UK's petroleum resources effectively. (Potential operators must demonstrate to the DTI that they are solvent and are likely to remain solvent.) Further, they must be able to demonstrate that they will not adversely affect future work being carried out under a licence by not being able to pay their share of the costs. The DTI offer some guidance as to what information they expect to be provided to them. This includes two copies of the latest annual report and accounts, together with those of the parent company if applicable. Projected balance sheets and cash flow statements for the next five years, together with the assumptions on which these statements are made, should also be provided. In circumstances where a company seeking to become a licensee is a subsidiary, then a letter of support from the parent company should also be provided to the DTI, stating that they will ensure that sufficient technical and financial resources will be made available to the subsidiary in order for it to meet its obligations and liabilities under the licence. Where a subsidiary is applying for a licence, the DTI will wish to see financial information regarding the parent company.

Applicants for a Promote Licence, by virtue of the nature of the licence, are not required to meet the financial criteria set by the DTI before the licence is awarded. However, the financial criteria are applied by the DTI after two years and unless the applicant satisfies the DTI financial requirements at this point, the licence will simply expire.

Other types of licences will only be granted to those companies who demonstrate their ability to fund the Agreed Work Programme. For the multinational oil companies this will obviously not be a problem, with the net worth of these companies being sufficient for the DTI to be confident that funding will not be an issue. Given the vast resources of the major oil companies, there is less risk of a lack of funding which will leave licence areas fallow. There have been a number of new entrants recently, including small and start-up companies entering the sector, and it is these companies that the DTI are likely to scrutinise closely to determine that they have the financial capacity to carry out any proposed work. These companies tend to have specific funding arrangements and often, apart from Promote Licences, those arrangements may be in place before the award of a licence. Very occasionally, the DTI will award a licence where there is a firm funding commitment in place, but such commitments must come from a recognised financial institution independent of the company. This is to avoid the situation where a licence is awarded on the basis that funding will be in place, only for the funding to be withdrawn and a licence granted to a company that can no longer fund the Agreed Work Programme.

In terms of the documentation that needs to be sent to the DTI, as discussed earlier, Appendix A of the application form for a Production Licence must be sent to the DTI. Part 3 of this form is a financial capacity questionnaire whilst Part 4 is an expenditure profile for each block that is applied for. Applicants should also submit two copies of the company's most recent accounts together with information as to the corporate structure of the company, including an organisation diagram. In the case of a subsidiary, details must also be given of the parent company's place of incorporation, principal place of business and company registration number.

Technical expertise

In addition to demonstrating financial capacity, prospective operators also need to demonstrate to the DTI that they possess the relevant technical expertise to enable them to exploit the petroleum resources effectively within the licence area. Given the challenges faced by operating in the North Sea, potential licensees are thoroughly screened and must demonstrate their competence in terms of maximising hydrocarbon recovery. The DTI expects prospective operators to display sound technical aptitude and, thus, those wishing to become operators must outline their actual managerial and technical staff structure. The DTI are particularly keen on understanding the role of contractors in the process as they play a vital role in the operation of facilities in the North Sea. In addition, applicants are required to have an adequate in-house team to oversee and manage the project and it is expected that the key technical staff have substantial experience in operating in the North Sea. It is common for new operators to come into the North Sea from elsewhere in the world and those who do so require to outline to the DTI their prior experience.

Appendix B of the application form for a Production Licence incorporates the technical aspects of the application, whereby the applicant can demonstrate their technical case and competence as an operator. During the application process, the applicant will be interviewed to clarify any issues relating to the technical side of their application. The requisite technical information is divided into four sections. Part 4 of the application form contains the Lead/ Prospect Summary Sheet where the applicant gives a geoscientific evaluation of potential prospects within the area covered by the licence. This should also include an assessment of the risks and reserves within the area and whether the area requires further seismic research or whether it is ready to be drilled immediately. Part 5 of the application form, as previously discussed, is the means by which the applicant sets out their proposed Work Programme. In addition to the information to be provided within the application form itself, the applicant should also include their technical proposals and ideas for exploiting the area covered by the licence.

Environmental

Developments initiated by OSPAR and the EC have resulted in a range of environmental regulations relating to offshore oil and gas activities in the UKCS. Strategic Environmental Assessments (SEAs) need to be carried out (the first was for an area to the west of Shetland) covering the entire UKCS before further licences can be awarded. SEAs have now been completed for virtually all the UKCS although there is still an outstanding requirement for the English Channel and in the Western Approaches (SEA8).

As part of the environmental competence assessment, potential applicants have to demonstrate to the DTI an awareness of environmental issues and provide evidence that they have an environmental management system in place. The prospective operator should outline to the DTI the environmental policy that they have in place.

The DTI Guidelines state that: 'Applicants for Seaward Production Licences (other than Promote Licences) must demonstrate that they possess an adequate level of competence in relation to environmental protection.'[7] Applicants must support their application to the DTI with submissions which allow the DTI to assess the environmental competence of the prospective operator properly. Oil and gas companies that have previously acquired a Traditional or Frontier Licence generally go through a simplified process for demonstrating environmental competence. This is because earlier licence applications by the companies will already have covered the basic environmental submissions and, therefore, only a summary environmental assessment is required. The DTI are able to check the company's track record on environmental compliance and look back to previous submissions for information relating to their environmental proposals. Only if there have been significant changes in the arrangements should new submissions be provided.

However, new applicants which have either a limited or no track record may not be in a position to provide the DTI with comprehensive submissions to satisfy the environmental requirements. In such cases the DTI Guidelines state that:[8]

> 'Applicants will therefore be expected to provide brief submissions to demonstrate that they understand the environmental requirements, including an outline timetable, or timetables, for meeting the specified requirements prior to undertaking any offshore activities on the United Kingdom Continental Shelf. The timetable(s) should be clearly linked to the work programme submitted in support of the application, and it is important to realise that environmental consents will not be issued until new licensees have satisfied all the environmental requirements.'[9]

For applicants wishing to obtain a Promote Licence, an environmental submission is not required and becomes necessary only if they wish to continue their licences into a third year. The submissions relating to environmental competence contained in Appendix C of the application form and all ancillary documentation in support of the application should be supplied in CD-ROM format.

Following licence award, environmental consents and approvals are required for most offshore oil and gas operations and a detailed Environmental Statement is required for all new developments in the UKCS.

Marks scheme

The DTI has created a 'Marks Scheme' as a means of assessing applicants for Seaward Production Licences. The scheme covers Traditional, Promote and Frontier licences and is the method by which the DTI gauges applicants under eight different categories: geoscientific database; geoscientific evaluation of the whole block; specific prospectivity identified and evaluated; new plays; geoscientific work programme; drilling work programme (with marks only awarded for Traditional and Frontier applications); promote assessment; and existing discoveries and redevelopments. Each of these eight sections is further subdivided in terms of what the DTI are looking for (eg more marks for deeper prospects in older formations than shallower prospects in younger formations) and marks are awarded on the basis of stated aims. The marking of each application takes place immediately after the interview process with the applicants and on the basis of the interview and how well the various applicants perform under the Marks Scheme, a decision is made by the Secretary of State as to whether or not a licence should be issued for that particular area. In normal circumstances, it is the applicant with the highest score under the Marks Scheme that is offered the licence. However, this is not always the case and, as the Secretary of State has an overriding discretion, there are rare cases in which the applicant that attains the highest score under the Marks Scheme is not awarded the licence; the DTI instead opting for a lower-scoring applicant. It should be stressed that such cases are uncommon and it is usually the case that the top-scoring applicant under the Marks Scheme is offered the licence.

Residence requirements

In order to become a licensee, a company must have a place of business within the UK, failing which they will not be permitted to hold a licence. A prospective licensee must have a staffed presence within the UK, be a registered UK company at Companies House, or be registered as a UK branch of a foreign company at Companies House. However, for those wishing to hold a licence in a producing field, the residence requirements are slightly different. In those circumstances, a would-be licensee must evidence the fact that they are registered as a UK company at Companies House or control the activities of a company through a place of business in the UK.

2.7 Licence terms and conditions

Licence restrictions

Certain parts of the offshore sector of the UKCS are primarily reserved to the Ministry of Defence. Hence, there are submarine exercise areas (eg in the Moray Firth), army firing/target areas (eg between the Outer Hebrides and St Kilda or off St Bees Head in Cumbria) and so on. Within these areas, offshore activity may be licensed by the DTI following consultation with the Ministry of Defence.

There are also designated shipping lanes from which drilling operations are prohibited. So, to evaluate a potential target below a sandbank or a shipping lane, the operating company must deviate its well from an approved location away from that sandbank or shipping lane.

Model clauses

The licences granted by the DTI have a number of conditions attached to them known as the Model Clauses. The Model Clauses are amended from time to time and as such the Model Clauses applying to a licence depend upon the Licensing Round in which the licence was granted. The Petroleum Act 1998 states that: 'The Secretary of State shall make regulations prescribing … (e) model clauses which shall, unless he thinks fit to modify or exclude them in any particular case, be incorporated in any such licence.'[10] The Model Clauses are published in secondary legislation and in older licences are incorporated by a single paragraph at the start of the licence. An example taken from a 1979 licence states that:

> 'Clause 1, Clauses 6–8, Clauses 12–24, 26–30 and 32–41 of the Model Clauses for production licences in seaward areas set out in Schedule 5 to the Petroleum (Production) Regulations 1976 (SI 1976 No 1129) as amended by the Petroleum (Production) (Amendment) Regulations 1978 (SI 1978 No 929)

> shall be incorporated herein and shall have effect as if herein set out at length subject to the following modifications.'

However, in new licences granted by the DTI the Model Clauses are set out in full within the licence, in order to make it easier to read and understand the licence without having to refer to the legislation. Currently the Model Clauses are found in the Petroleum Licensing (Exploration and Production) (Seaward and Landward Areas) Regulations 2004 (SI 2004 No 352). However, the licence terms in the 1979 licence example are not affected by the current Model Clauses in issue and so anyone wishing to become a party to this licence should refer to the Model Clauses in the licence itself and not the current set of Model Clauses. It is vital that companies check which Model Clauses apply to a particular licence and these will vary depending on the type and vintage of licence.

A licence is in the form of a contract between the Secretary of State and the licensees and, as with any contract, can only be amended by agreement between the parties or by legislation. Thus, subsequent amendments to the Model Clauses contained in new regulations after the date on which the licence was granted do not have any impact on existing licences unless an agreement is made between the parties or brought into effect by legislation.

Current licence terms

After the section incorporating the Model Clauses into the licence, the next common clause relates to the right to search, bore for, and get petroleum. Such a clause will normally state that:

> 'The Minister hereby grants to the Licensee EXCLUSIVE LICENCE AND LIBERTY during the continuance of this licence and subject to the provisions hereof to search and bore for, and get, petroleum in the seabed and subsoil under the seaward area comprising an area of 578.2 square kilometres more particularly described in Schedule 1 to this licence being the area comprising Block(s) [number] and [number], and parts of [number] and [number] on the reference map deposited at the principal office of the Department of Energy: Provided that nothing in this licence shall affect the right of the Minister to grant a methane drainage Licence in respect of the whole or any part of the licensed area or affect the exercise of any rights so granted.'

This is the clause that gives the licensee the right to search for and produce 'petroleum' (which includes oil, condensate and gas) and defines the geographical area which the licence covers. The licence grants an 'exclusive' right to the holders of the licence to explore for and produce petroleum in the blocks described in the licence. The exclusive nature of the licence is important and anyone subsequently wishing to become a party to the licence must have prior approval from the Secretary of State for Trade and Industry. After such approval is obtained the new party will enter into a Deed of Assignment with one or more of the existing licensees as the means by which they become a licensee under the licence.

Term

The next common clause in older licences is the term of the licence, outlining when it commences and when it expires. These clauses are straightforward and easily understood. As an example it may read: 'This licence unless sooner determined under the provisions hereof shall be and continue in force for the term commencing on the date hereof and ending on 15th March 2018.'

There will be other provisions within the licence which can lead to the licence coming to a premature end. However, normally the licence will run until its expiry date. This does, however, raise an interesting issue. What happens if the licence expires prior to the cessation of production from a field? Generally, there is no right to extend the period stated in the licence and it simply terminates at the end of the term stated in the licence. When a licence is granted initially the term should afford the licensee sufficient time to carry out the works in the field and complete the production phase by the time the licence expires. Nevertheless, the position is not inflexible and the Secretary of State for Trade and Industry has discretion to extend the period of a licence should he see fit. If a licensee is in the production process, it is clearly not in their interests for this to be brought to an abrupt end by virtue of the fact that the licence term has expired. Instead, it is most likely in these circumstances that an extension to the term of the licence would be granted. If it looks likely that the production phase will overrun the period of the licence, then the DTI will make a formal extension to the licence term provided that the obligations under the licence continue to be performed. Clause 6 of the current Model Clauses states:

> 'Where this licence has continued in force by virtue of clause 5 of this licence for a total period of eighteen years after the expiry of the Third Term, the Minister, on application being made to him in writing not later than three months before the expiry of such period, may in his discretion agree with the Licensee that this licence shall continue in force thereafter for such further period as the Minister and the Licensee may agree and subject to such modification of the terms and conditions of this licence (which modification may include making provision for any further extension of the term of this licence) as the Minister and the Licensee may then agree is appropriate.'[11]

Licence surrenders

The Model Clauses also regulate the surrender of parts of the licensed area. Licensees are able to either surrender the entire licence or merely part of a licence should they wish, subject to certain conditions imposed by the DTI being met. Clause 7 of the Model Clauses states: 'Without prejudice to any obligation or liability imposed by or incurred under the terms hereof the Licensee may at any time by giving to the Minister not less than one month's notice in writing to that effect determine this licence or surrender any part of the Licensed Area being a part which complies with clause 9 hereof.'[12]

However, the right to relinquish areas is subject to two main restrictions. First, Model Clause 9(2) states that: 'The surrender by the Licensee of any area pursuant to clauses 4, 5 or 8 of this licence shall not, unless the Minister has otherwise agreed in writing before the date on which the appropriate notice is given by the Licensee to the Minister, result in the creation of a Fragmented Licensed Area.'[13] Second, if there are obligations under the licence that are incapable of being fulfilled should a surrender take place, then the DTI will not permit the relinquishment.

The licensees under recent Seaward Production Licences incorporating these Model Clauses, therefore, require to give the DTI one month's notice prior to relinquishing an area by submitting the Licence Determination Form to the DTI. Some of the early Seaward Production Licences specify a six-month notice period that must be given to the DTI prior to surrendering an area. The DTI guidelines do suggest that irrespective of such notice period within the licence, they will generally accept only one month's notice. However, licensees should be aware that the DTI are entitled to insist upon the six-month notice period if it is specified in the licence, particularly where wells require to be plugged and abandoned. The DTI guidance to licensees is that they should ensure that there are no producing or suspended wells within the area they wish to relinquish prior to submitting an application to surrender. Licensees should also make sure that if they do relinquish an area under a licence they enter into an assignment of their rights under the licence to the remaining participants, leaving the exiting licensee with no beneficial interest under the licence. It is usual for the assignment to be effective on the same date as the surrender. The assignment is not automatic and failure to do so could result in the licensee continuing to have obligations under the licence despite the fact that they no longer retain a beneficial interest in the licence. All assignments need the Secretary of State's prior permission.

Keeping records

Under the current Model Clauses the DTI requires licensees to record the quantity of petroleum which they are producing. Clause 12(1) of the Model Clauses states that:

> 'The Licensee shall keep within the United Kingdom full and correct accounts in a form from time to time approved by the Minister of –

(a) the quantity of Petroleum in the form of gas won and saved;
(b) the quantity of Petroleum in any other form won and saved;
(c) the name and address of any person to whom any Petroleum has been supplied by the Licensee, the quantity so supplied, the price thereof or other consideration therefor and the place to which the Petroleum was conveyed pursuant to the agreement for such supply; and
(d) such other particulars as the Minister may from time to time direct.'[14]

Further, Model Clauses 26 and 27, entitled 'Licensee to Keep Records' and 'Returns', prescribe the procedure with regard to making the quarterly returns of petroleum production required by the DTI.

Working obligations

Clause 12 of the Model Clauses for Production Licences outlines the work obligations imposed on the licensee and declares that 'the Licensee shall before the expiry of the Initial Term of this licence carry out the Work Programme'.[15] The Work Programme is the amount of work that the prospective operator is committed to carry out if a licence is to be awarded by the DTI. It is agreed between the DTI and the applicant and takes the form of a firm commitment within the application to carry out particular exploration work. As part of the application, the prospective operator puts forward a Work Programme and after discussions between the applicants and the DTI, almost invariably involving an interview to clarify any matters, an Agreed Work Programme becomes part of the licence which is granted. At the end of the initial term the licence will expire if the Work Programme which was agreed has not been adhered to. The Agreed Work Programme is, however, a minimum criteria and there is nothing to stop a licensee from carrying out work over and above the Agreed Work Programme should they have the capacity to do so.

Commencement and abandonment of wells

The Model Clauses also deal with the issue regarding the drilling of wells, with clause 15(1) stating that 'the Licensee shall not commence or recommence the drilling of any Well without the consent in writing of the Minister'.[16] Once a well (whether exploration, appraisal, production or injection) has been drilled and production has ceased there is the issue of abandonment which is also addressed by the Model Clauses, with clause 15(2) outlining that, as with the drilling of a well, 'the Licensee shall not abandon any Well without the consent in writing of the Minister'.[17] Further, clause 15(5) states that 'the plugging of any Well shall be done in accordance with a specification approved by the Minister applicable to that Well or to Wells generally or to a class of Wells to which that Well belongs and shall be carried out in an efficient and workmanlike manner'.[18]

Appointment of operators

Under the Model Clauses attached to each licence, the Secretary of State must approve the appointment of an operator. Model Clause 20 states that:

> 'The Licensee shall ensure that another person (including, in the case where the Licensee is two or more persons, any of those persons) does not exercise any function of organising or supervising all or any of the operations of searching or boring for or getting Petroleum in pursuance of this licence unless that other person is a person approved in writing by the Minister and the function in question is one to which that approval relates.'[19]

The parties to a licence nominate an operator and thereafter seek approval from the DTI for their appointment. Frequently, it is the participant in the licence with the largest percentage interest that is nominated as the operator. However, this is not always the case as it is not viable for the large oil companies that have large interests in a number of licences to be operators in the large number of licences to which they are party.

Essentially there are two main types of operator – exploration operators and production operators. The production operator receives approval from the DTI to explore for petroleum, drill for it and produce it, whereas the exploration operator, as the name suggests, simply has DTI approval for the exploration phase, including exploratory drilling but not production. Should an exploration operator, on conclusion of the exploration phase, wish to move into the production stage, a further approval as a production operator would be required before it could commence production. The limited operator, meanwhile, is not approved to do any drilling or production.

However, the DTI can also revoke their approval of an operator should they see fit. Under Model Clause 20(2): 'the Minister shall not refuse to give his approval of a person in pursuance of paragraph (1) of this clause if that person is competent to exercise the function in question, but where an approved person is no longer competent to exercise that function the Minister may, by notice in writing given to the Licensee, revoke his approval'.[20]

2.8 Trust Deeds

The concept of Trust Deeds entered into between parties is also an important aspect to deal with in relation to licensing. Because a licence is granted by the DTI relating to a defined geographical area it is possible, and in the case of older licences, probable, that a licence may cover more than one block. It is in such cases that a Trust Deed is entered into. If the ownership of individual blocks covered by one licence is held by different parties from those who hold another licence then that split ownership interest is normally evidenced by a Trust Deed.

For example, if a licence covers four blocks, 1, 2, 3 and 4, and is granted to companies A, B, C and D, it is not uncommon to find a situation where, although the entire licence area is granted under licence to companies A, B, C and D, only companies, A and B, may be interested in blocks 1 and 2. At the same time, companies C and D may be the only parties interested in blocks 3 and 4. The DTI do not tidy this position up by accepting surrender of a licence and issuing two new licences in order to reflect that ownership interest. Thus, it is the responsibility of all the licensees to enter into a trust arrangement in terms of which they collectively agree to hold blocks 1 and 2 in trust for companies A and B and blocks 3 and 4 in trust for companies C and D. The Trust Deed will contain reciprocal indemnity arrangements in terms of which any liabilities under the licence, or otherwise relating to blocks 1 and 2, are to be met by parties A and B and those relating to blocks 3 and 4 are to be met by parties C and D. In situations where a licence covers more than one block and the ownership of the various blocks is governed by a Trust Deed, each time the licensees change there should be a corresponding novation of the Trust Deed. The purpose of novating the Trust Deed is to clarify the ownership and indemnity arrangements for the blocks covered by the licence.

A Trust Deed is also required where all or part of an existing Licensed Area is require to be divided vertically. (This may happen where the shallow part of a licence is operated by one company or consortium and the deeper parts of a licence is operated by a second company or consortium, whether in the exploration/appraisal phase or in a production phase.)

2.9 Fallow Initiative

With the DTI becoming increasingly worried about certain licensed areas of the UKCS failing to be thoroughly evaluated, and with licensees failing to carry out any substantive work over a period of years during the third term of a licence, PILOT introduced the Fallow Initiative in an effort to address the problem. PILOT originated from the Oil and Gas Industry Task Force which was established in 1998. PILOT itself was formed at the beginning of 2000 to work on the recommendations of the Oil and Gas Industry Task Force and part of its remit related to initiatives on fallow areas within the UKCS.

Each year the DTI announce the blocks or licences which, in their opinion, are fallow and these blocks or licences are classified as being either Fallow A or Fallow B. Licence areas falling within Class A are those licences held by technically competent companies that are doing 'all that can be reasonably expected' of them. As a result, the DTI permits those fallow areas in Class A to be retained by the existing licensees. However, fallow areas whereby the licensees have been unable or unwilling to progress in their activities, as a result of either commercial barriers or the fact that they believe it is uneconomical for them to do so, are classified as Fallow B.

Prior to the DTI classifying the fallow areas, the licensees have the opportunity to attend meetings with the DTI in order to make representations as to the classification of the area in question and thereafter the DTI determines whether the area is Fallow A or Fallow B. The classification process is clearly vital to licensees because a failure to convince the DTI that they are doing as much as can be expected of them as licensees can ultimately lead to them losing the licence. This initiative is in line with the DTI's ethos of 'use it or lose it', with the DTI aiming to maximise the exploitation of the oil and gas potential of the UKCS.

If a licensee fails to convince the DTI that they are doing all that can reasonably be expected of them then the licence area will fall within Class B and the licensees will have a three-month time frame in which they can generate a plan of renewed activity in the area. However, after that period has elapsed, if the area remains as Fallow B then it will be released onto the Fallow Asset Register of the Licence Information for Trading (LIFT). The area will then be listed as Fallow B on the DTI website for two years, during which time licensees are free to market the asset. After a period of 21 months, licensees and any parties interested in the area are required to report to the DTI with any plans for proposed 'significant activity'. ('Significant activity' could be a commitment to acquiring a new 3D seismic survey or drilling a well – whereas re-processing an existing seismic survey would be unlikely to be deemed to be 'significant'.) If a licensee does not have a firm plan of activity by then, it is required to assign its interest to any co-licensees or third parties that do have a firm plan in place if they request them to do so. If there is a 'significant activity' in the planning stage but it has not yet taken place, then the DTI may allow the licensees a temporary reprieve by re-categorising the area as Fallow BR (Rescued) until it is completed.

The DTI allow a one-year period from the date at which the activity plan is agreed in which this 'significant activity' should take place. Assuming the work is carried out to the satisfaction of the DTI then the discovery will no longer be classified as fallow and will enjoy immunity from fallow status for a period of three years. However, where the DTI are not satisfied with the level of work performed by licensees during the two-year period when the area was categorised as Fallow B, then the licensed area must be relinquished. The relinquished discoveries are then made available by the DTI in the next licensing round. However, before the area is relinquished, licensees must come to an agreement with the DTI to abandon all wells within a particular time. The abandonment obligations can also be assigned at the same time that the interest assignment of the licence to third parties or co-licensees takes place.

The Fallow Initiative is clearly something that licensees should bear in mind from the outset when applying for a licence. As discussed earlier, the DTI do not want companies simply adding to their asset base by taking on licences and not utilising them and the Fallow Initiative goes a long way towards ensuring that activity levels remain at a high level by encouraging licensees to work the areas under their control.

Notes

1 http://www.og.dti.gov.uk
2 http://www.og.dti.gov.uk/upstream/licensing/licawards.htm
3 DTI Guidance Note – Applications for Production Licences (http://www.og.dti.gov.uk).
4 Petroleum Act 1998, s 3(1).
5 Petroleum Act 1998, s 3(3).
6 DTI Guidance Note – Applications for Production Licences – http://www.og.dti.gov.uk
7 DTI Guidance Note – Applications for Production Licences – http://www.og.dti.gov.uk
8 http://www.og.dti.gov.uk/upstream/licensing/licawards.htm
9 DTI Guidance Note – Applications for Production Licences – http://www.og.dti.gov.uk
10 Petroleum Act 1998, s 4(1)(e).
11 The Petroleum Licensing (Exploration and Production) (Seaward and Landward Areas) Regulations 2004 – Model Clauses for Standard Production Licences – cl 6.
12 The Petroleum Licensing (Exploration and Production) (Seaward and Landward Areas) Regulations 2004 – Model Clauses for Standard Production Licences – cl 7.
13 The Petroleum Licensing (Exploration and Production) (Seaward and Landward Areas) Regulations 2004 – Model Clauses for Standard Production Licences – cl 8(2).
14 The Petroleum Licensing (Exploration and Production) (Seaward and Landward Areas) Regulations 2004 – Model Clauses for Standard Production Licences – cl 11(1).
15 The Petroleum Licensing (Exploration and Production) (Seaward and Landward Areas) Regulations 2004 – Model Clauses for Standard Production Licences – cl 12(1).
16 The Petroleum Licensing (Exploration and Production) (Seaward and Landward Areas) Regulations 2004 – Model Clauses for Standard Production Licences – cl 15(1).
17 The Petroleum Licensing (Exploration and Production) (Seaward and Landward Areas) Regulations 2004 – Model Clauses for Standard Production Licences – cl 15(2).
18 The Petroleum Licensing (Exploration and Production) (Seaward and Landward Areas) Regulations 2004 – Model Clauses for Standard Production Licences – cl 15(5).
19 The Petroleum Licensing (Exploration and Production) (Seaward and Landward Areas) Regulations 2004 – Model Clauses for Standard Production Licences – cl 20(1).
20 The Petroleum Licensing (Exploration and Production) (Seaward and Landward Areas) Regulations 2004 – Model Clauses for Standard Production Licences – cl 20(2).

— 3 —

EXPLORATION AND PETROLEUM GEOLOGY

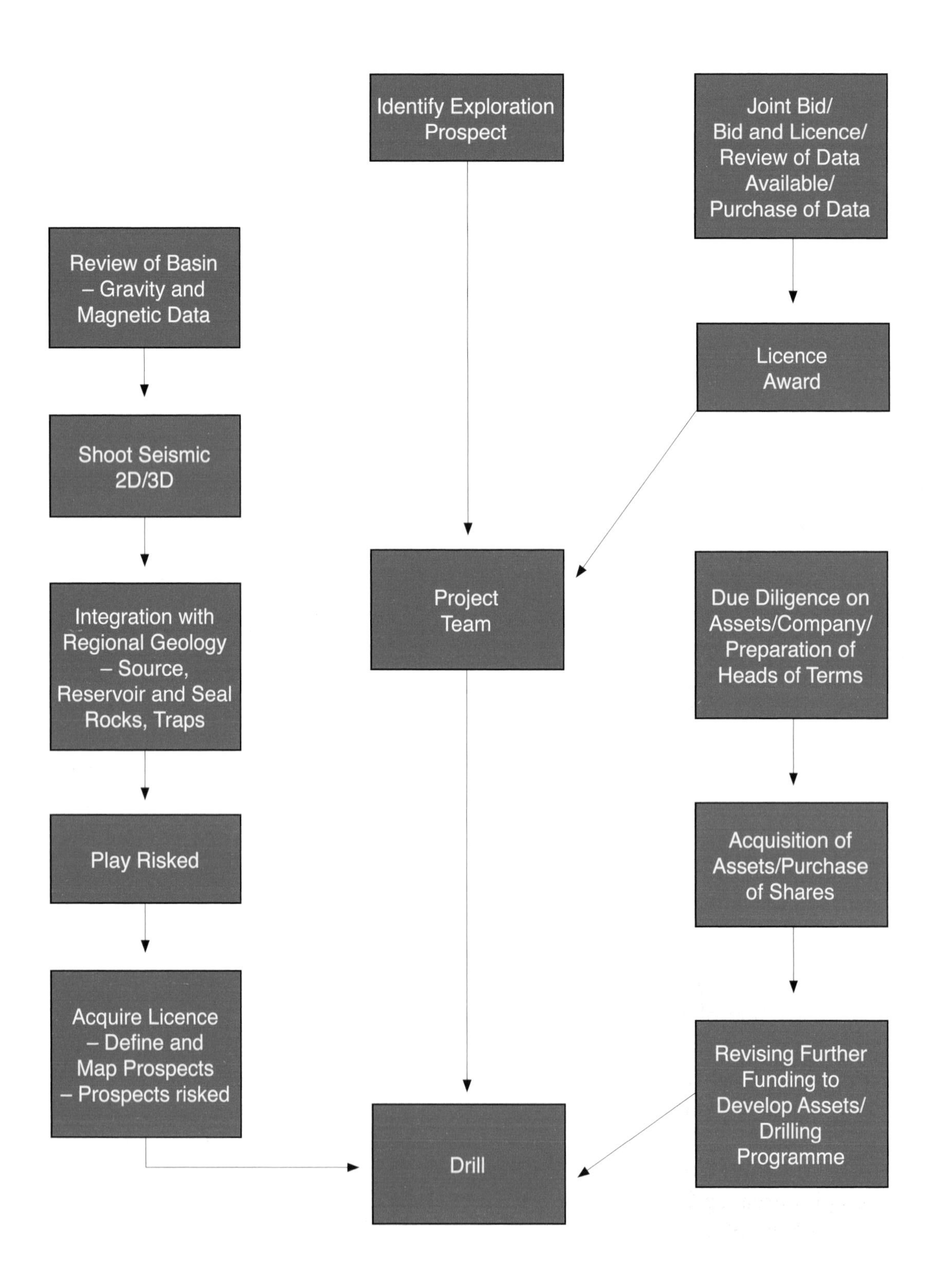

Identify Exploration Prospect
Joint Bid/ Bid and Licence/ Review of Data Available/ Purchase of Data
Review of Basin – Gravity and Magnetic Data
Licence Award
Shoot Seismic 2D/3D
Project Team
Due Diligence on Assets/Company/ Preparation of Heads of Terms
Integration with Regional Geology – Source, Reservoir and Seal Rocks, Traps
Play Risked
Acquisition of Assets/Purchase of Shares
Acquire Licence – Define and Map Prospects – Prospects risked
Revising Further Funding to Develop Assets/ Drilling Programme
Drill

EXPLORATION AND PETROLEUM GEOLOGY

TECHNICAL

3.1 Introduction

Petroleum geology is a complex business full of risks. It is a multidisciplinary science involving geologists of varied backgrounds specialising in structural geology, sedimentology, geophysics, geochemistry and palaeontology. It is, however, the fundamental building block for the discovery and production of hydrocarbon accumulations.

Prior to drilling for hydrocarbons, an area of interest must be identified and analysed with the tools available to the exploration geologist. A **hydrocarbon play** must be identified and all the necessary elements of that understood and risked.

3.2 Concepts and tools

Hydrocarbon play

A hydrocarbon play is a geologic model that describes the source rock (for the hydrocarbon in the reservoir), migration of hydrocarbon (into the reservoir), the reservoir (rock which contains the hydrocarbon), the trap (configuration of the reservoir that holds the hydrocarbon) and the seal (impermeable overlying and lateral rock which retains the hydrocarbon in the reservoir) for an area (Fig. 3–1). The chance of finding all of these geologic aspects needs to be risked for each play area (eg Gluyas and Swarbrick, 2004). This then allows the size/aerial extent of the play, or of individual prospects within the play, to be assessed so

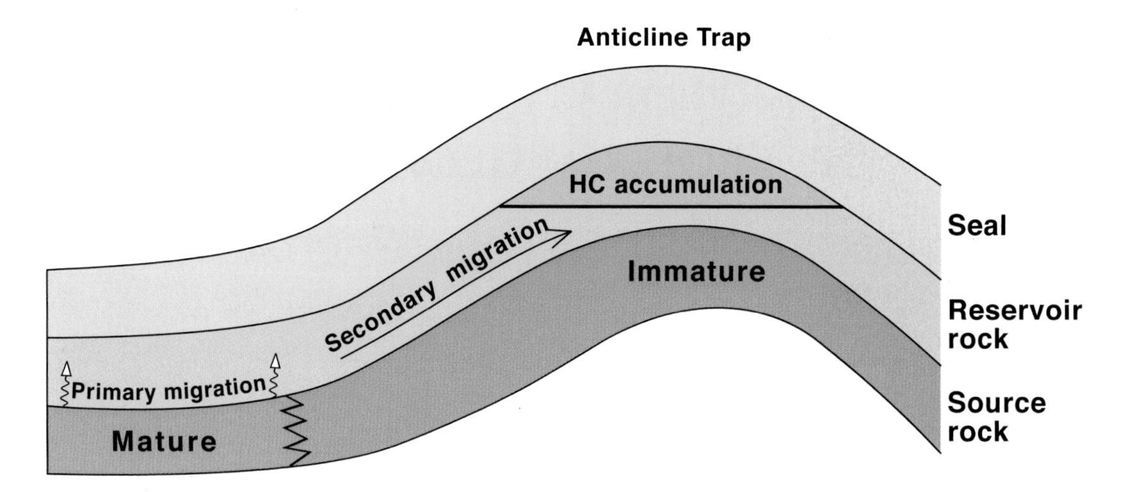

Figure 3–1 Geologic aspects of a hydrocarbon play
Note the five geologic aspects needed for a hydrocarbon accumulation or play: reservoir rock (yellow band – sandstone or carbonate), trap (the dome shape – anticline), seal (overlying blue layer – salt or shale), source rock (underlying red layer – organic rich shale or coal), and hydrocarbon migration (note the vertical and lateral arrows – timing of migration is also important).

that an economic evaluation of the hydrocarbon potential for the area can be made. Combined with considerations of the area's infrastructure and markets, the economic evaluation will then determine the type of commitment a company might be prepared to make in order to obtain a licence for the area (ie typically comprising the acquisition of (more) seismic data, and/or drilling a number of wells).

Data used

The types of information used to define and assess hydrocarbon plays include data from the subsurface (ie well boreholes and seismic) and from surface rock outcrop. The subsurface data are measured either directly from information derived from well boreholes, or from seismic, gravity or magnetic surveys. Borehole data include core and cuttings (actual rock taken from the borehole, Fig. 3–2a), a wide range of electric wireline logs (Fig. 3–2b), and various measurements made while drilling (such as rate of penetration of the drill bit, and fluid and pressure surveys within the borehole). Borehole data contain detailed information about the specific well borehole location (1D depth aspect, Figs 3–2a, 3–2b). Seismic data are not very detailed at the vertical scale (1D depth aspect), but cover a large horizontal area (2D lateral aspect, Fig. 3–2c). A group of 2D seismic lines can be acquired close to each other (12.5 m or 25 m spacing between lines), which creates a seismic volume over an area: the 3D survey (Fig. 3–2d). Seismic data will be discussed in more detail later (see section 3.3).

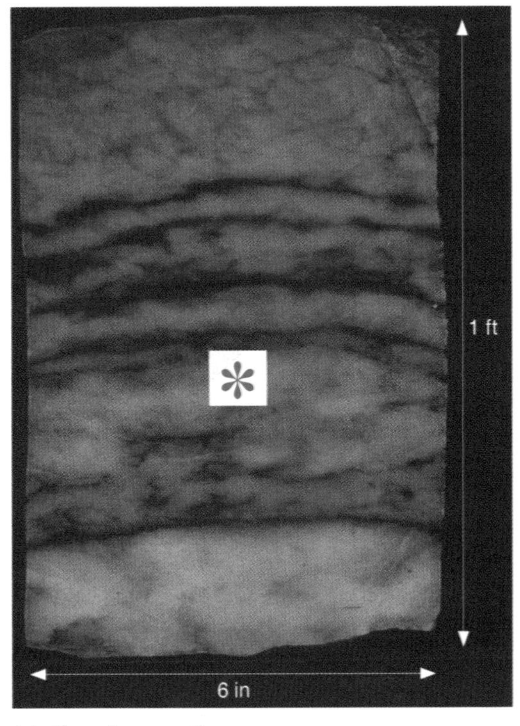

(a) Core from well

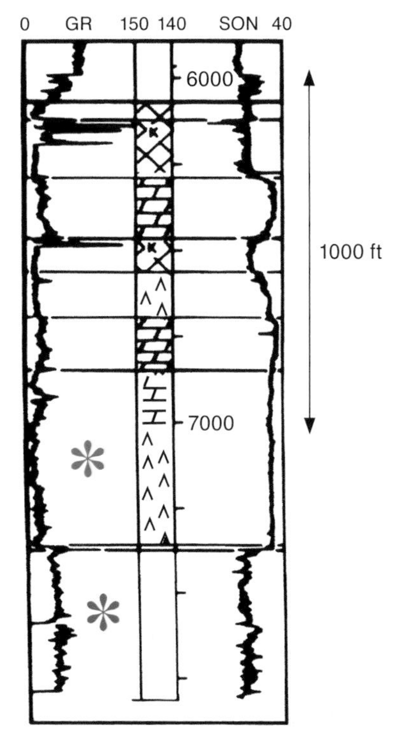

(b) Electric wireline well logs

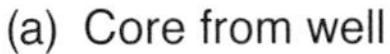

* Salt * Sandstone

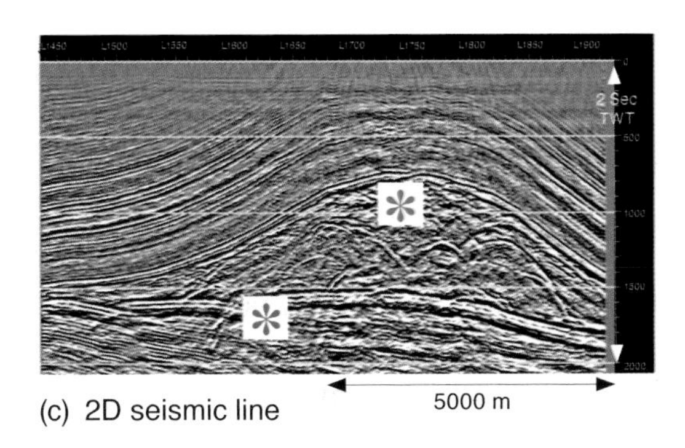

(c) 2D seismic line

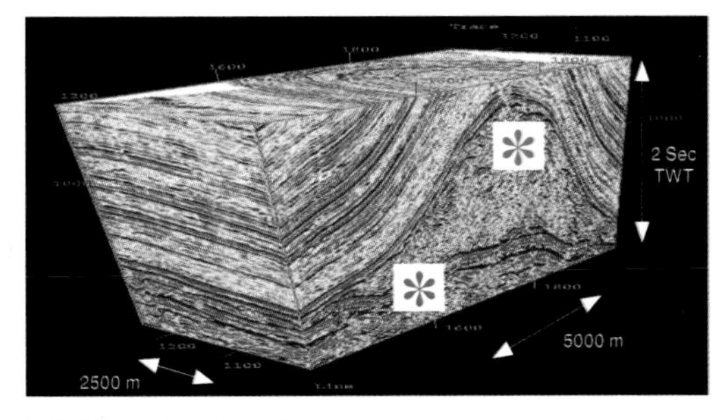

(d) 3D seismic volume

Figure 3–2 Types of subsurface data
(a) A piece of salt core from a borehole: note that the diameter of the core is 6 inches. (b) A set of electric wireline well logs from a borehole. The log on the left is a gamma ray and the one on the right is a sonic log which measures velocity of the rock. Note that this 2000 ft of log passes through both salt and sandstone, and each different rock type has a different log pattern. (c) A 2D seismic line through a salt dome: note the mound-shaped feature in the centre of the line. The vertical scale is 2 seconds of TWT (two-way time), while the horizontal scale is distance. (d) A 3D seismic volume from a workstation. The 3D volume is made of a number of closely spaced 2D seismic lines, and can be sliced in the horizontal plane (top of the cube).

Each type of data provide a different scale of geologic information (Fig. 3–3). The outcrop allows the identification of great detail in the rock, but not for a large lateral extent (photo in Fig. 3–3). The electric wireline well log gives detail around the well borehole location (note the red line in Fig. 3–3 which is a gamma ray log that shows the difference between sand and silt). A seismic trace images poor vertical detail (note that a single black and white wiggle of the seismic averages 30 m of rock information in Fig. 3–3), but covers a large lateral extent with a seismic survey (Fig. 3–2d).

The well borehole data are used to assess and predict the extent and quality of the reservoir, seal and source rock potential in the area, while the seismic data are mainly used to image large-scale subsurface structures (traps and possible hydrocarbon migration routes). Surface outcrops of areas analogous to the subsurface data are studied for detailed vertical and horizontal information that will enhance the subsurface data interpretation. The goal of the geologist and geophysicist in a company is to incorporate all the available subsurface data to define a coherent and geologically feasible hydrocarbon play for an area. This play is then risked to assess the economic interest and level of commitment a company will make in a potential hydrocarbon area.

3.3 Seismic data

The largest subsurface data set used in the oil industry is reflection seismic data. Information about buried rock layers within the earth can be obtained from seismic data. Seismic data are used at various scales, from mapping out large-scale structures (ie the salt dome in Figs 3–2c, 3–2d), to looking at detailed rock changes within the reservoir layer (ie using 4D seismic in the development field stage to find remaining hydrocarbon to produce). Seismic surveys are recorded and displayed as 2D lines (Fig. 3–2c), where the horizontal axis is distance (metres) and the vertical axis is two-way time (TWT) in seconds. A 3D seismic survey (Fig. 3–2d) is a group of closely spaced 2D lines (ie 12.5 m or 25 m line spacing). A 4D seismic survey is a second 3D seismic survey acquired a number of years after the initial 3D survey and production of a field, thus any changes on the second 3D seismic survey (4D) are due to fluid and pressure changes in the reservoir caused by production over a number of years. The following section will discuss some of the basic concepts of the reflection seismic principle, acquisition, processing and interpretation of reflection seismic data.

Concepts

Reflection seismic data are the recording of sound waves which are reflected off subsurface rock layers (seismic traces in Fig. 3–4). This is the same principle

Figure 3–3 Scale of data: outcrop to well log to seismic wiggle trace
The vertical scale of the outcrop is about 30 m (90 ft) high, 45 m (130 ft) in width. Note the detail available on the geology at this tidal channel sand outcrop. The red line shows what a gamma ray log would look like at that vertical location on the outcrop (ie if a well had been drilled at that spot): note that the deflection to the right indicates less sand. The black line shows a black and white seismic wiggle for this location: note that the seismic wiggle combines a large amount of rock information into a single wiggle.

as a sound echo, which is what happens when one shouts in a canyon and the sound (ie shout) is echoed (ie reflected back) off the canyon wall. In the subsurface, different geologic layers (ie shale, sandstone and carbonate in Fig. 3–4) have different acoustic impedance properties (ie velocities and densities). The surfaces between these geologic layers are called reflectors (ie reflectors 1–4 in Fig. 3–4) and cause the reflection of sound waves back off these surfaces up to the receivers (coloured arrows on Fig. 3–4). The depth to the subsurface reflectors can then be calculated by measuring the time taken for the reflected sound to reach the receivers (ie the reflections on the seismic traces in Fig. 3–4).

Acquisition and interpretation

The acquisition of reflection seismic data requires an acoustic source, and a number of receivers. The acoustic source is usually an air gun for offshore seismic (Fig. 3–4), and either dynamite or vibroseis for onshore seismic. The receivers are called hydrophones and are towed on a cable behind the ship for offshore data (Fig. 3–4), or are called geophones for onshore data. The acoustic source sends a sound wave down into the earth (downgoing black lines in Fig. 3–4). As the sound wave hits the reflectors, some of the sound energy is reflected back up to the receivers (coloured arrows in Fig. 3–4). The time it takes for this reflected energy to arrive at the receiver is recorded, and plotted as a reflection on the seismic trace (Fig. 3–4). A seismic line is composed of a number of traces (ie the recordings from each receiver, R1–R3 in Fig. 3–4), which are plotted on a vertical axis of two-way time (TWT), because the recorded sound waves are composed of the downgoing wave from the source and the reflected upgoing wave from the geologic reflector.

Once the seismic reflection data have been recorded, various processing steps are done to enhance the geologic reflections and to decrease the noise on the data. The types of processing are not discussed here, but the reader is

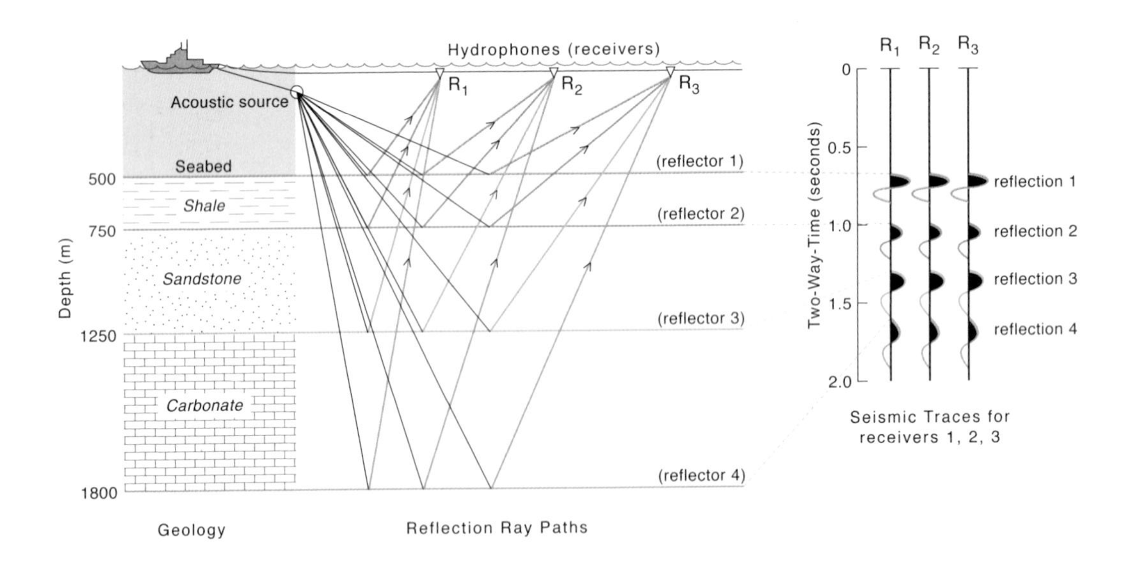

Figure 3–4 Reflection seismic acquisition

The subsurface geology is shown on the left, the reflected sound ray paths in the centre, and the resulting recorded seismic traces from the receivers on the right. Each layer of different subsurface geology (reflector) causes a reflected wave (coloured arrows) which is recorded at a receiver. The recordings are plotted in two-way time and make the reflections on a seismic line. The figure is colour coded to indicate the geologic reflector which produces a reflected wave that is then recorded as a distinct reflection on the seismic.

referred to Keary et al. (2002) for more information on processing. The final processed seismic line is then interpreted to produce a geological play concept, or reservoir model for an area. The interpretation of a seismic line is not always straightforward, and one needs to keep in mind the 'scale' of the geology that is averaged and represented by one seismic wiggle, ie one black and white loop of a reflection (Fig. 3–3). In a seismic interpretation, all available well data need to be used to calibrate the seismic response.

Figure 3–5a shows an interpreted seismic line, where the top of salt reflection has been interpreted as the green line and the top of an underlying sandstone reflection in red. Once the reflections are interpreted on the seismic lines, time maps of the reflections are made (top of salt map in Fig. 3–5b) and these maps are used to locate subsurface structures and potential areas to drill for hydrocarbon plays. This particular map shows a dome (anticlinal) shape which is a good type of structural trap. Seismic lines are interpreted in time, and are then converted back to geologic depth by using the velocity of the rock layers causing the reflections.

Seismic data rooms

Large volumes of seismic data (2D and 3D) have been built up worldwide over the years. These are owned either by the exploration companies or by seismic service companies (speculative surveys).

When acreage is put up for sale, the vendors invite prospective buyers to view all proprietary data, including seismic, in 'data rooms'. Non-proprietary data sets (owned by the seismic service companies) are also available in virtual data rooms which use the internet where clients can view the data online.

Effect of shooting seismic on the environment

Certain areas in the North Sea (and other offshore areas) are particularly sensitive in terms of the wildlife associated with them, eg fisheries, seabirds, etc. Seismic surveys, because they utilise sound, can have a disturbing effect on marine animals. Any seismic survey therefore requires permission from the DTI. It is necessary to submit an environmental assessment to support the application together with an additional 'survey close-out form' at the end of the survey.

3.4 Source rocks and the origin of petroleum

The carbon cycle

Most carbon on the earth is held in sediments in the form of limestones. Less than 20% is in the form of organic carbon (eg trees, algae, plankton) and

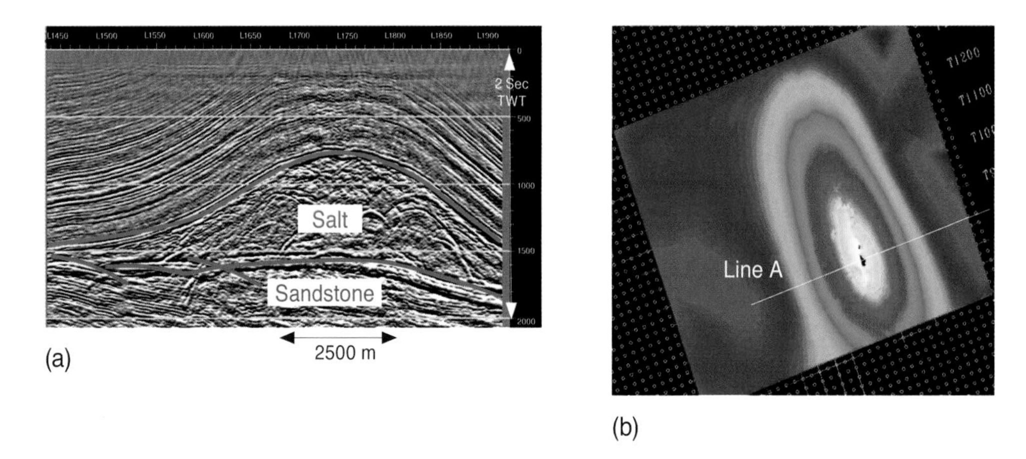

Figure 3–5 Seismic line and horizon map
(a) A 2D seismic line (Line A) where the top of the salt reflection (seal) is interpreted in green, and the top of the sandstone reflection (reservoir) is interpreted in red. (b) This is a time map of the top of the salt reflection, and the dome shape can be clearly seen. Yellow = shallow, purple = deep. The horizontal width of the dome is c. 7000 m.

most of this is quickly changed to the gas carbon dioxide which goes back into the atmosphere or hydrosphere. Only a tiny proportion of the organic carbon becomes trapped in sediments which, given time and burial, may become a source rock (Fig. 3–6), eg shales.

Kerogen

Kerogen is the organic matter that is found in sediments which turns into oil and gas. It is both physically trapped and chemically bonded within the source rock. High temperatures are required to break these bonds and generate hydrocarbons.

There are two main types of kerogen (Fig. 3–6):

- *oil-prone kerogen* which is derived from marine phytoplankton, algae and the waxy components of land plants (leaf cuticles, resin, spores and pollen); and
- *gas-prone kerogen* which is derived from the woody material of land plants.

Source rocks were deposited many millions of years ago and the type of kerogen found depends on the sedimentary environment at the time. For example, the kerogen which sourced the gas in the Southern North Sea was deposited during the Carboniferous geological period (c. 300 million years ago) in freshwater swamps and is dominated by land plant material in coals. Much of the oil in

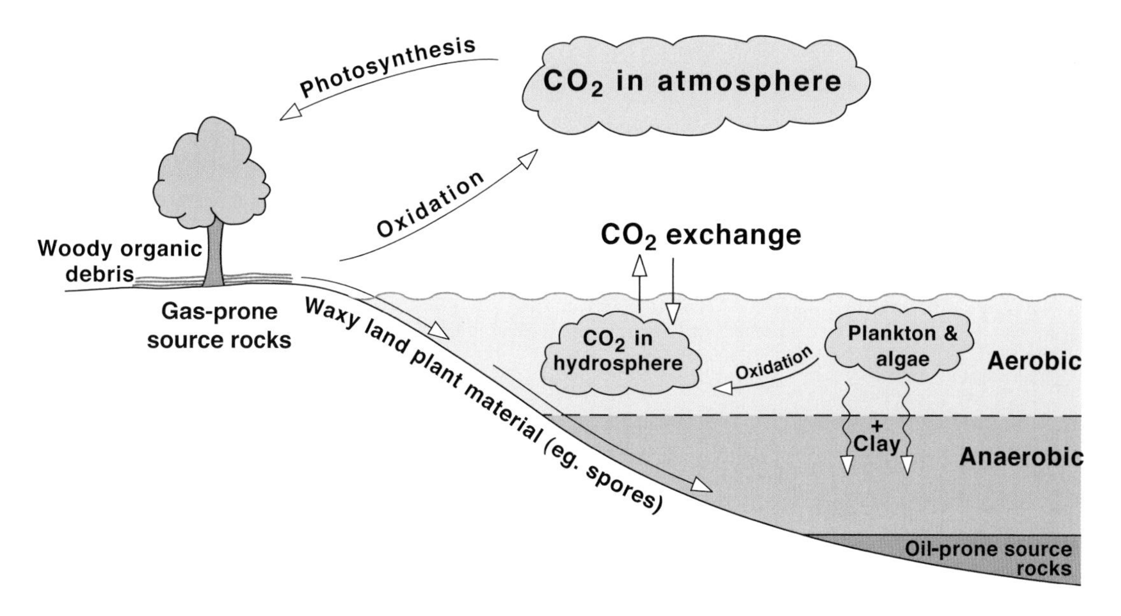

Figure 3–6 The carbon cycle
The carbon cycle showing exchange in carbon between the atmosphere, hydrosphere and geosphere. Oil-prone source rocks originate from marine organic matter and waxy land plant material while gas-prone source rocks are derived from woody organic debris. Most organic matter decays and is recycled in the hydrosphere and atmosphere. Much less than 1% is stored in the geosphere as source rocks.

the Central and Northern North Sea, however, was generated from source rocks which were deposited during the Jurassic geological period (c. 150 million years ago) in a deepwater, marine environment (the Kimmeridge Clay, a shale). Different types of source rocks are found across the world.

Source rock richness

It is important to measure how much organic matter a source rock contains – referred to as the source rock richness. One of the most common measurements is the Total Organic Carbon (TOC). To be considered a potential source rock, a sediment should contain more than 2% TOC. As the sediment generates hydrocarbons (ie as it matures), this figure will decrease. An exceptionally rich source rock such as the Kimmeridge Clay in the North Sea can contain between 6 and 12% TOC when immature (ie prior to generating hydrocarbons).

Generation

Whether or not a source rock will generate hydrocarbons depends on three factors:

- temperature;
- kerogen type; and
- source rock richness.

The most important of these is temperature. A source rock can generate hydrocarbons only if it has been subjected to very high temperatures over a period of geological time. This happens naturally as a source rock is buried within the Earth's crust. The deeper it is buried, the higher the temperature to which it is exposed.

- Oil is generated from oil-prone kerogen (eg marine phytoplankton) at burial temperatures around 80–150°C. If any oil is trapped in the source rock, it will be cracked to gas within the source rock at temperatures of around 150–180°C.
- Gas is generated from gas-prone kerogen (eg wood) at temperatures around 150–230°C.

Migration

Two main phases of migration occur:

- *primary migration*; and
- *secondary migration.*

Primary migration is the expulsion of hydrocarbons from the source rock into the porous carrier bed. The generation of hydrocarbon molecules is accompanied by a large volume increase, which increases the pressure within the source rock. This overpressure is released by fracturing and this allows the hydrocarbons to flow out of the source rock.

Expulsion is easier from organic-rich source rocks where multiple episodes of generation can take place. Rich, oil-prone source rocks expel most (70–90%) of their petroleum yield as oil over the temperature range 100–150°C. A lean oil-prone source rock will generate oil over the same temperature but may not generate sufficient hydrocarbons to cause fracturing and therefore no expulsion occurs. If raised to higher temperatures, the oil will be cracked to gas and the resulting volume increase and overpressure may allow expulsion.

Secondary migration occurs once the hydrocarbons have been expelled from the source rock into the carrier bed (Fig. 3–7). The carrier bed is a porous and permeable rock which hydrocarbons can move through to reach a reservoir rock and trap structure given geological time, a process which will take millions of years.

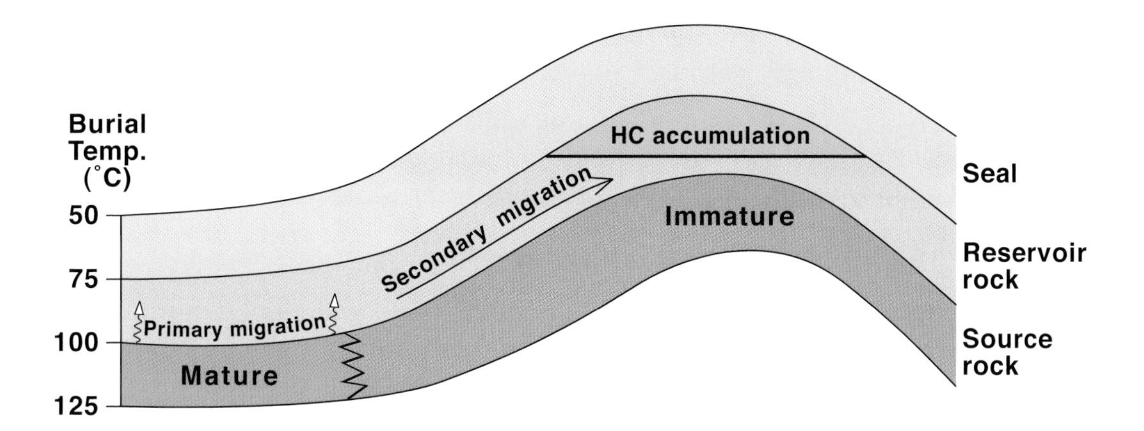

Figure 3–7 Generation and migration
At shallow burial depths, a source rock is said to be immature, ie no hydrocarbons have been generated. As burial depth (and hence temperature) increases above 80°C, the source rock begins to mature. Hydrocarbons are then generated and expelled into the carrier bed during primary migration. They move up-dip along the carrier bed into the reservoir due to buoyancy where they accumulate if a suitable trap and seal are present.

One of the main driving forces behind secondary migration is buoyancy, which is a function of the difference in density between hydrocarbons and the pore waters that are found in the carrier beds. Hydrocarbons will rise through the more dense water filling the carrier rock pores until they reach a sealing rock (a rock in which the pores or spaces are too narrow to allow movement) where they will either stay in place or move laterally until a seal and trap are encountered (Fig. 3–7).

Classification of natural gas and oils

Petroleum is made up of mainly carbon (C) and hydrogen (H). Thousands of different molecules exist in petroleum and source rocks, ranging from methane (CH_4) to very complex chemical structures (Fig. 3–8). Because of this, it is necessary to classify them into a small number of groups. In the laboratory, hydrocarbons can be physically separated into five main groups:[1]

(a) *Natural gas and natural gas liquids*: methane, ethane, propane, butane, pentane. Low-number alkane hydrocarbons with the general formula C_nH_{2n+2}, where n is less than 6.

(b) *Paraffins*: a common name for high molecular weight alkane hydrocarbons with the general formula C_nH_{2n+2}, which are liquids at room temperature. These are the most common and best understood of the oils. Sometimes they are referred to as saturated hydrocarbons or alkanes and have straight chains. Naphthenes (C_nH_{2n}) are paraffins which have a cyclic structure (eg cyclopentane).

(c) *Aromatics*: eg benzene, toluene, each having the chemical formula C_nH_n and have a cyclic structure containing double carbon bonds.

(d) *Asphaltenes.*

(e) *Residues.*

The latter two groups are relatively minor and less well understood, although in some cases, eg heavy oils, the proportions of these fractions can be significant. A considerable amount of specialised literature exists as deposition of these products in pipelines can create major problems.

Composition of natural gas and oil

The principal component of natural gas is methane (CH_4) but it is often present with smaller quantities of higher hydrocarbons such as ethane, propane, butane and pentane (n = 2 to 5).

Most oils comprise a mixture of long-chain alkanes where n > 5 and aromatic compounds. Additional elements may be present such as sulphur, nitrogen, oxygen, nickel and vanadium. Of these, sulphur is the most common, mainly in the form of organo–sulphur compounds. Sulphur contents are known to reach

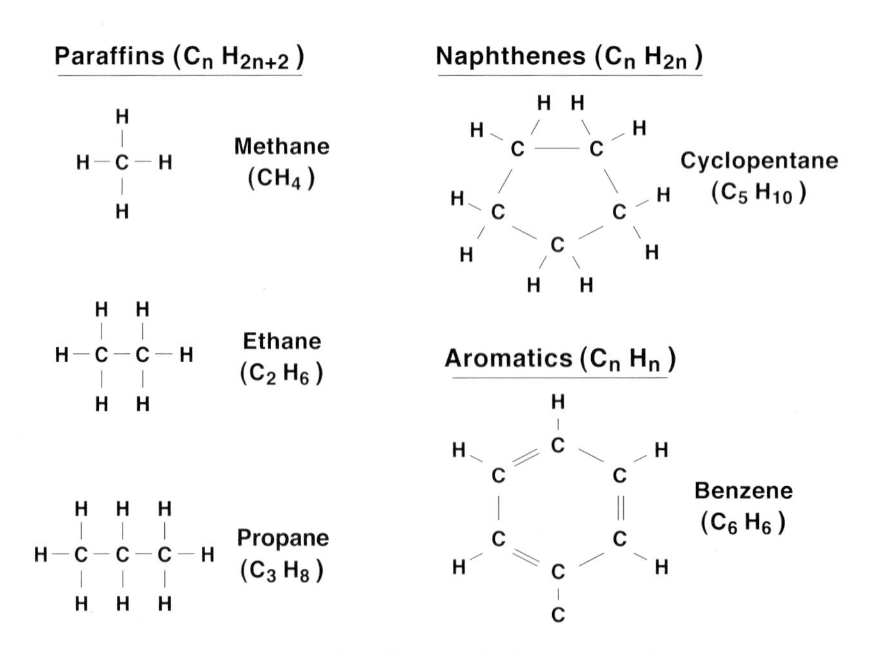

Figure 3–8 Classification of oils and natural gas
The chemical structure of common hydrocarbon molecules. Most oils and gases are composed of straight-chain hydrocarbons but can contain some cyclic hydrocarbons (naphthenes and aromatics).

up to 10% in rare cases although usually it is between 0 and 5%. Excess sulphur in crudes can present significant difficulties during both the production and refining stages.

API and heavy oils

API gravity or °API (American Petroleum Institute), is an arbitrary scale based on the specific gravity (SG) of an oil at 60°F calculated using the following formula:

$$°API = (141.5/SG) - 131.5, \text{ or}$$
$$SG = 141.5/(131.5 + °API)$$

Typically, oil will float on water as it has a lower specific gravity (water has a specific gravity of 1 and hence an API of 10°) and light crudes will have APIs in the range 22–40°. There are cases, however, where oils have higher specific gravity than water (eg heavy oils, tar sands, asphalts) and in these cases API gravities will be less than c. 22° (Fig. 3–9). These oils pose greater production problems in terms of their viscosity and often contain more undesirable impurities such as sulphur.

3.5 Reservoirs

Reservoir rocks need to be both porous and permeable. Porosity and permeability are controlled by the characteristics of the sediment (eg grain size and type) and the changes that have occurred during burial of that sediment (diagenesis). There are two main types of reservoir rock:

- *clastic*, eg delta sands, deep water sands; and
- *carbonate*, eg reefs, shoals, chalks, dolomites.

Reservoirs can also occur in other rock types if they have been fractured, eg fractured granite in Vietnam. These, however, are more unusual.

Clastics

Clastic sediments are generated by the erosion and weathering of pre-existing rocks such as granite, metamorphic rocks or pre-existing sandstones. This occurs in continental areas. The sediments that are generated by these processes are carried downstream and deposited in a variety of environments such as alluvial and river systems, beach and shallow marine environments and, eventually, deep marine environments. An example of this process are the sediments generated by erosion in the Cairngorm mountains some of which are deposited along major river systems such as the Spey and the Dee, with finer grains finally reaching coastal areas and further out into the deeper waters of the Moray Firth and the North Sea.

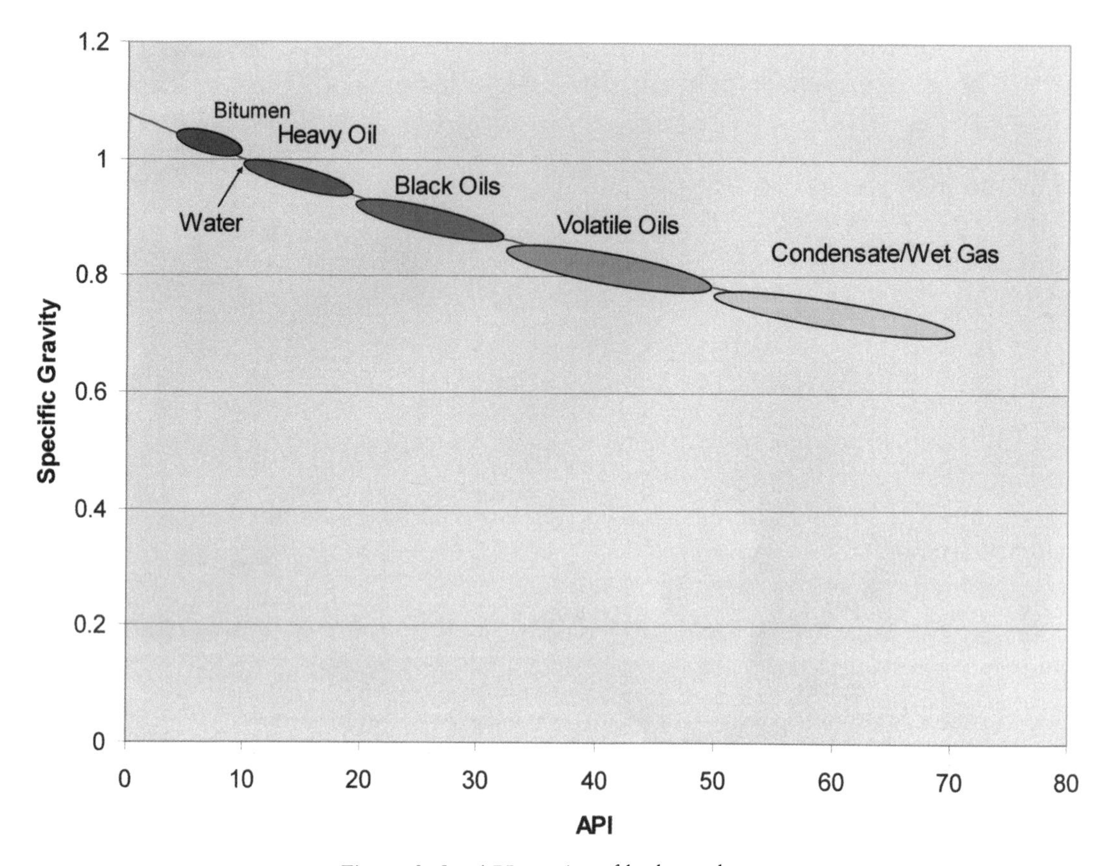

Figure 3–9 API gravity of hydrocarbons
API gravity gives an indication of the thickness or viscosity of a hydrocarbon. Heavy oils are very difficult to move or pour while bitumen is near-solid. Significant proportions of the world's hydrocarbon reserves have APIs less than 20 and present significant difficulties when trying to extract them from a reservoir or move them downstream to a refinery.

Each environment has its own sedimentary characteristics which can be used to identify in which environment the sedimentary rocks were deposited. This can be particularly useful in the oil industry when trying to predict the occurrence and geometry of reservoir rocks in the subsurface.

The reservoirs of the North Sea are dominated by clastic sands, eg the Brent Delta system (Fig. 3–10). Clastic sediments are also important in the Gulf of Mexico, the Southern Atlantic and elsewhere worldwide.

Carbonates

Carbonate sediments (or limestones) are generated on shallow marine shelves due to the accumulation of shells (eg mussels, corals, etc.) with additional contributions from other carbonate grains such as mud pellets and inorganic

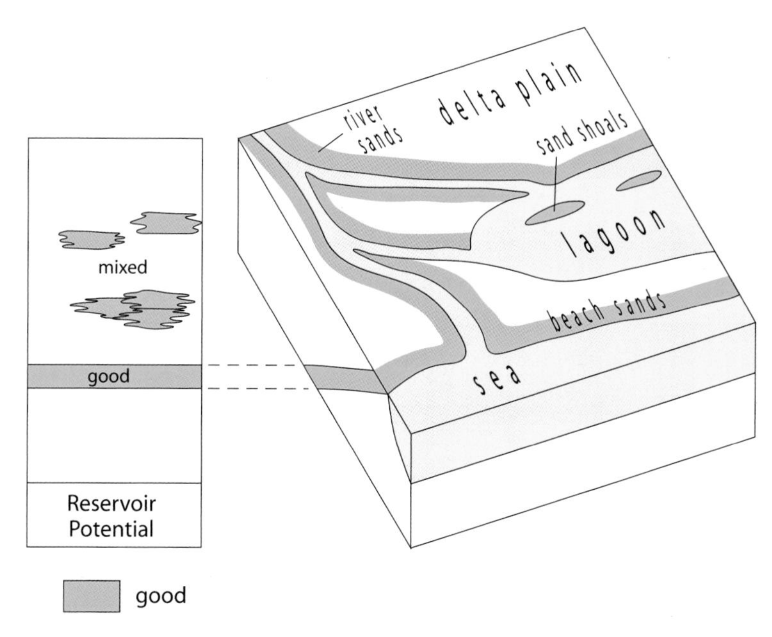

Figure 3–10 Schematic diagram of a clastic reservoir
(eg Brent, modified after Schlumberger, UKOOA/NHM, 1997)
Rocks with good reservoir quality are only found in the sands that were deposited by water (eg the river system, along the palaeo-coastline).

grains (ooids). Unlike clastic sediments, carbonates have a predominantly biogenic origin and are usually produced locally. As such, the distribution of carbonate sediments is controlled by environmental factors such as water depth and temperature. The typical setting for modern-day carbonate sedimentation is shallow, warm, tropical seas, eg the Caribbean or the Middle East.

Figure 3–11 shows the typical pattern of sediments found on a carbonate shelf with reefs and carbonate sand shoals along the margin at the 'drop-off' and a quieter water lagoon behind it. In the supra-tidal environment there may be mangrove swamps (eg Florida) or arid sabkhas (eg Middle East) depending on the climate.

Carbonate reservoirs dominate in the Middle East but are also found elsewhere worldwide, eg Western Canada Basin, the Far East, the Caspian Sea.

Porosity

The porosity of a rock is the space between or within its grains or crystals. It is here that the oil is stored. A reservoir rock must be sufficiently porous to hold enough petroleum within a trap to be economically viable. The porosity value therefore has a significant impact on the 'total' reserves or hydrocarbons in place. Porosity can be measured both downhole by well-logging techniques and in the laboratory using core samples. Porosity data are therefore readily available.

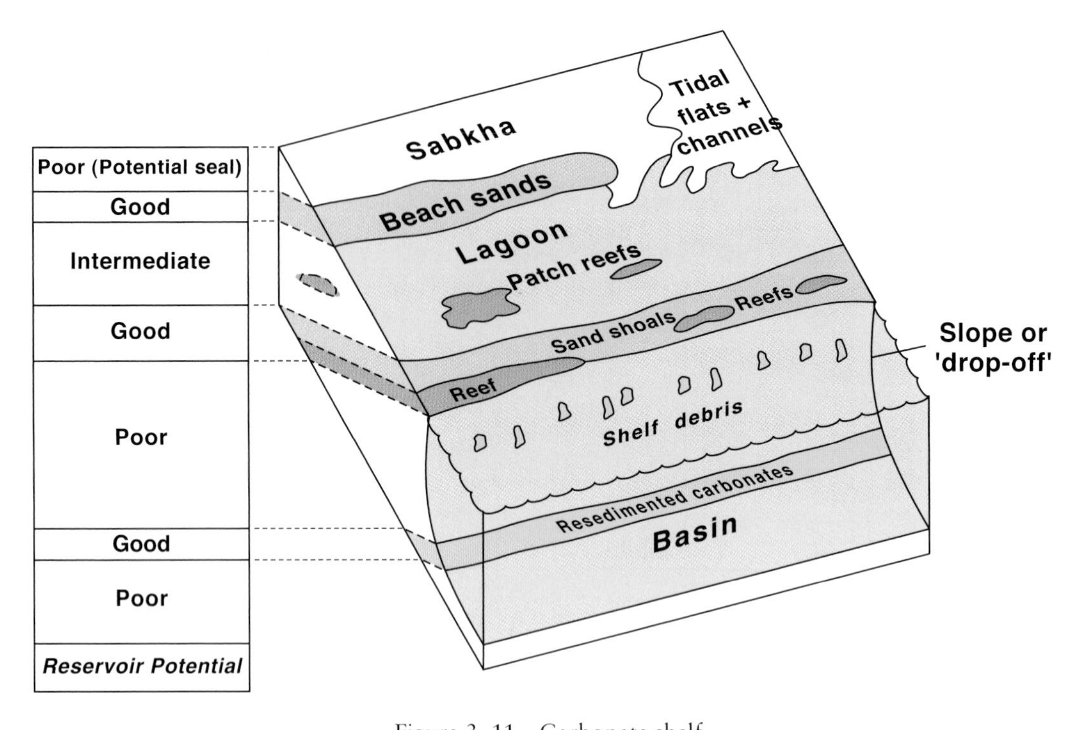

Figure 3–11 Carbonate shelf
Schematic diagram of a carbonate shelf showing where potential reservoir layers are found. Only certain rock types and hence layers will act as reservoirs.

Permeability

If the hydrocarbons in place are to be successfully produced, however, the pores must be sufficiently well connected and this is measured by permeability. The permeability of a rock is a measure of its ability to transmit fluids and is governed by Darcy's Law:

$$Q=KA(dP/dl)$$

Where:

Q= flow rate
K = permeability
A = cross-sectional area
dP/dl = pressure gradient over distance l.

Permeability therefore depends on both the rock properties and the medium being transmitted. It can be measured only in the laboratory, not downhole by well-logging techniques. Although critical to understanding the characteristics of a reservoir, it is not as easily available as porosity data.

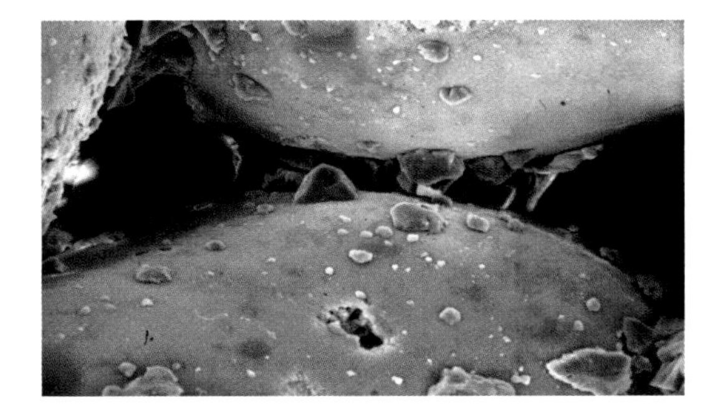

Figure 3–12 Porosity in reservoirs
3D image showing open pore spaces (black) in a permeable reservoir that have been partially filled by mineral growth during burial. This process is called diagenesis. (Circa 1.5 mm wide.)

Reservoir quality

Reservoir quality is therefore a function of both porosity and permeability but the two factors are not simply related. Due to the lack of permeability data, it is common practice to plot porosity against permeability and to look for trends in the data. The implication is that if porosity is known, permeability can be predicted. Most datasets, however, reveal a wide scatter of data where a given porosity value can be associated with permeability values that are several orders of magnitude in difference. Poorly connected porosity or microporosity will have low permeability while fractures can significantly enhance permeability but not porosity.

In both clastics and carbonates, good reservoir quality is only found in specific layers which act as reservoirs (Figs 3–10 and 3–11). Sandstones have an original porosity and permeability controlled by the sediment grain-size, its degree of variation and how the grains are packed together (Fig. 3–12). The growth of minerals during burial (Fig. 3–12) can destroy some of the original porosity and affect permeability. In carbonates, the relationship between porosity and permeability is much more complex due to the physical nature of the original sediments (eg many different types of grains such as different types of shell fragments and peloids) but also because carbonates are much more reactive than sandstones. Once the carbonate sediments have been deposited, any change in water composition will cause both dissolution and cementation of the sediments.

Heterogeneity

Because rocks are natural materials, they will never display identical properties over an area and this is particularly true of reservoir rocks. The degree of internal complexity is termed the 'reservoir heterogeneity' and measures factors such as:

- vertical and aerial distribution of reservoir and non-reservoir facies; and
- porosity and permeability.

It requires an understanding of the depositional setting, burial effects (eg compaction and diagenesis) and the location of barriers to fluid flow (eg depositional or faults).

It is vital to understand reservoir heterogeneity because the models are used in reservoir simulation packages. These are the key to effective production. The degree of heterogeneity influences a project's value in terms of:

- volumetrics and recovery;
- amount of appraisal required; and
- reservoir management and production.

3.6 Traps and seals

Oil and gas fields occur where hydrocarbons have become trapped in porous and permeable reservoir rocks. Migration towards the surface is stopped or slowed down by impermeable rocks such as shales or evaporites which act as seals (Fig. 3–1).

Oil and gas accumulate only where the seal and reservoir rocks are in the right shapes and relative positions to form a trap in which the seal is known as the cap rock.

Traps

There are two main types of trap:

- *Structural traps* (Fig. 3–13) are formed by earth movements which fold or fault rocks into suitable positions.
- *Stratigraphic traps* (Fig. 3–14) occur where a suitable combination of rock types are deposited in a particular sedimentary environment, eg a porous and permeable river sand sealed by clays deposited in the surrounding swamp.

Most traps are usually a complex combination of types. A group of oil or gas fields with similar trap structures or reservoir rocks is called a play, as discussed earlier.

Seals

The existence of a petroleum play depends on the presence of an effective regional *topseal* or *cap rock*. A cap rock is effective if its capillary displacement pressure

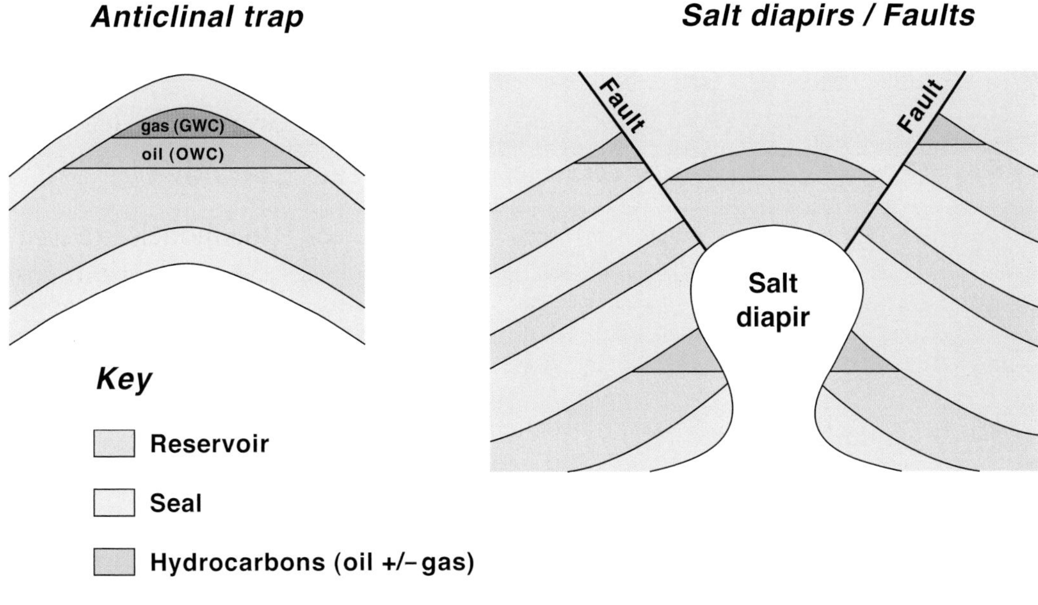

Figure 3–13 Structural traps
Structural traps are formed by movements in the Earth's crust (eg folding, faulting and salt diapirism).

exceeds the buoyancy pressure of an underlying hydrocarbon column and this depends on the diameter of the pore throats in the cap rock. A rock will seal if the displacement pressure of its *largest* pore throat is greater than or equal to the buoyancy pressure of the hydrocarbon column. The seal potential or capacity of a cap rock can be expressed as the maximum column height that it will support without leakage.

Capillary displacement pressures can be measured in the laboratory but problems with sampling occur. Areas with the largest pore throats will be the weakest and it is these which must be sampled. This is not always possible when dealing with rocks in the subsurface.

Shales and evaporites are the most effective seals as these rocks have the smallest pores. Finer pore sizes are required for gas than for oil, as the gas molecules are smaller. If the cap rocks are sufficiently tight, however, they do not need to be thick but need to be laterally persistent to cover the whole play area.

Since few seals are perfect, oil and gas escape from most traps. For a hydrocarbon accumulation to have formed, the traps and seals must have existed before hydrocarbon generation ceased in the source rock, eg some North Sea trap structures are 125 million years old but were not filled until 100 million years ago, giving plenty of time for hydrocarbons to be generated, expelled and migrated into the reservoirs and traps.

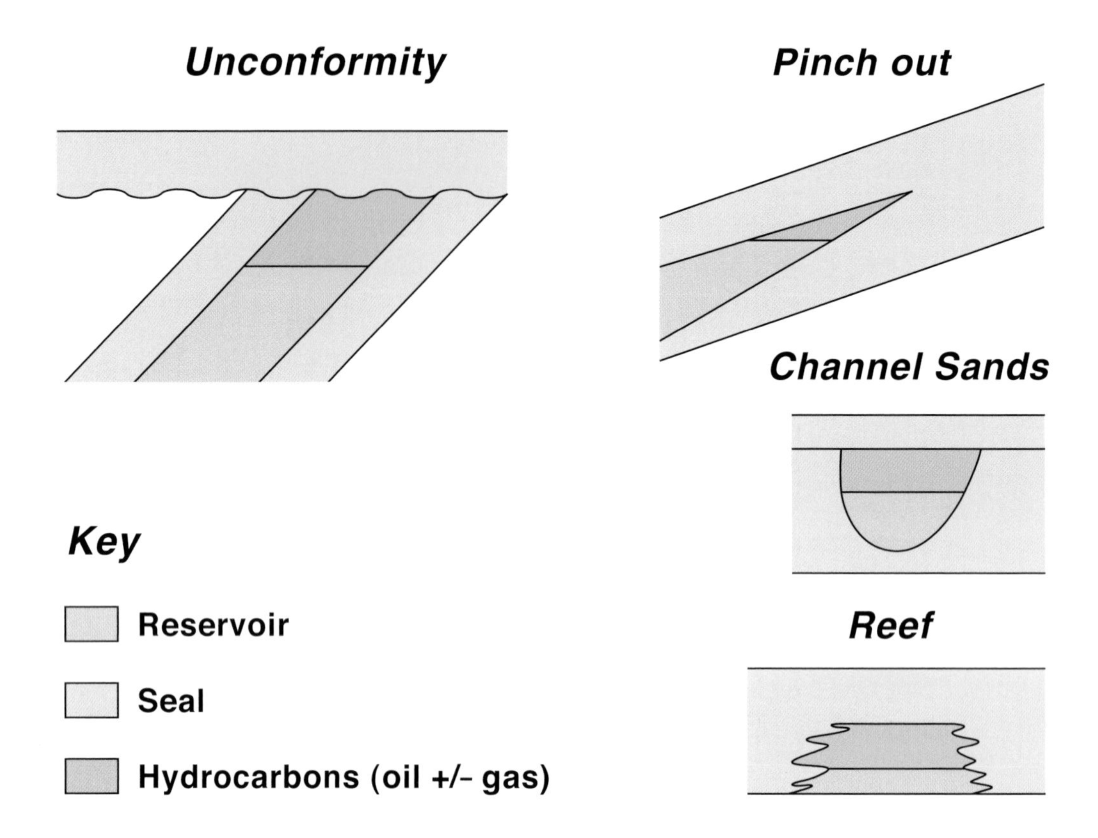

Figure 3–14 Stratigraphic traps
Stratigraphic traps are caused by the relative positions of reservoir and seal rocks in a particular sedimentary environment, eg the Brent Delta contains channel sands which act as stratigraphic traps.

3.7 North Sea geology

The North Sea can be subdivided into three main areas: Northern North Sea, Central North Sea and Southern North Sea (Fig. 1–1). A summary of the reservoir, traps and source rocks is set out below but for more detailed information on North Sea geology and hydrocarbon production, the reader is referred to Glennie (1998) and the articles by Bernard et al. therein (pp 1–29).

Northern North Sea

The Northern North Sea is mainly composed of oil fields associated with the Viking Graben structure, which follows the border between the UK and Norwegian sectors of the North Sea. The main reservoirs are the sandstones of the Triassic, Jurassic, Cretaceous and Palaeocene (Fig. 3–15), which are contained in structural traps. The Upper Jurassic Kimmeridge Clay Formation is the source rock for the oil and gas found in the Northern North Sea.

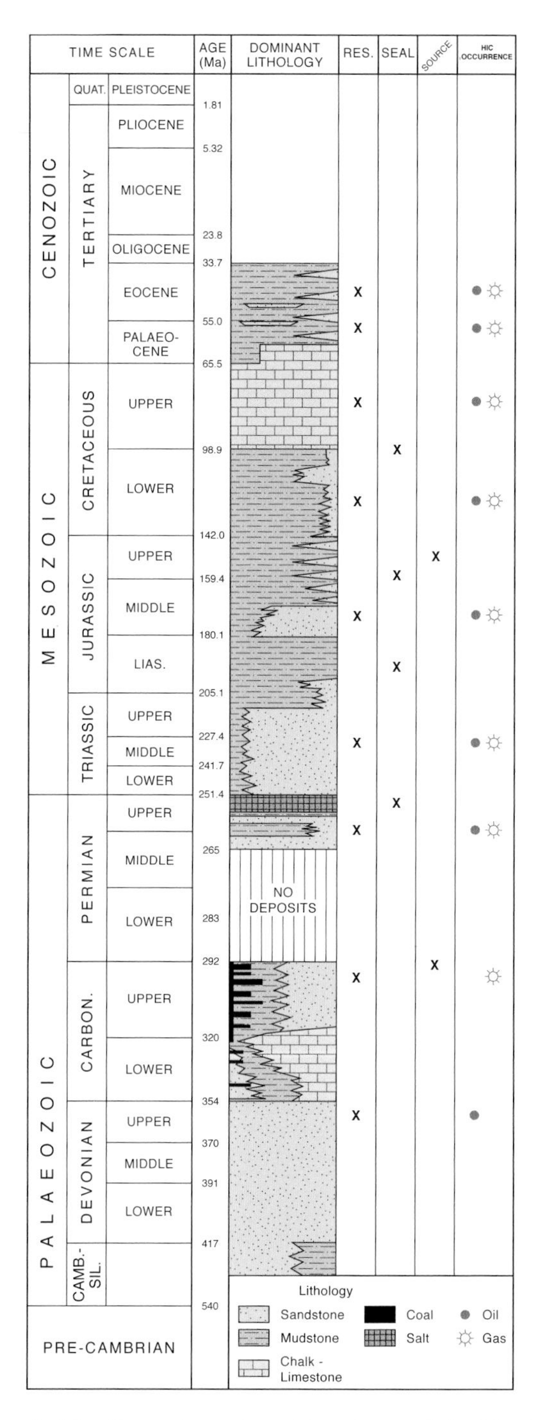

Figure 3–15 General stratigraphic column of the North Sea
This simplified stratigraphic column of the entire North Sea shows the ages and general lithology of each age. The location of reservoir, source and seal rocks are marked by an X in the appropriate columns, and the types of hydrocarbon found in these plays are indicated by either an oil or a gas symbol.

Central North Sea

The Central North Sea is mainly composed of oil fields associated with the Central Graben structure, which transect the UK, Norwegian, Danish and Dutch sectors of the North Sea. The main reservoirs are the sandstones of the Permian, Triassic, Jurassic, Cretaceous and Palaeocene, and the fractured Cretaceous Chalk Group (Fig. 3–15), which are contained in mainly structural traps with some stratigraphic trapping components. The Upper Jurassic Kimmeridge Clay Formation is the main source rock for the oil and gas in the central North Sea.

Southern North Sea

The Southern North Sea is mainly composed of gas fields within the Southern Gas Basin, which are contained in the UK and Dutch sectors of the North Sea. The main reservoirs are the sandstones of the Carboniferous, Permian and Triassic (Fig. 3–15), which are contained in structural traps associated with salt movement in the area. The Carboniferous Coal Measures are the main source rock for the gas in the southern North Sea.

Notes

[1] As with all aspects of the industry, the nomenclature of petroleum is confusing. Those in the downstream – refiners and traders – have their own highly specialised subdivisions not included here.

EXPLORATION AND PETROLEUM GEOLOGY

LEGAL

3.8 Introduction

Companies whose business is the search for, and production and sale of, hydrocarbons are often referred to as 'upstream oil and gas companies' or 'upstream companies'. Such companies try to obtain rights to explore, appraise and produce hydrocarbons from pre-defined areas, which areas can be located either onshore or offshore. These rights may be contained in licences or concessions granted by a government or state entity or may be contained in production sharing agreements or other such contractual arrangements. In the UK the relevant rights are granted by way of licence (see Chapter 2 for full details of the UK licensing system). The first stage of searching for hydrocarbons following the award of a licence is referred to as the 'exploration and appraisal stage'.

A licence or concession evidences the grant by a government of proprietary rights to the parties to whom it has been granted, though they may be personal in nature. These rights are usually exclusive and last for a specific period set out in the relevant document of grant.

A Production Sharing Agreement (PSA) is a contractual agreement between a host government (or, more usually, the relevant national oil company) and one or more upstream companies. In a PSA the national oil company permits the upstream company to exploit an area. The PSA will usually provide that on stabilised production from that area the upstream company can first recover its exploration and production costs and is then entitled to a share of production from the area (or entitled to some other form of return on capital employed). The amount recovered will obviously depend on the level of production and, therefore, there is an incentivisation to maximise production.

Exploration and appraisal is a costly business. No upstream company will want to expend large sums of money and resources exploring and appraising areas before it has obtained exclusive rights in respect of those areas. States are keen to encourage investment in their oil and gas industries and so are normally willing to award at least a period of exclusivity to upstream companies which want to invest in exploring the area.

The precise terms of the exclusivity granted to the upstream company will be set out in the licence, the concession or the PSA (as applicable). Chapter 2 sets out the relevant exclusivity provisions in the case of UK licences.

There are basically two ways to obtain such licences or concessions: they are either awarded to the upstream company by the relevant state or national oil company or an existing licence or concession is transferred to the upstream company. The licence or concession may impose obligations on the party to whom it was awarded (and its successors) to carry out certain activities and undertake defined work obligations. An assignee of such rights will be expected to fulfil these obligations.

In a competitive commercial environment, upstream companies will be competing with one another to discover and develop oil and gas reservoirs. One of the key tools available to them in their search for hydrocarbons is the use of data. Such companies may also have access to new technology which can be used to maximise production and to reduce costs. Data can be used to work up detailed reservoir models which can, in turn, be used to attract capital for the development of those fields.

The upstream company will treat its data, know-how and information in respect of its technology as a valuable asset and will therefore be keen to protect confidentiality. It must ensure that it has robust confidentiality agreements in place to protect those assets.

3.9 Nature of data – Technical information – Technology

An upstream company will own different types of information and a large part of the information may be confidential. Such information may include geological and geophysical data on the reservoir in question. The data may comprise wireline logs, seismic, fluids and flow analyses, drilling data, 2, 3 and 4D modelling data, which together will be analysed to determine whether the structure contains commercial reserves. The asset team of an upstream company may compile this data in circumstances of absolute secrecy, drawing together a multidisciplinary team which reworks the data as further drilling is completed and further tests are carried out.

Confidential data might also include technical information such as specifications for wells, details of well design and architecture and economic modelling on the reservoir, drilling rigs, pipelines, export routes and transportation systems. It might also include analyses of hydrocarbons extracted from a well which are then carried out in laboratories. These hydrocarbon assays may be analysed for sulphur content, metal content and other compounds, and the analyses will give oil and gas companies an idea of the quality and the likely value of the hydrocarbons in place.

Multidisciplinary teams will establish the type of technology they wish to utilise in all stages of the exploration, production and transportation of hydrocarbons from the reservoir in question. The teams may have identified technology companies with specific technology which they wish to use in the reservoir. Contractual relationships will be set up with those companies for the provision of project management and design in relation to the reservoir.

All this information, as it is confidential, should be the subject of confidentiality undertakings.

In this chapter there is a review of the steps to collate data and then to trade oil and gas assets. The trading of assets may happen for many different reasons. The first phase of oil and gas companies exploring for hydrocarbons in the UKCS tended to be dominated by the large international oil and gas companies. In the mature phase of exploration development and production there are a greater variety of companies, ranging from those that are small exploration and development companies to those creating hubs of assets and others who are specialists in extending the life of mature assets. A number of large companies have divested some of their assets in the UKCS to concentrate on larger fields elsewhere. This chapter also focuses on the processes and documents in trading assets.

3.10 Confidential information

An upstream company will wish to ensure the confidentiality of its information at all times, whether at the stage before it considers spending money trying to secure licences, at the stage of bidding for exclusive concessions or licences to explore and appraise or at the stage after the award of such concessions or licences.

It would be normal for an upstream company (and any other well-advised company, for that matter) to enter into a confidentiality agreement prior to entering into negotiations, whether these be for the disposal of a field interest, transportation and tariffing arrangements, discussions on possible unitisations or such like. A confidentiality agreement is an important yet short document. It is a contract in terms of which one party (the 'disclosee') undertakes that it will hold information which the other party (the 'discloser') is to disclose to it confidential and will only use that information for the purposes for which it was disclosed (the 'Permitted Purpose'). The undertakings of confidentiality may last for a specific time or may last indefinitely. In the case of agreements which deal with technology the confidentiality period is often unlimited whereas in the case of upstream oil and gas licensing or asset transfers the period is often limited by time (typically for around five years). If the disclosee breaches the terms of the agreement the discloser can seek damages for breach of contract and other remedies such as injunction (in England) and interdict (in Scotland) to stop the guilty party from breaching the agreement. A variant on the theme is where both parties are swapping confidential information. In such a scenario the confidentiality agreement would impose reciprocal confidentiality obligations, with each party being bound to respect the confidentiality of the other party's confidential information.

An upstream company may be in a group of companies and also have other 'affiliates'. A definition of an 'affiliate' may include any subsidiary company (ie a company or party that controls the majority of voting rights or exercises such control over the subsidiary company), a holding company and may include the ultimate holding company of a company. All those affiliate companies may be required to enter into confidentiality undertakings in a form acceptable to the discloser of the information or for the upstream company to procure that those parties or other companies will maintain that confidential information as confidential.

It is worth being vigilant when reviewing confidentiality agreements, as very often they will contain provisions which go beyond an obligation to keep information confidential. For example, sometimes one finds that rather than simply protecting confidentiality, a 'confidentiality agreement' contains unexpected clauses such as clauses creating areas of mutual interest (ie a provision that a party will not try to acquire rights in an area without including the other party to the agreement), non-solicitation clauses or restrictive covenant provisions. A party entering into such an agreement has to be on guard for such matters and not simply expect that a confidentiality agreement will restrict itself to issues of confidentiality.

3.11 Consultancy contracts/service contracts

Both small independent oil and gas companies and large multinational oil and gas companies sometimes find it necessary to contract with consultants to carry out specialist work or to increase their in-house resources.

Consultants generally operate as individuals or, more commonly in the UK, through their own limited liability companies. They are not employees of the upstream company which engages them although there can be situations where such consultants will be deemed to be employees and, in such a case, the upstream company will be responsible for payment of PAYE and employer's NI. It is therefore important to ensure that any consultants are not deemed to be employees for tax purposes.

Such consultants may be engaged by the upstream company to work for a short period of time to carry out a specific piece of work or might be engaged on a more long-term basis. The consultant may be working exclusively for the upstream company on the project or he may have contracts with a number of different upstream companies and split his time up amongst those different companies.

The relationship between the upstream company and the consultant is normally documented in a consultancy agreement. A well-advised upstream company will ensure that the consultancy agreement provides that all intellectual property rights, other know-how and any confidential information which arises as a result of the consultancy services will be owned by the upstream company and is assigned by the consultant to the upstream company. Without an express provision as to ownership, the consultant would own the confidential information and intellectual property rights in whatever he invented or created during the consultancy (although in some cases there might be an implied right for the upstream company to utilise the information and intellectual property rights). Of course, however, a company paying for a service expects more than a possible implied right.

The consultancy agreement should be very clear as to what the consultant is required to do and what he will be paid for doing it. Payment is usually dealt with by reference to an agreed day-rate but it can be more complex, with some form of incentivisation. It should also state how long the consultancy arrangement is to last.

In some cases, an upstream company may instruct a service company to design part of a well or to provide other services. This could be on a turn-key basis or on an EPIC basis (Engineering, Procurement, Installation and Construction). The arrangement between the upstream company and the service provider/contractor will be documented in some form of service agreement between the upstream company and the service company. More details on such contracting issues can be found in Chapter 10.

3.12 Heads of Terms

Once confidentiality agreements are in place, the parties can proceed to negotiating the appropriate form of contract. The parties may find it useful to negotiate 'Heads of Terms' (which are also known as 'memoranda of understanding' or 'letters of intent') prior to commencing the drafting of the fully termed agreements. These documents can be useful in all contract negotiations and not just in oil and gas transactions. They seek to set out the major principles agreed between the parties so that the parties can be clear that they are actually in agreement on key terms and principles before proceeding to documenting the arrangement fully. They are also quite useful in that having them in place sometimes makes a party unwilling to depart from the agreed position in the Heads of Terms even in circumstances where the Heads of Terms are not legally binding.

The Head of Terms may provide for a period of exclusivity in which the parties will negotiate the terms of an agreement and they may deal with issues such as payment of expenses in the event of a breach of exclusivity. The Heads of Terms may be legally binding or they may be stated not to be legally binding. If a party does not wish to be legally bound by the Heads of Terms then this should be stated explicitly.

3.13 Pre-Licence Award Agreements

As indicated in Chapter 2, upstream companies are often keen to spread risk and therefore they often apply for licences in conjunction with other upstream companies. The companies which co-operate in applying for licences and in developing fields are usually termed 'co-venturers'.

Upstream companies which agree to work together to apply for licences and to explore areas may enter into an agreement prior to the award of a licence or concession. In such agreements (which are commonly known as 'Bidding Agreements' or 'Joint Bidding Agreements') the parties aim to define their relationship and to document the terms upon which they will work together to try to secure licences or concessions. It is common for such documents to be entered into in the UK in the period before the annual UK Licensing Round.

Such agreements normally deal with matters such as defining the areas in respect of which the parties will seek licences, ie the area in which they interested (also known as the 'Area of Mutual Interest' or 'AMI'), how they will make decisions on applications for licences (ie which licences to apply for), the procedure which will apply if they cannot decide which areas to apply for, the sharing of data, the costs which they will share, their participating interests in any acreage awarded to them, their voting rights and who will be appointed as operator for the purposes of the application and as licence operator if the licence is awarded to them. There will normally also be provisions detailing how the application process is to be funded (who is to pay what and when). At the point of application the contracting parties will have to decide whether they want to continue to be applicants or withdraw from the project.

Seismic contracts

As described above, the operation, control and ownership of geophysical data and technical information are crucial to the building of reservoir models and determining the net present value of a particular reservoir. There are, therefore, well-defined contracts which are negotiated between upstream companies and contractors for data acquisition, licensing, storage and retrieval. The co-venturers having an exclusive right to explore in certain areas may wish to contract a seismic vessel owner to provide seismic in that area under a contract for services or they may wish access to seismic which has been shot by seismic companies on a speculative basis.

Sometimes licensees on different blocks will exchange seismic information under the terms of an exchange agreement ('Seismic Exchange Agreement') in order to further evaluate reservoirs which may straddle several blocks or in order to make estimates of the position as regards one block by making comparisons with neighbouring blocks which may have a similar geological profile.

It may be the case that one party wishes to acquire seismic or data on a particular field from another party to consider whether to carry out further work and the parties may enter into either a Data Acquisition Agreement or some form of licensing agreement to obtain access to the seismic or data.

3.14 Post-Licence Award Agreements

On the award of a licence, co-venturers will need to negotiate and establish Joint Operating Agreements (JOAs) if they have not already done so. These are required to regulate the exploitation of the asset by the co-venturers. The development of the field may involve contracts with large service companies to assist in the formulation of a field development programme.

A company which has been awarded or acquires a licence may try to acquire other licence interests (by grant of a licence or acquisition of licence interests in respect of neighbouring areas) in order to create a hub within a particular area. This can be done by acquiring assets in neighbouring exploration acreage areas or acquiring companies which hold licence interests to complete a portfolio of oil or gas assets within a certain area. The award of a new licence may provide a company an opportunity to drill a number of wells within a defined well programme area over a number of blocks or it may be that acquiring other acreage may make it more likely to lead to the development of an entire field rather than part of a field area.

The purchase of oil and gas interests can take a variety of forms. The most common of these are the acquisition of assets under an Asset Acquisition Agreement or at the acquisition of a company by the purchase of the shares in that company under a Share Acquisition Agreement. A purchaser might first enter into Heads of Terms with a prospective seller, then undertake due diligence on the assets for sale. The remainder of this chapter will consider these two scenarios.

3.15 Due diligence

Due diligence in oil and gas transactions

Ownership of petroleum in the UK rests with the Crown. In terms of the Petroleum Act 1998, the Secretary of State has the right to grant licences to search, bore for and get petroleum from the seabed.

Where a company wishes to sell an oil and gas asset, the 'asset' referred to is an interest in a certain licence together with its collection of contractual rights attaching to that area. As with any sale and purchase transaction, before transferring an oil and gas asset, due diligence will require to be carried out by a prospective purchaser to ensure that the seller is in fact the legal and beneficial owner of that particular asset and to ascertain exactly what rights and obligations the purchaser will acquire on transfer. The due diligence exercise is carried out prior to entering into the sale and purchase agreement and is essentially the only opportunity for the purchaser to identify and, where possible, remedy any problems with the seller's title to the asset. It is also an opportunity for the purchaser to verify whether what it has been told about the asset by the seller corresponds with the purchaser's understanding derived from the documents exhibited. The contents of the documentation provided by the seller to the purchaser (often referred to as the 'data set') will be disclosed against any warranties given by the seller to the purchaser. It is therefore important that the exercise is carried out thoroughly and that nothing is missed. The diligence exercise will include reviewing the licence and all licence assignments from the date of grant of the licence, the JOA and any subsequent novations/amendments and any other contractual arrangements which are in place among the licensees and field partners.

The licence

The licence, which will cover certain 'blocks' in the UKCS, will require to be carefully reviewed. The type of licence will dictate the kind of activities that may be carried out within the designated licence area. For example, a Petroleum Production Licence is required in order to produce petroleum. In addition, the duration or 'term' of the licence should be noted in any due diligence report, as each licence has an expiry date.

Newer licences will incorporate model clauses which can be found in the Petroleum (Current Model Clauses) Order 1999 (SI 1999 No 160). These model clauses set out certain rights and obligations on the licensees and these require to be carefully reviewed.

The licence area is defined by a set of co-ordinates and is set out in a schedule to the licence. It may be that the area stated on the original licence does not reflect the current position, as some parts of the licence may have been surrendered and the licence area redetermined since the date of grant.

Once the licence has been reviewed, the next step is to ensure that the changes in 'ownership' in the licence from the date of grant to the present day have been properly documented. The data set provided by the seller to the purchaser should include the licence and all assignments of the licence. Each of such documents will require to be carefully reviewed. For instance, a document purporting to be an assignment of licence should be exactly that – the terms of the document should be checked to ensure that the licence has been correctly assigned. There should be an unbroken chain of assignments showing, each time there is a change in the licence group, the identity of the licensees, the identity of the assignor (transferor of the licence) and the assignee (transferee of the licence).

Joint Operating Agreement

When licences are granted by the Secretary of State, they may be granted to one or a number of parties. Where they are granted to more than one party they are granted jointly and severally.

The licence itself will not set out the relationship between the parties in conducting operations under the licence, nor will it state how the costs of such operations are to be shared or how revenues are to be shared. Therefore, where there are a number of parties to the licence, a JOA will be entered into in order to govern operations and to indicate the ownership interests of the co-venturers. There is currently no compulsory standard style of JOA for use in the oil and gas industry, however, the Oil and Gas Industry Task Force (OGITF), in aiming to improve relationships between licensees, has introduced a number of standard agreements for use within the industry. These can be found on the UKOOA website (www.ukooa.co.uk). One of these standard agreements is the 20th Round JOA. Details of JOAs can be found in Chapter 9.

Any proposing purchaser (or its agents) should, at the outset, ascertain whether there are any pre-emption provisions in the JOA. These are provisions which would give existing co-venturers the right of first refusal of the asset which is being sold. Historically, pre-emption provisions tended to take one of two forms. Under the first example the seller and proposed purchaser were required to agree the terms of any transfer, at which point the other co-venturers had the option to purchase the interest which was up for sale on the same terms as those agreed between the seller and the proposed purchaser. The alternative was that of first refusal; ie the seller was required to inform the other co-venturers of its intention to dispose of all or part of its interest and they had a certain period of time in which to make an offer for the interest. In the former case, there was always the risk for the proposed transferee that once negotiations and due diligence had taken place (which may have proven time-consuming and costly) and the terms finalised, one of the other parties to the JOA pre-empted the transfer. In the latter case, another party/parties could decide whether to pre-empt any transfer prior to negotiations taking place. However, it was sometimes the case that a lengthy time period (perhaps as much as 90 days) was given to the other parties in which to decide whether to pre-empt and therefore the transaction could not complete until either the time period for the exercise of the right had expired or the parties holding the rights had waived their rights of pre-emption.

In recent years, various industry bodies have considered the use of pre-emption provisions and their effect on the industry. The general view is now that pre-emption provisions generally have the effect of restricting trade. With that in mind, the Master Deed (developed by PILOT and PPWG) has standardised pre-emption provisions on terms which it is hoped will be acceptable to new entrants. The Master Deed now provides that where a party enters into bona fide negotiations to transfer all or part of its rights under an existing operating agreement which contains pre-emption provisions, it must first notify the other parties to that operating agreement of its intention to do so. The remaining parties to the JOA then have seven days to either reserve or waive their rights of pre-emption. Failure by a party to respond is deemed to be a reservation of the right. Where a party reserves its right of pre-emption, under the new standard provision, it will have 30 days in which to exercise that right even where the operating agreement gives a longer period in which to exercise the right. Where there are no pre-emption provisions contained in the relevant JOA, the Master Deed pre-emption provisions do not apply. The DTI will no longer approve operating agreements which contain pre-emption provisions unless they can be justified. Even then, such provisions must be on terms equivalent to those contained in the Master Deed. Therefore, over time, it is anticipated that pre-emption provisions will become less of an issue.

There is normally a financial capability test contained in the JOA in terms of which the proposed purchaser must demonstrate to the other existing co-venturers that it has the financial, economic and technical capability and expertise to fulfil obligations under the JOA. This would include its share of the costs of the Work Programme and work obligations contained in the licence and the JOA and the development programmes devised by the operator. It would also be required to show that it has sufficient financial resources to meet all decommissioning obligations set out in the JOA or in a decommissioning agreement. Arguments about whether or not a party has the financial capability are not uncommon, especially in the case of new entrants to the UKCS. In the event that agreement cannot be reached, sometimes the other co-venturers require some form of security in respect of financial capability. Those obligations may require the proposed purchaser to arrange the issue of letters of credit by a well-rated financial institution, or to provide cash collateral or a parent company guarantee for decommissioning obligations. It would be common, therefore, for a prospective purchaser to make presentations to the co-venturers before acquiring the assets in order to demonstrate its capability and desire to become a co-venturer in that field.

In some transactions, and more commonly where companies are invited to bid for assets, an Information Memorandum (IM) will be provided to any proposing purchaser setting out background information in relation to the asset(s) offered for sale. Depending on the size of the transaction, this can include a description of the relevant field along with geological data (including seismic), the history of any well, production, facilities and expectations. Perhaps most importantly, the IM will set out the percentage interest(s) held by each of the parties to the licence and JOA and which is offered for sale. The JOA and any subsequent amendments and novations should be reviewed against any IM produced by the seller prior to the transfer of assets. The percentage interest of each party stated in the JOA (or most recent novation and amendment thereof) should coincide with that stated in the IM. Where it does not coincide, further investigation will be required as to why this is the case. Perhaps there has been a missing novation or amendment and this may require to be rectified prior to any transfer.

With regard to operations under the licence, the JOA will state who is to be appointed in the role of operator. The operator is the party given the responsibility of managing the day-to-day operations under the licence, on behalf of the joint operating committee. Typically, the duties of the operator will include preparing and implementing programmes, budgets and Authorisations for Expenditure (AFEs); providing each party with reports and data concerning joint operations, planning for and obtaining services and material; directing and controlling statistical and accounting services and preparing a development plan. A prospective purchaser will require to ascertain how such operations are to be funded, how decisions are taken in relation to the budget for operations and in what circumstances the operator can require the other parties to advance funds in order to meet expenditures (referred to as 'cash calls'). Where the operatorship is being transferred along with an interest in the licence and JOA, provisions relating to the duties, responsibilities and liabilities of the operator will require to be reviewed carefully.

Although the operator will be in charge of conducting day-to-day operations under the JOA, the operator's activities will be governed by the JOA and be subject to control via the operating committee. It follows that in any JOA, provisions relating to the joint operating committee, which is in charge of supervising and controlling all matters relating to joint operations, will require to be carefully reviewed. In particular, provisions in relation to representation at meetings of the joint operating committee and the voting pass mark should be considered. Usually, and as is provided for in the 20th Round JOA, a party's voting rights will correspond with its percentage interest under the JOA and any prospective transferee should consider whether these provisions are acceptable to them. For example, it may be that the interest to be transferred is 20% and there are four other parties holding 80% in aggregate. If the voting pass mark contained in the JOA is three parties holding 60% then it is likely that the proposed purchaser will have little power over decisions of the committee and that decisions may be forced upon them. The implications of this will require to be carefully considered by any prospective purchaser.

Where agreement cannot be reached under the JOA, one or more parties may wish to undertake certain work at their own cost and risk. Most JOAs provide for this by way of 'sole risk' provisions. Although only certain parties to the JOA take part, sole risk provisions often allow the other parties to join in such operations at a later date, provided that they pay a share of the costs incurred by the sole risk parties, together with a premium. Where an IM suggests that sole risk operations are taking place, any proposing purchaser should carefully review these provisions.

A JOA will state whether the parties are entitled to grant security over their interests. It may be that the prospective transferee is reliant upon funding from a bank or other financial institution, and the bank will require security over the asset in return for such funding. Any provision which restricts the granting of security over assets may be of concern to the prospective purchaser.

Provisions covering default under any JOA will require to be carefully reviewed and considered. For example, the 20th Round JOA provides that on default by any party, the operator is required to notify all of the participants of such default and such non-defaulting parties are required to pay their percentage interest share of the amount in default. The defaulting party will usually have the opportunity to remedy the default, however, if it does not do so, ultimately, it may be required to assign its percentage interest under the JOA to the non-defaulting parties. From the point of view of a prospective purchaser it is therefore necessary to ascertain whether any default has occurred under the JOA.

Unit Operating Agreements

Sometimes a reservoir straddles more than one block. 'Ownership' of the different blocks may be held by different parties. In these circumstances it may be commercially logical to enter into a Unit Operating Agreement (UOA). The UOA is similar to a JOA but will also contain provisions for determining and redetermining how the oil or gas in the unitised reservoir should be owned as between the parties on one block and the parties on the other block. One way of doing this is to allocate unit percentage interests based upon periodic geological interpretations of, for example, how much gas there is and where it lies on the particular blocks. When reviewing a UOA, a prospective purchaser should be concerned with the issues associated with any other JOA. They will also be particularly interested in how and when redeterminations are to take place because these may change the percentage interests of the parties.

Other Agreements

As previously stated, in order to fully understand the 'ownership' interest of a party in a licence it is necessary not to look at just the licence, the JOA and any unitisation agreement (which broadly, will identify the percentage interest of a particular party) but also to consider the whole package of contractual rights which allow that party to exploit that percentage interest and derive economic value from it and other agreements which may impose obligations or give rights to other parties to acquire part of the interests to be sold.

Transportation and Processing Agreements

When carrying out due diligence in relation to any oil and gas asset, it is vital to be satisfied as to the mechanisms for transportation and processing of that oil or gas.

In some fields, the oil or gas is lifted from a particular block through subsea tie-backs and piped to a processing platform on another block, owned by entirely different partners. In order to govern the relationship between the parties in these circumstances, a platform operating and services agreement (or POSA) is entered into. The agreement will provide for a royalty to be paid by the parties using the pipeline. The level of such royalties will be important for the prospective purchaser. Transportation and Processing Agreements can allow the owner of a block in the middle of the North Sea to lift oil or gas from that block, transfer it through other parties' pipelines or processing systems and to take delivery of the gas following processing and delivery back onshore.

Farm-in/Farm-out Agreements

Where a party does not wish to (or simply cannot afford to) carry out certain work on its blocks it may agree with another party that such other party will carry out certain work (such as drilling a well) in exchange for which, on the satisfactory completion of the work commitment, the owner will transfer a percentage interest in the asset to the party who has carried out the work. The main terms of any such agreement will require to be carefully considered as the contract may lead to a variation in percentage interests. For example, a purchaser may be about to buy a 100% interest from a seller. The seller may have entered into a Farm-out Agreement with another party (B), in terms of which on the drilling of a well to a certain depth, B is entitled to receive one half of the seller's interest. If the purchaser purchases the interest from the seller and novates into the Farm-out Agreement the purchaser will be obliged to transfer 50% of the interest to B on completion of the work obligation under the Farm-out Agreement. Farm-in Agreements are a useful way for smaller, independent companies to carry out exploration and production in situations where they do not wish to take all of the risk themselves.

Carry Agreements

A Carry Agreement is an agreement in terms of which a party agrees that it will meet the costs of another party under the relevant documents (eg under a JOA) and which may provide that that party can recover those costs from revenues produced from the assets. Where there are carry arrangements in place, these will require to be carefully considered by any proposed purchaser. A carry arrangement may mean that the proposing purchaser will be under an obligation to bear more than its percentage interest share of costs in relation to the asset.

Royalty/Net Present Interest Agreements

The consideration for the sale of an asset may be partly satisfied by both parties entering into a Royalty Agreement or Net Profit Interest Agreement the terms of which will provide that, perhaps in addition to some cash consideration, a royalty will be payable to the seller in consideration of the sale of the asset. A royalty is often stated as a percentage of the production from an asset which is paid to a royalty holder free and clear of the costs of production and can be taken either in the form of petroleum from a designated delivery point or in cash. A net profit interest entitles the holder of the interest to a share of profits from production revenues after deduction of all costs of production relevant to the asset, sometimes including interest on capital employed. Again, prior to any sale, it is important to ascertain whether there are any Royalty Agreements or Net Profit Interest Agreements in place and a prospective purchaser will require to consider whether they are willing to take on responsibility for such agreements.

Oil and Gas Sales Agreements

Where oil or gas is being produced, there will probably be Oil and Gas Sales Agreements in place which will require to be reviewed. Particular attention should be paid to provisions in these agreements which might restrict the assignability of the contracts. Commonly, there will be provisions in oil sales contracts to the effect that they will terminate on the sale of the asset in question. In addition, any prospective purchaser will require to consider carefully whether there are any provisions which could lead to liability on the part of the party selling the oil or gas, such as shortfall provisions. For details of oil and gas contracts and the issues involved see Chapters 19 and 20.

Key Operator Agreements

Key Operator Agreements can include contracts such as rig contracts, survey agreements or other field agreements. These will be of particular interest to a purchaser where the purchaser will be taking over the role of operator. These may contain risk/reward elements and future payment obligations (based on production and cost recovery) which can survive for many years after the work has been done. A prospective purchaser should be alert to such contingent liabilities.

Seismic survey licences

Many survey companies shoot seismic in the UKCS on a speculative basis and licence the information to oil and gas companies on request. As a result, seismic data might not be owned by the seller but rather may be licensed to it. The terms of the seismic licence may prohibit the transfer of the right to use the seismic data. It may be that the seismic company can demand a fee for agreeing to allow the purchaser of the asset access to the data. If there are such seismic agreements, any restrictions on assignment (and likely resultant fees) should be considered by the parties and the cost of acquiring access to such data should be considered in establishing the acquisition costs.

Procedures for undertaking due diligence

Make sure that the right parties are parties to the relevant documents. When looking at licences and the history of the licence (the various transfers which have occurred) it is important to check that there is an unbroken chain of transfers of licence. If companies A and B held the licence at grant of the licence and then transferred it to companies D and E then the next transfer of the licence should be by companies D and E. Where this is not the case then the reason for any difference will require to be investigated. It may be that since the date of the last assignment, one or more companies have changed their names. This information is easily accessible on the Companies House website (www.companieshouse.gov.uk) in the case of UK registered companies. Where that is the case, provided that the legal entities stated as assignors on the previous assignment are assignees on the next, title is complete. Where that is not the case, there may be an assignment which has not been exhibited to the proposing purchaser. This will require to be requested from the seller. It might be the case that there is no missing assignment but that the name(s) of the party(ies) were simply misstated on one of the assignments. Where there is no assignment showing why a company is not a party to the licence or indeed a new company has been added then, quite simply, title is defective. The reason is that a licence is granted to all licensees jointly and where not all of the licensees have agreed to an assignment, that assignment is defective. Accordingly, all future assignments will be defective. In practice, this is remedied by a corrective deed of assignment which will be entered into between the current licensees and the party which was missed from a previous assignment. That party will require to confirm its approval of all subsequent transactions relating to the licence. The consequence of this defect may be that the seller has no title whatsoever to sell. Where they were not an original licensee, or they acquired their interest after the date of the defective assignment, then they may have no interest in the licence at all.

If a licence covers more than one block, there should be a Trust Deed which provides that the parties to a block will hold the other block in trust for the licensees of that particular block. It follows that for every assignment of licence there should be a corresponding novation of Trust Deed in order to clarify the ownership and indemnity arrangements for the various blocks covered by the licence. Any defective novation, for example because a company has been missed as a party or because the wrong company is stated as a party, can affect the validity of a Trust Deed. Where that is the case, the best solution may be to put in place a new Trust Deed among all of the current licensees in order to clarify the matter.

There should be a corresponding novation of any JOA recording the change in the parties to it and their new percentage interests. Where a party is withdrawing from the licence and the JOA, the novation relating to such withdrawal should include provisions covering the assumption of the withdrawing party's obligations under the JOA. In addition, the percentage interest transferred and the resulting percentage interests of the parties should coincide with each other.

It should be noted that under the new Master Deed procedure it is common for a number of documents to be assigned or novated in one document – the Execution Deed. If an Execution Deed has been used then there will not be separate assignments and novations but one or more execution deeds which list the documents which they are transferring or novating.

In relation to agreements which have been entered into by the operator on behalf of the parties to the licence, where the role of operator is being transferred these documents will require to be carefully reviewed to ensure the benefit of such contracts will transfer to the new operator. Often, transportation and processing agreements are not entered into by the operator alone but are entered into by the operator and all co-venturers of the block. In that event, as with the licence or JOA the benefit and burden of the transportation agreement requires to be assigned to the purchaser of the interest. Similarly, any pre-existing defective assignment could be a problem but can probably be remedied as part of the completion process.

In summary, in order to check whether there is good title to an oil or gas interest the documentation provided by the seller should disclose a complete, unbroken and correct series of assignments and novations for every contract governing the ownership and operation of the interest. Any gaps are a defect in title and these should be considered and, where possible, remedied as part of the completion documents process.

3.16 Acquisition of assets/shares

An overview of the legal documentation involved in the acquisition of oil and gas assets and the purchase of an oil and gas company is set out below. Once a prospective purchaser has reviewed the due diligence documentation and data (or contemporaneously with that review) it will negotiate the terms of the acquisition. The first consideration for any prospective purchaser is what form the acquisition will take. The two main options open to the purchaser are as follows:

1. Acquisition of assets

This is the most common way in which oil and gas assets are acquired. It involves the purchase of an interest under a licence or licences from the seller, together with any property, other assets (eg infrastructure and other moveable property, data, books and records) and any contractual rights relating to such licence(s). The acquisition of assets can also take the form of an exchange or a farm-in/ earn-in and these are essentially variations of the straight asset acquisition.

2. Acquisition of shares

Although not as common as an acquisition of assets, an acquisition of shares quite simply involves the purchase of shares in a company which holds oil and gas assets. Unlike an acquisition of assets, an acquisition of shares involving the purchase of all of the shares in a company will mean that the purchaser acquires that company with the company still holding all of its assets and, crucially, all of its liabilities.

The choice between an acquisition of assets and an acquisition of shares will depend on a variety of factors (such as tax, extraction of value, avoiding pre-emption rights, etc.) and each route has its own advantages and disadvantages. As indicated above, currently the more common method of acquiring oil and gas assets is by way of an assets deal.

Acquisition of assets

The Sale and Purchase Agreement (SPA) is the contract between the seller and purchaser in respect of the sale and purchase of the relevant assets. In oil and gas transactions the first draft of the SPA is normally prepared by the seller. The SPA sets out the rights and obligations of both the seller and the purchaser in respect of the acquisition. The main issues dealt with in the SPA include: the identity of the parties; what the assets are which are being sold; what the price is and how the price is to be satisfied; what warranties are being given in connection with the sale; whether any indemnities are being granted; and tax issues. Each of these and some other key issues will now be considered in further detail.

1. Who are the parties?

Normally the parties are the seller (or sellers) and the purchaser (or purchasers). In some circumstances, there may be more than one purchaser or more than one seller and this is common where a number of assets are being acquired by, or purchased from, different companies within the same group.

Sometimes there are parties to the SPA other than just the seller and the purchaser. In situations where the seller has concerns about the purchaser's ability to meet its financial obligations under the SPA (eg its ability to pay the price at completion or to honour obligations post-completion) the seller might require that a third party guarantees the obligations of the purchaser. If the parties agree that the parent of the purchaser will guarantee its obligations then the parent company may be a party to the SPA for the purposes of giving that guarantee. Sometimes a seller is unhappy with accepting a parent company guarantee in support of the purchaser's obligations. The seller might insist upon a bank guarantee being provided. If a bank guarantee is required this would be documented in a separate bank guarantee rather than having the bank as a party to the SPA. An SPA also imposes obligations on the seller – eg warranties. The purchaser might request a parent company guarantee (or a bank guarantee) in support of such obligations where the seller has concerns about the purchaser's ability to meet its financial or other obligations under the SPA.

2. What is being bought?

The SPA will contain details of the assets which are being bought and this is of crucial importance. As stated above, an interest in an oil and gas asset comprises interests under a licence and under various other contracts. The SPA should provide that the relevant interest will be transferred (including the rights under all relevant contracts, etc.). As indicated above, the seller will normally prepare the first draft of the SPA and will insert a definition of the assets which are to be acquired (normally referred to as the 'Transferred Interest' or simply 'Interest'). It is then up to the purchaser to ensure that this definition of the assets accurately reflects not only what the purchaser is expecting to acquire but also what is evidenced by the various licence interest documents – clearly, the seller cannot sell more than it actually owns and neither party will want to become embroiled in disputes over what assets have been sold.

From the purchaser's point of view, it is extremely important to ensure that everything that is being bought is caught in the definition of the assets, especially where these are unusual assets that would not normally be acquired as part of a package of oil and gas assets. Otherwise, the purchaser could find itself in a situation where it does not hold an asset which is essential to the operation of the interest as a whole and this could seriously impact upon the purchaser's ability to conduct its business.

3. Sale and purchase

The fundamental purpose of the SPA is to deal with the terms of the sale and purchase of the assets. As a result there will always be a clause dealing with the obligation of the seller to sell the assets and the obligation of the purchaser to purchase the assets. Such a clause might take the following form: 'Subject to the terms of this Agreement, from the Effective Date, the Seller agrees to sell and transfer the Transferred Interest free from all Encumbrances and the Purchaser agrees to purchase the Transferred Interest.' There are two points worthy of note here. First, the clause provides that the seller agrees to sell the assets 'free from all Encumbrances'. The definition of Encumbrances will include things such as securities in favour of banks. The existence of such bank securities is reasonably easy to spot as in the case of UK companies the security or charge will have been registered with Companies House and so a search of Companies House records will disclose their existence. If they exist then one should insist that they are formally released or that (in the case of floating charges) letters of non-crystallisation /consent are obtained from the holder of the charge.

The definition of 'Encumbrances' will not only encompass securities granted by companies but will be framed as widely as possible so that the purchaser can try to ensure that the assets being acquired will not be burdened by any security or other third party rights such as net profit interests, royalties and such like. Such interests do not require to be registered and so there is no register which can be searched to check for their existence. The purchaser could rely on the sale and purchase clause to take action against the seller, if it turned out that the assets which it had acquired were in fact subject to an Encumbrance (this being a breach of contract).

The second point worthy of note is the reference to the assets being acquired 'from the Effective Date'. This is a very important concept which will now be discussed in more detail.

4. Effective Date

Perhaps one of the more complicated concepts to understand in an oil and gas transaction is that of the 'Effective Date' and how this links in with the other time frames contained within the SPA.

There are three key dates which must be differentiated in order to understand how an oil and gas SPA works.

In its most simplistic terms, an SPA is signed by the parties on one date (the signing date or execution date) but completion of the sale and purchase (ie the actual transfer of ownership of the assets) will not take place until a later date (completion date). The reason for the delay between signing of the SPA and the actual completion of the sale and purchase is to enable the various conditions set out in the SPA ('conditions precedent') to be satisfied by the seller and/or the purchaser so that the transfer can take place. However, the parties will normally agree that as between themselves, the sale and purchase of the assets will be deemed to have taken place and have an economic effect on another date (the 'Effective Date'), notwithstanding the date of signing of the SPA or the date of completion. For example, an SPA might be signed on 30 June 2007 with completion taking place on 30 September 2007. The parties might have agreed that the Effective Date will be deemed to be 1 January 2007.

So what does this mean in practice? In essence, the seller and the purchaser will agree to treat the assets as having been acquired by the purchaser on the Effective Date and, therefore, the purchaser will be responsible for all costs and other expenses relating to the assets from the Effective Date to the date of actual completion (the 'Interim Period') and will be entitled to all income and other receipts arising from the assets during the Interim Period. Given that these costs and income will have been paid already or received when completion takes place the SPA has to contain a mechanism in terms of which there is an adjustment to the price paid by the purchaser to reflect the net amount of such costs and income.

5. The price, adjustments and interest

Ideally, an SPA would simply provide that the price payable for the assets will be a specified cash amount but this is rarely the case. It can often be difficult to ascertain at the time of signing the SPA what the total price payable will be. The price may consist of part cash and part other assets, it may also include an element of deferred consideration (payable on a certain future date) or contingent consideration (which is payable if a future event occurs). As indicated above, if the date of completion and the Effective Date are different then the consideration will need to be adjusted to take account of what has happened between the signing of the SPA and the date of actual completion (normally known as the 'Interim Period').

The normal adjustments can be summarised as follows:

(a) Working capital adjustment

Most oil and gas assets will include an element of working capital. This may include cash balances in a joint account, stocks and materials, sums due by the operator of the asset or other third parties and sums due to the operator or other third parties. Obviously, the working capital figure will change constantly and so the working capital figure as at the Effective Date and as at the date of actual completion will be different. For the purposes of our example, let us assume that the value of the working capital at the Effective Date is £250,000 but on the date of actual completion this figure is £450,000. As the working capital has increased, the difference between the two figures will be for the account of the purchaser and will result in an increase in the price payable by the amount of such difference (ie £200,000).

(b) Cash call adjustment

Where there is activity in respect of the interest which is being acquired there may have been a number of cash calls made upon and paid by the seller during the Interim Period. Similarly, the seller may have received credits or other income during the Interim Period and both these cash calls and credits/income require to be taken into account when calculating the price. Both sums will be calculated and netted off against each other and if the result is that the seller has paid more than it has received, there will be an upward adjustment in the price payable. Conversely, if the amount received by the seller is more than the amount paid, there will be a downward adjustment in the price payable. It should be noted that sums received by the seller during the Interim Period which relate to petroleum/gas sales are normally dealt with separately (see below).

Example: In the Interim Period the seller is cash called by and pays £100,000 to the operator. There are no other cash calls or credits. The purchase price should be adjusted upwards by £100,000 as a result (ignoring any tax adjustment required – see below).

(c) Petroleum sales adjustment

During the Interim Period if the assets being acquired are producing assets, the seller may have received income from the sale of petroleum or gas produced from the assets. It may also have had to pay various costs relating to the sale of such petroleum/gas (eg transportation or processing tariffs). If, after deducting the relevant costs, there is a net amount which has been received by the seller during the Interim Period (which one would usually expect), then this will be for the account of the purchaser and would be dealt with by a downwards adjustment in the price payable.

(d) Taxation adjustment

As discussed above, there will be various payments made by and to the seller during the Interim Period. Although the seller and the purchaser will have agreed that these are to be allocated between them with effect from the Effective Date, in reality it will be the seller which will receive payments and make payments during the Interim Period. There will be tax consequences for the seller in doing so. For example, the seller may incur capital expenditure in the Interim Period. The seller may receive capital allowances in respect of such expenditure. The purchaser is responsible for reimbursing the seller for such capital expenditure. It would be unfair if the purchaser were required to reimburse the seller for the full amount of such capital expenditure in a scenario where the true cost to the seller was less due to the application of available capital allowances. The tax adjustments clause deals with this by providing for an adjustment to the consideration (in this example, downwards) by an amount which equates to the tax relief received by the seller in respect of such payments.

Another example is that the seller will receive income relating to the Interim Period. The seller will have to include such income as income in its corporation tax return notwithstanding that as between the seller and the purchaser the income will be for the account of the purchaser and, accordingly, the seller will not benefit from it. As a result, the tax adjustment provisions will provide that the consideration will be increased by an amount equal to the tax which the seller will be obliged to pay as a result of having received such income relating to the Income Period. In this way, the purchaser pays the seller an amount equal to the seller's tax liability.

From a practical point of view, it will be difficult to ascertain on the date of completion what the precise adjustments to the price are likely to be. Various payments and income which relate to the Interim Period might not be ascertainable or not actually be paid or received until after the completion date. As a result, the amount that is paid at completion is usually based on a preliminary calculation (normally know as the 'Preliminary Completion Statement') which will show the consideration with such adjustments relating to the Interim Period as are quantifiable as at the completion date. The Preliminary Completion Statement is normally prepared by the seller who sends it to the purchaser for approval. The SPA will also normally contain detailed provisions setting out when the Preliminary Completion Statement is to be prepared, the basis upon which it is to be calculated and the procedure to be adopted in the event of a dispute.

The Preliminary Completion Statement will set out the net price payable by the purchaser to the seller (although in some cases there may be an amount due by the seller to the purchase) after the application of the adjustments detailed above. It is this net amount which is paid on the date of completion.

As stated previously, it is extremely unlikely that the Preliminary Completion Statement will accurately reflect the true position as regards adjustments as at the completion date (although this might be the case with exploration acreage where nothing is happening other than payment of licence rental). It is normal practice for a further statement (normally known as the 'Final Completion Statement' or 'Completion Statement') to be prepared within a certain period of the completion date (perhaps 60–90 days after completion). This statement will be in the same form as the Preliminary Completion Statement and will set out the final adjustments required to the consideration to reflect the position on the completion date. Again, this will normally be prepared by the seller and then submitted to the purchaser for approval. Once approved, there will be a final payment made by the seller or the buyer (as the case may be).

One final point which often arises in relation to the price payable is whether or not interest should be charged on the consideration from the date of signing to the date of actual completion. There are numerous arguments for and against the inclusion of such a provision but looking at it from the point of view of the purchaser, it would be unwise to accept such a clause – if the seller is getting a commercial interest rate, there will be little or no incentive for the seller to act quickly in relation to the satisfaction of the conditions precedent (some of which will be entirely within the control of the seller). The seller will argue that interest represents the cost of money used by it in funding and running the business effectively for the purchaser and also that they would have earned interest on the price had the transaction completed on the Effective Date.

6. Conditions precedent

The SPA will set out a number of conditions that require to be satisfied before actual completion of the acquisition takes place ('Conditions Precedent'). These will vary from transaction to transaction but will normally include the following:

(a) DTI/Secretary of State consent

Before any interest in a licence is transferred or any transfer of operator occurs, the transfer must first be approved by the DTI. In deciding whether to consent, the DTI will consider a number of factors with the ultimate aim being to assess the financial and technical capability of the party to perform its obligations under the licence. A licence or operatorship cannot be transferred without the consent of the DTI. In very simple cases it can take two weeks from the date of the application for consent to the date of grant of consent. In cases involving the transfer of a more complex asset or the transfer of an operatorship the consent process can take considerably longer.

(b) Waiver of pre-emption rights

The JOA for the asset might contain pre-emption rights. As indicated above these rights can give other parties to a JOA or UOA a right to acquire the interest which is being sold. If these pre-emption rights exist then it will be necessary to obtain waivers of pre-emption rights from the relevant parties or to wait until the period during such pre-emption rights can be exercised, has expired. Pre-emption rights can often lead to potential problems in the acquisition of oil and gas assets. A potential purchaser can spend a great deal of time and money carrying out due diligence in relation to the assets being acquired and negotiating the SPA only to find that one or more parties pre-empts. In such a scenario the purchaser is left with nothing other than bills for the costs of the abortive transaction.

In order to try to limit the possibility of the deal being aborted due to pre-emption rights, the purchaser and the seller might try to structure the transaction in such a way as to make it unattractive to those parties that would be entitled to pre-empt, for example by making it a condition that a party acquiring the asset to which the pre-emption rights relate also acquires an interest in some other area.

(c) Completion documents

As we have previously seen, the title to an oil and gas asset is made up of a collection of licence and contractual rights. These have to be assigned or novated as part of the completion process. The purchaser will need to step into the shoes of the seller *vis-à-vis* these agreements. Many of these agreements will be between more than one party and so those other parties will also need to sign the relevant assignments/novations along with the seller and the purchaser. As signature of these documents is necessary to effect completion it will be a condition precedent that all parties (other than the seller and the purchaser) have signed all of the assignments/novations which require their signature (or as is now more common that all relevant parties have signed the

Execution Deed(s) in respect of the transfer (see above) which effectively means that the number of documents which require to be signed by third parties is reduced).

A common issue which is often dealt with as a condition precedent (but which is more appropriately dealt with in the section which deals with whether any party has the right to resile from the SPA) is the question of what happens if there is catastrophic damage to the assets being acquired during the Interim Period? As indicated above, the acquisition of the assets will be deemed to have been effective as at the Effective Date and, therefore, a situation could arise where the assets being acquired are totally destroyed during the Interim Period and thus do not exist on the completion date.

Obviously, a purchaser does not want to remain contractually bound to buy and pay for assets which no longer exist (and neither does its bank) and this is sometimes dealt with by providing that it is a condition precedent that no damage has occurred to the assets having more than a specified monetary value. Whether or not the seller would be willing to agree to such a provision is a purely commercial matter and one that will vary from transaction to transaction. If a seller is willing to accept such a provision in the SPA it will normally only be on the basis that the threshold at which it is triggered is set very high. Alternatively, a seller may simply refuse to agree to such a provision and instead insist that this is a matter which should be dealt with by claiming under the relevant insurance policy.

7. Completion

The SPA will contain a clause which deals with the mechanics of what happens at completion and which sets out what the obligations of the seller and the purchaser will be at completion. The completion clause will normally provide for the following:

(a) *When completion will take place.* This is normally stated as being a specified number of days after the satisfaction of the last of the conditions precedent.

(b) *Where completion is to take place.* This will normally be at the offices of the seller's solicitors but can be any mutually agreed venue. Historically, prior to changes to UK law on stamp duty, the SPA would provide that completion would occur outside the UK, eg in Amsterdam to avoid the possibility of being required to pay stamp duty on the purchase price.

(c) *Who is to deliver what and to whom.* The various completion documents will be delivered to the purchaser (having already been signed), both parties will then sign the interest assignment (ie the document which transfers the seller's interest in the assets to the purchaser) and finally, the purchaser will electronically transfer the consideration to the seller's bank account. There is also normally a provision that each party will provide the other with a copy of the authority under which the documents are being signed at completion (board approvals, powers of attorney, etc.).

8. Warranties

The warranty coverage contained in the SPA will be of fundamental importance. In essence, warranties are statements of fact, confirming that something is or is not the case. They are used as a form of price adjustment and risk allocation. The purchaser will have carried out due diligence but will still be acquiring the assets based on certain assumptions (eg that the seller is the owner of the assets and is entitled to sell them) and so the purchaser will expect the seller to warrant the position. If the position is otherwise than as warranted there should be a claim to adjust the price.

If any of the warranties given by the seller subsequently turn out to be untrue, the purchaser will have a claim against the seller for a breach of warranty and if successful in proving such breach, will be entitled to claim damages from the seller. Often the damages for a breach of warranty will reflect the reduction in the value of the assets acquired.

The warranties will encourage the seller to make disclosure of any matters that would render any of the warranties untrue. Any such disclosure is normally documented in a separate disclosure letter from the seller (or the seller's solicitor) to the purchaser (or the purchaser's solicitor). The purchaser will not have a claim in respect of any matter to the extent that it is properly disclosed by the seller in the disclosure letter.

This is probably better from both parties' points of view as it allows any possible problems to be identified early on and, if of sufficient severity, for the parties to agree a reduction in the consideration or some other mechanism such as a retention of part of the consideration to recognise the magnitude of that problem. Clearly, this is a more attractive alternative to finding out about a problem post completion and then having to go to court to resolve the matter.

There are a number of warranties which a purchaser will look for the seller to give. Some common warranties are as follows:

(a) that the seller is a licensee of the licence;
(b) that the licence is in full force and effect;
(c) that there has been no breach of any of the terms of the licence which might entitle the DTI to revoke the licence;
(d) that the seller owns the assets being acquired;

(e) that the assets being acquired are free from Encumbrances (as defined in the agreement);
(f) that the seller is not in default under any of the field agreements which relate to the assets;
(g) that the various field agreements exhibited to the purchaser by the seller are the only documents relevant to the assets being acquired;
(h) that the seller has and is complying with all relevant laws and other regulations which apply in respect of the licence and the assets being acquired; and
(i) that neither the seller nor any other party to any of the field agreements (if any) are involved in any actual, pending or threatened litigation.

There will also be warranties of a more corporate nature and it is quite often the case that the seller will look for these warranties to be given by the purchaser as well. These warranties include:

(a) that the party has the corporate authority and power to enter into the SPA and all ancillary documents;
(b) that when signed, the SPA and all ancillary documents will create binding obligations on the party; and
(c) that the party is not insolvent.

9. Warranty limitations

Given that the seller will have potential exposure to litigation and damages being awarded against it should any of the warranties given by it turn out to be untrue, the seller will want to ensure that the level of its exposure is limited. As a result, the SPA will normally contain limitations on the warranties. These limitations may include the following:

(a) no claim can be made for a breach of warranties unless the claim is made within a specified period of time. The period of time is a matter to be agreed between the seller and the purchaser, with the seller wanting the period to be as short as possible and the purchaser wanting the period to be as long as possible. Normally the period will vary from between one year and two years but for warranties relating to tax matters, the period will generally be for six years (which is the seventh anniversary from completion);
(b) no claim can be made unless the amount of the claim is above a certain value (known as the '*de minimis*' limit). This avoids the seller being subjected to low value claims. The level at which the *de minimis* is set will be for the parties to negotiate. Whatever the *de minimis* value is set at, the purchaser will want to ensure that in the event of a claim being over the *de minimis* limit, it will be entitled to claim the whole amount

and not simply the amount by which the particular claim exceeds the *de minimis* limit;

(c) no claim can be made where it would take the amount of all claims made to date above a certain figure (known as the '*de maximis*' limit). Again the level at which the *de maximis* is set will be a matter for negotiation between the parties but in most cases this limit will be set at the amount of the consideration being paid for the interest. If any claim would result in the *de maximis* limit being exceeded then the purchaser would only be entitled to claim the amount that would bring the total amount of claims up to the *de maximis* limit and no more;

(d) no claim can be made in respect of a matter that has been fairly disclosed in the disclosure letter;

(e) no claim can be made where that claim arises as a result of a change in legislation after the date of completion or where the loss suffered by the purchaser has been suffered as a result of the actions of the purchaser (or to the extent that such loss has been contributed to by the purchaser);

(f) no claim can be made in respect of a matter which is contained within any of the field agreements relating to the assets being acquired. This means that it is important for these agreements to have been identified and defined in the SPA and for them to have been fully reviewed as part of the due diligence process.

In some cases, the seller will try and add other limitations such as a limitation on making a warranty claim where the purchaser was aware or ought to have been aware of the matter giving rise to the warranty claim. This is a difficult limitation for a purchaser to give as it would be impossible to say what someone 'ought' to have known.

10. Obligations in the Interim Period

As discussed above, there may be a period between the Effective Date of the SPA and the completion date in order to allow the various conditions precedent to be satisfied. As previously indicated the period between signing and completion is known as the 'Interim Period'. During the Interim Period, the seller will remain the legal owner of the assets but will have entered into a binding contract in terms of which it is required to sell the asset to the purchaser and similarly, the purchaser will be legally bound to purchase the assets. Clearly, the purchaser has a vested interest in having some control over what the seller does with the assets during the Interim Period and does not want to be in a position where the seller can legally do something with the assets that reduces their value. In order to prevent such an occurrence, the SPA will contain various protections for the purchaser in respect of the Interim Period. This takes the form of a list of things that the seller has to do during the Interim Period and a list of things that the seller must not do without consulting (and preferably obtaining the consent of) the purchaser. These Interim Period provisions might include the following:

(a) a provision that the seller will act as a reasonable and prudent operator in respect of the assets (if it is operator);
(b) a provision that the seller will continue to sell oil/gas and to collect revenues generated by the assets during the interim period;
(c) restrictions on entering into new field agreements without the consent of the purchaser;
(d) obligations on the seller to consult with the purchaser prior to voting on any particular issue at any meeting relating to the assets (for example, a meeting of the joint operating committee);
(e) obligations on the seller not to agree to any variations of budgets without the consent of the buyer;
(f) restriction on the seller granting any security over the assets; and
(g) obligations on the seller to maintain any policies of insurance in respect of the assets.

As with most of the provisions of the SPA, a balance will have to be struck in respect of these Interim Period obligations and not surprisingly, the purchaser will be looking for as much protection as possible whereas the seller will be looking for as few restrictions as possible (as at the end of the day if completion does not occur the seller will be left with the asset). Perhaps one of the most important Interim Period obligations is that the seller maintains its current insurance policies in respect of the assets and the purchaser is noted on such insurance policies so that in the event of any damage and a claim being made, the purchaser will be entitled to receive the proceeds of any such insurance claim. The purchaser may also want to put in place its own insurance policies in respect of the assets where the assets are being bought from a large company. The reason for this is that the seller may be part of a large group of companies with a group wide insurance policy in place and the excess of such policy may be extremely high (for example, $50 million). In such a case, the benefit of being noted on the seller's insurance policy will be of little effect if the purchaser is not entitled to recover the first $50 million and so the purchaser would want its own insurance in place to cover the majority of this excess (bearing in mind that the purchaser's insurance policy will also include an excess provision). It might even be the case that the seller self-insures.

11. Tax issues

In any transaction, tax will play a major role and this is no different in relation to the acquisition of oil and gas assets. The SPA will contain detailed tax provisions and it would be normal for the purchaser to take specialist tax advice in respect of these provisions. This will include the allocation of the consideration between different elements, eg licence, MEAs, etc.

12. Condition of the assets

Almost invariably there will be no warranties given by the seller in relation to the physical condition of the asset being acquired and the seller will not give any warranty in relation to the recoverability of oil and gas from the assets or the existence of reserves or the state of the reservoir. It will be up to the purchaser to satisfy itself with the condition of the assets and the recoverability of oil and gas, which will form part of the purchaser's technical and operational due diligence process.

13. Assumption of obligations

As a consequence of the Effective Date principle, the SPA will contain provisions which effectively allow there to be a 'clean break' as at the Effective Date. There may be liabilities which arise after the completion date but which relate to events that occurred prior to the Effective Date and in such an event, the purchaser will want to ensure that these are the responsibility of the seller. Similarly, a benefit may accrue after the completion date that relates to something that occurred prior to the Effective Date and the seller will want to ensure that it is entitled to this benefit.

Accordingly, the SPA will contain provisions that (i) the seller will be responsible for and indemnify the purchaser in respect of all liabilities and obligations in respect of the assets in the period prior to the Effective Date and that the seller will be entitled to all benefits accruing as at the Effective Date; and (ii) conversely, the purchaser will be responsible for and indemnify the seller in respect of all liabilities and obligations in respect of the assets being acquired in the period from the Effective Date and that the purchaser will be entitled to all benefits accruing after the Effective Date.

An exception to the above provisions can sometimes arise in relation to the decommissioning (or abandonment) costs in respect of the assets and the seller will often try to include a provision whereby the purchaser will be responsible for these decommissioning costs irrespective of when they arise (for further details on decommissioning provisions, see below).

14. Decommissioning

Of increasing importance in any acquisition of oil and gas assets is the question of decommissioning. The basic position in relation to decommissioning of assets is that all parties who have ever been a party to the licence can be held responsible for the decommissioning of the assets relating to that licence and for all associated costs. Decommissioning costs can be very high. The practice of the DTI tends to be that it will first look to the current licensees to undertake the decommissioning of assets and it is only if those licensees are unable to meet the costs of such decommissioning that it will look to past licensees to pay for the costs of decommissioning. As a result of this, a seller will often try to insist that it will be a condition precedent to completion that the DTI grants it a release from its obligations relating to decommissioning. In practice, the DTI will be reluctant to grant such releases unless it is satisfied that the remaining licensees will have the financial ability to meet the decommissioning costs without the exiting licensee. However, even if a release is obtained, the DTI still has the power to look to the released party to contribute to the costs of decommissioning so there is doubt over the practical significance of such a release.

If the seller cannot get such a release (and sometimes even where such a release is given) the seller might require the buyer to put up some form of security for its share of the decommissioning costs. This might take the form of a parent company guarantee but would more usually be some form of bank security or letter of credit which can be called up if the purchaser defaults on any of its decommissioning obligations. Even where the seller does not insist on such security it may be the case that other co-venturers of the seller require such security to be put up by the purchaser as a condition of consenting to the transfer.

Acquisition of shares

An oil and gas company may wish to purchase the shares in another energy company rather than acquiring its oil and gas assets. This part of the chapter looks at the purchase of the shares of such a company.

The important point to keep in mind is that in a shares deal the purchaser cannot pick the assets which he is willing to buy. The purchaser acquires the shares in the relevant company and not the assets themselves. For example, A is the purchaser; B is a company which holds all the shares in C; C holds interests in numerous oil and gas assets (licences, participating interests under JOAs etc.). If A is interested in the assets held by C then it could enter into a sale and purchase agreement to buy the assets held by C and at completion the assets would transfer from C to A. Alternatively, A could buy the shares in company C from company B. A would then be the holding company of C. C would still own the assets and would be responsible for all of its own obligations. A would own all of the shares of C.

There may be a number of circumstances in which a purchaser wishes to buy a company rather than buying its assets; it might be that a group of companies holds a whole collection of oil and gas assets over a number of jurisdictions. A quick way for a purchaser to increase its reserves base or reserves and production base would be to buy the parent company. Perhaps the seller has kept its assets in different group companies to make it easier to sell one part of its business; for example a selling company may have assets in several jurisdictions and hold them in different companies (one per jurisdiction) or it might separate assets into different companies depending on the type of the asset (eg gas in one company and oil in another). If it wants to sell all of its assets in one jurisdiction it could do so by selling the company which holds those assets.

Another reason for structuring the transaction as a share sale rather than as an asset sale might be to get round any pre-emption rights. As indicated previously, some JOAs/UOAs contain pre-emption rights in terms of which if a party wishes to sell its interest then the other co-venturers have a right to acquire that interest. Usually such a pre-emption right takes effect only where there is a transfer of the asset and not where there is a change of control of the company which holds the interest. By buying the shares it might be possible to get round the whole pre-emption issue (although one has to check carefully as some operating agreements do have more sophisticated pre-emption rights which would apply in a change of control scenario).

The structure of a Share Purchase Agreement is similar to an Asset Purchase Agreement in certain respects but is very different in other ways.

1. Due diligence

As indicated above, in a share acquisition, the purchaser will be acquiring the target company. The company which is being acquired will still have its existing assets and all of its existing liabilities. The extent of due diligence required, therefore, may be substantially greater as it will require to deal not only with the assets of the company, but also all liabilities, tax liabilities, environment liabilities, health and safety issues and employee issues which exist in respect of that target company.

It should be noted that in any share acquisition where the target company holds an interest in a UK licence it is necessary to obtain comfort from the DTI that they are happy with the change of control of the licensee. Strictly speaking, DTI consent is not required to a change of control of a licensee but it can give rise to a termination of the licence in certain circumstances. The safe course of action is therefore to seek consent from the DTI before a change of control occurs.

2. Share Purchase Agreement

The sellers and the sale clause

The purchaser (which will normally be a company) will be purchasing the entire issued share capital of the target company from the sellers (the shareholders of the target company). The sellers may be individuals, financial institutions or a holding company, etc. It is important to ensure that if the purchaser wants to buy the entire issued share capital of the target company that all shareholders are sellers. The purchaser will usually want to acquire the whole of the target company rather than acquiring less than all the shares.

A Share Purchase Agreement will include a provision in terms of which the sellers agree to sell their shares in the target company and the purchaser agrees to buy those shares for the stated consideration on reliance upon representations, warranties, covenants and undertakings contained in the agreement. The purchaser will want to buy the shares free from encumbrances.

The purchaser will want to ensure that none of the shares which it is buying are encumbered. It will also need to ensure that the companies it is buying are free from debt or, if there is debt, that the debt holder has given its consent to the purchase and that the purchase will not trigger a right on the part of the lender to call for repayment of the borrowing facilities. It is almost invariably the case that bank facility agreements will contain provisions in terms of which the bank can call in the loans if there is a change of control of the borrower.

3. Purchase price

The purchase price for the sale shares can take many forms. The simplest is obviously a specific amount of cash per share.

The consideration might include an amount paid per share with adjustments which will take into account forecast cash in the target company at an Effective Date, the forecast working capital amount at an Effective Date and which will take account of any estimated payments or accruals to be made by the target company. The aggregation of that price may then be less any bank debt that has to be repaid to a bank together with any interest. All distributions made by the target company beyond a certain accounting date may also be a deduction from the purchase price. Sometimes fees paid to professionals on the acquisition can be a deduction from the acquisition price.

The consideration could be subject to adjustment depending on the level of the assets of the target company as at completion. All distributions made by the target company after a certain accounting date might also give rise to a deduction from the purchase price.

In order to arrive at the amount of working capital in the company at either completion or a given Effective Date there will need to be an agreed basis of preparation of a Preliminary Completion Working Capital Statement which will set out the accounting principles on which both purchaser and seller calculate and agree the amount of working capital in the target company at that date. The Preliminary Completion Working Capital Statement is normally drawn to the date of completion and this is because working capital amounts can only be estimated at any given date and cannot be fully accounted for until it is possible to accurately state the working capital. There is normally a Final Working Capital Statement produced 30–60 days after completion which will show the final working capital amounts to be included in the adjusted consideration to be paid by the purchaser to the seller.

The purchase price may be alternatively based on a net asset valuation which is a valuation of the target company's fixed assets plus current assets less its liabilities. There is then an estimated net assets calculation which is adjusted after the completion accounts have been prepared and agreed between the parties or verified by an independent accountant or other professional.

The purchase price might be payable in cash or it could be satisfied by the issue of new shares in the purchasing company. There could be a combination of cash payable at completion and cash payable on deferred terms. For example, the purchaser might issue loan notes to the seller or simply agree to pay in the future.

It is possible to structure the deal so that the level of the consideration can change depending on the level of the profitability of the target company post-completion (known as 'an earn-out'). The agreement could provide that additional payments are to be made to the sellers if specified future financial targets are met.

Where the sellers are concerned about the purchaser's ability to pay any element of deferred or contingent consideration they could ask for the purchaser to provide security for payment of such additional consideration. Such security could take the form of a bank guarantee, parent company guarantee or other form of security.

4. Interim Period

Unlike a deal involving the acquisition of oil and gas assets it is common in share acquisitions for the signing of the sale purchase agreement and the completion of the acquisition to occur simultaneously. There are no assignments or novations of field agreements (as the target company will still be the party to these – not the purchaser).

It is possible for there to be a delay between signing and completion in a shares deal (although it is much less common than in an assets deal). Usually, there will be a delay where the parties wish to be bound by the terms of the sale and purchase agreement but there are matters which need to be dealt with before completion can occur (such as obtaining consents). If there are such issues these are dealt with as conditions precedent to completion. An example would be obtaining comfort from the DTI in respect of the change of control of the licence holder.

If there is a delay between signing and completion then the agreement may contain a number of covenants by the seller in respect of the operation and management of the target company and its assets in this interim period. These are along the lines of the interim period obligations of the seller found in an asset purchase agreement but will include other matters given the corporate nature of the acquisition. For example, there may be other covenants in terms of which the sellers agree not to change the memorandum and articles of association of the company, and not to materially change the business operated by the target company.

5. Warranties/indemnities

As with an asset deal (and for the same reasons) the Sale and Purchase Agreement will contain representations and warranties. These warranties are likely to be more extensive than the warranties in an asset acquisition transaction given that the target company in its entirety is being acquired and not simply the assets. The warranties may include matters which are normally included in an asset deal but will also include warranties as to matters such as the seller's capacity to sell the sale shares, that the sale shares are not encumbered, that the sellers have waived all pre-emption rights on selling the shares, that the information given in respect of the target company is correct and accurate, that the sale of the company or group of companies will not put the target company into default under any agreement, that the licences and the documents relating to the licence will all remain in full force and effect notwithstanding the change of control of the target.

There are also likely to be warranties on employees and pensions and warranties on financial records, management accounts, annual accounts, taxation, insurance, intellectual property rights, information technology systems, environmental matters, abandonment obligations and safety matters.

As in an asset sale, the sale and purchase agreement may contain limited warranties given by the purchaser as to its capacity to enter into the sale purchase agreement and its solvency.

There will also be limitations on the warranties (*de maximis*, *de minimis*, time period for claims, etc.) and the seller will ordinarily prepare and deliver a disclosure letter making disclosures against the warranties.

In a shares deal, in addition to the Sale and Purchase Agreement there is normally a tax deed granted by the sellers to the purchaser in which the sellers undertake to indemnify the purchase against all tax liabilities (to the extent to which these have not been provided for) which relate to the period prior to completion. The tax deed will be a fairly complex document with exclusions and carve-outs to the indemnity.

As mentioned previously the extent of the warranties is normally capped in terms of amount and duration, etc. If there is a warranty claim this will give rise to a claim by the party to which the warranty was granted against the party to which the warranty was given.

The difference between a warranty and an indemnity is that a warranty is a statement (which may be qualified by the seller's awareness and knowledge) about an aspect of the state of the target company's business. In order for the purchaser to make a successful claim for breach of warranty the purchaser needs to evidence that the warranty was breached and that the effect of the breach is to reduce the value of the company or business acquired and that there is a quantifiable loss. An indemnity is an obligation on the part of the sellers to reimburse the purchaser for a specific liability in the event that the liability arises. In effect it is a straight allocation of risk – if a specified problem arises then the costs of that problem are for the account of the party which has granted the indemnity.

A claim under the tax indemnity or any other specific indemnity is a claim for a pound for pound recovery. A purchaser has a duty to mitigate its loss in the event of a warranty claim. In the case of a breach of an indemnity there is no such obligation.

6. Restrictive covenants

In order to ensure the goodwill which resides in the target company stays in that company, the purchaser might require the sellers to give restrictive covenants that they will not attempt to compete against the businesses of the target company, that they will not solicit or poach employees from the target company and that they will not solicit customers or try to stop suppliers of the target company dealing with the target company.

7. Process of acquisition

Only a limited number of people, both in terms of the purchasers' and seller's representatives and their professional advisors, will be involved in the negotiation of the transaction.

The process after the transaction is over is sometimes as difficult as completing the transaction itself. The first employees and co-venturers may know of the transaction will be when it is announced in the press, and senior management teams of the purchaser may spend many weeks and months trying to consolidate the target company's businesses, incentivise acquired employees and management teams and dispose of non-core assets.

— 4 —

DRILLING OPERATIONS

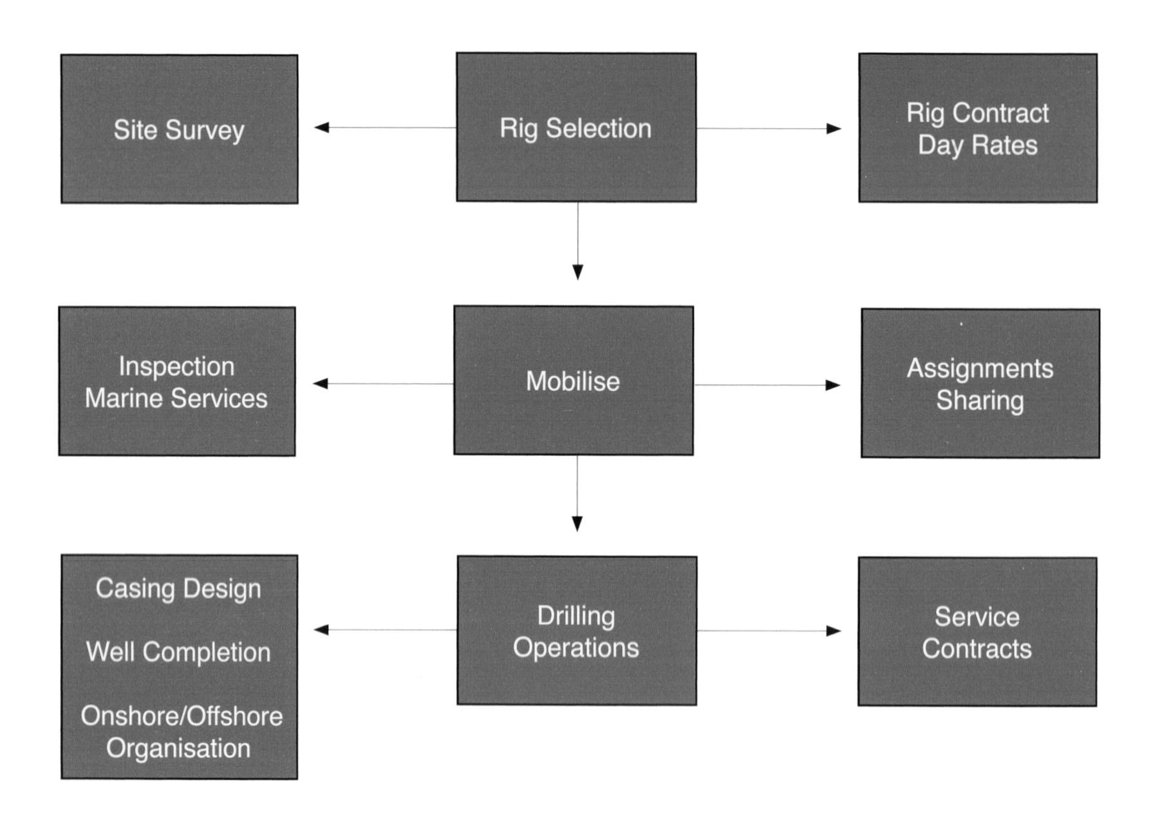
Site Survey
Rig Selection
Rig Contract
Day Rates
Inspection
Marine Services
Mobilise
Assignments
Sharing
Casing Design
Well Completion
Onshore/Offshore
Organisation
Drilling
Operations
Service
Contracts

DRILLING OPERATIONS

TECHNICAL

4.1 Introduction

The use of hydrocarbons for practical, medicinal and military purposes goes back to biblical times and natural seeps of hydrocarbons occur worldwide, eg the Eternal Fires of Kirkuk (Iraq) and Kazakhstan, and the bitumen seeps of the Athabasca River, Alberta, where the Cree Indians used it for mending their canoes.

The commercial development of hydrocarbons did not, however, begin until the late 1800s – early 1900s. While early uses involved the collection of hydrocarbons deep into the Earth, the commercial development required penetration of the Earth's crust to reach accumulations. In order to do this, the development of the drilling rig was essential. Early drilling made use of a primitive device called a cable-tool rig. A heavy, chisel-like bit was suspended on a cable and dropped repeatedly into the rock at the bottom of the hole.

Cable-tool drilling was very slow, hard and dangerous work. It was not uncommon to drill only 300 ft per month. The bits had to be pulled out and sharpened frequently. Drillers poured water into the well bore and removed the rock fragments by bailing out the resulting mud. If the bit encountered a reservoir, both bit and oil would shoot back up, resulting in the 'black gushers' with which we are familiar from old photographs – dangerous for both workers and the environment.

As the industry developed, it was essential to develop a better way of drilling and so the rotary drill was, therefore, invented. Further developments in drilling have taken place with horizontal and multilateral well designs.

Although experimentation with horizontal wells began in the 1950–1960s, significant advances did not occur until the 1980–1990s. A horizontal well is commonly defined as any well in which the lower part of the well bore parallels the pay zone. Although much more expensive than conventional vertical wells (two or three times), the production factor can be increased by as much as 15 or 20 times.

As with horizontal wells, multilateral wells are more expensive but can again increase production rates. These are wells in which one or more well bore branches radiate from the main borehole. Multilateral well technology is not as advanced as horizontal well technology.

4.2 Rig types and costs

Drilling rigs are owned and managed by specialist companies called drilling contractors, who hire out their rigs, complete with crews and management systems, to oil companies who are the operators. The operators own the right to exploit hydrocarbons from their licence blocks, which can be on or offshore, but need the drilling contractors' rigs to drill the wells.

There are a finite number of rigs available at any one time, so this creates the classic supply and demand rollercoaster. When the price of oil is low, operators do not want to spend money drilling, so rigs are cheap. When the oil price increases, operators want to increase their reserves or production by drilling more wells, so the cost of hiring a rig increases and, as the number of available rigs declines, the price increases even more.

Figure 4–1 Land rig

Onshore

The cost of land rigs is defined by the depth they can drill. A typical unit,

Figure 4–2 Platform rig

able to drill to 20,000 ft, fitted with a Top Drive, will cost $20,000 to $25,000 a day (24 hours), (Fig. 4–1).

Offshore

There are four common types of offshore rig:

- *Platform rigs (fixed or modular)* (Figs 4–2 and 4–5): these are similar to land units but installed on an operator's fixed offshore platform. These rigs were once owned by the operator, but now it is usual for a drilling contractor to own and manage them. Depending on the crew size and type of drilling or workover operation to be performed, platform rigs cost $30,000 to $40,000 a day.
- *Jack-up rigs (Mobile Offshore Drilling Unit or MODU)* (Figs 4–3 and 4–5): the drilling package is mounted on a hull fitted with three or more legs. The hull is towed to location by specialist tugs and the legs jacked down to the seabed. Once the legs contact the seabed the hull is driven up the legs

to a predetermined working air gap above mean sea level. Jack-up rigs can be used in open water locations to drill exploration, appraisal or production wells. Alternatively, they can be positioned alongside a production platform and the drilling package skidded out over the platform to drill production wells. Standard jack-up rigs work in water depths of between 20 ft and 150 ft and cost $60,000 to $140,000 a day. Newer, harsh environment jack-up rigs can work in water depths of up to 500 ft and can cost up to $250,000 a day.

Figure 4–3 Jack-up rig

- *Semi-submersible rigs (MODU)* (Figs 4–4 and 4–5): the hull, which supports the drilling package, is connected by columns to submerged pontoons (usually two); the unit is always floating. The height of the hull above sea level is controlled by flooding or emptying the pontoons with sea water. The rig is towed to location by specialist tugs and then, depending on the design, either anchored in position or held in place by computer-activated thrusters in the pontoons (Dynamically Positioned (DP)). Semi-submersible rigs are used in open water to drill exploration, appraisal or production wells which are usually part of a template tied back to production facilities. Depending on the size, sophistication and age of the rig, they can work anywhere between 150 ft and 10,000 ft of water and cost from $120,000 to $500,000 a day.
- *Drill ships (MODU)*: the drilling package is an integral part of a ship-shaped vessel which is normally self-propelled and able to position itself on location. Once there, it will either be anchored in relatively shallow water

Figure 4–4 Semi-submersible rig

up to 2,000 ft or held in place – like the semi-submersible rig – with dynamic positioning in water depths up to 10,000 ft. Also, like semi-submersibles, drill ships drill exploration, appraisal and production wells. Depending on the size, sophistication and age of the drill ship, it can command from $150,000 to $500,000 a day (Fig. 4–5).

These day-rates cover only the cost of hiring the rig, crews and management systems; the operator also pays the drilling contractor for fuel to run the rig, lubricants to maintain the rig's equipment, some spare parts, and transporting crews and equipment to and from the rig.

The process of drilling is the same for all rigs but variations are due to the position and distance of the wellhead relative to the drill floor and the method of

Rig Type	Water Depth (ft)	Location Example	Rate Per Day US$
Platforms	<500	N. North Sea	30,000–40,000
Jack-ups	20–150	S. North Sea	60,000–140,000
Harsh environment jack-ups	20–500	North Sea, Norway	100,000–250,000
Semi-submersibles	150–10,000	N. North Sea	120,000–500,000
Drill ships	2,000–10,000	West of Shetland	150,000–500,000

Figure 4–5 Examples of rigs and day-rates

connecting the two. This is relatively simple for a land rig but the cost increases with more complex offshore rigs.

4.3 Rig market and mobilisation

With a few exceptions, rigs are designed to be mobile so that drilling contractors can take advantage of the international nature of the oil and gas industry and get the maximum return for their investment. If required, a land rig working in West Texas can be mobilised to a desert in the Middle East, a jack-up working in the North Sea can be towed to West Africa or a drill ship working in the Mediterranean can sail to the Indian Ocean.

Although the planning of these moves is done by either the drilling contractor or the operator, it is the operator who pays for the move. With such potential to relocate rigs, operators have to be continually aware of the international market place. A deepwater drilling campaign planned for west of the Shetlands by one operator could be delayed because another operator has contracted all the spare suitable rig capacity for a programme offshore Brazil.

The type of contract drives the type of management relationships so it is logical to look at contractual arrangements first. The types of contract that have been, or may be, used include:

- *Day-rate contract.* The operator pays an agreed amount of money each day to the contractor. Responsibility for all operational decisions rests with the operator.
- *Turn-key contract.* The contractor is paid an agreed lump sum for drilling the well. Responsibility for all operational decisions rests with the contractor.

- *Incentive contract.* This is a day-rate contract with some kind of bonus scheme for the contractor if certain performance criteria are met.

Turn-key contracts are now quite rare. They might be used on simple, shallow wells where many wells have been drilled and the subsurface conditions are well known but day-rate contracts are the most common. Bonus schemes seem to come into fashion from time to time but are probably used on less than 10% of contracts worldwide at present.

4.4 Rig positioning and moving

Land rigs can be dismantled, mounted on trucks and moved along roads, across deserts, or onto ships and across oceans. There are even specialist land rigs that can be broken down into small enough units to be flown to a new location by helicopter; typically this would be an inaccessible jungle or mountainous location where road building would be impossible.

Jack-up rigs and most semi-submersibles are towed to a new location. It is normal to use at least two vessels and, depending on the distance and sea currents, quite often three, to allow for redundancy and emergencies.

Drill ships have the ability to move themselves to location by transferring their power generating system from the drilling facilities to their propulsion system.

Once the rig arrives at its new destination it has to be positioned accurately so that the well is drilled where the geologists want it. The final position is now usually managed by Global Positioning System (GPS) but even using this accurate system it is still normal to wait 24 hours before drilling operations start, to ensure sufficient satellite passes have occurred to guarantee the required level of accuracy.

4.5 Rotary drilling

Rotary rigs were introduced in Texas in the 1890s but it was not until after the Second World War that cable-tool rigs were finally retired. Today rotary rigs form a key element of the industry.

The main features of a rotary drilling rig (Fig. 4–6) are:

- The *derrick* which supports the weight of the drill string.
- The *drill string* which consists of 30 ft lengths of drill pipe, which are screwed together as drilling proceeds.
- The *drill bit* is attached to the base of the drill string using very heavy pipes called drill collars. These put weight on the bit and aid the drilling

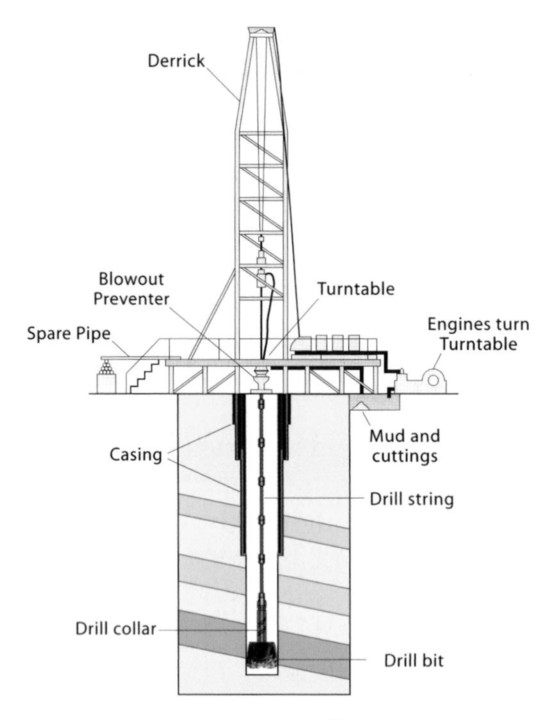

Figure 4–6 Drilling rig
Schematic diagram of the main elements of a drilling rig apparatus.
(Modified after www.howstuffworks.com)

procedure. This part of the drill string is also known as the Bottom Hole Assembly (BHA).

- The *rotary table* (now superceded by a top-drive on most rigs) turns the whole drill string. This allows drilling to be a much more rapid procedure than with the old cable-tool rigs and 300 ft can be drilled in a few hours as opposed to weeks.

The cost of removing the drill string from the well bore is significant in rig-time and so is kept to a minimum. The process of removing and subsequently re-entering the drill string is termed a 'round trip'.

4.6 Drilling a well

Most rig-time is taken up with drilling and well completions and it is the responsibility of the driller to monitor and control the drilling procedure. The first step is to hammer a conductor pipe into the ground (outside diameter 30") using a pile driver or drill a 36" hole with the conductor pipe lowered in afterwards. The purpose of the conductor pipe is to guide drilling. As drilling continues, smaller and smaller bit sizes are used (Figs 4–7 and 4–8).

On the rig, the driller has instruments which indicate the total weight of the drill string. As the bit touches the rock and presses into it, the drill string weight goes down because it is supported by the rock. The difference between the drill string weight with the bit above the rock and when it is pressing into the rock is called the Weight on Bit (WOB). By applying weight on the bit, the teeth of the drill bit are pushed into the rock. As the drill bit is turned with weight on bit, chips of rock are dislodged. The mud flowing out of the bit and up the annulus (space between the drill string and borehole wall) lifts the rock chips, called cuttings (Chapter 5) to the surface. As the rock below the bit is removed, the drill string weight increases (WOB decreases) due to the lack of rock support. The driller therefore lowers the drill string slowly to keep up with the progress of the bit. If the drill string is lowered at exactly the same speed as the bit drills, the WOB will stay constant. Drilling is, therefore, a highly skilled operation.

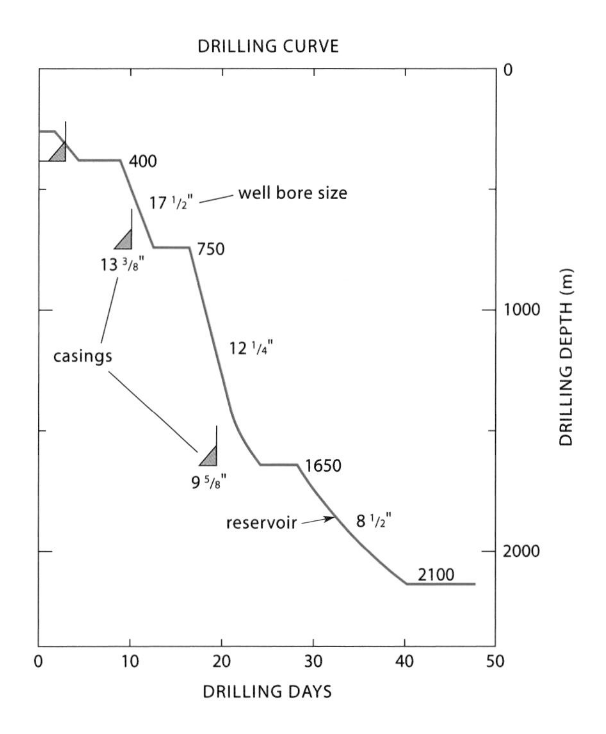

Figure 4–7 Drilling record
Drilling record showing how the well bore and casing diameters decrease with depth. (Modified after Rider, 2002).

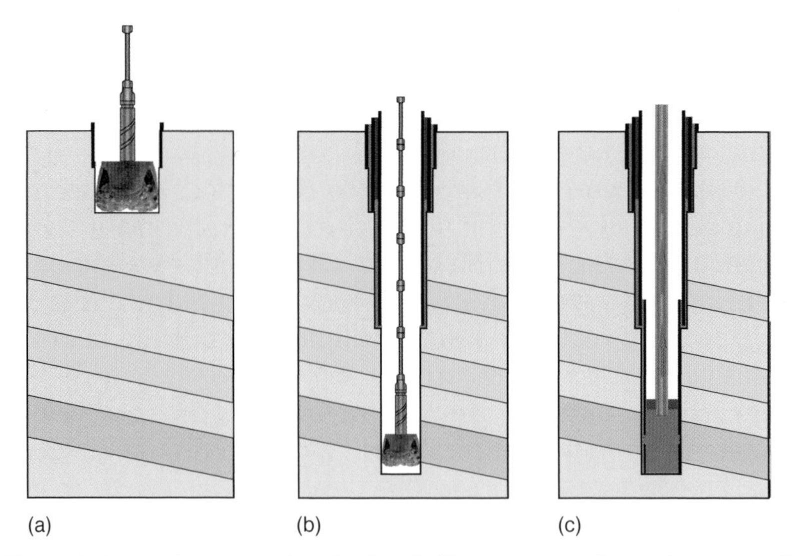

Figure 4–8 Various stages involved in drilling, casing and completing a well
(a) The first stage is to drill a 36" hole for the conductor pipe. (b) Subsequently, the well bore is drilled using smaller bits. Casing is set after each stage of drilling. (c) The final stage is the setting of the completion and perforation of the reservoir (green) to allow fluids to flow into the well bore.

4.7 Drilling fluids

As drilling proceeds, drilling fluid (called drilling mud or just mud which can be either water- or oil-based) is pumped continuously down the drill string (Chapter 5, Fig. 5–1) and is monitored by the mud engineer (or mud logger). It comes out of the bit at the bottom of the drill string and flows back up the annulus.

The drilling mud has several roles. It:

- cleans, cools and lubricates drilling tools;
- washes up rock cuttings from the subsurface to the surface (Chapter 5);
- balances the pressure of the fluids in the rock formations to prevent 'blow-outs'. The drilling mud weight can be increased by adding barite; and
- helps to seal off permeable formations by leaving a mud cake on the borehole wall while the liquid infiltrates the reservoir.

4.8 Casing

As discussed in section 4.6, a well is drilled in different stages, each section having a smaller diameter than the previous (Figs 4–7 and 4–8). At the end of each stage, and after all well logs have been run (see Chapter 5), the casing is set. This is a length of pipe placed into the well bore and fixed by pumping cement down the hole which then flows back up the annulus. Once the cement is hard, the casing then protects the well bore and prevents formation fluids being contaminated by drilling mud.

The first casing run inside the conductor is known as the surface casing. Subsequent casings are known as intermediate casings with the casing over the reservoir interval known as the production casing. These are shown in Fig. 4–8 where the cement is shown in grey.

While a surface casing always has the annulus completely filled with cement, subsequent casings do not require this – 500 ft of cement above the base of the previous casing is adequate to provide a seal, reducing the cost of the cementing process. A column of drilling mud (purple, Figs 4–8(b) and (c), will remain above the hard cement.

4.9 Well completion

A set of tubes, screwed together, is run in to the well. These tubes, together with any tools included, are called the completion. In Fig. 4–8(c), a special tool is run on the bottom of the completion, which forms a seal between the bottom of the tubing and the casing. This tool is called a packer.

Once the completion is in place, the logging wireline unit is used to run special guns in the hole. These guns are positioned at predetermined depths in the reservoir, then shaped explosive charges are fired which perforate holes in the casing and through into the formation. Modern perforation charges are capable of penetrating steel and a couple of feet of formation, forming a path for hydrocarbons to flow from the reservoir to the well.

When a new reservoir first starts to produce oil, there is usually enough pressure inside the reservoir to force the oil to the surface through the completion, termed natural drive. Some reservoirs, however, lose pressure as oil is extracted and so the flow slows down over the years. Eventually, there might not be enough pressure to give a reasonable production rate. The completion can be removed from the well and a different type of completion employed in these circumstances.

4.10 Rig management structure

When an oil company (the operator) decides to drill a well, they would normally hire the rig, equipment and services needed. Oil and gas fields are typically found in remote, inhospitable places – deserts, jungles and offshore. As the costs of operations (and rewards) are high, personnel and machines have to work 24 hours a day, 365 days a year in these environments. By necessity, drilling rigs become self-sustaining communities where:

- all the power required to run the rig- and life-sustaining systems have to be generated on site;
- hotel facilities like meals, bunking and recreation have to be provided for all on board;
- communications systems to the rest of the world are needed; and
- on-site medical support in the event of illness or an accident must be provided.

The major contractor on a drilling project is the company that owns the drilling rig (the drilling contractor). The management and contractual relationships between the operator and the drilling contractor are important to the success of the project.

Operator company organisation

A typical operating company drilling department will be organised along similar lines to that shown in Fig. 4–9. If there are several rigs working for the operator,

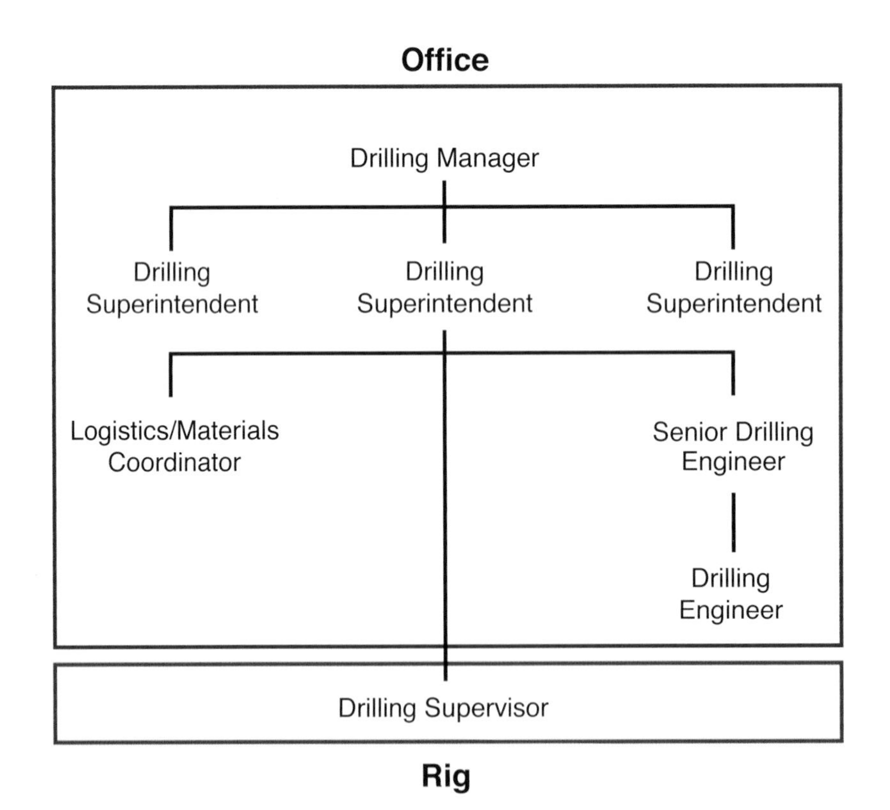

Figure 4–9 Operating company organisation

there may be several drilling superintendents, each responsible for one or two rigs, depending on the complexity of the operation.

The drilling superintendent is the main point of contact with the rig and he will talk to the rig-site drilling supervisor several times a day. Supporting the drilling superintendent may be one or more drilling engineers and geologists, who might be dedicated to that particular rig or might form a pool of personnel who work as needed on any project. A drilling department usually has one dedicated logistics expert, who arranges to get supplies to and from the rig as needed by the operation. Efficient logistics are crucial to drilling in terms of rig-time and costs (thousands of pounds per hour).

Responsibility for a drilling operation is usually divided between the drilling contractor, taking care of everything above the wellhead (ie the rig, maintenance, personnel and safety) and the operator, managing everything below the wellhead (ie well quality, drilling performance, casing setting depths, etc.).

The drilling contractor will supply the operator with a drilling rig, crews and management systems to run the rig, and the operator will need to supply drill bits, downhole drilling tools, mud systems, casing and accessories, cement and accessories, wellheads, formation evaluation tools and specialist engineers to run and manage these tools and services. In order to achieve this, contracts will be set up with various service companies to supply the operator with one or more of these services. The operator can mix and match equipment and personnel from several smaller suppliers or choose to source everything from one of the integrated companies.

More complex well designs and locations require more sophisticated and expensive rigs and support services. This has a large impact on the cost of drilling a well. As a guide, the daily spread cost (the cost of the rig plus all tangible and non-tangible costs) for drilling a well is typically double the rig day-rate. Thus, an onshore operation using a land rig with a day-rate of $25,000 a day will cost the operator $50,000 a day to drill the well. A deepwater operation using a fifth-generation semi-submersible at a day-rate of $500,000 will cost the operator $1,000,000 a day to drill the well.

Drilling contractor organisation

The drilling contractor will supply the operator with a drilling rig, crews and management systems to run the rig (Fig. 4–10). The person in charge of the department may have the title of Drilling Manager although, of course, different companies worldwide may use other titles. If the contractor is set up for day-rate operations, they would not need the support of drilling engineers to design wells and plan how best to drill them.

Each rig has a rig manager but it is also possible that one rig manager might be responsible for more than one rig. The rig manager is the main point of contact

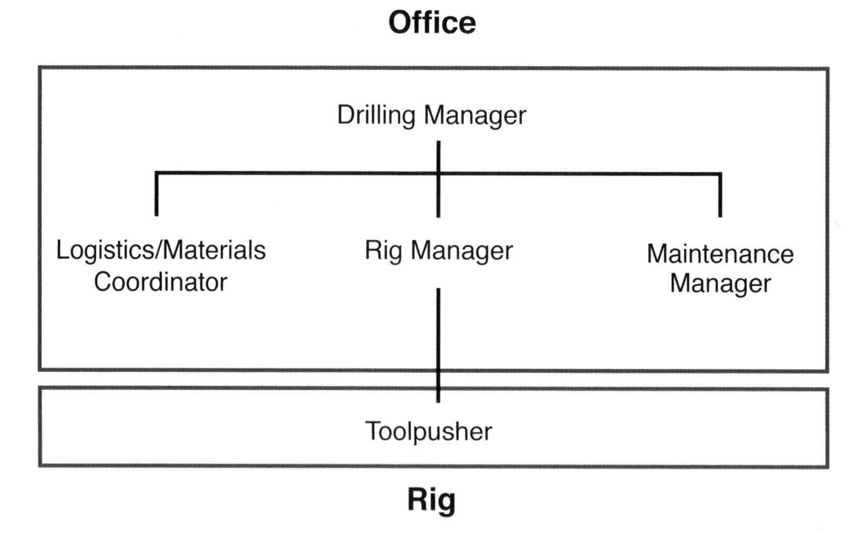

Figure 4–10 Drilling contractor organisation

with the toolpusher, who is the senior employee of the drilling contractor on the rig. The toolpusher has responsibility 24 hours a day for the rig, personnel and ongoing operations. He may be assisted by a night toolpusher who will work from 6pm to 6am. On an offshore rig there will also be an Offshore Installation Manager (OIM) who will have overall responsibility for both the drilling and marine functions of the rig.

Maintenance of the rig is very important. If the rig stops working for more than a set number of hours in a month (defined in the contract and often 24 hours) the rig goes on to zero rate and is not paid until the problem is solved. Logistics are also crucial for the drilling contractor, who must handle crew changes (replacing crews or individuals on the rig with fresh crews each week) as well as materials and other supplies.

Drilling rig organisation

The operator has a senior representative on the rig, the drilling supervisor (Fig. 4–11). This person has 24-hour authority to make the day-to-day decisions required in drilling the well, in terms of downhole drilling tools and bits, mud systems, casing, cement, wellheads and formation evaluation tools and personnel. Contracts will be set up with various service companies to supply the operator with one or more of these services.

Reporting to the drilling supervisor will be several other operator staff plus personnel from other companies providing services for the operation.

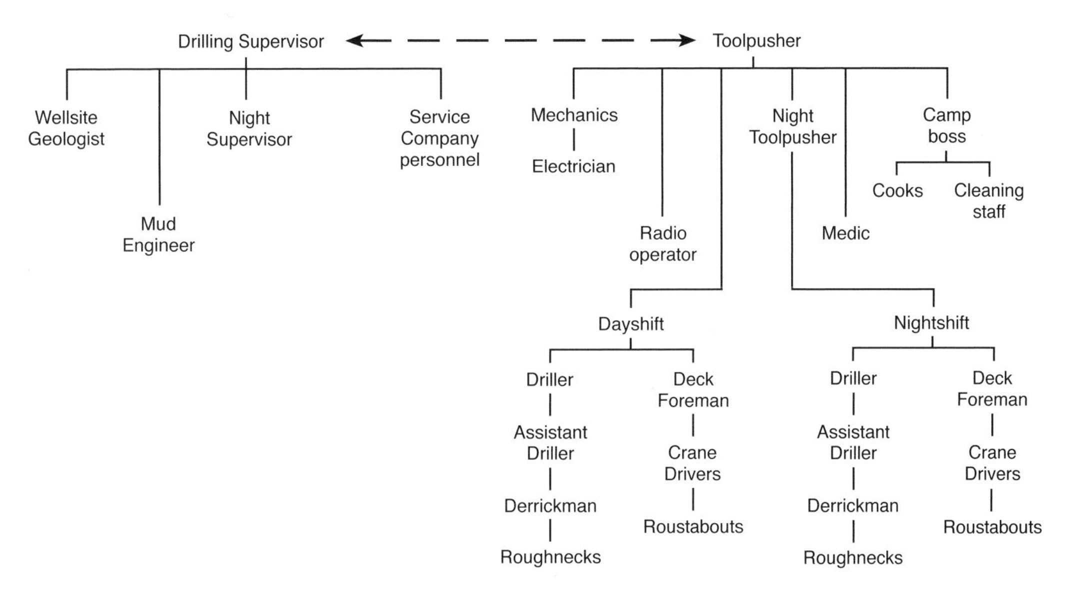

Figure 4–11 Drilling rig organisation

- *Night drilling supervisor* – works 6pm to 6am, ensures that operations continue as planned.
- *Mud engineer* (or *mud logger*) – looks after the drilling fluids, which are pumped around the well while drilling, the drill cuttings, mud volumes going in and out of the hole, gas levels and drilling performance.
- *Wellsite geologist* – examines samples of rocks retrieved while drilling and witnesses the wireline logs run in the hole.
- *Directional driller* – works for the company which supplies the directional drilling and Measurement While Drilling tools (MWD). He is responsible for the condition of this equipment before it is run in the hole and ensuring that the wellpath follows the required plan set out in the drilling programme. This is particularly important for high-angle or horizontal wells.
- *Formation evaluation engineer* – works for the company which supplies the well-logging equipment. This could be run either as part of the drill string (Logging While Drilling tools – LWD) or as separate tools run after a section of the well has been drilled on an electric wire line (Chapter 5).
- *Service company personnel* – apart from the drilling contractor, there may be up to 30 other contracts for services which require particular expertise on the rig. Where these service company personnel are paid for by the operator, they will report to the drilling supervisor while on the rig.

The size of crews and service company personnel will change with the type and size of rig and complexity of the well to be drilled.

The drilling supervisor has an office which is normally located on the same corridor as the toolpusher and is usually either next door or very close. These two people must communicate frequently during the operation. The drilling supervisor should not pass instructions directly to the drilling contractor personnel, but should work via the toolpusher who will instruct his people accordingly. This is necessary so that conflicting instructions are not given and to make sure that all of the work going on around the rig – including maintenance – is properly co-ordinated.

The toolpusher is responsible for the rig itself and the drilling contractor personnel (Fig. 4–11). On most rigs there is a night toolpusher who is on shift from 6pm to 6am. There are various support personnel, such as the mechanic, the electrician, the camp boss and catering staff. There are two sets of crews which normally work 12-hour shifts, most often 12am – 12pm – 12am.

The drill crew, supervised by the driller, work on the drill floor which is the focal point of drilling operations on 12-hour shifts. The driller operates the drilling process from a console that controls all the functions on the drill floor. The assistant driller supports the driller by managing the drill crew, checking and measuring equipment before it is run in the hole and helping run the drilling console. The derrickman is responsible for managing the stands of drill pipe as they come in and out of the hole, and for ensuring that the mud-circulating system is functioning efficiently.

The drill floor crew is made up of at least three roughnecks who handle the physical side of drilling, screwing and torquing-up the drill pipe and tools as they go in and out of the hole, preparing tools and equipment before they are run and keeping the rig floor clean.

The deck crew supply the drill floor with equipment from around the rig, work with supply boats and helicopters and keep the deck organised plus provide labour as needed. Normally, around four roustabouts work for the crane driver, offloading boats (or trucks on a land rig), laying out drill pipe and casing so that it is ready to go up to the drill floor for the drill crew. They also help the mud man (see Service Company Personnel) and the derrickman in the mud pit room mixing mud chemicals.

The maintenance crew consist of mechanics, electricians, welders and helpers, who all work on a 12-hour shift basis. On offshore rigs there will also be a marine crew, whose size and complexity will depend on the type of rig.

DRILLING OPERATIONS

LEGAL

4.11 Introduction

This chapter considers the formal legal framework between the operator and the drilling rig contractor and the process that is undertaken to secure a drilling rig 'on contract'. It also discusses the specific standard terms and conditions that are in use and would typically be included within the contract documentation, together with the overall structure and content of the drilling contract. Arrangements for rig assignment and rig sharing are also reviewed. Finally, there is a brief look at the associated well services and materials supplied that complement the drilling contract.

4.12 Types of contract

The foregoing technical section of this chapter described the types of drilling rig that are commonly used in North Sea operations. The most commonly used drilling rigs are the platform-based rig and the Mobile Offshore Drilling Unit (MODU) (typically a semi-submersible jack-up or drill ship). Irrespective of what type of rig or category of well is to be drilled (eg exploration, appraisal or development well) the principles and processes in contracting for the rig are very similar.

There will be differences in contract details as MODUs, by their nature, have a distinct marine flavour about their modus operandi. The fact that platform-based rigs are located on an operator's production platform means that some of the contractual clauses required for a MODU will not be required for the platform-based drilling operation contract. This review will concentrate on a contract for a MODU although a brief look at platform-based drilling is included.

Day-rate contracts

The most common type of contract in use today is the simple 'day-rate contract' where the drilling contractor is paid a hire fee by the operator, based on a 24-hour day, known as the operating day-rate, for the use of the rig. The operator will usually also pay a mobilisation fee to cover the cost and time required to move the rig from the previous operator's well location to the new contracting operator's well location. The fee may be a lump sum but more usually, from 2004/2005 onwards, will be a day-rate for the duration of the move to the work site.

At the end of the drilling operation there may be a demobilisation fee to provide for the cost and time to move the rig to a predetermined spot but this arrangement varies depending on the contract in place, ie if the rig is moving immediately onto a new operator's well, the new operator would most likely be paying a mobilisation fee or day-rate during mobilisation, with the releasing operator perhaps paying only for a short demobilisation from its well location to, say, 500 metres away.

As day-rates payable by the operator to the rig contractor can be considerable (up to $500,000 in the 2006 buoyant market), the operator needs to ensure it is getting value for money and that operations are conducted in an efficient and timely manner. The day-rate contract will therefore contain varying rates in monetary value that will apply should operations not go according to plan.

For example, if the rig breaks down due to the fault of the contractor, the operator would not want to pay $500,000 a day for the privilege of hiring an unservicable rig, therefore a repair day-rate will be included; this may be zero or could be stepped down over time, eg day one – 90% of the day-rate; day two – 80% of the day-rate; day three – zero.

In certain instances, the operator may also wish to suspend drilling operations and in this event a standby rate will become payable. The value of the standby rate will depend on whether the rig contractor will be able to mitigate costs by, for example, standing down non-essential personnel, etc.

There are other day-rate structures in use and their application will depend on the specific programme that is being undertaken and also the market forces in play at the time of contract negotiation. In all day-rate contracts the operator will provide associated well services and materials via other contracts of service placed with specialist contractors and vendors. As described in the technical section of this chapter, the rig contractor is under the direction of the operator and the risk involved in well design and reservoir characteristics lies with the operator, although the risk in terms of the safety of the rig and the personnel on board lies with the rig contractor.

Turn-key contracts

This type of contract usually takes the form of a lump sum fee that is to be paid by the operator to the rig contractor for the complete execution of a drilling programme with the risk and organisation of the entire drilling operation in the hands of the drilling contractor.

The operator will design the well and set the target and prognosis for the campaign, and the rig contractor will then execute the drilling programme. The rig contractor will enter into all the ancillary contracts for associated well services and takes the operational and financial risk in that regard. These contracts are less common when demand for rigs is high.

In times of low oil price, the operators may try to get a good deal at a competitive price with low risk by suggesting this type of contract.

Footage contracts

This type of contract is not common in the UKCS. In such contracts, the operation is identical to the day-rate arrangement but payment is made in US dollars or pounds sterling per foot drilled so the rig contractor is incentivised to get the hole drilled as quickly and efficiently as possible. This type of contract is not necessarily in the operator's interest as it may be more important to drill slowly and carefully to maximise the potential from a difficult reservoir. The risk with such a contract is that the rig contractor will be keen to complete the task and move on to their next project as soon as practicable.

Incentive contracts

The basis for this contract type is likely to be the day-rate contract. The operator and rig contractor will agree a time basis for the drilling operation, for example a 60-day well, and then set out an incentive scheme that will reward the rig contractor if the well is successfully completed either ahead of, or on, time.

If there is an overrun due to the rig contractor's fault then liquidated damages may be payable to the operator by the rig contractor. The attraction of this type of contract is that it can benefit both rig contractor and operator. If the job is finished early, the rig contractor gets his bonus and can move to the next job.

For the operator, as well as getting the programme completed early and maybe improving cash flow for 'early oil', it will save considerable costs not only on rig hire, but on all ancillary well service costs that are payable over and above the rig operating day-rate. A rough rule of thumb would be to double the rig day-rate to calculate the approximate total daily cost of the rig and all other specialist contractors that are required to drill the well.

A $300,000-a-day rig will therefore have a total 'spread' cost of approximately $600,000. By the reduction of three days off the programme in a successful incentive contract the operator saves $1.8 million. Even if the bonus payable to the rig operator is 50% of the saving it is a worthwhile consideration when agreeing the drilling contract terms.

Platform-based drilling

Located on many production platforms are in situ drilling modules that are installed as part of the platform structure so that the platform can drill its own wells or perform workovers without the need to bring a MODU alongside the platform. In this instance, the operator normally contracts with a specialist platform contractor for the operation and maintenance of the platform rig. The specialist contractor will supply the crew and/or may even own the platform rig. Contracts will be drafted in a similar manner to the MODU contract, and will provide for the particular contracting arrangement that is required.

4.13 Process for entering into a contract for a drilling rig

Assuming we are contracting a drilling rig in the UKCS Northern North Sea to drill a well on a day-rate contract, the process for entering into the contract is fairly straightforward.

The industry is very cyclical and in 2006 drilling rig supply was tight, with demand from the operators high due mainly to the oil price of over $60 per barrel.

Despite the fact that there may be limited availability, tendering, as opposed to single-source negotiations, is still feasible. The operator will normally invite rig contractors to submit a competitive bid based on a drilling programme and to a required rig specification. Included with the invitation to tender will be:

- *Instructions to tenderers* – basic information about the tender process. Return time/date, contact for queries, etc.
- *Scope of work* – a brief description of the drilling campaign.
- *Specification of the rig* – the minimum characteristics the rig must have to be considered technically acceptable.
- *Terms and conditions of contract* – the operator's proposed legal framework that the drilling contract is to be based upon (these are various standards and specific forms which will be discussed later in the chapter).

- *Remuneration structure* – to be completed by the drilling rig contractor as part of his tender and submitted with the form of tender – this forms the legal 'offer' to perform the work and will be signed by the contractor's representative who has the contractor's legal and binding authority to submit their offer.
- *Ancillary information* – this could include the operator's health, safety and environmental policies that it would expect the rig contractor to comply with whilst undertaking the work. Also, the operator may wish to review the rig contractor's track record, personnel experience, etc. These aspects would be reviewed as part of the tender evaluation process and rig and rig contractor selection.

Assuming the rig contractor has a suitable rig, he would complete his tender proposal, his 'offer', and submit it with the required information and day-rates to the operator for evaluation and hopefully selection.

A bid closing date and time are stated so as to ensure that collusion on bid submission is avoided and that a level playing field is in place so tenderers can be sure the content of their bid will not be disclosed to a competitor. Normally, bids are all opened at the same time by a bid-opening committee after bid closing and witnessed as authentic true bids by the operator's team. In this age of digital information technology it is also common for bids to be submitted electronically via a secure website, although paper-based tender submissions are then offered as backup to confirm the electronic offer.

As part of his tender submission, the rig contractor will have been asked to confirm that he will carry out the work in accordance with the terms and conditions of contract that were included in the invitation to tender documentation.

In virtually all rig tender submissions the rig contractor will take exception to some of the proposed terms and conditions. This is commonly known in the bid response as 'qualifications'. The rig contractor may also be uncertain as to what some clauses are intended to achieve, so here, more than likely, there will be 'clarifications' sought from the operator prior to signing any contract.

Any qualifications and clarifications of the rig contractor will be reviewed by the operator. Clarifications are normally dealt with in a routine manner whilst qualifications usually form the focus of contract negotiations. Proposals and counter-proposals flow between the rig contractor and operator until agreement on specific terms is reached.

Once the operator has finalised its tender evaluation it will hold a series of meetings with its short-listed rig contractors to try to formulate an agreeable basis for the contract using the qualifications as a starting agenda.

Market conditions at the time of tender will set the scene on relative positions by both parties and the stance taken on contractual qualifications. In a tight market where rigs are in short supply, the rig contractor will not accept the same risk profile as he would in a market where rigs are underutilised and some are laid up in sheltered waters with no work. Here, the skills of the respective negotiating teams come into play. At the end of the day, hopefully, a mutually agreeable form of contract, with qualifications negotiated to mutual satisfaction, will be in place. The duration of the contract will require to be defined. It may be that a single well contract is all that is required or perhaps options for further wells may be added. These will require to be exercised on giving the rig contractor the prior notice set out in the contract.

In today's market place, with rigs in short supply, it is common for rigs to be contracted on a term basis, some in excess of five years, where the operator guarantees revenue to the rig contractor and hopefully has work in the form of continuous wells for the contractual term. Given that the operator has committed to pay for the rig on a long-term continuous basis, the operator should ensure he has assignment rights written into the rig contract so as he can 'assign' the use of the rig to another operator should he run out of work for it prior to the end of the contract. It will be costly for the operator if he has to pay the rig contractor for time when there is no work for the rig. Rig assignment and rig sharing are dealt with later in the chapter.

It would be normal practice to award the contract by issue of a letter of intent by the operator to the rig contractor. In the letter of intent will be a clear statement of the operator's desire to enter into a formal agreement with the rig contractor and a list of 'subject to' conditions will appear, for example:

- the form of contract to be used, including the resolution to qualifications;
- the name and specification of the rig;
- the rates payable;
- start time and location of the well; and
- duration/time of the contract term.

If the rig contractor is agreeable to the content of the letter of intent, the contractor will formally accept by return and the basis of the drilling contract is now in place. Thereafter, the operator will draw up a contract document for the rig contractor to review. Once all the documentation is agreed, and wording finalised, the contract documents will be signed.

4.14 Common forms of contract and contract structure

Over the past 40 or so years there have been various attempts made to standardise the wording of the terms and conditions of contract for use in the UKCS contracting environment.

Operators' standard forms

The origins of many of the clauses in use today stem from standard forms of contract used in the civil engineering and building industries. Also imported from the USA, forms of contract drafted by the International Association of Drilling Contractors (IADC) provided a template whereby the operators' own commercial and legal teams could formulate their own in-house 'standard form of contract'. This was the most common format in use in the 1970s and 1980s where each operator had its own set of terms and conditions for each specific service it required to contract for, including drilling rigs.

IADC Standards

As noted above, the IADC publishes a series of standard contract forms to cover a variety of contracting scenarios. The website www.iadc.org will provide a comprehensive list as to what standard formats are on offer and their intended application. The use of IADC formats in their published form is not common in the UKCS; they are more likely to be used internationally or in the USA, both for land and offshore rig contracts. Many of their clauses and principles, though, have found their way into use in operators' own forms of contract or in the LOGIC standard forms (below).

Leading Oil and Gas Industry Competitiveness – LOGIC

In the early 1990s it was recognised by the operator community that for each operator to have its own 'standard form of contract' for each application was time-consuming, costly and highly inefficient. It seemed prudent to formulate a set of standard forms for use by all operators in the UKCS, thus ensuring the contractors were all tendering their services based on the same terms and conditions.

At this time, through CRINE (Cost Reduction in the New Era), an initiative was undertaken to create the CRINE Standard Contract Library. Representatives for operators and contractors drafted a set of terms and conditions covering various service disciplines which were intended to be used across the industry. One of these contract forms was intended to be used in the contracting of MODUs and the *Mobile Drilling Rigs – Edition 1* was published in December 1997. These standard contracts are now administered and issued by LOGIC and further information on these forms including the MODU contract can be found at www.logic-oil.com

The LOGIC forms are supplemented by each operator's special conditions that relate to specific topics or areas of special interest to that operator. An example would be the indemnity provisions which inevitably require detailed discussion and negotiations to find a mutually agreeable distribution and acceptance of risk.

The most common format in use today is the LOGIC form together with the operator's special conditions supplementing the standard form, although many operators still insist on using their own in-house drafted standard. IADC forms are seldom seen in the UKCS.

Contract structure

When drafting a drilling contract, there are various sections to be included. The contract usually begins with a Form of Agreement. This sets out the contracting entities, briefly summarises what the contract is about and may list the documentation which follows and which forms the entire agreement between the parties. The authorised signatories for the respective operator and drilling rig contractor will execute the contract here.

This will be followed by the Terms and Conditions, be it an Operator Standard or LOGIC Standard with Special Conditions. Examples of specific clauses are included later in the chapter. The Scope of Work or Summary Drilling Programme follows, setting out the technical terms of the contract, eg to drill an exploration well at location X to depth Y. A detailed technical specification of the rig to be provided will also be included. This will be important if there is a later dispute on the technical capability of the rig. The Remuneration Section will include all commercial terms and the day-rate monetary amounts. Also, provision for any escalation to rates and the methodology for escalation calculations will be detailed here.

Finally, the Additional Information section will typically include the operator's health, safety and environmental standards, administration instructions and supplemental information provided by the rig contractor such as personnel details.

There may also be a requirement for the rig contractor to provide a parent company guarantee or a bank guarantee to provide the operator with financial security to ensure the work scope is complete in the event of the contractor's default. There may also be some further information required to cover well specifications but in the main the contract format is now complete.

4.15 Rig assignment and rig sharing

The operator should ensure the contract contains provision for the operator to be able to assign the use of the rig to another operator at any time during the term of the contract. This is important in multiwell or term contracts where, for instance, the operator may have a change of plan and have to alter its drilling campaign programme. This may be necessary due to funding issues or reservoir problems which make further drilling impossible or uneconomic.

In today's market where rig availability is an issue, operators are speculatively contracting rigs on long-term contracts in order to ensure security of supply. It is inevitable as time progresses that the operator may wish to offer their joint venture partners or other operators access to the rig so the assignment clause is very important from the operator's perspective. It would be common for the rig contractor to have a say in the arrangement and his approval would be sought but it would be incumbent on the operator's part to ensure that approval from the rig contractor to assign 'was not unreasonably withheld or delayed'.

The new operator taking over the rig would be expected to assume all the contractual responsibilities that the original operator had agreed to under the original contract. It is also common for the ancillary well services and associated contracts to go with the rig to the assignee operator so there will be a requirement to prepare for each original contract an assignment agreement. This would set out the terms of the assignment and refer to the original contract; it would be signed by the original parties to the contract and the assignee.

At the end of the assignment the original operator takes back the rig for the unexpired term if the contract is still in force or another assignee might be sought if the original operator still has no use for the rig. The rig contractor would still expect to be paid in accordance with the original contract.

Rig sharing

A similar proposition occurs when two or more operators decide to contract for a rig on a shared basis. They combine their work scopes and go to the market place looking for a rig to carry out all of their work. This, again, is common when rigs are in short supply and the operators, hopefully by combining their work scopes and the term they require the rig, will get a more attractive day-rate.

The contract documentation for a rig share could be based on the lead operator's format. However, it is sometimes difficult to get operators to agree to the same terms and conditions, especially in terms of the liability and indemnity regime. This is because each operator has its own view on risk and the level of liability it wishes to assume.

An alternative is to have a broad form of agreement setting out the sharing mechanism and for each operator to take the rig for its own scope based upon its own standard form of contract or perhaps using the LOGIC form with its own special conditions agreed on an individual basis with the rig contractor.

4.16 Examples of drilling rig contract clauses

It is recommended that the reader, if requiring detailed sight of a standard contract form, accesses the LOGIC or IADC website where particulars of how to obtain these publications are given. This section will attempt to give an indication of what should be expected to be included in the drilling contract clause coverage and wording. It looks briefly at standard boilerplate clauses and then specific clauses which require further detailed consideration. The LOGIC general conditions of contract for *Mobile Drilling Rigs Edition 1* (December 1997) have been used for ease of reference.

(a) Standard boilerplate clauses

All contracts, those for mobile drilling rigs included, will have a number of standard boilerplate clauses that for sound legal considerations it is advised to include. These clauses should require little, if any, redrafting and will give both contracting entities the comfort that the contract includes provision for basic legal principles, rules and general conditions that govern the legal framework of commercial business contracts. Legal advice should be sought but in the main the LOGIC conditions should provide a solid basic structure for any UKCS-based rig contract.

Some examples of boilerplate clauses would be:

- the definitions and interpretation provisions (although some definitions will require specific drafting to suit individual company situations);
- company (operator) and contractor's representatives;
- contractor's general obligations;
- offshore transportation;
- contractor's personnel;
- assignment and subcontracting (important in term contracts);
- force majeure;
- taxes;
- ownership;
- law and regulations;
- confidentiality;
- audit;
- liens;
- business ethics; and
- general legal provisions to cover such items as waiver; independent contractor; notices; entire agreement, etc.

(b) Specific clauses that require further detailed consideration

As well as the standard boilerplate clauses, there are certain specific clauses that will require to be included. These additional clauses and their wording will depend on the circumstances, negotiated position, and commercial terms that have been agreed. These aspects will dictate the extent of detail and drafting over and above the basic LOGIC wording that is required to be incorporated into the final contract. Some examples of areas that may require further consideration are as follows:

- *Definitions.* The definitions for 'Affiliate', 'Company Group', 'Contractor Group' and 'Co-Venturers' will have a significant bearing on the indemnity clauses and therefore on who ultimately may be liable should a problem arise.
- *Company and contractor provided items.* These clauses attempt to put a boundary around what each party to the contract is supplying. It is wise to spell out in an Appendix the exact extent of who is providing what, to avoid costly disputes.
- *Ingress and egress at the location.* This provision outlines the responsibilities of the operator to provide sufficient information about the location to enable the rig contractor to ensure that his rig is positioned in a safe location where there are no obstructions which might damage the rig. The rig contractor's insurers also require this information.
- *Variations.* Not everything goes according to plan and changes will be required. It is prudent to include a method or standard by which variations can be valued or calculated so that the contract can be changed or varied at ease should the need arise.
- *Terms of payment.* Each commercial negotiation should take into account how long the operator will take to pay its bills and what happens if it does not pay on time or at all. The cash flow position of the rig contractor could have an effect on its performance of the contract if funds are not available on time, for instance to pay the crew.
- *Patents and other proprietary rights.* Usually the operator will want to protect its position on an item or idea that has been developed as a direct result of work undertaken within the scope of the contract. The rig contractor may wish to negotiate a share of any benefit to which it has directly contributed.
- *Indemnities.* Both parties will attempt to protect their respective positions in the 'Liabilities Clause'. This clause normally results in the majority of complex qualifications which have been referred to earlier and will form a significant item on the contract negotiation agenda. In summary, each party will usually give the other an indemnity against loss of, or damage to, their respective personnel and property, commonly known as a 'knock

for knock' or 'back to back' indemnity. The problem arises where there has been a negligent act and, depending on the negotiated position, the question of who has been negligent and who pays for the consequences will need to be addressed. The rig contractor may also look to the operator for an indemnity for its mooring equipment or any of its equipment used down hole that the operator is in 'control of'. The operator usually takes responsibility for the well and reservoir so if there is an incident down hole the rig contractor should seek to rely on wording that favours his position. An indemnity in respect of a pollution incident should also be clear. It is common for the rig contractor to be responsible only for pollution originating from its own equipment. Reservoir pollution would normally be covered by the operator.

- *Insurance.* The type and minimum value of insurance cover required are usually an area for debate and negotiation. The liability and indemnity structure should be taken into account when arranging insurance. It is sometimes the case where both the operator and the rig contractor will have insurance cover for the same unplanned event so the indemnity and insurance provisions need to be clear. Evidence that the rig contractor's insurance coverage is in place to the required amounts will need to be provided by the rig contractor to the operator. The operator will need to ensure the insurance coverage is placed with a reputable broker and, ultimately, a reputable insurance company, as if an event triggers a claim this could be of significant value, given the financial magnitude of drilling an offshore well. In recent times there has been a trend for rig contractors to self-insure the rig due to its high value and the increasing cost of insurance.
- *Consequential loss.* Normally each party to the contract indemnifies the other against its consequential losses. It is important that consequential loss is adequately defined.
- *Termination.* The operator should be able to terminate the contract for a variety of reasons of its own choosing. Normally, the default of the rig contractor would be the main reason. However, it is normal for the operator to be able to terminate at its own convenience. This is an uncommon event but the provision to be able to do so is contained in most drilling contracts. The rig contractor may wish to negotiate into the contract an early termination fee that would cover some or all of its costs if the operator terminates for its own convenience. In the tight market of 2005–2007 this fee could be the day-rate multiplied by the number of days remaining on the original contract. Other events which trigger termination may include bankruptcy of the contractor, breakdown of the rig for so many days in

succession; loss of the rig, etc. It is uncommon for the contractor to have any specific termination rights.

- *Resolution of disputes.* In the event that the parties are in dispute, the contract may contain procedure which can be followed in an attempt to rectify the situation without recourse to the courts, such as mediation or arbitration. If no agreement is forthcoming there should be a legal provision as to how disputes should be handled and where they should be heard, for instance in the English judicial system. Care should be taken when structuring the contract as to where, and in what country the entities are registered, where the work is taking place and which governing law applies to the contract.

These are just some of the main legal clauses which are discussed in detail during contract negotiations. In addition, the commercial terms surrounding payment for services or time the rig is in transit will require detailed attention and clear drafting as part of the remuneration section of the contract.

4.17 Associated well services and materials procurement

As explained in the technical part of this chapter, the operator will engage the rig contractor under the terms of the contract to provide the rig and associated rig personnel. In addition to this, various specialised contractors will be required to assist with the well construction. In the case of a day-rate contract (as opposed to a turn-key contract), the operator will contract for all other required services directly with the well service contractors.

Examples of associated services, or well services contracts as they are commonly known, will typically include:

- downhole drilling services;
- provision of fluids and cements;
- rental of specialist drilling tools;
- drill cuttings treatment;
- well testing and completions; and
- underwater TV/remotely operated vehicles.

The methodology and process for placing contracts for these services broadly follow the same process as for the rig: tender invitations to competitors, bidding against minimum specifications for equipment standards, and competing on price and value. Technology capability will also play a part in contractor selection, with perhaps the most expensive being selected as they may have a specific tool that saves rig-time and, inevitably, money in the longer term.

In addition to the specialist services contractors organised to work on the drilling rig under the direction of the operator, specialist materials that will be incorporated within the well structure will also require to be purchased by the operator. Items such as OCTG (oil country tubular goods), tubing and casing, wellheads, liners, gauges and well completion assemblies will be bought from specialist vendors. The purchase agreement will be specifically tailored to the equipment specification and will normally take the form of a purchase order. Purchase orders will contain specific language particular to material supply and detailed attention should be paid to warranty clauses in particular. It is important to ensure the operator is protected against faulty goods or poor workmanship associated with the materials installation. Delivery timing will also be of importance to the operator. A provision for liquidated damages should the materials arrive late may also be included in the purchase agreement.

A clear specification with regard to design and intended purpose of the material is necessary so as to make it clear as to what is expected technically of the material being procured. It may also be the case that technical support in the form of technical experts to go offshore to install the material will be included in the purchase order. In this case it is important to ensure the purchase order terms and conditions provide cover for the personnel to travel offshore as well as the material supplied. Needless to say, well service contracts and purchase order agreements require to be drafted with attention to detail to ensure the contract for service or supply complies with the purchaser's requirements.

Marine charter parties

The MODU will require to be towed by a vessel from well location to location. It is normal practice for the operator to contract for the vessel with the vessel owners via a shipbroker. Various types of vessel will be required at certain stages through the drilling campaign: tugs for the tow, anchor handlers to run the rig's anchors (if it has them) and supply vessels to transport materials, chemical and general supplies between the rig and the shore base.

— 5 —

RESERVOIR EVALUATION

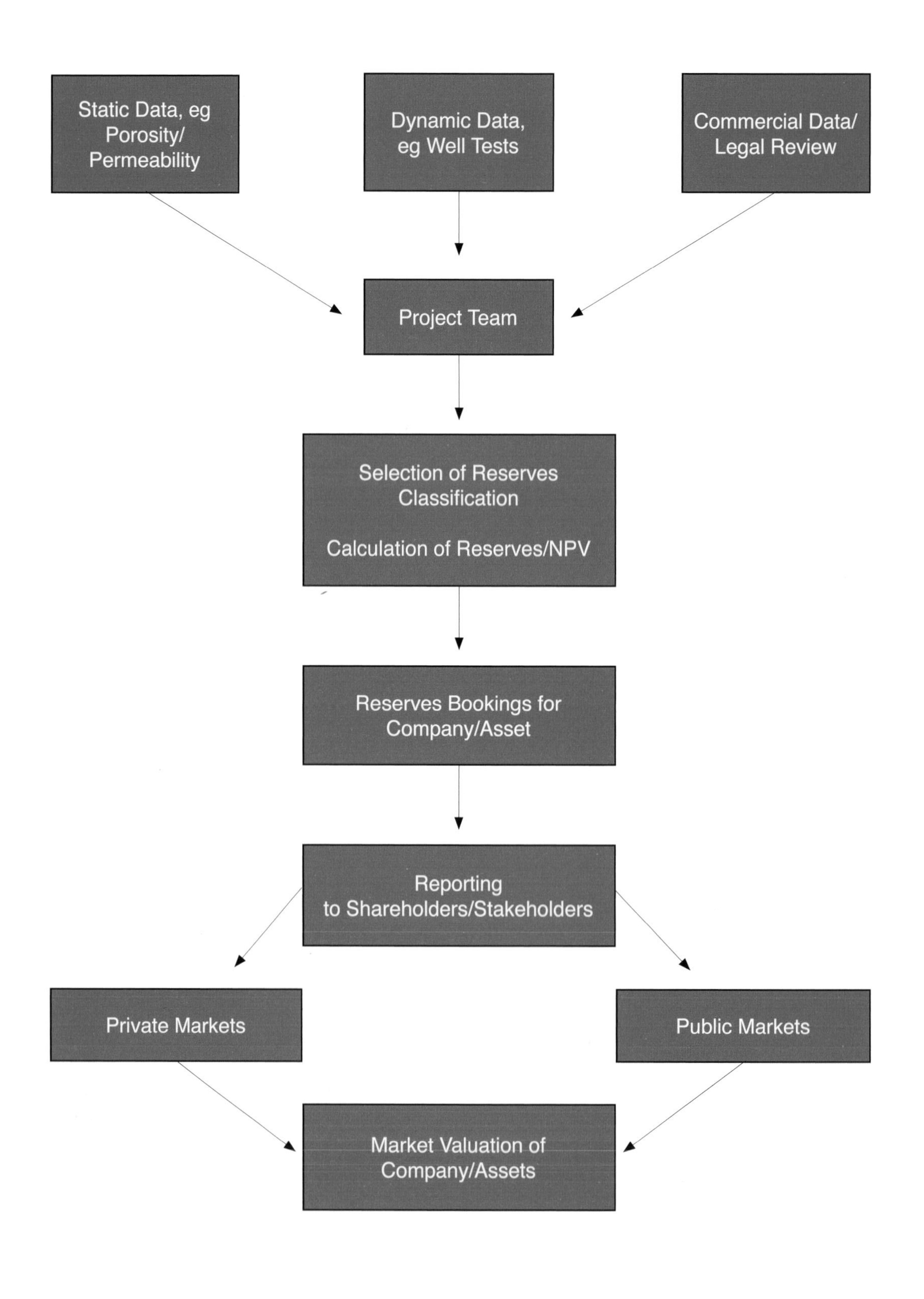

Static Data, eg Porosity/ Permeability
Dynamic Data, eg Well Tests
Commercial Data/ Legal Review
Project Team
Selection of Reserves Classification
Calculation of Reserves/NPV
Reserves Bookings for Company/Asset
Reporting to Shareholders/Stakeholders
Private Markets
Public Markets
Market Valuation of Company/Assets

RESERVOIR EVALUATION

TECHNICAL

5.1 Introduction

Once a well has been drilled and hydrocarbons discovered, the amount of hydrocarbons in place have to be estimated and a work programme to develop a reserve has to be put in place. This is the realm of the reservoir engineer.

Reservoir evaluation involves the estimation of hydrocarbons in place in a reservoir, the calculation of a recovery factor and the period leading up to the development of a production profile as well as day-to-day optimal management of the reservoir. This work often consists of four main activities namely observations (ie data acquisition, etc.), assumptions, calculations (normally resulting in a reservoir simulation model), and development and/ or production decisions. The reader is referred to Daker (2001) for further information.

- *Observations*: This activity involves a whole range of data acquisition, such as geological cores, well logs, well tests and fluid samples, production rates, temperatures and pressures. The important fact to note is that, as most development and production decisions rely on the output from very complex reservoir simulation models, the accuracy of the input data is essential – *the output from a computer model is only as good as the accuracy of the basic input data*. There are numerous examples of inadequate data acquisition leading to erroneous development decisions which have then cost millions of pounds to correct. Data acquisition is often expensive and time-consuming and it is the duty of the reservoir engineer to persuade management of the necessary justification so as to reduce the potential development risk.

- *Assumptions*: Having collected a range of data, the reservoir engineer has then to make a range of assumptions about the specific reservoir. For example, will there be water influx into the reservoir or will there be adequate pressure communication across the reservoir? Often these assumptions will be proven, or not, as the case may be at some stage in the future but it may only be after production over a significant number of years.
- *Calculations*: Ultimately the acquired data and the assumptions are used to perform a range of complex calculations (sections 5.2 and 5.3) from estimating the hydrocarbons in place through to complex fluid property calculations. Often this leads to the generation of a reservoir simulation model which can be used to provide estimates of future reservoir performance including production profiles. These models are often used to examine different development options and different assumptions as well as providing various performance scenarios.
- *Decisions*: The work performed by reservoir engineers has to provide the basis for a range of development and/or production decisions, eg the provision of a new platform, the drilling of extra wells, shut-in of wells and remedial actions. Often the cost impact of these decisions can be very significant, ie hundreds of million pounds.

Today, the reservoir engineer normally plays a central role in a multidisciplinary team either planning the development of a new reservoir or enhancing the performance of an older one. The reservoir engineer receives data from others, such as geologists (core data, geological models), geophysicists (seismic data) and petrophysicists (well logs) and assimilates it with his own data (eg PVT fluid properties, well test results, etc.) to construct some form of reservoir model that is used to predict field performance for a range of scenarios. The results of this work are then shared with production, process and project engineers and economics engineers such that production facilities can be designed and the economics of a range of production scenarios studied. This whole process is nearly always iterative and can be very lengthy, especially for a complex reservoir in which there is a high degree of uncertainty about reservoir performance.

5.2 Data acquisition

In order to understand the significance of data acquisition it is important to review what data are used, the calculations that are performed and how the resulting information is used in developing/producing the reservoir. Most well and reservoir data acquired at the well site are used to calculate the volume of hydrocarbons held in a reservoir, how the hydrocarbons will flow through the reservoir and how much will be recovered (ie the recovery factor). Once the field is on production, the data are also used to monitor and enhance the reservoir performance.

The initial development decision is based on the data acquired during the exploration and appraisal campaign. With the possible exception of well tests and some core flooding data, these data will be of a static nature (ie the non-moving parts of the reservoir as opposed to dynamic data which deal with the measurement of flow through the reservoir). Static data includes seismic which reveals the size and shape of the reservoir, core and well log data which reveal

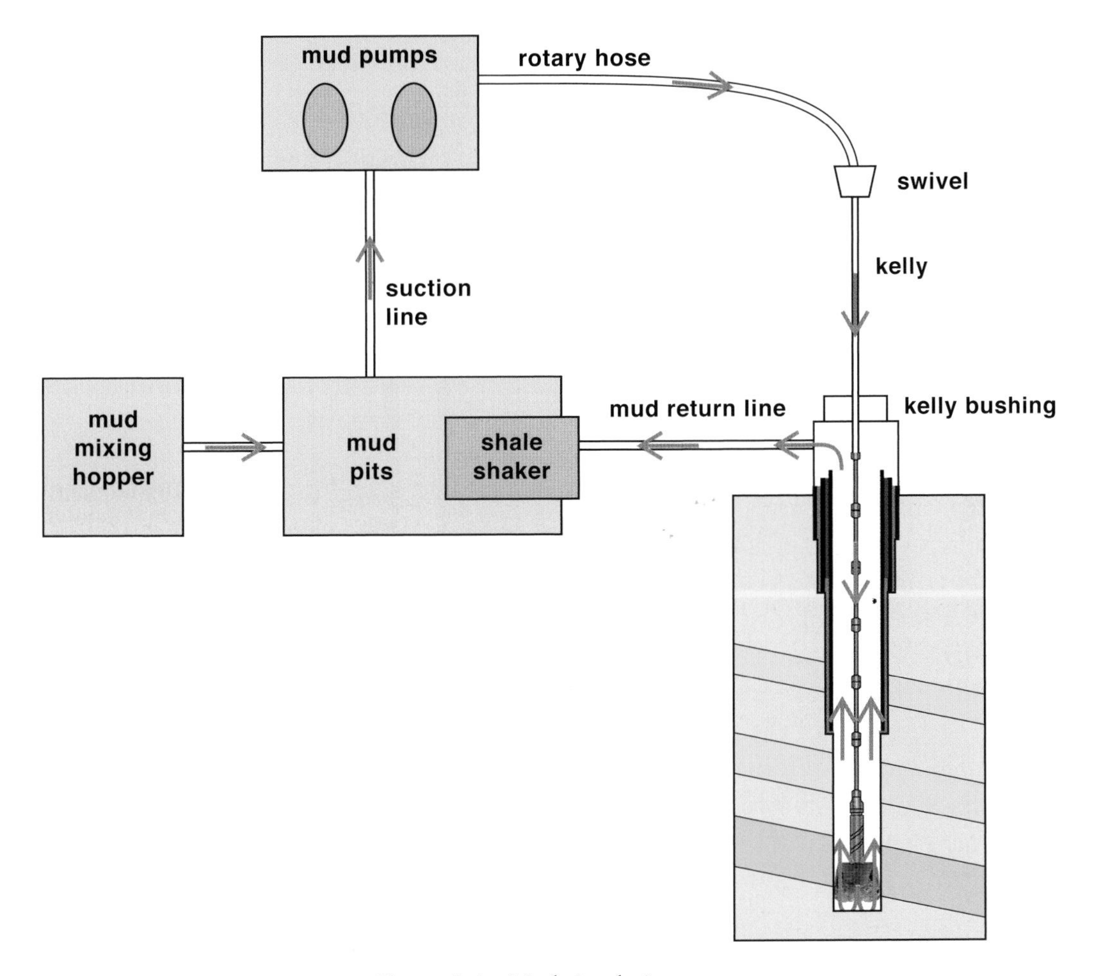

Figure 5–1 Mud circulation system
Drilling mud is continually circulated in the well bore during drilling helping to lubricate the bit, maintain temperatures and pressures and to bring the rock cuttings up to the surface where they are separated in the shale shaker for analysis.

the reservoir properties and initial hydrocarbon content and some reservoir fluid data.

Rock sampling

The process of drilling (Chapter 4) grinds the rock into tiny fragments (mm size). These are known as cuttings and are brought back to the surface with the drilling mud. The mud passes over the shale shakers (Fig. 5–1) which act as sieves and the cuttings are removed by the mudlogger. The onsite geologist then examines them to determine the geological sequence and if there are any hydrocarbons present by using ultraviolet light and/or gas analysis. Although these cuttings provide a basic understanding of the rock sequence, interpretations based on these have many problems. The samples are very small and hence no porosity or permeability data can be gained from them. Also, because they are collected by the drilling mud, the rock lithologies are often mixed up. 'Cavings' (fragments from higher up in the well bore which have fallen to the base) are also a problem.

It is necessary, therefore, to collect samples of the rock at specific depths. This is done by taking solid cores of the rock (see Chapter 3, Fig. 3–2(a)). These are cut in sections (30 ft) using a special drilling bit and pipe (core barrel). It is, however, a very expensive process in terms of roundtripping time and is done only where essential, eg sampling the reservoir horizon. This is typically carried out during the exploration and appraisal stages of a field's life. These cores are retained as a record of the geology and are looked at extensively by specialists (eg sedimentologists) to determine the geological history of the reservoir rock (Chapter 3).

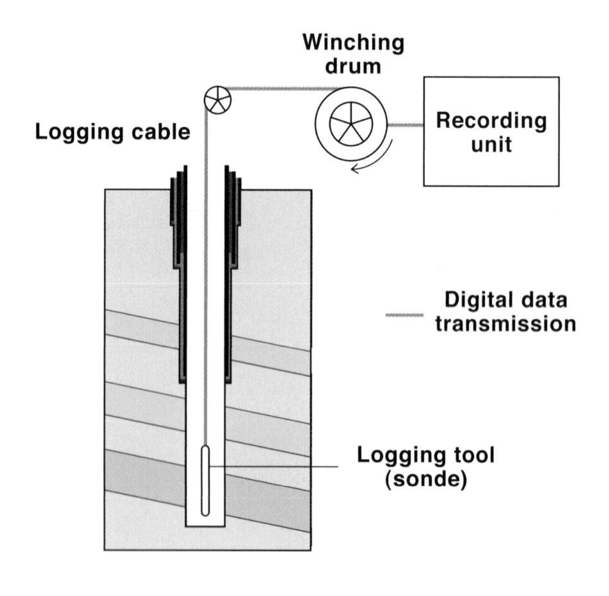

Figure 5–2 Wireline logging operations
Schematic diagram of the wireline logging system showing the recording unit and winching drum which are housed on the drilling rig or platform floor. The logging tool (sonde) is lowered into the well bore attached to the logging cable prior to the casing being set. Recordings are made as the sonde is drawn out of the well bore and data transmitted digitally to the computers housed in the recording unit. (Modified after Rider (2002)).

Wireline logs

Due to a lack of rock samples and data in the form of core material, alternative methods of measuring the properties of the rocks had to be found. In the 1920s, the Schlumberger brothers in France developed wireline logging tools. They believed that if they could measure the electrical resistivity of rocks in oil wells then they could acquire information about the nature of the rock (eg sandstone, limestone) and the presence of hydrocarbons. In 1927 they produced the first measurements of an oil well in France. Their methods were so successful that it lead to the formation of Schlumberger and subsequent logging companies. The technology of wireline logging was born and it now forms a significant part of the oil industry. A detailed account of the various wireline log tools is beyond the scope of this publication but a summary is provided below. The reader is referred to Rider (2002) or Darling (2005) for more detailed information.

Well logs have been developed to investigate rock types, porosity, nature of the fluids within the rocks (eg hydrocarbons or water) and are used to correlate rock units between wells, across fields and regionally. Logs are run after drilling but prior to casing a well by lowering a 'tool' or 'sonde' into the well bore which sends information back to the logging equipment on the drilling rig or platform where it is recorded (Fig. 5–2).

Well logs are divided into two main groups.

- *Passive tools* which measure the natural properties of the rocks and the fluids contained within them. These are the caliper, gamma ray and spontaneous potential (SP) logs.
- *Active tools* which measure the response of the rocks and the fluids contained within them to an external signal. These are the sonic, resistivity, density and neutron logs.

Basic details of the main well logs and their uses are given below.

- *Caliper Log* is a basic tool that measures the diameter of the well bore and any variation in it due to geological factors, eg fracturing.
- *Spontaneous Potential (SP) Log* measures the natural electrical variation in geological formations and is used to calculate the formation water resistivity and lithology.
- *Gamma Ray (GR) Log* measures the natural radioactivity of rocks and is used to identify lithology, eg clean sandstones (potential reservoirs) or mudstones (potential seals or source rocks).
- *Sonic Log* is an acoustic log and measures the ability of the rocks to transmit sound waves. This varies with lithology and rock texture (mainly porosity) and hence it is used to estimate porosity. It is also important in lithological correlation and for tying wells to seismic lines via synthetic seismograms.

- *Resistivity Logs* measure the resistance of a geological formation to the passage of an electrical current. Most rock materials are insulators whilst fluids are conductors. The exception to this is hydrocarbons which are resistive. Resistivity logs, therefore, can help identify the presence of hydrocarbons in a rock formation.
- *Density Log* measures the bulk density which is a function of rock matrix and porosity (free space). It is one of the nuclear logs where the lithological formation is bombarded by a gamma ray source. It is used to calculate porosity.
- *Neutron Log* measures the hydrogen content of a formation (mainly water) and is another of the nuclear logs where the formation is bombarded by neutrons. Again, it is used to calculate porosity and is usually used in conjunction with the density log.

None of these tools is used entirely on its own. They are usually run in various combinations as a suite (Fig. 5–3) and plotted against depth with or without lithological and fluid interpretations alongside.

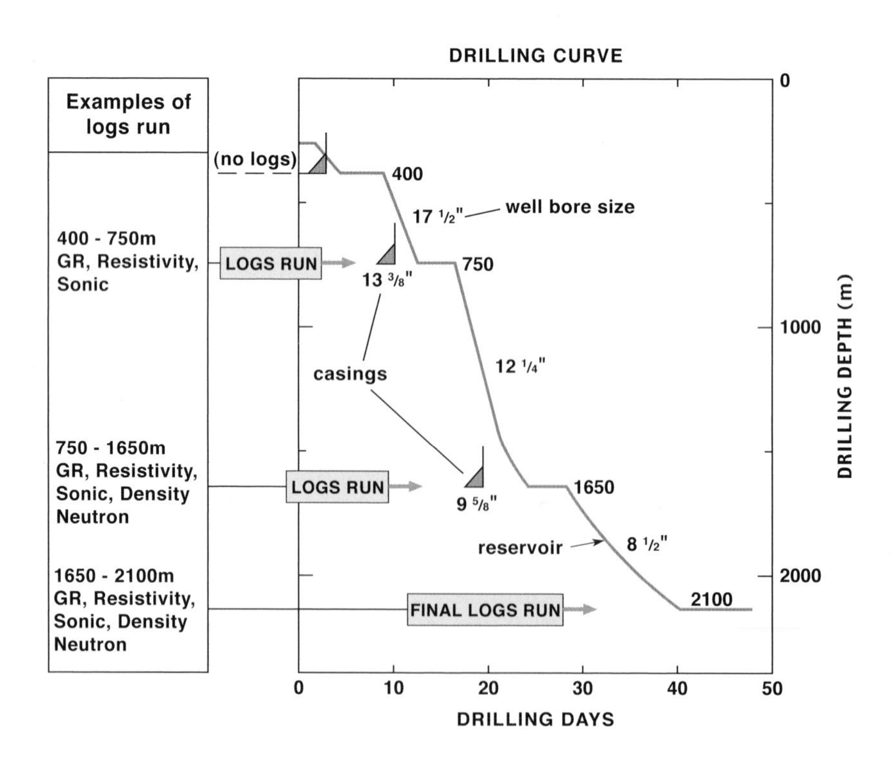

Figure 5–3 Logging record
Logging record showing the suites of wireline logs that are run during various stages of the drilling of a well. (Modified after Rider (2002)).

The techniques are always being refined and improved. New advances not discussed here are image logs and MWD (Measurement While Drilling) logs.

Well testing and the flow of oil/gas

The well logs discussed above give an initial indication as to whether a formation contains oil or gas but these data can be misleading. To establish whether a find is economic or not requires a flow or well test. The most common form of well test is the drill stem test (DST).

DSTs measure both fluid flow and reservoir pressure and can be conducted in both open and cased holes. The drill bit is replaced with a test assembly which comprises valves, a packer to seal off between the drill pipe and an open hole and a pressure recorder. When the packer has been set and a sufficient seal achieved, the mud weight is removed from the tool and the downhole pressure recorded for around 15 minutes (initial pressure). Flow of formation fluids is then allowed to occur up to the surface for at least half an hour. If there is sufficient pressure, the reservoir is permeable and filled with gas or oil, these phases will flow to the surface. At the end of the flow test, the valves are closed again to obtain a final reservoir pressure. The rate at which the pressure builds up again is critical. If a reservoir zone has sufficient permeability, then the fluids produced in the flow test will be replaced rapidly.

In open holes, many DSTs are unsuccessful because the packer fails to seal the well bore properly. Further problems can arise when the reservoir has been drilled right through. Testing then requires packers either side of the assembly and hence more uncertainty with the seal. Testing, therefore, is best done before the reservoir zone has been penetrated completely or in a cased and perforated hole. The latter option, however, carries increased costs.

The results from well tests provide key information on the content of the reservoir and its performance. They also allow estimates to be made about how much oil or gas is likely to be produced (recovery factor).

This depends on the reservoir energy system (or drive, section 5.3) and the permeability of the various reservoir layers. The basis of fluid flow through reservoirs is always governed by Darcy's Law (Eqn 1) which is one of the most important equations in petroleum engineering. The equation describes the radial, homogeneous, steady state flow of oil into a well and, in typical oilfield units, is shown as:

$$q_{sc} = \frac{k.h.\,(P_e - P_w)}{141.2 \times \mu.B.[\ln(r_e / r_w) + S]} \qquad \text{(Eqn 1)}$$

Where:

q_{sc} = Flow rate (bopd)
k = Permeability (mD)
h = Thickness (m)
P_e = Pressure at the limit of the well's drainage area (psi)
P_w = Pressure in the well (psi)
μ = Viscosity (cp)
B = Formation Volume Factor (see Eqns 3 and 4)
r_e = Radius of well drainage area (m)
r_w = Radius of well (m)
S = Mechanical Skin Factor

Full discussion of this equation could cover an entire book but the most important point to note is that the flow rate from a well is dependent on all of these factors.

During well tests, the most important parameter that is measured is pressure, preferably downhole pressure, and the results of these tests can be used to estimate future reservoir performance. The typical order of priority in data collection from a typical offshore appraisal well test is:

- measurement of the oil (or gas) flow rate (q);
- calculation of the well skin factor (S) – a measure of the formation damage during drilling – an important factor in well performance;
- collection of fluid samples (see below);
- evaluation of formation characteristics (eg permeability (k), fractures, layering, etc.);
- influence of boundary conditions (eg fault patterns, depletion, etc.);
- determination of initial reservoir pressure (P_i).

In a typical well test, the well is flowed through temporary (and portable) production facilities and the resulting fluids (oil/gas/condensate) are flared. During this process various gauges are suspended in the well and used to monitor downhole pressure and temperature. Typically a downhole flow meter is also used in order to estimate the flow distribution across the producing zones. As discussed above, one of the most important tests is based on the so-called 'build-up' test during which the well is flowed at a number of different rates and after each flow period the well is shut in and the pressure allowed to build up. The reservoir engineer then uses a range of calculations to produce graphs based on, for example, the Horner (1951) or Millers, Dyes, Hutchinson (1950) methods. The reader is referred to Earlougher (1977) or Lee (1982) for further information. These plots can then be analysed and estimates of the average effective permeability of the formation made, as well as whether there any other factors such as dual porosity and/or fractured behaviour, and whether there are any boundary effects, ie depletion and/or faults, etc. The Productivity Index (PI) of a well expressed in bopd/psi is a direct measure of well performance and can be expressed as:

$$\mathbf{PI} = \frac{\mathbf{q}}{\mathbf{P_e - P_w}} = \frac{\textbf{Flow rate}}{\textbf{Pressure drawdown}}$$

Which by using Eqn 1 can be stated as:

$$\mathbf{PI} = \frac{\mathbf{k.h.}}{\mathbf{141.2 \times \mu.B.[\ln (r_e / r_w) + S]}} \qquad \text{(Eqn 2)}$$

As discussed later, one of the aims of production optimisation is to make the PI of each well as high as economically and practically possible. The ways in which this can be done rely on altering the individual parametres in Eqn 2 so as to increase the PI .

Fluid sampling

Inspection of the pressure-volume-temperature (PVT) fluid properties of any reservoir is critical as the PVT functions are required in practically every aspect of reservoir engineering, eg calculation of reservoir content, well performance, recovery calculations and calculations for the design of production/export facilities, etc. For further information on the properties of petroleum fluids, see McCain (1990), Danesh (1998) or Dandekar (2006). The main responsibility of the petroleum engineer in this area is to ensure the collection of valid fluid samples that can be transferred to the laboratory where the basic PVT experiments are performed. Detailed sampling is normally conducted during appraisal well testing when the well has been flowing at a steady state. It is vitally important that the initial reservoir temperature and pressure is accurately measured since many of the laboratory analyses will be conducted at these conditions. Fluid samples can be taken both downhole (eg using an RFT[1] or MDT[2] wireline tool or during a DST with a downhole sampler) or at the surface either at the wellhead or after separation at the surface.

Production logs

Unlike the logs routinely run in open hole (ie uncased), described earlier, production logs are normally run in a cased hole. Typically, logs are run to inspect production tubing and/or casing, evaluate cementing programmes, ie behind casing, and also to evaluate well flow and associated properties. A range of logs can be run to evaluate the status of tubing such as calipers (examining the internal surfaces), electric potential and electromagnetic logs (measuring thickness and losses due to corrosion, etc.). At several times during the life of a production well, a full production test is normally carried out, utilising downhole pressure and temperature sensors with a downhole flowmeter. This enables the relative flow from particular intervals and the fluid composition (% water, oil or gas) to be examined and compared with previous measurements providing information for potential remedial action to improve hydrocarbon production and/or reduce water production.

Field monitoring

The field model that can be built from the data and calculations above has to suffice for making the development decision, but any production forecast derived from it should have enormous error bars attached to it.[3]

During development drilling and initial production, an enormous amount of data is acquired, often of a different and more revealing nature than that which was available when the original development decision was made. The new data often throw an entirely new light on the field, and invariably, the field turns out to be more complicated than initially thought. The well performance data, in the form of rates and pressures, provide better indications of the internal reservoir architecture, or to put it more crudely, the internal 'plumbing' of the reservoir. Dedicated observation wells are sometimes drilled with the sole objective of gathering data to better the understanding of the field. Permanent downhole monitoring of pressures in production and injection wells is becoming the norm.

The incoming information is used to update the models of the field regularly. A good 'history matched' model of the field is one that is capable of reproducing all the historical production and pressure data. A model with a good 'history match' inspires enough confidence for its predictions to be relied on. Regularly, the underlying framework of the model, ie the understanding of the geology and internal reservoir architecture, has to be completely revised in order to explain the production performance. Increasingly popular are successive sets of seismic data (4D seismic).[4] These can sometimes reveal changes in the reservoir that cannot be seen directly in the wells.

5.3 Reserves

Natural resources (eg hydrocarbons or mineral deposits) are defined by geological knowledge. There is, however, a difference between resources and the reserves that can be economically extracted from the resource base. As the oil price fluctuates, the oil in a marginally commercial field may be an economic reserve one day but only a resource the next and vice versa.

Volumetric calculations

Once the initial data gathering has been completed, and prior to development of a field, it is essential to calculate the *volume* of oil and/or gas held in a reservoir (Eqn 3). This is sometimes referred to as the STOOIP value or stock tank oil originally in place.

$$\mathbf{N\ (or\ G)} = \frac{\mathbf{A.h.\phi.(1-S_w)}}{B} \qquad \text{(Eqn 3)}$$

Where:

- N = Volume of oil in place (m^3)
- G = Volume of gas in place (m^3)
- A = Productive area of the reservoir (m^2)
- h = Net thickness of the reservoir (m)
- ϕ = Porosity
- S_w = Water saturation
- B = Formation Volume Factor (B_o for oil and B_g for gas)

The productive area (A) of the reservoir is normally calculated from maps produced from geophysical data, geological considerations and pressure measurements. The net thickness (h) of the reservoir is usually obtained from downhole wireline log measurements (ie SP and resistivity logs) and other information from cores and cuttings. The product of these is the net volume (V) of reservoir rock (ie A.h in Eqn 3), and this is often provided in the form of a probability distribution or as the sum of the volume of a number of cells from a gridded mapping package.

The porosity of rocks is dependent on rock type and how the grains are fitted together (Chapter 3). The average porosity (ϕ) is normally measured in the laboratory from cores or by various downhole measurements such as sonic log, neutron measurements and density logs (section 5.2). Again, a probability distribution and/or the average over the number of cells in a reservoir model are used in the calculation. Rock porosity varies within a wide range and for oil/gas reservoirs it is normally in the range 0–40% with an average 15–25%.

The reservoir is never entirely filled by oil or gas, there is usually a residual amount of water within the pores, know as the water saturation (S_w). This is a major factor and is best established by capillary pressure measurements carried out on cores although it can also be calculated using the Archie Equation and data from resistivity wireline logs.

The Formation Volume Factor (B) is the factor that is used to convert the volume at reservoir conditions into the stabilised volume at the surface. For oil reservoirs B_o is the number of reservoir barrels of oil and dissolved gas that must be produced to obtain one 'stock tank' barrel of stable oil at the surface. For gas reservoirs B_g is the volume in barrels that one standard cubic foot of gas at the surface occupies as free gas in the reservoir. The situation is thus more complex because natural gas does not behave as an ideal gas under high temperature and pressure. The reservoir pressure and temperature are therefore required as well as the compressibility of the gas (ie the Z–factor), which requires information about the gas composition in order to calculate B_g.

$$B_g = \frac{Z.\,T_r}{264.43.\,P_r} \qquad \text{(Eqn 4)}$$

Where:

B_g = the gas formation volume factor
Z = the super compressibility factor at pressure P_r
T_r = reservoir temperature and
P_r = the reservoir pressure

Thus, assuming that average values are used, the content of the reservoir can be calculated. Routinely, however, this is calculated using probability distributions for each of the factors producing a 'central' oil/gas in place figure with an estimate of uncertainty. Volumetric calculations are, therefore, never an exact science and estimates of reserves need to be treated with caution.

Reservoir performance and recovery factor

Not all oil or gas in a reservoir can be produced. The recovery factor is therefore the percentage of the oil/gas 'in place' in the reservoir that can be economically recovered. Typically, the recovery factor for an oil reservoir is 20–45% whereas for a gas field it is 70–85%. Sandstone reservoirs tend to have higher recovery factors than carbonate reservoirs.

Estimating the recovery factor for a reservoir is very complex and requires information on both technical and commercial aspects such as:

- reservoir drives;
- flow regime within the reservoir;
- fluid behaviour;
- development plan; and
- commercial constraints.

(i) Reservoir drives

The reservoir drive is the mechanism that forces the fluids to flow through the reservoir into the well bore. It is possible to classify reservoirs by the type of reservoir energy although often more than one force is active. The main driving forces are:

- *Expanding gas*: as the pressure in the reservoir decreases due to production, dissolved gas in the oil is liberated. This then expands, helping to drive the oil into the well bore.
- *Gas cap*: the force of gravity is prevalent in reservoirs creating gas caps. Again, as oil is produced, the gas cap expands to fill the reduced volume created through production.
- *Encroaching water drive*: where underlying water, which is under substantial hydrostatic pressure, replaces the produced volume of oil either entirely or in part.

(ii) Flow regime

As discussed in section 5.2, it is important to understand how the oil/gas flows through the reservoir into the well. This can be affected by:

- poorly connected porosity (hence poor permeability) within the reservoir,
- a high degree of compartmentalisation in the reservoir due to depositional or structural geological factors; and/or
- the presence of heavy oil which is very viscous and difficult to produce.

All of these will have an impact on how much of the oil/gas can be recovered.

(iii) Fluid behaviour

How the fluids behave during the life of a reservoir is especially important in gas condensate reservoirs where the hydrocarbons are in a gaseous state under reservoir conditions but become liquid either in passage up the hole or at the surface. Information about the type of reservoir fluids, ie gas, oil and water, is therefore essential.

(iv) Development plan

The proposed development plan has a significant effect on how much of the oil/gas will be recovered. This is ultimately determined by how many and what type of wells are drilled, the production and processing facilities available, the export route and oil/gas sales and marketing.

Often a reservoir simulation model (3D and 3-phase) is used to produce production profiles for oil/gas and water and hence a recovery factor based on the technical data. This information can then be used as input to a full-field economic model to produce the standard economic parametres such as Net Present Value (NPV) at a range of discount rates and the internal rate of return (IRR). This whole process is iterative as the recovery factor is related to all these factors. Assuming there is one, however, an economic development plan is then agreed and the information is used to support a corporate development decision.

(v) Commercial constraints

The ultimate aim for an oil company is to make a profit and commercial issues *at the time of development* are a key factor. As noted earlier, a discovery may be a reserve one day but be downgraded to a resource another, depending on the economic climate. Key commercial issues include:

- estimates of the total capital expenditure required for field development and estimates of operating costs over the field life;
- details of the commercial sales terms – especially relevant for gas fields;
- details of all related tax terms – often this is also very complex;
- forecasts of long-term oil/gas and commodity prices, etc.; and
- corporate discount rates and cost of capital, etc.

The field development, cost estimating, commercial, taxation and economic factors which are necessary to calculate the recovery factor are described in later chapters.

Notes

[1] Repeat Formation Tester.

[2] Modular Formation Dynamics Tester.

[3] The range of reserves for an undeveloped field should typically be 'base case' ±50%.

[4] Successive seismic surveys are often called 4D seismic, with the fourth dimension referring to the time dimension.

RESERVOIR EVALUATION

LEGAL

5.4 Introduction

This chapter considers the stage at which an oil and gas company and their co-venturers on a block or under a licence evaluate the options for developing a field and define the potential reserves. Having spent money on applying for licences, initial studies, shooting seismic and drilling a discovery, and possibly acquiring further assets around the field, the next questions for the reservoir team to decide are whether that field is commercially and technically capable of commercial production and, if so, what are the likely reserves in the field. The reservoir team will also want to know what the capital and operating expenditure costs are in developing the field and whether that field will receive sanction for development. The sanction in a large company may depend on competing for capital as against other field developments, and in a small company will depend on the private equity and debt funders approving its development.

Having carried out exploration and appraisal drilling, it may be that the reservoir team recommend that the drilled block or blocks form part of a larger field or basin and that the co-venturers on that part of the field should enter into a joint study agreement or data swap agreement to evaluate the whole field or basin with other co-venturers in other blocks in order to maximise the likelihood of successful commercial development. It is a requirement of the licences issued by the DTI that the parties consider maximising commercial production within the area being considered for development. This may lead to various co-venturers under different JOAs combining and entering into a Unitisation Agreement (UOA) which is discussed further in Chapter 12. This important phase in the appraisal of a field may require the full re-evaluation of all data on the field to establish whether there are economic reserves. Consideration will first be given to the concept of data as this often differentiates an upstream oil and gas company from a service company.

5.5 Data

Data may take many forms and might include legal title documents which evidence the legal title of ownership to assets, documents evidencing the operating and other contracting arrangements relative to a field, technical data on a field derived from past exploration activities and commercial data which will include economic assumptions developed in financial models for a field.

Upstream companies normally treat such data as being highly confidential and will allow contractors to work on such data only if they have entered into confidentiality agreements or given confidentiality undertakings. They will also require their own employees to enter into employment contracts which will contain confidentiality provisions. In some cases, most companies may expect co-venturers or other parties they are working with on joint studies to enter into restrictive covenants which may take the form of an area of mutual interest agreement or some other form of agreement before they will release data to another party. The legal title to the data and ownership of the data will also depend on the nature of contractual documentation entered into and the terms in it which deal with ownership of the data. It will also depend on the binding confidentiality undertakings given to an oil and gas company by other parties.

Joint Operating Agreements will set out confidentiality undertakings which each of the co-venturers enter into by signing the JOA in which they agree not to divulge confidential information in respect of a field to other third parties. These confidentiality provisions will extend to joint operations and that information will normally be kept confidential for a period after that particular co-venturer has exited from the field. A co-venturer may divulge information to an affiliate in the same group, to a governmental agency if required and to comply with relevant applicable law and regulations or to engage with prospective or actual contractors or consultants.

Confidential information in itself is recognised as a legal concept in English and Scots law but it is not strictly recognised as always being property. Confidential information will not, in common law, include all information which one company or person nominates as being confidential; generally, it must be trade secrets or commercial information which a party treats as being confidential. It may be protected by a company requiring other companies to enter into written confidentiality undertakings or it may be protected as an implied right. A right to require information to be kept confidential may arise where a party has given another party information which the donor party has treated as confidential, that information has the necessary quality of confidence about it, the information has been imparted in circumstances importing an obligation of confidence and there has been an unauthorised use of that information to the detriment of the donor party communicating. If there has been such an unauthorised use, then the party with the proprietary right in that confidential information can seek from a court an order restraining the other party from using it if it is not already in the public domain. The aggrieved party may apply for an interdict (in Scotland) or injunction (in England) on an interim and ex parte basis (ie without notice to the defendant) and seek a court order to restrain the release of the confidential information. It can also apply for an order for damages to be paid or an account of profits. There could also be an order for destruction of the information in unauthorised third parties' hands.

The data which are generated and produced by the operator and co-venturers in connection with a field will normally be kept highly confidential. It is these data from which each of those co-venturers will report their percentage interest of reserves in that field and therefore the value of those reserves in their own balance sheet in their accounts. The sensitivity, therefore, of data is their direct link to reserves reporting and, as companies are valued on the amount and quality of their reserves, this goes to the heart of the company's valuation and its viability to raise and deploy capital.

Intellectual property data

Intellectual property data may include data which are know-how or trade secrets and relates to patents, design rights, rights in inventions or may be database rights. It may be know-how itself which has not been registered, as, for instance, a patent.

As an example, there may be valuable trade secrets in the mixture and application of chemicals into the well or reservoir in order to test flow assurance. The chemicals may either be protected by a patent from being copied or the data which leads chemists to methods of application may be secret and form part of a company's know-how or confidential information.

Legal data

Legal data will often include data contained in major operating contracts in which goods and services were acquired, contracts dealing with title to the field interests (for instance the JOA, the UOA and other agreements), and the agreements dealing with the creation and management of data itself. There will be sensitive data contained in minutes of meetings of, for instance, the operating and technical committees under a JOA or internal team meetings of a co-venturer. There will be commercially sensitive data in the farm-out and farm-in agreements, drilling contracts and other such field contractual documents. The terms of these documents will evidence the ownership of data and will range from the price and terms of payment, the work obligations to be fulfilled and the warranties, indemnities and extent of any liabilities. There may also be highly sensitive information on pending, threatened or actual litigation in connection with those liabilities or contracts which would also be treated as confidential as it may affect the value of the company. This kind of information is often kept strictly confidential as it is relevant to a company's valuation in both a public and a private company.

Legal data can also include information in transportation agreements and other agreements on infrastructure, the processing of hydrocarbons and agreements on terminal operations. This information may be crucial to determining whether a field is economically capable of development and therefore whether it can be included in the commercial reserves of a company.

Technical data

Technical data may include all geophysical data, for example field tapes, surveys, maps, reports, specifications, computer programs, navigational data, seismic data, FEED (front-end engineering and design) studies and other such information. It would also include well logs, the results of well tests, including wire-line logs, core logs and flow assurance tests. This information may go to determine whether a field is technically capable of development and therefore whether it can be included as proven and probable reserves.

Technical data may result from years of testing wells or of highly expensive core-logging exercises and its relationship with different technologies.

Commercial data

Commercial data may be a much broader category and may include information which the geological and engineering teams do not have sight of but might be kept in treasury departments, finance departments or at board level. It could include budgetary expenditure plans for forthcoming years, information on banking covenants, information on covenants in connection with shareholder arrangements, sensitive accounting and financial information and internal hurdles to be crossed before a field can be sanctioned. There will also be economic assumptions on the future price of oil and gas.

5.6 Data agreements

There are many different types of data agreement depending on what different co-venturers in the field wish to do. Data licensing, data commissioning, licensing storage and data swap will now be considered.

Data services and data acquisition agreements

Seismic contract

An operator may enter into a contract with a seismic contractor to commission the contractor to provide its own vessel or someone else's vessel to trawl over a given field on given traverse lines and point co-ordinates within a given period to shoot seismic on a pre-agreed specification. It will also be commissioned to process the data and provide it to the operator capable of reprocessing or further analysis. The operator may be keen to retain ownership of the seismic and, therefore, will include a provision to take ownership to all title and proprietary interest in such data. These are normally agreements for the provision of services to the operator by a contractor whereby the contractor warrants he has a vessel technically capable of performing the service. There will, therefore, normally be a scope of work section in a schedule which sets out the contract area and a programme of operations. It will also state the format of the document and whether any processing of the seismic data recorded on tapes will be required. Such data normally start out as field data and then have to be processed to remove acquisition-induced artefacts and become usable for workstation interpretation. The data may be further reprocessed to increase the sharpness of the reservoir image, such as in pre-stacked depth migration. There will also be navigation data which are recorded and which will set out the location of the vessel and where the equipment has been stationed to carry out the seismic study.

The main provisions in such contracts will deal with ownership of data, mobilisation of the vessel and equipment and completion of the scope of work, the degree of skill and prudence to be exercised by the contractor, compensation and payment, provisions dealing with mobilisation fee, any demobilisation fee, a fee for full coverage of traverse area, minimum programme fee, any force majeure rates and any additional services to be conducted, such as processing raw data and standby rate. There will be provisions dealing with indemnities and liabilities, insurance and safety, health and environment and taxation. One of the difficult clauses in this agreement is force majeure and the problem of adverse weather conditions and other 'acts of God'. Another provision which would be key is the quality control on producing and processing the seismic data in accordance with the given standards and guidelines.

Data licensing

It may be the case that seismic contractors who own or have access to a vessel will speculatively shoot seismic and may offer for licence the use of that data to operators or other co-venturers. Such licences are normally non-exclusive and non-transferable, irrevocable and sometimes may convert to ownership on payment.

Under such an agreement, the seismic contractor will own the seismic data and will process it and format it ready for market use. However, there will then be restrictions on the use to which that data can be used by the licensee. For instance, the seismic contractor will put constraints on reformatting or reprocessing such data by the licensee. It will prevent modifications to it or disposal of it by the licensee or disclosure to other third parties and will often make further charges by way of increased licence fees for the use of the data by other co-venturers within the same co-venturing group, contractors or other third party users on the field. There could be escalation fees depending on the number of users and change of control provisions in which the licensor will terminate the contract on the licensee being sold or the field being sold by the licensee. The licensor may give no warranties as to the quality or condition of the data.

Data Storage Agreements

There may be substantial technical data which an operator or co-venturers have no warehouse base to store. An operator may enter into a Data Storage Agreement for storage in warehouses of such technical data and other stock on the field. This may be hire of storage space which will include retrieval and dispatch services or it may be for full access at any time.

Oil and gas companies are required by the DTI to keep all data on the reservoir in which they have a licence by the DTI and must not destroy it.

Data Access Agreements

One operator may hold data on the field which another operator wishes to use and there may, therefore, be a Data Access Agreement to allow such access to data or to swap data on different fields.

In some cases the field owners may set up a jointly owned data holding company to allow access by the parties to its field data.

Joint Study Agreements

When reservoir teams are reappraising a field, it may be that their studies at that point indicate that the field is part of a larger field or basin and they will, therefore, enter into negotiations with adjacent field owners for joint studies to work up a field development plan for a larger area. This may lead, if a larger field is commercially capable of development, to a Unitisation Agreement. Parties may also enter into a Joint Study Agreement.

This will be an agreement whereby co-venturers in different fields through their operators enter into an agreement to pool information and data on the field, to set objectives for joint field development and set out budgets and a system of co-ordinating and managing those budgets. It may be the case that a field co-ordinator is appointed by the various operators to the different fields who will bring together the operators in the field and co-ordinate the study programme and budgets. That co-ordinator may take on specific responsibilities and will negotiate a restriction to its liabilities, normally restricting liability for wilful misconduct and restricting its liability in common law to gross negligence. A steering committee might be set up to approve the policies and the joint studies. There may be voting rights and percentage interests allocated which will be dependent not on the potential reserves of the fields but simply on an equal shared basis of the field owners until such time as the reserves have been set. Various committees might be set up for undertaking different field studies. The agreement might deal with data exchange, withdrawal from a default, assignment of interest, confidentiality and contain restrictive covenants in the form of non-compete provisions.

Joint Data Agreements

It may be the case that parties just simply want to swap information on respective fields rather than enter into a formal Joint Study Agreement. There could be provisions dealing with the sharing of data, provisions for jointly carrying out seismic surveys and swapping information on a proposed contract. Parties may be under the same licence but be different owners of blocks and they may come to an agreement on how that licence is to be managed in a co-ordinated way.

Joint Planning Agreement

There could be an agreement between operators that states that after joint studies have been entered into and reserves have been established for the different fields, the owners of adjoining blocks agree to joint rules for field development and application for sanction by the DTI for that development. These are really pre-unitisation agreements which will lead to the negotiation and conclusion of a UOA.

5.7 Reserves

Hydrocarbons in the subsurface reservoir are called oil in place or gas in place and economic value may be determined by the recovery factor which is a percentage of oil in place or gas in place that the reservoir will produce. The recovery factor depends on a number of different technical factors which, in the case of oil, will include reservoir drive, reservoir permeability, reservoir heterogeneity, oil and gas viscosity and other factors. The recovery factor typically ranges from 20–45% for oil and about 70–85% for gas. Gas which is in the subsurface may be entirely dissolved in the oil that is known as under-saturated oil, the amount of gas within the oil is known as the solution or producing gas-oil ratio and is measured in scf/bbl. When the oil reaches the surface, the gas will bubble out of the oil and the volume of oil will decrease. There will, therefore, be a shrinkage factor in the oil volume. In order to determine what a barrel of oil is, there is a definition for a stabilised barrel of oil under surface conditions and this is known as a stock tank barrel of oil. The number of reservoir barrels (rb) required to make up one stock tank barrel, accounting for the shrinkage, is known as the oil formation factor and is measured as rb/stb, where stb means stock tank barrels. In the same way, a volume of natural gas when it arises from the subsurface reservoir, expands to one cubic foot at surface conditions. This is known as the gas formation volume factor and can be measured in rb/scf or rcf/scf. In order to value gas, it is taken as natural gas measured in standard cubic foot (scf) which is the volume in cubic feet of natural gas under defined surface conditions (namely 60°F and 1 atmosphere).

Not all oil and gas can be produced and it is only that oil and gas which is capable of economic and technical production which is known as reserves. The Society of Petroleum Engineers (SPE) defines reserves as 'those quantities of petroleum which are anticipated to be commercially recovered from known accumulations from given data'.[1] The DTI states that 'Economic reserves are those reserves which have a (pre-tax) market value greater than the (pre-tax) resource cost of their extraction where costs include both capital and operating costs but exclude sunk costs and costs (like interest charges) which do not reflect current use of resources'.[2] As reservoir teams will estimate the reserves based on the type of definitions of oil and gas which are referred to above, these will simply be estimates and there will be some degree of uncertainty. The uncertainty arises from the amount of geological and engineering data available at the time the estimate is given and the interpretation of that data. There are generally accepted reserve classifications throughout the world and there are different statements of practice produced by different authorities and professional societies on what will come within the principal classification.

The Society of Petroleum Engineers and the World Petroleum Council (WPC) jointly approved classifications of reserves as either being proved or unproved: 'Unproved reserves are less certain to be recovered than proved reserves and may be further subclassified as probable and possible reserves to denote progressively increasing uncertainty in their recoverability.'[3]

There are, generally, two methods of estimation:

1. '*deterministic*': a single best estimate of reserves is made, based on known geological, engineering and economic data.
2. '*probabilistic*': 'when the known geological, engineering and economic data are used to generate a range of estimates and their associated probabilities'.

The US Securities Exchange Commission, for instance, requires deterministic disclosures, while the UK follows probabilistic reserves disclosures.

Reserves are normally identified as being proved, probable and possible, which gives an indication of the probability of recovery. However, reserves do not include petroleum which has been produced and held as stock, or hydrocarbons used for processing in the field or other such usage. They can, however, include reserves attributed to natural recovery or improved recovery methods. Proven, probable and possible reserves therefore represent a degree of certainty that a reserve does exist, based on geological and engineering data and the interpretation of that data.

The table overleaf produced by the SPE shows the different categories of reserves and their recoverability.

Proved reserves are normally categorised as developed or undeveloped but are estimated with reasonable certainty to be commercially recoverable from a given date. Using a probabilistic method of determination, they have a 90% probability that the quantities actually recovered will equal or exceed the estimate. This assumes that current technology is being used and a given set of current prices on known commercial terms. They are often known as P90 or 1P reserves.

Probable reserves are reasonably probable of being produced, based on geological and/or engineering data similar to those used in estimates of proved reserves and using the current technology at current prices on known commercial terms. When probabilistic methods are used there should be a 50% probability that the quantities actually recovered will equal or exceed the sum of estimated proved plus probable reserves.[4] They are often referred to as P50 or 2P or Proven Plus Probable reserves.

Possible reserves, as the SPE states, 'are those unproved reserves which analysis of geological and engineering data suggests are less likely to be recoverable than probable reserves'.[5] Using probabilistic methods they have a 10% probability 'that the quantities actually recovered will equal or exceed the sum of estimated proved plus probable plus possible reserves'.[6] They are often known as P10, 3P or Proven Plus Probable Plus Possible reserves.

There are, then, reserve status categories for the development and producing status of wells and reservoirs. They are categorised into developed reserves which are expected to be recovered from existing wells and include reserves behind the pipe.[7] These reserves are then characterised as being 'producing' and 'non-producing'. Producing reserves are those which 'are expected to be recovered from completion intervals open at the time of the estimate'[8] and producing to the market, whereas non-producing reserves are shut-in reserves and 'are expected to be recovered from completion intervals open at the time of the estimate'[9] though currently are not producing. There may be mechanical export and transportation or market reasons why they are not producing.

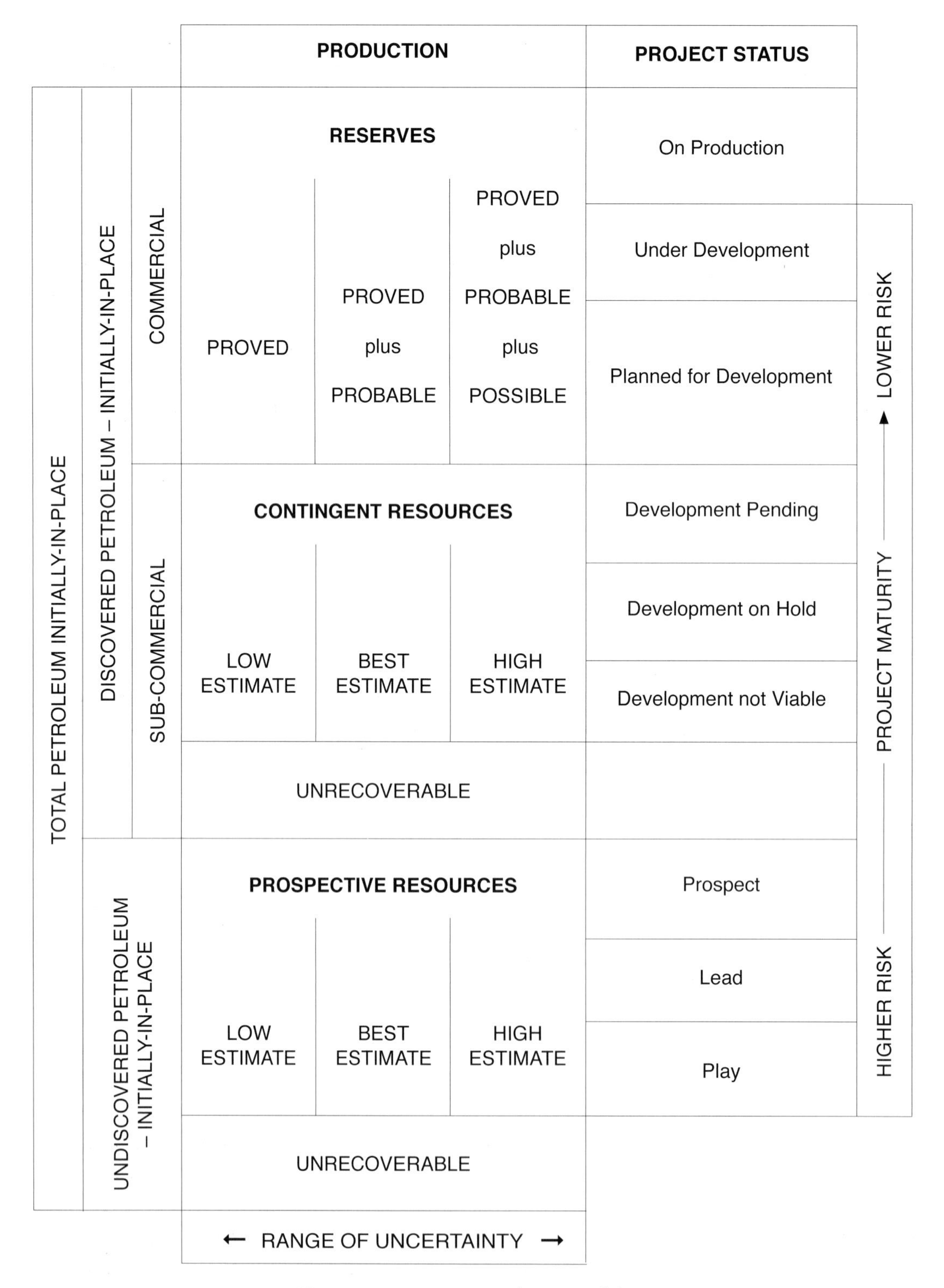

Figure 5–4 Reserves and recoverability

Finally, undeveloped reserves are not producing and are expected to be recovered from, for instance, new wells, deepening existing wells to a different reservoir or where a large expenditure is required to recomplete an existing well or install production or transportation facilities.

Future developments in reserves classification

There have been a number of attempts to standardise the definitions of reserves and resources which began in the 1930s. The SPE and the World Petroleum Council (WPC) (formerly known as the World Petroleum Congresses) published separately in 1987 reserves definitions which were similar. In 1997, they together developed a system of Petroleum Reserves Definitions, which was updated in conjunction with the American Association of Petroleum Geologists (AAPG) in 2000 and followed by Guidelines for the Evaluation of Petroleum Reserves and Resources (2001) and a Glossary of Terms (2005). The SPE, the AAPG, the WPC and the Society of Petroleum Evaluation Engineers (SPEE) produced a draft paper entitled 'Petroleum Reserves and Resources Classification, Definitions and Guidelines 2006'. This provides an update and clarification of the classification and estimation of petroleum quantities. The aim of the definitions and guidelines was 'to establish a technical-based reserves and resources evaluation standard and provide a common reference for the international petroleum industry, national reporting and regulatory disclosure agencies'.[10]

In addition, the United Nations have, since the 1990s, been developing the UN Framework Classification for Fossil Energy and Mineral Resources (UNFC). It is an umbrella framework to harmonise existing terminologies and definitions worldwide and onto which other systems can be mapped. It is intended to be a universally applicable scheme for classifying and evaluating energy and mineral reserves and resources. In 2004 it was recommended for worldwide application and it has been successfully applied or tested in over 60 countries. It continues to be developed with the support and direct contribution from various international organisations (including WPC) and professional associations (including SPE and AAPG).

The 2007 SPE/WPC/AAPG/SPEE classification system

The basic classification system has been expanded and the result is the Petroleum Resources Management System 2007 (prepared by the Oil and Gas Reserves Committee, WPC, AAPG and SPEE) which consolidates and replaces the 1997 Petroleum Reserves Definitions, the 2000 Petroleum Resources Classification and Definitions Publications and the 2001 Guidelines for the Evaluation of Petroleum Reserves and Resources. The basic classification system is shown in Figs 5–5 and 5–6 and provides a clearer explanation of, and differentiation between, resource classification (vertical axis) and resource categorisation (horizontal axis).

Major principles underpinning the revised guidelines are that:

- the system is 'project-based';
- resource classification is based on project chance of commerciality;
- resource categorisation is based on certainty of quantities recovered by applying a defined project to a reservoir; and
- the base case uses forecast conditions (prices and costs, technology available, etc.) with several sensitivity cases which typically would include one which assumes that current conditions will remain constant throughout the life of the project.

Resource classification requires the setting up of criteria for a discovery and then the differentiation between commercial and sub-commercial projects in known accumulations (and hence between reserves and contingent resources).

The revised guidelines state:

> '**Determination of Discovery Status:** A discovery is one petroleum accumulation, or several petroleum accumulations collectively, for which one or several exploratory wells have established through testing, sampling or logging the existence of a significant quantity of hydrocarbons that is potentially economic to recover under a technically feasible development plan.'[11]

> '**Determination of Commerciality:** Discovered and potentially recoverable volumes (Contingent Resources) may be considered commercially producible, and thus Reserves, if the organisation claiming commerciality has, with reasonable certainty, committed to developing and producing them. The commercial value of a project would include the net present value of future cash flows obtained as a result of the production and sale of recoverable quantities. If the degree of commitment is not such that the development of the accumulation is expected within a reasonable time frame, the estimated discovered recoverable quantities for the accumulation should remain classified as Contingent Resources.'[12]

Commerciality can be further subdivided according to project status or maturity: 'As an accumulation moves to a higher level of maturity, there will be an increasing chance that the accumulation will be commercially developed within a reasonable time frame.'[13]

The following diagrams illustrate the two options for classifying resources at various stages of a project based on 'decision' or 'economic' status.

Resource categorisation is shown along the horizontal axis in the classification diagrams (Figs 5–5 and 5–6) and defines the range of uncertainty in estimates of the quantities of petroleum associated with a project. The guidelines state: 'The range of uncertainty of the recoverable and/or potentially recoverable volumes

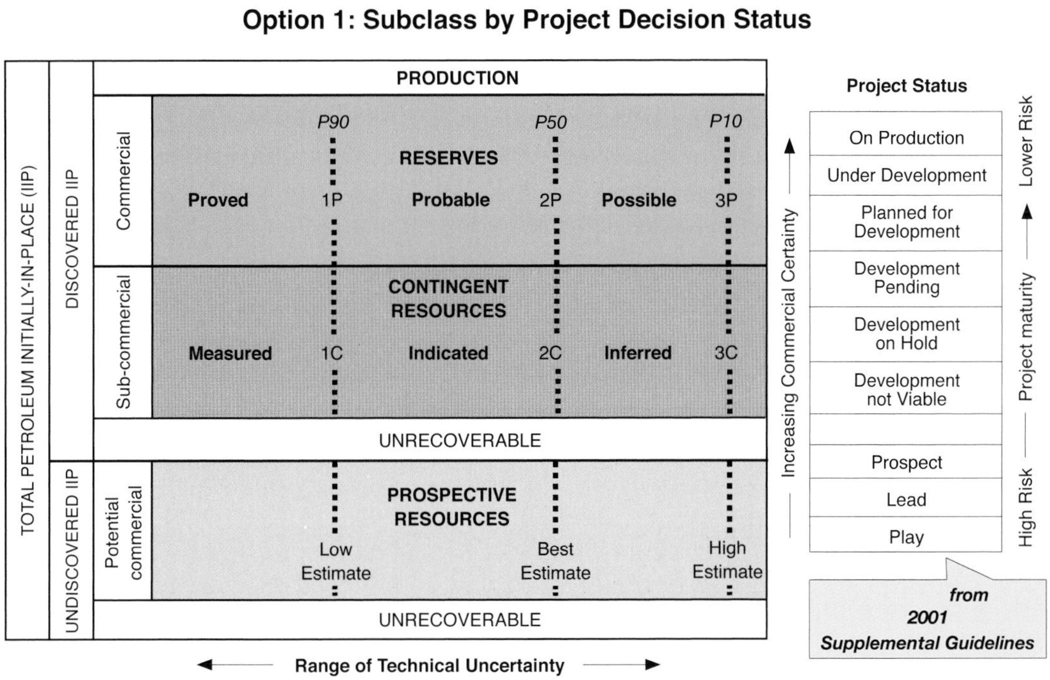

Option 1: Subclass by Project Decision Status
TOTAL PETROLEUM INITIALLY-IN-PLACE (IIP)
DISCOVERED IIP
UNDISCOVERED IIP
PRODUCTION
Commercial
Sub-commercial
Potential commercial
P90
P50
P10
RESERVES
Proved
1P
Probable
2P
Possible
3P
CONTINGENT RESOURCES
Measured
1C
Indicated
2C
Inferred
3C
UNRECOVERABLE
PROSPECTIVE RESOURCES
Low Estimate
Best Estimate
High Estimate
UNRECOVERABLE
Range of Technical Uncertainty
Increasing Commercial Certainty
Project Status
On Production
Under Development
Planned for Development
Development Pending
Development on Hold
Development not Viable
Prospect
Lead
Play
Lower Risk
Project maturity
High Risk
from 2001 Supplemental Guidelines

Figure 5–5 Subclass by project decision status

Option 2: Subclass by Project Operational/Economic Status
Project committed and funded/ implemented
Project committed but not yet funded/ implemented
Economic or near-economic but no project committed
Uneconomic (or analysis incomplete)
New sub-classes for Contingent Resources
TOTAL PETROLEUM INITIALLY-IN-PLACE (IIP)
DISCOVERED IIP
UNDISCOVERED IIP
PRODUCTION
Commercial
Sub-commercial
Potential commercial
Economic
Sub-economic
Developed (PDP, PNP)
Proved
Undeveloped (Pud)
P90
P50
P10
RESERVES
1P
Probable
2P
Possible
3P
CONTINGENT RESOURCES
Measured
1C
Indicated
2C
Inferred
3C
UNRECOVERABLE
PROSPECTIVE RESOURCES
Low Estimate
Best Estimate
High Estimate
UNRECOVERABLE
Range of Technical Uncertainty
Increasing Commercial Certainty
Option to use Dev/Undev for all reserves categories

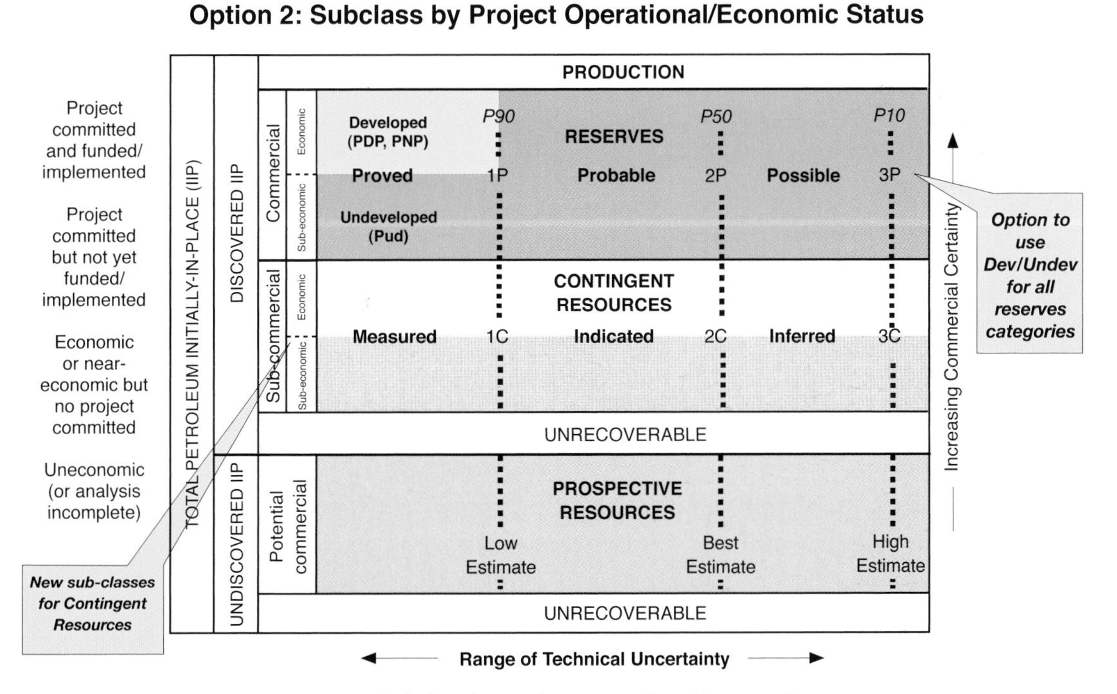

Figure 5–6 Subclass by project operational/economic status

may be represented by either discrete deterministic scenarios or by a probability distribution. This same range of uncertainty applies to Reserves, Contingent Resources and Prospective Resources.'[14]

'For Reserves, the general cumulative terms low/best/high estimate are denoted as 1P/2P/3P respectively. The associated incremental quantities are termed Proved, Probable ... and Possible ... For Contingent Resources, the general cumulative terms low/best/high estimates are denoted 1C/2C/3C respectively. The associated incremental quantities are termed Measured, Indicated and Inferred.'[15]

The UN Framework Classification for Fossil Fuel and Mineral Resources (UNFC)

The complete UNFC framework superimposed with the SPE/WPC/AAPG classification system for petroleum (in colour) is illustrated in the following diagram:

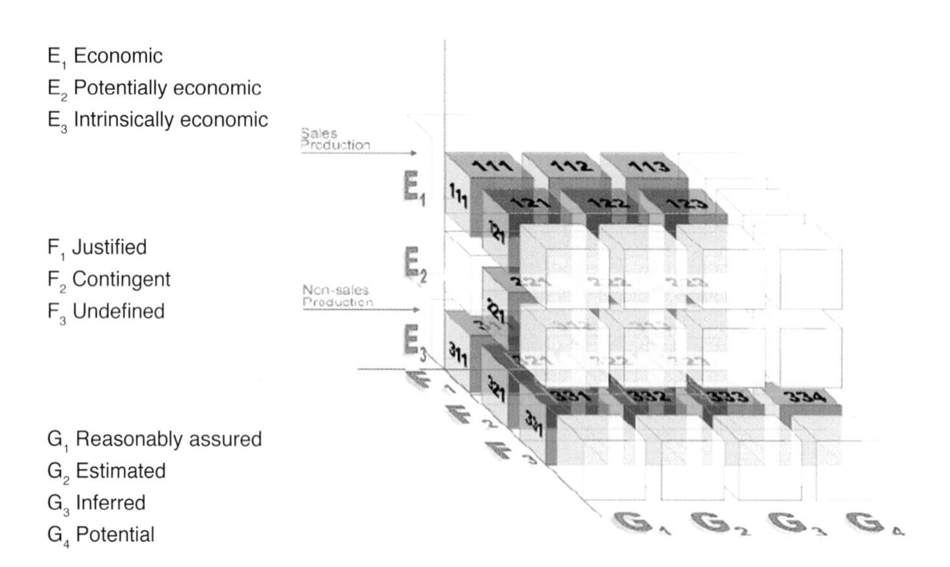

Figure 5–7 UNFC for Petroleum

The framework incorporates the principal criteria that recur in many of the classification systems applied to energy and mineral resources, namely:

- economic viability (E);
- technical feasibility/project maturity (F);
- geological knowledge (G).

The categories are quoted in fixed order (EFG) and the category letters are removed but the numbers are retained. The resources are identified by a number code ((111), (334), etc.) to facilitate communication independent of alphabet. The UNFC provides for 42 theoretical possibilities, not all of which are relevant – there being 19 relevant to the petroleum industry. For example, under 'geological knowledge' category G1 equals proved, G2 probable and G3 possible reserves and G4 prospective resources.

More information on the UNFC can be found at www.unce.org/ie/se/reserves.html

Reserve booking

Reserves are largely the means by which an oil and gas company is valued. There are different sets of rules to determine what can be booked and what is not bookable and these rules often differ widely between different administrators of the rules. The main rules are set out in the UK by the UK Statement of Recommended Practices (SORP – 2001), US Securities and Exchange Commission, the Canadian Security Administrators, the Russian Ministry of Natural Resources under the Russian Federation Classification Scheme (RF – 2005), China Petroleum Reserves Office, the Norwegian Petroleum Directorate, US Geological Survey and United Nations Framework Classification. Many countries are now adopting the International Financial Reporting Standards (IFRS) which are described below.

The published reserves are some of the most important data for oil and gas companies to be judged on. It enables the financial sector to analyse, compare and contrast past and prospective operational performance of oil and gas exploration and production firms.

This chapter began by looking at the classification system for reserves reporting. This section now looks at reserves reporting in the public and private markets.

The basis of reserves reporting is to provide more information on the underlying value of an upstream oil and gas company than can be obtained from a balance sheet or profit and loss account. There is, therefore, a balance between a company's desire to keep information on its reserves confidential against the shareholders and other stakeholders desire to receive information on reserves in order to value the company and monitor its performance.

Financial institutions generally prefer to see consistency and transparency in reserves reporting over time.

5.8 Regulation of private and public companies in the UK

The Financial Services Authority (FSA)

The FSA regulates all investment activity in the UK which includes all regulated investment exchanges (ie AIM and Official List) and all private equity, debt funding and all public issue of bonds or stock by any oil and gas company which deals in, or issues, stock in the UK or has other investment interests here. The FSA is an independent non-governmental body, given statutory powers by the Financial Services and Markets Act 2000. It regulates the financial services industry in the UK and it has been given a wide range of rule-making, investigatory and enforcement powers. It has four statutory objectives: ensuring market confidence, public awareness, consumer protection and reduction of financial crime.

The FSA regulates most financial services markets, exchanges and firms. It sets the standards they must meet and can take action against firms if they fail to meet the required standards by applying civil and criminal sanctions. It regulates the two main public markets for companies in the UK: the Alternative Investment Market (AIM) and the Official List.

Public companies

Outlined below are the rules for being admitted to AIM and the continuing obligations which affect UK publicly listed oil and gas companies.

1. Alternative Investment Market

There are specific rules for companies admitted to the Stock Exchange, and there are also guidelines which have been more recently issued. This chapter reviews the reporting of reserves by public companies on AIM.

The London Stock Exchange plc (LSE) issued guidance in March 2006 to Resource Companies which are admitted to, or are seeking admission to, AIM of the London Stock Exchange.[16] The LSE expect the Guidance to be followed where applicable in interpreting AIM rules.

Resource companies include exploration, prospecting and production companies (but do not include consultancy companies providing advice to resource companies). The Guidance reflects best practice in the market. The LSE requires companies listed on AIM to appoint a 'nominated advisor' ('nomad') who is suitably qualified and has been approved. The nomad must ensure that the rules and guidelines of AIM are applied in practice by the company that has appointed the nomad and report to the LSE on all areas of non-compliance.

The Guidance needs to be read alongside and interpreted with AIM rules. Where an applicant to AIM is also issuing a prospectus the rules applicable to the prospectus take precedence over the Guidance.

Resource companies seeking admission to AIM. One of the most important documents provided to analysts, financial institutions and others regarding a public listed oil and gas company is the Competent Person's Report.

Competent Person's Report. A Competent Person's Report (CPR) needs to be prepared and forms part of the document admitting a company to AIM; a CPR needs to be prepared by a 'Competent Person' (CP) who is a suitably qualified person. The CP would report on all material assets owned by the company or proposed to be exploited or utilised by it. As well as reporting on such assets he also needs to report on all the company's liabilities. The CPR must be up to date. If a CPR has been prepared within 12 months of another CPR, there needs to be a future note on why the first CPR was not used in the current admission document.

Nominated Advisers. AIM Rule 39 sets out the responsibilities a nomad owes to the LSE and provides that a nomad who is advising resource companies listed on AIM should ensure that 'it has appropriate access to suitably experienced and qualified individuals' in the relevant part of that sector.

A CP should at least:

(a) be professionally qualified as a member in good standing of a properly recognised professional association;
(b) have at least five years relevant experience and understanding of the estimation, assessment and evaluation of the type of mineral or fluid deposit under consideration;
(c) be independent of the applicant, its directors, senior management and advisers;
(d) not be remunerated by way of a fee that is linked to the admission or value of the applicant; and
(e) not be a sole practitioner.

The nomad has the responsibility of ensuring that the CP producing the CPR does have the necessary qualifications and experience. The work of the CP will be subject to an internal review.

The CPR should be prepared, as a minimum, no more than six months prior to the date of the admission document and must be addressed to the company and the nomad. It should comply with an internationally recognised standard of reporting for mineral and oil and gas reserves and resources.

The CPR should include:

- a summary table of assets (set out in a specific format);
- the disclosures (set out in a specific format);

- the relevant tables (set out in a specific format);
- details of which standard was used in the preparation of the CPR;
- an up-to-date no material change statement; and
- a report on any existing reserves and resources statements, stating clearly what work was undertaken or include a derivation of any reserve or resource estimates.

The admission document should include descriptive sections about the applicant – usually at the beginning of the document. Any information taken from the CPR and used in the descriptive section must not be used misleadingly, and must present a balanced view of the CPR – ie there are to be no omissions of information included in the admission document.

The CP should review the document and confirm in writing to the applicant and the nomad that the information relating to the CPR is accurate, balanced and complete.

Assets. In relation to the assets the LSE gives various guidelines which should be followed by a company seeking admittance to AIM.

(a) *Material contracts* relating to the resource companies are to be summarised and included in the admission document. The meaning of material contracts includes all material subsisting agreements which are included within, or relate to the assets and liabilities of the applicant.

(b) In relation to *due diligence*, the nomad should conduct full due diligence. Overseas legal opinions are to be sought from reputable overseas counsel. This opinion should include issues of jurisdiction and the title to, or validity and enforceability of, any assets. This is in addition to the standard legal due diligence report on the company's business and assets.

(c) It is expected that the nomad undertake a *site visit* and physical inspection of the applicant's physical assets in order to properly consider the suitability of the applicant company for admission to AIM.

(d) *Payments* amounting to £10,000 or more made by, or on behalf of, the applicant to any government or regulatory authority, in relation to the operation of the assets owned or to be acquired, should be disclosed in the admission document.

(e) Any exploration or development companies who have not been independent and earning revenue over the past two years should ensure all connected parties and relevant employees observe the relevant *lock-in requirements* contained in AIM Rule 7.

(f) Within the '*Risk Factors*' section of the admission document the applicant should ensure that any risk factors specific to them be set out before any general risks which may apply.

Ongoing obligations of resource companies listed on AIM. The previous guidance relates to companies wishing to be admitted to AIM; there are also obligations which must be followed by companies already listed which we have summarised below.

Notifications. The resource company should adopt an internationally recognised standard for the purposes of all notifications which must also be referred to in the relevant notification. Such notifications include results and reserve estimates and are known as a 'resource update'. There needs to be a glossary of key terms used in the notification.

Drilling updates should be issued and include information in relation to ore and minerals on the depth of zones tested.

Each resource update should be reviewed by a qualified person who will take responsibility for the resource update. In that event, a company must state in its notification that any estimate as to its resources or reserves is not false or misleading. Sometimes notifications are required urgently and there is not enough time to produce a resource update. Such a notification should also comply with the adopted internationally recognised accounting standard.

Dual listed resource companies. Where an AIM company is also admitted to trading on another recognised investment exchange, the AIM Rules need to be complied with as well as the regulatory requirements of the other exchange.

2. Official List, London Stock Exchange

UK Listing Authority rules. Generally, mineral, oil and natural gas companies (collectively referred to as mineral companies in the rules of the LSE) are subject to disclosure requirements before being listed. A CPR must be contained in listing particulars of a new applicant. Companies that are involved only in exploration for mineral resources and are not undertaking or proposing to undertake their extraction on a commercial scale are not suitable for listing on the LSE.

For the purposes of the LSE a 'mineral company' is defined as a company or group of companies of which a principal activity is, or is planned to be, the extraction of mineral resources (which may or may not include exploration for mineral resources). In determining what constitutes a principal activity, the UK Listing Authority will have regard to all the circumstances, including whether the activity represents 25% or more of gross revenue, operating expenses, assets or market capitalisation of the company or group.

The previous listing rules for the Official List were set out in the Purple Book. The Purple Book was replaced on 1 July 2005 by the Listing, Prospectus and Disclosure Rules. These Rules have few provisions in relation to mineral companies, but are supplemented by the Committee of European Securities Regulators' (CESR) guidelines (CESR's recommendations for the implementation of the European Commission's Regulation on Prospectuses No. 809/2004).

A public company which wishes to be admitted to the Official List, and issue its shares to the public, will need to issue a prospectus to potential subscribers and other stakeholders which complies with the Prospectus Directive (which came into force in the UK on 1 July 2005) and the Prospectus Rules.

Such a company must also comply with the Listing Rules LR 6.1.8 to LR 6.1.10 which sets out the new rules governing mineral companies listed on the Official Exchange. These are a lot less detailed than those contained previously in Chapter 19 of the Purple Book. In accordance with LR 6.1.10 a mineral company which is a 'new applicant' and does not hold a controlling interest in the majority of its assets has to demonstrate that it has a 'reasonable spread of direct interests in mineral resources and has rights to participate actively in their extraction'. In addition, the CESR recommendations suggest certain disclosures in all mineral company prospectuses.

The CESR's recommendations for Prospectuses for *all mineral companies* should include:

- details of reserves;
- expected period of working;
- any licence details;
- progress of actual working; and
- any other exceptional factors.

In addition, it is suggested that Prospectuses for those mineral companies which have not been mineral companies for *at least three years* should include:

- statements of interests and rights of extraction (where there is no controlling interest of the majority of assets in which the company has invested);
- estimate of funding requirements;
- particulars of estimated cash flow – expected prices, grade structure, extraction costs, etc.;

- confirmation from an accountant or auditor that the cash flow particulars have been prepared appropriately;
- an expert's report – the content of which to be agreed with the competent authority.

Under the Listing, Prospectus and Disclosure Rules LR 10.7.5 to 10.7.7 there are specific rules which apply to transactions involving 'significant mineral resources'. In these situations, the 'reserves test' should be applied to determine the percentage ratio. LR 10.7.5(2) provides that: 'The reserves test is calculated by dividing the volume or amount of the proven reserves and probable reserves to be acquired or disposed of by the volume or amount of the aggregate proven reserves and probable reserves of the mineral company making the acquisition or disposal.'

LR 10.7.7 also provides that when calculating the ratio, account must be taken of any associated transactions or loans effected or intended to be effected, and any contingent liabilities or commitments.

There is no one definition of reserves in the CESR's recommendations (ie when a mineral company has to give 'details of its reserves') nor in the UKLA Listing Rules.

A Competent Person's Report will also be required which has to be approved by the LSE.

Private companies

Private companies may be required to report their reserves to their equity financial institutional investors and to banking institutions which may have lent them money based on the Net Present Value of their reserves. There may be included within the banking documentation a definition of Borrowing Base Amount which is generally based on collateral security based on the bank's estimated P90 or P50 reserves.

Providers of equity finance may be lending against reserves and may put conditions in their investment and shareholders agreements by which companies are required to take certain actions if reserves fall below a certain limit. Their reserves reporting may in such circumstances have to be substantially recalculated. In certain cases, a bank may demand repayment of their loans if the reserves fall below a certain level.

Reporting standards for companies

The reporting of reserves in the accounts of a company has to comply with accounting rules adopted by that company. In the past 25 years, companies based in the UK have adopted UK GAAP and, in terms of accounting for disclosure of commercial reserves, will comply with the relevant practice rule which is now the Oil and Gas Industry Statement of Recommended Practice. The reporting standards are now changing so that UK GAAP is converging with International Financial Reporting Standards (IFRS). EC Regulation EC/1606/2002 (the IAS Regulation) came into force in September 2002 and is directly applicable in the EU Member States. The IFRS, formerly referred to as the International Accounting Standards, are currently issued by the International Accounting Standards Board.

International Financial Reporting Standards (IFRS)

It is now a requirement of all EU companies which have equity or debt securities listed on a regulated market to prepare consolidated accounts from 1 January 2005 in accordance with IFRS. This means that all public companies listed on the Official List of the LSE must comply with this; while AIM is not an EU regulated market it has chosen to adopt IFRS and now all AIM listed companies must comply with the same reporting standards as on the Official List. The adoption of IFRS may cause some problems for companies as IFRS is an accounting system that adopts fair value, unlike UK GAAP which is based on a historic cost accounting system. IFRS places more emphasis on a fair value of assets and liabilities and takes into account a wider range of assets and liabilities and such assets and liabilities are valued at current fair values as opposed to historic costs. This will, therefore, have an effect on the company's distributable reserves and the dividends it can pay. The net present fair value of assets and liabilities can be more volatile than on a historic cost accounting basis. For instance, under IFRS only those realised profits which are in the form of cash or other assets which can ultimately be realised in cash can be assessed with reasonable certainty and therefore can be treated as realised profits. For example, under IFRS, preference shares will be treated as debt or a combination of debt and equity and not as share capital. The liability for repayment of preference shares by way of redemption may be recognised as the present value of redemption payment and treated as a balance sheet liability. There will also be complications for those companies setting up merger or pre-acquisition consolidated reserves.

IFRS must be adopted by listed companies for reporting accounts on a consolidated group basis; however, individual companies in a group are still free to apply UK GAAP standards.

There are particular issues for oil and gas companies and their reserves reporting under the new IFRS regime. It is not clear whether the reserves should be included in the company's balance sheet and, if so, how they should be included. The ISA issued IFRS 6 'Exploration for and Evaluation of Mineral Resources' to try and remedy the lack of authoritative international guidance in relation to minerals resources asset. The standard sets out the times when companies should test exploration and evaluation costs for impairment and how that information should be disclosed. There is likely to be more detail of accounting practices in this area in the future. IFRS 6 also seeks to improve transparency by requiring improved disclosures for exploration and valuation assets.

Under IFRS there is no single comprehensive guide on IFRS accounting issues unique to the oil and gas industry and therefore different oil and gas accounting practices have been followed. Some companies believe that IAS 18 'Revenue' should be followed to recognise pre-production oil and gas revenues. Should revenue be recognised, the amount of capitalised costs will need to be expensed. Many oil and gas companies believe that the products produced from the sale of the product in the commissioning phase of the operation should be treated as a reduction of capitalised costs rather than revenue. In other cases, costs which lead directly to finding of mineral reserves are capitalised, while costs that do not lead directly to mineral reserves are charged to expense.

For private companies and individual companies in a group of public listed companies they may adopt UK GAAP as described below.

Oil and Gas Industry Statement of Recommended Practice (SORP)

In the UK the disclosure of commercial reserve quantities is stated in the Oil and Gas Industry Statement of Recommended Practice (SORP) which is simply a UK reporting standard published in January 2000 and revised in June 2001. It is not a classification system. It is, however, an accounting standard which is commonly adopted in the UK. Under SORP the company may at its discretion disclose either:

1. proven developed and undeveloped oil and gas reserves (known as 1P); or
2. proven and probable oil and gas reserved (known as 2P).

In point (1) above, SORP does not subdivide proven developed into producing and non-producing. This definition is close to SEC guidance (1P).

Under point (2), there needs to be 'a 50% statistical probability that the actual quantity of recoverable reserves will be more than the amount estimated as proven and probable and a 50% statistical probability that it will be less ("2P")'.[17] For the proven component of proven and probable reserves there should be an equivalent statistical probability of 90% or more and 10% probability respectively. There should be actual production or conclusive formation tests; this involves immediately adjoining undrilled portions which can be judged on available geophysical, geological and engineering data, successful pilot tests or other reasonable evidence. Management of a company also has to have a reasonable intention of developing such resources.

Government reserves reporting

Reserve booking is important not only for private and public companies but also for governments. For instance, governments may suddenly revise their estimates of their reserves. In 1985, Kuwait revised its reserve estimates by 50% overnight which coincided with the change in the way that OPEC decided to switch to a quota production system based on the size of the country's reserves. Another example is the Canadian oil reserves which were increased from 5 to 179 gigabarrels moving Canada to second place in world oil reserves because they determined that there was a change in the learning curve of technology combined with disruptive technology to produce oil from tar sands. The Alberta Energy and Utilities Board recalculated the numbers on that basis and thereby quadrupled North American proven oil reserves. However, under the US Securities and Exchange Commission those reserves cannot be booked by the US Securities Exchange (SEC) which include bitumen and tar sands.

Notes

[1] Draft Petroleum Reserves and Resources Classification, Definitions and Guidelines, September 2006. Taken from www.spe.org/specima/binary/files/5806700Revised%20Definitions%20Draft.pdf

[2] Guidance Notes on procedures for regulating offshore oil and gas field developments, January 2006. Taken from DTI website at www.og.dti.gov.uk

[3] Petroleum Reserves Definitions, approved by the Board of Directors, Society of Petroleum Engineers (SPE) Inc., and the Executive Board, World Petroleum Congress (WPC) March 1997. Taken from World Petroleum website at www.world-Petroleum.org/publications/Petroleum%20Reserves%20Definitions%2doc1.doc

[4] Society of Petroleum Engineers and World Petroleum Council.

[5] Petroleum Reserves Definitions, approved by the Board of Directors, Society of Petroleum Engineers (SPE) Inc., and the Executive Board, World Petroleum Congress (WPC) March 1997. Taken from World Petroleum website at www.world-Petroleum.org/publications/Petroleum%20Reserves%20Definitions%2doc1.doc

[6] Petroleum Reserves Definitions, approved by the Board of Directors, Society of Petroleum Engineers (SPE) Inc., and the Executive Board, World Petroleum Congress (WPC) March 1997. Taken from World Petroleum website at www.world-Petroleum.org/publications/Petroleum%20Reserves%20Definitions%2doc1.doc

[7] *Bank of Scotland – Oil and Gas Handbook* (6th edn, 2005).

[8] Petroleum Reserves Definitions, approved by the Board of Directors, Society of Petroleum Engineers (SPE) Inc., and the Executive Board, World Petroleum Congress (WPC) March 1997. Taken from World Petroleum website at www.world-Petroleum.org/publications/Petroleum%20Reserves%20Definitions%2doc1.doc

[9] Petroleum Reserves Definitions, approved by the Board of Directors, Society of Petroleum Engineers (SPE) Inc., and the Executive Board, World Petroleum Congress (WPC) March 1997. Taken from World Petroleum website at www.world-Petroleum.org/publications/Petroleum%20Reserves%20Definitions%2doc1.doc

[10] Draft Petroleum Reserves and Resources Classification, Definitions and Guidelines, September 2006. Taken from www.spe.org/specima/binary/files/5806700Revised%20Definitions%20Draft.pdf

[11] Petroleum Resources Management System 2007, para 2.1.1.

[12] Petroleum Resources Management System 2007, para 2.1.2.

[13] Petroleum Resources Management System 2007, para 2.1.3.

[14] Petroleum Resources Management System 2007, para 2.2.1.

[15] Petroleum Resources Management System 2007, para 2.2.2.

[16] AIM Rules for Companies: Guidance for Mining, Oil and Gas Companies (AIM 16) 16th March 2006.

[17] Statement of Recommended Practice, Accounting for Oil and Gas Exploration, Production and Decommissioning Activities, 7th June 2001 (Part 2; Definitions of terms 12(c)).

— 6 —

WELL DESIGN AND INTERVENTION

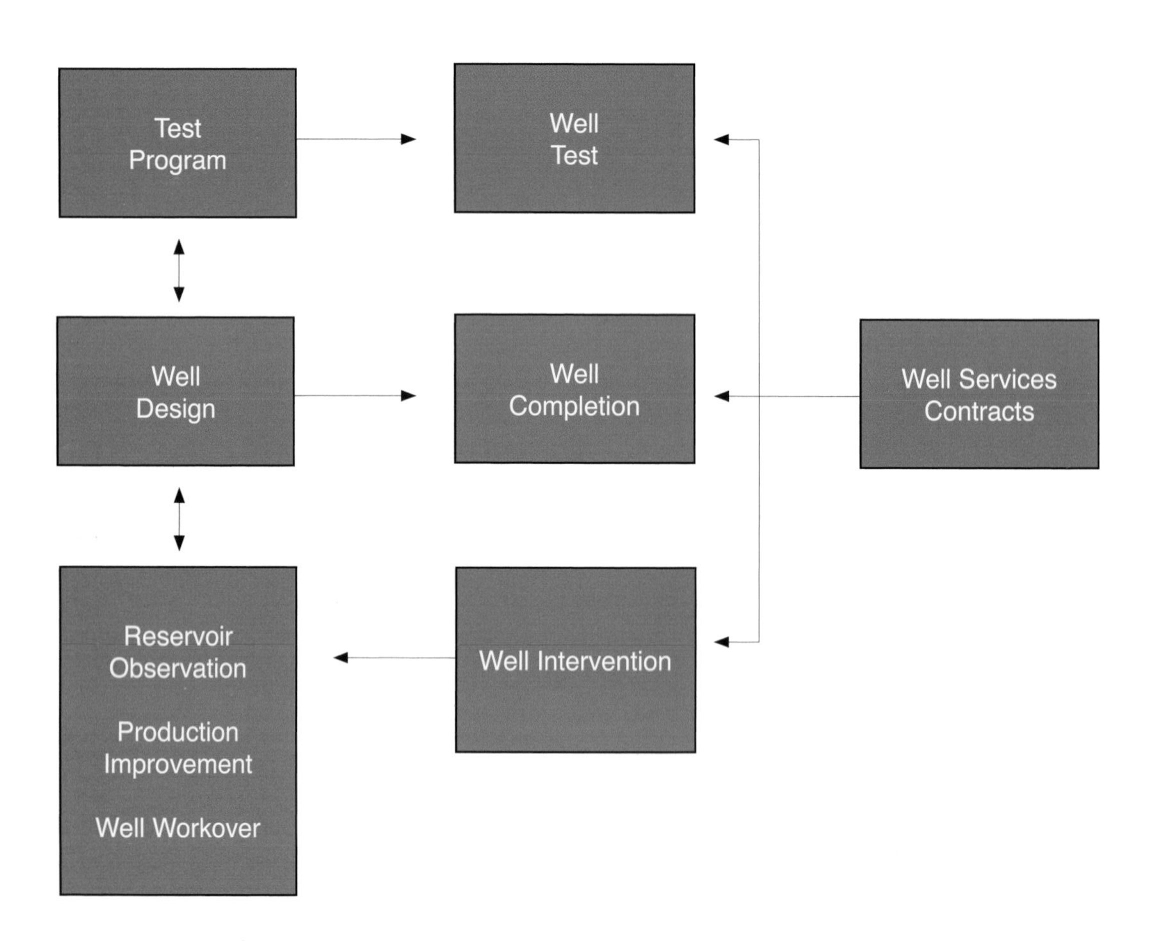
Test
Program
Well
Test
Well
Design
Well
Completion
Well Services
Contracts
Reservoir
Observation
Production
Improvement
Well Workover
Well Intervention

WELL DESIGN AND INTERVENTION

TECHNICAL

6.1 Introduction

The wells are a critical part of a producing oil or gas field. They link the reservoir with surface facilities, connecting two extremes of pressure and temperature. They are subjected to erosion and corrosion from the well fluids and risk blockage from produced sand and scale.

They are expensive to drill, to complete for production and to maintain. Nevertheless, if damaged or their condition is allowed to deteriorate below their design specifications, they must be shut in, causing lost production.

This part explains what equipment is installed in an oil or gas well, what can go wrong and what options are available for remedial work.

6.2 Well design

An oil or gas well is best described as a 'pressure vessel', designed to resist extremes of pressure from both inside and out. If properly designed and correctly operated, it will neither burst nor collapse.

The design of a well can be said to have two main parts: internal and external. The external part is the sequence of casing strings, as seen in Fig. 6–1. The physical properties of these casing strings and the depths at which they are set are selected to ensure that the well can be safely drilled to total depth, accommodating all hazards encountered en route. The end result is a steel-lined borehole connecting the reservoir to the platform (or subsea manifold) which will resist the external pressures acting upon it.

However, the internal geometry of the well must be configured to allow safe, optimised production for the life of the well. The well is completed for production by installing a string of steel tubing with an array of components, each selected and located along the well bore for a specific purpose – termed the 'completion'.

The design of the completion is critical; it must contain the well pressure and corrosive fluids for the 'design life' of the well – 10 years or more in some cases. The information on which this design is based is gathered during an operation called a 'well test'.

Post-drilling well preparation

After the reservoir has been penetrated and the well drilled to Total Depth (TD) (usually 200–300 ft below the reservoir), the rock properties and distribution of hydrocarbons are evaluated by wireline logs or LWD. This is discussed in more detail in Chapter 5.

At this point, the well is a concentric series of steel casing strings, each cemented in place and extending back to surface. The lowermost section of the well is 'open hole'. If the decision is made to test the well, then a steel liner is run and cemented across the open hole. Liners are not normally run all the way back to surface but overlap the bottom of the last casing string by 300–400 ft.

Perforating

In order to allow the reservoir fluids to flow into the well, the production liner must be perforated. The earliest perforating guns came into use in the 1920s. These fired a steel bullet through the liner and into the reservoir, creating a flow-path. The Bazooka was developed early in the Second World War and used a shaped explosive charge to penetrate tank armour. At the end of the war, the Bazooka technology was adapted for use in oil wells and totally replaced bullet perforators.

Modern perforating guns use hollow conical-shaped explosive charges held in a steel case. The hollow profile of the charge faces the inside of the production liner. When detonated, a jet of gas and metal vapour travelling at up to 20,500 miles per hour passes through the steel production liner, through the cement sheath and into the reservoir rock.

There are a great many types of charges available, utilising different types and weights of explosives. The charge selected depends on the application, but charges fall broadly into two categories: 'deep penetrating', which produce a long thin hole, typically 0.3" in diameter but up to 30" long in soft rock and 'big hole' which produce a much shorter tunnel (about 5") but with a larger diameter (0.6").

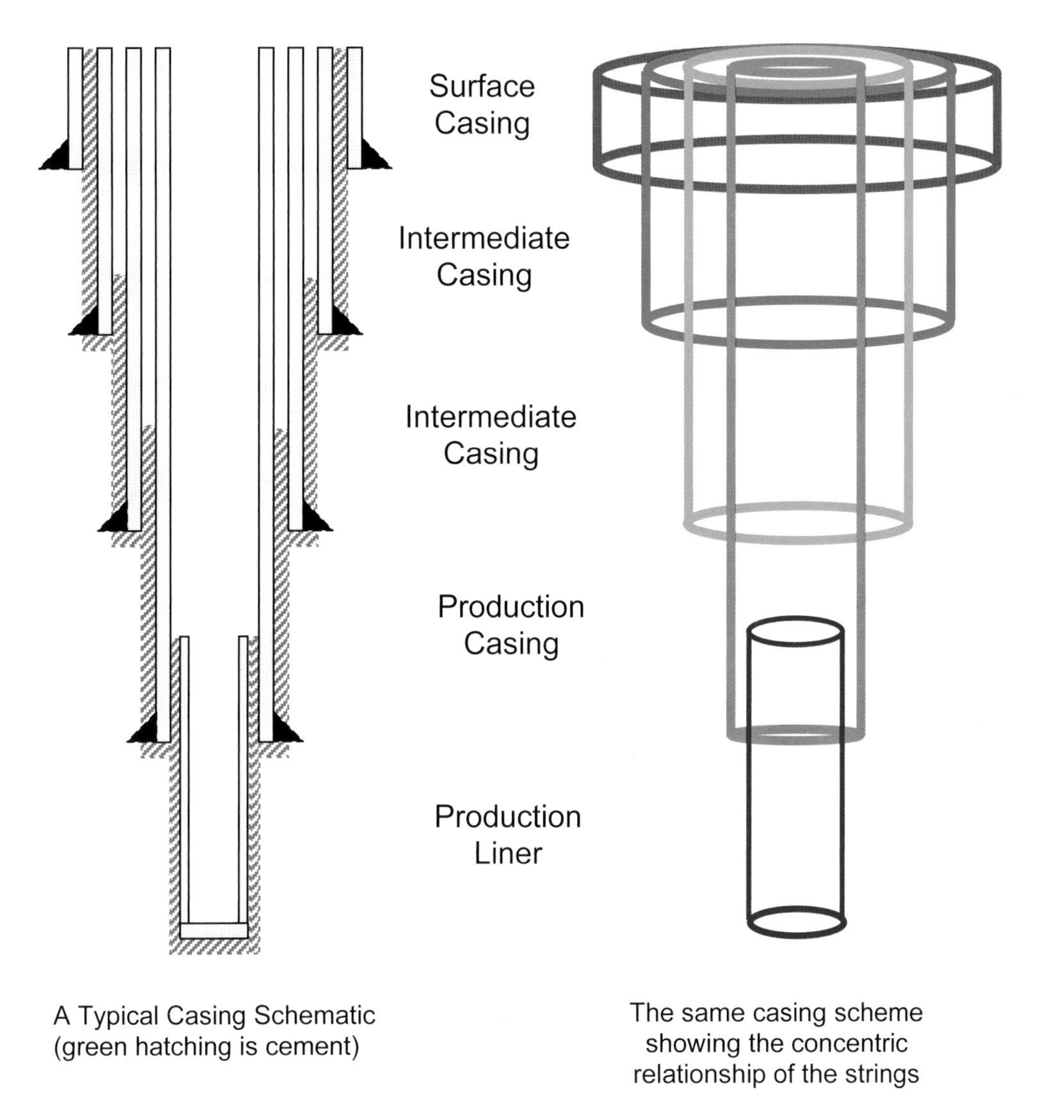

Figure 6–1 Casing schematic

The charges are loaded into a gun carrier and are connected to each other by detonating cord. The shot density or 'shots per foot' is determined by the carrier diameter (dictated by the narrowest constriction in the well) and the size of the charges selected (Fig. 6–2).

The orientation of the charges in the gun carrier or 'phasing' is also taken into account. Many applications will use phasing on the guns to fire shots radially round the well bore, with an angle between the charges generally of 60°. However, some wells require guns with 180° phasing, firing shots in only two directions, for example in horizontal wells.

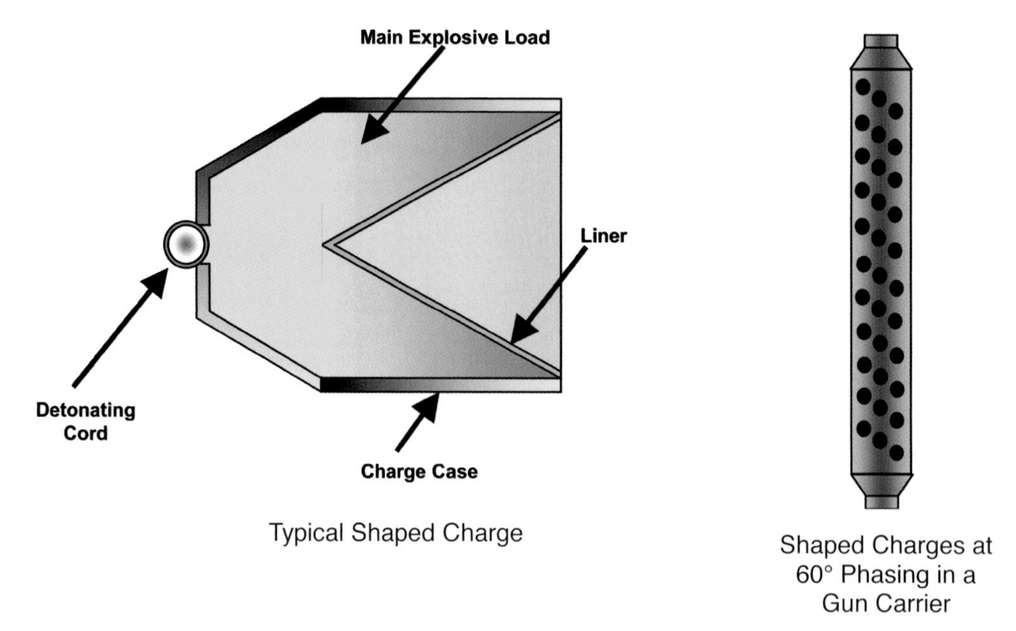

Figure 6–2 Perforating charges

Perforating guns can be run on slickline, electric line or coiled tubing. The guns may also be run on the bottom of a completion or test string, normally referred to as TCP: Tubing Conveyed Perforating.

Electric line (eline) operations have very accurate depth control. In addition, this allows selective perforating and discrete reservoir zones can be accessed.

Under normal circumstances, a well will only be perforated with a completion or test string in place.

Well testing

When a reservoir is drilled, traces of oil and gas are normally circulated to surface in the drilling mud and the location of the hydrocarbons in the well can be accurately determined using electric logs. This evidence, however, does not indicate whether the well is economically viable or not. The production capability of the well can only be determined by a well test, allowing the well to flow under carefully controlled conditions.

A well test serves a number of purposes. In terms of the completion design, the flow rate of the well fluids can be metered and the ratio of oil, gas and water assessed. The fluids are sampled to evaluate their chemistry, to determine, for example, their corrosivity and wax content. In addition, the well flowing pressures and temperatures are measured.

The well test is also used to determine a range of reservoir parametres including permeability of the rock to the flow of fluids, the lateral extent of the reservoir structure itself and the identification of any damage caused by the drilling fluids referred to as 'skin'.

Testing operations commence once the well has the liner in place and final logging has been completed. The actual equipment used depends on a number of variables such as location, rig type, oil or gas, high or low pressure, viscous crude, etc. However, the layout in Fig. 6–3 gives a range of equipment which will be common to most well test operations.

- *Test string.* This is a temporary completion installed in the well. It has most of the features found in a production completion but contains additional components, including circulating valves (to allow the annulus and tubing to be circulated to brine) and a test tool (to isolate the well down hole).
- *Surface test tree.* This is a temporary Christmas tree consisting of four valves, which perform similar functions to those on a production tree (see Fig. 6–5).
- *Data header.* These are placed upstream and downstream of the choke manifold. They are used to allow access to the wellstream for pressure and temperature instrumentation. They are also a fluid sampling point.
- *Choke manifold.* This is used to control the flow of fluids to the surface equipment and to shut-in the well.
- *Heat exchanger.* A test spread for an oil well will often include a heat exchanger to maintain the temperature of the well stream. Heavy

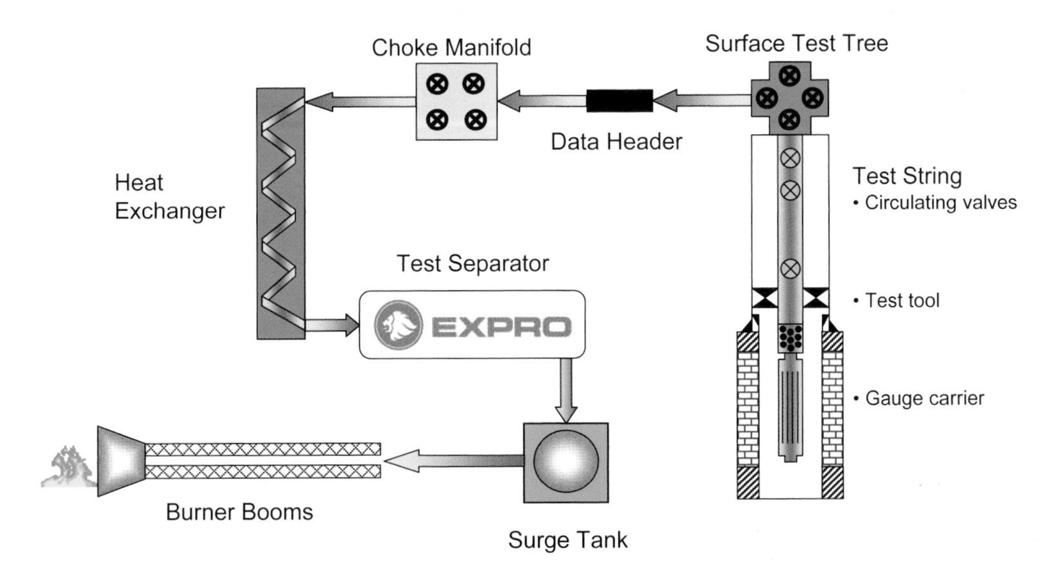

Figure 6–3 Well test spread

oils may thicken due to wax solidifying, therefore heating the fluid ensures that flow through the system is maintained.

- *Test separator.* The reservoir fluids are separated into oil, water and gas in the test separator. The separator is also used to measure the flow rate of the produced fluids and allows the fluids to be sampled.
- *Surge tank.* The primary use of this vessel is for the calibration of oil meters prior to and during the test.
- *Burner booms.* These are frames which support the oil burners over the side of the rig. The burner is the main method of disposing of produced oil and gas during well tests. A water curtain is usually pumped to contain the flame and minimise radiant heat. There are normally two burner booms on a well test to allow for changes in wind direction.

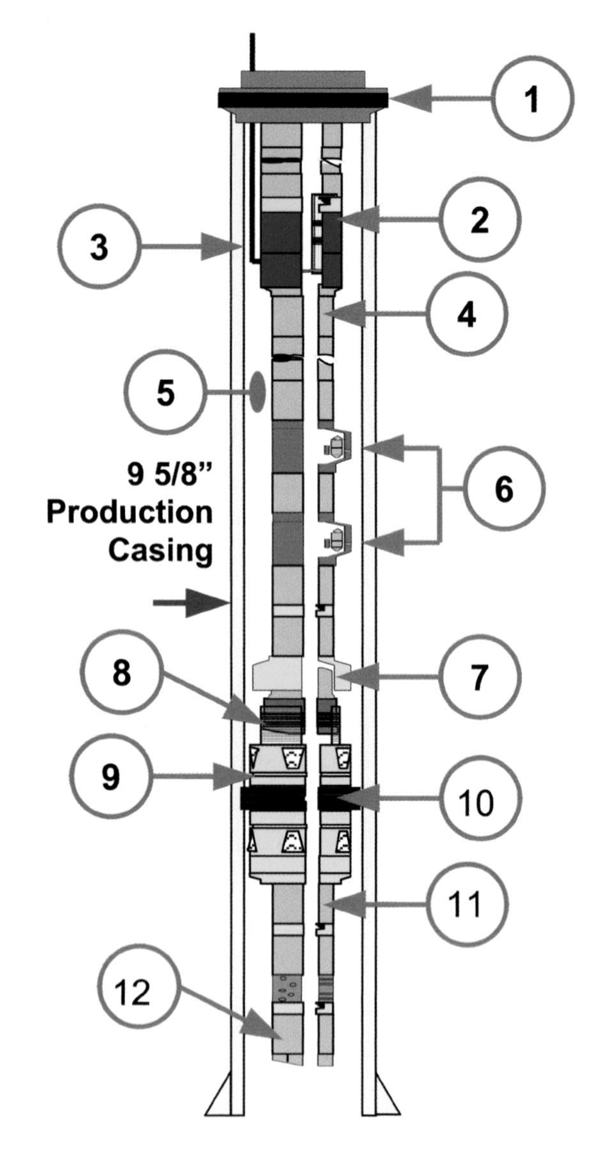

Figure 6–4 Completion schematic

The well test itself takes place once the test string, surface equipment and associated pipework have been installed and pressure tested. The actual sequence of events on a well test varies according to the test, but a typical operation will comprise a series of alternating flowing and shut in periods of, say, 12–24 hours each, spread across three to four days. While flowing, the rates of oil, gas and water are metered in addition to downhole flowing pressures and temperatures. When shut in, the downhole pressure build-up is recorded.

Not all wells are tested. Normally, only discovery or appraisal wells will be the subject of a full-scale well test. Once the reservoir and fluid properties are known for a reservoir, these will be used for all subsequent completion designs on that field, updated by routine reservoir surveillance and sampling. New production wells, however, may be flowed initially to surface well test equipment after completion, for 'clean-up', to remove solids and debris from the well.

Completion design

Every well is different. A field or operator may have a 'house style', but each completion is designed in detail specifically for the well in which it will be installed. The completion diagram in Fig. 6–4 shows a 'typical' gas lifted oil well for the purpose of discussion.

- *Tubing hanger.* This is a large steel mandrel which locates in a cavity in the wellhead. The tubing hanger supports the weight of the completion at the top of the well. Elastomeric elements provide a pressure and fluid seal between the hanger and the wellhead.
- *Downhole safety valve.* These are flapper-type valves normally set between 500 and 2000 ft below surface. In the open position, the flapper is extended downward into the well where it locates in a recess. In the closed position, the flapper is forced upwards and held against a sealing surface, thereby cutting off flow from the well.
- *Control line.* The downhole safety valve is held in the open position by a positive pressure applied from surface via the control line, a plastic coated ¼" steel tube. If the control line is cut or damaged, pressure is released causing the safety valve to close. The downhole safety valve is therefore a 'fail-safe' device ensuring that flow from the well will cease if the wellhead or platform is damaged.
- *Tubing.* The bulk of the completion comprises 'tubing'. There are a great many types of tubing – different diameters, wall thickness, metallurgy, etc. In each case the physical properties are selected for a particular reason. For example:
  - the metallurgy of the tubing is selected to withstand the effects of well fluids – in benign conditions carbon steel may suffice, however in hostile downhole environments more exotic, and therefore expensive, alloys may be required;

- the pipe wall thickness is selected to ensure the completion can withstand differential pressures without either bursting or collapsing; and
- the actual diameter of the pipe, such as 4½", 5½" or 7", is selected to ensure optimum production over the life of the completion.

In North Sea operations, tubing is generally supplied in 40 ft lengths or 'joints'. The joints are connected to each other by threaded couplings which, when properly tightened, provide a gas-tight seal.

- *A annulus.* This is the void between the inner casing and the outside of the completion. It is always full of fluid (treated water or brine) unless the well is gas lifted.

- *Gas lift mandrels.* These are tubular components which have a much larger outer diameter than the tubing and a distinct excentric 'belly'. Machined into the steel of the 'belly' are pockets where various downhole tools can be installed within the well but out of the main fluid flowpath, they are termed Side Pocket Mandrels.

  Side Pocket Mandrels are commonly used in gas lift applications. The gas lift valves themselves are one-way check valves. At a predetermined pressure on the A annulus side, they open to allow lift gas to flow from the annulus into the wellstream. They do not allow flow from inside the completion out into the annulus.

- *Expansion joint.* The completion connects the hot, high-pressure environment of the reservoir with ambient surface conditions. These extremes can impart a number of stresses within the completion due to expansion and contraction.

  The computer modelling of these and all other stresses that the completion will endure is a critical part of completion design. It is called Tubing Stress/Movement analysis and is used to ensure that each component and the combination of components is fit for purpose under all anticipated well conditions.

  In many cases, the modelling will indicate that the combination of forces will exceed the tensile or compressional limits of the completion. This problem can be overcome by using an expansion joint which will accommodate all movement as indicated by the modelling, plus a safety factor.

- *Anchor seal assembly.* The anchor seal assembly connects the lower, static section of the expansion joint to the top of the production packer.

- *Production packer.* The completion is mechanically supported at the lower end by the production packer. There are many different types of packer and they may be permanent or retrievable depending on the application. More complex completions may have two or more packers, particularly if the well penetrates multiple reservoirs.
- *Packer sealing element.* The second, but equally important, function of the packer is to isolate the casing (in the A annulus) from both reservoir pressure and produced fluids. In many cases the casing is carbon steel and may not withstand their corrosive effects. When the packer is set, an elastomeric ring is compressed forcing it to extrude and seal against the casing walls.

  In completions where two or more packers are run, the sealing elements provide hydraulic isolation between different production zones.
- *Tailpipe.* The tailpipe is a section of tubing which extends below the packer. It is generally less than 100 ft in length but can incorporate a number of components including:
  - *Nipples.* A nipple or Landing Nipple is a series of ledges or profiles machined into the internal surface of short sections of tubing. Their function is to engage a locking mechanism attached to specific tools run into the hole.

    An example would be landing gauges (see Pressure Surveys). The gauges are loaded into a gauge carrier and run to the lowermost nipple on slickline and the lock engaged.
  - *Perforated joint.* This is merely a joint of tubing with large holes drilled in a regularly spaced pattern. It provides an alternate flowpath for hydrocarbons into the tubing if a gauge carrier is set in the lowest nipple.
- *WEG – wireline entry guide.* This forms the very end of the completion string and is designed to ensure that any wireline tools run across the reservoir will not get stuck when being pulled back into the completion.

Different types of completion

ESP completion

An Electric Submersible Pump (ESP) is another method of artificial lift. The pump is run on the bottom of the tubing below the production packer and powered by cables run from surface in a similar manner to the control lines.

Although very effective, ESPs are very prone to failure, often caused by sand and debris being drawn into the pump mechanism. A failed ESP will require a full workover.

Water injector

Not all wells are used for hydrocarbon production; many wells are used to inject water into the reservoir. (See Chapter 12.) The two main reasons for this are: to maintain the reservoir pressure and to sweep oil towards the production wells.

Completions used in injector wells are very similar to production wells but during the design there is greater emphasis on containing the high pressures involved during injection.

Liner top completion

Some completions do not include a production packer. In a Liner Top Completion, a PBR (polished bore receptacle) is incorporated into the top of the drilling liner. A seal stack is run on the bottom of the tubing and engaged into the PBR, acting as both an expansion device and providing annulus isolation from the well fluids.

Horizontal wells

Wells with a long horizontal section have become almost a North Sea standard. This profile allows a much longer section of the reservoir to be exposed to the well. The actual completion is often very similar to a conventional well, however the horizontal section may pose zonal isolation problems. When cementing a liner in a horizontal hole, it is difficult to get a cement seal 360° around the well. This means that should an interval need to be shut off, there still might be communication with adjacent intervals through the cement.

This problem can be avoided by the use of Expanding Cement Packers (ECPs). These are circular elastomeric elements located on the outside of the drilling liner. During the cementing process, cement is diverted into the ECPs which inflate and seal radially against the reservoir. Pressure on the ECP is maintained until the cement sets.

Dual completion

In cases where two or more reservoirs are penetrated by a single well, the ideal scenario in completion terms is for co-mingled production, ie all fluids flow to surface through the same completion.

There may be circumstances, however, when the fluids from two reservoirs are incompatible either for pressure or chemical reasons. In this situation, a dual completion may be an option, using two tubing strings and producing each reservoir in hydraulic isolation.

Dual completions are more complex to install than a single string, plus the smaller tubing used may limit both the hydrocarbon production rates and the well intervention options.

Multilateral wells

In the last 10 years there have been significant advances in multilateral technology. From a single parent bore, it is possible to have a number of laterals accessing different parts of the reservoir or even different reservoirs.

Multilateral wells are categorised into six types on the TAML classification (Technical Advancement of Multilaterals) depending on the level of sophistication of the junction between the bores. This ranges from a simple exit from the parent bore at one end of the scale to full pressure integrity at the other.

The upper completion may be any of the designs above if production from the laterals can be co-mingled, or may be a dual completion if not.

Smart wells

The first intelligent well system was installed in Saga's Snorre field in 1997 and although still not in common use, the technology has continued to develop.

Smart wells use permanent downhole sensors to monitor pressures, temperatures, flow rates, fluid composition and, in some cases, sophisticated reservoir imaging devices. These parametres can be constantly monitored at surface via signal cables.

Power cables are also installed in the well and can be used to activate remotely an array of downhole devices which are used to optimise production. These are predominantly flow control devices which can open or shut off particular zones to production depending on current well conditions.

In the latest generation of 'intelligent' wells, the monitoring and downhole regulation of flow is automated.

Christmas tree

The Christmas trees are the most visible parts of the wells. They appear complex but are essentially a pressure control manifold at the wellhead. They interface between the well and production facilities and have a number of functions, principally to allow flow from the well to be stopped as required or 'shut in'. They also facilitate the pumping of fluids into the well from surface and allow the safe deployment of intervention workstrings.

On a modern Christmas tree (as used on North Sea platforms) there are normally five valves (Fig. 6–5). These valves are opened and closed by manually turning a wheel which uses a thread mechanism to move a heavy metal 'gate'. The five valves are:

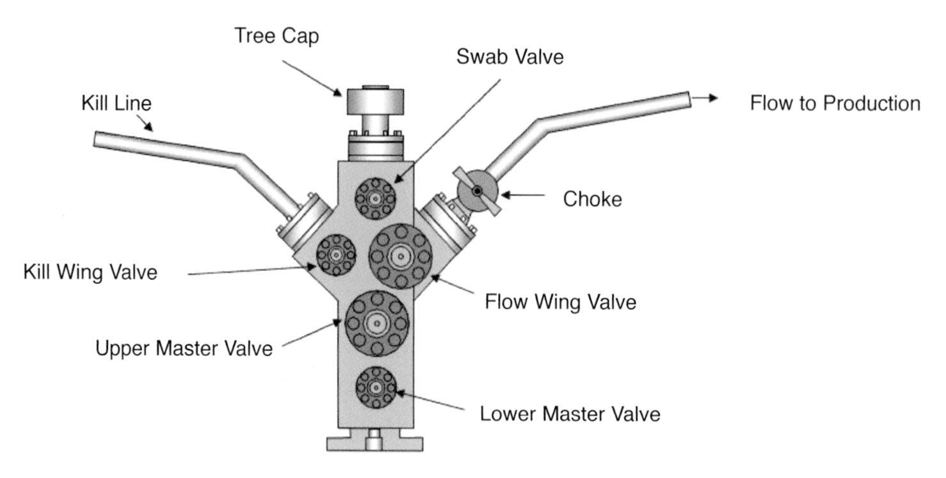

Figure 6–5 Christmas tree

- *Flow Wing Valve (FWV).* When the well is on production, well fluids leave the tree via the flow wing. The FWV is therefore used to shut off flow from the well when required.
- *Kill Wing Valve (KWV).* The KWV is on the opposite side of the tree from the FWV. If the well has to be killed by bullheading brine from surface, the tanks and pump are lined up to the flow wing.
- *Lower Master Valve (LMV).* The LMV isolates the well regardless of which other valves are open.
- *Upper Master Valve (UMV).* The UMV performs the same function as the LMV but is normally hydraulically operated.
- *Swab Valve (SV).* Located at the top of the tree. CT (Coiled Tubing) and wireline BOPs (Blow Out Preventers) are bolted to a flange above the valve and it is opened to allow toolstrings to enter the well.

Subsea trees perform the same function as platform trees. Their operation, however, is more complex and their component terminology may differ between companies.

6.3 Types of well intervention units

Slickline

Slickline evolved in the USA in the early 1900s. Initially, fence wire was coiled around the back axle of a truck and used to run simple tools in and out of the well. They quickly developed into built-for-purpose units and today are still the most important means of well intervention. Historically, slickline was used only to deploy plugs and simple mechanical tools. In recent years, however, there has been significant developments in the design of memory tools and accurate depth-tracking systems. As a result, there are now very few tools which were formerly restricted to electric line that cannot be run on slickline. Figure 6–6 below is of a dual drum slickline unit. The operator sits in the control cabin, looking out over the drums of wire and in line-of-sight to the well. The two drums of wire can be seen to the front of the cabin. The wire spools off to a pulley at the base of the rig-up and from there to another pulley at the top.The lubricator/stuffing box assembly is used to contain the well fluids/pressure while the tools are run in and out of the hole.

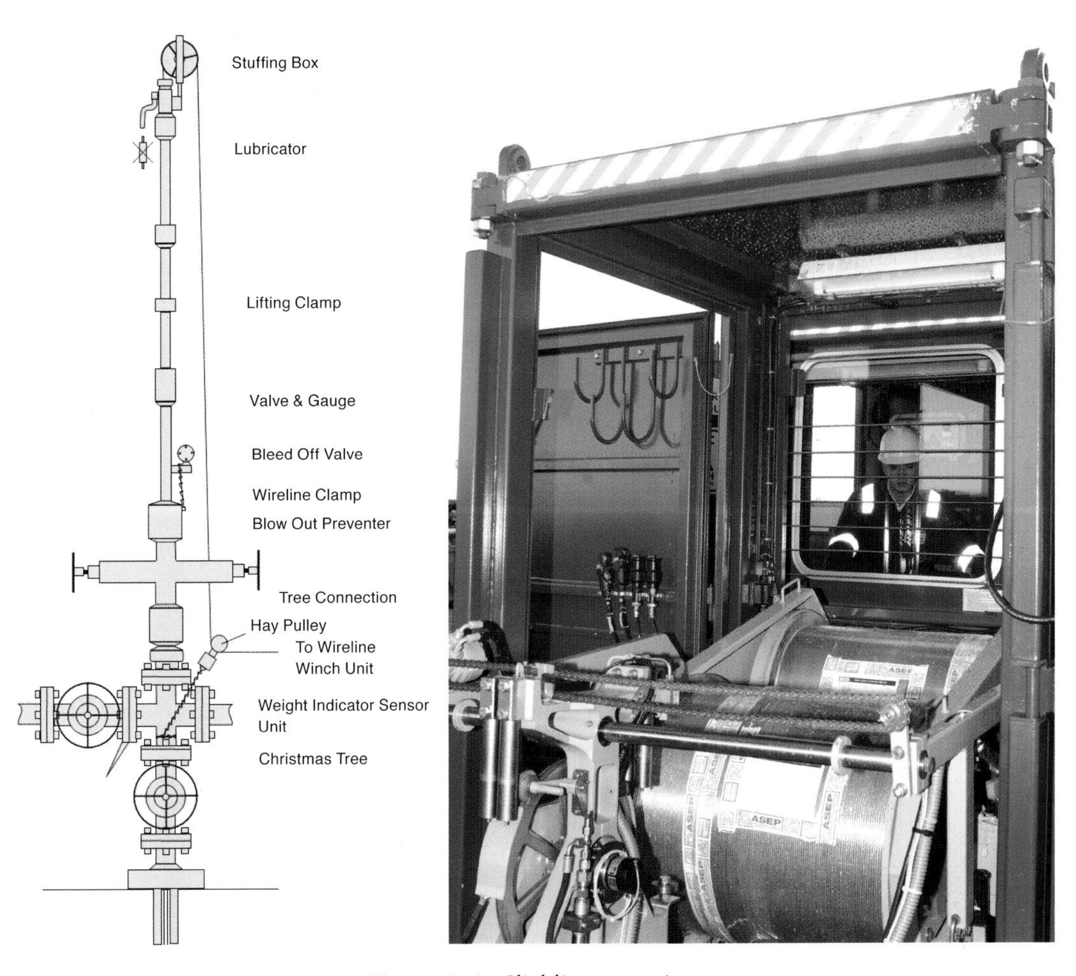

Figure 6–6 Slickline operations

Visually, the wire is identical to the fence wire from which it was developed, however it is manufactured to very precise specifications; for example, there is a range of different diametres such as 0.092", 0.108" and 0.125", selected on operational requirements. The wire is also available in different alloys to accommodate different well conditions.

Some wireline units employ braided wire, normally for running and pulling heavier loads. There are complications, however, with braided line in terms of well fluid containment. (See Electric line below.)

The wire is coiled on a drum which is located immediately in front of the control cabin. A spooling device ensures that the wire is accurately coiled on the drum. A counter head in contact with the wire is used to determine tool depth by measuring the amount of wire run in and out of the hole.

Attached to the end of the wire is a toolstring. The actual components vary according to the operation but standard tools common to most toolstrings include:

- rope socket – provides a means of attaching the wire;
- stem – circular steel bar providing weight to overcome friction and pressure;

Figure 6–7 Selection of wireline tools (racked in workshop)

- power jar – provides an upward jarring action;
- mechanical jar – provides an upward and downward jarring (hammering) action; and
- knuckle joint – provides flexibility.

Attached to the bottom of the toolstring is whatever equipment is going to be deployed in the well. This could be a simple mechanical tool such as a gauge cutter to check for scale build-up or a plug to shut off the lower part of the completion. Conversely, it could be a sophisticated caliper or memory PLT (Production Logging Tool) string.

Electric line

Electric line is very similar to slickline but with two notable exceptions.

- The wire is conductive. This means that downhole tools can be electrically powered from surface, but also that data from downhole tools is available on surface in real time.
- As the wire is braided, a stuffing box will not seal around it. If electric line is used in live-well conditions, a 'grease injection' system must be used to provide a barrier to well fluids.

Coiled tubing

The use of coiled tubing began in the early 1960s. The development of the technology was in response to a need for a continuous conduit that could be injected into a live well. The first fully functional coiled tubing unit was used for washing out sand from wells in California in 1962.

The coiled tubing (CT) itself is a continuously milled steel tube. CT comes in a wide range of diametres from 0.75" up to 4". CT of 1.5" and 1.75" diameter are probably the most widely used in the North Sea. The metallurgy is selected according to well conditions. The length of the coil may be up to 15,000–20,000 ft when new, but sections are regularly cut off during normal operations.

The injector head provides the surface drive force to run the CT both in and out of the well. The CT Pressure Control Equipment typically consists of a Blow Out Preventer (BOP) with a section of tubing and a stuffing box mounted on top. The stuffing box is very similar to that found on a slickline unit, and provides the same primary seal between the well fluids and the surface environment, whether the coil is moving or static. A typical arrangement is shown in Fig. 6–8.

There are many advantages to running CT over wireline, such as:

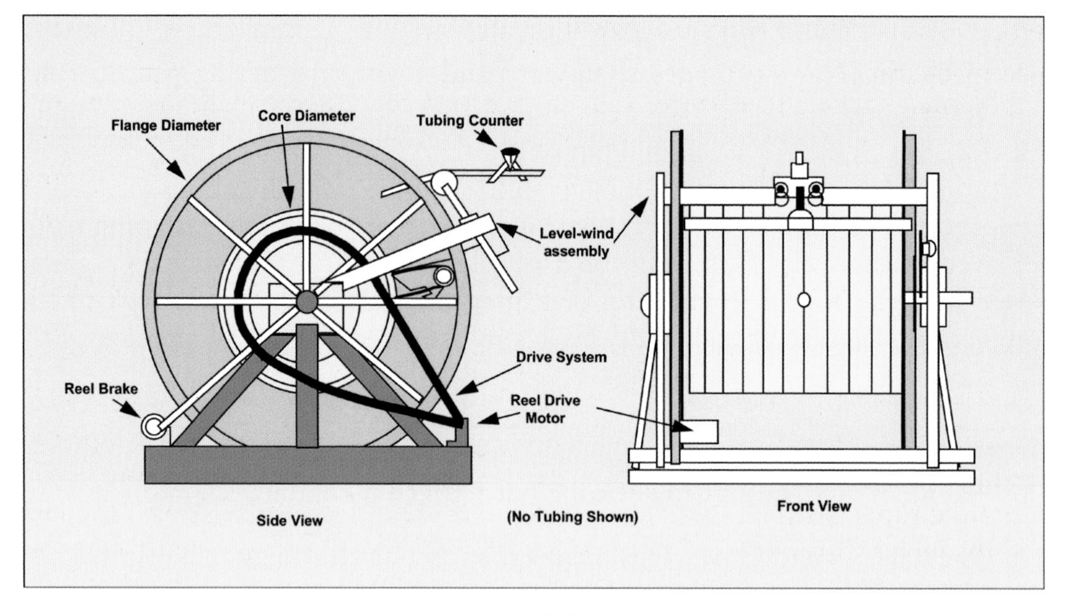

Figure 6–8 Coiled tubing unit

- the ability to circulate fluid or spot chemicals;
- the coil can be pushed around corners or along high-angle holes;
- hydraulic motors (turbines) can be used to mill or drill;
- heavy weights can be run into or pulled from the well; and
- electric cable can be installed inside the coil for logging horizontal wells.

However, the disadvantages include:

- slow to rig up, slower than wireline to run;
- more personnel are required to operate;
- very heavy, crane limitations are a regular problem; and
- the coil itself can be prone to cyclic fatigue and failure.

Hydraulic Workover Unit

Hydraulic Workover Units (HWUs) have been in use since the 1930s but were traditionally used to enter and control problem wells. They have most of the capabilities of a platform rig but rather than moving pipe with a block and tackle, the string is pulled and pushed using hydraulic rams.

Their use in the North Sea has increased significantly in the last 10 years. They are used for concurrent operations with the platform rig or may be used stand-alone where the platform rig has been removed or is out of certification.

Although slower to operate than a platform rig, they can be used to pull and re-run a completion (workover) and also have a drilling capability. Due to the hydraulic rams, the string can also be jacked into the hole against well pressure, allowing live-well operations in a similar manner to coiled tubing.

Hydraulic workover units come in many forms and are often modular. Figure 6–9 shows typical features found on most hydraulic workover units.

In Fig. 6–9, the unit is running tubing with a Side Pocket Mandrel. In A, the pipe is held by the upper slips while the lower slips are stroked upwards by the hydraulic rams. At the top of the upstroke, the lower slips grip the pipe and the upper slips release. Then in B the pipe is jacked down into the hole by the hydraulic rams. At the bottom of the downstroke, the upper slips grip the pipe and the lower slips release. The cycle is repeated until the whole string has been run into the hole. The sequence is reversed to pull the pipe out of the hole.

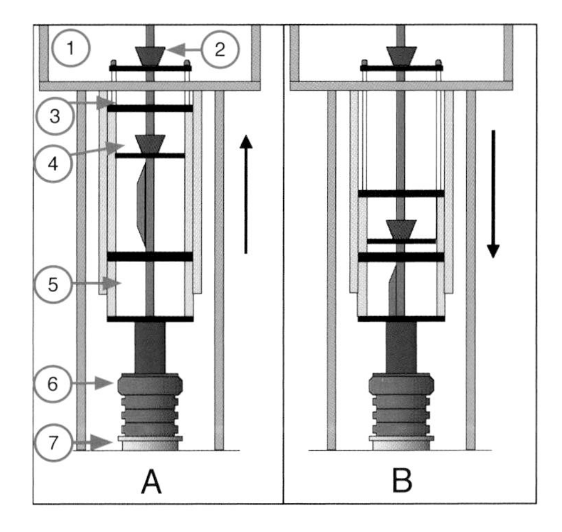

Key

1. Work Basket – where the crew operate the unit.
2. Upper Slips – hold the pipe at the top of the jacking system.
3. Hydraulic Rams – jack the pipe in and out of the well.
4. Lower Slips – hold the pipe at the bottom of the jacking system.
5. Work Window – where large bore components are added/removed from the string.
6. Blow Out Preventer (BOP).
7. Wellhead.

Figure 6–9 Hydraulic workover unit

6.4 Well integrity/maintenance

Operating companies have a legal responsibility to keep their wells in good working condition: they must 'maintain the pressure vessel'. Companies who allow their wells to deteriorate below design requirements risk losing their licence to operate. The well stock can be subject to scrutiny at any time from the regulatory authorities such as the HSE, so it is vital that all information pertaining to well integrity and maintenance is both up to date and accurate in order to withstand audit.

Figure 6–10 is a display from an on-line well integrity management system. Crews offshore follow a planned maintenance schedule of testing and inspection. The results are input to the system along with data from sensors monitoring pressures on each well. The information is then instantly available to the operations team onshore. Results which fall outwith pre-defined acceptance limits are flagged by the system. In Fig. 6–10, well A–40 has issues with two of the Christmas tree valves.

Corrosion/erosion monitoring

The tubing and component metallurgy is selected in order to resist the well fluids for the expected life of the completion. However, the completion may be in use longer than planned or the nature of the well fluids may change with time, posing a risk of corrosion. In addition, sand particles entrained in the well

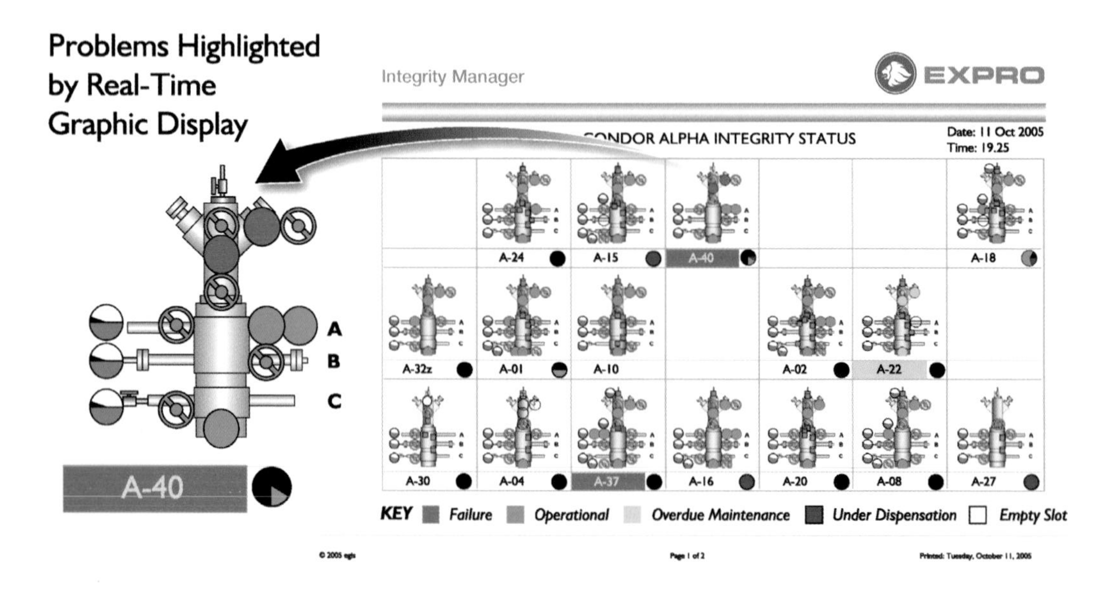

Figure 6–10 On-line well integrity management system

Technician working on a caliper. Note the extended feelers.

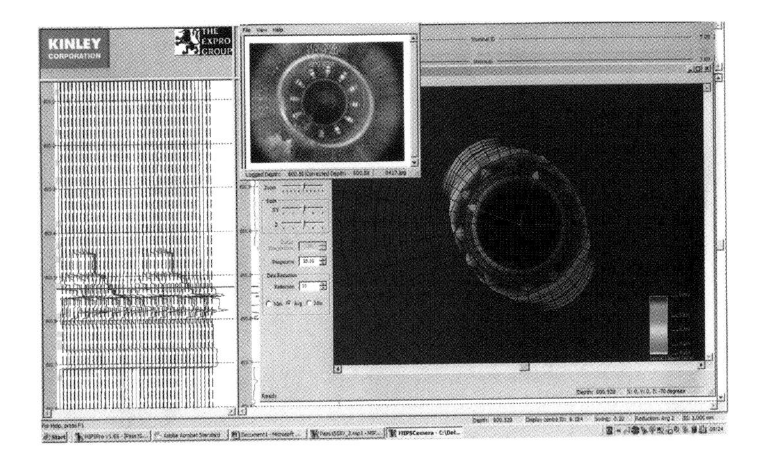

A caliper log across holed tubing. Each vertical trace was produced by a single feeler.

Here the same caliper data has been processed into a 3D image.

Figure 6–11 Caliper tool

stream can be highly erosive, particularly in high rate gas wells. Therefore, to ensure the integrity of the completion, the effects of corrosion and erosion must be monitored periodically.

There are two principal tool types used to monitor corrosion/erosion: caliper tools and wall thickness tools.

Caliper tools

The first tool to 'feel' the inside of the completion was patented by Myron Kinley in 1950 and was an immediate success. His inventions gave rise to a wide range of downhole tools called calipers.

These devices have radial arms or 'feelers' which extend to touch the internal walls of the completion or casing. The number of feelers depends on the tool but may be 15, 30 or 60. They are run into the well on slickline, electric line or coiled tubing to a point below the depth of interest. The arms are extended either by timer-switch or controlled from surface and the tool slowly drawn up the hole. Irregularities in the internal diameter of the casing or tubing are detected by the arms. In the case of slickline, this information is stored in memory where, as with electric line, there can be real-time surface read-out.

In both cases, the data is presented as a 'caliper log' of the well, displaying abnormalities in relation to depth. The tools can be used to detect variations in the bore of the completion caused by such problems as holes in the tubing, mechanical damage or scale build-up. Often calipers are used to provide time-lapse monitoring of corrosion and erosion by, for example, running a survey every six months and comparing the results (Fig. 6–11).

Modern electronic calipers are highly sophisticated tools capable of extremely fine measurements. However, the descendents of Kinley's original mechanical caliper are in daily use world wide, particularly in HPHT wells where the pressure and temperature is outwith the operating window of electronic devices.

Wall thickness tools

In recent years, tools have been developed to evaluate corrosion on the outside of the tubing. These tools are based on magnetic wave propagation. The magnetic wave is affected by the thickness of metal through which it has travelled. Therefore the tools can be used to measure variations in the wall thickness of the tubing, both pitting and gradual loss.

Wall thickness tools are run on wireline, normally in conjunction with an electronic caliper to provide a log of internal and external metal loss over the length of the completion.

Pressure testing

As previously described, a well is a 'pressure vessel' designed to withstand pressure from both within and without. It follows, therefore, that the best test of integrity is to pressure up voids in the well and monitor for leakage. In each case the void is charged up to a pre-determined pressure, using a high pressure pump and suitable liquid (often water treated with corrosion inhibitors), and monitored for decline over a period of time using a pressure gauge. Adjacent voids are monitored for pressure build-up over time, also using a pressure gauge.

Subsurface valve replacement

The downhole safety valve (SSSV) is run on the tubing as an integral part of the completion and termed Tubing Retrievable (TR-SSSV). However, should the valve fail to test or become damaged, it can be locked open using wireline tools and an insert valve set in a nipple above the TR-SSSV. The insert valve is also fail-safe and held open by pressure from the control lines. The insert valve is wireline retrievable (WL-SSSV) and may be changed periodically after a pre-determined working life or if it fails during routine testing.

Gas lift valves may also be replaced periodically if pressure testing suggests that they may be allowing tubing to annulus communication.

Direct inspection

Recent advances in technology have allowed the development of downhole cameras which can be used to take still photos and video clips. These tools can be run on slickline or electric line. Their use is best suited to gas wells or high water cut wells due to limited visibility in oil. However, most wells can be prepared for inspection by pumping clear fluid to the area of interest.

Figure 6–12 is a photograph of mineral scale on the inside of the tubing.

6.5 Reservoir management techniques

This section describes the techniques and equipment used to monitor the performance of the reservoir and make production improvements.

Reservoir observation

Production logging

Downhole tools to evaluate the flow regime in a well have been in use in their most basic form since the 1940s. Today, Production Logging Tools (PLTs) are highly sophisticated and capable of making very precise measurements in hostile downhole conditions.

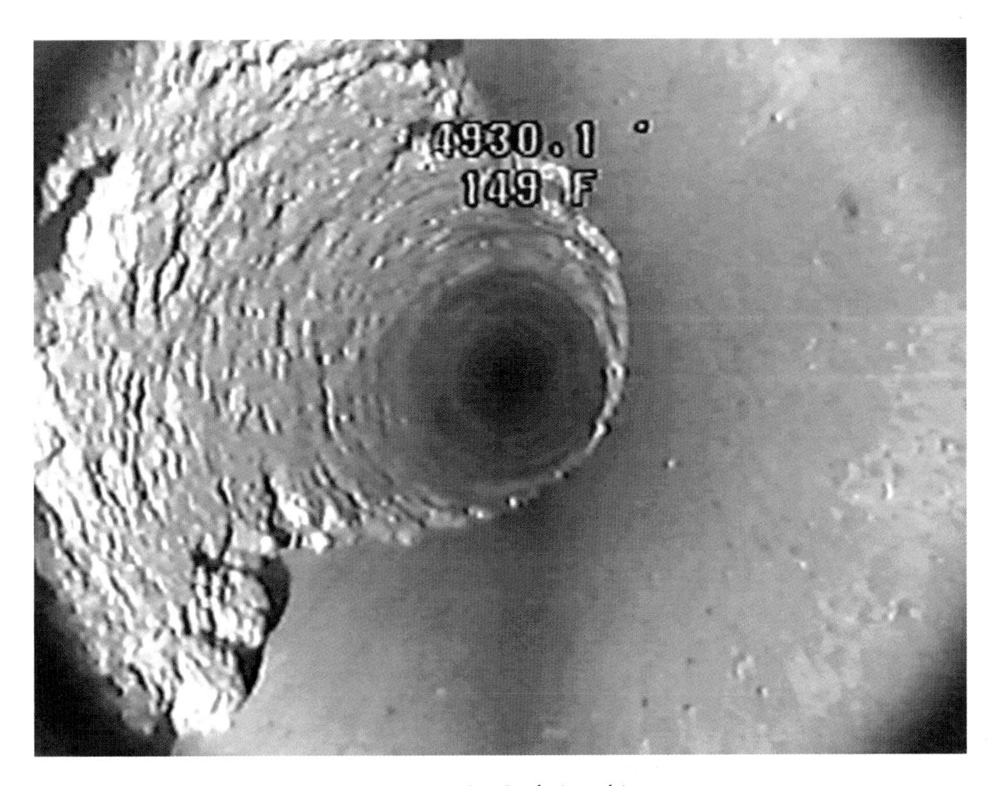

Figure 6–12 Scale in tubing

There is a range of component tools commonly incorporated into a PLT string. Many of these have trade or product names, however this section briefly describes them using generic nomenclature (Fig. 6–13).

- *Spinners*: there are a number of different spinner devices which are basically propeller like tools which record the flow rate.
- *Pressure gauges*: downhole pressure measured in flowing and static well conditions is valuable data to aid reservoir management. A quartz pressure gauge is standard on almost all PLT strings. Pressure surveys are discussed in greater detail below.
- *Water hold-up tool*: these are sophisticated capacitance devices which are used to record the location of water in the wellstream at any one point in the well.
- *Temperature tool*: records variations in temperature across the length of the well.
- *X–Y caliper*: this is a simple four-arm caliper tool, used to check the completion and liner for any signs of deformation.

Operationally, the sequence of events for PLT will vary according to the well. Typical activities, however, will include:

- *Spinner Calibration*. The tool is moved up and down in the tubing at three different speeds, commonly 30, 60 and 90 ft per minute. The resulting data are used to evaluate the response of the spinner at downhole conditions.
- *Static Passes*. The PLT is run up and down across the reservoir with the well shut in. This can be used to identify 'crossflow', the flow of hydrocarbons from a high-pressure zone to a lower-pressure zone, rather than up to surface.
- *Flowing Passes*. The PLT is run up and down across the reservoir at different flow rates. This is used to determine which zones are contributing to the flow.
- *Stations*. The PLT is used to monitor flow at different depths in the well. In practice this will usually involve holding the tool on-depth for 5 minutes every 2000 ft, while pulling out of the hole after logging.

During production logging operations, it is vital that the depth of the tools in the well is known. There are two main sensors used to cross-reference the position of the toolstring (this process is also known as depth correlation). These are Gamma Ray (GR) and Casing Collar Locator (CCL).

GR: gamma ray tools were originally Geiger Counters but are now more sophisticated scintillometres. However, both tools have the same function, they measure the naturally occurring radiation in the rock. Most sedimentary rocks contain radioactive minerals to some degree, generally containing traces of potassium, uranium or thorium. These minerals emit gamma radiation (GR) at a constant rate proportional to the abundance of radioactive minerals present. In general, shales and mudstones are more radioactive while sandstones and limestone are less so.

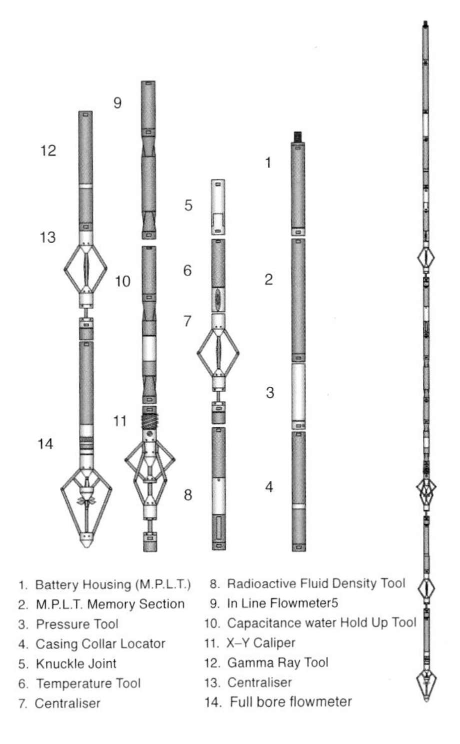

Figure 6–13 M.P.L.T. Toolstring (showing individual components and positioning)

At the end of each hole section, the well is logged with electric line or LWD and a GR log is recorded. As the GR can be measured through steel, the well can be re-logged on every PLT run. The GR signature of the well does not change, so the PLT-GR logs can be correlated with the EL-GR allowing very accurate depth control. This is particularly important when the PLT is run in memory mode.

Often a radioactive 'pip-tag' will be incorporated into the completion which is detected by the GR tool, again used as a reference point.

CCL: the joints of tubing which form most of the completion are joined together by threaded connections or collars. Therefore at the connection, there is a greater thickness of steel.

The Casing Collar Locator (CCL) works on the same principle as a wall thickness tool, although it is much less sophisticated. The tool detects the change in steel thickness and records a spike on a trace. The resulting log is used to correlate the depth of the PLT string. Often a short 'pup-joint' of tubing, 10 ft in length is included in the completion. This is used as a reference point of known depth.

Reservoir saturation

After the reservoir section has been drilled, the rock properties are evaluated by electric logs or logging while drilling (LWD) in the case of high angle or horizontal wells. Many parametres are measured but three of the most important in defining which intervals will be produced are the porosity of the reservoir rock, the hydrocarbon distribution (which horizons contain oil and/or gas) and hydrocarbon saturation (the relative % of gas, oil and water at any particular depth).

The measurement of these parametres in the open hole is straightforward, utilising technology that has been in use for many decades. However, once the liner has been run and cemented across the reservoir it becomes more complicated. For example, the resistivity logs used to indicate the location and concentration of hydrocarbons do not work in a steel-lined hole.

In more recent years, highly sophisticated nuclear saturation tools have been developed to evaluate reservoir fluids behind steel. Their mode of operation is extremely complex; they are, however, highly effective in identifying the distribution and saturation of gas and oil. In addition, they can in some circumstances be used to differentiate between formation water and injection water.

Over the life of a well, these parametres will change as hydrocarbons are produced. It is therefore important that saturation tools are run periodically to monitor the changing distribution of well fluids. These tools require power and are normally only run on electric line or electric-CT but may be used to identify former oil zones which are now producing water, zones of unproduced hydrocarbons and zones where injection water has 'broken through'.

This information is invaluable for both reservoir management and well maintenance. See *Re-perforation and Zonal Isolation* below.

Pressure surveys

Since the 1920s, the performance of a well has been expressed as a graph of the pressure recorded at the bottom of the well while flowing versus the flow rate of produced fluids at surface.

By measuring the bottom hole pressure at different flow rates, the Productivity Index (PI) can be calculated. The PI is a simple numeric value which allows us to compare the performance of a specific well with other wells. More importantly, it allows us to monitor the performance of an individual well over time.

The pressure data are recorded by highly sensitive gauges run on slickline, electric line or even coiled tubing. The data is invaluable yet relatively cheap to acquire, as the gauges are normally run routinely during every well intervention operation. To provide data gathered over a longer period of time, the pressure gauges may be left down hole then recovered days or weeks later. These are highly accurate, based on quartz technology and measure both pressure and temperature. Their operating pressure range may be typically 0–15,000 psi with an accuracy of ± 3psi, while the temperature range may be 0–150°C with an accuracy of ± 1°C. The data is stored in memory and, depending on gauge type, up to 1 million data sets can be stored. The pressure survey can therefore be used to provide a 'health check' on the well. Changes to the Productivity Index (PI) over time can be used to determine artificial lift requirements or to schedule future workovers, thereby optimising production.

Production improvement

As a result of reservoir observations and interpretation of deteriorating well performance, remedial actions may be required to restore the well productivity or to minimise sand or water production. This section discusses the available options.

Re-perforation

During the operational life of a well it may have to be re-perforated in order to restore or enhance production. There are two main reasons why it may be required:

- *Formation damage.* The sand face exposed by the original perforations may be damaged in that the pore spaces become blocked, limiting the flow of hydrocarbons into the well. The damage may be due to mineral scale, solids resulting from operations or fine particulate material such as clay from the formation itself. In this case, the objective of re-perforating is to gain access to the reservoir beyond the zone of damage.
- *Access to additional reserves.* When first brought onstream, not all hydrocarbon bearing zones penetrated by the well may be perforated. It is a common practice to produce from a lower zone first.

Acid wash

The use of acid to stimulate oil production was first attempted in 1932 on the Mt Pleasant Field, Michigan, USA, reputedly using a garden hose to pump the acid into the well.

Today, acid is pumped into the well through coiled tubing or jointed pipe and 'spotted' at the required depth, then left to react. After 'soaking' for the required period of time, the spent acid is circulated out of the well and in most cases the treatment is repeated several times.

Hydrochloric acid (HCl) dissolves calcium carbonate ($CaCO_3$), the principal mineral in limestone. The acid is used to etch or enlarge the natural fractures in limestone reservoirs or to create 'worm holes' through areas of formation damage, thereby enhancing the flow of oil into the well.

HCl is also used to dissolve calcium carbonate scale within the well itself. The formation water produced with the oil contains dissolved mineral salts including calcium carbonate. This often re-crystallises within the completion or even in the perforations in response to changing pressure/temperature and is termed 'scale'. This will build up, eventually blocking the flow of oil. HCl can be pumped to reduce scale periodically, thereby avoiding the need to remove it by mechanical means.

Hydrofloric acid (HF) is used to stimulate sandstone reservoirs by dissolving crushed quartz grains and clays in the pore spaces or in the perforation tunnels. In addition to being corrosive, HF is highly toxic which requires detailed planning and specialist medical facilities.

'*Mud acid*' is a generic term for proprietary mixtures of HCl and HF in varying proportions, often including organic acids. It is used to treat damage to the formation caused by drilling mud.

Zonal isolation

During the life of a well, it is often necessary to isolate a particular zone in the reservoir. This is commonly performed to limit water production. High water cut (ie a high proportion of water) limits the flow of hydrocarbons from the reservoir, plus as the water is 'oily', treatment is expensive. There are a number of methods that can be used to isolate sections of reservoir.

Plugs. If the lowermost perforations or zone is producing water, the solution is simple in many circumstances. A mechanical plug is run on wireline and set in the liner at an appropriate depth.

Straddle packer. If the zone to be isolated is in the middle or upper part of the reservoir, then it is more complicated as access to the lower zone is still required. In this application, we can use a tool called a straddle packer. This is a solid pipe of the required length, with a packer at either end. It is run to depth on wireline and the packers set in the liner. A straddle packer reduces the internal diameter of the well significantly but still permits tools to be run to lower zones.

Expandables. The use of expandable tubular technology has increased significantly over the last 10 years. There are many types on the market but the principle is always the same; a lightweight steel pipe is run into the well on wireline in a compressed state to the depth required. Then an expansion tool forces the pipe to open out and make close contact with the inside of the liner. Thin rubber elements may be used to provide a hydraulic seal if required.

Chemical methods. There are several proprietary methods of zonal isolation by chemical means, predominantly to shut off water-producing zones. In each case, a reagent is spotted across the perforations, normally using coiled tubing.

The compound reacts with water to form an impermeable solid. The theory is that the compound will react with the sections of reservoir producing water but not those producing oil. Across the industry as a whole, chemical shut-off operations have very mixed success.

Sand control

The wireline logs run in the well after the end of drilling are used to predict the likelihood of sand production during the life of the well. Sand failure is a problem in many wells, particularly those in older fields where the rock is under increased stress due to depleted reservoir pressure. If anticipated, then primary sand control is addressed before the completion is installed, for example by running screens or a slotted liner.

However, sand production can also start unexpectedly during the life of the well for a number of reasons, such as water breakthrough which can again weaken the rock. With a completion in place, the options for remedial sand control are limited but can be very effective (Fig. 6–14).

Figure 6–14 Sandscreens
Left: Wire-wrapped screen *Centre*: Premium sandscreen *Right*: Expandable sandscreen

Stand-alone screens. Retro-fit sandscreens can be run through the completion on wireline (depending on weight) or on coiled tubing. They are set across the perforations, normally hung from a packer-like device. The mesh size is carefully selected to ensure that it is the optimum size for the sand produced from that well. Eventually, the space between the liner and the screen may pack with produced sand and limit production.

Through tubing gravel pack. Gravel packing is a technique that has been in use for decades. The system is very similar to the stand-alone screen except that when the packer has been set, the space between the liner and the screen is circulated to sand (or gravel) which is precisely sized in relation to the formation sand (normally 6× larger diameter grains). This gravel 'packs' the space, keeping the formation sand in place yet maintaining a high production rate.

Expandable sandscreens. As described in the Zonal isolation section, expandable technology is in widespread use. Expandable sand screens are installed in the same manner as solid expandables. The mesh is designed so that when fully expanded it will still exclude the sand particles.

Chemical methods. There are a number of commercial products designed to consolidate loose sand while remaining permeable to the flow of oil. However, they have had limited use in the North Sea.

Sand production is a major problem for a number of reasons, the most important being that sand entrained in the wellstream can be highly erosive. In addition, it can fill the lower section of the well, limiting production and reservoir access. On the surface, sand can block flowlines, etc. and if it is oil-wet then disposal will be expensive.

Well clean-out

A well may need to be cleaned out for a number of reasons, including the accumulation of produced solids such as sand at the bottom of the well or the build-up of scale, wax or asphaltene deposits at various places in the well.

With a completion installed, the usual method of performing a well clean-out is to use coiled tubing, due to the ability to circulate fluid. The fluid pumped through the coiled tubing can have a number of functions:

- to power hydraulic drilling motors (turbines) to mill scale or asphaltene;
- hot crude oil may be pumped to dissolve wax (termed 'hot oiling');
- acid may be pumped to dissolve scale; or
- the fluid may be thickened with viscosifiers so that when circulated, it transports loose material and debris to surface.

6.6 Well workover

To workover a well is to remove and replace the completion. This is a very expensive process due to time, materials and man-power, plus the well might be off-line for several weeks, deferring production. However, it may be necessary for a number of reasons, including:

- the existing completion may be damaged or corroded;
- the completion metallurgy or tubing size may be out of specification for current well conditions;
- the well conditions may now require artificial lift;
- downhole equipment no longer functioning, such as electric submersible pumps; and/or
- the well may be 'junked' with dropped equipment which cannot be retrieved.

Sequence of events

The steps involved in a workover are specific to an individual operation, although all will require the use of the platform rig or a hydraulic workover unit. The following sections describe typical stages common to most wells. As with all well operations, the job is planned in meticulous detail and a plan is produced which incorporates all activities, equipment, guidelines and objectives. This plan is signed off by all key players in the operations team and is known as 'The Programme' (as in a programme of work).

Pulling the completion

The well is first 'killed' by pumping heavy brine from surface down to the perforations, called 'bullheading'. Then mechanical plugs are set in the tubing to act as physical barriers to flow while the Christmas tree is removed and drilling Blow Out Preventers are installed. The platform rig is positioned over the well and the two mechanical plugs removed from the tubing.

The tubing hanger is engaged with a pulling tool and the completion is pulled upwards by the rig (normally parting at the expansion joint). The joints of tubing and components are unscrewed one by one and laid out on the deck. As the completion is removed, the well is continually topped up with brine to replace the volume formerly occupied by steel.

Running the new completion

The bottom hole components are assembled and run into the hole on tubing. As each joint of tubing is screwed onto the completion, the torque required to tighten it is carefully monitored to ensure that a gas-tight seal is formed.

Depending on the well, the new completion may engage the lower completion that was left in the well or may have a packer. The last sections of tubing run in the well are of shorter lengths such as 5 ft, 10 ft, etc. and are called pup joints. They are selected so that the completion correctly engages the lower part of the expansion joint or puts the new packer at the desired depth. This process is called the 'space-out'.

The tubing hanger is picked up and screwed onto the completion, then landed in the wellhead. Pressure tests are used to ensure that the new completion has successfully engaged the lower completion.

Mechanical plugs are set in the tubing to act as physical barriers to flow while the Blow Out Preventers are removed and the Christmas tree installed. With the Christmas tree in place and tested for both pressure containment and valve function, the plugs are removed from the well and it can be handed over to production.

6.7 Well abandonment

The term 'well abandonment' implies a lack of concern for a well that has no further production value. This is not the case and effective decommissioning is a critical phase in the lifecycle of a well.

Abandonment has two principal aims:

- to reinstate the geology; and
- to restore the seabed (or land site).

Reinstatement of the geology is achieved with cement. Regulations require that all permeable zones (ie those capable of flowing water or hydrocarbons) are isolated from each other using cement plugs.

The perforations themselves are sealed with cement. This is pumped from surface and 'spotted' across the production zone. The cement is then 'squeezed' into the perforation tunnels using pressure from surface.

If a single reservoir is penetrated, the cement may be pumped down the completion. After pumping, the completion is pulled in the same manner as performing a workover, separating at the expansion joint. More cement is spotted above the packer before the completion is pulled out of the well.

If the well has produced from multiple reservoirs or different geological horizons, the completion and packer is removed and the cement pumped down drillpipe. This allows the placement of a mechanical plug between each production zone in addition to the cement plug. More cement is pumped to leave a cement plug extending several hundred feet above the liner lap or the top perforation, whichever is greater.

In both cases, a mechanical plug is set above the cement plug, isolating the production zone.

Further cement plugs are set higher up the well, again pumping the cement down through drillpipe. Each plug may be thousands of feet long. They are allowed to set for a number of hours then tested for hardness using the drill string. If the set cement can support the weight of the drill string then it is considered to be a viable barrier and the next cement plug can be set higher up the well.

The removal of the casing from the well varies from job to job depending on well type. But in general, each string of casings is cut in sequence using a mechanical cutter, spearing the free section and pulling it to surface. A cement plug is set across the area of the cut.

The seabed is restored by cutting the outermost casing using explosives. This is done by running a shaped explosive charge on wireline. The casing stub and wellhead are then recovered on drillpipe.

The remaining hole is allowed to fill naturally with soft sediment, although all efforts are made to restore the seabed around the wellsite to normal conditions. This normally involves a detailed underwater survey and the removal of any remaining debris.

WELL DESIGN AND INTERVENTION

LEGAL

6.8 Introduction

This chapter concentrates primarily on the topic of well services. Its purpose is to give insight into the basic legal requirements which must be considered when entering into any well services contract. First, key pieces of legislation will be set out, with a brief description as to how each relates to the field of well services. Then, the essential clauses of the contract will be covered in depth, to highlight what is expected from both the operator and the contractor in terms of their responsibilities and obligations towards each other. Finally, the key contractual issues of risk and insurance will be discussed – both major topics in any well services operation given the nature of the work involved.

6.9 Well design

Before going into any further detail on the topic of well services, it is necessary, for the sake of completeness, to briefly consider the process behind the actual *design* of the well. A detailed and complex assortment of specialist equipment and materials is required in well design and intervention. The design of the well will be set out in detail by the operator in a drilling programme. The programme is normally compiled by one or more members of the operator's drilling team, a senior drilling engineer and perhaps then reviewed by the exploration and drilling management team.

As well as detailing the design of the well, the drilling programme will also describe the sequence of work and materials that will be required, for example bit and casting selection, bottom hole assemblies and mud and cementing specifications. The programme will also include a section for the testing of the well. There may also be a summary of operations, pre-spud procedures including environmental considerations, general drilling practices in regard to running, casting and cementing, a list of reports that will be required, as well as the progress and specific vendor material data sheets. The programme, therefore, essentially contains all relevant information in respect of a well design and the sequence of work to be undertaken. It is an important document for when government approvals and consents are sought.

It may be the case that external assistance will be contracted in drawing up the programme, for example if the operator does not have sufficient in-house resources or particular expertise in a specific well design or reservoir type. Many technical experts have formed their own companies and enter into consultancy agreements with one or more operators. Once approved, the programme will be distributed to all interested parties, the drilling team, drilling and specialist well services contractors, and to the relevant governmental agencies which provide consent to the drilling or workover of oil and gas wells.

6.10 Well services

When commencing any drilling operation it will be necessary to enter into a series of different contracts in order to preserve and maintain the well. The activities involved come under the general term 'well services'.

Well services is a highly competitive market, and usually the operator in charge of the particular operation will take control of the organisation of the various contracts involved. The requirements for drilling-related services are rather complex and will vary depending on the nature and formation of the well. Different services will be required at the different stages of the well life, for example exploration, testing and, ultimately, production. However, a typical production well will require various *general* services during the well lifecycle, and these are outlined below.

Typical production well services

Drilling phase

- drilling rig;
- rental of pipeline and drilling tools;
- drilling fluids and cementing;

  - drilling fluids supply and services (mud services);
  - completion fluids; and
  - cementing services;
- OBM (oil-based mud) drill cuttings treatment:
  - mud cuttings;
  - onshore cuttings handling and disposal; and
  - offshore cuttings re-injection facilities;
- tubular make-up and running:
  - casing and tubing running; and
  - tubular inspection services;
- downhole drilling services:
  - MWD (measurement whilst drilling) services;
  - LWD (logging whilst drilling) services;
  - directional drilling;
  - fishing and milling services; and
  - surveying services;

Tubing and completion phase

- well completion and maintenance:
  - well testing;
  - wireline;
  - coiled tubing;
  - pumping; and
  - well perforation;
- completions:
  - downhole gauges; and
  - completion sub-assemblies.

The drilling and well services activities are typically performed by specialised drilling and well services companies on contract to the oil field operator. Contract types can vary, with well services being supplied by a single contractor who provides the total package of services or multiple contracts with either the drilling contractor or the oil field operator.

6.11 Legal requirements

There are various legal requirements which must be complied with in the provision of well services. The key legislative sources are summarised below.

The Petroleum Operations Notices

These notices replaced the Continental Shelf Operations Notices. The notices include details of the following: applications for consent to drill exploration, appraisal, and development wells (Notice No 4), the reporting of petroleum production (Notice No 7) and applications to complete and/or work over a well (Notice No 8). Well Workover Consents are considered in more detail below.

Petroleum Act 1998

This Act consolidated legislation that has developed since 1934. It vests with the Crown the rights to petroleum resources in the UK. It enables the Secretary of State to grant licences to search for, bore for and get oil and gas within UK and to grant licences for such activities.

Health and safety legislation

As there will be numerous personnel involved in the operation, various health and safety legislation will have to be adhered to, including the following:

- *The Health and Safety at Work, etc. Act 1974, Part 1*, which forms the foundation for all subsequent health and safety legislation. It imposes general duties on all employers and employees to ensure general health, safety and welfare. The duties must be strictly adhered to or else penalties will be incurred. From an offshore operations perspective, compliance with this Act will involve ensuring the proper construction and safe dismantling of equipment used and securing the safety of all persons engaged in the operation. The Offshore Safety Act 1992 extends Part 1 of the 1974 Act and increases the penalties for certain offences.
- *The Offshore Installations and Pipeline Works (Management and Administration) Regulations 1995* (SI 1995 No 738) require the operator to appoint a competent Installations Manager on his behalf to ensure the safety of all those involved in the operation, which includes the right to restrain and remove a person from the offshore installation if it appears that that person is endangering the safety of others, and to keep records of all persons involved in the installation.
- *The Offshore Installations and Wells (Design and Construction etc.) Regulations 1996* (SI 1996 No 913) ensure that the installation design and construction are structurally strong and stable so as to guarantee the health and safety of all persons and to ensure that installations are decommissioned and dismantled safely.
- *The Offshore Installations and Wells (Design and Construction, etc.) Regulations 1996* (SI 1996 No 913), in particular regulations 13–21

(relating to wells), confer the general duty of the operator to ensure that a well is designed, operated and maintained so that there can be no unplanned escape of fluids. The well operator must also ensure that suitable well control equipment is provided to protect against blowouts and make sure arrangements are in place to examine the well.

- *The Offshore Installations (Safety Case) Regulations 2005* (SI 2005 No 3117) (replacing the 1992 Regulations) require a 'Safety Case' to be prepared and sent to the Health and Safety Executive (HSE) for acceptance before operating in UK waters. A Safety Case should be as detailed as possible to ensure it is accepted. Regulation 12, and Schedules 2 (relating to production installation) and 3 (relating to non-production installations), set out the particulars to be included in the Safety Case. These particulars include details which demonstrate that there is a sufficient management system in place, the identification of all hazards with the potential to cause a major accident, descriptions and diagrams of the installation structure and materials required, and details of the maximum number of persons expected to be on the installation at any time (including details of whom accommodation is to be provided for). Arrangement details for controlling the well operations, such as controlling pressure in the well and preventing the uncontrolled release of hazardous substances will also need to be given. Schedule 5 gives further details of what must be included in a Safety Case in respect of dismantling a fixed installation.

  The Regulations also set up a general notification procedure for the carrying out of any well operation. Notification is to be made to the HSE, containing particulars detailing information such as the name and address of the well operator, the type of well, a description of the well operation such as the date each operation is expected to commence and finish, and any activities with the potential of creating hazards.

Well Workover Consent

Well Workover is the process of performing the maintenance and repair of a well. It is likely that a Well Workover or intervention will be required during the life of the well. Prior to carrying out any maintenance, it is necessary to obtain consent from the DTI, known as a Well Workover Consent, in accordance with Petroleum Operations Notice No 8. Such consent is required only in certain circumstances, for example for the entry of subsea wells, rig operations, snubbing operations using a hydraulic workover unit, operations which involve the changing of the downhole status of the well (eg zone isolation or additional perforating) or the removal of the Christmas tree for any reason. For platform wells, consent is not normally required for wireline logging, coiled tubing logging or coiled tubing nitrogen lift. A minimum of 28 days' notice is required for a consent to work over or recomplete a well.

Applications for consent to work over a well, where required, should contain information such as (1) the reason for the workover, (2) the present status of the well and its proposed recompleted status; (3) a revised completion diagram showing the downhole equipment to be installed, with approximate depths, together with the producing formation(s) and proposed perforated interval(s); and (4) proposed reservoir monitoring logs (pressures, fluid flow, water saturation).

6.12 Model well services contracts

The field of well services is a highly complex area. Considering the amount of money that is involved in a typical operation, and the risks that can be encountered throughout, it is important not only that the quality of equipment and personnel are of a high standard but that such contracts are drafted with precision, so as to ensure that all eventualities are covered.

LOGIC (Leading Oil and Gas Industry Competitiveness) provides a standard style Well Services Contract for use in the oil and gas industry. However, while the LOGIC contract certainly serves as a useful starting point in the legal process, it should be remembered that it is intended, merely to be a *stylistic* form of agreement, setting out the basic requirements that ought to be provided for in any typical operation. The body of the contract will therefore not be suitable on every occasion and will undoubtedly require specific tailoring depending on the nature and circumstances of each individual operation.

It is worthwhile noting that well services operations and the equipment used in this area of the offshore industry are of far greater importance than the level of cost of such services would indicate. The Piper Alpha catastrophe was caused by a gas leak from a well, and there have been many near misses since which, fortunately, have not produced another such disaster. It is of vital importance therefore for great care to be taken in the contractual terms, as well as in the quality of equipment and personnel involved.

6.13 Basic information required and general contract terms

The following key details should be provided in any well services contract:

The parties

The operator and contractor should be correctly named and their registered address specified (as well as details of telephone numbers, fax numbers and email addresses).

Contractor selection

The operator will want to ensure that the selection of the technical team is undertaken in a structured and formal manner. There may be some proprietary design or areas of knowledge or expertise that restrict the selection of the contractor. However, in the majority of cases, the operator will invite competitive tenders from the contracting community. In order to streamline the selection process it has become common practice to use the services provided by First Point Assessment Ltd (FPAL), established in 1996, for this purpose. FPAL has compiled a database of contractors and records their technical and capability profile. This database is often used when selecting contractors to provide well design and well intervention services.

Prior to 1996, in order to comply with EU law in regard to open competition, operators individually compiled tender invitation lists of contractors, using a pre-qualification process that duplicated effort on the part of both the buyer and the seller. In order to eliminate this costly and time-consuming process, FPAL was formed. Contractors register with FPAL, submit their technical and capability profile and are therefore visible to the operators – the buyers of their services or products. The operators will interrogate the database and use it to draw up their shortlist of companies that will be invited to tender for a particular service or product supply. Also as part of the FPAL arrangements, buyers and sellers can share business performance information through a performance feedback process. Here, the parties to a contract complete a structured review of each other's performance.

Operators will of course also use experience and previous track record of contractors when compiling tender invitation lists. Multiproject or term contracts, sometimes referred to as 'call off contracts' will also be used to access services and supplies on an ongoing basis, eliminating the need for continual source and tender for services and materials.

The work

A clear and detailed description of the work to be performed under the contract is essential. It follows that a description of the worksite should also be given. Any relevant technical reports should be listed. A detailed inventory of materials and equipment (considered more fully below) should be included, and any spare parts and tools which are required to complete the work should be listed.

It may be desirable to include a clause to allow for certain parts of the work to be changed upon the written request of either party. There may be a number of reasons to include a variations clause in the contract; for example, it may not be financially viable for a certain portion of the work to be performed as originally contracted, or the operator may simply want to retain a degree of flexibility throughout the process. Whatever the reason may be to vary the work, any adjustments that are to be made will clearly have to be within the ambit of the contractor's reasonable capability in order for the contractor to effect performance. It may be in the contractor's best interest to try to have a negotiation period drafted into this clause, so that any adjustments that are to be made must be discussed and formally agreed between the parties.

Materials and equipment

It is a standard position that the contractor will be responsible for providing the necessary materials, equipment and personnel to enable him to carry out the particular operation. When material is incorporated permanently within the well structure, for example casing, such material would be procured by the operator from the contractor, using a purchase order agreement to set out the detailed terms and conditions applicable to the contract of supply. There are a number of additional agreements and documents which will be required in the provision of materials and equipment, some of which are summarised below:

- *Material Supply Agreements* will contain a clear description and specification of the material to be supplied. Quantities and delivery times should also be detailed so as to avoid disputes at a later date.
- *Data Sheets* or *Specification Summaries* will contain details of the equipment to be supplied or the technical description of equipment to be hired out.
- *Remuneration* or *Schedule of Prices or Rates*. It is common for well services contractors to publish a standard price book which is then marked up or discounted. A specific pricing table will normally have been included in the contractor's tender. This can be used as the basis of the payments section of the contract.
- *Conditions of Use Contracts* will be required. There is a standard form LOGIC well services and purchase order style that can be used for this purpose, however for more complex purchase agreements, operators will tend to use their own in-house standard which they have developed over the years from various sources.

The materials and equipment to be provided in any operation will have to satisfy certain standards and requirements, as laid down by the operator, before being used in the operation, in which case such specifications should be clearly set out within the contract. Where no standards are set out (almost definitely standards will be included in the contract), equipment will at the very least have to be of 'good quality', meaning new or relatively new. In certain circumstances, however, the responsibility may fall on the operator to provide certain materials and equipment. If this is the case, any materials, etc. to be so provided should be explicitly specified within the contract, for the avoidance of doubt.

Health and safety issues will always be at the back of the contractor's mind throughout the operation. The contractor will have to comply with the operator's instructions on all matters in order to ensure that any work being carried out is under the safest possible conditions. It will be the contractor's responsibility to remove all equipment that it has itself provided and made use of in the operation and leave the site in a safe and tidy condition.

Personnel

Details of all personnel who will be involved in the work should be listed, such as names, numbers, job titles and qualifications. Minimum training and certification requirements must be met and all personnel will have undertaken pre-employment physical examinations including drug screening. It is the responsibility of the contractor to provide sufficient and properly qualified personnel. The operator should reserve the power to remove any person involved in the operation whom he believes to be incompetent, acting contrary to the interests of all those involved in the operation or not conforming to relevant health and safety procedures. Although this will normally be included within the contract, this power will be implicit in any event.

Duration

The duration of the contract should be specified. The duration clause may be worded so that the time period is indefinite until the work is completed. Alternatively, if there is an expected duration this can be detailed, with options to terminate early if the work is completed sooner than this date, or with options to extend if the work is still incomplete by the end of the specified period.

Notification

To guarantee that the operation runs as smoothly as possible, there is a general duty on the contractor to inform the operator of any major incidents which would adversely affect the carrying out of the work. There will, therefore, be a notification procedure in place whereby the contractor will have to notify the operator of, amongst other things, any accidents that occur in carrying out the work, if there are instances of proposed or actual cessation of the work, and if any conflicts arise between the contract terms and the law of the country where the operation takes place.

6.14 Additional contract terms

Equally relevant are the following terms which must be, and always are, included:

- the operator's general work policies should be given, detailing information such as its safety and environmental standards, confidential information policy and security policy;
- price and payment method (all rates and prices should be properly specified); and
- confirmation of which laws apply (in the event of dispute arising).

The need for the inclusion of these terms within a contract is self-explanatory and there is no need to go into further detail with regard to these points. However, the following clauses merit more in-depth discussion.

6.15 Essential contract terms

Ownership

The operator will retain ownership over all materials, equipment and technical information which it has provided throughout the operation. Those materials and equipment which are provided by the contractor but are intended for *permanent incorporation* into the work will become the property of the operator either upon delivery to the worksite or once payment has been made (usually whichever is earlier). Any such equipment which is found not to conform to specified requirements will immediately re-vest in the contractor. All reports, charts and test results encountered in the operation which are created by the contractor will vest in the operator and, upon completion, suspension or abandonment of the well, the contractor must give the operator all related documentation that it possesses.

Patents and other proprietary rights

If any patent or other intellectual property right results from developments of either the operator or contractor prior to commencement of the contract, or outside the scope of the contract, then any intellectual property rights so created shall usually vest in the party that developed the right. This will equally apply if either party enhances any of its own existing intellectual property rights.

Where, however, any intellectual property rights arise during the term of the contract, then rights will vest in either the operator or the contractor absolutely, or jointly between the parties depending on how the agreement is drafted. Details of how rights are to vest will be set out in appendix form. Where a particular right is to vest in one party absolutely, it will be at that party's discretion whether or not to grant the other party a royalty-free, non-exclusive, worldwide licence to use the right (the use of such right will most probably not be sublicensable). Where a right is to vest jointly between the parties, both parties will jointly file an application for registration of that right.

Defective performance

Provision will have to be made for defective performance in instances where the work has not been performed in accordance with the contract. This is achieved by means of a notification procedure whereby the operator notifies the contractor of the specific nature of the defect, stating the specific section of the contract which the contractor has failed to meet. It will, thereafter, be the contractor's obligation to perform that part of the work again at its own expense and risk. The operator may alternatively decide that it is necessary to engage a third party to perform the works instead of the contractor. If so, the operator must notify the contractor of its intention. The operator will be able to recover from the contractor additional costs incurred in the reperformance of the contract by that third party.

Default

Default provisions should be included and should highlight precisely when default is deemed to have occurred. Such instances will usually include: if a party becomes insolvent; if receivership, insolvency or bankruptcy proceedings are commenced; if there is an unlawful assignment; and if the contractor does not complete the work in accordance with the requirements of the contract.

The party in default should be given a reasonable time period in order to remedy the default and the operator should give the contractor notice of the default without delay. If the default is not remedied within the time period specified, then the operator will be entitled to terminate the contract. These provisions will equally apply to the contractor in the event of default by the operator.

If the operator exercises its right to terminate in this way, it will be entitled to finish the work without incurring any liability to the contractor. In that instance, the contractor will be liable to pay the operator direct costs arising through the default (the contractor will want to cap its liabilities). If it is the contractor who exercises the right to terminate (and it is very unusual for a contract to confer rights of termination to a contractor), it will be entitled to payment for performance of the work through to the date of termination (this may be on a pro rata basis) and also non-recoverable costs which have been incurred in respect of specially manufactured equipment which was required for the specific operation.

Suspension

The operator will want to have the option to suspend performance of the work if certain circumstances arise, such as default on the part of the contractor, if suspension is necessary for health and safety reasons or just at the general convenience of the operator. This general 'convenience' ground, which may also appear in the termination provisions (see below), is extremely broad and gives the operator the right to suspend whenever it considers necessary (within reason of course). The operator must give notice to the contractor of its intention to suspend the performance, and upon receiving such notice the contractor must discontinue the work and ensure that the work that has been carried out has been properly secured and protected.

Termination

The operator will be entitled to terminate the contract under certain specified grounds, such as convenience of the operator, suspension, default, force majeure (usually defined as any event or circumstance beyond control of the parties such as an 'act of God', flood, earthquake or any other natural or physical disaster, act of war, act of terrorism, etc.), non-compliance with applicable laws, policies and procedures or in the event of the contractor becoming bankrupt (or some other similar insolvency procedure).

Upon exercising its right to terminate on the ground of convenience, the operator will be obliged to reimburse the contractor for costs directly incurred and which are non-recoverable in respect of the termination. Notification to the contractor of the operator's intention to terminate must be given.

With regard to termination following suspension, if the operator suspends the work for a given period then, in some cases, *either party* will be given the option to terminate the work at the end of that specified period. It may be the case, however, that there is mutual agreement to continue with the work, in which the case the contractor will have the opportunity to renegotiate its original price for the work.

Assignation

The precise terms of assignation should be specified within the contract. Not only does assignment result in the transfer of rights and obligations under the contract but, perhaps less commonly realised, the assignee will also assume liability for any *prior* acts and omissions of the assignor. Any assignment which occurs will be further effected by an assignation agreement (Scots law) or an assignment agreement (English law).

Operator's position

It will normally be the case that the operator will be entitled to assign its rights and obligations (whether in whole or in part) under the contract without obtaining the prior consent of the contractor. This right to assign will most likely be subject to various qualifications. For example, the assignation will have to be made to a subsidiary of the operator or to a holding company. Assignment to any other company will most likely require the contractor's consent. Whilst the operator ultimately retains control over the whole operation, the contractor will, at the very least, want to have some say over who it is contracting with. A 'prior written consent' provision will offer the contractor a good deal of protection in that regard. It follows that the contractor will want a provision stating that the assignee will be of 'sound financial standing'. This further protective provision is important to assure the contractor that the assignee has the financial capability to fulfil its obligations under the contract.

Contractor's position

Unlike the operator's position, the contractor's right to assign is not so standard and will vary depending on the particular operation. Some operators may require that consent must be granted to the contractor in any instance of assignment of the contract (whether in whole or in part). This may seem very restrictive from the perspective of the contractor; however there will usually be a provision stating that such consent is not to be unreasonably withheld or delayed.

Alternatively, the operator may be satisfied that no consent is necessary, but only if the assignation is made to a subsidiary, or holding company, of the contractor. The operator will similarly want assurance not only that the proposed assignee has financial standing to take on the contract terms but that it possesses the relevant degree of expertise and skill to perform the work adequately. A provision to that effect should therefore be inserted into the body of the contract. Background checks into the history of the potential assignee will be useful and will offer a great deal of comfort to the operator, as will parent company guarantees where these can be obtained. It will usually be the case that if the assignation results in any additional cost to the operator then this extra expense shall be borne by the assignee.

Subcontracting

Rights of the contractor to subcontract will be set out under the contract and are similar to the provisions relating to assignation – either consent must be obtained from the operator on all occasions or only when subcontracting to a party that is not a subsidiary or holding company of the contractor. Depending on the degree of control which the operator wishes to retain, the terms of subcontracting will vary.

Again, the operator will want assurance that the subcontractor is of sound financial standing and possesses the requisite degree of skill and expertise to perform the contractor's obligations under the contract. That being said, it should be borne in mind that subcontracting will not relieve the contractor of its obligations. Responsibility will still lie with the contractor in respect of all acts and/or omissions of the subcontractor.

The operator will want to have the opportunity to review the terms of the subcontract fully and will want to know the precise nature of the work which the subcontractor is being contracted to undertake.

Indemnities

It will be necessary to incorporate an indemnities clause into the contract to specify liability covering different eventualities. Indemnity clauses basically transfer liability from the responsible party. Their purpose is to allocate responsibility for certain risks between the parties, thus avoiding the time and expense of drawn-out litigation. Once responsibility is allocated, the relevant party is then free to arrange appropriate insurance cover.

The clause should be worded in terms of reciprocal indemnities between the operator and the contractor. The types of indemnities included in the contract should cover the commonly incurred instances of loss of, or damage to, property and personal injury (including death or disease) and instances of pollution and contamination. Pollution can easily occur through spills or it can arise out of a blowout, through seepage or uncontrolled well flow. It is necessary to be very careful in the drafting of pollution clauses and the contractor should ensure that it accepts liability only for pollution *originating from* its own equipment. By its very nature, a well services operation means that any pollution from the well bore may be processed through the well services equipment. Any pollution emanating from the reservoir or equipment of the contractor will be the operator's responsibility and the contractor should be held harmless. Indemnities in respect of claims for patent or copyright infringement will undoubtedly be included and liability for indirect, incidental or consequential losses or damages should also be included.

Instances of loss/damage to property and personal injury in respect of any third party involved in the contract should also be considered. Indemnities granted between the parties will be worded to be 'regardless of cause'. However, this is not the case in respect of indemnities granted in respect of loss/damage to third party property. It is unlikely to be the case that the operator or contractor is willing to accept liability for any loss/damage to third party property 'regardless of cause'. Rather, the operator is only is likely to accept liability and indemnify the contractor to the extent that the loss/damage is attributable to the negligence or gross negligence of the operator.

There are specific indemnities relating to well services which should be considered for inclusion in a well services contract, for example the performance of 'fishing' to recover downhole equipment (this will be at the expense of the operator). In addition, the operator may reimburse the contractor for the costs of repairing any equipment that is either lost or damaged in the well bore. Further, the operator may indemnify the contractor for claims in respect of damage to the reservoir and well. The liability in respect of the recovery or abandonment of any radioactive source in the well bore should also be considered, and will be performed at the operator's sole risk and expense. A provision in respect of liability for claims arising in respect of such recovery/abandonment may also be included.

There are certain optional indemnities which should be considered, many of which are beneficial to the contractor and the operator may feel are too burdensome for inclusion; for example, damage to surface equipment. If the contractor demonstrates abnormal damage to his equipment used in the operation then he should be reimbursed for the cost of repair (except where the contractor's negligence caused the said damage or where the damage is caused by fair wear and tear). 'Abnormal damage' is taken to mean damage that could not be reasonably expected and quite often occurs due to the nature of the well fluids which can be exceedingly corrosive. The similar indemnity provision may be granted in respect of marine transport equipment. Further indemnities for consideration include subsurface trespass, liability for claims resulting from fire, explosion or blowout at the 'work site' (ie the drilling location, the drilling rig or the platform) and the costs of controlling a wild well.

Warranties

The provision of warranties in the contract is important, particularly in the case of the operator who will want to obtain as many warranties as possible from the contractor. Typical warranties to be included in a well services contract are detailed below.

Operator

The only warranty which the operator will grant to the contractor is access to the work site.

Contractor

Service warranty. The operator will require the contractor to warrant that it is qualified and can perform the work. The operator may further require the contractor to warrant that it shall perform all services under the contract in a 'good and workmanlike manner', ie with the requisite special knowledge, training and experience. This is referred to as a 'service warranty' and will be limited to the extent that the contractor has relied on inaccurate information supplied by, or on behalf of, the operator. The service warranty period must be specified and 'downhole' services (ie in the well bore) may be distinguished from other services.

If the contractor does not perform the services adequately, the operator should notify the contractor of this position and may require the contractor to reperform the 'non-conforming' service to the reasonable satisfaction of the operator. If, once again, the contractor fails to perform to standard, or fails to perform within a specified time limit, then the operator will be entitled to complete or correct the work itself, and will be entitled to recover all reasonable costs in that regard from the contractor. The contractor should insist on capping any liability to be incurred here. If marine or air transportation is required for materials and equipment to effect any correction, then the operator should consider inserting a provision to recover expenses involved in such transportation.

Products warranty. In addition to a service warranty, the operator may want the contractor to warrant that any products, equipment and materials used in the operation conform to certain specifications, standards and requirements and that they meet with applicable laws and regulations. This is referred to as the 'products warranty'. For example, the operator may specify that the equipment must be new and, if not, the contractor must receive written approval before using it. At the very least, the operator will want a guarantee that the equipment is free from any defects. Again, the warranty period must be specified, the contractor notified in the event of breach and given time to remedy the breach. The operator may be satisfied that the equipment is simply repaired or he may require that it is replaced. Again, the contractor will want to cap its liability.

Consumable products and materials warranty. Warranties relating to 'consumable' products and equipment will usually be given. This relates to products which are ordinarily consumed in the course of the work, eg drilling fluids and completion fluids and certain service materials. Upon granting this warranty, the contractor will typically warrant that the product meets agreed specifications, will last a normal shelf life and that its quality will not be lessened during storage.

Rental items warranty. All rental items will similarly be required to meet with certain specifications and requirements, and should be in good working order throughout the rental period. The operator will probably request that all operating manuals, supplies and any spare parts be included with the rental product.

Interpretation of well data. It is accepted that one contractor's interpretation of well data (or indeed other data) will differ from another. It is simply a matter of opinion. It follows therefore that the contractor will *not* warrant the accuracy of any data interpretations or recommendations. This will be explicitly stated in the contract but would probably be implied none the less.

Assigning warranties
In addition to the warranties listed above, where there are subcontractors of the contractor, it would be in the interest of the operator to require the contractor, where reasonable, to receive warranties from its subcontractors and even from its vendors or suppliers. Thereafter these warranties would be assigned to the operator.

Responsibilities of the contracting parties
Each contracting party should have no doubt as to their individual roles and functions which are to be performed throughout the operation. Each party's rights and responsibilities should therefore be clearly spelled out.

Operator's responsibilities. The operator is obliged to provide the contractor with access to and from the work site without any limitations. This means that the operator must have obtained the correct permits, licences, any host Government authorisations and is acting in accordance with the applicable laws to enable the work to be carried out. It further means that the operator is required to provide the contractor and its team with suitable offshore transportation and accommodation, at no expense to the contractor. The operator will also have to assist the contractor in the performance of the work, including importing and exporting equipment, material and supplies in connection with the host Government.

Contractor's responsibilities. The contractor is working in the capacity of an independent contractor, not as agent of the operator. Its general responsibilities include making itself aware of all matters which arise in connection with the work, for example the geographic and climatic conditions in the area of operations, and familiarising itself with applicable government rules and regulations. The contractor will be responsible for providing all management, supervision, personnel, materials and equipment. It must perform its work with 'all due care and diligence' and with the skill expected of a reputable contractor.

The contractor will be required to prepare technical and production reports on a regular basis. If any defects or deficiencies in the equipment become apparent to the contractor, then he will be required to notify the operator. Any equipment which the contractor receives from the operator for use in the operation must be returned in the same condition in which it was originally delivered. In addition, the contractor has various obligations to the operator in respect of the personnel it employs to carry out the work. For example, it must ensure that it has at all times the minimum number of personnel to perform the work and that the personnel are of the requisite fitness and qualification and possess correct working visas and permits.

Long-term contracts for well facilities
Some well services contracts may be for a long duration. Such contracts may require onsite availability of well intervention units and will contain responsibilities on the contractor for such equipment. In these long-term contracts the contractor will often be required to provide specialist staff and equipment and to undertake the competency of such staff. There may be provision for the appointment of an operator representative and contractor representative under such a contract.

6.16 Key issues

There are essential key issues which ought to be considered in further detail when drafting a well services contract. They are as follows:

Risk
Risks and uncertainties are inherent in any drilling operation. It is, therefore, vital in order to ensure optimal performance in a given project, to identify, assess, manage and ultimately control these risks.

Risk identification involves identifying particular hazards and accidents that are likely to occur in the operation. It can be achieved through consultation with appropriate experts and professionals who will have a detailed understanding of the project. Past risks are easy to determine by looking to prior projects for guidance. It is advisable, however, to take precautions against new types of risk (it is here that the views of experts will be particularly helpful).

Risk assessment will follow. This is an avoidance mechanism through which anticipated risks can be avoided or, at the very least, their impact can be minimised. Consideration of prior risks that have been encountered in similar operations in the past will be useful in assessing the most effective means of preventing these risks arising in any future operation. It will further be necessary to consider those risks which may be specific to the operator, to the project as a whole and also to the contractor and therefore to *allocate* risk accordingly.

The obvious risks that will be encountered in any operation involve fire and explosion since well services activities involve the extraction of highly flammable hydrocarbons. Not only could this result in major damage to the structure of the well itself, but it could ultimately delay or cease production entirely, with severe financial implications being incurred. Contractual risks may also be encountered and therefore measures must be taken to prevent their occurrence. There is always the risk of the competency of staff – do personnel possess the correct qualifications and training? Are personnel under adequate supervision? Strict procedures will be in place to ensure that all staff employed in the operation possess the required qualifications, therefore controlling any risk that they could pose to the operation.

Equally important is that the correct materials are being used and that they are of the correct quality. Control checks will be in place to ensure that all specialist equipment and machinery conform to the correct specifications and are pre-approved, inspected and certified prior to its use. Stringent checks will be in place to avoid any accidents that may arise due to faulty or improperly installed equipment.

Other risks commonly encountered include health and safety risks and environmental risks (for example, severe weather conditions and hazards on site such as subsoil conditions and faults). Catastrophic risks are a particular concern in today's society. Natural hazards such as earthquakes, hurricanes, flooding and tsunamis regularly dominate news headlines. Given the large-scale losses and damage associated with such disasters, private insurance is the primary mechanism to secure funds following these hazards.

There are also risks involving changes in the price of materials that are used in the operation, and there is also the risk of sudden changes to a country's economy. Financial risk is a particular worry in any operation; however this can be reduced, or at least managed, by allowing for multiple funders.

Insurance

Given the nature of the work involved, insurance is a vital clause in any well services contract and precise requirements will vary depending on the nature of each individual contract. It will be necessary to specify a minimum insurance coverage which each party must meet. Some examples of common insurance policies which ought to be considered include:

- employer's liability insurance and/or worker's compensation insurance, covering personal injury or death of an employee of the contractor and specifying a capped liability level per accident;
- commercial general liability insurance to cover injury or property damage;
- general third party insurance for any incident or series of incidents covering the operations of the contractor;

- excess liability insurance; and
- insurance may also be required in respect of any vessels involved in the works or aircraft.

The contractor will be responsible to arrange the minimum insurance cover specified in the contract. The operator will want to satisfy itself that insurance is being taken out from 'reputable and substantial' insurers. It may, therefore, be the case that the operator will want to see the certificates of insurance which are issued to the contractor and, in the case of employer's liability insurance, it is mandatory for those certificates to be displayed on the notice board at the offshore installation. If there are any subcontractors involved in the operation then the contractor must ensure that they too are adequately insured up to appropriate levels. If any claims are made under any of the policies, it is the contractor's duty to notify the operator immediately – it is vital that, despite the fact that it is essentially the contractor which performs the work, the operator *always* remains in control throughout the entire operation.

It follows, therefore, that the operator should always be notified (not only in the case of insurance claims) if there is anything at all which will affect the performance of the work. This includes, for example, undue delay, any contradictions or ambiguities in the contract, any conflicts with applicable laws or any accidents which occur in connection with the work. Equally, the operator is obliged to notify the contractor of any information it has knowledge of, which is likely to affect the work. The inclusion of reciprocal duties between the operator and contractor to inform each other throughout the contract is important to ensure not only the efficiency of the operation but also that if any 'blips' do occur, then they can be ironed out as quickly as possible to ensure both minimum disturbance to the operation and lessening of the financial blow.

— 7 —

PROJECT ECONOMICS

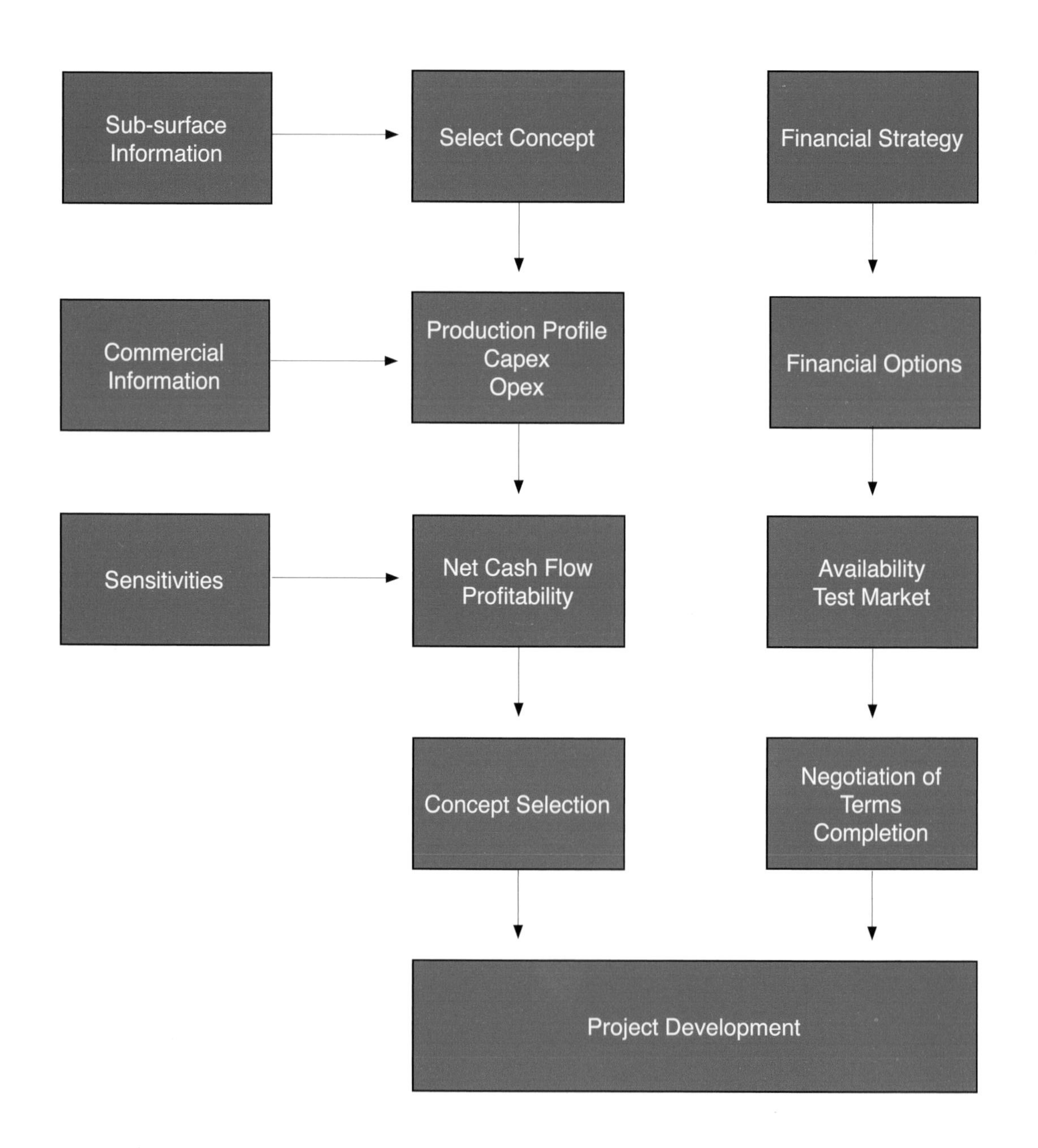
Sub-surface Information
Select Concept
Financial Strategy
Commercial Information
Production Profile
Capex
Opex
Financial Options
Sensitivities
Net Cash Flow
Profitability
Availability
Test Market
Concept Selection
Negotiation of Terms
Completion
Project Development

PROJECT ECONOMICS

TECHNICAL

7.1 Introduction

There are many ways to assess and compare projects, such as strategic or corporate portfolio fit, cost per unit reserves developed, and cost per unit production. Economic analysis is the method which brings together the various aspects for the lifecycle of a project or venture and allows them to be assessed objectively.

This chapter will outline ways in which economic analysis can be used to achieve this and will describe key inputs and their characteristics.

Projects use the same economic modelling basics to assess development feasibility, determine whether or not additional field appraisal is justified, compare alternative development options, underpin commercial agreements and support budget proposals.

7.2 Economic modelling

The economic models for screening purposes or to support requests for major funding use the same basic concept; a series of inputs is required to build a model for a particular development case, and the outputs are then assessed against a series of bench marked economic measures. Typical inputs comprise: the production profile, capital expenditure (capex) for field development, operating expenditure (opex) for life of field, with typical outputs being: net cash flow, discounted cash flow and profitability assessment. These are used in turn to generate sensitivities.

Needless to say, an economic assessment is only as good as both the input upon which it is based and the bench marks against which the output is compared. It is essential to have an expert assessment of each aspect, and that consistency and integration between each of these often separate strands is assured.

Production profile

Determination of a production profile requires to take account of subsurface parameters, facility issues, design constraints, evacuation bottlenecks and also commercial matters, especially sales contracts.

Subsurface considerations include expected reservoir size, fluid transmission characteristics, modelled residual saturations (how much gas and oil will remain in the reservoir) and the impact of any reservoir pressure maintenance schemes. This itself will depend on the degree of pressure support modelled from aquifers or gas expansion. Combined with water ingress estimates and optimum well type and placement (eg vertical, horizontal, multilaterals, injection, gas lift), this leads to estimates of the 'technically possible' ultimate recovery.

The design offtake rate, and hence basis for 'production plateau' is, however, not solely a technical matter but is rather the result of an optimisation process (described below). Initial estimates of plateau rate will reflect facilities constraints, eg pipeline ullage, and/or bench marking from other developments of typical 'optimum' rates for an assumed field size. Final field-rates, prior to abandonment, will depend on the lowest flowing well pressure which the facilities can handle, eg for a gas field this will reflect compression facilities.

Whilst the production profile is the functional responsibility of the reservoir engineer, the selected design rates and production rate maintenance options will result from the input of all disciplines, such as engineering and commercial, typically determined through economic analysis. The profiles need to reflect downtime of wells and facilities, as this will reduce production volume over a given period and hence extend the duration of the production profile.

Capex

The capital expenditure (capex) required to develop a field depends principally on the planned wells and surface facilities, their scope and type. Key criteria include the design offtake rate, specific assumptions or information about the fluids and physical conditions (gas, oil, contaminants, pressure/temperature), and safety and environmental requirements. Geographic and market factors can also play a significant role. In the concept selection phase a series of development options (and capex) cases will be considered. This is part of an economic and broader business optimisation process.

Capex typically peaks prior to start of production, although subsequent capital expenditure may be required to maintain production from depleting reservoirs. Any such post-production 'development' should be reflected in the economic model if its impact is assumed in the production profile assessments.

Capex estimation is the domain of the facilities engineers working closely with the reservoir engineers, drilling engineers, cost estimators, planners and contracts and procurement specialists. The cost estimation process is discussed in section 7.5 below.

Opex

Operating expenditure (opex) is largely determined by the facility's scope, complexity and size, as well as geographic and logistical factors. In the early phases of a project there may be very little information on which to base opex estimates, hence bench marking and rules of thumb are typically applied. For example, for an offshore production platform, annual opex might amount to some 5% of capex. Despite this uncertainty there remains a need to evaluate possible opex/capex trade-offs to maximise lifecycle value. Once facilities are better defined, more detailed manning, consumables and logistics cost estimates can be made. Future requirements, such as additional wells, enhanced facilities or the necessity to meet stricter environmental regulations, need to be considered. Tariff payments (use of third party facilities and/or receipts from third parties), royalty payments and, last but not least, tax need to be included. Tax can, in certain situations, completely change the economics of a project and is all too often neglected. The subject is, however, exceptionally complex, and is specific both to individual countries and individual projects and accordingly is not dealt with in any depth in this overview.

Initial opex estimates will be provided by the cost estimator. Detailed verification of manning, consumables and logistics, however, will need to be made by operations staff who understand the specific issues associated with a particular location and type of plant.

Net cash flow

The various inputs described above allows the net cash flow to be estimated – the net cash flow being the difference between gross income and the sum of all expenditure. This is typically presented on an annualised basis and reflects phasing of costs and production. Income is assessed from the expected volumes of oil, gas and natural gas liquids, and estimates of the future selling prices. Expenditure comprises capex and opex, taxes, royalties (assuming where paid as cash, otherwise royalties in kind are deducted from the production). General parametres such as inflation and exchange rates need to be included. The net cash flow forms the basis for the economic analysis of the project. Note that economics used for decision-making will be forward looking, and will ignore past expenditures and production; the only exception is to include any tax effects from past expenditures.

Inflation, discounting and present value

The economic analysis needs to allow for the impact of inflation, ie the loss of purchasing power of a currency over time. A project's future cash flow components, eg capex, opex and revenues, have to be 'escalated' to allow for inflation. They are then described as being in 'Money-of-the-Day' (MOD). Note that any budget requests should be in MOD terms.

A project cash flow used in economic analysis, however, requires the year-by-year figures to be presented in units of constant purchasing power. To make this possible the concept of constant value money, or Real Terms (RT), is used, based on a selected reference year. Note that these two adjustments, inflation (to MOD) and deflation (from MOD to RT), are different. Whilst the deflation is based on the general inflation rate, inflation to MOD should account for any special market influences for individual items, eg a tightening contractor or materials supply market based on increased demand and/or fewer willing bidders or, in times of reduced demand, a willingness for suppliers to reduce margins to sustain workloads.

The RT cash flow is then discounted to reflect the cost of capital, ie the fact that money tied up in an investment is lost liquidity. An organisation will require some compensation for this and also the exposure to future uncertainty and risk. A range of Discount Rates (DR) is typically used to determine this 'time value' of money or Present Value (PV). For example, the PV of £1 million in three years at a DR of 10% is:

$$1/1.10 \times 1/1.10 \times 1/1.10 = (1/1.10)^3 = 0.751, \text{ ie £}0.751\text{m.}$$

Applying this concept to revenue, £1 million received each year for three years has a PV (at 10% DR) of:

$$1/1.10 + (1/1.10)^2 + (1/1.10)^3 = 0.909 + 0.827 + 0.751 = 2.487, \text{ ie £}2.487\text{m.}$$

Profitability assessment

Using cumulative cash flows, various profitability measures are used (Fig. 7–1):

- discounted ultimate cash surplus, ie Net Present Value (NPV);
- Profitability or Value to Investment Ratio (NPV/PV capex);
- Unit Technical Cost (PV capex + PV opex/discounted production);
- earning power or rate of return;

- exposure; and
- payout time.

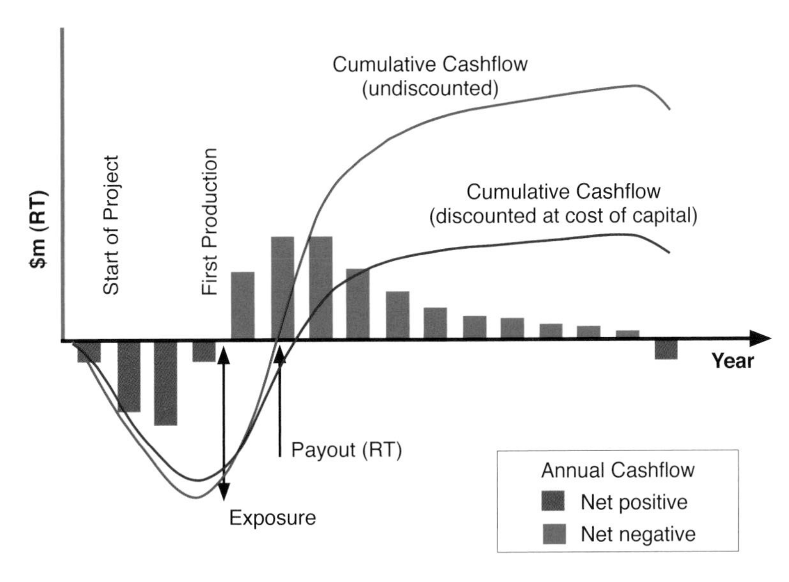

Figure 7–1 Economic measures

Each of these measures has its merits, but some are more useful and commonly used than others. Ultimate cash surplus or NPV is the standard measure of 'value', and is the amount of money ultimately generated by investing an amount of money in a project reflecting the loss of liquidity and risk over time by making this investment. NPV does not, however, indicate how effective the investment is per unit capex. For this, the Profitability or Value to Investment Ratio is a more useful measure to compare projects of different size and scope. Another measure sometimes used to compare projects is Unit Technical Cost, a measure of cost efficiency versus production. Earning power is defined as the discount rate at which the NPV is zero. This is a screening tool to check project robustness but is of limited use for comparison purposes; nevertheless, it is an often quoted measure. Exposure, the maximum amount that an investor would risk prior to or just after commencement of production, and Payback, how long he must wait to get his money back, are checks to assess the viability and risk of the investment.

Sensitivities

It is essential not just to consider a 'deterministic' case, ie single parametres for all inputs. The entire economic analysis is full of uncertainties or ranges of possibilities, eg reserves, sales prices, production, capex, opex. To assess the impact of input uncertainties the parametres are each varied around their base values to amounts appropriate to the uncertainty. The project base value is then the NPV of a case built on the assessed P50 values, ie values where there is a 50% chance of the actual outcome exceeding the value and a 50% chance of the outcome being below the value.

These variations are typically shown as individual parameter impacts on NPV in a 'Spider Diagram', as shown below (Fig. 7–2). The parametres of most interest are those which have the greatest influence on NPV and those over which the engineers and project team can have a major influence, ie capex, capex phasing, production availability and production delays. Note that to compare different parametres, the range in uncertainties should be consistent, eg the P90 and P10 values for each parameter, ie 90% chance of exceeding and 10% chance of exceeding respectively. For example, in Fig. 7–2 reserves has the largest range of uncertainty (eg the P90 being 35% below the base level and giving a negative project NPV).

7.3 Evaluating concepts

The greatest opportunity to influence the value of a possible development occurs in the front end phases of the design process. At this stage, value can be maximised, exposure to uncertainty reduced and less robust development

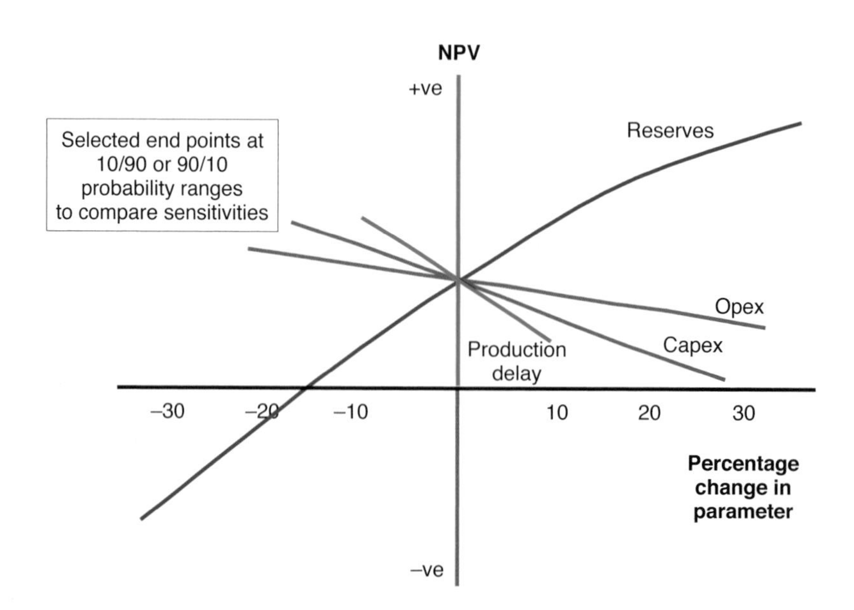

Figure 7–2 Sensitivities

solutions eliminated. The influence/time curve illustrates this potential, which is at a maximum before concept selection and declines as the development solution is defined and expenditure on facilities design increases (Fig. 7–3).

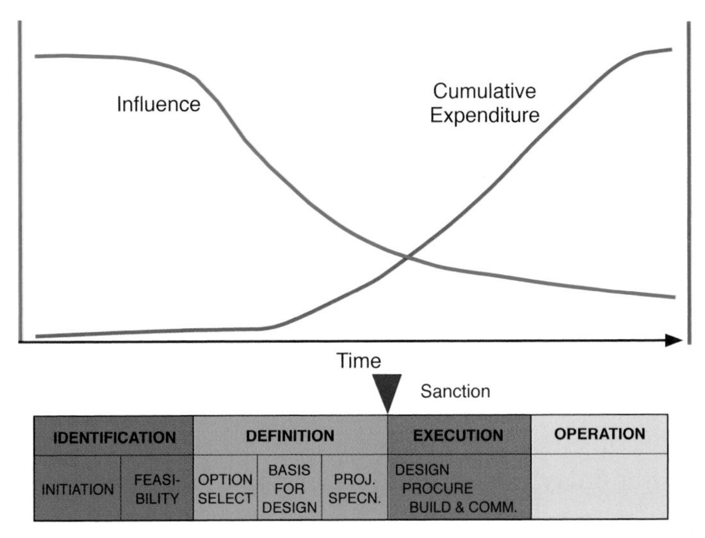

Figure 7–3 Influence diagram

Whilst the potential to influence the out-turn value exists in the early stages, ie identification and definition, it is these phases that are often compressed to meet business aspirations, eg for rapid production start-up. A term used to describe the resources applied and development analysis/decisions at this stage is 'Front End Loading'; greater input at this stage can lead to improved project delivery (capex and schedule) and project operability.

In these stages, project economics are used to assist decision-making in terms of deciding whether or not to progress with a potential development, and to help optimise the basis for the development. These decisions will depend on the availability of, or more significantly, lack of, information.

Subsurface information is critical at this stage, and includes: volumes, reservoir variability, fluid properties and contaminants. Commercial information, eg constraints such as evacuation routes for products, also needs to be acquired. Decisions will therefore be made concerning the need for additional information, ie is field appraisal necessary?

Value of information

If field reserves, well productivity or data regarding fluid properties are key uncertainties then additional appraisal may be required to meet two objectives, namely to establish development viability/commerciality, or to optimise a development.

Evaluating whether it is economically justified to appraise can be estimated by use of the technique known as Value of Information (VoI). This is defined as the difference in the NPV of the project with and without the additional information, reflecting a range of uncertainties. Thus, if the information will not change the development plan then the VoI will be zero. The Value of Appraisal (VoA) is the VoI less the cost of that appraisal.

Appraisal required to demonstrate commerciality requires to establish if the reserves, productivity and development costs will meet economic hurdle requirements, ie minimum level of measures below which a project is likely not to secure budget support. Without appraisal the development uncertainty may be too great leaving the risk of developing a sub-commercial field, or leaving a commercial field undeveloped (see Fig. 7–4).

Appraisal to optimise a development, eg design production rate, needs to be assessed carefully considering that whilst the NPV of a project may be increased this may result in a delay for appraisal, and the additional appraisal will itself introduce additional cost. For example, a small oil field may be most economically developed using a tie-back to an existing facility, but a larger field might be more profitably developed via a stand-alone facility such as an FPSO (floating production storage and offtake vessel). The analysis needs to consider production profiles for both options, associated capex and opex, including tariffs for any

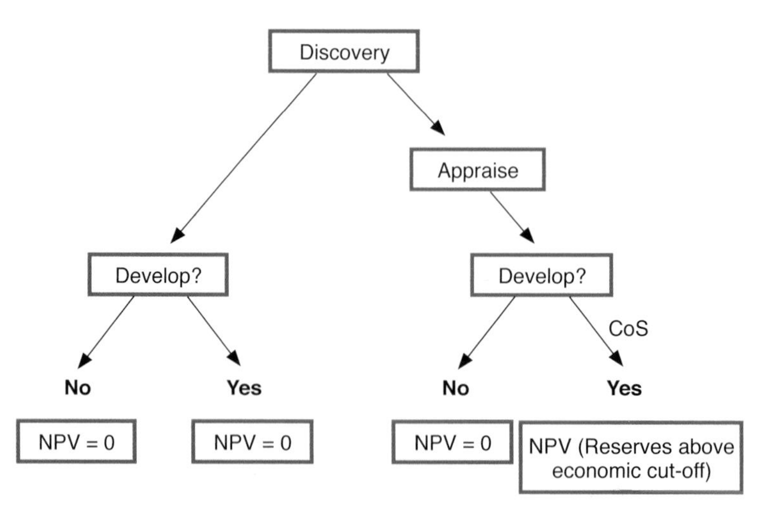

Figure 7–4 Value of information to demonstrate commerciality

use of third party infrastructure, and the time to start-up. This latter point may well be critical, as this could be less than a year for a tie-back but three/four years for a stand-alone development, excluding appraisal.

The diagram below (Fig. 7–5) illustrates the wider range of reserves uncertainty that will need to be catered for without appraisal versus a narrower range (better estimate) having been appraised. The case on the left might result in selection of a stand-alone facility whereas on further appraisal it might be found that only a tie-back is justified.

Option selection stage

Critical requirements for economic evaluation at this stage are good estimates of reserves, production rates, capex and opex, at a time when the definition of options is low and there is a limited time to determine these criteria. This requires experienced input and a co-ordinated approach between functions, ie subsurface, facilities and commercial.

A key factor in successful evaluation will be bench marking against similar (recent) projects and experience of similar reservoirs. Benchmarking should include the scope of wells/facilities, ie have similar developments required additional facilities for certain production problems, or have others shown that a simpler more cost-effective approach is possible – and robust? Benchmarking of costs should also consider market factors relating to material supply and

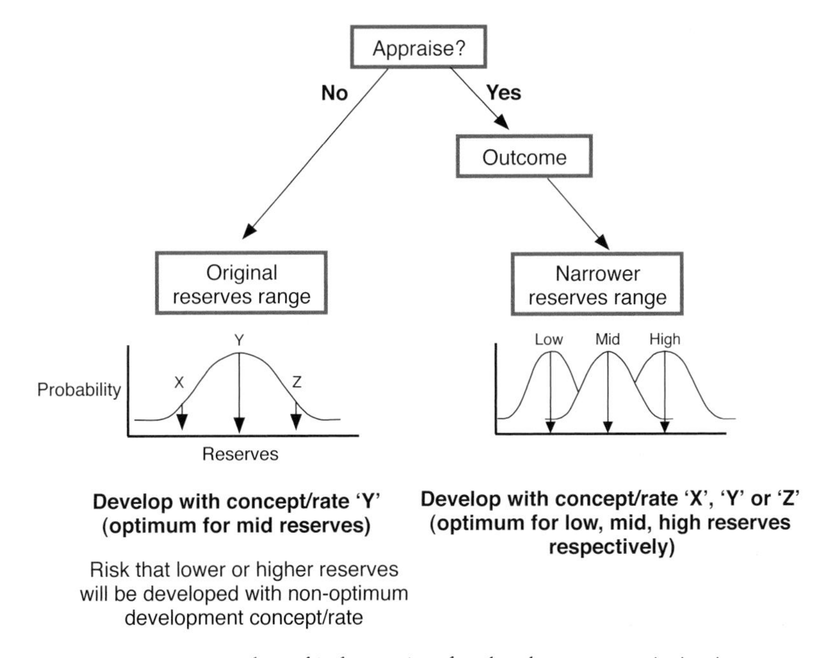

Figure 7–5 Value of information for development optimisation

availability of contractors. It should also identify if other operators have experienced operational difficulties that should be addressed in any new development.

The same principles apply for assessing modifications to existing ('brownfield') facilities. In this case the reservoir information should be more mature, with less uncertainty, and decisions will focus on how best to develop existing facilities, eg improving reliability, debottlenecking, or maintaining or expanding production through additional wells or compression.

As well as conventional economic analysis, other criteria are essential for robust option selection. Various factors may not be adequately covered by the economic model, eg safety and environmental impact/risk, cost/cashflow (rather than NPV), stakeholder/political considerations, technical uncertainty, eg new technology and future business. Such factors should be considered alongside NPV in selecting a preferred concept (Fig. 7–6).

7.4 Basis for Design and Project Specification stages

Having selected the development concept, including general requirements such as the number of wells, production rate, general facilities scope and future development/expandability, the focus is on improving the definition of the concept and how it will be executed, eg contract strategy, supplier options. This will lead to improved understanding of project schedule and cost.

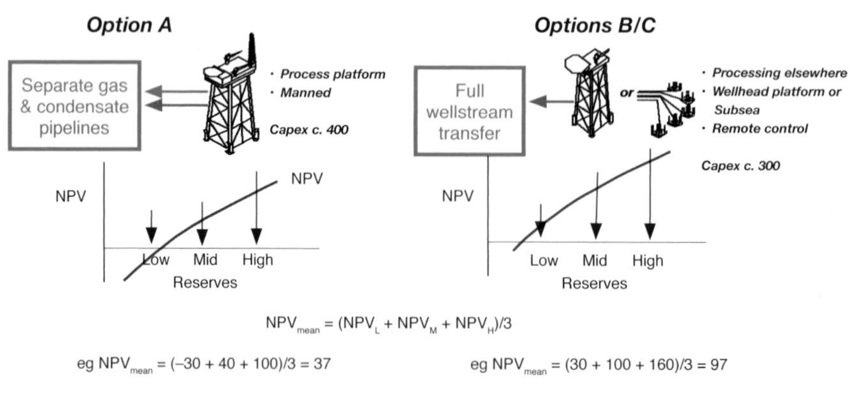

Whilst the mean NPV is much higher for Option B/C than A the relative risks need to be considered:

- Not economically robust at low reserves
- Proven scheme/less cost uncertainty
- Offshore processing and monitoring (but leads to higher safety risk in operation)

- Flow assurance risks (hydrates, wax, slugging)
- Water/sand management (reduced production?)
- Less operational flexibility
- Wells – jack-up rig for platform vs. semi-submersible rig for subsea wells – cost/availability?
- Brownfield or onshore plant cost risks
- Possible onshore environmental concerns

Figure 7–6 Comparing options

This phase is typically split into two stages: Basis for Design (BfD) (sometimes referred to as Pre-FEED) followed by Project Specification (sometimes known as FEED – Front End Engineering and Design) (Fig. 7–7).

During these stages, detailed economic models are required to support commercial negotiations, application for government approval and to secure investment funding. These may include modelling of others' commercial positions and detailed modelling of tax effects and tariffs. The trick at this stage, however, is to maintain the overview and ensure that an internally consistent and integrated set of numbers is used. It will also be necessary to revisit the evaluation on a continual basis as new information arrives, eg during negotiations and as bids arrive.

Whilst it is not feasible to describe the process for determining subsurface uncertainties and reserves in this overview, it is of merit to address the often poorly understood area of cost estimation.

7.5 Cost estimation

Cost estimation techniques alter during the course of development. Initial feasibility estimates are likely to be based on limited scope definition. Therefore,

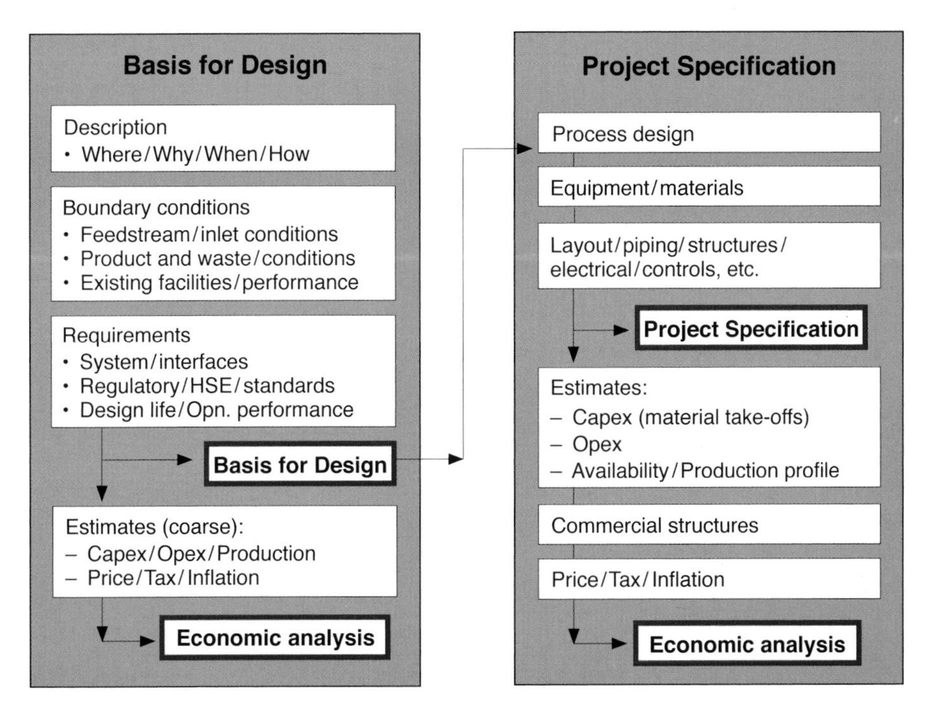

Figure 7–7 Project definition

out-turn costs for similar recent facilities in the same geographic area are likely to be useful for bench mark purposes.

As scope definition increases, through option selection and developing the BfD, a range of commercially available and proprietary estimating tools have been developed. These employ historic data such as materials costs, hours per construction activity, vessel day-rates, with factors for design, project management and insurance and certification.

Cost estimating for the Project Specification stage is a more complex task. Here, estimates will be developed in line with a defined work breakdown structure, ie physical building blocks of the project. Such estimates will be based on detailed estimates of the quantities of materials required, such as tonnes of structural steel, bulks (piping, cabling, secondary steelwork), construction man-hours, construction camp costs, vessel rates and efficiencies and hours of design time. This requires a 'bottom-up' approach, building on good definition of the facility's scope. It is also important to define the contracting strategy, project management resources and to understand the prevailing market conditions including supply/demand sensitivities relating to products and services. Such an estimate is referred to as a 'Base' estimate.

For economic evaluations, '50/50' cost estimates are employed. These are costs which have an equal chance of being too low or being too high. To ensure that costs are not underestimated, through incomplete scope definition and omissions,

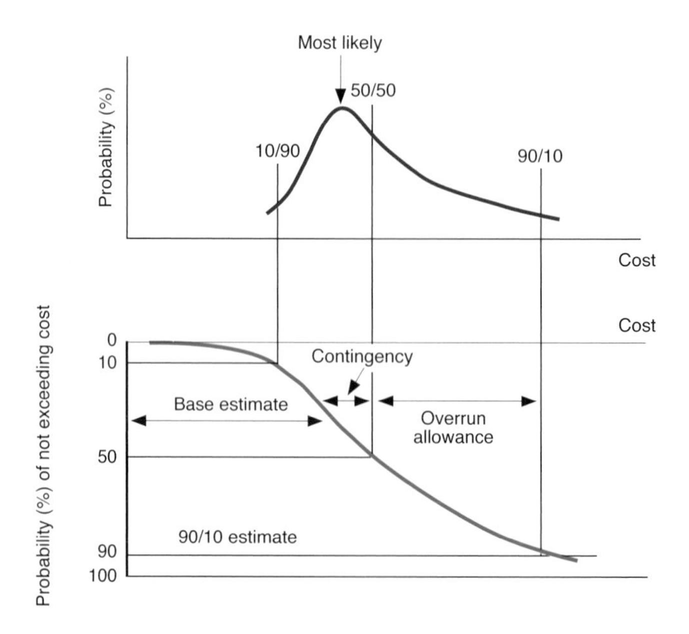

Figure 7–8 Cost probability curves

a *contingency* allowance is added to the Base estimate. Note that contingency is to cover these 'unknown uncertainties' – major scope changes are not covered by the contingency allowance, nor are 'force majeure' risks.

Having developed a 50/50 estimate, it can be seen that there is a range of uncertainty around this value. This range above and below the base estimate is referred to as the *accuracy*. Where this range is referred to as the 10/90 level this implies that there is a 10% likelihood of the out-turn cost being below this value, and for the 90/10 level, a 10% chance of exceeding this value. The 90/10 value is sometimes referred to as the *overrun allowance* (Fig. 7–8).

The size of contingency allowance and uncertainty will tend to decrease as project definition and understanding of the relevant market conditions improve. An example of contingency and accuracy levels through project development is illustrated below (Fig. 7–9). It should be noted that in early stages, option selection and BfD, uncertainty ranges will provide typically generic values. Actual probabilistic estimates based on cost–risk analysis are more complex and will not be undertaken until the Project Specification stage when there is a clearer understanding of the project scope and market factors. This difference, generic range or based on risk analysis, should be noted when quoting estimate accuracy.

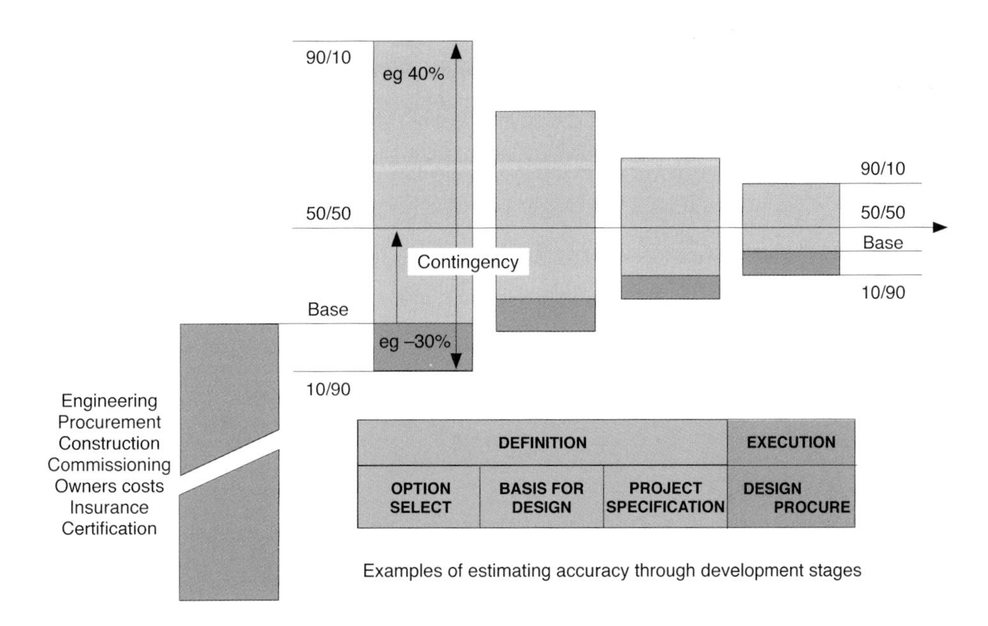

Figure 7–9 Estimate accuracy

7.6 Conclusions

There are many ways to assess and compare hydrocarbon projects but economic analysis is the only method which brings together all financial aspects for the lifecycle of a project. The technique is essential for effective decision-making through the early stages of a hydrocarbon venture, in terms of assessing viability, determining the value of additional appraisal, supporting commercial negotiations, underpinning applications to government for necessary licences and to seek investment funding.

The greatest potential to maximise project value, or guard against a risky investment, occurs during the feasibility and concept select stages. This is, however, at a time when there is most pressure to compress the schedule to meet business aspirations for rapid start-up to repay some of the costs incurred with making the discovery. The best result might be a non-optimised development; an inappropriate design solution could result in reduced production capacity and deferred, or lost, production, whilst inadequate field appraisal could lead to an uneconomic development. Economics has a role to play here in terms of informing and warning the decision-makers.

Reliable economic modelling requires robust, integrated input data, combining the contributions across different technical and non-technical functions. Here, economics can play a pivotal role to ensure that this happens, but more typically if the inputs are not understood in an integrated way the economic analysis can generate and give credence to wrong data and results.

Several measures can be used to assess the 'economics' of a project, but it is essential that economic sensitivity to the uncertainties and potential variations in key input parametres is understood. It is easy to use economics inappropriately and without thorough understanding, but potentially at a cost. What is required is a thorough understanding of the business, across all facets, and how these can be connected through project economics to make decision-making truly effective.

PROJECT ECONOMICS

LEGAL

7.7 Introduction

As will have been seen from the preceding comments in the technical section of this chapter, economic modelling is not an exact science – it is simply a method by which a project is assessed for feasibility, based on certain assumptions. The model should identify, for any particular project, the amount of capital required for that project and the likely return on that capital employed. The type of funding required for any project (whether debt, equity or other forms of third party financial support) will be determined by the following:

- The nature of the party carrying out the project – is it a large, publicly quoted company with access to the public capital markets, whether for debt instruments or equity? If so, then, to the extent that it does not have sufficient working capital on its own balance sheet, it may choose to fund a particular project or series of projects by way of a fresh issue of shares on the market or perhaps by issue of a debt instrument, which may or may not be convertible into equity. If the company does not have access to the public capital markets and is not suitable for listing on an investment exchange then it will have to look to the private equity markets (including specialist equity funds and high net worth individuals) and to banks as sources of funding for its project.
- Whether funds are to be raised for a specific project or for the more general corporate purposes of the party raising finance so as to enable it to fund a number of acquisitions or development projects without going back to seek additional funding for each one.

- The risk inherent in the project – the riskier the project, the less certain its likely cash flows, the more suited that project is to equity finance; whereas the more certain the cash flows from a given project, the more likely it is to be suited to funding by way of debt. Equity investors expect a higher rate of return on their capital invested in order to reflect that greater risk, whereas debt providers usually accept a lower rate of return, reflecting the lower risk inherent in the project.

Once the particular type of funding instrument for a project has been selected (whether debt or equity), the party raising finance for the project may then wish to look at hedging arrangements so as to underpin the cash flows upon which that funding depends, eg by entering into hedging contracts to underpin the assumptions in its model as to oil price, or interest rates attaching to its debt. In this way, if the oil price turns out to be materially lower than expected in the model or interest rates, and so debt service liability significantly higher, those finance risks in the project can be laid off onto the hedging counterparties. In exchange, the project company may give up some upside in that if the oil price turns out to be higher than expected or interest rates are lower than expected, then some of that additional revenue from a higher than expected oil price or lower interest charge may have to be paid to the hedging counterparty – the trade-off for reducing risk in the project and therefore making it more likely that the project will succeed rather than simply being a 'bet' on the oil price or interest rates. There are enough uncertainties in oil and gas projects without making every project a gamble on the way in which oil prices or interest rates move, and so some element of hedging particularly for smaller companies may be desirable.

7.8 Project finance versus corporate funding

Corporate funding is general funding for a company, in contrast to a company raising funds for a specific project. Such funding for a project by a corporate entity is done by raising money for a range of projects or opportunities rather than a specific project.

There are different types of corporate and funding structures, depending on whether an investment is being made in a company at a corporate level or investment capital is for a specific project, but there are many features common to each. For example, if equity finance is to be raised for a specific stand-alone project then it may be that a stand-alone joint venture company is established by the company carrying out that project – that project company would take ownership of the relevant asset to be developed and would enter into its own equity and debt financing arrangements with finance providers without exposing any other assets of the company owning that project to liability towards those shareholders and debt providers. Such 'ring-fenced' or 'limited recourse' funding is quite well suited to a stand-alone project company. That type of funding can be more expensive than raising new equity or debt finance for the main commercial party to carry out the project. If equity providers and debt providers are allowed to invest in, or lend to, a company or group of companies which own(s) a portfolio of assets, that spreads the risk of any particular project being unsuccessful and so reduces the risks to the equity and debt providers of losing on their investment. A stand-alone project company may be used if, for example, the company seeking investment does not wish to open up its general portfolio for investment by outside parties or if other elements of its portfolio are not seen as suitable investments by the relevant equity and debt providers. For example, some equity funds may be restricted in the geographic scope of their investments to the UKCS and therefore may not be able to invest in a company which has interests in West Africa as well as in the UKCS. In that event the company may establish a UKCS project company into which the investor makes its equity investment.

The remainder of this chapter does not seek to draw any distinction between project finance, ie finance raised by a stand-alone vehicle for a particular project, and corporate funding where investment is made at a higher level in the group of companies, permitting the investor and lender access to the entire portfolio of projects. Whichever funding model is chosen, the debt and equity documentation is likely to be very similar.

Consideration is given below to different types of funding and the documentation that lies behind it.

7.9 Tax

The tax liabilities and reliefs applicable to a project and its participants will need to be considered in detail, as tax issues can often change the expected return on a project or prevent the project happening at all and may also have an effect on corporate structure used for the funding.

7.10 Types of funding

Funding for a project may comprise equity funding or debt funding (in both of these cases involving the investment of funds in the company to carry out the project) or may take the form of a farm-out or sale in which project costs are borne by a third party or under a risk/reward contract under which project risk is shared by a contractor. These types of funding are commented on below.

1. Equity funding

Equity funding is funding by way of share capital. True 'equity' share capital is share capital which does not have any limited right to a return, as distinct from preference share capital where the return may be limited to a fixed redemption premium or a particular dividend or 'coupon' on the share. In this section 'equity' refers to both such types of share capital.

In most cases, equity funding is not raised specifically to acquire a particular asset. The time scale, costs and complexities of raising equity funding on a case-by-case basis, for each incremental acquisition by a company, coupled with the uncertainties in any acquisition process introduced by pre-emption risk (the risk that a third party which is a co-venturer under the JOA for the assets exercises its pre-emption rights), third party consents and timing issues, generally rule this process out. However, notwithstanding those issues, it can be appropriate for smaller companies, when acquiring their first assets, to seek equity at the initiation of each acquisition.

Although bench marks vary over time, typically, a private equity investor putting funding into an oil and gas company will look for an internal rate of return on their investment of at least 15–30%. Short of striking oil and gas in much larger quantities than expected, or a substantial and unpredicted hike in oil and gas prices, it is highly unlikely that any project funded entirely by equity will be able to generate that level of return. However, that level of return per annum can be achieved where part of the overall funding from the project is by way of debt finance at, say, 1% or 2% per annum over base rate. It may be that the overall rate of return on a particular project is, say, 12% but if half of the funding is provided by way of bank debt at, say, 6% then it is possible for the party providing the remaining 50% of the funding required to achieve a return of something in excess of 12%. This mechanism for achieving a higher rate of return on equity is known as 'leveraging' and is the concept which underpins the feasibility of most development projects. Without some level of debt finance somewhere in a corporate entity, it is difficult to achieve the required rate of equity return. That higher equity return is usually justified because the equity providers are either funding early stage development work and/or exploration (where banks are typically unwilling to lend, at least on normal debt terms).

Equity funding comes in many different forms and the precise type of equity funding required for any company or transaction will depend upon the projected cash flows and exit strategy for that project. There is no point in capitalising a company with redeemable preference shares, to be redeemed in, say, five equal tranches over the first five years following investment, if the company's cash flows demonstrate that it will not be cash generative until year four. Some common examples of equity funding instruments and the circumstances in which they are appropriate are as follows:

(1) Ordinary shares

Plain ordinary shares may be issued with no preferred rights to dividends or to return of capital on a winding-up in private companies. These are most appropriate for longer-term investments where the return to the equity provider is expected to come out of a future sale or flotation of the company, creating a market for those ordinary shares to be sold for cash or converted into some tradeble security. Just as such shares have no minimum return, they have no maximum return. Investors may seek a different class of ordinary share from a management team in order to create special class rights which attach to their investor shares, eg to control changes to the company's constitution, restrict the issue of further shares and so forth.

There can be different types of ordinary shares issued; for instance convertible redeemable preferred ordinary shares (CRPOs) may permit the holder to have the shares redeemed and may have certain preferred rights as against the ordinary shareholders to dividends or return of capital. The CRPOs may also be capable of conversion on some event into ordinary shares (for instance a listing of the shares on AIM or the Official List).

Management incentivisation – private company ratchets. In some cases, in order to incentivise the management shareholders in a company, the institutional shareholders may agree to the incorporation of a ratchet mechanism in the equity structure. Ratchets come in many different forms, however, the underlying principle behind them is that they are designed to vary the equity percentages of the shareholders, as between each other, by reference to the internal rate of return or some other performance bench mark achieved over the life of the investment. For example, the financial model for a company may indicate that in order to generate, say, a 30% internal rate of return per annum (IRR) on its investment, the investor needs to have, say, 75% of the issued ordinary shares at the time the company is set up. If the company performs better than expected such that the return to the investor is, say, 40% then a ratchet might apply so that the 'excess profit' generated by the investor, in excess of the required bench mark, is shared more generously with the management team than the starting equity percentages of 75%/25% would provide. For example, the equity structure of a company can be set up such that all profits up to a 30% IRR are shared between the management team and the investors in the ratio of 75/25 but that all profits in excess of that bench mark are shared 50/50. A ratchet can operate as a substantial 'carrot' to management teams in order to try to encourage superior performance.

(2) Preference shares

Preference shares come in many different types. They can have a fixed or floating rate of return based upon the amount paid for the preference share and/or on the profitability of the company. They may be redeemable, ie designed to be bought back by the company at some point in the future, either with or without a premium on redemption, or non-redeemable in which event their preference nature comes purely from their ability to attract a preferred dividend or return of capital on a winding-up. Preference shares may also be convertible into plain ordinary shares. Such conversion rights can provide a measure of downside protection to an investor (enabling them to keep preference shares should things go wrong, so that their investment ranks ahead of any ordinary share capital) but also the potential for enhanced upside so that should the value of plain ordinary shares exceed that of the preference shares then the investor may elect to convert them into ordinary shares.

(3) Options to subscribe

Although the grant of options themselves would not ordinarily raise capital for a company (the options sometimes being granted free of charge), options can form part of an investor's package of investment rights. These are attractive to investors as they allow them to hedge their bets and only participate in the shares subject to option if things are going well and the options are profitable. From the company's point of view, options may also be attractive as they have the potential to enhance the investor's upside and therefore make the investor perhaps less demanding on the terms of their initial cash investment. In this way the non-investor shareholders give away some equity but only in the event of future success of the company resulting in options being 'in the money' rather than giving away substantial amounts of equity early on. Options can be granted either without limit of time or with some trigger events at the time of which the investor must either exercise their option or lose the right to do so. Trigger events might include, for example, a future round of funding raised by the company, possibly a time limit by which options must be exercised or lapse, a strike price to be achieved or a requirement that they be exercised on or before the time of any sale or flotation.

(4) Warrants

Warrants are very similar to options but are normally issued by a company borrowing from an investor as part of the funding package. They are issued under a warrant instrument and entitle the holder to subscribe at a pre-determined price for a given number of shares (normally ordinary shares) on an event occurring (for instance, the flotation of a company or the price of ordinary shares reaching a given strike price).

(5) Convertible debt instruments

Convertible debt instruments can give attractive downside protection for an investor, in much the same way as convertible preference shares, save that by using a debt instrument the investor's interest ranks ahead of all classes of share in issue and, if secured, can also rank ahead of ordinary creditors. That downside protection may be useful in capitalising an oil and gas company which, typically, should be asset rich and therefore second ranking security, or ordinary unsecured debt, ranking after secured bank debt, might well have some commercial value. The debt instrument would normally contain quite a soft rate of interest (substantially less than the bench mark return of between 15% and 30% required by an equity investor, reflecting the lower risk attaching to a debt instrument).

Any substantial fund-raising, using private equity, may well contain two or more of the funding mechanisms referred to above, designed and based on certain assumptions, to produce an acceptable rate of return to the equity investor.

Equity documentation

There are many different types of legal documentation depending on the nature of the transaction or fund-raising. We summarise below some of the documents on the fund-raising referred to above.

1. *Articles of association.* A company will always have documents incorporating the company, which include a memorandum of association which sets out the objects for which the company was formed and articles of association which are the rules by which a company is governed. The articles set out the rights attaching to the different classes of share, dividend rights, rights on a return of capital, board composition, share transfer restrictions and, perhaps, mechanisms for forcing a sale of the company. There may be leaver provisions which provide that if a member of the management team leaves the company he may be forced to sell back his shares to the other shareholders. These may operate, for example, on dismissal, resignation or death, or on a shareholder's bankruptcy or on a shareholder becoming disabled or otherwise unable to do his work. There will be provisions dealing with the transfer of shares and those will often in a private company generally prohibit the transfer of shares but permit some transfers of shares to, for instance, family members of the management shareholders or between members of the same group of funders. There will normally be a pre-emption mechanism on a shareholder wishing to sell his shares entitling the other shareholders to purchase them in the event that that shareholder obtains permission to sell.

There will also normally be rights for institutional investors with more than, say, 50% of the voting rights to procure the sale of the entire issued share capital of the company – known as a 'drag along' right. Conversely, there may be 'tag along' rights which state that the majority of shareholders cannot transfer or sell their shares having voting rights of, for instance, 50% of the entire shareholding of the company without the proposed buyer of the shares making an offer to all shareholders on the same basis.

2. *Investment Agreements*. Equity funders will normally fund on the basis of an Investment Agreement which is an agreement between the shareholders of the company in which they agree how the company is to be run.

The Investment Agreement is likely to set out the type of investment being made and the subscription mechanics, how much money is being invested and what sort of securities are to be issued. It may contain a list of conditions precedent which must be met before the funding will happen (eg completion of acquisition of an interest in a field) and warranties which are statements of facts to be given by the management team to the institutional investors. Those warranties will normally be limited in extent of financial liability and duration. The management team will normally be required to put in some cash of their own to provide evidence that they are aligned with institutional funders and the Investment Agreement will document that. There will be clauses including negative covenants which place negative controls on the management of the company; for instance, that the company cannot borrow above certain limits without institutional investors' consent or cannot issue new shares or alter the share capital of the company or the articles of association or memorandum of association without institutional investors' consent. There will also be positive covenants in which the management team are required to undertake various matters and financial covenants. The management team are normally required to provide monthly or quarterly management accounts and audited accounts to all shareholders. There will be clauses dealing with the board of directors who are to be appointed and whether there are to be any non-executive directors appointed. There may be a statement that a proportion of non-executive directors are independent and others are to represent the institutional investors.

2. Loan notes

Funding may include the issue of loan notes (effectively, debt) by the company as issuer to institutional investors who are the loan note holders. The company issues the loan notes under a Loan Note Instrument. The Loan Note Instrument is a document which sets out the rights and obligations owed by the issuer (ie the company raising the money) to the note holder. The Instrument will set out the interest to accrue on the notes and the terms for repayment. It may also contain provisions allowing the holders to convert their notes into fully paid shares in the issuing company – effectively allowing them the option of converting relatively 'low risk, low return' loan notes, with a fixed rate of interest return, into riskier but potentially more profitable equity shares. Other provisions dealing with the holding of note holder's meetings or clauses dealing with the calling in of the debt and a demand to repay the debt on an occurrence of an event of default will be set out in the Loan Note Instrument. The Loan Note itself simply evidences the amount of debt which has been borrowed by the issuer. Loan notes are usually unsecured and postponed to any bank debt and so carry a rate of interest higher than bank debt, as well perhaps as conversion rights, to compensate the noteholders for that higher risk.

3. Debt finance

Any financing party considering making a debt facility available to a borrower for an upstream oil and gas project will do so on the basis that the projected cash flows to be generated by that borrower are sufficient to service the debt with a reasonable margin for error. Those projected cash flows may be from a single asset, where the bank is lending against that asset, or they may represent the combined cash flows from a number of assets at different stages of development by the company.

The degree to which the bank is comfortable that those cash flows are sustainable determines the level of debt which the bank will be prepared to provide and the rate of interest charged on that debt – the more stable and predictable the cash flows, the higher the debt capacity of the asset and the lower the rate of interest to be charged.

For this reason, debt funding, unless to be repaid out of existing cash flows from currently producing assets, is seldom appropriate for exploration, seismic or preliminary development work pre-production. It may not be always appropriate for certain projects with a high degree of risk or uncertainty. Similarly, towards the end of the life of a project, the banks lending against a particular asset will wish to be assured that their loans are repaid in full before the net present value of the relevant asset, taking into account the prospective abandonment liability and future net cash flows from the asset, goes negative. Banks do not wish to be in a position where their borrower has no net economic interest in the field (as abandonment costs may well exceed the likely income from the field towards the end of the field's life; see Chapter 15 on Decommissioning) leaving the bank in a position where it is the only party interested in successfully producing oil from the field.

It follows that there will almost certainly be some element of expenditure on any project which requires funding other than debt funding to be raised.

There are different ways of raising loans in both the private and public markets which are as follows.

Private debt funding

Private debt funding (ie debt funding not raised on the public capital markets) is governed by a Facility Agreement entered into between the borrower and a bank or a syndicate of banks – for larger facilities, banks may group together to form a syndicate in order to spread the risk of lending to a particular borrower. Only where a facility is in excess of £10–£20 million is it likely to be syndicated.

Bank debt may be offered to a borrower in the form of a single facility or may be divided into senior and junior facilities. Debt which is ordinarily secured and first-ranking on any insolvency of the debtor is termed 'senior' and any debt which is either secured or unsecured and ranks after that senior debt is referred to as 'junior', subordinated or mezzanine debt. Reflecting the higher level of risk attaching to subordinated or unsecured debt, the junior facility would normally carry a higher margin or rate of interest on that debt. Senior debt would typically be provided at a margin over base rate of 1–2.5% whereas mezzanine debt would typically carry a rate something in excess of 3% over base.

It is beyond the scope of this work to consider all the permutations for different types of debt facility or to analyse a Facility Agreement in detail, however, in the context of oil and gas project economics it is worth noting that debt facilities are often made available by reference to a 'borrowing base calculation'. The calculation, which is redetermined periodically throughout the life of the bank facility, is intended to calculate the net present value of the future cash flows expected to be generated from the sale of petroleum from the producing fields against which the facility is secured. As the development and production from the field continue changes are made in the P90 and P50 reserves attributable to that field, the market price expected to be achieved for the sale of petroleum from the field, the opex applying to that field and the expected costs for decommissioning that field – all of these variables are taken into account in order to redetermine periodically the amount which the borrower can draw under the facility. The intention behind the redetermination is that the amount of debt outstanding to the bank at any point in time is more than covered, with a significant margin, by the expected net future cash flows from the field.

Capital markets – debt instruments/bond issues

A large company with sufficient high revenue earnings before interest, tax and depreciation may raise capital by issuing high-yield bonds, whether on the private or public markets, to refinance existing bank debt (perhaps incurred as a result of the company acquiring a series of assets) or for capital borrowing on a very large project. High-yield bonds pay fixed interest over the period of the term of the bond, they tend to be repaid at the end of the term of the bond and the bond would normally have a term maturity of between 6 and 12 years after its issue. The minimum size of a high-yield bond issue is usually in the region of £65 million.

A large upstream oil and gas company may issue Commercial Paper, Bonds or Medium Term Notes (MTNs). Bonds and MTNs may be listed and admitted to trading on a regulated market (and therefore subject to the Prospectus Directive). In terms of Bonds and Medium Term Notes, a ratings agency will give a 'grading' on an issue which states that agency's opinion as to the creditworthiness of the issuer or as to the issuer defaulting on its repayment obligations. There are three main agencies which include Moodys Investors Services, Standard & Poors Corporation and Fitch Ratings.

Commercial Paper is a short-term debt instrument which will normally need to be repaid within a year and provides short-term working capital. It is normally issued under a Programme Platform and not listed directly on a public market.

Bonds are again debt instruments which may have maturity of anything between 2 and 50 years but are normally about 2–10 years.

Medium Term Notes are normally issued like Commercial Paper under a Programme Platform and are now commonly used for longer-term working capital requirements. Both MTNs and Commercial Paper will generally be issued under Programme Platform which is an uncommitted ongoing facility put together by an issuer, arranged by an arranger and underwritten by investment banks known as dealers. It should be noted that issues of Commercial Paper are not normally issued on a public market and normally fall outside the Prospectus Directive regime.

4. Other forms of capital-raising

Farm-out or sale

If a company is unable or unwilling to commit all of the funds necessary for a particular project, then it can derive economic benefit from that project either by farming out part of the interest in the field in exchange for the incoming party bearing some or all of the proposed development costs or, after having undertaken some preliminary work to identify an opportunity for a party with capital resources to meet the ongoing costs, a company can dispose of the field interest entirely, at a profit over the original acquisition cost.

Contractor 'equity'

Some contractors (for example, drilling contractors or the major service companies) may be prepared to reduce their rates for the provision of manpower and equipment in exchange for a risk/reward-type contract which entitles them to a higher fee on 'success'. In effect, the field owners lay off some of the risk of the project being unsuccessful onto the service companies who, in accepting this exchange, provide a quasi-equity form of funding to the project. This can be attractive, particularly to Exploration and Production (E&P) companies, as it enables the oil and gas companies to retain complete ownership of the licence, operatorship of the field and to book all of the reserves as their own for reporting purposes, whilst using third party contractors to bear some of the cost and risk of the development. This has some of the advantages of a farm-out but without the need to sell reserves or take in a field partner.

Where the oil company is relatively small and the service company is particularly large, this can be quite an efficient means of deploying capital. The average weighted cost of capital for a large service company is likely to be significantly less than the cost of capital for a new entrant oil company and allows the new entrant oil company, in exchange for giving away some of the upside, to benefit from the strength of balance sheet and lower cost of capital available to the larger partner.

5. Different models

Traditionally, an upstream oil and gas company wishing to carry out a project had to have enough capital to cover the following:

(a) acquisition of the asset;
(b) initial exploration/appraisal/preparation of a Field Development Programme (FDP);
(c) implementation of the FDP;
(d) ongoing, capital expenditure and operating expenditure; and
(e) ultimately, abandonment of the field.

Each of the forgoing steps involves the provision of working capital and, cumulatively, these can amount to a significant capital commitment.

In the case of a large multinational upstream oil and gas company the project team that is working on the project will need to make the case to the relevant asset management committee to develop the project and prove that it meets bench marks internationally for that company. Such a project will compete against other projects for capital and the project team will need to demonstrate that its project will meet an internal target for the internal rate of return on the capital of the multinational before that project will get internal sanction. Large multinational companies may, therefore, hold on to assets which are regarded as exploration or appraisal assets for years without carrying out much work on these assets because they do not meet their current internal criteria for development. However, they may not wish to relinquish those assets or to sell the assets as the internal criteria could change. For instance, a heavy oil asset may not currently be capable of development at a cost which meets the investment return target but the price for heavy oil may go up or there may be new technologies or downstream facilities for handling such oil, in which case that asset may be capable of development within a few years' time.

In a smaller upstream oil and gas company its cost of capital might be higher because it is unable to access, for instance, debt on low interest rates on the debt capital market or its shares may be less liquid than a bigger company or it may not have sufficient capability to attract investors to a large rights issue for its shares and therefore fund certain projects. Lack of sufficient working capital may leave it unable to fund field development.

Traditionally, both such companies may have gone into a project on the basis that they could fund its way through the whole project from exploration, appraisal through to production and abandonment. For both those types of company there may be opportunities for partnering with another company who will provide development capital for a project but not the capital necessary to decommission the field – in that way, new external sources of capital may be accessed, so making it easier for a project to meet internal return on capital criteria.

7.11 Hedging

Any financing model for a project is simply a hypothetical series of cash flows. In the real world, there are risks to those cash flows – interest rates may go up and correspondingly the liability of a company to service debt incurred on a project; similarly, oil price or gas price may go down, resulting in lower income from a project. Use of hedging contracts can assist in managing these risks.

There are numerous forms of hedging arrangement which may be entered into and new forms are developed every year. If there is a financial risk involved in a project it is almost certain that the capital markets will have created a hedging instrument to manage that risk.

As a simple example, a hedging contract may be taken to guard against a fall in the oil price. For example, a model for a particular project may assume that there are 100,000 barrels of oil produced every calendar month in 2007, at an average price of $40 per barrel. The company carrying out that project wishes to underpin that assumption and may be prepared to give away some upside in return for doing so. It may be more concerned about a low oil price jeopardising the project and making it loss-making than about the likelihood of an extremely high spike in oil price resulting in a super profit. The company could enter into a hedging agreement in respect of, say, a hypothetical 100,000 barrels of oil for each of January, February, March and so on in 2007, at a price of $40 per barrel with a hedging counterparty. Under the contract, if the actual oil price in any of those months is less than $40 per barrel then the hedging counterparty would undertake to pay to the project company the difference between the actual market price of oil and $40 per barrel for 100,000 barrels. Conversely, if the actual oil price is higher than $40 per barrel, the project company undertakes to pay the difference between the actual oil price, say $60 per barrel; and the nominated contract price of $40 per barrel to the hedging counterparty for the same 100,000 barrels. By this mechanism, the project company guarantees that for a *hypothetical* production of 100,000 barrels per month throughout 2007 it would never receive less than $40 per barrel and in exchange it gives up any excess over $40 per barrel. This helps the project company to de-risk its project and give some comfort that actual cash flows from the project will be more in line with those assumed in the model. It is important to note that such contracts are based on *hypothetical* and not *real* production – if, because of production difficulties or delays, the project company produces, say, only 10,000 barrels of oil in May 2007 at $60 per barrel it will still be obliged to account to the hedging party for $20 per barrel for a hypothetical 100,000 barrels of oil in that month.

Similar hedging contracts can be put in place to guard against the risk of an increase in interest rates or fluctuations in currency rates where field costs and debt may be incurred in sterling but yet all production is sold in dollars.

Other forms of hedging can take the form of forward sales of production in terms of which the project company, rather than taking a spot price for its oil on the market and risking that the market falls, agrees to deliver oil in the future at a fixed price. Such contracts may reduce one risk (that of a falling oil price) but they also expose the company to significant financial loss if for some reason production fails and it cannot deliver the oil as contracted. If the spot price for oil has risen by the delivery date and the company is unable to deliver the oil at the lower price agreed then the company is usually exposed to paying to the oil buyer the difference between the contract price of the oil and the price which the buyer has to pay in the open market in order to purchase barrels on the spot market. That financial exposure can, of course, be further covered by another hedging contract and so on.

Hedging documentation

Documentation for such hedging agreements can take many forms, however, the most common is that produced by the International Swaps and Derivatives Association (ISDA). For example, the ISDA has produced a Master Agreement which may be entered into between a project company and a hedging counterparty – once in place, individual hedging contracts can be put into place under that Master Agreement. It is beyond the scope of this section to describe that Master Agreement in detail, however, some features are worth noting as they do have a bearing on the project economics and the working capital required of a party to a hedging agreement. One aspect of particular note is the requirement for a party to a hedging agreement to put up security in certain circumstances. By its nature, a hedging contract can expose a party to significant financial risk. In the above example, if the oil price were to rise significantly then the contingent liability of the project company to account for the difference between the high actual price of oil and the relatively low price hedged in the contract may be significant. In theory, that liability is matched by real production, ie real barrels of oil being sold at the real spot price in the real world, and, therefore, the project company should have sufficient cash to meet the liability under the hedging agreement, but what if the production is not there? This credit risk exposure of the hedging counterparty is usually accepted by the hedging counterparty up to a particular limit but if that credit limit is exceeded then the hedging counterparty may require the project company to put up security for its contingent liability under the hedging contract, usually by way of a bank letter of credit. If real production has not at least matched the hypothetical production in the hedging contract there is a real risk that the demand on that letter of credit will arrive at a time of a particular cash flow crisis in the project company – hedging contracts require to be used with care.

— 8 —

NORTH SEA TAXES

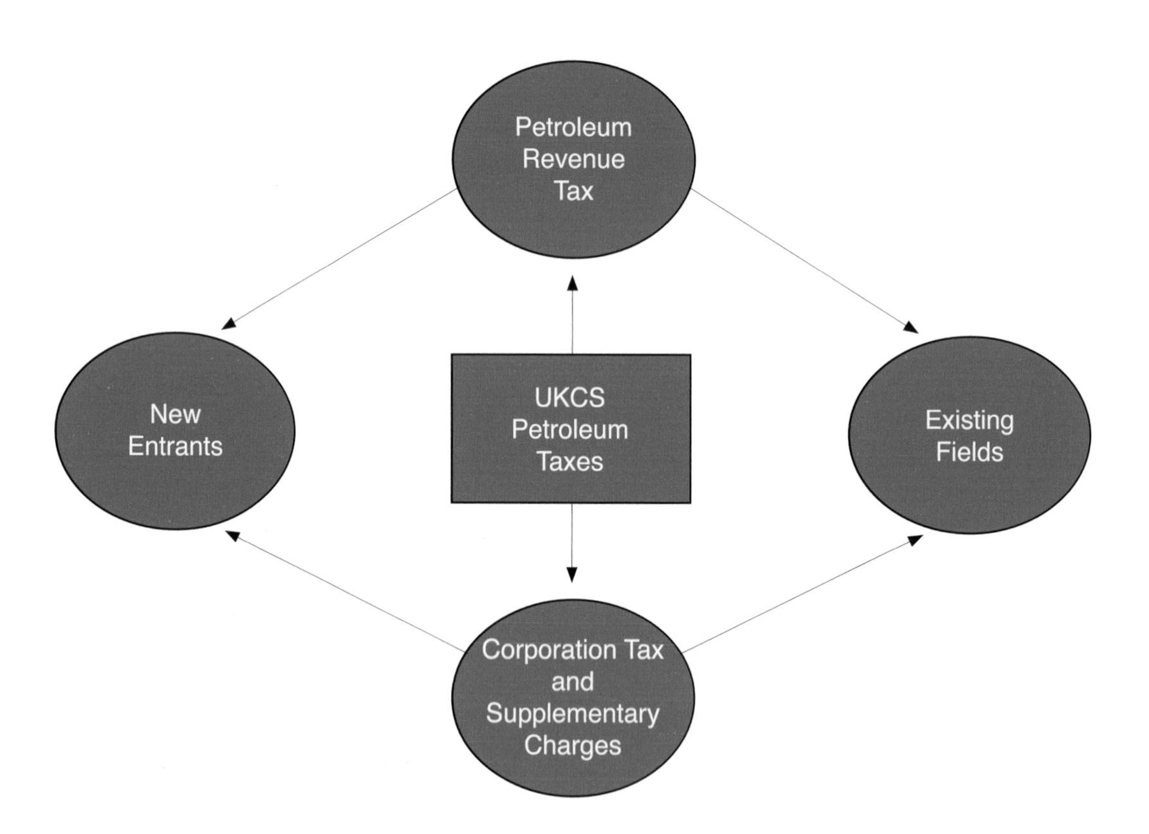
Petroleum Revenue Tax
New Entrants
UKCS Petroleum Taxes
Existing Fields
Corporation Tax and Supplementary Charges

NORTH SEA TAXES

8.1 Introduction

The UK North Sea fiscal regime has seen many changes over the years as the government of the day has continually sought to find the right balance between maximising government take and encouraging investment. There have been some periods of relative stability, for example between 1993 and 2002, but rarely has a year gone by without some adjustment to the rules.

Generally speaking, as the North Sea has matured, the fiscal regime has shed its more regressive elements (such as Royalty) and moved to a more progressive system of taxation. All direct taxes that currently apply to companies operating in the North Sea are essentially profit-based and allow companies to recover all their major costs before tax is charged. The playing field is not a level one, however, since profits are taxed at different rates according to the age and size of the field from which they are derived. Large, old fields are taxed much more heavily than new fields to which an internationally more competitive rate applies. This disparity in rates, combined with the frequent tweaking of the rules over the years, does unfortunately lead to some complexity in the regime.

Before 1975 there were two elements to the North Sea fiscal regime: Royalty charged at 12.5% of the wellhead value of gross production and Corporation Tax (CT) charged at 52% on companies' taxable profits. Against the background of soaring oil prices it became clear in the early 1970s that a fiscal regime based only on these two elements would not achieve the then Government's objective of securing a sufficient share of the 'super profits' (economic rent) that were likely to arise from the large oil fields in prospect to the north and east of Scotland. So, in 1975 two new elements were added to the regime:

- a new tax – Petroleum Revenue Tax (PRT) – to be charged at 45% on the profits arising from individual fields; and
- a 'ring fence' for CT around a company's entire profits from the North Sea.

Both these elements still remain, although as explained below, PRT, while still very significant where it applies, is now limited to profits from larger, older fields.

There were many upward changes to the regime in the late 1970s and early 1980s, with the marginal tax rates rising at one point to 90%. These rises led to a significant decline in the number of projects being brought forward so tax rates started to come down again and specific reliefs introduced, most notably the abolition of Royalty on certain fields and the introduction of cross-field reliefs for PRT. However, the latter led to a significant loss of tax revenue which prompted the Government in 1993 to reform the system by abolishing PRT for all 'future' fields (and with it the costly cross-field reliefs) and reduce the PRT rate to 50%.

No further significant changes were made to the tax regime until 2002 when a new 10% Supplementary Charge on ring fence profits for CT was introduced. At the same time, significantly more generous CT investment allowances were introduced and Royalty abolished entirely from 2003. Finally, in the 2005 Pre-Budget Report the Government doubled the Supplementary Charge to 20% from 2006 in response to much higher oil prices. This rise was accompanied by a guarantee that there would be no further increases for the life of the current Parliament.

8.2 Summary of the current tax system

Following the abolition of Royalty in 2003 there are three taxes that currently apply to profits from extracting oil and gas in the North Sea, though most field profits are subject to only two of the taxes.

- Petroleum Revenue Tax (PRT) at 50% on profits from fields given development consent before 16 March 1993, though, as explained further below, many such fields do not pay any PRT because of the allowances available.
- Corporation Tax (CT) at 30% on company profits with a 'ring fence' around profits from the North Sea.
- Supplementary Charge (SC) at 20% on 'ring fence' profits as computed for CT but with financing costs added back.

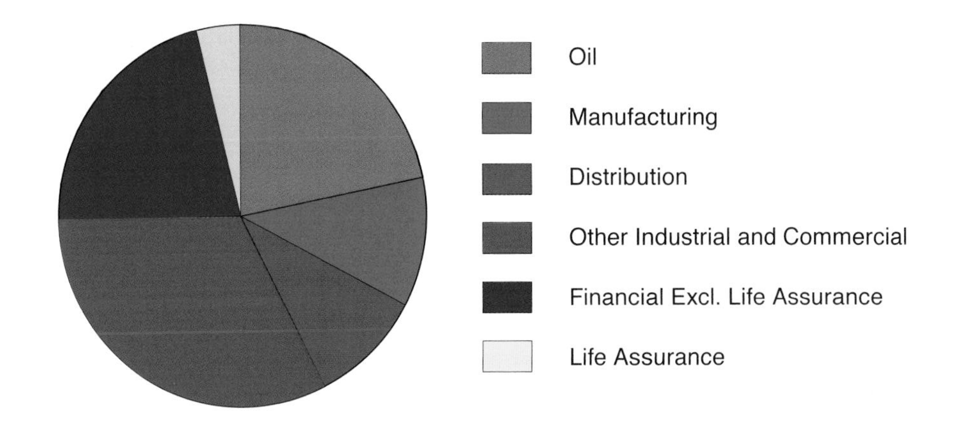

Figure 8–1 Corporate tax revenues from HMRC National Statistics in 2005/2006

PRT is deductible for CT and SC so that the marginal rate of tax for profits from PRT-paying fields is 75% and for profits from all other fields is 50%.

Decisions on North Sea tax changes are a matter for the Chancellor of the Exchequer in his annual Spring Budget (though now often made at the time of the late autumn Pre-Budget Report), with general oversight of North Sea tax policy resting with officials in the Treasury. Responsibility for ensuring that the present rules remain fit for purpose and general administration of the taxes lies with the Large Business Service, Oil and Gas (LBSOG), previously known as the Oil Taxation Office, which is part of HM Revenue and Customs (HMRC). In addition to taxes on UK oil production LBSOG also deals with the tax liabilities of all oil companies with UK downstream operations and UK resident oil companies with overseas operations, upstream or downstream. It also handles the tax liabilities of non-resident contractors operating on the UK continental shelf.

With the recent hike in oil prices, oil has once again become an important source of State revenue. In the tax year 2005/2006 North Sea tax revenues are estimated to be £9.6 billion (made up of £2 billion PRT, £5.6 billion CT and £2 billion SC): around 22% of UK corporate tax revenues for that year (see Fig. 8–1). While these revenues are much larger than they have been for years, they are now dwarfed by oil revenues accruing to its North Sea neighbour, Norway, which for 2005 amounted to around NOK 200 billions.

8.3 Petroleum Revenue Tax

Basic structure

PRT, which was introduced by the Oil Taxation Act 1975, is a tax on profits derived under licence from individual oil and gas fields, in the UK or its continental shelf, other than in respect of gas sold to British Gas under contracts made before 30 June 1975. As part of the major tax reform of PRT in 1993 its application was restricted to fields first given development consent before 16 March 1993. Fields developed on or after that date which are outside the scope of the tax are described in the legislation as 'non-taxable fields'. (Under proposals made in the 2006 Pre-Budget Report non-taxable fields may also include decommissioned fields first developed before 16 March 1993 but which are subsequently redeveloped.) PRT is charged on individual participators (invariably the licensees) at a rate of 50% on their net income from the field in a six-month chargeable period. The boundary of each field is determined by DTI strictly on the basis of geological criteria. There are special allowances designed to ensure that it bites only on the larger, more profitable fields. As it is a field-based tax, the costs of developing one field cannot be set against the profits of another.

There are around 120 North Sea fields potentially within the scope of PRT but, due to the special reliefs available, only around half that number are ever likely to pay any PRT. The vast majority of the tax is paid by only a handful of fields. In the first half of 2005, for example, only 31 fields paid PRT, eight of which paid around two-thirds of the tax.

Though the rules of PRT can be very complex, it has a simple underlying principle. It is computed by taking for each six-month chargeable period the difference between 'positive amounts' (income) and 'negative amounts' (expenditure) which produces either an 'assessable profit' or an 'allowable loss' for each participator in the field. From any resulting profit is deducted allowable losses (for other periods) and 'oil allowance'. The tax payable may then be capped in certain circumstances by a relief known as 'safeguard'. A simple example of a computation is given below as an Appendix.

Measurement of 'gross profit'

The main element of the positive amounts is, of course, revenue from the disposal of oil or gas which is described in the legislation as the 'gross profit'. Where the disposal is a sale on the open market ('arm's length') then the sale price is included in the computation. Where the disposal is not at arm's length, for example where oil is appropriated for refining, then the income to be taken into account for PRT is the 'market value' of the oil or gas, as determined by LBSOG. In addition to production disposed of in the period, 50% of the value of any production in stock at the end of the period, less an equivalent amount in respect of opening stock, has to be brought into account. There are also special rules known as the 'nomination scheme' that can apply to change the amount of income that is taken into account for arm's-length sales of oil (not gas) on the forward market.

The definition of 'arm's length' is much tighter for sales of oil than it is for other products. Very broadly, the contract has to be a cash sale with the terms unaffected by any kind of connection or arrangement between the parties.

Valuation of oil

Some significant changes to the way North Sea oil (not gas) is valued were made in the Finance Act 2006. Previously, oil was priced on a monthly basis, taking the average value of arm's-length sales over a six-week reference period. From 1 July 2006 the monthly market value has been replaced by a system which values each cargo of oil around its delivery or appropriation date. There are separate rules for blends with a readily quoted price, such as Brent and Forties, where the price is determined by taking an average of published prices over a five-day period and for other blends where the rules allow more discretion on the method to be employed, taking account of how arm's-length sales of oil of that kind would be priced.

In certain circumstances, an additional amount from the sale of oil, called a 'nomination excess', may be included in the 'gross profit'. Following changes to the nomination scheme made in the Finance Act 2006, only companies which sell oil on the forward market (such as the 21-day BFO market) need be concerned with this. They must notify LBSOG within two hours of the forward deal if they wish the actual sales price to be included for tax rather than the market value at the time of delivery. This is to prevent a practice known as 'tax spinning' whereby producers enter into a range of deals on the forward market and choose the lowest price for tax.

Valuation of gas

Where gas is sold to a related (marketing) company the tax price is that which gas of the kind in question would have fetched under an arm's-length contract, taking into account all the circumstances relevant to the particular disposal. The legislation requires a hypothetical contract to be constructed between the seller and the buyer by reference to arm's-length contracts struck in similar circumstances. The aim is therefore to mirror the arm's-length market for the product in question. These values are not easy to find and may require considerable negotiation with LBSOG.

Tariffs

In 1983, immediate relief for expenditure was extended to all North Sea assets regardless of whether they might be used in other North Sea fields. As a *quid pro quo* the scope of the PRT charge was extended to cover tariff receipts for the use by third parties of field assets, such as pipelines and treatment facilities (described in the legislation as 'qualifying assets') and the full receipts from their disposal.

However, not all tariffs received in PRT-liable fields are charged to PRT. First, there is an allowance known as the Tariff Receipts Allowance which exempts from PRT tariff receipts for the first 250,000 tonnes of throughput per six-month chargeable period from each user field. No allowance is due where the user field is outside the scope of PRT. Second, there is an important exemption for new tariffing business introduced in the Finance Act 2004. This exempts from PRT tariffs received from 1 January 2004 under a contract entered into on or after 9 April 2003 in relation to any field receiving development consent from that date or any older field that has not previously used a 'qualifying asset'. This latter category is primarily aimed at Norwegian fields which have not previously made use of infrastructure in the UK sector. The exemption for new tariffing business was introduced to maximise the useful life of such infrastructure and to encourage the development of further UK fields in their vicinity.

Field expenditure

Unlike CT, there is no distinction between capital and revenue expenditure for PRT. As a general rule only expenditure which meets one or more of a number of field-based purpose tests may be allowed. All qualifying expenditure is allowable in full as it is incurred. The qualifying field purposes cover exploration (up to 5km out from the field), appraisal, production, transportation (to the UK or the nearest reasonable delivery place abroad), initial treatment and storage, sales, and decommissioning the field at the end of its life.

All expenditure incurred in acquiring or improving major items of equipment used in the field are allowable for PRT provided they are used for the purposes set out above, even if the assets concerned are shared with other fields under a cost-sharing or tariffing arrangement, though in the former case the expenditure may be apportioned between the relevant fields. Expenditure on mobile assets which are not dedicated to a field (such as a drilling rig) is given over their expected life. There are some complex anti-avoidance provisions to prevent costs being shifted from non-PRT liable or non-PRT-paying fields into PRT-paying fields or being inflated in such fields, especially where transactions are between related companies. In particular, in these circumstances there is no write-up of assets to market value on transfer.

Certain cross-field reliefs have been allowed in the past (and some past expenditure may still be utilised now) but the only current non field-related expenditure that may be claimed directly in a field now is that incurred on research that has not been allowed in a field within three years of the costs being incurred.

Some field expenditure is specifically prohibited as being allowed for PRT. Most notably no relief is given for interest or other financing costs. This disallowance has applied from the outset of PRT owing to concerns that regulating its allowance under a field-based system would be wrought with difficulty leading to considerable loss of tax revenue. Also, no relief is available for the costs of onshore land, or onshore buildings to the extent that they are used for any downstream process.

Supplement

To compensate for the disallowance of financing costs there is a supplement of 35% (often referred to as 'uplift') which is added to certain allowable expenditure incurred up to the end of the six-month chargeable period in which the field reaches 'payback', ie when the cumulative cash flow of the field first turns positive. The expenditure qualifying for supplement is the major (generally capital) expenditure incurred to bring the field onstream or improve the rate of production or transportation. The relief is of little value now as most PRT fields will have long passed 'payback'.

Special reliefs for PRT

There are two special reliefs – oil allowance and safeguard – to protect small or economically marginal fields from paying PRT.

Oil allowance gives a PRT-free 'first slice' of production to each field. It is given after all expenditure relief and losses, but only so far as to reduce the profit for the period to nil. There are three levels of allowance given per six-month chargeable period, with a cumulative limit over the life of the field of 20 times the allowance per period, as follows:

- 250,000 metric tonnes (cumulative limit of 5 million tonnes) for fields given development consent before 1 April 1982;
- 125,000 metric tonnes (cumulative limit of 2.5 million tonnes) for all Southern Basin fields and onshore fields given development consent on or after 1 April 1982; and
- 500,000 metric tonnes (cumulative limit 10 million tonnes) for all other fields given development consent on or after 1 April 1982.

The allowance is converted by a formula to a cash amount and allocated between the participators in accordance with their share of the oil produced in the period. Many of the older fields have now exhausted their oil allowance. Nevertheless, the allowance continues to protect many smaller fields from paying any PRT and can be a valuable allowance in PRT-paying fields. Over £1.2 billion assessable profits were covered by the allowance in such fields in the first six months of 2005.

Safeguard was designed to give companies a degree of assurance about the minimum level of profit they could expect to enjoy after PRT (but before CT) with a view to ensuring that marginal fields remained profitable. Under safeguard no PRT is payable if the 'adjusted profit' of the field is less than 15% of accumulated capital expenditure. If more, then the PRT cannot exceed 80% of the excess. The 'adjusted profit' for safeguard is broadly the gross profits less operating costs. As the allowance is only available to fields for periods until 'payback' is reached plus half as many periods again, the relief is of diminishing value in the North Sea.

Losses

Allowable losses may be carried backwards against assessable profits of earlier periods (beginning with the latest such period) or forwards against future profits until the losses are exhausted. If the field has ceased production then any losses are first carried back to exhaust any profits of that participator for previous periods and then any profits of participators that previously held the loss-maker's interest in the field. Once all such field profits are exhausted (and providing the winning of oil from the field has permanently ceased) then any balance becomes an 'unrelievable field loss' which may be relieved against the profits of any other field of the loss-maker. This is the only rule, other than that for research expenditure, which now allows a breach of the strict PRT field 'ring fence'.

Transfers of field interests

From the outset PRT has been a tax on the proceeds of North Sea oil less the actual costs of producing it. It does not seek to tax the profit on sales of licence or field interests, nor does it allow the costs of acquiring such interests. Consistent with this philosophy therefore the rules on transfers of interests are designed to ensure that, as far as possible, the new owner inherits the full PRT position of the old owner, including any expenditure relief not yet allowed, any unused allowable losses and the 'cumulative capital expenditure' for safeguard purposes. The transfer does not give rise to any disposal receipts chargeable to PRT.

PRT returns and payment of tax

The PRT system works on the basis of assessments being made for each of two six month chargeable periods ending on 30 June and 31 December. Returns of income are kept quite separate from claims for expenditure – the two only coming together in assessments made by LBSOG.

First, *the responsible person* for each taxable field (invariably the operator) has to submit a return of the total amount of oil and gas produced from the field, together with each participator's share, within one month of the end of each chargeable period (PRT2). Second, *each participator* has to submit a return of all their own incomings, including revenues from all sales of oil and any tariff and disposal receipts, within two months of the end of the chargeable period (PRT1). In addition, within two months of the end of the chargeable period, *each participator*, has to render a return showing all arm's-length sales during the period by each company in the group in each type of crude which are not otherwise included in a PRT1 return (PRT1A).

Before any expenditure is allowed in an assessment it has to be claimed by participators and agreed by LBSOG (or determined on appeal), although a provisional allowance of 5% of gross profits, subject to later clawback, may be given. Most of the expenditure is claimed by *the responsible person* and allocated between the participators (PRT30), but companies can make individual claims for expenditure which is commercially sensitive, such as insurance premiums (PRT40). Typically, expenditure claims will be submitted for a period by the two- month deadline for returns of income so that the expenditure can be agreed in time for inclusion in the assessment which is normally made not later than five months after the end of the chargeable period.

PRT is paid by means of instalments, payment on account, and payment (or repayment) against an assessment. The payment on account must be made when the return of income is delivered, two months after the end of the period, ie on 31 August and 28 February, and is based on the participator's calculation of the PRT payable for the period (PRT6). This may include expenditure for the period which has not yet been formally agreed. This payment on account is then used to calculate monthly instalments for the next chargeable period on the basis of six equal payments, each one being one-eighth of the payment on account. When the assessment is finalised any excess of the final PRT liability over the payment on account and instalments becomes due and payable or any balance repayable, with interest on any underpayment or overpayment calculated from the payment on account date.

8.4 Corporation Tax and Supplementary Charge

General CT rules

Corporation tax is charged on the net profits of all companies operating in the UK, including profits from oil or gas activities on the UK continental shelf. The main rate of tax (for profits over £1.5 million) is 30%. All the general CT rules apply to oil companies but with certain modifications, most notably the special 'ring fence' (explained below) which is used as the vehicle to apply additional tax to North Sea profits in recognition of the special nature of oil operations and the importance to government of securing tax revenue from this important national resource. In the 2007 Budget, a reduction in the general rate of CT to 28% from 1 April 2008 has been proposed. However, this general reduction is not to apply to 'ring fence' profits which will continue to be taxed at 30%.

UK tax resident companies are chargeable to CT on their worldwide profits while non-resident companies are chargeable on profits attributable to a 'permanent establishment' (a fixed place of business) in the UK. The UK continental shelf (outside of the 12-mile territorial sea limit) is not part of the UK. However, non-resident oil companies involved in UK oil production, offshore or onshore, will invariably have a permanent establishment in the UK but, in any event, there are special rules to treat an exploration or exploitation connected activity on the UK continental shelf as carried on through a permanent establishment in the UK. If that were not enough, as a condition of a licence for operating on the UK continental shelf, companies are required to have a taxable presence in the UK proper through which they conduct their offshore operations.

CT is charged on the profits made in each accounting period of the company, ie the period over which the company draws up its accounts. A company's profits comprise its income and capital gains. Trading profits are taxed on an accruals basis, generally in accordance with the accounting treatment. Capital gains are taxed on realisation. An important distinction is made for CT between revenue and capital expenditure. Revenue expenditure, which is wholly and exclusively incurred for the purpose of the business, is allowed in full. No deduction is available for capital expenditure or depreciation as such but instead relief is given by way of a system of capital allowances. Trading losses can be set off against other profits and gains, including capital gains, arising in the same, or previous, accounting period, or carried forward and set off against future profits arising in the same trade. There is a system of group relief whereby a trading loss made by one group member can be surrendered for set off against the profits accruing in an equivalent accounting period of another.

North Sea ring fence

The most important modification of the general CT rules for oil companies is the 'ring fence' that treats UK oil extraction activities as a separate 'ring fence' trade. The original purpose of the 'ring fence' was to prevent profits from UK oil chargeable to normal CT being eroded by costs or losses arising from other activities. However, it is now used additionally as the basis for charging a higher rate of tax on such profits. It determines the tax base for the special Supplementary

Charge (explained below) and proposals in the 2007 Budget are that it should also be used from 1 April 2008 to apply a higher CT rate (30%) to such profits than will apply to profits from other corporate activities (28%). In computing ring fence profits only expenditure incurred for the ring fence trade may be allowed and losses arising from any non-ring fence activity of the company, whether downstream, overseas or any other type of activity, cannot be deducted. Similarly, group relief is denied for losses which emanate from activities outside the ring fence. Interest and other financing costs are only allowed against ring fence profits to the extent that the money borrowed is used to finance UK oil extraction activities or in acquiring UK oil rights.

The ring fence operates in only one direction and so there is nothing to prevent ring fence losses being used to reduce profits from other activities, providing the normal CT rules for the offset of losses are met. Ring fence losses may be carried forward or back (under the general CT rules) but only against ring fence profits.

It should be noted that companies that are not searching for, or producing oil or gas on their own account but merely providing services (as contractors or subcontractors), to those companies that are, pay CT under the normal rules. They are not subject to the special ring fence rules nor are they liable to Supplementary Charge.

Ring fence profits

The PRT rules for determining the amount of revenues to be included for tax from the disposal of UK oil or gas apply also for CT, even where the field is outside PRT. The income, therefore, will be the actual price from arm's-length sales or the market value as determined by LBSOG in other cases. Any nomination excesses on forward sales (see 'Valuation of oil' on page 269) are also brought into charge as ring fence income (but with a corresponding deduction given against non-ring fence profits to prevent double counting). Tariff receipts for the use of North Sea assets which would not otherwise be within the ring fence are brought in by specific legislation. Receipts on the disposal of North Sea assets which may be also charged to PRT, however, are not profits for CT, though any capital gains arising on the disposal of North Sea assets are within the charge (see 'Capital gains' on page 278).

Commencement of trade

Relief cannot be given for any expenditure, either of a revenue or capital nature, before a company has commenced a trade. Exploration is not generally regarded as a trade. Capital expenditure incurred prior to commencement of a trade, and revenue expenditure incurred within seven years of commencement, is treated as incurred on the first day of trading. The date on which a trade commences is a matter of fact to be determined on long-established general principles but in practice LBSOG will accept that a company has commenced to trade when a decision has been taken to proceed with the commercial development of a discovery which will lead to production.

Revenue expenditure

All operating costs and overheads related to the production of oil are allowable in full as they are incurred. Genuine R&D research work of a revenue nature can qualify for 125% relief. It is possible for innovative research by oil companies to qualify for this special relief but it should be noted that exploration and appraisal activity is specifically excluded.

Capital expenditure

There are some generous reliefs available to North Sea oil companies to encourage investment. The fact that they pay tax on their ring fence profits at a much higher rate than other companies makes the allowances economically very valuable. Some major changes to the general capital expenditure allowance have been proposed in the 2007 Budget, largely to take effect from April 2008. However, none of these changes are to apply to North Sea ring fence activities which retain their existing capital allowances treatment. The three most relevant allowances for North Sea oil companies are Research and Development Allowances (R&DA), Mineral Extraction Allowances (MEA) and Plant and Machinery Allowances (P&M).

The capital costs of exploration and appraisal (E&A) activity specifically qualify for relief under the R&DA code. Immediate 100% relief is available in the year the expenditure is incurred. Following longstanding practice the costs of E&A activity up to the time a decision is made to develop a field are allowable under this code. If assets representing R&DA expenditure are disposed of, the value attributable to that activity is clawed back as a trading receipt of the company (described in the legislation as a 'balancing charge').

Certain costs incurred by oil companies may qualify for relief under the MEA code as 'mineral exploration and access'. Mineral exploration and access includes both 'searching for and testing mineral deposits' and 'winning access to such deposits'. It therefore covers both E&A (as an alternative to R&DA) and the capital costs of drilling development wells after oil has been discovered. Since 17 April 2002 a 100% first year allowance (FYA) has been available for this expenditure incurred as part of a ring fence trade. MEA is also available for secondhand mineral exploration and access costs, for example on transfer of a licence interest where part of the value is attributable to drilling expenditure incurred by the seller. In such cases, the relief given to a purchaser cannot exceed the costs incurred by the seller. MEA also covers expenditure on mineral assets (such as the cost of a licence) where relief is available at 10% on a reducing balance basis. As for R&DA, there is a clawback of allowances on disposal of assets representing MEA expenditure.

Finally, all the major capital costs of acquiring or building infrastructure such as oil platforms, treatment facilities, pipelines and other capital equipment used in the production of oil and gas qualify for relief under the P&M code. As for MEA, since 17 April 2002, a FYA of 100% has been available for all such expenditure incurred for a ring fence purpose, other than that which is incurred on long-term assets (assets with an expected useful life of more than 25 years) in which case a FYA of 24% is available. The allowances may be clawed back as a balancing charge on disposal of the assets. If P&M assets are sold as part of the transfer of a field interest the allowance available to the purchaser is limited to the cost of the assets to the vendor. This is to prevent excessive allowances being given for North Sea assets which have been known to increase considerably in value as a result of new discoveries in the area or oil price rises.

A 100% immediate allowance is also available under the P&M code for the costs of decommissioning offshore infrastructure in accordance with an approved UK abandonment programme. Where a North Sea company has ceased to trade and incurs decommissioning costs within three years of the cessation, the company can claim a 100% allowance in respect of the expenditure in its final trading period. Where the company has losses arising from decommissioning these can be carried back for set off against profits of the trade in the preceding three years (instead of the normal one year). The costs of obtaining a bank guarantee or letter of credit against future abandonment costs are allowable in full though it should be noted that there is no allowance for any sums set aside (or provisions made in accounts) for future abandonment costs.

All the 100% allowances for major capital expenditure set out above (other than post-trade cessation decommissioning) are available only in the year the expenditure is incurred. However, the Finance Act 2006 made a one-off provision for companies to elect for expenditure incurred in the calendar year 2005 to be treated as incurred on the first day of the company's accounting period beginning on or after 1 January 2006. This was introduced alongside the doubling of the Supplementary Charge from 1 January 2006 and enabled companies to obtain relief for the sunk costs of recent investment at the new higher rate.

Ring Fence Expenditure Supplement

Exploration companies which have not yet commenced trading, or other companies without an existing income stream, are at an economic disadvantage compared to producing companies because of their inability to take advantage of the timing benefit of the 100% immediate tax reliefs. This is particularly the case for some North Sea new entrant companies which may not wish, or have the resources, to buy into a producing field. To compensate companies in this position, any unrelieved expenditure carried forward from one period to another (either as expenditure incurred before the trade commences or as a trading loss) is increased by a compound 6% per annum. This Ring Fence Expenditure Supplement applies to expenditure from 1 January 2006 and replaces a similar relief (introduced in 2004) which applied only to unrelieved exploration and appraisal expenditure. The Supplement may be claimed for a maximum of six years.

Capital gains

Capital gains realised on the disposal of North Sea assets (ie the difference between the sale proceeds and acquisition costs plus any enhancement expenditure) are chargeable to CT at 30% under normal rules. Indexation allowance (to take out gains attributable to inflation) is available to reduce the chargeable gains and rollover relief (to encourage further investment in the business) may be used to defer the gains. Some special rules, however, apply to capital gains of oil companies involved in North Sea operations. The most important of these is the ring fence which means that gains on the disposal of assets used in the ring fence trade cannot be reduced by losses arising outside the ring fence and rollover relief is available only if the sale proceeds are used to acquire other North Sea assets. There are also special rules applying to North Sea assets acquired before 1982 and to licence swaps.

Transfer pricing

The special market value rules that apply for PRT on the transfer of oil between related companies (see 'Valuation of oil' on page 269) apply also for CT. On other transactions, such as the provision of services between related parties, the same transfer pricing rules apply to oil companies as apply to other taxpayers, the general principle being that if the consideration does not represent an arm's-length price then that price is to be substituted. The ring fence, however, adds another dimension to the transfer pricing rules for oil companies. The rules apply across the ring fence boundary, even to transactions within a single company where it carries on both ring fence and non-ring fence activities. In such cases, the two types of activities are treated as if they were separate businesses carried on by separate companies under common control. Transfer pricing adjustments to cross ring fence transactions are subject to the 'one way street' principle: they can be made only where the substitution of an arm's-length price would increase ring fence profits.

Oil companies are also subject to the general transfer pricing rules that apply to loans ('thin capitalisation') but these too are extended for oil to apply across the ring fence boundary. Very broadly, this means that where a loan that crosses the boundary exceeds the amount that the borrower would or could have borrowed from an independent lender, or where the interest rate or other terms of the loan differ from those that would have been agreed with such a lender, the excessive interest is disallowed as a deduction in arriving at the assessable ring fence profits. There are rules for making corresponding adjustments in the hands of the lender where appropriate. LBSOG pay special attention to North Sea financing operations to ensure that ring fence profits are not diluted by interest on inter-company loans.

Supplementary Charge

Since 2002, an additional tax, known as Supplementary Charge (SC), has applied to the profits of companies producing oil or gas in the UK or on the UK continental shelf. SC applies to the profits of oil companies as computed for ring fence corporation tax purposes except that no relief is available for financing costs. All such costs deducted for CT have to be added back in computing SC. The reason given for this restriction at the time of its introduction was to guard against companies manipulating their levels of borrowing between ring fence and non-ring fence activities to minimise their SC liability. When it was introduced in 2002 the rate of SC was 10% but this was raised to 20% for profits arising from 1 January 2006 in the wake of much higher oil prices. The tax is administered in the same way as CT and companies pay SC at the same times as their CT liability.

CT and SC returns and payment of tax

Unlike for PRT, where responsibility for making assessments lies with HMRC, CT is self-assessed by the taxpayer. Every company liable to CT, including oil companies, must file a return within 12 months of the end of its accounting period, subject to penalties for late filing. The return (CT 600) contains the company's self-assessment to CT which, for an oil company with ring fence income, also includes its liability to SC (supplementary pages showing the SC liability also have to be completed). The company then has 12 months to amend its return, for example if it wishes to change a claim to capital allowances, and HMRC is allowed the same period to initiate an enquiry into its completeness and accuracy. This may be a straightforward request for information through to a full review of the company's business and records. HMRC must issue formal notice when it starts and ends an enquiry. (Budget 2007 proposes linking the 12 months enquiry 'window' for most companies, though not large groups, for accouting periods ending on or after 31 March 2008, to the date the return is received.) HMRC may also make a 'discovery' assessment if the return is later found to be inadequate as a result of fraudulent or negligent conduct, or of incomplete disclosure.

There is a single fixed due date for the payment of CT: 9 months and 1 day after the end of the accounting period. However, large companies have to pay their tax earlier than this by estimating their eventual tax liability and paying the tax by means of instalments of that estimate. The normal rule is that companies with a 12-month accounting period pay their tax in four equal instalments, in the seventh, tenth, thirteenth and sixteenth months following the start of the period. Oil companies have to meet that schedule of payments for tax on their non-ring fence profits, but tax on their ring fence profits, including SC, has to be paid by three equal instalments in the seventh, tenth and thirteenth months.

8.5 Taxation for new entrants

The tax consequences of commencing operations on the UKCS will depend on the nature of the organisation and the method of entry. Where, for example, a new entrant purchases an existing North Sea company through a share acquisition, the CT and PRT liabilities of the target company should remain unaffected by the change of ownership, providing it continues to trade as before. It should be noted, however, there will be no allowance for financing costs on the purchase (because the interest would fail to meet a ring fence purpose). So, while some selling companies may favour this route new entrant companies which rely on finance may not do so.

If entry is by means of a farm-in to an existing North Sea field or licence the new entrant will want to establish how much of the value of the acquisition is likely to qualify for 100% allowances for CT and whether there will be any restriction to the vendor's costs and, most importantly when it can expect to start paying CT on the profits from its new acquisition. Where financing is involved, the extent to which interest will be allowable for CT and what level of debt in the company will be permitted by the LBSOG will be important considerations. If a PRT field is involved then the transferee will step into the shoes of the transferor for PRT. So it needs to establish exactly what PRT position the field has reached, eg how much oil allowance has been used up and are there any losses being carried forward, etc.? If the field is within PRT, but no PRT has been paid to date, it will want to establish whether PRT is ever likely to be due in the future.

Where the new entrant is a pure exploration company then it will need to consider how long it can bear the costs without a tax offset in the UK and to what extent the Ring Fence Expenditure Supplement will provide compensation if it finds oil. If the company is a foreign independent then how it initially structures its operations in the UK, its home country tax position and the availability in that country of relief or credit for UK taxes will, of course, be relevant considerations.

Whatever its situation, any company proposing to enter the UKCS should make early contact with the LBSOG. This is important so that the tax authority understands from the outset the extent and nature of the new company's operation in the UK so as to minimise unnecessary enquiries. It will often be worth seeking LBSOG's views on how proposed transactions will be treated under UK tax law. LBSOG is bound by the same general rules for administering taxes and giving rulings as apply to other parts of HMRC but because of the importance of North Sea oil to the national economy it has traditionally placed a wide interpretation on the circumstances in which it is appropriate to give 'informal clearances'. It is generally prepared to comment on the tax implications of a major project or acquisition in advance of it taking place providing that all the relevant facts relating to the transaction are clearly set out and a view given on the tax consequences.

8.6 The present and future impacts

How should the North Sea fiscal regime currently be viewed by potential investors and what does the future hold for the regime? With the recent capital allowances changes to the CT rules (which apply equally to SC) all three taxes now essentially tax only cash flow. All income is recognised as it is earned and virtually all expenditure is relieved as it is incurred. Cash flow taxes target economic rent and are generally accepted as some of the most efficient forms of taxation for natural resources, with only a limited impact on investment rates of return and associated investment decisions. Despite that, however, against the background of falling production and rising costs, sudden tax increases in recent years are seen by some to have created instability in the regime leaving potential investors uncertain about future returns on their investment, particularly as there is no assurance that tax rates will come down if there is a substantial fall in oil prices. The opposing view is that the tax regime needs to be kept flexible and increases in the tax rate when profits soar are an inevitable concomitant to a neutral and progressive tax system.

Companies must make their own judgment on whether the UK Government has currently got the balance right between the two competing priorities of extracting a fair share of economic rent for the nation and leaving companies with a reasonable return on their investment, given the risks and high costs associated with North Sea activities. The Treasury continuously monitors very closely the impact of the regime on these twin objectives. Overall, perhaps, new investors can take some comfort from that and the fact that the history of North Sea taxes has shown that successive administrations have been ready to take action if tax is seen to inhibit activity or reduce profits below an acceptable level. Despite recent increases, the tax on profits from new discoveries in the UK still remains reasonably low by international standards and some of the other recent tax changes such as the removal of PRT from new tariff business and introduction of the Ring Fence Expenditure Supplement, have demonstrated a continuing desire by the present administration to encourage new investment, particularly by new entrants.

It is possible there could be some significant changes to the regime in the future in the wake of the very large decommissioning costs that are looming in the next 10 years or so. PRT revenues will drop substantially when that happens and at some point will go negative. It is unlikely that any government will want to maintain a tax that is bringing in little or no revenue. So some major decisions will almost certainly have to be taken at some stage in the future on how the regime as a whole is to be adjusted to remove PRT from the system and accommodate these significant costs whilst maintaining tax yields on much lower volumes of production. The Government has already opened discussion with industry on this issue alongside a range of other wider structural issues and published a discussion paper at Budget 2007 setting out some tentative initial conclusions. It will be interesting to see whether anything concrete emerges from these discussions or whether the issue is merely deferred until a more critical time.

APPENDIX

8.9 Example of a simple PRT Assessment

Positive amounts

		£m
Gross Profit		
Proceeds from arm's-length sales	75	
Market value of oil disposed of non-arm's length	24	
Stock adjustment	1	100
Tariff Receipts (net of tariff receipts allowance)		10
Disposal Receipts		2
		112

Negative amounts

Provisional allowance	Nil	
Expenditure and any Supplement (claimed by responsible person and agreed by LBSOG)	25	
Expenditure and any Supplement (claimed by participator and agreed by LBSOG)	4	
Research expenditure	1	
	30	
Less: reversal of provisional allowance (for earlier period)	Nil	30
Assessable profit for period		82
Less: assessable loss brought forward		10
		72
Less: Oil Allowance		12
Amount chargeable to PRT		60
Tax at 50%		30

— 9 —

PROJECT DEVELOPMENT

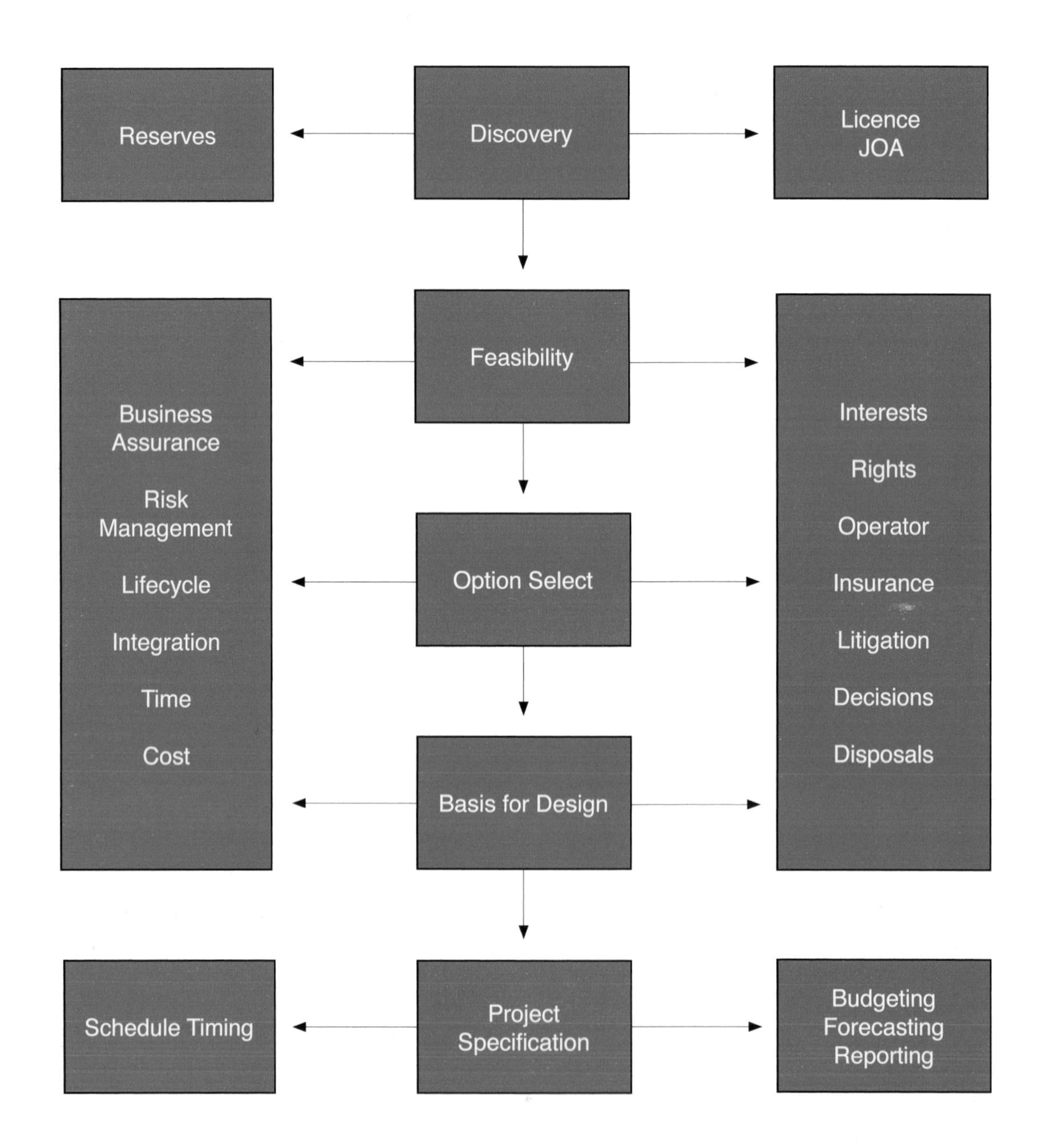
Reserves
Discovery
Licence
JOA
Feasibility
Business
Assurance
Risk
Management
Lifecycle
Integration
Time
Cost
Interests
Rights
Operator
Insurance
Litigation
Decisions
Disposals
Option Select
Basis for Design
Schedule Timing
Project
Specification
Budgeting
Forecasting
Reporting

PROJECT DEVELOPMENT

TECHNICAL

9.1 Introduction

Many individuals and companies have gone bankrupt after discovering oil, and trying to develop a 'field'. This chapter intends, by examining the complexity of the development process, to explain how this can happen, and to clarify some of the techniques typically employed to maximise the likelihood that a development will be robust when full funding is committed.

The techniques described have been hard won by generations of oil and gas developers. There is no right answer about how to develop hydrocarbon accumulations. They (and their developers) come in all shapes and sizes and the fact is that to a greater or lesser extent they are all bespoke. That is both the challenge for the development team and its attraction.

That there is no 'one-size-fits-all' solution can be demonstrated by considering even simple examples: the small onshore project in Louisiana is more than just geographically remote from a $1 billion west of Shetland deep water adventure. No less diversity is seen in the companies developing these resources: for the same discovery the major oil companies of this world face quite different challenges than entrepreneurial companies with only one or two assets to their names.

Similarly, the focus of a development operator differs from the overview of a non-operator in the same development. Development generalisations, are therefore nearly always suspect. That said, some principles have been established over the years, particularly with regards to processes, organisational structures and generic thinking applicable to managing the development process. This chapter aims to allow the challenge to be better understood, but first it is necessary to define more fully some of the jargon used in the world of resource development.

9.2 Development phases

The nomenclature used to describe the post-discovery, pre-execution phase of the hydrocarbon lifecycle often gives rise to confusion, with various companies using different terms when referring to the same stages and, worse still, the same terms being used to refer to different stages of the process. This employs terms typically used in the UK, but note that it is neither universally applied *nor is it universally applicable.*

Th*e* Proven Undeveloped Discovery, or PUD, is our starting point. It is an accumulation which has been successfully drilled and tested, ie flowed hydrocarbon, and accordingly is a discovery capable of sustained flow. Once a PUD starts to receive serious consideration by development engineers it is commonly referred to by engineers as a prospect. This, however, can create confusion; explorationists use the same word to refer to undrilled exploration targets, so beware. A field is a hydrocarbon accumulation which is, or was in the past, in production.

The first phase in developing a PUD is known as Identification (subdivided into Initiation and Feasibility). Here, the PUD's potential to become a successful field is assessed.

Analysing subsurface parametres, and bracketing their uncertainties are the critical activities during this stage: volumes, fluid properties, contaminants, reservoir variability and pressure support are evaluated.

Parameter uncertainties need to be honestly addressed, and decisions will be made as to whether additional information is required, eg appraisal drilling, or possibly additional exploration drilling.

The commercial environment will be mapped out: evacuation routes, potential partners/competitors, and importantly markets. Initiation ends when sufficient understanding is achieved to say for sure that an economic development is possible. Feasibility ends when several development options have been scoped out sufficiently to say that they would meet corporate objectives, and look sufficiently interesting economically to pass onto the next phase – Definition. This is split into Option Select, Basis for Design and Project Specification (Fig. 9–1).

Option Select is self-explanatory and without doubt the single most critical event in the development process. Sometimes it may appear straightforward, eg a single small onshore discovery next to existing facilities. Generally, however, several potential options present themselves: for example, should the development combine several discoveries? If offshore should it have subsea or platform wells? Should new processing facilities be built or is it more economical to go to third

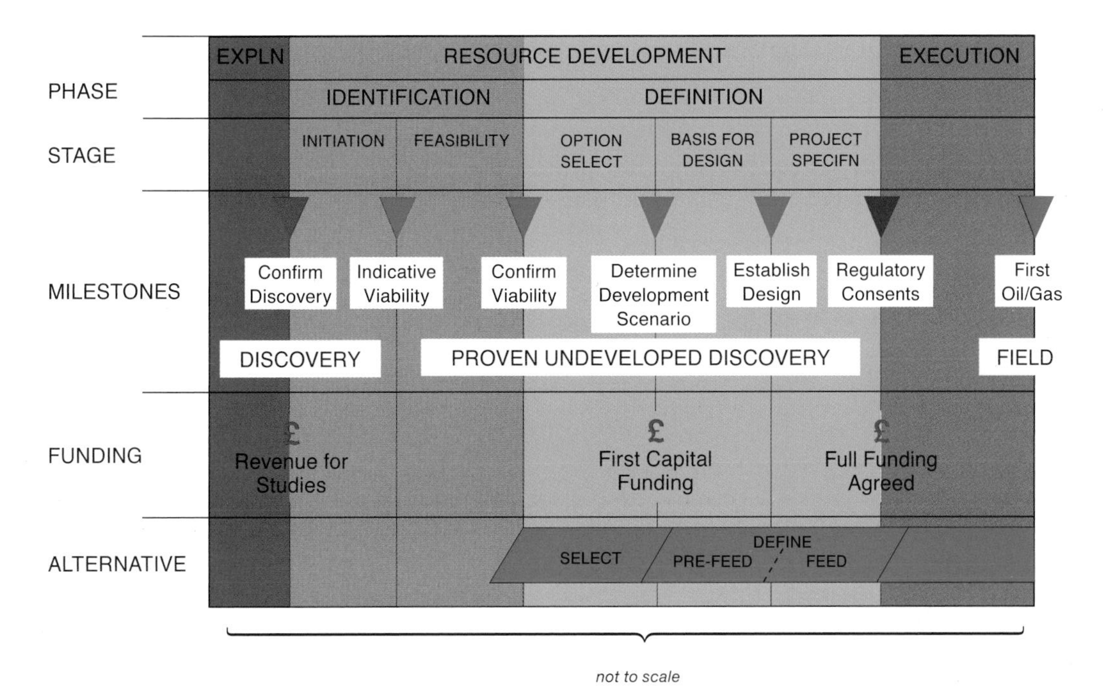

Figure 9–1 Early phases in the hydrocarbon lifecycle

party facilities? If new facilities should they comprise an FPSO[1] or a fixed platform?

And then there are the multifarious commercial options, eg which partners, which business models, and the financial options, eg equity–debt models, forward sales, etc. The selected option is therefore *not just a technical choice*, but rather the result of balancing many complex and potentially conflicting factors. The selection must also consider not least the 'fall-back' positions which each option affords – for rarely do developments go completely according to plan.

Basis for Design takes the selected concept, defines its functional aspects, and prepares these in a form which can be developed in a full Project Specification (sometimes referred to as preparing the conceptual design). Basis for Design (BfD) deliverables include details of fluids, pressures, temperatures, product specifications, production rates and availability requirements, together with an outline description of the facilities required and, importantly, will shape operating philosophy.

Commercially and financially, extensive amounts of work are done in parallel with the engineering; negotiations for Partnership, Operating, and Sales Agreements are progressed typically to the stage known as Heads of

Terms, where the major issues are recognised and conditionally accepted, whilst funding plans and arrangements need to be matured sufficiently to enable the development to proceed confidently into Project Specification.

Project Specification evolves the functional requirements described in the BfD into a clear definition of the facilities required. Subsea, pipeline, piping, mechanical equipment, electrical and control requirements are detailed such that appropriate materials can be selected and ordered; manpower levels, accommodation, layouts, civil and structural requirements are determined; costs are hardened up allowing estimates to be made for full field lifecycle capital and operating expenditures.

The system availability and hence adjusted production profile is 'fine-tuned' to ensure that the commercial, financial and technical elements all add up consistently, robustly and economically. Commercial agreements should be fully termed, regulatory requirements, eg DTI, planning, HS&E and various licences (Field Development Consents 'sanction') will need to be met and financial arrangements to carry the entire costs of the developments will need to be put in place. Only when everything is ready and signed off will the project be ready to launch into next phase – Execution – when the 'building work' truly begins.

There are many variations on the above nomenclature. A frequently encountered term is 'Front End Engineering' or 'FEED'. Some companies interpret this as the design work done during the BfD, in particular ensuring that out-turn costs, schedule and operability are understood and that the contracts to be let for Project Specification are properly defined. Others may refer to FEED more loosely and will include all the preparatory engineering done prior to letting the contracts for Project Specification. The amount of work done during the FEED is often referred to as the 'front-end loading'.

The purpose of any development process scheme, like that shown above, is to allow activities, milestones and stage deliverables to be established clearly, and thereby ensure that each stage can be verified before progressing further.

These schemes tend, however, to adopt a language that, whilst familiar to engineers, is often slightly alien to economists, commercial negotiators or sub-surface specialists. This can result in the development phase wrongly being thought of largely as a series of technical activities. It should rather be considered as a business opportunity requiring a series of staggered investments, based on structured study and risk analysis.

The prize is to proceed with an attractive economic investment, but being too hasty will almost certainly result in major investments being committed either too early (costly to fix) or to a fundamentally unsound project (potentially catastrophic).

Attempting, however, to remove risk altogether, say by over-extending 'front-end loading' is likely to result either in missing opportunities, 'paralysis by analysis' or both.

The development process therefore is a fine balance, which needs to progress neither too quickly nor too slowly. It also requires the ruthlessness to 'kill' the project, if that is the economically correct decision, and in some ways can be compared with preparing for battle: it must make sense strategically, the tactics should be clear, the resources must be adequate, and the opposition must be understood. Then decisions need to be taken: select the ground, choose the right moment to advance, know when to retreat – get it right and you're a winner, but get it wrong and you (or your company) may not survive.

9.3 Fashion and experience

Resource development is, then, something of an art and unsurprisingly many theories have been advanced about the 'correct' way to go about it. Like fashions, these come and go – one year projects should engage in 'aggressive cost reduction', the next 'fast-track development', then 'parallel engineering', while 'alliancing' might be regarded as a hardy perennial. The principal themes being argued over can, however, be represented in a ternary diagram (Fig. 9–2).

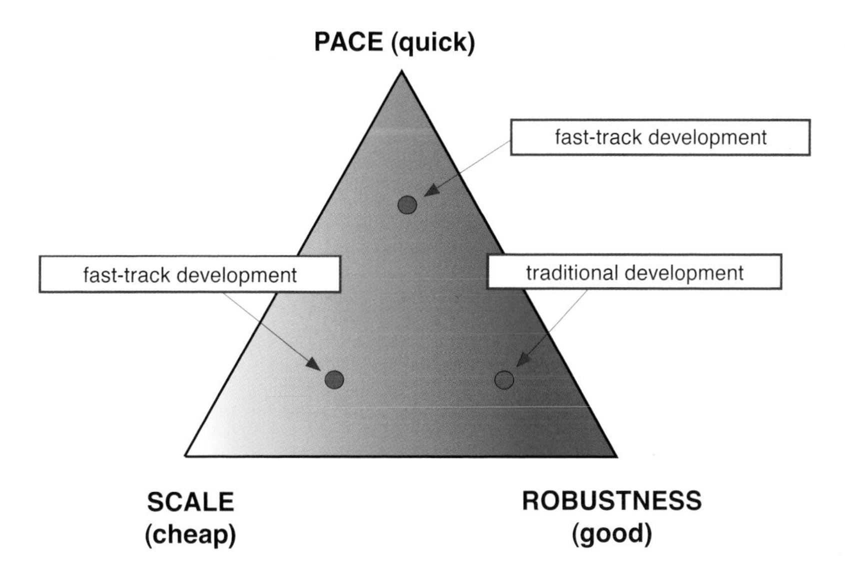

Figure 9–2 Pace, scale, robustness

The three issues are pace, scale and robustness, or as expressed in that well-known office quip, you can have quick, cheap or good – choose any two, but you cannot have all three simultaneously. Another way of looking at the problem is shown in the 'bath-tub' curve (Fig. 9–3).

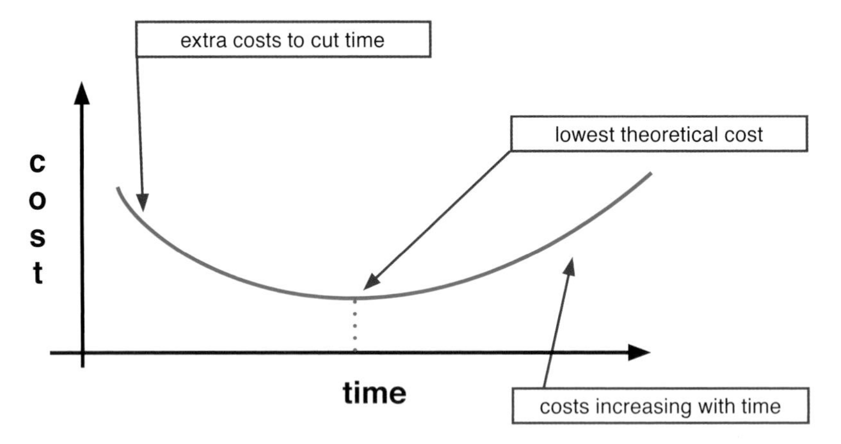

Figure 9–3 The 'bath-tub' curve

The idea is straightforward: namely it costs extra to complete anything quickly (extra resources, etc.), and it costs extra to do something 'too slowly' (time is money). Therefore, there is an optimum schedule for any development if costs are to be minimised.

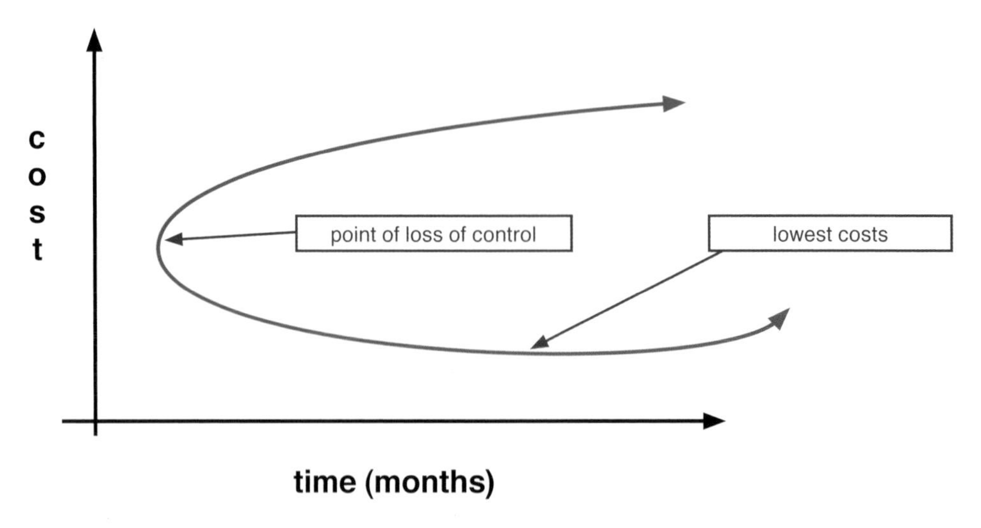

Figure 9–4 The real bath-tub – more like a cold shower

Some gurus argued, however, that the extra costs necessary to speed up a development could, in the right circumstances, be more than offset by the earlier hydrocarbon production stream, ie if value rather than cost were plotted against time, an earlier optimum schedule would emerge. This is the 'fast-track' philosophy in a nutshell. Like many theories, reality has proved recalcitrant and the 'bath-tub' curve has shown itself to be rather more complex than that shown above. Costly experience suggests it to be more like Fig. 9–4.

Aggressive 'fast-track' developments, trying to achieve extremely fast first-oil schedules, can reach a point where lack of sufficient subsurface, engineering, commercial and financial specification, combined with inadequate risk analysis, leads to costs spiralling (literally) out of control.

The lack of engineering specification not only leads to spiralling costs but the necessity to correct and re-engineer results in the schedule suffering from repeated and significant slippage.

Matters are only worsened with the use of 'off-the-shelf' equipment which is cheap but inadequate, meaning that after being late and over budget the development itself failed to deliver the production uptimes promised. The UK has witnessed several very large projects and many smaller ones which sought the holy-grail of 'fast-track' and ended up with such enormous cost and schedule overruns that potentially lucrative developments actually lost money when considered in terms of full-lifecycle economics.

9.4 Integration

The lesson has been that technical, commercial, economic, financial, stakeholder, legal matters and organisational issues need to be progressed as an integrated whole.

Developments, however, are generally complex and present various uncertainties, which can be both large and interrelated, such that unique options or solutions rarely present themselves.

A way of tackling a new development is to establish a reference value chain from a reference technical solution. Here, a 'standard' conventional technical solution is worked out in enough detail to allow costs and hydrocarbon production streams to be analysed. Bench-marked assumptions regarding the reservoir, well productivity, processing tariffs, schedules and costs are derived from whatever sources are available. An example is given in Fig. 9–5.

Here we have an offshore PUD capable of producing oil and gas. The reference technical option is a standard offshore production platform with full processing facilities which can produce several saleable products, from partially separated natural gases through to stabilised crude.

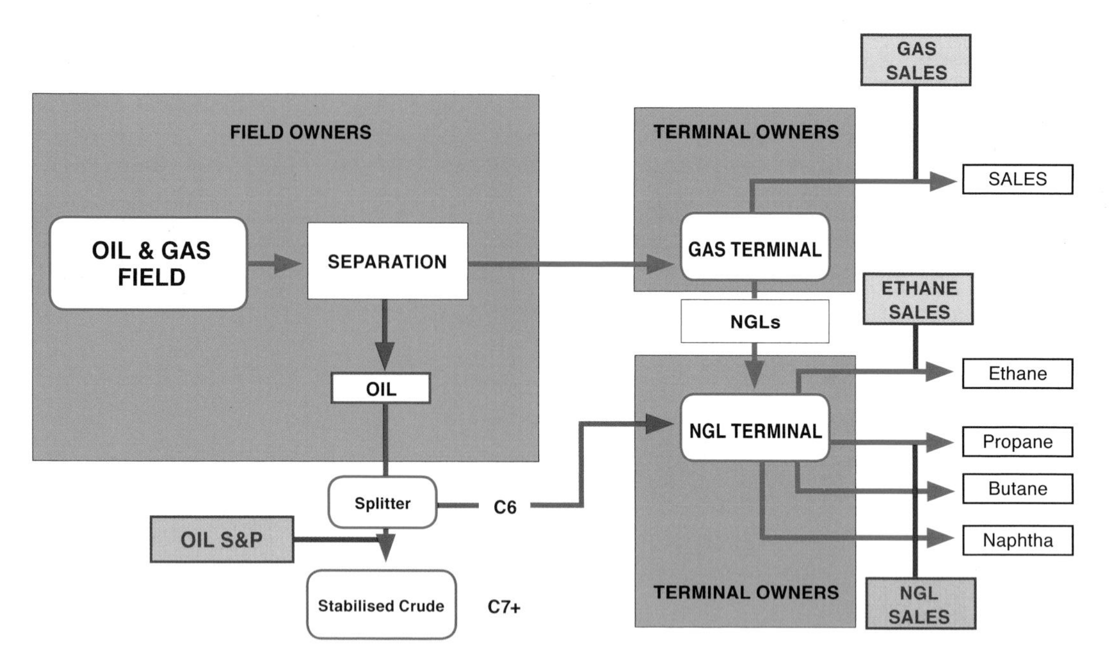

Figure 9–5 Typical value chain

Even here, however, each product may have several possible routes to market, and may indeed have its own idiosyncratic market. That notwithstanding, a reference value chain can be established and economically interrogated and optimised. This allows alternative technical options to be examined in terms of their impact on the reference value chain.

Experience shows that altering the hydrocarbons flows (eg less/more processing offshore resulting in less/more natural gas liquids) can be of greater impact than the cost differences between technical alternative. Such an exploded value chain allows more parts of a development to talk around the same technical, commercial and economic material than conventional economics.

The 'downstream'[2] can see directly how their products are changed as a result of the facility engineers attempting to save costs – they can then explain perhaps that the changes could result in paying unnecessarily high processing tariffs and selling discounted products. The reference value chain can be used as an internal bench mark for the team's explorers, reservoir engineers, facilities engineers and commercial negotiators and facilitate better integration.

The necessary integration comes through appropriate organisation, planning and management. An integrated team means that the various individuals have a clear understanding of what others are doing and the possible importance of any new piece of data or analysis. This requires proactive engagement to ensure that the impact of their particular discipline is fully disseminated throughout the team – eg the geologist has a responsibility to know what the facility engineer's problems are, and they both need to ensure that the economist is fully in the loop.

Likewise, those dealing with commercial aspects better be aware if the reservoir engineer has just changed the production profiles. In practice, a development team evolves through time and might look something like that shown in Fig. 9–6.

The numbers will vary depending on both size and complexity but certain activities cannot be avoided.[3] Some smaller prospects may indeed have a higher degree of risk attached to them, eg the infamous single-well development, where one mistake could see the entire project fail. Here, in order to achieve an acceptable degree of development robustness, more rather than less 'de-risking' work may be required.

Presently, there is a growing tendency to 'contract out' some or even most of the front-end work to minimise the in-house staff required. That is fine, but

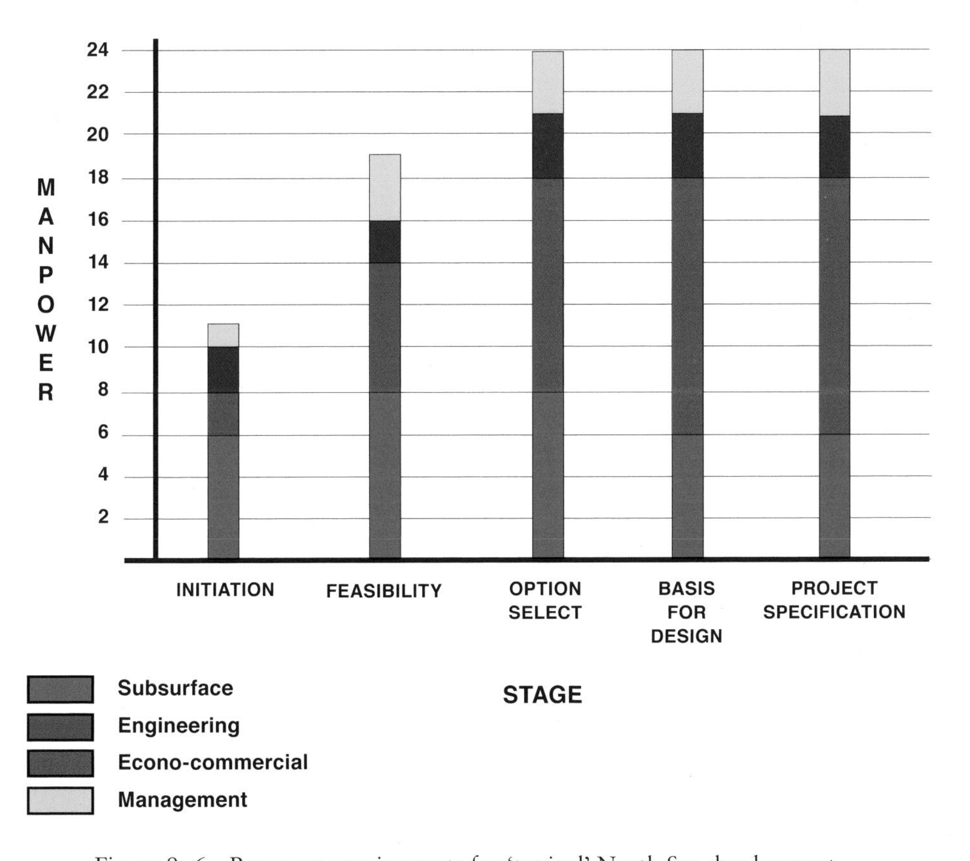

Figure 9–6 Resource requirements for 'typical' North Sea development

integration remains absolutely critical. It helps hugely to keep the team physically co-located, contractors or not, and it is obvious that personnel continuity is highly desirable.

9.5 Business assurance

Business assurance is the process applied to ensure that the deliverables required at each key milestone are reviewed externally prior to closing out that particular phase. This should not be confused with 'peer reviews' (they should take place as part of general working practice) but is a formalised decision-making process where critical assessment is made of whether the development should proceed, and what might be done to enhance its value or risk robustness. This business assurance process is, ironically, particularly important for small companies where a single development could make or break it.

For the business assurance process to be fully effective, it is desirable to have some three to four reviews between Identification and Execution (Fig. 9–1).

The first review is commonly held to close out the *initiation* stage and considers whether the opportunity is truly worth pursuing: strategically, commercially, economically and technically. The development team should expect and welcome tough challenges to the overall concept and its corporate value.

For most companies there will need to be a compelling business case to attract the necessary investment. The next review may be at the end of *feasibility* confirming that there is indeed something worth pursuing and agreeing to the necessary funds to continue studies.

Review three is likely to look at the *option selected* and verify that it is indeed optimum for the shareholders. Details of the development's expenditure profile should be examined to see exactly where and when investment will be required. Financial planning should clearly match spending profiles and the 'commercials' should be maturing at the right pace to match the development's technical resolution.

Whether another review is needed prior to the full-funding review will be determined by the overall size and complexity of the project. The team will be under frantic pressure at this stage, with investors, funders, partners and regulators all demanding tomorrow today. The last thing the team will feel like doing is having yet another review, but if managed well, with experienced practitioners it will undoubtedly generate value and inspire confidence.

The final pre-full funding review should be especially rigorous as it provides investors the confidence to commit funds for the execution phase. Key commercial agreements should have been executed by this point, otherwise the investors run the risk of being 'squeezed' in continuing negotiations. The 'other-side-of-table' (contractors, facility owners, etc.) know that once into execution the investors are so heavily committed that they are likely to settle on terms which might otherwise be unacceptable.

9.6 Risk management

The development phase may be thought of as a discrete set of exercises in risk recognition, and risk quantification followed by decision-taking about risk management. More technically, it involves risk identification and assessment, followed by designing risk controls and/or recovery procedures (these are also known respectively as mitigation and remediation).

Risk identification involves the whole team considering those events which might occur within their individual disciplines and together identifying the potential impact any 'event' might have across the project. Subsurface experts, however, tend to think rather in terms of 'uncertainty', for example volumes being represented by some type of probability density function. This then needs to be converted to a risk 'event', eg certain volume levels lead to consequential change in production profile, and in turn at a certain break-over point this will impact processing equipment design. This could impact not only on costs and cash flows but also on commercial considerations such as tariff negotiations.

Risk management requires, therefore, that the seismic interpreter has some feel for the facility engineer's risks and that the commercial negotiators are aware how they might be impacted by uncertainty.

Conditionally dependent risks are notoriously difficult to capture adequately, since not only is excellent interdisciplinary communication needed but quantification is problematic. Shakespeare, in *Richard III*, captured just how catastrophic small 'events' can become if a conditional chain exists when the 'kingdom was lost but for the want of a nail'. It can and does happen in oil and gas projects. In one huge project the reservoir and process engineers forgot to mention to the oil traders that there was a risk of some residual heavy metal (parts per billion) in the offshore processed oil stream. This led to the receiving refinery refusing to take the first shipment, the field being closed in, a new onshore facility having to be built post-haste, and extensive renegotiations for oil sales – all for the sake of a few parts per billion!

Business assurance, however, is not all doom and gloom – upsides should also be captured – just what will you do if you start to produce twice as much as prognosed: can you readily process it, evacuate it, sell it?

Assessing risk is yet another art rather than science, certainly when considering the high-level 'strategic'-type events (oil price, civil unrest, etc.) and it pays initially not to over-science matters. A simple scheme is to subdivide the probability of an event occurring as either very low, low, medium, high or very

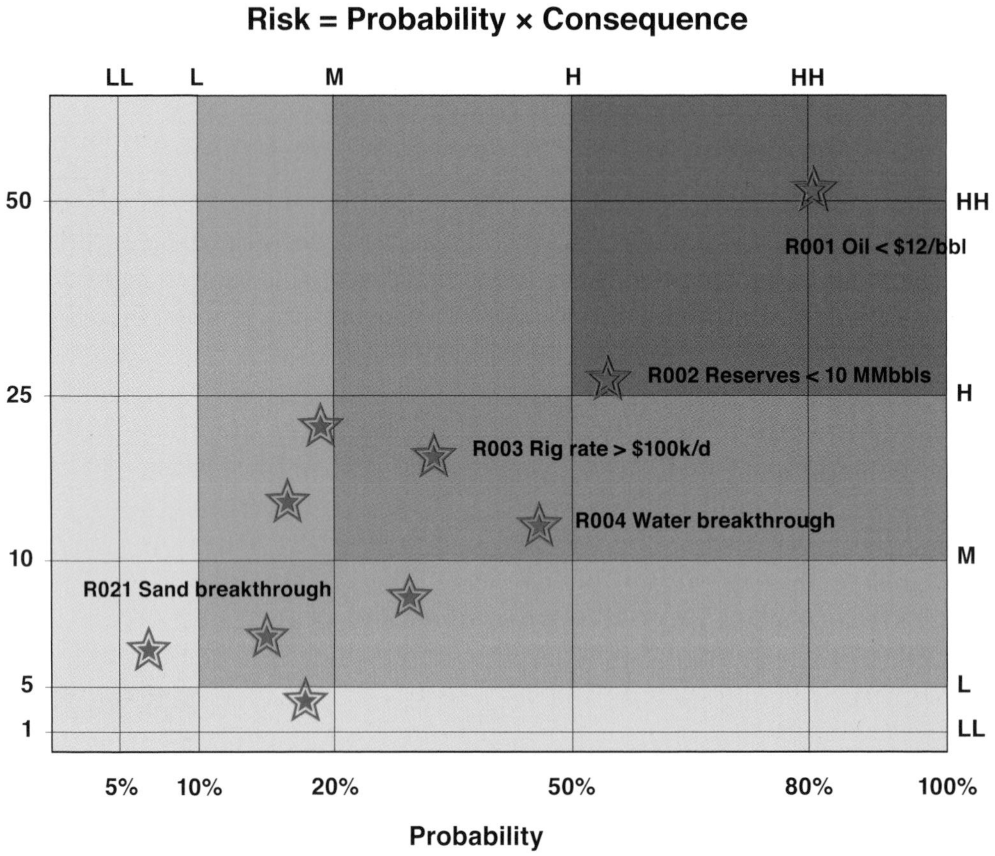

Figure 9–7 Risk assessment

high (LL, L, M, H, HH) and cross-plot this against consequence, estimated in money terms. An example is shown in Fig. 9–7.

Having assessed the magnitude of the risks, the next step is deciding which risks need to be managed and determining a strategy for doing this. Often it will be a choice between accept (do nothing!), control (mitigation), ie early expenditure to reduce the probability of an event occurring, or allowing for its eventuality, or recovery (remediation), ie measures designed to reduce the consequences should a particular event occur. For example, drilling extra wells upfront to protect a gas development's production profile would be an example of mitigation, whereas allowing extra deck space to allow for retro-fitting water separation in the event of water breakthrough would be an example of a remediation measure.

Some 'technical' risks, such as uncertainties in reservoir size can have complex interactions, potentially impacting the required number of wells and the revenue stream. Should there be plans, say, to forward sell oil, calculating the commercial and financial impacts of such a risk would be vital and a full probabilistic economic analysis would be required.

9.7 Conclusions

Developing discovered hydrocarbon resources is really about looking at a business opportunity in a structured and critical manner. A major part is risk and uncertainty analysis together with informed decision-taking. It most definitely is not just a technical challenge. Unlocking maximum possible value, whilst minimising the potential of significant financial loss, requires wide-ranging and multifaceted thinking, with experience showing that the front-end-loading should be optimised.

Too much detail too early can, however, lead to 'paralysis by analysis' and keeping a balance between study and progress is vital. No amount of internal risk management or front-end engineering can hope to capture any one project's possibilities – whether good or bad. External reviews and challenge will greatly improve any development's likelihood of success.

Integration, identification of risks (and opportunities), being open to challenge and having structured reviews at the major project milestones will go a long way to ensuring that a development will be delivered on budget, on time, and producing the predicted volumes. Leadership with the appropriate level of experience and authority is necessary to make it happen and to ensure that the development delivers its maximum value.

Notes

[1] A Floating Production Storage and Offtake vessel – eg a converted tanker with processing facilities topsides.

[2] That part of the hydrocarbon value chain dealing with refining, marketing, chemicals and sales.

[3] Ideally, a drilling engineer should be part of the integrated team, particularly given that some 50% of a smaller project's costs can be drilling, and 100% of the revenue stream comes out of the wells.

PROJECT DEVELOPMENT

LEGAL

9.8 Introduction

Once the co-venturers in a project have secured the relevant licence under the Petroleum Act 1998, the co-venturers will be required to carry out certain work obligations to develop the area covered by that licence (the Licensed Area) within a given time frame. To project manage these work obligations, the co-venturers will usually enter into a Joint Operating Agreement (JOA) governing operations relating to the development of the licensed area. One of the co-venturers will be chosen to act as operator and will be responsible for managing development and production operations under the JOA on behalf of itself and the other co-venturers.

If the area to be developed covers more than one licence area and the percentage interests of the co-venturers are different in each, a JOA will not necessarily be the appropriate agreement to govern operations in the Licensed Area and in some instances the co-venturers may require to enter into what is know as a Unitisation and Unit Operating Agreement (UOA). This would be appropriate where a reservoir straddles two different blocks which are owned by different co-venturing parties and where the owners of the blocks agree to jointly develop the reservoir. The overriding aim of the UOA is very much the same of the JOA: each of the co-venturers is looking to combine its respective resources jointly to develop and exploit oil and gas from the reservoir. The detailed provisions of a UOA will be much the same as a JOA with a few variances and is further discussed in Chapter 12.

This chapter discusses the legal background to a development plan and the key provisions of a typical JOA as it is these which provide the contractual framework among the co-venturers for the conduct of a development.

9.9 The development programme

Following the exploration and appraisal phase, the co-venturers may decide that there are deposits of oil and gas in a reservoir which are sufficiently large to be considered 'commercial'. In other words, the revenue that will be generated from the production of oil and gas would provide an attractive rate of return on investment to its investors, taking into account the risks and costs of development and production. In order to bring an oil and gas field commercial discovery to first production, an extensive development plan will have to be prepared by the co-venturers, normally under the leadership of the operator, in accordance with the rules and regulations published by the DTI and others and in accordance with the agreement among the co-venturers contractually set out in the JOA.

That development plan will typically encompass:

- all of the engineering and economic considerations relevant to the development of the field, including the number and type of production platforms to be installed in the field (if any), the facilities to be used and reservoir management (including flow capabilities of the reservoir);
- an environmental assessment;
- the entering into of contractual relationships with drilling companies, pipeline operators and tanker operators, etc.;
- the negotiation of offtake arrangements, transportation arrangements and, if petroleum is brought ashore by pipeline, terminal arrangements;
- decommissioning arrangements.

Over the years there have been different licence procedures which have required to be followed by the licensees in preparing such a plan and submitting it to the DTI for approval before implementation. The latest procedures are now set out in the Guidance Notes, 'Procedures for Regulating Oil and Gas Field Developments', which became effective from September 2000. In these Guidance Notes, the DTI sets out its policy objectives which are to maximise the economic benefit for the use of its petroleum resources, minimise environmental impact, ensure security of supply, ensure the recovery of all economic hydrocarbons, ensure adequate and competitive provision of pipelines and facilities and take account of environmental impacts in the interests of other users of the sea. In this new streamlined process, the Field Development Programme is the supporting document under which the development and production authorisations will be issued by the DTI. There will normally be considerable discussion between the co-venturers and the DTI on technical aspects of commissioning the field, as well as the contractual arrangements, before a Field Development Programme is finally submitted for approval. The Field Development Programme therefore becomes itself only a summary document unlike the former Annex B which would run into a considerable number of volumes.

Along with the Field Development Programme, the co-venturers need to submit an Environmental Impact Assessment Report which is a new requirement under the revised procedures.

If the Secretary of State is satisfied with the Field Development Programme and the Environmental Impact Assessment Report, the Secretary of State will authorise the development of the field, following which commissioning and mobilisation can take place. Since 1993, the DTI no longer imposes conditions in terms of which it can order production cutbacks by the issue of 'Substitution Notices'. However, production levels can be controlled if it is in the national interest.

The duration of the production authorisation is normally between five years and the life of the field. If the DTI issues an authorisation for less than the life of the field it will normally issue letters of assurance, if requested to do so, giving comfort that other consents will be awarded after the initial authorisation. Following the authorisation of the Development Programme, licensees will be required to provide periodic field reports, normally on an annual basis.

The issue of decommissioning in connection with the development process has vastly increased in importance over recent years with the number of smaller co-venturers entering the UKCS. The DTI have issued comprehensive guidance notes on decommissioning. These notes set out guidance on changes to field operators and address issues on the contracting out of field management responsibilities. There is a desire by the DTI to scrutinise new operators and their relationships with contractors carefully to maintain good oil field practice in the UKCS. Health and safety is another important issue in respect of the development process and this is the responsibility of the Health and Safety Executive under the Health and Safety at Work, etc. Act 1974, as opposed to the DTI.

The establishment of safety zones, procedures for the protection of offshore installations, the construction and operation of pipelines and offtake arrangements are also important issues which will arise in connection with the development process. For instance, the Secretary of State has to authorise all construction of submarine pipelines and, under the Petroleum Act 1998, the Secretary of State can make various orders in connection with proposed or existing pipelines. Guidelines have now been issued for the completion of pipeline works and it should be noted that on the expiry of an authorisation, the pipeline transfers to and vests in the Secretary of State by virtue of section 17 of the Petroleum Act 1998.

In order to improve competitiveness in the UKCS there are various initiatives which include new procedures for licensing, a new Code of Practice on operating matters, recommended changes to JOAs, standardisation of agreements and recommendations on decommissioning arrangements. In addition, there is now a streamlined process and initiatives aimed at increasing access to infrastructure. Guidelines were initially stated in the Code of Practice on Offshore Infrastructure, which was adopted by the industry in 1996 but which has since been superseded by the Code of Practice on Access to Upstream Oil and Gas Infrastructure on the UK Continental Shelf, adopted in August 2004. The Code of Practice applies to all offshore infrastructure and onshore receiving terminals and applies to owners of infrastructure and non-owners. It sets out guiding principles to those involved in negotiating third party access to offshore infrastructure.

In the event of disputes over access to infrastructure there are also new guidelines by the DTI, entitled 'Guidance on Consideration of Applications for Resolution of Disputes over Third Party Access to Infrastructure', July 2002, under which the DTI will make a decision in the case of disputes referred to it.

It should be noted that where field developments are authorised under earlier procedures then those procedures will still apply.

9.10 Joint Operating Agreement

The JOA forms the basis of the joint venture between the co-venturers and sets out their contractual relationship in conducting operations under licence. Once a production licence is awarded it would be normal for the licensees to negotiate a JOA and there are various types that can be used; for instance, the Association of International Petroleum Negotiators' model form International Operating Agreement (Addition 2002) is one such form. In this chapter, we will concentrate on the JOA which was produced by the Progressing Partnership Working Group and published on the UKOOA website in April 2002 (which is itself a variation of the old British National Oil Corporation (BNOC) pro-forma JOA). However, in practice every JOA is likely to be different.

Alternatively, it may be more appropriate for a UOA to be entered into at this stage if the reservoir to be developed straddles different blocks, each with separate groups of co-venturers. In addition to the JOA (or UOA, if appropriate) there will normally be a raft of other commercial agreements entered into by the co-venturers, dealing with matters such as transportation, processing, pipelines, terminal operations and the sale of oil and/or gas. While JOAs will vary in terms of detail in respect of each different field, their general characteristics will be the same. The main terms in the JOA are summarised below:

Scope and understanding

In this clause, the co-venturers state the scope of the JOA. This will normally include exploration for, and production of, petroleum under the relevant licence, the treatment, storage and transportation of the production, the decommissioning or other joint disposal of the property and the conditions for carrying out sole risks projects in the licensed area. It will then set out what is excluded from the scope of the JOA, which will normally be any joint financing arrangements, joint marketing or joint sales of petroleum as, ordinarily, it is up to each co-venturer to arrange for lifting and sale of its own petroleum.

Percentage interests

The co-venturers do not establish a partnership for the purposes of the development nor do they enter into a formal joint venture arrangement involving the setting up of a joint venture company. The JOA will set out the co-venturers' respective percentage interests in all joint property and all joint petroleum and will state that the participants' share of all costs and obligations incurred in the conduct of the development (known in the JOA as 'joint operations') shall be borne by the participants in accordance with their percentage interests. While there is a joint tenancy created by the licence, this is effectively severed under the JOA by establishing a tenancy in common between the co-venturers. In terms of the JOA each co-venturer holds an undivided interest in its percentage interest in the joint property and each party is responsible for its own obligations but not that of its co-venturers. Nevertheless, there are important exceptions to this rule. For example, decommissioning obligations are joint and several and a licensee may well be liable for the decommissioning cost of an impecunious co-venturer.

It is, therefore, possible for each co-venturer separately to sell, mortgage or charge their respective percentage interests under the JOA. However, the DTI has in the past not favoured certain types of dealing in licensed interests which have included arrangements involving net profit interests.

It is the key to the joint venture relationship that each co-venturer is liable up to its net percentage share of the joint venture's obligations and it is not liable on a joint and several basis for all costs and liabilities on the development and operations. The co-venturers can, therefore, raise finance against their percentage interest (subject to the limitations contained in the JOA) and can also obtain their own insurance in respect of their percentage interest in the joint property. Nevertheless, this is uncommon as co-venturers tend to make use of a joint policy obtained by the operator. In addition, co-venturers will provide mutual indemnities up to the extent of their percentage interest for the liabilities relating to joint operations.

Operator

One of the co-venturers is appointed to operate and manage the operations.

Detailed provisions dealing with the resignation and removal of the operator and the election of a successor operator are contained in the JOA. The operator and any successors require to be approved by the DTI. The operator is normally a company which has sufficient experience and a good track record of operating other upstream assets. The DTI vet applicants for operatorships and obtaining a first operatorship in the UKCS is difficult.

The JOA will provide that the operator has the right, and is obliged, to conduct the joint operations by itself, its agents or its contractors under the overall supervision and control of the 'Joint Operating Committee'. In addition, the JOA will provide details of the responsibilities of the operator and these will normally include the preparation of programmes, budgets and Authorisations for Expenditures (AFEs), the implementation of those programmes and budgets, the provision of reports, data and information to the co-venturers, the planning for, and obtaining of, all required services and materials. It will also include the direction and control of statistical and accounting services, the provision of technical and advisory services and prior to the production, the preparation of a Field Development Plan and Environmental Impact Assessment Report, and their submission to the Secretary of State with any other information required.

The JOA will also provide that the operator must conduct operations in a 'proper and workmanlike manner' in accordance with methods and practices customarily used in good and prudent oil and gas field practice. In addition, the operator will be required to conduct operations in accordance with any instruction of the Joint Operating Committee and with a degree of diligence and prudence reasonably and ordinarily exercised by experienced operators engaged in a similar activity under similar circumstances and conditions.

Due to the extent of the operator's responsibilities, its liabilities are often limited to wilful misconduct or a failure to obtain or maintain any insurance (except where the operator has used all reasonable endeavours to obtain it). In either case, the JOA usually provides that the operator will not be responsible for any consequential loss or damage, including lost production or loss of profits. In addition, any restriction based on wilful misconduct usually limits liability to the actions only of senior and managerial personnel of the operator. That said, the operator's liability is not always limited in this fashion, particularly in older agreements.

It is normal practice for the operator to be entitled to reimbursement of all costs incurred by it in carrying out joint operations. The operator can therefore employ its own personnel and materials and can charge the costs incurred in doing so to the account established for the purposes of the joint venture (known as the joint account) in accordance with the detailed accounting procedure set out in the JOA (see below). These joint accounting records can be reviewed by the Joint Operating Committee but the operator does not have to divulge commercially sensitive information relating to any multifield or multioperator agreements. In some cases, the operator can provide a certificate of costs or charges certified by its auditors. If a contract to be awarded is above a certain *de minimis* level, then the operator must consult with the co-venturers and get the approval of the Joint Operating Committee to the tender enquiry document, bid list and proposed tender evaluation criteria. As referred to in Chapter 10, in procuring services and materials by tender the operator must comply with European and UK procurement legislation. Whilst the operator is agent for the co-venturers when contracting, the JOA usually provides that contractors are to look only to the operator for the due performance of commitments.

In addition to its other duties and responsibilities, the operator is also normally required to submit to the Joint Operating Committee for its approval a Health and Safety and Environment Plan setting out policies to govern the joint operations with various objectives and targets.

Rights of the participants

The JOA will normally provide that each of the co-venturers has the right to inspect all books, records and inventories maintained by, or on behalf of, the operator and relating to the joint operations. There will usually be restrictions as to the time (usually normal business hours) and notice required to be given for any such inspection. In addition, the co-venturers will also have the right of access to the Licensed Area and the joint operations provided that reasonable notice is given to the operator. In the event that such access relates to offshore operations, the operator is usually required to provide suitable transportation and accommodation (if required) at the cost of the joint account.

Insurance and litigation

The operator is required to obtain and maintain all insurance required by legislation, the licence and any other applicable laws in respect of both the joint operations and all joint property used in connection with such operations. The operator may, in addition to the insurance referred to above, be required by the Joint Operating Committee to take out further insurance but, in such event, each of the co-venturers may elect not to participate in such insurance. If any co-venturer chooses not to participate in such insurance obtained by the operator then they are required to obtain their own insurance in respect of their percentage interest share of any liability which may arise. In addition, each of the co-venturers is entitled to obtain such other insurance as it may require, but that insurance must contain a waiver of subrogation by the insurer in favour of the operator and/or the other co-venturers.

In terms of the JOA, the operator is also obliged to take reasonable steps to ensure that any contractors performing work in respect of the joint operations obtains and maintains all insurances required in terms of the licence, legislation and any other applicable laws.

The JOA will usually contain provisions in terms of which the operator confirms that it is a party to the Offshore Pollution Liability Agreement dated 4 September 1974, as amended (OPOL) and a member of the Offshore Pollution Liability Association Ltd ('the Association'). The operator will further agree (in its capacity as operator) to be bound by, and comply with, the provisions of OPOL, the memorandum and articles of association and the rules of the Association.

The operator will be under a duty to notify each of the co-venturers of any incident, accident or other circumstances resulting in damage to joint property, where the costs of such damage are in excess of a specified amount. In addition, the operator will be required to notify each of the co-venturers of any litigation in excess of a specified amount. The JOA will normally then provide that the operator will have the authority to deal with any such litigation, subject to certain exceptions (the most notable of which is where the litigation is in excess of a specified amount) in which case the operator requires the consent of the Joint Operating Committee before dealing with such litigation.

The Joint Operating Committee

The JOA will contain provisions relating to the establishment of a Joint Operating Committee, which will consist of one representative of each of the co-venturers. The powers and duties of the Joint Operating Committee generally include the consideration and determination of all matters of general policy, expenditure, press announcements, strategies and development, to name but a few. It would be normal for each co-venturer to have a voting interest equal to its percentage interest and that all decisions of the Joint Operating Committee will require to be made by the affirmative vote of a specified number of co-venturers (normally two, but this will depend on the particular circumstances) holding an aggregate percentage interest of a specified amount (this tends to be in the region of around 70–90% but will depend on the particular circumstances). However, some decisions will require only a simple majority (for example, agreeing the location of a well to be drilled as part of work obligations under a licence where the co-venturers have been unable to agree) and some decisions will require unanimous agreement (for example, the voluntary relinquishment of part of the licensed area or an amendment to the JOA).

Programmes and budgets

The operator prepares budgets for each forthcoming year for exploration and development. The operator will also have to prepare an annual work programme and budget for operating costs.

Upon a discovery being made, the operator, under direction of the Joint Operating Committee, will normally be required to prepare an appraisal programme and budget for that particular discovery. If, at a later stage, a Field Development Programme is required, then the operator prepares a Field Development Programme and budget for the discovery, for approval by the Joint Operating Committee. When any discovery or field reaches the production phase of development, the operator produces an annual production programme and budget for the following year.

Any authorisation to enter into a commitment for expenditure (AFE) normally has to be submitted to the co-venturers for approval. Once approved, the operator is entitled to incur the relevant commitment for expenditure and there will normally be a provision which allows the operator to overspend on the amount of the AFE by a given percentage (normally 10%) without having to first get the approval of the Joint Operating Committee.

Capital and operating expenditures in joint operations are normally shared by the co-venturers according to their percentage interest. This will not always necessarily be the case. One example is in the case of a 'carry'. In a carry, one party agrees to bear a disproportionate share of the costs for a period of time. For example, Company A may own an asset. It may transfer a percentage in the asset to Company B. Part of the consideration payable by Company B may be that for a period of time Company B will bear part of Company A's costs in respect of Company A's interest.

The operator is normally given the power to cash call each of the co-venturers for their percentage interest share of expenditure in advance of that expenditure being made. There are normally fairly tight deadlines to be adhered to for payment of cash calls and if a cash call is not met, then there is potential for a co-venturers to be in default and, therefore, subject to the default provisions in the JOA (see below). All income and expenses relating to the joint operations accrue to the joint account.

Further details of the accounting procedures in terms of which the operator is obliged to operate the joint account are set out below.

Sole risk

The JOA often provides that where a co-venturer proposes to the Joint Operating Committee a plan which is outside the current programme and budget of the operator and that plan is not agreed upon by the Joint Operating Committee as forming part of the current programme for all of the co-venturers then the proposer (and such of the other co-venturers who wish to participate) can carry out the work at its or their 'Sole Risk'. Any co-venturer may propose a sole risk seismic programme, sole risk testing and logging, sole risk drilling or sole risk development (all being generically referred to as a 'Sole Risk Project'). There are different provisions within the JOA dealing with each type of Sole Risk Project. If, for instance, a co-venturer has proposed a Sole Risk Project which has not been adopted by the Joint Operating Committee, then that co-venturer may elect with other sole risk parties to carry out a programme and may ask the operator to carry out the operations, failing which, it could elect to carry out that programme itself. There are circumstances in which a sole risk party will be entitled to use joint property. Generally speaking, no Sole Risk Project may be carried out if it is substantially similar to, or conflicts with, all or part of any programme approved by the Joint Operating Committee. In the event that a Sole Risk Project takes place, the Sole Risk participants have incurred costs and expenses in connection with that project and have taken the risk that it would not succeed. To reflect the risk and investment, if a co-venturer which did not participate in the Sole Risk Project later wishes to participate there is a cost in doing so. For instance, if a co-venturer does not take part in a sole risk seismic programme but wants to use the seismic data later on, it may have to pay, say, five times the cost of the seismic data which it would have borne had it approved the seismic as a joint operation. In any event, a Sole Risk Project cannot jeopardise or interfere with the joint operations.

Default

In certain specified circumstances (the most common of which is failure by a co-venturer to meet its percentage interest of a cash call) a co-venturer will be deemed to be in default under the relevant provisions in the JOA. In the event of a co-venturer being in default, there are detailed provisions set out in the JOA which set out the consequences of such default. If one co-venturer has defaulted it is usual for the others to have to contribute the funds to the operator. The defaulting party has to pay interest on the amount in default. While, and for so long as the default continues, the defaulting co-venturer is not normally allowed to attend meetings of the Joint Operating Committee, to vote on any matter to be determined by the Joint Operating Committee, to receive information or receive its entitlement to any petroleum produced as a result of the joint operations. If the default continues for a specified period, then the JOA will usually provide that the defaulting co-venturer forfeits its percentage interest under the JOA. The non-defaulting co-venturers will normally have rights to acquire the defaulting co-venturer's percentage interest on a pro rata basis. If none of the non-defaulting co-venturers wants to take an assignment of the defaulting party's percentage interest then the JOA will normally provide that the parties elect to abandon the joint operations.

Non-consent

In some JOAs, there are non-consent provisions whereby if a party did not vote in favour of a particular programme but the majority of the co-venturers did, then the party cannot be compelled to participate in the operations which it voted against. The BNOC style JOA does not include non-consenting provisions for exploration and appraisal operations, however, there are normally non-consent provisions for field development operations in the BNOC style. A co-venturer may, upon the Secretary of State authorising a field development plan and by giving notice to the other co-venturers, elect not to proceed with the field development. Each of the co-venturers also has the right to refuse to participate in a field development on the relevant Field Development Programme being approved by the Joint Operating Committee.

Assignments

In terms of the JOA an assignment of a co-venturer's interest under the licence and the JOA is permitted (subject to DTI consent) as long as it is in respect of an undivided interest in all and not part of its interest under the licence and JOA. Historically, JOAs quite often contained pre-emption rights which provided that where a co-venturer wished to assign its interest under the licence and the JOA, it had to first offer its interest to the other co-venturers on a pro rata basis and on the same terms as the proposed deal with the third party. Pre-emption rights are no longer permitted in new JOAs but are quite often still found in older (pre-2003) JOAs, albeit now as modified by the 2003 Master Deed. If a co-venturer wishes to sell its interest under the licence and JOA then it will also have to demonstrate to the other co-venturers that the purchasing party has the financial capability to meet its prospective obligations under the JOA and the licence. Notwithstanding the transfer of its interest, the co-venturer assigning its interest under the licence and JOA will remain liable to the other co-venturers for all obligations which were incurred prior to the date of assignment.

This clause will also contain provisions which allow a co-venturer to grant security over its interest in respect of any finance provided that the co-venturer remains liable for all obligations relating to its interest and that the right of the secured creditor are subject to the rights of the co-venturers under the JOA and that any necessary consent of the Secretary of State has been obtained.

Disposal of petroleum

The JOA will usually provide that the operator has the right to use as much petroleum as may be necessary for the joint operations. All other petroleum is to be available to the co-venturers for sale in proportion to their percentage interest; each of the co-venturers therefore has a right and obligation to lift and separately dispose of its percentage interest share of all petroleum produced and stored. Each co-venturer will normally enter into offtake agreements or other arrangements for the disposal of its percentage interest share of petroleum.

Confidentiality

All data and information collated and produced while exploring, appraising, developing or producing a field are confidential to the co-venturers and cannot be disclosed to third parties unless consent is obtained from the other co-venturers or it comes within certain restricted exemptions. A breach of confidentiality will normally be regarded as a serious breach by other co-venturers.

Withdrawal

Participants are not allowed to withdraw from the JOA except under certain defined circumstances. A participant may withdraw if, for instance, the work obligations in Schedule 4 to the licence have been completed. Generally, if a party wishes to withdraw the other parties have the right to acquire its interest (either for no consideration or for salvage value of joint property). If none of the other parties wishes to acquire the interest then the JOA is normally terminated and the interests relinquished.

Governing law

North Sea JOAs are normally governed by English law and will normally contain a provision stating that the parties to the JOA submit to the jurisdiction of the High Court in England. In the event of assets located in countries other than the UK, there will always be a question of which law should govern the contract. This will clearly depend on the circumstances but where a UK company is involved it will normally attempt to have English law govern the JOA.

Accounting procedure

The JOA will contain detailed accounting procedures and, although it is beyond the scope of this chapter to provide a full summary of the various provisions, a brief overview of the main provisions of the accounting procedure is set out below.

Normally, the accounting procedure will be divided into five sections. The first section contains general accounting provisions, the second section relates to chargeable expenditure, the third section deals with income and receipts, the fourth section deals with budgeting, forecasting and reporting, and the fifth section deals with the provision of reports. Each of these sections will now be considered briefly in turn.

1. General accounting provisions

This section will normally set out the purpose of the accounting procedure which is to establish the principles of accounting which reflect the actual cost to the operator so that it neither gains nor loses by reason of it being the operator. This section will also provide that each of the co-venturers will be responsible for maintaining their own accounting records in order to comply with all legal requirements and to support all fiscal returns and other reports to be made to or required by any governmental authority in respect of the joint operations (other than those which are the obligation of the operator). The operator is also under a duty to provide such accounting information to the co-venturers in order for them to comply with any statutory accounting obligations.

The operator will be required to keep and maintain accounting records with details of all expenditure incurred by the operator, all payments made to the operator by the co-venturers and all income received by the operator.

It is generally provided that the initial cost of the joint operations will be funded by the operator and then reimbursed to it by each of the co-venturers (in proportion to their respective percentage interests). In such a case, the operator will, in addition to reimbursement of the amounts paid, be entitled to payment of a financing fee. This section of the accounting procedure will normally set out a detailed formula that is to be used in calculating the financing fee that will be due by each of the co-venturers. In the case of more major items of expenditure, the operator has the option of cash calling each co-venturer for its share of any such expenditure by written notice a specified number of days prior to such expenditure being incurred. Where a cash call is made the operator will not be entitled to any financing fee as it will have the funds from the co-venturers prior to having to utilise the funds.

This section of the accounting procedure also sets out when invoices are to be submitted by the operator is respect of expenditure incurred by it, the form of such invoices and the date by which these are to be paid by the co-venturers. The invoices will show the net total of all payments (ie less all receipts and income) relating to the joint account and the amount payable by each co-venturer. There will also be provisions relating to the invoicing of the operator for any services which have been agreed to be provided by any co-venturer.

Also included within this section are provisions relating to the keeping by the operator of records of all joint property (assets, stock, equipment and supplies) and the taking of periodic inventories of such joint property. There are also provisions relating to adjustments in the event that any amount invoiced to a co-venturer is disputed and there are very detailed audit provisions, in terms of which the co-venturers have the right to audit accounts and records of the operator.

Finally, this section will normally provide that the accounting procedure can be revised or amended from time to time by agreement between the co-venturers or, in certain circumstances, with the agreement of the Joint Operating Committee.

2. Chargeable expenditure

This section of the accounting procedure sets out those items of expenditure which the operator can charge to the joint account. These include the cost of all salary and related benefits of all personnel engaged on joint operations (which includes personnel employed by the operator, personnel seconded to the operator by the co-venturers or hired by third party employment agencies, and personnel employed by the co-venturers who provide services to the joint operations). All direct expenses incurred by personnel working under the direct control of the operator (including travel and relocation expenses, and any living allowances) can also be charged by the operator to the joint account. This section also contains detailed provisions on the amounts that are to be charged to the joint account in respect of such personnel and how this is to be determined.

Another expenditure which is chargeable to the joint account (and which relates to personnel) is administrative overhead costs. This includes property costs, personnel department costs, office services, routine computer applications and costs of other support departments but specifically do not include costs and expenses of a corporate nature.

Property, equipment and supplies purchased by the operator from third parties or transferred from the operator or any of its affiliates can be charged to the joint account and this section contains details of what can be charged for such property, equipment and supplies. The operator is also under a duty to ensure that only such property, equipment and supplies as are required for immediate use is acquired and that there are no surplus stocks of joint property. The cost of transporting personnel and any property, equipment and supplies in connection with joint operations can also be charged to the joint account by the operator (unless otherwise charged to the account in accordance with this section of the accounting procedure).

Other costs which are chargeable to the joint account include the cost of services provided by the co-venturers or any third parties, the cost of services provided by the operator of by any of its affiliates, and all costs and expenses arising out of any loss or damage to joint property, all costs and expenses of litigation and other legal services relating to joint operations. It also includes all taxes and other governmental levies assessed or levied upon, or in connection with, joint operations and all premiums paid for insurance carried for the benefit of the co-venturers. The cost of establishing and maintaining shore bases, warehouses, camps and other field facilities used in connection with joint operations, the costs of providing technical support and general expertise (including health, safety and environmental advice, technical services, research and development support, geological, geophysical, drilling, petroleum engineering and other support activities), are chargeable to the joint account as well as costs associated with licence rentals and fees paid by the operator on behalf of the co-venturers and any other expenditure not covered elsewhere in this section. Those costs which are deemed to be necessary and proper for the conduct of joint operations (provided it is approved by the Joint Operating Committee).

The above list of items chargeable to the joint account is not intended to be exhaustive and the precise items that are so chargeable may be the subject of some debate between the operator and the other co-venturers when negotiating the JOA.

3. Income and receipts

This section will generally provide that the operator will promptly credit to the joint account all net proceeds received in connection with joint operations as a result of:

(i) sale of property equipment, supplies and other joint property;
(ii) services provided to third parties or individual participants whether using material, other joint property, facilities or expertise;
(iii) reimbursement by third parties of any sums expended by the operator on behalf of the participants;
(iv) insurance or other claims made by the operator on behalf of the participants;
(v) material returned to the operator from joint operations or transferred to other activities; and
(vi) grants from governmental sources and all taxes in addition to any other event giving rise to a receipt (including interest) by the operator on behalf of the participants.

The disposal of material purchased for joint operations generally requires notice of this fact to be given to the co-venturers along with the applicable price. Prior approval of the Joint Operating Committee is often required for higher value items, for example items of material with an original unit cost of greater than £100,000 or original unit costs totalling more than £500,000 ('Major Surplus Items') which are no longer needed or suitable for joint operations.

The JOA will typically then set out procedures for the purchase of such material by the co-venturers. Such provisions would allow the operator to purchase any surplus material other than Major Surplus Items, which can typically be purchased by any of the co-venturers during a 30-day period from date of approval given by the Joint Operating Committee. A bidding procedure will govern the situation where more than one co-venturer wishes to purchase an item of material. The procedures provide that the operator is to determine the price to be paid and set out the basis for this. Material can be classified as new, good used, other used, bad-order or junk with the price to be paid dependent upon such classification.

Where there have been no bids for material, the operator prepares a list of the items for sale and competitive bids are requested from third parties, with the highest offer customarily accepted. Where no such bids are received or the nature or value of an item makes tendering impractical or uneconomic, the operator is to dispose of the same as it thinks fit, other than to itself or its affiliates. Similar provisions will apply in relation to disposal of other forms of joint property.

The operator may provide services to third parties or individual co-venturers using material, other joint property, facilities, expertise or other resources provided that such a provision does not jeopardise, hinder or unreasonably interfere with joint operations. This limitation does not apply, however, in the case of emergencies. A further limitation generally found is that where services are to be supplied with an original cost of greater than, say, £250,000 to the joint account. In such an event, notice must be given to each co-venturer along with details of the service, the identity of the person requesting the service and a recommendation on the terms on which the service should be provided. Prior approval of the Joint Operating Committee is required before any such service can be provided. Any services provided below this threshold are to be provided at rates which are not less than those charged by third parties for like services on comparable terms in the same location.

4. Budgeting, forecasting and reporting procedure

This section sets out what is required to be included in exploration budgets, appraisal budgets, development budgets and production budgets. In all cases, this will generally include:

(i) an estimate in Pounds of the total relevant programme and a subdivision of each total into each main classification and subclassification of cost;
(ii) an estimate of any material amounts to be paid in a currency other than Pounds, together with the estimated exchange rates;
(iii) the amount of any escalation allowance or contingency allowance added;
(iv) an estimate of the timing and value of AFEs and of the costs and the total number of man-months budgeted; and
(v) a statement indicating which budget items, if any, are contingent upon the outcome of other budget items such as the testing of appraisal wells.

Approval of any budget provides the operator with general approval of the proposals and shall permit the operator to enter into commitments or incur any expenditure included in the budgets approved by the Joint Operating Committee.

A review of, or amendment to, any budget shall include actual cash payments, net of receipts and accruals to date and actual commitments to date.

Each budget must typically be divided into separate classifications and subclassifications of cost in order to provide a breakdown of the workscope into work elements in sufficient detail to allow adequate cost allocation and control. AFEs required will be established for each classification or subclassification as appropriate. The operator may transfer sums between budget subclassifications after budgets have been approved provided there has been prior approval of the Joint Operating Committee.

The operator is to request approval of an AFE when the main details of the relevant commitment can be ascertained and the AFE can be approved by the participants. The AFE is to describe the scope of work, provide estimates for the items of equipment required and timings of such expenditure and show separately the base cost, escalation and any contingency. The total of these three sums is the estimated final cost. The JOA will also set out the procedure for approval of an AFE by co-venturers, typically allowing 30 days for voting in favour of it. After approval by the Joint Operating Committee the operator will notify all co-venturers of the identity of those co-venturers whose authorisations formed part of that approval. The operator must also notify co-venturers where the future commitments will, or are likely to, exceed the estimated final cost by more than 10%.

A cost control report is typically to be provided on a quarterly basis unless the aggregate annual expenditure exceeds a specified figure (say £10 million). In such an event, the report is to be provided monthly. The report shall be a comparison of the latest final estimated costs for each AFE with the approved budget cost for each AFE in addition to a comparison of actual costs against the approved AFE values.

Finally, it will be provided that any major contract which is forecast to exceed its approved level by more than 10% or by a specified amount (say £750,000) is to be added as a memorandum item on the cost control report with the estimated final cost for such contract. A major contract is one exceeding a set value (say £3 million) or as may be determined by the Joint Operating Committee.

5. Summary of reports

This section will simply set out the reports to be prepared by the operator and the frequency of each report required under the JOA.

— 10 —

PROJECT MANAGEMENT

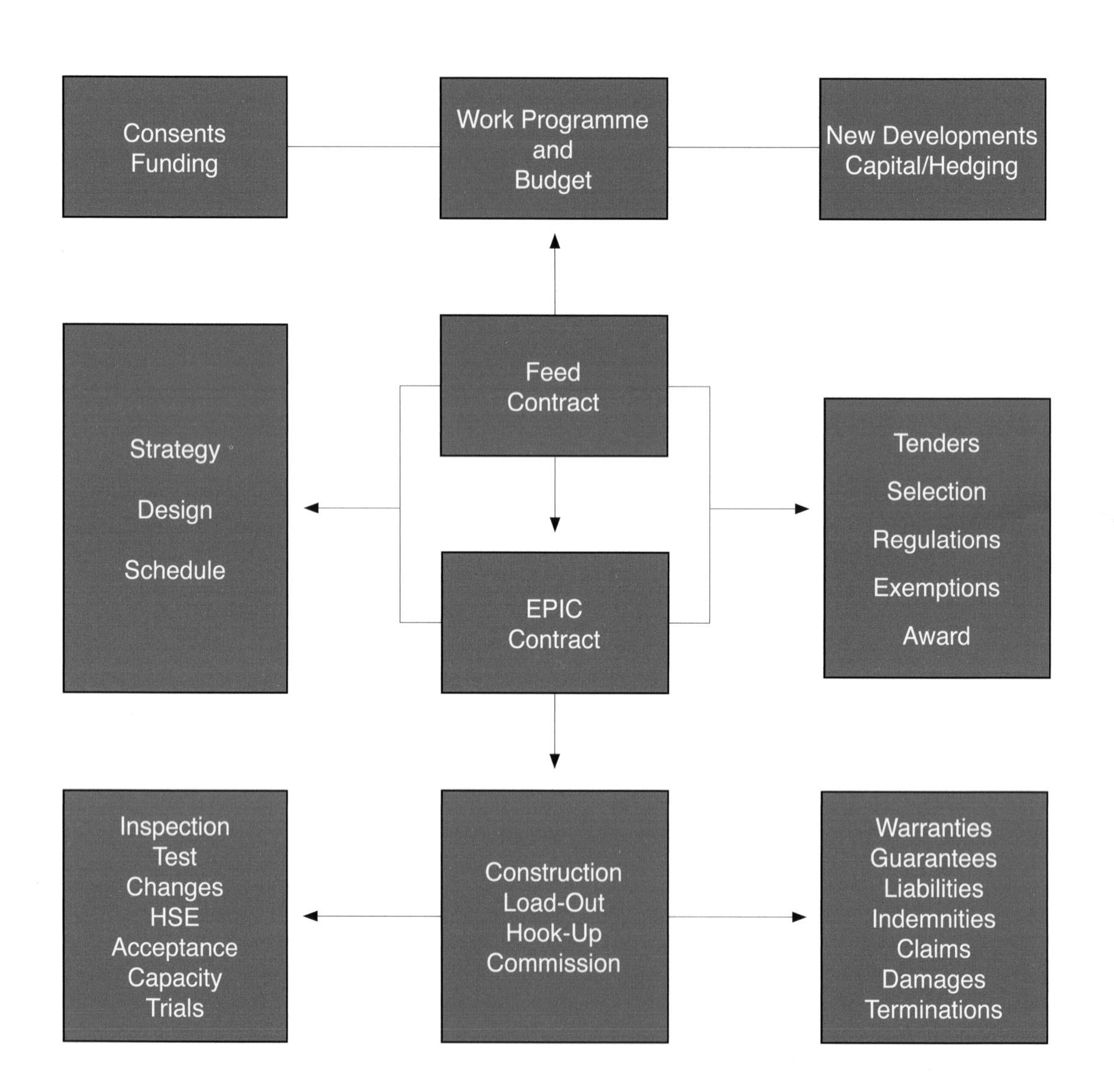

Consents
Funding
Work Programme
and
Budget
New Developments
Capital/Hedging
Strategy
Design
Schedule
Feed
Contract
EPIC
Contract
Tenders
Selection
Regulations
Exemptions
Award
Inspection
Test
Changes
HSE
Acceptance
Capacity
Trials
Construction
Load-Out
Hook-Up
Commission
Warranties
Guarantees
Liabilities
Indemnities
Claims
Damages
Terminations

PROJECT MANAGEMENT

TECHNICAL

10.1 Introduction

The execution phase of a project is when topsides, substructures, pipeline and all the other hardware necessary to process and transport hydrocarbons are constructed and installed. On most successful projects, the project manager will also have participated in the previous phase of the enterprise: the development phase. This allows him to take part in the concept selection, the way the field will be developed. More important, it allows an opportunity to gain ownership and commitment to the project.

The development team and the emerging project team will work together for some months to ease the transition into the execution phase. In many cases, two or three of the development team will remain with the project team for some time, occasionally until the very end of the execution phase.

The execution phase has the primary aim of delivering an asset that is ready for start-up in accordance with the project objectives of Health, Safety and Environment (HS&E), cost, time and quality. The activities during this phase are:

- detailed design;
- procurement;
- construction;
- commissioning;

- preparation for asset operation; and
- project closeout.

During the development phase of a project, free and creative thinking is prominent. How is this field best developed? Can existing infrastructure be used? Is new technology available? In the advance towards the execution phase, thinking will converge towards a more focused conclusion. This means the removal of uncertainty, providing better definition and detail. In turn this provides improved accuracy in terms of the expected out-turn cost and schedule. To give further confidence it is customary to bench mark. This is a simple comparison with previous projects. Do the promises and expectations sit with an acceptable range of previous outcomes in terms of cost, schedule and complexity?

10.2 Project Execution Plan

One of the first tasks of the project manager is to prepare the Project Execution Plan (PEP), the 'roadmap' to deliver the project. The PEP describes the scope of work and the principal steps of the execution phase which are: detailed design, procurement, fabrication, installation, commissioning and ultimately handover of the project or asset to the operations team. The PEP conveys to the reader not just what is to be done, but how it is to be done. It is comprehensive, covering wide-ranging issues such as health, safety and the environment, stakeholder engagement, permits and consents, resources, the project schedule, a breakdown of costs and the contracting strategy to deliver the project. All of these are essential components to deliver a project.

10.3 Contracting strategies

At the start of the execution phase a contracting strategy will already exist. It is in essence the combined plan for all major contracts within a project. It addresses the commercial form of the contracts, the method of selecting contractors and the combination of interfacing activities.

Most of the work within a project will be contracted out, representing some 80–90% of the budget. Consideration for choosing a contracting strategy will evolve around risk, scope definition, etc. The different types of contracts entail to what degree direct company involvement is deployed. There can be direct management by company staff; sometimes key company staff can be supplemented by third party contract staff. In this case, company control may be less effective in response to changing circumstances.

A project services contractor may help staff a team. In this case, some contractor procedures and systems may be employed, but the company remains in control, and there is a single, integrated project team with company staff in key positions.

At the other end of the spectrum a managing contractor may be employed. In this case they are responsible for the administration of most of the major contracts, under the direction of a very small company team.

Finally, a very much hands-off approach whereby an 'EPIC' contractor (Engineer, Procure, Install and Commission) is directly contracted to execute the total scope of the work within a project (as opposed to a managing contractor who manages other contracts on the company's behalf).

Alliance contracts have evolved from EPIC contracts. They work on the principle that client and contractor(s) work together using their joint skills and resources. The starting point is usually an EPIC bid proposal, adopted as a base cost schedule. There is an initially agreed target value acceptable to both the client and the contractor, where the contractors' participation in project risk is already taken into account. Thereafter both parties have the objective of beating the target through enhanced performance. Both parties become, in effect, shareholders in the contract: sharing the rewards, ie savings under target on an agreed shareholder basis, and sharing the risks on cost overruns, usually to some predetermined limit, after which the client assumes total liability.

Selection of the contractor involves availability and compatibility, host government's influence, market forces and local content issues. The contract plan should highlight the prequalification, tender and award process to be followed. Contracts may take many forms, ranging from fully reimbursable, where the operator pays all costs that are incurred, to a lump sum where the contractor proposes a fixed cost for delivering the scope. This implies some risk to the bidder. Contracts may be bundled together and awarded. The contracting strategy and selection underpin the success of every project, or indeed the failure if the wrong approach is adopted.

10.4 Contractor remuneration

A number of different methods of contractor remuneration can be used, with advantages and disadvantages as shown.

Lump sum contracts

The distinguishing feature of a lump sum contract is that the contractor is responsible for performing and completing the work as defined for a fixed price. For lump sum contracts to be successful, a good definition of scope, and a reasonable split of risk between company and contractor is required. It is essential to minimise subsequent scope changes.

In order to achieve this, a significant amount of project planning and definition prior to awarding a contract is required and a long lead time is therefore necessary.

Advantages

- Once signed, the cost should only vary as a result of agreed variations and claims.
- Costs are known ahead of the project execution, are easy to control, and a low risk to the company.
- Straightforward contract, management and administration.
- Contractor usually has strong incentive to perform well.

Disadvantages

- Long lead time before actual contract commences.
- Less influence over deliverables.
- Potential for claims (particularly if there are many variations in the orders, causing delays or disruptions to the project).
- Unless the scope of work is very specific, the contractor may tend to increase the contract price as a protection against potential risks in the contract.

Unit rate contracts

In unit rate contracts, rates are fixed for specific items of measurable work. The contract price is then determined by measurement of the work actually performed. The prime characteristic of this type of contract is that although the overall quantity of work ('scope') is unknown at the time of contract signature, the scope of work for each unit is defined. This provides a reasonable approximation of the scope of work and quantities involved and all significant jobs should be identified within the agreed schedule of rates. Furthermore, clearer definition of indirect costs needs to be included in the agreed rates. Finally, an accurate measurement of the quantity and quality of the work as it is completed is very important. The key cost monitoring control in unit rate contracts is at the commitment stage, when the company's own estimate of the number of units to be constructed or provided is translated into a single Authorised Contract Value (ACV).

This type of contract is usually used for front-end design services, and open-ended service contracts where a scope of work cannot be properly defined. The key drivers are usually when time is of the essence, and where significant changes to the scope of work or the specifications are to be expected.

Advantages

- Some degree of control over the final cost without precise definition of the scope of work.
- Project execution can commence prior to completion of detailed design.

Disadvantages

- Cost control requires considerable effort by contract holder.
- There is usually considerable scope for accumulating variations to the contract.

Reimbursable cost contracts

The main characteristic of the reimbursable cost type of contract is that all direct and indirect expenditures incurred by the contractor are paid on the basis of actual cost without an overlay for profit. Often, incentives are included to provide a profit for the contractor provided certain objectives are met. Usually these include time, budget, quality and HS&E.

Advantages

There are no particular advantages to reimbursable cost contracts, but they are appropriate in the following circumstances:

- for major front-end design services, and various other major open-type service contracts;
- for time-driven EPIC contracts of a major nature with international contractors who have experience in this type of contract;
- if proper 'milestones' for the payment of incentives can be established;
- if there is a sufficiently accurate budget which can be used for setting a financial target;
- if a buyer's market operates.

Disadvantages

- The need to establish the true cost of the contractor without embarking on an onerous financial administration by the company.
- The establishment of clear and measurable parameters for assessing achievements in the field of quality, health, safety and environment.
- The requirement for close monitoring by the company, and detailed financial and administrative procedures.

Bills of Quantities contracts

Bills of Quantities (BOQ) contracts are contracts with detailed bills of quantities that form the definition of the work. BOQ contracts list all the quantities of work to be performed to a standard level of detail. BOQ contracts are usually approximate, with the actual quantities being measured upon completion. The final quantities will be agreed; this is the basis upon which the contract price is assessed.

Advantages

- Straightforward execution.
- Costs of variations readily derived from contract.
- Low possibility of claims by contractor.
- Perceived lower risk than other contract forms by contractor.

Disadvantages

- Detailed scope of work requires considerable upfront effort.
- Significant engineering and administrative effort to measure work.
- The risk of the project is mainly with the company.

Day-rate contracts

Day-rate (or time) contracts are those where the major element of contractor remuneration consists of a fixed rate per day (hour or month) for work performed. Day-rate contracts occur usually in the context of a drilling or construction project, where the contractor is to provide the main item of equipment, such as a drilling rig, construction lay barge, or similar pieces of equipment.

Under such contracts, as much as possible of the scope of work should be covered by unit rate contracting, such as drilling a specified footage of a well, laying a length of pipeline per specification. Usually this mechanism is used when the scope of work cannot be sufficiently defined to allow lump sum contractor remuneration, or where significant or unquantifiable risks are present which it would be unreasonable or uneconomic for the contractor to carry alone.

Day-rate contracts may also use an incentive scheme (eg based on footage drilled). There is also an option of 'milestone' payments. Ideally, incentives should create a win–win situation for both parties. The company wins by getting a quality product delivered on time, and the contractor wins the financial incentive.

With an incentive-based contract the contractor will:

- work efficiently;
- improve performance;
- apply new technology; and
- deliver quality products or work.

With non-incentive based day-rates:

- there are difficulties in controlling the cost of the work;
- the company carries the total risk for poor performance or productivity on the part of the contractor; and
- there is a need for extensive and detailed company supervision and skilled and experienced manpower.

Time and Materials contracts

Time and Materials contracts apply when the major element of contractor remuneration consists of a fixed rate per unit for materials supplied by the contractor. The unit rate is a fixed price based on specified materials, or other project requirements. All contractor costs are covered in these all inclusive materials prices. Examples are concrete structures by volumes of concrete (cubic metres), installed roads of a specified length, provision of a length of pipeline, and so on. Under such contracts, scope is clearly specified by the materials requirements. Incentives to complete or progress the work on time are a critical element of such contracts. They are usually in the form of bonus (or penalty) scheme in which completion on time is a key factor.

Advantages	Disadvantages
• Provides incentives to work efficiently. • Deliver quality work according to specifications. • Minimum company supervision.	• Difficulties in controlling the quality of work performed. • Carrying the risk of poor performance by the contractor.

10.5 Project costs

By the time the project is ready for approval, sometimes referred to as sanction or Final Investment Decision (FID), a high level of definition is required. At the FID the project manager should have a cost estimate that accurately reflects the work to be done, and typically would be within a range of accuracy of minus 10% to plus 15%.

The cost estimate is expressed as an expectation case, or likely outcome, that reflects confidence in the way that the estimate has been put together: there is a 50:50 chance of overrunning or underrunning, within the prescribed level of accuracy. The estimate also contains some contingency for what is referred to as 'known unknowns'. Known unknowns are a reflection of what can typically happen. The sources are vested in history and experience – such as productivity, weather downtime, late materials and so on. The project will take a view on the level of contingency to be applied to discrete elements.

For example, a heavy-lift vessel required to install a 10,000-tonne topsides may be required for a period of only 10 to 15 days. However, if this activity is delayed by bad weather, it may cost as much as $750,000 a day waiting for conditions to improve. It is not difficult to imagine how quickly the costs escalate.

Another example, but over a much longer period, would be during the construction of the topsides which can take 18 months to two years. A forecast of productivity is required over that duration. A drop in the productivity expectation of 1 or 2% over this period would lead to a significant increase in cost and schedule.

The second category of contingency is unknown unknowns – a much more difficult concept. Every possible occurrence cannot be included, nor should it be. Nevertheless, there are a number of potential impacts outside the project's control – exchange rates, rapidly increasing steel prices, a hardening market and so on – all of which will typically appear on a project manager's list of risks to be managed or mitigated. Risk management requires some degree of market intelligence and often entails developing various 'what-if' scenarios, applying probability analysis and then taking a view on possible outcomes, and this is an area where experience and judgment really come into play. During the 1970s there was considerable industrial unrest and many projects were subject to significant delay and cost overruns.

A range of possible out-turn cost estimates is developed around the 50:50 or 'expectation' case. A 'least likely' or 10:90 scenario (ie a 10% chance that the out-turn cost will be within the estimate figure) may be viewed as, say, 15% under budget, perhaps due to a soft market or low steel prices. At the other end of the scale, steel prices may escalate and such a factor might well have a significant effect. This is referred to as the 90:10 scenario, where there is a 90% chance that the out-turn costs will be within the estimated figure. A project on the UKCS can take three to five years from sanction to first production and may cost around $1 billion, so these sensitivities are important

In the cost estimate, the build-up of cost is done on a line-by-line item basis, so it is important to have a high level of definition of the scope to be executed. Once again, the significance and value of getting the 'front-end' conceptual thinking right come right to the fore.

10.6 Project schedule

The schedule has a critical path, which is the longest path of sequential activities. This is also the shortest duration in which the total project can be completed. This is often presented as a simple Gant or bar chart. This representation very much understates the complexity that underlies the plan. A North Sea project involves thousands of activities, some largely independent of one another and many interdependent (Fig. 10–1).

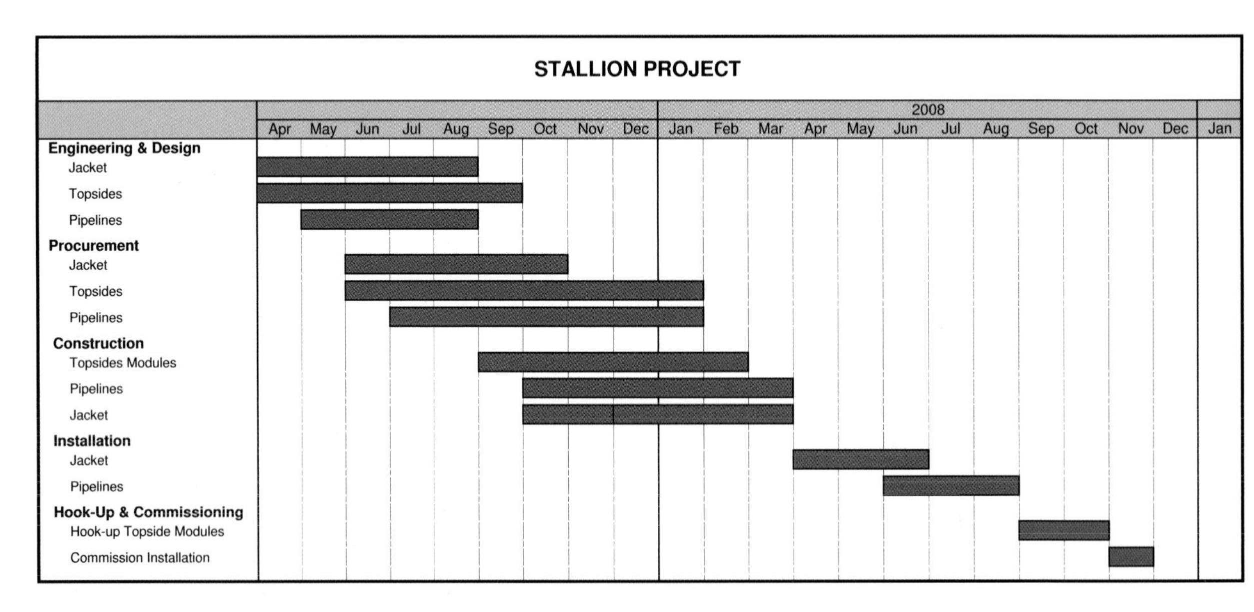

Figure 10–1 Typical project planning chart

A properly networked plan links in all of these interdependencies and this creates a critical path. The trick in planning a very complex schedule is to recognise the sub-critical activities, the ones waiting to take prominence as the new critical path. These plans need to be updated regularly and accurately to manage a complex project. Once again, this needs objective challenge, otherwise we see the 'triumph of hope over experience' and teams reduce durations in the belief that they can maintain the end date.

Just like the cost estimate, planning the time from project sanction to first production involves complex variables. Imagine a 10,000-tonnes topside for processing oil and gas. Aside from the support structure, there is a great deal of processing equipment: vessels, pipe work, valves, electric cable, instruments and pipe supports. Some of these topsides may be built offsite as a separate 'box' or module. There will be an expectation that this is delivered by a certain date, as there is for all equipment such as large vessels, valves and processing equipment. On occasions this can delay the installation of the entire topsides. In certain circumstances this can escalate and the delay may move the installation of the facilities into a poor weather window, or into the heart of the winter season. This may result in as much as three to five months' delay to schedule.

Often, in an attempt to mitigate such delays, the incomplete facilities may be loaded out and installed as originally planned. The unfinished work would then be completed offshore. Mobilising construction workers offshore, with the attendant helicopter flights, logistics and reduced productivity, is likely to cost between two-and-a-half and four times the onshore hourly cost. Why do this? The answer is: to try to protect the schedule.

There are a number of other interfaces to manage between other contractors and activities. It is likely that specialist contractors will each work in its/their own area of expertise. One may construct and build the pipeline, another the substructure or 'jacket', and yet another may install the facilities. Locations for these construction sites are likely to be spread around Europe. The interface with the drilling activities also has to be planned very carefully. Each interface presents the possibility of each activity potentially impacting adversely on the other.

10.7 Detailed design

Before project sanction, the Front-End Engineering and Design (FEED) should be sufficiently mature to give the definition and understanding of scope, to underpin accurate cost estimates and a robust schedule. Detail design is what it suggests: filling in the detail. This is a significant effort in terms of man-hours and time. It also encompasses specifying and purchasing all of the long-lead (long delivery) equipment and all the bulks (piping, flanges, nuts, bolts, etc.).

Detail design is a significant effort and can entail thousands, even millions, of man-hours over one to two years. It involves many different engineering disciplines, such as electrical engineering, process engineering, mechanical engineering, structural engineering, in fact almost every kind of engineer one can imagine. This has to be a very ordered process since it is a multidiscipline effort. A change by one engineer can seriously impact other areas of design. This can also lead to recycling of information.

During the detail design process numerous reviews are conducted around constructability, operability and safety, for example. This is not only good practice but also essential to demonstrate that a case for safety (Safety Case) has been made and that the plant will operate in a safe and effective manner.

To some degree the construction work can begin before detail design is complete. The risks are that this may result in changes, or late delivery of equipment which can adversely affect construction. At the end of detail design a complete package of drawings is issued, showing exactly what is to be constructed.

When schedule becomes the key driver, this can lead to a significant overlap of design with construction. Too much of an overlap carries excessive risks of rework, delays to the construction programme and cost overruns. This approach even has gained a title: 'design while build'. A good rule of thumb is: a project should not be more than 20% into construction unless detail design is 90% complete.

10.8 Construction

Construction is exactly what it says, just in the same way as it would describe building roads, houses or schools. However, these are often massive structures that have to be transported out to sea when completed. This has led to an incredible amount of innovation over many years.

Many factors have contributed to evolution in the approaches to construction. Three aspects have been very real drivers for change. These are water depth, heavy-lift capability and innovation. Throughout the design phase, the value-drivers are to reduce weight – steel is heavy and costly to fabricate and install. Ease of build, access and maximising what can be done onshore are other key factors.

Initially, the complex processing plant or topsides was constrained by the ability to lift and install these units offshore. The original lift vessels were constrained to lift weights of about 1,500 to 2,000 tonnes. A 10,000-tonne topside would be constructed as a number of modules, often as many as 10 or 12. This in turn dictated the way the modules were constructed. In the early days, different construction yards would specialise, so these modules could be spread around the UK or even Europe.

Figure 10–2 Jacket installation

The substructure may be a concrete, gravity-based structure or steel tower that is pinned to the seabed with tubular piles. While the substructure would be only 1,000 tonnes and 30-metres high, as, in shallow waters such as the Southern North Sea, this translated into megaliths for the likes of BP's Forties field or Shell's Brent field.

In the Northern North Sea, the water is around 300–500 ft deep. The substructure needs to survive a more challenging environment such as '100-year storms' in addition to carrying heavier topsides. Typically, such a structure would be in the region of 50,000 tonnes. For large finds such as the massive Forties or Brent fields, this was not prohibitive but still an expensive solution (Fig. 10–2).

From this came the idea of developing fields with subsea technology. A number of production wells could be placed on the seabed and tied back to nearby platforms. Initially, these tie-backs were restricted to around 15 km from the host platform. No single concept could be universally applied to field developments, owing mainly to the nature of the reservoir, fluid characteristics and flow-assurance issues.

In parallel to this emerging concept, the heavy-lift companies recognised the opportunities that could ensue if heavier topside lifts were possible. This allowed more work to be completed onshore, a much cheaper option than flying

Figure 10–3 Crane barge

hundreds of people out to sea for months to hook-up or tie together the smaller modules.

There was significant investment in new lift barges. These initially lifted around 5,000 tonnes, then, using two cranes in tandem, as much as 9,000 tonnes. The largest lift to date was Shell's Shearwater platform. Completely constructed and commissioned topsides were put into position in a single lift of 11,638 tonnes (Fig. 10–3).

Despite the obvious benefits of subsea developments, large processing platforms were still required. Innovation came into play again: flexible pipes or risers from the seabed to the surface. This enabled 'floaters' or FPSOs (Floating Production Storage and Offtake vessels). These are ship-shaped vessels with process equipment on the deck, tethered to the seabed with chains or cables. The production wells are linked to the surface through a special turret or swivel. The swivel is installed within the hull of the vessel and remains fixed relative to the wells on the seabed. The vessel is allowed to rotate or 'weather vane' around the turret. The enables the pipe work on the vessel to remain fixed relative to the wells, while the vessel is permitted excursions within a defined envelope. This allows the vessel to cope with differing sea states and wind conditions (Fig. 10–4).

These vessels manoeuvre much like oil tankers. In fact, some were conversions and many used standard ships' hulls. This enabled oil to be stored in the hull,

Figure 10–4 Floating production facility under construction in dry dock (© Shell)

with ocean-going tankers coming alongside to offload the oil in batches of, say, 500 million barrels upwards.

In the meantime, in the USA, Tension Leg Platforms (TLPs) were being designed. They were similar to a conventional topsides platform but able to float, their movement being restricted by cables tethered to the seabed. These were to become more and more important as finds in 'deepwater' became

Figure 10–5 Topsides being installed on substructure by 'float-over' method (© Shell)

more prominent. Deepwater, by definition, means depths of 6000–10,000 ft. The cost of the substructure for this kind of water depth is most certainly prohibitive.

The UK offshore construction industry has built massive integrated topside structures, in the range of 20,000 to 30,000 tonnes, well beyond the lifting capability of any lift barge. The solution was to be the 'float-over concept'.

These structures are 'jacked up' and transferred onto a barge. The barge is towed offshore and then sails between the existing substructure 'legs', then is de-ballasted to lower the massive topsides onto the support structure (Fig. 10–5).

This method means that construction and indeed pre-commissioning and commissioning onshore is maximised, resulting in lower costs and faster schedules – the primary project-drivers.

10.9 Hook-up and commissioning

Hook-up refers to two operations – the tying together of the modules of the topsides described earlier and also linking the vertical pipes or risers and tying in the pipe work to pre-drilled wells. This work can only be done offshore following the mating of topsides and substructure.

There is an interim step before commissioning and that is pre-commissioning. Once the construction phase is complete, testing is conducted to verify that the work has been carried out correctly. This takes a different form in each of the disciplines.

To test systems that will contain gas or liquid, often at high pressures, the pipe work is filled with water and pressurised up to one-and-a-half times the design pressure. This is within the limits of the steel and rarely fails, in view of the close scrutiny given to pipe manufacture and welding. The system usually operates at a pressure below the design pressure, giving another margin of safety.

The pipeline will then be de-watered, dried and filled with nitrogen. It is usual to run one or more 'pigs' which are spherical or bullet-shaped devices, through the line. This verifies the integrity of the pipeline and is also is used to clear any liquids or debris out of the system. Later, it may be necessary to send an 'intelligent' pig down the line to inspect for damage or corrosion.

Switchboards and electrical equipment are powered up, motors are turned, and every instrument loop and electric cable is checked for correct connection. Vessels are sometimes inspected and finally they are 'boxed up' ready for service. Level gauges and instruments are set and calibrated to ensure they are reading correctly. Pipe work that will contain hydrocarbons is leak-tested with nitrogen/helium. If the system proves leak-tight when filled with these gases, it will certainly not release any hydrocarbon molecules.

Commissioning is the final phase before start-up. Hydrocarbons are introduced, initially at a low pressure and then gradually built up to 'operating pressure'. Once this is achieved, motors are run, pumps and compressors operated, valves turned and ultimately hydrocarbons begin to flow. The pipeline will have been dried and left full of nitrogen previously. Nitrogen is pushed out of the system by the hydrocarbons.

Once it is established that all is in order, the remainder of the producing wells will be opened up and full export from the platform established. In order to verify that the facilities are performing to design, the final step of capacity trials is then undertaken.

PROJECT MANAGEMENT

LEGAL

10.10 Introduction

In the first part of this chapter, consideration was given to a specific scenario. Here, the legal and commercial aspects of a situation where the project team of a licence holder (the 'Company') have discovered a play, have appraised the field and have entered into a Joint Operating Agreement (JOA) with the other interest holders in respect of that block ('Block A'). It may be the case on some occasions that the block represents an entire field or the same co-venturer's own adjacent blocks and one JOA covers the whole field. Alternatively, further drilling may disclose that the structure is actually a structure which extends beyond the boundaries of the block covered by the co-venturer's licence and well into a neighbouring block held by different parties under a separate licence ('Block B'). The owners of Block A and Block B have agreed to unitise their interests in respect of Block A and Block B and so have entered into a Unitisation and Unit Operating Agreement ('Unit Agreement' or UOA) to unitise their interests and allow them to develop the whole structure as one 'unit structure' in respect of which they all have an interest.

The party which has been appointed as operator may be for the unit area and other co-venturers under the UOA ('co-venturers'), or may be under a single JOA; that operator will have successfully applied to the Secretary of State for sanction of their Field Development Plan. They have produced and submitted a Project Development Plan, an Environmental Study Report and Health and Safety Report together with all other ancillary information which has been requested by the DTI. On the basis of this information the Secretary of State has granted permission to the operator and the co-venturers to develop the unit.

The technical part of this chapter described the different contracting strategies which can be employed. The project management team for this development may have started with front-end engineering and design studies under a FEED contract and consultancy contracts which may then lead to the award of commissioning contracts for the construction of the facilities required to produce oil and gas from the field.

During this phase, from field development sanction to mobilisation and production of first oil, there will be numerous contracts entered into by the operator as agent for the co-venturers. The operator and the co-venturers will have agreed a Work Programme and a budget for the Work Programme. The UOA or JOA may provide that the operator can overspend on the budget, say by up to 10%, without requiring the consent of the co-venturers. A more substantial increase in spend will need to be authorised by the operator by applying to the Joint Operating Committee for approval to carry out the spend (other than in emergency situations where the operator has to act to protect lives and property).

In this part of this section, some of the different types of contracts which the operator might enter into with contractors will be reviewed. Then, the legislation on procurement in the UK and EC and procurement procedures which may be used by an operator will be discussed.

The second part of this section will look at ways in which some companies may wish to attract capital to a project by selling part of their percentage interest in a field or by selling forward part of their production. For instance, this may happen where a small oil and gas company does not have access to the public and private capital markets to fund their share of cash calls made by an operator. Rather than sell out the interest to a party which is able to fund the expenditure, the company may wish to transfer part of its interest in the field whilst retaining the rest of its interest. It is not just where a company needs to find cash that it might transfer an interest. Large oil and gas companies may not wish to deploy capital into a particular field development (because, for instance, they consider it to be too small) but may wish to retain an interest in the field going forward (for example, in case there is a large discovery). Finally, a company may consider entering into a derivatives contract to hedge risk. This type of arrangement is reviewed in section 10.14.

10.11 Contractual arrangements

Development stages

Most oil and gas companies have well-defined project management processes which are used when developing a field or re-entering a producing or abandoned field. Each project team will need a strategy for contracting in the resources which it will need to carry out the development.

There are commonly four stages which the project management team in upstream oil and gas companies will typically go through in bringing a new field onstream or redeveloping an existing field after a project development plan has been approved by a committee or board of that company.

The first stage is front-end engineering and design (FEED) in which the project team resolves the engineering options into one single engineering solution that has been the subject of a major hazard review and which can then be taken to the next stage which is the design and development stage. There will also need to be contemporaneous separate drilling and completion FEED processes. During this whole process the company will be looking for a single engineering solution which will minimise the costs of the project. At this stage it would be normal to identify those items of equipment which will take the longest times to get hold of (which will be long lead items).

The project manager in charge of the project may use outside contractors to support the project management team, especially for engineering solutions. These contracts are normally entered into on the basis of either a fixed fee plus reimbursable costs or on a day-rate contract plus reimbursable costs. Work is normally controlled through the use of cost time resources sheets (CTRs) for each element of the project.

During this process, the operator may bring in a large contractor on an EPIC contract for design, procurement, installation and commissioning of plant and equipment and this may especially be the case for smaller operators who may have less in-house resources or a large operator who may be employing resources on larger projects that it does not have the in-house expertise available to dedicate to the development of a small field.

It is the operator who enters into contracts with the contractors. The operator may be contracting with independent contractors and with consultancy firms. The operator may also engage manufacturers of equipment in the design studies on a reimbursable basis so that all those companies involved in manufacture and installation of equipment, as well as other companies providing contractual services, can be brought together to collectively work on the FEED study. At this stage, consultancy services or design services by manufacturers might be provided on standard terms and conditions of service. The contractors may be pre-qualified and selected from a panel of contractors previously approved by the operator. The operator may opt to use the services of the First Point Assessment Limited (FPAL) database in order to select suppliers of goods and services, when awarding contracts.

After completing the front-end engineering studies (FEED studies), the operator may seek approval from its own board (and the consent of the Unit Operating Committee established under the UOA) to award a contract to a design contractor, to start the design and development stage.

In the Design and Development Stage, the operator and contractors will produce a design package and detailed work packages to enable procurement and construction activities to be carried out. They will produce drawings, specifications, standards and requisitions in sufficient detail (quotations of which will be issued) to enable the purchase of specialised and bulk material and to allow for the fabrication of equipment and construction of the plant to be carried out. The contracts placed for this work are usually of a lump sum or fixed fee type. It may be that the same company involved in the FEED study will be involved in the design process or the process may be handled by one large contractor under an EPIC contract.

When the design and development stage has been completed, the design is then frozen and the operator may then give approval to move to the construction stage. At the construction stage, work packages and specifications produced at the design and development stage are taken and the project team will use detailed networks and plans to carry those out so that plant and machinery can be manufactured ready for the next stage, which is commissioning. The construction stage ends when the plant and equipment have been installed and successfully tested. It is the construction stage which has the greatest cost component of any part of the project and normally accounts for more than all the rest of the project stages put together. It therefore carries the greatest financial risk of all. The key management issues at this stage will be in preventing time slippage and maintaining cost control.

The activities during the construction stage include progressing construction activities in accordance with concise scopes of work and a detailed overall plan and programme. This will involve managing the production of materials by delivery dates, payment for goods and services, inspecting the technical aspects of materials received and fabrication work to ensure quality material traceability and certification are adequately carried out by contractors. Furthermore, the construction stage involves acceptance testing of packages to ensure compliance with specifications and testing of plant, assembly of data packages and documentation required for certificate of fitness requirements.

There are two parts to the commissioning stage. First, there is a dry stage (pre-commissioning) where plant and equipment is tested, for instance, with water. It then moves to wet commissioning in which hydrocarbons are used to test the system.

As explained previously in this chapter, the project management team of the operator will have developed a contracting strategy and may also have its own distinctive terms and conditions for all contractors. This approach aims to ensure consistency in warranties, indemnities, indemnity and warranty limitations, pricing and payment, key dates for delivery and the testing and installation of equipment.

Packages of work may be divided up into work for services, work for goods and then work according to the extent of the cost of the package and liabilities under it.

Types of contracts

There will be different types of contracts used for different development stages and the nature of the work. For instance, the design contracts used in the FEED studies will be entirely different in scope and extent from construction contracts and installation and hook-up and commissioning contracts. Some of these are analysed below.

In the UKCS the DTI introduced an initiative to harmonise contractual relationships and reduce costs. This was known as Cost Reduction Initiative in a New Era (CRINE). This was managed and sponsored by the United Kingdom Offshore operators Association (UKOOA) and included the DTI and all sectors of the industry. As part of that process a new approach was introduced which aimed to harmonise relationships between oil and gas companies and contractors. CRINE is no longer operational and Leading Oil and Gas Industry Competitiveness (LOGIC) has since taken over all of its former responsibilities. A number of standard form contracts have been produced by LOGIC including General Conditions of Contract for Construction, General Conditions of Contract for Design, General Conditions of Contract for Marine Construction, General Conditions of Contract for Onshore Services and General Conditions of Contract for Offshore Services. It was the intention of the industry at that time to use these contracts wherever they could to streamline processes. Since the mid-1990s when these contracts were first produced they have formed a template for the industry; however, they are not used by everyone. Some operators have their own style documents and some of these are heavily revised versions of LOGIC contracts. Throughout all those contracts there are certain general conditions which apply to all of them and which will be considered in detail below.

Contracts for design

Design contracts may include all the terms and conditions outlined under the heading 'Contract for manufacture of substantial facilities' below except for terms dealing with construction, inspection and testing, handover and completion, customs procedures and procedures dealing with, for instance, offshore vessels and pollution.

In a design contract, the operator will wish to own all technical information and intellectual property rights created during the design process.

An engineering services contract might be entered into with a contractor to provide engineering designs. This would typically contain a detailed scope of work in which the contractor would design the equipment in accordance with the scope. Any change to this would require a variation order to be agreed by the parties to the contract. There would be clauses dealing with the conduct of work, term of contract, relationships of parties (ie one of operator and independent contractor and not agency or partnership) and a clause setting out the members of the contractor's personnel who are to be engaged on the project. There would also be clauses on the nomination of representatives for each party, compensation to be paid, payment mechanics and the requirement for the operator to audit the project records of the contractor. Moreover, there would be clauses on trade, early termination, suspension of the contract, unsatisfactory performance, mutual hold harmless clauses, insurance policies the contractor is obliged to take out, remedies, a clause dealing with assignment of the contract, governing law, force majeure, resolution of disputes and conflicts of interest.

The ownership of the intellectual property in inventions (for example, if new mechanical processes are invented), of trademarks, of copyright in the design drawings and in the data relating to the field is of crucial importance. This question of ownership of intellectual property can be fraught with difficulty. The contractor may have pre-existing intellectual property of its own ('Background IPR') which it will utilise in carrying out the services. The contractor is only likely to be willing to use its Background IPR in the design process if the operator acknowledges in the contract that the contractor owns such Background IPR. The operator may wish to ensure that the co-venturers have complete ownership of all existing data relating to the field by making it clear that such information is Background IPR of the co-venturers. The solution is normally that the parties each agree that they own their own Background IPR, that the other party owns its own Background IPR and that each party grants the other a licence of such Background IPR for use on the project. Alternatively, the intellectual property may have been invented by the contractor and everything within that field use may be owned by the contractor.

Another area of complication is the warranty coverage in the contract. From the contractor's point of view it can only give limited warranties. It can warrant that the work will be expeditiously carried out in a diligent, skilful, safe and workmanlike manner and in accordance with good industry standards. The contractor could go further and say that it will use its reasonable efforts to achieve certain results by a target date. Unlike warranties given on goods or, for instance, hook-up and installation, the contractor's work is, to an extent, intangible and as a result the extent of the warranties given is very limited.

Smaller work packages

The operator may contract for the manufacture of smaller work packages, such as well heads and trees, on its own standard terms and conditions using a purchase order. These contracts may be issued to pre-qualified contractors or go to external tendering. The actual terms of such a contact will be in a much shorter form than a subsea facilities manufacturing contract but will cover similar issues. For small work packages it is likely that the contractor's work obligations will be restricted to the manufacture of specified items, the factory testing and acceptance of such items and systems integration tests. The risk and timing of payment may be stated to be in accordance with certain INCOTERMS. For instance, the risk may transfer to the purchaser when the equipment is delivered ex-works (ie when the goods are delivered at the contractors works premises) or FOB (free on board, ie the operator accepts risk when the goods are taken into the operator's vessel or other method of transport) or may be under CIF arrangements (the contractor pays for carriage freight and insurance to the operator's delivery point). The INCOTERMS 2000 will often apply to this type of contract. Title to the goods may pass from contractor to operator at delivery, payment or completion of factory acceptance testing, whichever is first.

The scope of the warranty provided by the contractor will be limited to the equipment being supplied. The contractor may warrant the title to the goods sold, that any goods and/or services provided under the purchase order will conform as to quantity, quality, applicable specification as set out in the contract and that they are free and clear of all liens and encumbrances. In addition, they may warrant that the goods and services are of sound materials and workmanship and that the products manufactured by the contractor and work performed by the contractor will be free from defects which are not inherent in the quality required or contractually permitted. The warranty period may be, for example, 12 months from the date the items are first put into service or 18 months from the date of delivery. Where goods are repaired or replaced, a new warranty period may start and may run for a further period. Items which do not conform to specification may be rejected by the operator and the contractor would be required to replace or repair and return them. The contractor's warranties would, therefore, be limited to providing the equipment on time and in accordance with the operator's specification. There will be exclusions of liability under the warranties and, more importantly a cap on the aggregate liability for the contractor; this could be up to, say, 10–15% of the contract value or, where a small business is contracting, it could be up to the entire value of the contract.

The contractor will normally represent and warrant that the equipment provided does not infringe any licence, patent, copyright or any other intellectual property rights and will undertake to indemnify and hold harmless the operator from any claims or losses or for any infringement. The operator may therefore not own any intellectual property rights in the equipment or goods supplied.

In a smaller contract for purchase of subsea facilities there will normally be no obligation on the contractor to install or provide vessels to ship the goods out to the site.

The project team may have authority to make orders for smaller work packages for FEED contracts or for the purchase of small items of equipment. However, where the work package is more substantial it may need to be reviewed by the operator's in-house or external legal team. Along with the purchase order terms there will normally be a front sheet and annexures stating how the goods are to be shipped, a specification of the work, an introduction to the project, standard codes and reference material. There would also be specific requirements for equipment to be manufactured to, description of the installation and test requirements, a description of the test equipment requirements and testing requirements, description of materials to be used in the manufacturing process, a description of all deliverable spare parts and a description of project reporting.

Contract for manufacture of substantial facilities

Tender. A substantial international contractor may be selected to supply major items of equipment and associated services. In such a case, the operator is likely to have issued documentation to potential contractors as part of a tender exercise. The tender documents sent to potential contractors include the operator's style of contract documentation. Bidders will submit their tender price for carrying out the work together with details of any exceptions or revisals which they wish to make to the contract. The operator and the successful bidder then finalise the form of the contract.

Contract. The project may not be new to the contractor as it may have been previously involved in the FEED study and/or as a contractor in respect of certain design packages. The main contractor in this case might be asked to manufacture the bulk of the subsea facilities and provide all resources and personnel required to carry out all aspects of the Work. The definition of 'Work' in the contract is one of the key provisions as it will specify exactly what work is to be carried out by the contractor in respect of the contract. Contracts of this nature are likely to be substantial documents and will include the main contractual terms and exhibits including a scope of Work, details of operator supplied information (specifications), operator supplied information (drawings), operator supplied items, contractors' supplied items, contractors' data requirements list, contractor equipment lists and a contractors' subcontractors list, the workplan, compensation details, parent guarantee (if any) and a health and safety and environment statement.

The contract will contain a schedule of key dates by which the contractor is required to perform aspects of the Work and a Scheduled Completion Date by which the Work is to be completed.

The contractor is usually obliged to furnish all required vessels, personnel, supervision, facilities, equipment, machinery and other materials, transportation licences, permits, bonds, labour and services and to do all other things necessary to carry out the work in a timely manner. Moreover, it will undertake to perform the work as a 'reasonable and prudent contractor'. The term 'reasonable and prudent contractor' is often a defined term in the contract and might mean, for example, 'the contractor seeking in good faith to perform its contractual obligations and in doing so and in the general conduct of its undertaking exercising a degree of skill, diligence, prudence and foresight which would be reasonably and ordinarily expected from a skilled and experienced international contractor complying with all applicable laws and legislation engaged in a similar undertaking'. The contractor is also to work with all due skill and diligence, and in accordance with 'Best Industry Practice' which is typically defined as meaning 'those practices, techniques, methods, specifications, standards of safety, engineering design and construction observed by experienced and qualified international contractors in the international petroleum industry'. The contractor is also obliged to work in accordance with all applicable law and legislation and meet all agency requirements.

Representatives. Both the operator and contractor normally appoint representatives who can bind their respective companies in terms of the contract.

General Obligations. The contractor then covenants to carry out certain general obligations such as providing qualified, competent and skilled personnel, ensuring the work site is clean, ensuring all health and safety and environment codes of practice are met, obtaining all permits, authorisations, licences and all customs clearances and governmental authorisations and to provide personnel and equipment. It is often the responsibility of the contractor to ensure that it can manufacture or import equipment (where necessary) and provide the equipment to the site designated by the operator within the stated time schedule.

Independency. The contractor will be recognised in the contract as being independent of the operator and the contract will state that there is no agency or partnership relationship between them.

Assignation. While it is usual for the operator to be entitled to assign its obligations under the contract to an affiliate of the operator or a co-venturer or to a successor operator, the contractor is normally not permitted to assign the contract without the permission of the operator (given the fact that the contractor will have been selected by the operator on the basis of the contractor's experience and ability). The contract would normally provide that such permission would not be unreasonably withheld or delayed in a case where the proposed assignee can comply with the obligations of the contractor under the contract. The operator will be particularly concerned to monitor the award of subcontracts by the contractor and the contract may provide that the contractor will have to obtain the operator's permission prior to awarding any subcontract. The contract will usually provide that where subcontracting has been permitted by the operator the contractor remains entirely responsible for the work of the subcontractor. In addition, the contract usually permits the operator to step into the subcontract in the place of the contractor. There may also be a statement in the contract that the subcontracting work will form part of the Work which will then be owned by the operator at completion of installation.

Ownership of the Work. The contractor would normally declare in the contract that the Work will be owned by the operator and that there are no liens or encumbrances on the Work. Moreover, the contractor will assert that it has not committed any breach of local corruption or bribery legislation nor has it paid any commissions, payments, gifts of substantial value, kick-backs, lavish or extensive entertainment of person in government or any member of the operator's group.

The contractor is required to acknowledge that before it has started work it has satisfied itself as to the extent and nature of the Work and that it can carry it out.

Completion of the Work. It is essential for both the operator and the contractor that the Work is completed in accordance with the given schedule of key dates as many work packages are coming together at that time and one late subcontractor can delay the whole programme. It is the contractor's job to ensure that it achieves the completion of the Work by the dates set out in the schedule of key dates. It is therefore the contractor's responsibility to schedule the Work and to provide a Work Plan. There are provisions for regular monitoring of the work performance and for the production by the contractor of progress reports to be given to the operator.

Changes to the Work. During the contract it is possible that the Work set out in contract might change as a result of the operator's requirements or because the contractor believes that it is being required by the operator to carry out work which is outside the specification of the Work set out in the contract. In such an event, either the contractor or the operator may propose a change notice or variation order. If a change notice is accepted by the operator (or where the operator does not accept it and the parties have the issue dealt with by arbitration) then there may be an adjustment to the contract price and there could be a consequential change to the schedule of key dates. Where there are numerous variations to the Work there is an increased risk of cost overruns or time slippage.

Supply of information. Both parties are keen to ensure that the right information is supplied to the contractor to ensure the Work is carried out. It is, therefore, the operator's responsibility to provide operator-supplied items and operator-supplied information to ensure that the contractor can carry out its Work. There are also provisions in terms of which the contractor has to supply contractor supplied items in addition to the manufactured equipment which it is to supply.

Inspections and testing. There will be inspections by the operator and testing of manufactured equipment throughout the contract. The two main testing bench marks are Factory Acceptance Testing (FAT) which is carried out when equipment has been manufactured initially; sometimes prototypes or substitute parts are tested. The main testing comes on System Integration Testing (SIT) which will then lead to equipment going into the field. It is the contractor's responsibility to carry out all tests and inspections and to provide the operator with certified copies of all test records and reports. The operator can reject any part of the Work and may require a rework of Work packages as a result of those tests. Any such rework normally has to be carried out at the expense of the contractor.

Supply of vessels. In an offshore operation, the contractor may have to supply vessels to take equipment and personnel to the work site. The contractor will be under certain obligations to provide marine vessels which are seaworthy, serviceable and in first class condition and prepared for operation in navigational waters of the UK. Vessels have to be certified in conformity with international standards (which might be International Convention for Safety for Life at Sea (1974) SOLAS and the International Convention for Prevention of Pollution from Ships (1973) (as modified by the Protocol of 1978 relating thereto) MARPOL. The vessel is presumed to be safe and without risk to vessel or crew until the contractor or the master of the vessel objects. All tugs, pilots and marine crew are under the responsibility of the contractor.

Health, safety and environment. In large work packages there may be substantial elements of the contract which deal with health, safety and environment management systems. The risk for the operator here is that the contractor will be responsible for taking large items of equipment on its site and arranging for their commission.

Force majeure. There will always be a force majeure clause ('FM clause') in the contract. The operator may want to ensure that this clause does not trigger a termination of the contract. In an FM clause it would be normal to list the occurrences which the parties consider to constitute FM. These might include riot, war, invasion, act of foreign enemies, acts of terrorism and sabotage, civil war, rebellion, ionising radiations or contamination by radioactivity from nuclear fuel, earthquake, fire, flood, explosion and other natural physical disasters, strikes or work stoppages at a national level or maritime or aviation disasters. If such an event occurs then a party may claim that there has been an incidence of FM. The contract will provide what the effects of an FM are to be. If the FM continues for a period of more than a few days then the contractor may be free to demobilise and the parties will then have to agree a new completion of work programme.

Suspension of the Work. The contract will provide that the operator has a right to suspend the Work. This right may arise in the case of the contractor's default or because of a safety reason. The contract may be suspended for an issue connected with the development itself. During the period of suspension the contractor may be entitled to payment under the contract at the standby rate. If the suspension is temporary, there will be a rescheduling of the contract price (to provide the contractor with standby rights) and there may also be a rescheduling of the Schedule of Key Dates.

Termination. In addition to the suspension provisions the contract will contain separate termination provisions. If there is a breach of the terms of the contract then this could lead to a termination of the contract. The contract may provide for termination where the contractor has committed a breach of its obligations under the contract, where an FM event has occurred and has not been remedied within a period set out in the contract or where the operator wishes to terminate at its convenience.

Breach. The contract will contain various provisions aimed at protecting the position of the operator where the contractor is in breach of contract. For example, the contract may state that the operator is to have full access to the site and can require that the contractor cease to carry out any more Work. In addition, the operator may require the contractor to move all items of equipment and materials which belong to it from the site and may require the contractor to assign to it all of its rights to any parts of the Work, including all subcontracts relating to the Work. There may also be a right to the contractor to payment for all work carried out on that part of the contract in the event of termination.

Warranties. One of the key commercial considerations for the contractor is the extent of the warranties it will be required to give in the contract and the undertakings to rework the Work if the operator is not satisfied. The contractor normally warrants and guarantees that all work will be performed as a reasonable and prudent contractor in accordance with best industry practice, that all work including all materials and equipment provided by the contractor are free from liens and defects and that all materials and equipment provided by the contractor shall be suitable for their intended purpose as specified in the contract. The contractor might further warrant and guarantee the performance of the Work and the equipment for anywhere between 12 and 24 months following the issue of the mechanical completion notice or 12 months after the first production through the equipment or 'permanent work'.

Mechanical completion. Mechanical completion is normally the stage at which the operator accepts the Work or the rework, as the case may be. Final completion, in contrast, might only take place on the issue of the final acceptance certificate when the warranty and guarantee period has expired. On mechanical completion, the operator has accepted that the contractor has completed the Work. However, the operator will issue a notice of provisional acceptance only once it is satisfied that the Work is in accordance with the requirements of the contract. At that point the contractor can demobilise from the site. The operator can use the Work from the time of mechanical completion.

Payment and security. Very importantly for the parties there are provisions which deal with how much the contractor will be paid, the procedure and timing of invoices and when payment will be made. The operator may require the contractor to provide a parent company guarantee to support its obligations under the contract. The operator might also request that the contractor provide an unconditional irrevocable bank guarantee (the amount of which will be calculated as a percentage of the contract price for all work carried out) until the issuance of the notice of mechanical completion and then a second bank guarantee for a percentage of the contract price which will expire at issuance of the final acceptance certificate. Of course, depending on the perceived financial capability of the operator, the contractor may seek some form of security for payment from the operator, such as a guarantee from the parent company of the operator or a bank guarantee.

The contractor is normally responsible for all taxes, duties and fines except for value added tax and the operator may withhold certain payments if required by tax authorities in order to pay the contractors' taxes. All contractors' records and accounts relating to the project are normally available for inspection by the operator at the contractor's offices.

Liability and indemnity. Liability and indemnity clauses are among the most important provisions of any contract, but even more so in oil and gas contracts where the risks and liabilities involved are considerable. It is, therefore, important that particular care and consideration are given in negotiating the scope and extent of their terms to ensure that they reflect all parties' intentions and ultimately to avoid the expense incurred in drawn-out litigation. Indemnities are covered in greater detail elsewhere in the book but in general terms the purpose of indemnity provisions are to apportion risk between the parties to an agreement; one party will agree to be liable for the loss or damage of another, or of a third party, from a specific act.

The contract will set out a liability and indemnity regime which is to apply. This is of fundamental importance in oil and gas contracts given the potentially huge exposure which could be faced by a party to a contract in the event that something goes wrong and there is injury to people, the environment or property.

Liability for third party claims. The contractual position in respect of third party liability will also need to be addressed. It may be agreed that the contractor and operator will each be responsible for their own liabilities, caused by their own negligence or, alternatively, the operator may agree to indemnify the contractor of its liabilities (such liabilities not being the result of a negligent act or omission of the contractor).

Where at all possible, a contractor will attempt to exclude third party liability altogether. If it is unable to do so then it will at least want a cap on its liability. This will usually be limited to the level of the contractor's insurance or, in the event that the negligence or fault is caused by or the result of a negligent act or omission or fault of the contractor itself, then the contractor's indemnification obligation may be limited to its share of such joint negligence or fault. In certain circumstances, such as in the event of wilful misconduct, the contractor may agree to unlimited liability to third party claims.

Mutual hold harmless indemnity. There will be mutual indemnities given by the operator to the contractor and the contractor to the operator. For instance, the operator will indemnify the contractor against injury, death or, illnesses of the operator's employees and against damage to the Work not caused by the contractor's negligence or wilful misconduct. It may also indemnify the contractor against all damages or losses to equipment and material supplied or hired by the operator and all damage to or losses of third parties' property, which is part of the site or located beneath the seabed. The operator will normally also grant an indemnity in respect of all injuries, deaths and illnesses of third parties and property of third parties which arises as a result of the negligence of the operator's group. The contractor will give similar indemnities to the operator, and will also indemnify the operator from pollution and contamination claims which emanate from its vessel or equipment.

Generally, for manufacture and construction contracts a contractor will not enter into mutual hold harmless indemnities with other project parties, as this tends to be the case in operational or drilling contracts.

Insurance. The contract will set out the contractual insurance requirements. The contract will list minimum insurance coverage which will have to be obtained by the contractor. For example, the contractor will be expected to take out workers' compensation insurance, employers' liability insurance, commercial and general liability insurance, automobile liability insurance, insurance for vessels, hull and machinery protection indemnity insurance, hull and machinery insurance in each vessel covering fire, explosions, marine perils and an element of collision and running down.

Liquidated damages. The contract may provide that the contractor will be required to pay liquidated damages in certain scenarios. For instance, the timing of completion of the work might be of fundamental importance to the operator and so the contract might provide that the contractor will be required to make certain payments to the operator where the contractor has failed to meet the time frames contained in the contract. The amount payable by the contractor might be an amount which increases depending on the period by which it goes beyond the time period for delivery as set out in the contract. It is crucial that the amount payable by the contractor is a genuine pre-estimate of the amount of the loss which might be suffered by the operator as a result of the contractor's failure to deliver on time rather than being a figure plucked from the air which acts as a penalty against the contractor. Whilst English and Scots law recognise the concept of liquidated damages provisions, they will not give effect to provisions which are merely penalty provisions.

Governing law. Finally, such a contract will have a governing law clause. It will also provide either that there will be arbitration in the event of a dispute or that the matter may be dealt with in a court in a specific country. UKCS contracts are usually governed by English law with the contract providing that the English courts are to have jurisdiction to dealt with any litigation arising from the contract.

Contract for installation and hook-up

It may be that the main contractor providing a large part of the subsea facilities is also the contractor providing the installation of the facilities at the site. The terms of the contract would be very similar except that the scope of work and the schedule of key dates will be different. The contract may also require more integration of other work packages.

Licence consents – Field Development Plan

It should be noted that the consent of the Secretary of State is required to mobilise and produce in a field; the first step in this process is submitting a Field Development Plan. This subject has been covered in Chapter 9 above.

10.12 Procurement

Procurement in the North Sea

The operator as agent for its co-venturers must decide how it will procure the services which it requires to carry out the project. The JOA or UOA (as appropriate) will contain details of the procedures which the operator must follow in awarding contracts and the operator will have to comply with these. However, the provisions of the relevant operating agreement are not the only place one would have to look in going through a procurement process.

UK and EC legislation exists which has a dramatic impact on how an operator must go about the procurement process. The Utilities Contracts Regulations 2006 (SI 2006 No 6) and its Scottish equivalent (the Utilities Contracts (Scotland) Regulations 2006, SI 2006 No 2) (collectively referred to as 'the Regulations') came into force on 31 January 2006. They implement the European Parliament and Council of Europe's Utilities Directive (2004/17/EC). The Regulations lay down provisions governing the award of supply, works and service contracts by 'utilities' for the purpose of carrying out activities in the water, energy, transport and telecommunications sectors. The Regulations provide detailed rules to be followed when awarding contracts. However, there is an exemption in respect of certain utilities operating in the energy sector which means that compliance with certain sections of the Regulations is not required. Where the exemption applies the utility can use a less onerous procedure than those set out in the Regulations.

Scope of the Regulations

Only 'utilities' come within the scope of the Regulations. Schedule 1 to the Regulations details the type of persons and processes which are caught as a 'utility'. 'A person operating by virtue of a licence granted or having effect as if granted under the Petroleum Act 1998' for 'the exploitation of a geographical area for the purpose of exploring for or extracting oil or gas' are utilities in terms of Schedule 1 Part M to the Regulations. The Regulations cover both supply and works contracts.

Where the Regulations apply, a utility is not permitted to discriminate between providers. In this respect, the utility is not permitted to treat a person who is not a national of, and is not established in, a relevant state (as defined in the Regulations), more favourably than one who is. The Regulations apply where a utility seeks offers in relation to a proposed supply, works or certain other services contracts (unless those contracts are excluded by the Regulations). Certain contracts, such as research and development, technical testing and analysis services, are subject to all the provisions of the Regulations, while other contracts, such as personnel placement and supply of services, are subject to only a limited number of the provisions.

The Regulations do not apply to activities which are not specified in Schedule 1 to the Regulations nor to activities outside the EU. In addition, they do not apply in certain other specified circumstances. Regulation 6 sets out the general exclusions to the Regulations. They include carrying out an activity outwith the Communities where that activity does not involve the physical use of a network or geographical area within the Communities, by a utility which engages in an activity specified in Parts 2–6 of Schedule 1 for the purchase of energy or of fuel for the production of energy, for the acquisition of land, for employment and other contracts of service, for arbitration or conciliation services and for certain research and development services. The Regulations also exclude service contracts awarded to affiliated undertakings and to co-members of a joint venture (Regulation 7). In practice this means that in a joint venture constituted by a JOA the co-venturers could appoint one of their number as operator without having to make a call for competition. In addition, the exclusion of service contracts awarded to affiliates means that an operator could award a contract to one of its affiliates. In addition, there are certain exemptions from the Regulations, namely exemption by certain utilities operating in the energy sector (Regulation 8), and contracts where the activity is directly exposed to competition (Regulation 9). These are considered in more detail below.

Exemptions

Regulation 8 permits the European Commission to grant exemptions so that contracts awarded by certain utilities in the energy sector may be exempted from the detailed provisions of the Regulations. The UK Government applied for an exemption in relation to petroleum licensees and the current exemption is contained in the Commission Decision 97/367. As a result, companies operating within the UK which are exploring for, or extracting, oil or gas may follow 'alternative arrangements'. Utilities relying on the exemption need not comply with Parts 2–5 of the Regulations and certain other specific parts of the Regulations. There is no detailed guidance as to what 'alternative arrangements' actually are. It would appear that any utility relying on the exemption must still observe the principles of non-discrimination and competitive procurement set out in the Regulations and that the utility should hold a competition (tendering process) unless it can objectively justify not doing do. In practice this may mean that although there is no obligation to publish notices in the *Official Journal*, a genuine call for competition should be published in an appropriate publication. In addition, the utility must make decisions in respect of certain parts of the tendering process objectively on the basis of relevant criteria.

If a utility relies on this exemption for contracts awarded with a value above a specified amount, certain information must be sent to the European Commission within 48 days after the awarding of the contract.

In addition, the Regulations will not apply, in accordance with Regulation 9, in respect of activities specified in Column 2 of Schedule 1 where that activity is directly exposed to competition in markets to which access is unrestricted. Under the Regulation applications can be made by either the UK Government or the particular utility concerned.

The Regulations do not apply to contracts where the value is less than the relevant threshold. The relevant thresholds are detailed in Regulation 11 and depend upon the type of contract. The thresholds as at the date of publication are currently €422,000 in relation to a supply or services contract and €5,278,000 in relation to a works contract.

The Regulations give detailed guidance on how the value of the contract is to be calculated. The estimated value is taken to be the total consideration payable net of VAT, taking into account factors such as any form of option, renewal of the contract, any payment awarded by the utility to the economic operator and any fees or commissions payable for banking services. Guidance is given on estimating the value of supply contracts for the hire of goods and for service contracts which do not include a total price. In calculating the value of a series of contracts that have to be entered into to fulfil the single requirement of goods, services or carrying out works, the aggregate value of the consideration which the utility expects to be payable under each of those contracts shall be the estimated value. In instances where goods and services are required over a period of time, the aggregate value of (1) similar characteristic contracts and (2) contracts which are for the same types of goods or services will be calculated.

As there is a lack of practical guidance on the requirements of the alternative arrangements (set out in Regulation 8) it has been suggested that the full provisions of the Regulations should be used as a bench mark as to whether or not the alternative arrangements have been complied with. In practice, notwithstanding the waiver, many upstream oil and gas companies continue to comply with the full procedure set out in the Regulations. For this reason the remainder of this section deals mainly with the full procedure.

Procedures leading to award of contract

The utility must use the open, the restricted or the negotiated procedure when seeking offers in relation to a proposed contract. The open procedure is a procedure leading to the award of a contract whereby all interested persons may tender for the contract. The restricted procedure is a procedure leading to the award of a contract whereby only persons selected by the utility may submit tenders for the contract. The negotiated procedure is a procedure leading to the award of a contract whereby the utility negotiates the terms of the contract with one or more persons selected by it.

The general rule is that for the purposes of seeking offers a utility has to make a call for competition. The Regulations detail what is required to satisfy the making of a call for competition for contracts to be awarded using the different procedures. The utility may seek offers in relation to the proposed contract without a call for competition in certain stated circumstances. These are set out in Regulation 17 and include the following circumstances: (i) in the absence of tenders, suitable tenders or applications in response to a procedure with a call for competition but only if the original terms of the proposed contract offered in the discontinued procedure have not been substantially altered; (ii) when the contract is to be awarded purely for the purposes of research, experiment, study or development but not where it has the purpose of securing profit or of recovering research and development costs and insofar as its award will not prejudice the competitive award of subsequent contracts which are, in particular, for the same purposes; and (iii) when, for technical or artistic reasons, or for reasons connected with the protection of exclusive rights, the contract may only be performed by a particular economic operator.

The Regulations also specify time limits within which the tenders must be received. In accordance with Regulation 22, utilities must take account of the complexity of the contract and the time required in drawing up tenders when fixing time limits. Generally speaking, for utilities using the open procedure, the time limit must not be less than 52 days from the date of dispatch of the notice. For utilities using the restricted or negotiated procedure, the time limits for the receipt of tender requests with a call for competition shall be at least 24 days from the despatch of the invitation to tender and not less than 10 days. Where the call for competition is made by means of a periodic indicative notice, then the time period will be at least 37 days but not less than 22 days, unless the notice is transmitted by fax, in which case the time period shall be 15 days.

Qualification and selection of providers

Utilities may use a system of qualification of providers if certain rules are met. For example, selection criteria are to be made available to the providers and they may also request to be provided with an explanation as to why any tender has been unsuccessful.

There are different rules for the selection of providers when the restricted or negotiated procedure is being used. The utility using those procedures (with or without a call for competition) must select the providers who are to be invited to tender on the basis of objective criteria and rules which should be made available to the providers if requested. The Regulations list certain criteria which a utility may use for deciding not to select a provider, for example, bankruptcy or misrepresentation of information to the utility. In certain circumstances the utility is permitted to ask providers for certificates or other evidence of technical capacity.

Award of contract

The Regulations provide that the utility should award the contract to the most economically advantageous offer or the offer with the lowest price. When considering whether an offer is economically advantageous matters such as delivery date, quality, environmental characteristics and technical merits can be considered. The general rule regarding the most economically advantageous offer/lowest price offer does not apply to offers from suppliers if greater than 50% of the value of the goods to be supplied originated in countries with which the EC does not have a trade agreement. Once the contract has been awarded, the utility must notify the European Commission.

10.13 Funding a project without borrowing

Introduction

Before the operator applies to the Secretary of State for Field Development Plan sanction (FDP sanction) the operating committee of the JOA and/or UOA will have agreed with the co-venturers a Work Programme and a time scale within which the operator is likely to cash call co-venturers for funding that Work Programme. The cash calls on the co-venturers prior to FDP sanction are likely to be much less than the substantial cash calls to fund capital expenditure through the mobilisation stage after the FDP sanction. The cash calls at the commissioning stage are particularly substantial.

A small company may specialise in exploring, finding and appraising oil and gas fields and adapt a strategy of farming out sufficient percentage interest in the field to a third party in order to have a larger company carry its costs through to production of first hydrocarbons, or maybe through a certain Work Programme. In Chapter 3 there was an analysis of trading assets by way of the sale of the entire assets or shares in a company. This may be to raise money for another development or simply as part of a divestiture programme. In Chapter 7 there was a review of raising money by borrowing at a corporate or asset level to fund a development. In this part of this chapter there is a review of the different ways for a company to raise capital to fund its share of a work programme.

Farm-outs/farm-ins

A farm-out or farm-in may happen at any time after the original licence has been awarded to a co-venturer. They are most likely to happen after a field has been discovered but before first production. In certain circumstances there might be a farm-out in a producing field, for instance to carry out a new drilling programme.

A farm-out is where a co-venturer (the 'farmor') holding a certain percentage interest transfers part of that percentage interest to a third party (the 'farminee') on the basis that the third party carries certain of the costs or the obligations of farmor.

The third party may carry all or part of the costs and/or obligations of the farm-in. It might, for instance, conduct seismic work or purchase seismic data. It may agree to pay the costs of drilling a well to a target depth as part of an exploration and appraisal drilling programme, or it may fund the costs of a whole drilling programme or the costs of taking a field to first production. In return for carrying the costs and taking over the obligations of the farmor, the farminee acquires a working interest in the field.

The negotiation of a Farm-out Agreement would tend to be around the nature and cost of work to be performed by the farminee in exchange for the interest and the size of the working interest to be assigned to the farminee by the farmor. A 'ground floor' deal is where a farminee is responsible for all costs in exchange for the entire interest held by the farmor. Alternatively, a farminee may farm in to a 50% working interest in return for carrying out, for example, all of the farminee's costs of a field development. This is known as a 'two for one promote'; the promote level is the ratio between expenditure incurred by the farminee and the working interest earned by it.

There are two basic legal structures which one encounters in farm-in/farm-out transactions. In the first scenario the farminee acquires the working interest prior to carrying out the work. If it fails to carry out the work as required by the agreement then it is required to retransfer the interest. In the second scenario the interest is only transferred to the farminee once it has completed the work. The risk for the farminee in the second scenario is that they do the work but the interest is never transferred to them.

The work obligations are very specific and tightly drafted. In the second scenario the agreement is also known as an 'Earn-In Agreement' in that the farminee only acquires the interest on fulfilling the earn-in obligations.

One of the difficult areas in farm-out negotiations is the issue of operatorship. Should the farminor continue to be the operator and the farminee act as a quasi-contractor fulfilling work obligations under a contract or should the operatorship be transferred to the farminee, allowing it more control of, for instance, field development or a drilling programme?

The farminee can only obtain title to the interest in the asset if the Secretary of State gives consent. Subject to the parties adhering to any pre-emption provisions contained in the JOA and/or UOA, there will also need to be an assignation of the licence interest and an assignment of any Production Licence.

The parties would now normally enter into an Execution Deed under the terms of the Master Deed.[1] In the event of the other parties consenting to the transfer by way of executing a Consent to Transfer document, the Administrator (UKCS Administrator Ltd), assignee and assignor would execute the assignment document.

The farm-out might be for a cash consideration or in fulfilment of working obligations or one or both of them. On small undeveloped fields there may be a transfer of the operatorship to the farm-in party who is taking over all the work obligations to drill exploration and appraisal wells in order to fulfil the terms of an exploration or promote licence.

A Farm-Out Agreement would, therefore, contain provisions about the consideration to be provided by the farminee, the terms of the transfer of the title to the asset and conditions precedent dealing with the conditions which have to be fulfilled before the farminee comes on the asset. There would be representations and warranties by the farmor as to its legal title, solvency and disclosure of material obligations in respect of the asset. There may be a stated Economic Date on which the farminee takes over all obligations on the percentage interest of the working interest being transferred to it. The farminee party would normally indemnify the farmor for all obligations after the Economic Date and the farminor would indemnify the farminee party for all obligations prior to the Economic Date. There might also be clauses dealing with the interim period before the time the farminee party has obtained a transfer of interest in the licence. Those interim obligations might include that the farmor must consult the farminee on all material matters and provide it with information on the assets. Finally, there would normally be a description of the asset in the Farm-out Agreement, a list of title documents and a list of material contracts disclosed within the agreement.

If a farminee is to come on a field, the other co-venturers would need to know that the farminee has sufficient resources, competence and capability to meet its obligations on the field; for this reason it is often large companies that are the farminee as they have larger resources to meet those obligations.

Due diligence

The due diligence exercise carried out by a company farming in or a company entering an earn-in is often less complex than the exercise carried out on the purchase of upstream oil and gas assets or shares in an upstream company. This is because farm-ins, earn-ins and overriding royalty arrangements tend to happen at an exploration, appraisal or field development stage. As a result, there may be less data available and there may be fewer commercial contracts and title documents to examine. The nature of the due diligence exercise has been described in Chapter 3 and the same principles will apply to farm-ins, earn-ins and royalty arrangements as for asset deals and share deals.

Overriding Royalty Agreements

An oil and gas company (which may be a large oil and gas company) may not wish to deploy its capital into, say, a small field but might be prepared to transfer the licence interest to a smaller company or consortium of co-venturers to appraise and develop the field in return for a royalty. The terms of the royalty and the transfer of the assets would be set out in an Overriding Royalty Agreement or Royalty Agreement. In that agreement the parties would agree the extent of the accumulation of hydrocarbons in the field, that the interest would be transferred and that the Secretary of State's consent obtained to the transfer. In consideration for the transfer the purchasing company would agree to develop the field and pay all capital expenditure costs and operating costs upstream of the Delivery Point. The Delivery Point might be the closest point of metering to that field. A royalty would be calculated on a percentage of production of oil or gas produced and would commence once the production company had paid back all its development costs.

If any remedial capital expenditure was incurred over and above the development costs then it would start when all remedial costs had been paid as well. The royalty holder would, therefore, have a contract with the development company and the development company would indemnify the royalty holder from all exploration, appraisal, development or production costs or liabilities of whatever nature. The royalty holder would be responsible for lifting its share of oil or gas at the Delivery Point in accordance with the applicable procedures for nomination and lifting of petroleum set out in that agreement and any relevant JOAs or UOAs. There would, therefore, be no responsibility on the royalty holder for any production, transportation, processing or other facility costs or liabilities. The royalty holder might be given the option of taking royalty in kind (for instance, taking physical possession of the hydrocarbons) or being paid the cash equivalent in accordance with a predetermined market price. It may also be the case that the royalty holder might book reserves based on its future royalty interest.

The development company would be responsible for producing production forecasts to the royalty holder based on preparing them on a reasonable and prudent standard of care and then in producing statements of total quantity of production to the royalty holder. The royalty holder would have a right to audit all metering equipment, accounts and records which relate to the allocation of petroleum and all development and remedial costs. There would be provisions set out in the agreement for pooling and unitisation and also mechanisms for settling disputes.

The Royalty Agreement is, therefore, a direct contract between the royalty holder and the development company and there is no encumbrance on the field. However, the royalty holder may have a right to prevent a transfer of the working interest of the development company or interest in the field by including an undertaking from the development company not to transfer the working interest without its prior written consent.

Net Profit Interest Agreements

As an alternative for an oil and gas company not wishing to sell its assets entirely, it could transfer the costs of development and production to another oil and gas company in return for that other party paying it a Net Profit Interest under the terms of a Net Profit Interest Agreement. In this case, the holder of the working interest would pay a net profit interest to a development company in exchange for the development company paying some or all of the development costs. Those payments would equate to all gross revenues less all capital expenditure and operating expenditure together with accrued interest on capital; it is, therefore, an interest in the revenue earned by the developing company less all expenses and costs of capital. Net Profit Interest Agreements tend to be less common in the UK because the arrangements may be treated as a form of deferred consideration by Her Majesty's Revenue and Customs (HMRC) and the total amount of deferred consideration would be charged to tax on the completion of the agreement.

Carried Interest Agreement

A variant on a Royalty Production Agreement is where one party holding a field interest funds the entire capital expenditure of another party. The carrying party would be entitled to receive and have transferred to it some or all of the carried party's percentage interest in production in that field until such time as the capital expenditure has been repaid together with accrued interest on the capital costs. When that point has been reached, the field interest would be returned to the original holder.

Forward Purchase Agreement

A Forward Purchase Agreement may be negotiated and entered into when a bank or syndicate of banks or other financial institutions purchase forward production (ie production that has not yet been produced) from an oil and gas company in return for that oil and gas company receiving early payments of estimated production (either before production has started or in some cases after production has started). In this way, an oil and gas company can fund its ongoing capital expenditure and operating expenditure costs without having to sell out its percentage interest in a field to another party. However, in the event that the oil and gas company receiving advance payment fails to meet certain production targets, and therefore fund the advance payments, there is a risk that the syndicate of banks or financing institutions might call an event of default and foreclose the security granted by the oil and gas company to the financing institutions.

In a Forward Purchase Agreement it would often be the case that the financial institution would have a Marketing Agreement under which they sold and marketed a certain proportion of production produced.

Earn-In Agreements

In an Earn-in Agreement the holder of a Field Interest might transfer a working interest in the field to another oil and gas company on the condition that the company wishing to take an interest in the field has fulfilled its earn-in obligations. The earn-in company might take operatorship of the field in return for paying for field development, well costs or undertaking well obligations, for example. The obligation on the earn-in company like the farminee is, therefore, to pay certain capital costs in drilling wells or bringing a working interest to production. The earn-in is earned by the earn-in company undertaking the well obligation and once it has been met the working interest is consequently transferred to that company, subject to the Secretary of State approving the transfer and the execution of the necessary completion documents transferring the interest. There may be payment of production bonuses by the earn-in company based on future production targets being met. There would normally be indemnity provisions so that the transferor (the original holder of the field interest) indemnifies the transferee (the earn-in company) for any obligations up to the Effective Date (which may be the signing of the Earn-In Agreement) and the transferee is responsible for all costs including decommissioning liabilities after the Effective Date. There would then be the usual warranties, tax provisions and a clause dealing with the field operations by the earn-in company. The transferor company would continue to manage the Transferred Interest until the earn-out had been earned and the working interest transferred to the earn-in company. The party holding the Transferred Interest until the earn-out is earned may be the operator who would continue to operate the field until the earn-out is completed. There may be detailed dispute clauses and expert determination clauses included in case of a difference of opinion about whether the well obligations had been completed.

Exchange Agreement

Exchange Agreements are quite common in the UKCS. In an exchange transaction the parties exchange an interest which they hold in respect of one asset for an interest in another asset. Basically they swap interests. For example, A Ltd holds an interest in Licence x Block a/b. B Ltd holds an interest in Licence y Block c/d. The two companies might agree to exchange the whole or part of the interest which they hold in their own asset for the whole or part of the interest held by the other company.

Such an exchange is documented by way of an Exchange Agreement. An exchange agreement is very much like a Sale and Purchase Agreement but there are some important differences to reflect the fact that there are contemporaneously two disposing parties and two acquiring parties.

Rather than providing for a cash consideration for the transfer of an interest the Exchange Agreement provides that the consideration payable by a party for the interest which it is acquiring will take the form of the transfer by it to the other party of the interest which it is exchanging. Where the respective interests have different commercial values it is common to see a cash payment being made in respect of the more valuable asset.

As with a normal Sale and Purchase Agreement, there will be adjustment clauses in terms of which the consideration payable for the interests will be adjusted up or down to take account of petroleum which has been sold in the interim period, cash calls which have been paid by the transferring party in the interim period and movements in the working capital position. Such adjustments have to be calculated in respect of both assets and commonly the adjustments are netted off with one payment being due by one party to the other.

The other provisions of Exchange Agreements are very similar to those contained in normal oil and gas asset Sale and Purchase Agreements.

Given the mutuality of interest involved when drafting Exchange Agreements, it can be quite easy to agree on certain aspects of the Exchange Agreement such as the warranty package and the vendor protections (*de maximis* and *de minimis* levels, etc.) which are to apply. Whatever a transferor gives by way of warranty coverage in respect of the asset which it is transferring it will receive as warranty coverage in respect of the asset which is being transferred to it.

10.14 Hedging – derivatives

At any point during field development, or during the production of hydrocarbons, an oil company may decide to hedge against the risk of interest rates or oil price fluctuations (as described in Chapter 7). It may sell oil forward to raise more money. It may alternatively trade in derivatives contracts or raise investment from hedge fund institutions who are actively engaged in trading derivative contracts. This section looks briefly at hedge funds and derivative contracts.

A substantial amount of money for investment purposes is now available through hedge funds. Hedging itself by using derivative contracts may be used to offset risks in the market or even raise funds based on future production.

Hedging is traditionally a form of protection against market risks and fluctuation involving a swap, option contract, forward or future contract, or credit derivative or a combination of these.

Hedging funds traditionally concentrate on hedging transactions by making an absolute return in all market conditions. They are normally highly flexible and streamlined in their credit decision-making so that the hedge fund managers can make decisions without a substantial amount of due diligence or verification. They will develop fund strategies which may be multifaceted and may include risk arbitrage or may develop a strategy of, for instance, activities which are closer to traditional private equity.

Private equity funds, on the other hand, tend to adopt a less conservative strategy with the aim of higher market returns on investment. Arbitrage is where an advantage is taken of a price difference between currencies, goods or securities in different markets. This may include selling short or buying long. 'Selling short' is a term to describe selling a security that is held in the expectation that the price will not fall; if a fund is buying long then it will acquire a security with the hope of an increase in price.

Derivatives

Derivatives are financial instruments whose value and price depend on the value of the underlying assets or some other variable. They can either be sold directly from seller to buyer by way of an over-the-counter transaction, which is a private arrangement between seller and buyer (OTC) or traded on a recognised investment exchange. Derivatives are normally taken out to protect against financial risk; the buyer of a derivative contract makes a small initial investment which is normally less than the underlying assets.

Traded derivatives are traded on the London International financial Futures and Options Exchange (LIFFE). All derivatives trading, whether on a recognised investment exchange or OTC, is regulated by the FSA and any advice given on such derivative is also within the scope of regulated activity under the Financial Services and Markets Act 2000.

Types of derivatives

Swap

A traditional swap is a bilateral contract whereby one party swaps, for instance, interest payments or currency payments to be made on a future date with another party (the counterparty). As an example, one company may be borrowing a loan from a bank at a fixed rate of interest and may wish to swap that fixed rate because it wishes to obtain a variable rate of interest and so will swap with another company which is borrowing on a variable rate of interest; the companies will net their payments. Currency swaps operate in the same way but the parties will make payments in different currencies.

Options contract

An options contract is a bilateral contract, whether traded or an OTC between an option holder and an option writer. An option writer can, on payment of a premium, grant an option holder the right to buy or sell an underlying asset at a fixed price at a future date. The option is not an obligation but only a right. The option may be a put option, in which the option holder has a right to sell or deliver an underlying asset at an agreed price at a future date. Alternatively, it may be a call option, where the option holder has the right to buy or receive an underlying asset at a new agreed price on a future date. The price on which the option is exercised is the exercise price or strike price. The settlement of an option contract can be by way of physical settlement/by deliveries of funds or by payment in cash.

Forwards and futures contracts

In a forward contract there is an agreement between parties to buy and sell an underlying asset on a future date at an agreed price and is an OTC contract. Unlike an option, a party that buys a forward contract must pay the agreed purchase price relating to the underlying asset.

A futures contract is normally traded on an exchange with limited credit risk; a party agrees to buy or sell an underlying asset at a future date at an agreed price.

In the case of a futures contract for oil, there is normally a standard specification for a particular oil and for a minimum quantity used in the regulated markets. In the futures contracts the clearing house acts as the central counterparty and will only transact with brokers who are registered institutions and have a seat at the relevant exchange. The broker will only take on clients whom they know and who have limited credit risk. Each broker will charge the margin payment on a contract which will be debited against a client's margin amount.

Credit derivatives facility for trading of a company's credit risk

A credit derivative is a contract for the separate trading of credit risk. There are different types of credit derivatives.

There may be a 'credit default swap' structured as a total return (which transfers market risks as a whole). Alternatively it may be a 'credit default option' (in which credit default risk is traded). Another example is one in which a credit derivative is embedded into a loan note or bond and is known as a 'credit linked note' or 'credit linked bond'.

A credit default swap is, for instance, a collateral contract between a seller (which may be, for instance, a bank) which will sell credit protection to protect a buyer. The buyer may be a company seeking to take credit protection against another company which it may be trading with. With a credit default swap a buyer buys a pre-agreed amount of credit protection on the obligations of a named company or entity. The credit events may include, for instance, a company's bankruptcy, a failure to pay the principal amount or the interest on its loan or bonds, or a restructuring of its debts facilities.

A Contract for Difference (CFD) may be entered into between two parties whereby one party swaps the difference of an opening and closing price of shares with another party. One party may go short so that it will be paid the difference between the closed price at the end of the contract if it is lower than that of the start price (in the beginning of the contract) for the underlying shares. A party may go long in the converse situation. Only a small initial outlay of capital is required to be paid a the outset on entering into the contract although the underlying liability may be substantially more.

Note

[1] The reader should note that Oil & Gas UK and LOGIC have recently produced a new short form Execution Deed for future transfers.

— 11 —

PLATFORM FACILITIES AND OPERATIONS

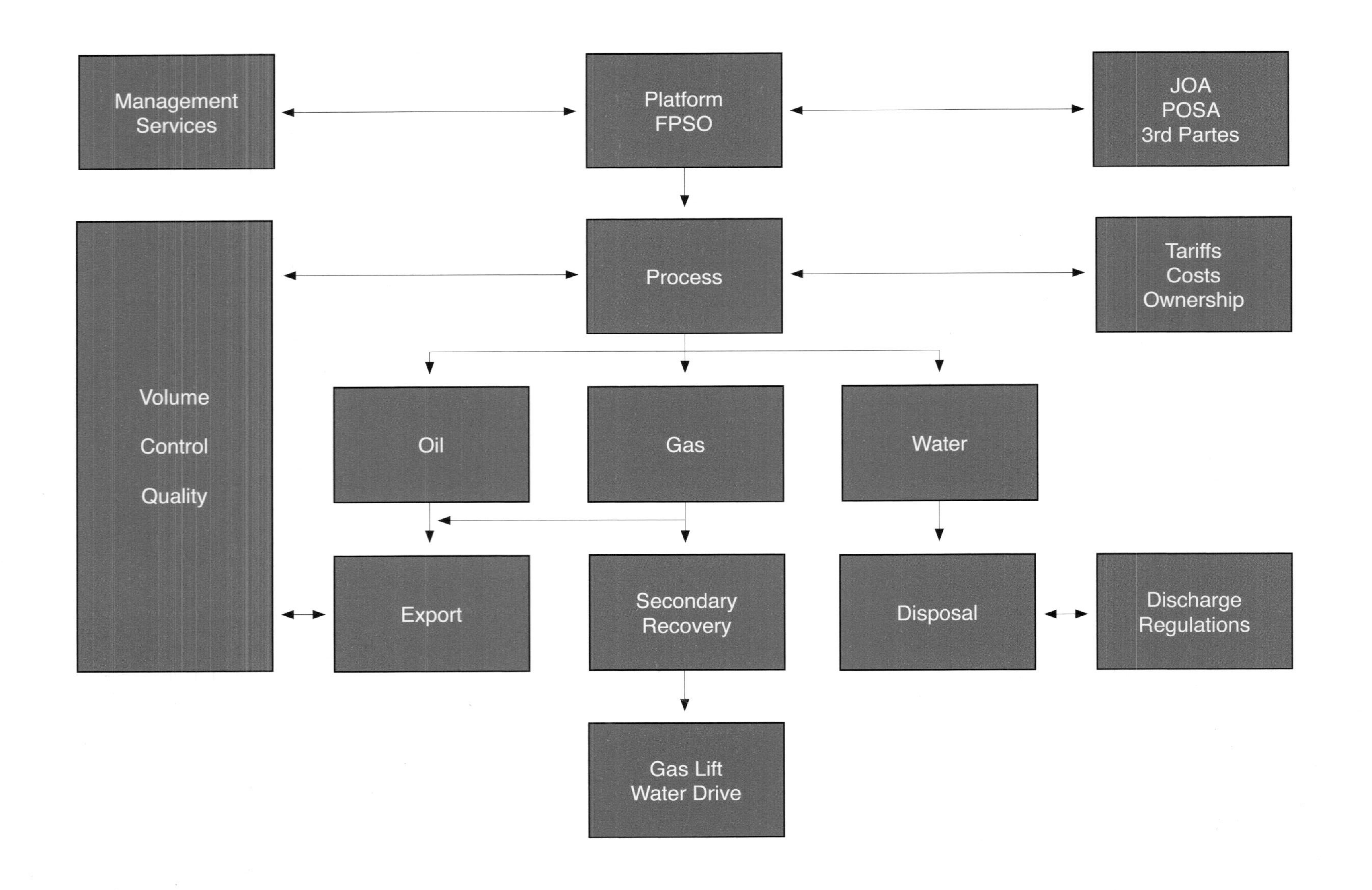
Management
Services
Platform
FPSO
JOA
POSA
3rd Partes
Volume
Control
Quality
Process
Tariffs
Costs
Ownership
Oil
Gas
Water
Export
Secondary
Recovery
Disposal
Discharge
Regulations
Gas Lift
Water Drive

PLATFORM FACILITIES AND OPERATIONS

TECHNICAL

11.1 Introduction

Although in the UK there is some onshore oil and gas production, the vast majority is offshore. Simplistically, most of the dry gas production is concentrated in the Southern North Sea and Irish Sea with typical water depths of 150–300 ft.

Most oil production occurs in the Northern North Sea, with the Central North Sea producing oil/gas and gas condensate and some heavy oil. Here the offshore environment can be very severe, with water depths up to 600 ft. Further north and west of the Shetlands, the environment is even more severe and water depths can be in excess of 1500 ft.

The purpose of offshore platforms is to provide access to facilitate the recovery of hydrocarbon reserves from formations under the seabed.

The designs for these installations are influenced strongly by the recovery mechanisms required to maximise the economic return of exploitation of the reserves, the need to condition the production to enable its transportation towards its market place and the technology available at the time of investment.

The designer's objectives are, therefore, to provide an economic solution to the exploitation of hydrocarbon reserves in the provision of the process equipment necessary to move the production towards its market place. In doing this it is the highest priority to provide a safe work environment over the economic life of the hydrocarbon reserves for people to operate and maintain the plant and equipment on the platform.

The functionality of the facilities is dictated by the reservoir characteristics and the rate of exploitation of the reserves. It is also dictated by the processing requirements for product 'export' and the size of organisation required to keep the operation running smoothly. Furthermore, technology available, appropriate design standards reflecting the understanding of the risks (business, political and human), and maximising the economic return, are major considerations at the design stage.

There are over 200 fixed platforms in the North Sea, many with some processing capacity redundant as a result of depletion of the original reserves for which they were built. Small subsea developments are now being tied back to these nearby host platforms to provide processing and export facilities subject to appropriate agreements. This will provide lower capital and operating costs for small field development, whilst extending the life of the fixed facility.

11.2 Offshore platform types

As the North Sea oil and gas business developed, so too did the network of infrastructure put in place, and this in turn influenced the decisions on the type of platform used for the particular project at hand.

Southern North Sea (SNS) gas developments

In the early days when gas was first discovered in the SNS in the 1960s, the available technology was non-existent in the UK, and USA technology from the Gulf of Mexico was used. These designs were modified to meet the environmental requirements of the North Sea.

All the early Southern North Sea developments were built using process equipment (called topsides) set on top of fixed multilegged steel structures (called jackets). These were placed onto the seabed and held in place with long steel pins – called piles – which were driven deep into the sea bed to allow the total facility to withstand the weather over the design life of perhaps 25–50 years (Fig. 11–1).

The production and accommodation facilities (the 'topsides') were fabricated onshore and then lifted on to the already positioned jacket by large cranes on barges. These early platforms included process plant designed for the flow capacity required by the well's flow potential and the gas sales contracted with British Gas (BG) – the distribution monopoly of the day.

Since 'raw' produced gas contains water, liquid oils – called condensate – and contaminants such as nitrogen, carbon dioxide and even hydrogen sulphide on rare occasions – and the sales gas specification demanded by BG requires that the gas must be able to meet domestic quality requirements, the operators usually 'cleaned up' the gas offshore and thereby reduced the internal corrosion problems and the water handling problems in the pipeline and at the shore landing point – often called the 'gas terminal'.

At the gas terminal the gas was given final treatment to bring it into specification for sales to BG and accurately metered to 'fiscal' standards – both for custody transfer to BG and to measure the volume on which government levies and taxes were to be paid as part of the operator's licence regulations and obligations.

Figure 11–1 Southern North Sea gas production platform

Central and Northern North Sea developments

Geologists' attention migrated northwards in the late 1960s and the discovery of the Forties field 160 km east of Aberdeen in 300 ft of water set new challenges to the companies and the designers of the jackets and topsides.

The design for this 600,000 barrels per day field needed a change in concept from the traditional land-based developments, which were characterised by process plant of typically 50,000 bpd and multiples thereof. The problem in the North Sea was that the process plant 'footplate' onshore for twelve 50,000 bpd-producing units covered acres of ground. In the deeper waters of the Northern North Sea such a design would not be economically viable – even if designing a jacket for North Sea conditions in this water depth could be done.

This was pioneering work and, unlike the USA Gulf coast developments built on a single level, the designers chose a stacked design – using a small basic footplate, but stacked on multiple stories – eight in all on Forties. In addition, whilst this gave them up to 150,000 bpd of process capacity, the technology did not exist to drill wells very far off from vertical, so the number of drilling sites required to cover the area extent of the field – 40 sq km – needed a minimum of four sites for the wells.

To pipe the oil ashore would need the largest diameter pipeline available: 30 inches. This required 100 bar (1500 psi) of pressure drop to get to landfall,

Figure 11–2 Steel jacket Northern North Sea production platform

requiring heavy-walled pipe for laying in the water depth at the limits of technology.

To drill all the wells (25 per platform) and to operate and main-tain the facilities to keep the oil pumping steadily to shore required at least 100 staff, and the associated life support services for them (Fig. 11–2).

In comparison to the North Sea, platforms in the shallower waters of the Middle East with bigger flow rates have multiple steel jackets to spread the facilities over a reasonable space.

More compact developments were required in the deeper waters of the North Sea, increasing the risk of gas leaks leading to catastrophic incidents. Such a failure happened on Piper Alpha in 1988 (see Chapter 21) with devastating results. Suffice to say that whilst much of the early design work was good, there were some inherent weaknesses coupled with flaws in the application of Safety Management Systems. This terrible accident resulted in many changes to design understanding and a significant series of design philosophy changes for UK North Sea production platforms to manage the risks.

With ever-increasing water depths as the development of oil/gas fields moved further north and greater distances from the coast, other platform designs had to be considered that were cheaper and more efficient for these water depths. The high cost overruns and design changes of the first very large steel structures opened the door to concrete structures. For water depths in excess of 300 ft there have been a number of Gravity Based Structures (GBS) which are constructed in concrete, sit on the sea bed and are kept in position by their own weight (Fig. 11–3).

These structures were normally towed from dry dock, anchored at the site, and ballasted with solid ballast. Often they also were able to provide oil storage in their legs, which was important in the early days of production before adequate pipeline infrastructure was built.

Figure 11–3 Gravity based structure

Whereas steel jacket technology was largely a product of the US, the concrete gravity structures were European designs and many are still in operation in both the UK and Norwegian sectors. An example of the use of a number of GBS platforms was the development of the Brent field by Shell with first production in 1976.

The Tension Leg Platform (TLP) is another structure used in the North Sea and in this case the platform is composed of a deck structure and buoyant hull tied to the sea bed by a number of tendons that are kept taut by excess buoyancy in the hull. The hull is normally made of a series of vertical cylindrical columns, horizontal submerged pontoons and tubular member bracings. An example of this type of development was the Hutton field developed by Conoco. In this case the TLP was placed in only 500 ft water depth, but this design has been used in water depths of up to 1000 ft.

Floating production units

At the same time that Forties was being developed, a much smaller discovery, the Argyll field, led the operator to try a different design – processing on a floating rig converted from drilling service to take the process plant for the development, and a local offshore loading system requiring relatively low-pressure design for the export system. Its challenge was to use relatively untried subsea well completions and offshore loading in the hostile conditions of the North Sea.

Argyll produced the first UK oil in 1975 – just ahead of Forties – and was an outstanding success for the operator.

This visionary and innovative development is now becoming more common for marginal field developments in the North Sea. In addition, semi-submersible mobile drilling rigs provide a stable floating drilling and production platform which can be moved from one field to another on depletion of the reservoir.

For deeper water still, the Floating Production Storage and Offloading vessel (FPSO) has become more common and can be either a purpose-built vessel or a converted commercial tanker that is used for the purpose of permanent field production (Fig. 11–4).

Typically these vessels can be used in water depths in excess of 1000 ft and many sophisticated FPSOs are being used to develop deepwater fields in many international areas such as the Gulf of Mexico and Brazil. With the increasing

Figure 11–4 Floating Production Storage and Offloading Vessel (FPSO)

number of smaller deeper water subsea developments, these types of production facilities should become more common in the North Sea.

Drilling rigs integral with platform operations

Most Northern and Central North Sea fixed platforms were also designed to include drilling rigs and associated facilities. Directional drilling techniques have allowed up to approximately 40 wells to be drilled and completed for production from one platform.

As soon as the platform was commissioned to produce oil and gas safely, the first wells were brought on stream and many years of concurrent drilling and production operations then followed.

Even when all wells were drilled, most rigs have remained available for well repair, servicing or redesign to accommodate changing reservoir conditions throughout the life of the field.

Recent platform developments

Whilst the fixed, floating and subsea technologies have increased the options open to facility designers to optimise the economics of development, the commercial and fiscal regimes of the day have also had their influences. One key milestone was the deregulation of the British Gas gas marketing monopoly and the opening up to normal market pressures. This transformed the Southern North Sea, its business re-emergence as a province, and the way in which gas fields were developed.

Treatment is now mainly done onshore at the landfall terminal even though environmental constraints are generally higher on the coast than far offshore.

The technology of both corrosion and hydrate control and management is much improved, as is the reliability of control and instrument systems, designs and digital control technology for information gathering and processing. This in turn has led to many platforms that were permanently manned for many decades being streamlined and demanned.

The tie-back of subsea wells to existing infrastructure is now the most common way of adding new reserves to the production system. The technology for finding and developing smaller reserves that can be processed on existing host platforms which may become marginally economic to operate is now doing much to extend the economic life of the host platform.

11.3 Oil, gas and water processing

The processing of the oil and gas production is primarily to remove unwanted well by-products, and treat the usable and sellable products into a quality for transportation to the onshore terminal and point of sale.

The production from the reservoir – and the substances pumped down wells to help get the reservoir fluids up to the process plant – can contain a diverse mix of components (though mainly crude oil, associated gas and water) that may vary with composition and time. This gives process designers a challenge to understand the variability and the performance consequences, yet not add excessive capacity to cover all eventualities. The cost of space and equipment 'foot print' offshore is very expensive.

Typically, the wellheads for the production wells are physically located on the platform or an adjoining wellhead platform bridge linked to the processing platform. Increasingly, the production wellheads are located subsea and the produced fluids are carried to the processing facilities via subsea pipelines and/or manifolds and/or risers. The produced fluids from the production wells flow to the platform for processing.

Fluids from a reservoir typically consist of hydrocarbons (ie oil and/or gas); other fluids such as water, and a range of chemicals that have been injected to reduce any barriers to flow; a range of non-hydrocarbon gases such as nitrogen (N_2) and carbon dioxide (CO_2); and solid impurities such as drilling mud, sand, silt and salt, etc.

The normal first step in processing these fluids is to 'separate' them into gaseous and liquid components. This is typically done by the use of a range of separating vessels which are pressurised enclosed steel 'containers' through which the fluids flow (Fig. 11–5).

These vessels can be vertical or horizontal and come in an enormous range of sizes, fluid-handling ability and pressure ratings, etc. In a typical system

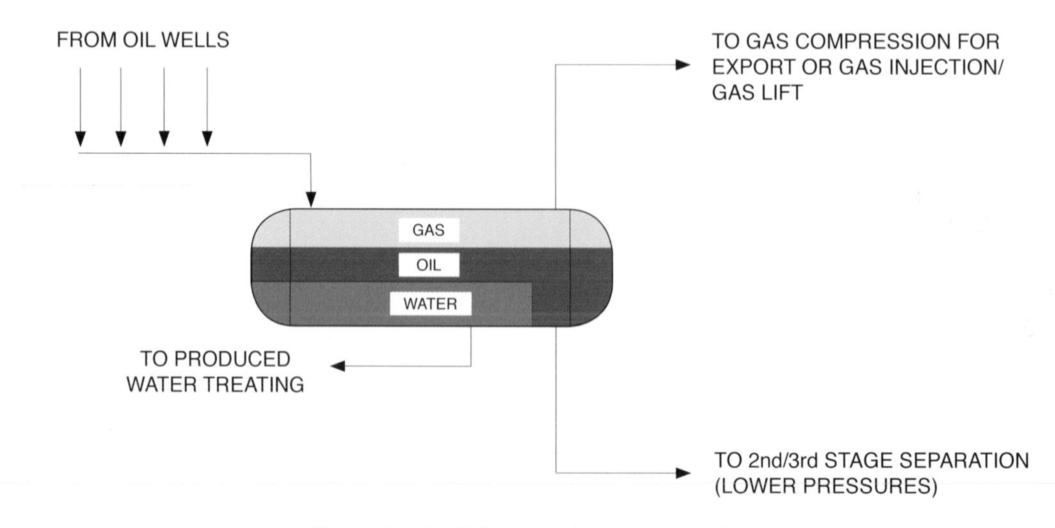

Figure 11–5 Oil, gas and water separation

there are differing separating vessels of various sizes, depending upon the specific fluid composition and flow rates, such that the first vessel separates liquids, namely oil and water, from the gas. The water and hydrocarbons are discharged from the bottom of the vessel whilst the gas is discharged from the top. There are often several stages of separation in order to increase the efficiency of this process.

The primary function of the oil/gas separators can be summarised as:

- *Removal of oil from gas.* The difference in density between oil and gaseous hydrocarbons may accomplish adequate separation in the oil/gas separator but, in some circumstances, it may be necessary to use mechanical devices such as 'mist extractors' to remove liquid mist from the gas before it is discharged from the separator. Oil can come in a range of qualities – depending on its original source and to what conditions the rock formations were subjected over the 10–200 million years that have transpired since they were deposited in the first place.
- *Removal of gas from oil.* The physical and chemical characteristics of the oil and its conditions of pressure and temperature determine the amount of gas it will contain in solution. The rate at which gas is liberated from a given solution depends on its pressure and temperature. Further agitation, heat, special baffling, coalescing packs and filtering material can assist in the removal of non-solution gas. Additional treatment is done for part of the produced gas to make it fit for use as fuel gas to drive the power generation needs on the platform and perhaps for process heating requirements.
- *Separation of water from oil.* In some cases it is preferable to separate and remove the water from the well fluid before it flows through pressure reductions, such as those caused by chokes and valves. Such water removal may prevent difficulties that could be caused downstream by the water, eg corrosion, hydrate formation, and tight emulsion, etc. The water can be separated by the use of a 3-phase separator utilising chemicals and gravity separation. If the separator is not big enough, it can be separated in a free-water knockout vessel installed downstream of the separators.

Once separated, further processing may be required, such as:

- *Oil.* The oil may be further processed to remove more water and/or gas as well as other chemicals, especially potentially corrosive ones, and then it is stabilised and either stored in a tank prior to export or directly exported via an export pipeline. Some platforms export their oil directly onshore, some to a gathering and 'hub' platform and others to tankers.

- *Hydrocarbon gas.* The gas may undergo further processing, again to remove more water, etc. but also to remove corrosive gases such as carbon dioxide and hydrogen sulphide prior to export via the pipeline. In the early days of oil production in the UKCS, gas was routinely flared but now it is mostly removed and exported to shore terminals. In certain circumstances, eg fields with a very low gas quantities, gas may still be flared but this is now becoming the exception. Gas typically requires compression before it is exported via pipelines.
- *Water.* The water normally undergoes further processing and cleansing such that it meets all the required specifications before it is either reinjected or disposed overboard to environmental standards. Generally, water production increases during the field life (particularly if water injection is used for pressure maintenance – see below) and thus the platform water handling systems may need to be enlarged during field life.
- *Other gases.* These are normally further processed and disposed of either chemically, such as hydrogen sulphide, or, if harmless and meeting all emission legislation, such as nitrogen, vented to the atmosphere.

11.4 Secondary recovery facilities

Many reservoirs also require secondary recovery facilities on their host platforms, such as *water injection* and *gas compression* facilities. These fields require pressure maintenance schemes both to improve the economic recovery of hydrocarbons and/or to maintain (sometimes increase) production rates.

A combination of the additional production from improved reservoir recovery and additional processing needed for these secondary recovery techniques present additional challenge to the process plant design. Furthermore, structural integrity management issues arise as result of platform operational life extended sometimes well beyond its original design life.

As a general rule, secondary recovery will cost twice that on a per barrel of recovered oil compared to the cost of primary depletion investments and operating costs.

Water injection

For UK offshore facilities, as indeed for most offshore areas of the world, sea water is used as the water supply for secondary recovery. Whilst this chapter will not detail the reservoir mechanisms of water injection, a basic understanding should be helpful.

Water flood is the name given to the water injection mechanism of secondary recovery and serves two primary functions:

- Reservoir pressure maintenance – adding at least as much water into the reservoir as oil, gas and produced water produced from the production wells.
- Reservoir sweep – pushing the oil and gas ahead of the injected water towards the producing wells.

The first requires the design of the right capacity of injection – at the right quality, and the right pressure to overcome the existing reservoir pressure. The latter requires the wells for injection to be located at the right position in the reservoir in relation to the producing wells (Fig. 11–6).

There are four key quality issues of injected water and one key consideration of the produced water.

- Sea water is saturated in dissolved oxygen, and this is the main cause of corrosion internally of the mild steel pipes and process plant. Oxygen is removed from the sea water by one of three methods: stripping by spare fuel

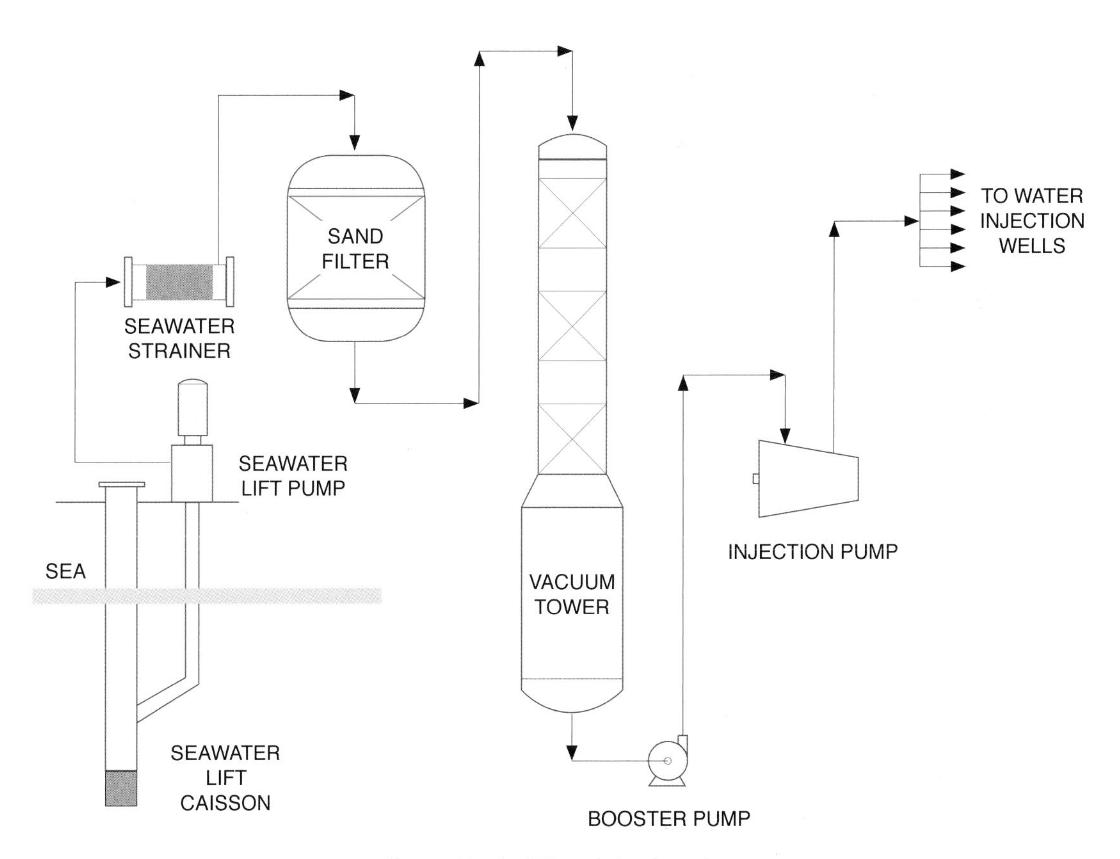

Figure 11–6 Water injection plant

gas on the platform, thus reducing the residual partial pressure remaining in the water; vacuum stripping done by reducing the pressure to only a few inches of water gauge and thus delivering the same result as gas stripping but without the use of fuel gas; oxygen scavenging using a chemical (such as sodium thiosulphite) to consume the oxygen chemically in the water. Often a combination is used and is determined by the perceived economic drivers. In addition, corrosion management requires additional surveillance and protection with corrosion inhibitors to retain plant and equipment technical integrity.

- Organic – especially bacterial – content can create the right environment for the rapid growth of bacteria in the reservoir, often Sulphate Reducing Bacteria (SRB), which consume sulphate in sea water and convert it to hydrogen sulphide. This causes additional production problems as the usually sweet North Sea crude oil becomes contaminated with hydrogen sulphide. This needs filtration of all the sea water and treatment with chlorine and/or biocides.
- Dissolved salts in sea water, and their compatibility with the indigenous water originally in the reservoir, often rich in barium and strontium. When mixed with the high sulphate content of sea water, these precipitate out barium and strontium sulphate. This deposits inside the reservoir. Once the water flood front reaches the production tubing of producing wells, it can be completely blocked with hard scale that cannot be dissolved away. In a few fields the expectation of this problem has been so severe that the sea water was treated prior to injection with sulphate removal – a very expensive treatment but cheaper than the consequential problems if not done.
- Solids content of sea water – often caused during storms disturbing the sea bottom and resulting in high solids content of a particle size bigger than the pore spaces in the reservoir and which would plug the reservoir and prevent injection. This requires filtration to provide the quality for long-term injection.
- Produced water from the North Sea contains LSA – low specific radioactive salts – mainly strontium and some caesium isotopes. These are only a problem during maintenance and internal cleaning, requiring special procedures and safety measures to be properly handled by specialist service companies.

Gas injection

Gas injection is also used to maintain reservoir pressure at a selected level or to supplement natural reservoir energy. The gas injected is normally hydrocarbon gas which can be either produced gas or gas imported from other fields/platforms or, potentially, supplied from onshore, for example carbon dioxide (CO_2).

In the UKCS there are no current CO_2 injection recovery schemes but this is being examined as a potential option for disposal of CO_2 produced from power generation and other industrial/commercial processes.

Gas injected into a reservoir has to be processed, dried and in some cases treated before it is compressed and injected into the reservoir via gas-injection wells. Several platforms also have a complement of gas compressors for gas injection which can be powered electrically or gas turbine driven.

Gas injection is carried out similar to water injection, but usually requires higher pressures and a lot of gas. There is a critical need for a plentiful supply of cheap gas, even though it can mostly be recovered at the end of field life by 'blow-down' of the remaining gas in the reservoir.

The only difference to water injection is that with the right composition and pressure, injected gas can become miscible with oil and 'thin' the oil so that it flows through the rocks more easily.

11.5 Control, monitoring and safety systems

Control and monitoring of the critical production, processing and other operations on an offshore platform is essential for both efficient and safe operation of the plant.

Offshore production facilities have the same basic requirements for electric power, control and monitoring systems as onshore facilities. In particular, there are requirements for a power source with a reliable distribution system, instrumentation to control and monitor production operations, and a safety shutdown system tailored for the specific installation.

Offshore electrical facilities have to be designed for minimum weight and space whilst offering high degrees of flexibility, reliability, access and maintainability. Due to deck space and layout limitations, hazardous area considerations are complex and governed by a host of HSE regulatory codes dependent upon type of structure and the hydrocarbon fluid type being processed.

Figure 11–7 Control room

Further environmental considerations are important so as to avoid the accidental discharge of fluids and chemicals into the sea or atmosphere.

The controls on an offshore platform tend to be very concentrated in a purpose-built secure Control Room where all operations are both monitored and controlled, often using the most advanced computer technology (Fig. 11–7).

Process controls frequently include a combination of pneumatic, hydraulic, electric and electronic instrumentation. The amount of remote control and electronic instrumentation and control depends upon the age of the platform with more recent installations being the most sophisticated.

Processing facilities – for whatever purpose – require the operators and management to know what is going on in the process, and to have the capability to vary and control conditions.

The first generation of North Sea platforms were designed and built before the advent of computers, and were mainly pneumatic systems with some electrical control systems using mechanical relays on low-voltage systems (0–24v). Modern day controls operate off milli-volts with electronic processors that can intelligently track, monitor, and calibrate the instrument control loops automatically.

With the continuing sophistication of computer simulations, the instruments and controls of today have probably changed more than any other component of the offshore installation. The larger platforms and fields with longer life expectancies have had to replace the whole control and instrumentation systems as the older systems have become obsolete, with spares essentially no longer available.

Modern instruments offer greater accuracy of control. This has been seen especially in such applications as gas compressor anti-surge control, which today have a continuous recalculation of the process conditions and the 'surge line' of the compressor. This has prevented the severe damage that was commonly experienced in earlier years of platform life.

The operations typically monitored and controlled on an offshore platform include:

- *Wells* – valve positions including downhole, pressure, temperature, flow and/or injection rates, etc.
- *Processing* – pressures and temperatures, valve positions, oil/water interface, gas/oil interface, flow rates, etc.
- *Power generation* – production rates, turbine controls, etc.

Safety and emergency shut down systems are normally kept separate from alarm and control circuits. Examples of key safety-related systems include combustible-gas detectors, poisonous gas sensors, fire detectors, subsurface shutdown valves (SSSVs), surface shutdown valves (SSVs), and emergency shutdown systems (ESDs). Proper design and installation of these systems is one of the most critical aspects of offshore instrumentation and control systems.

With a judicious combination of strategically placed fire detection sensors and shutdown valves it is possible to shut in production facilities, including wells, risers and pipelines, to blow down pressurised vessels and to activate the appropriate fire suppression system simultaneously and immediately, thus minimising escalation of the potential incident.

The well subsurface shutdown valves (SSSVs) are installed downhole in the production tubing on every well and are held open by hydraulic pressure in the control line. They are fail-safe in that if the pressure falls they immediately shut. These valves are normally used only in extreme emergencies as they are expensive to repair. The SSVs are situated between the wellhead and the production manifold. They are activated in most platform and process shutdowns.

The final element in most safety systems is the manual ESD (Emergency Shutdown) with controls that activate various shut down facilities around the platform. ESD stations are normally located on boat landings, helicopter decks, and process areas and in control rooms.

On many platforms the control rooms also control and monitor unmanned platforms and/or a range of subsea facilities including individual wellheads, subsea manifolds through to subsea processing systems. Safety systems and controls have improved beyond all recognition over the years.

Serious safety incidents experienced in the North Sea and elsewhere have provided valuable learning to the design of the safety equipment, the application of Safety Management Systems, the understanding of the consequential effects of incident escalation and the design criteria to reduce these consequences.

The result of all this learning is a major reduction in both accidents and the consequences of the initial events in comparison to the earlier days in the North Sea. Technology has played its part, but at least as important has been the change in management approach to lead safety in the workplace properly. The combination of improved understanding of the real risks and hazards, the design and improved management of systems, and training of the workforce have all resulted in significant improvements on offshore installations.

Fire and explosion from a release of hydrocarbons, often from under great pressure, are still the major accident hazards on any offshore production facility. Designs now separate 'safety' systems from operational control systems. These require higher levels of redundancy and reliability and priority on maintaining schedules of safety-critical elements. These include safety controls and shutdown systems for wells as well as the process plant

11.6 Accommodation, utilities and life support

Although many of the smaller platforms in the North Sea are unmanned, the vast majority of the larger platforms are continuously manned. The need to support a workforce on a platform involves a host of additional facilities and services. These include potable water, accommodation units, increased power generation, larger heli-decks, more storage, and more sophisticated safety systems.

Most accommodation facilities are normally situated as far away as possible from the production and processing areas, for obvious safety reasons. The accommodation units are normally self-contained and provide all the normal 'hotel' services such as beds, cooking and eating areas, rest areas, laundry facilities as well as office space, communication systems, medical support, etc.

A typical northern platform accommodates between 50 and 200 people on board at any one time – the size of a small village. The workforce covers all the requirements – of the plant and of the 'hotel facilities' – their operations and their maintenance.

Supporting permanent personnel on board a platform requires a large increase in power generation. The modern new generation of Southern North Sea wellhead towers can produce and control production with as little as 1 KW, the majority of the bigger platforms can consume 80–100 MW – and all produced and distributed on the platform and managed and maintained by the staff on board.

In some cases, the power is imported via submarine cables either from land, or from a neighbouring platform. With the advent of new DC technology it is now possible to transport electricity more efficiently than with the large voltages required for AC generation.

Essential loads on the platform must remain energised when the main power generation fails if there is an unscheduled platform shutdown. Secondary/emergency generators are required to enable continued supply to critical systems such as navigation lights, foghorns, communications, emergency lighting, personnel safety systems, etc.

A modern platform will typically have microwave communication and/or fibre optic cable for speech and data as well as a backup satellite communication system. In future it is expected that these systems will be expanded such that various activities on the platform can be controlled and monitored remotely, as is the case for many unmanned platforms.

Whilst logistical and technical support is organised onshore, day-to-day business is conducted on and from the platform and through its people.

Few North Sea platforms are accessed by sea, and the vast majority can be accessed only by helicopter. The North Sea is the most concentrated arena for commercial helicopter usage in the world, even if it is affected by periods of fog, high winds and electric storms.

There is also an effective array of safety equipment and backup equipment for evacuation of the platform if the circumstances require people to abandon the installation and the heli-deck becomes unusable.

11.7 Manning and organisation

The origin of the offshore legislation was derived from that encompassing the marine industry. The captain or Offshore Installation Manager (OIM) is accountable in law for all that happens on the installation. His priority role is to ensure the safety and welfare of all on board, with all operations and administrative managers and supervisors reporting to him for the day-to-day activities on the platform. Each discipline has functional lines of communication for technical, material or logistical support from onshore.

Platform organisations

Platform organisations have changed at various levels of field maturity together with the continuous quest for maximising operational efficiency and optimisation of operating costs whilst maintaining flexibility of skilled and semi-skilled offshore staffing.

In the early days of offshore production operations, the operating and maintenance staff was predominantly employed by the oil company that was designated as platform operator. This is usually the operating partner of the licence who has the highest percentage interest in the ownership of the licence.

Additional labour requirements to cater for higher than normal work levels were added from manpower contractors or agencies. Catering crews and other more specialist services were employed under service contracts.

As more experience has developed within the major production and maintenance contractors, the oil companies started to reduce their offshore staff on most facilities to a core group of technical supervisory roles, or on many platforms to the OIM as the sole company representative. This has now further resulted in some major contractors becoming 'Duty Holders' of the platforms. Offshore contractor staff report to the contractor technical and administrative offshore supervision. Responsibility for all onshore logistical and technical support for the day-to-day running of the platform facilities support also lies with the contractor.

The role of the licence holder operator has therefore now focused on the lifecycle issues of reservoir management and future investment decisions for sustaining and optimising production.

Manpower levels

The sizes of the organisations are related to the style, complexity and magnitude of the equipment on board, for production, drilling, life support and maintenance, and administration. Larger platforms may have 250–300 persons permanently on board. On the smaller Southern North Sea platforms there may be no permanent staff, with only visits to perform maintenance or perhaps to intervene to correct a malfunction. While control technology has had a significant impact on reducing the operations staff, this has required significant changes to the skill requirements of the maintenance staff.

In the early years of production, operating teams were split into day and night shifts in almost equal numbers. Today the majority of staff only work on day shift with a much smaller 'watch-keeping' night shift – supported in the event of an incident or malfunction by calling out the daytime staff. Reliability and better maintenance planning have also enabled this staff reduction option.

With the employment of operating and maintenance staff by a 'Duty Holder' contractor who also supplies and manages operating and maintenance staff, flexibility in variation of numbers and skills is better accommodated. In periods of high maintenance and during scheduled shutdowns for major work, better manpower planning can be achieved by a contractor with responsibilities for operations and maintenance on a number of platforms.

11.8 Future production facilities

Since the start of production of oil and gas from the UKCS, it has been calculated that just over half the reserves have been produced. Typical of the majority of petroleum basins throughout the world, it would seem that the majority of the large reservoirs have already been discovered and significantly depleted, and smaller fields now remain.

Many of these fields have become more accessible by better seismic and drilling technology, or may have been considered uneconomic to develop with the more traditional platform technology. Advances in subsea technology will now enable these fields to be produced from subsea wells tied back to existing platform and pipeline infrastructure, which now have spare capacity.

These facilities will not require additional manpower on the host platform. In view of their remoteness, such facilities will need to be better instrumented to allow the downhole real-time data to be accessible at the platform to aid the monitoring and maximisation of oil or gas recovery.

The emphasis will therefore be on the technology and the skills capable of ensuring the reliability and continuous production of subsea wells, whilst maintaining integrity of the existing topsides production and life support facilities.

PLATFORM FACILITIES AND OPERATIONS

LEGAL

11.9 Introduction

Aspects of the construction and decommissioning of platforms are dealt with elsewhere in this book. This chapter focuses on the use of a platform following construction and prior to decommissioning. Such use may be by the operator who forms part of the platform-owning group for the benefit of that platform-owning group, by the operator for the benefit of third parties, or by a contract duty-holder appointed by the operator to manage the platform.

In the case of a platform for the production of petroleum from fields where the ownership interests are the same, then the contractual mechanism for ownership, management and operation of the platform is the same as with any other joint property, ie it is governed by a typical Joint Operating Agreement (JOA), with provisions for Work Programmes, budget approval and cost recovery, as with any other JOA. The detailed provisions of a typical JOA are considered in Chapter 9.

Where a platform is to be utilised for the production of petroleum from fields where the ownership structure of the field differs from the ownership of the platform itself, then use of a single JOA is no longer appropriate and a separate agreement is required between the owners of the platform and the owners of the relevant field(s) wishing to use the platform facilities. Such an agreement is normally termed a 'Platform Operating Services Agreement', or POSA, and the key commercial terms of a typical POSA are considered below.

Where a platform is to be managed not by the operator directly but by a subcontractor on behalf of the operator, that service is governed by an agreement termed a 'Facilities Management Agreement' and typical key terms of such an agreement are also considered below

11.10 Platform Operating Service Agreements (POSAs)

Each POSA will be tailored to the particular circumstances of the fields and platform concerned and there is no 'standard form'. However, most will have common features and issues to address. As an example, assume there are two adjoining blocks in the North Sea, each involved in the production of oil, with a single, fixed platform located on one block and owned by the licensees of that block (the 'Platform Owners') and the other field is located on the adjoining block and is owned by entirely different third parties (the 'Third Parties'). In this case, the POSA between the Platform Owners and Third Parties should address the following issues.

Commencement and duration

A Construction and Tie-In Agreement should set out the work to be done in order to tie the Third Parties' field back to the Platform Owners' platform, the time scale in which that is to be completed and the allocation of costs for doing so (this would ordinarily be borne by the Third Parties). Once the construction and tie-in work has been completed and satisfactory commissioning on any tie-in facilities achieved the provision of ongoing services by the Platform Owners to the Third Parties is governed by the POSA. Under the POSA, it is usually provided that the rights of Third Parties to have their petroleum processed on the platform will continue until cessation of production from the Third Parties' field, however, the Platform Owners normally retain rights to terminate the POSA earlier than cessation of production on the Third Parties' field in certain specific circumstances. Earlier termination can be by reference to a fixed date (by which time the Platform Owners expect to be decommissioning their own platform) or when production from the Third Parties' field has fallen to the level where tariffs generated from that may make it uneconomic to continue to provide the service or where the Platform Owners' own field production has declined to the point where it cannot economically provide the service to the Third Parties.

Services

The POSA will set out the detail of the services to be provided by the Platform Owners. Typically, this would comprise an obligation to accept delivery of 'on-specification' production from the Third Parties' field at a designated Delivery Point on the platform, to carry out processing services on that petroleum and to redeliver it to the Third Parties at a redelivery point. Depending upon the ownership of infrastructure on the downstream side of the platform that delivery point may be to a terminal on land or may be the entry point to another offshore transportation system. In either event, the Third Parties will require to negotiate terms for the entry of their production at the redelivery point in to that third-party terminal or transportation system and for onward transportation of the petroleum to a further redelivery point for lifting and sale by them.

The nature of services to be provided under the POSA to the Third Parties will vary depending on the commercial circumstances, however, typically, those services would include the separation of gas, oil and condensate from the production received from the Third Parties, the handling of any waste water and other waste materials from that production, possibly the management of any subsea equipment operated from the host platform but owned by the Third Parties and the redelivery of production following processing.

Depending upon ownership of further transportation infrastructure required to transport oil back to the land, oil and/or gas produced by the Third Parties at the platform may be sold by those Third Parties to one or more of the Platform Owners – this may be attractive to the Third Parties as they would no longer require to negotiate capacity and tariff terms for the transportation of the production from the platform to the beach. Alternatively, the Third Parties may choose to negotiate terms for the transportation of their production back to the beach and arrange to lift and sell that petroleum on land.

Quantities and quality of petroleum to be processed

Rights to have petroleum processed on the platform are limited by reference to the quantity of petroleum which is expected to be produced and also the quality.

The Platform Owners will wish to provide for a minimum quantity of petroleum to be produced by the Third Parties (in order to ensure that tariffs generated make the provision of a service to the Third Parties economic) and also for a maximum quantity of petroleum to be produced by Third Parties. The Platform Owners primarily own the platform to produce their own petroleum and therefore wish to ensure that they themselves have adequate capacity for their own present and future production.

The quality of petroleum to be taken into the platform is also critical. It is important to ensure that an entry specification for the Third Parties' petroleum is agreed and that production of petroleum outside that specification entitles the Platform Owners to shut in the Third Parties' field and not to accept that petroleum. Off-specification petroleum can cause problems for the Platform Owners, for example, by including a high water content beyond the capacity of the platform to handle the disposal of that water, or perhaps a high sulphur content which might mean that the platform facilities are exposed to a risk of corrosion outside of their technical specification.

Tariffs, costs and ownership

The agreement will make provision for payment of capital costs incurred by the Platform Owners, for example, for installing additional processing facilities on the platform in order to cope with third-party production. The agreement will also make provision for payment of tariffs by the Third Parties to the Platform Owners for use of the platform.

Ordinarily, ownership of new equipment installed in the platform will pass to the Platform Owners, however, liability for payment for the installation of the equipment and ultimately payment for any incremental costs of decommissioning that equipment would normally fall on the Third Party.

Restriction and suspension of services

The POSA may make provision governing what happens in the event that the platform's capacity is restricted or the operations on the platform require to be suspended for any reason. Restriction of the platform's capacity (whether resulting from a problem with the platform itself or the evacuation system for petroleum from the platform) is one difficult area – is production capacity allocated first to the Platform Owners or is a set proportion of any reduced capacity to be allocated to each of the Platform Owners and the Third Parties? There is no set answer for this and it is a matter for commercial negotiation, linked with the calculation of tariffs and any capital payments for use of the platform.

Decommissioning

The question of who is to remain responsible for the decommissioning of the platform and any equipment installed in the platform at the request of the Third Parties should be addressed in the POSA, as well as the question of who bears the cost of that decommissioning.

Measurement, metering, sampling and allocation

It is highly unlikely that the quality of petroleum produced from the Third Parties' field will be exactly the same as the quality of petroleum produced from the Platform Owners' field. As a result, the POSA requires some mechanism for measurement, metering, sampling and allocation of the petroleum streams. Typically, once the Third Parties' petroleum is introduced to the platform it will be processed in a way designed to ensure that it can then be co-mingled with the petroleum produced by the Platform Owners so as to provide a single quality of petroleum exported from the platform. If the Third Parties' petroleum is of particularly good quality then their petroleum will, on average, improve the quality of the petroleum leaving the platform and there is therefore a case for the Third Parties to receive a higher allocation of that petroleum than would be suggested by a simple pro rata allocation based on the number of barrels produced. Equally, if the Third Parties' petroleum is of lower quality than that produced from the Platform Owners' fields, the reverse would apply.

Risk of damage and loss

The question of risk of damage to the platform and any petroleum produced should also be addressed and there should also be clarity in the POSA on who should carry which insurances. Just as with a JOA, liability of the operator providing services under the POSA is normally restricted so as to exclude liability for consequential loss and only include specific liability where wilful misconduct has occurred or perhaps a failure to carry relative insurances. Beyond that, the issues of liability allocation centre on the extent to which liabilities are to be shared by the Platform Owners and the Third Parties.

Given that it is the Platform Owners who are permitting the Third Parties to ship their production across the Platform Owners' platform, the normal starting point is that the Platform Owners require to be indemnified in respect of any losses or costs which they may suffer as a consequence of providing that service. Obviously, taken to its extreme, that position may make it completely uneconomic for the Third Party to enter into the POSA in the first place. The potential damage to a host platform, not to mention any liability for consequential loss, loss of production of the Platform Owners and so forth, may run into hundreds of millions of pounds if a catastrophic event were to occur as a result of the tie-in of the Third Party facilities or the production from the Third Party field. If, for example, the Third Parties' production were highly corrosive it may cause significant damage to the host platform. As a result there are normally financial limits agreed on such liabilities of the Third Parties with appropriate insurance cover effected by the Third Parties so as to provide comfort to the Platform Owners that the Third Parties will be good for any claims arising under the indemnities given.

The Platform Owners tend not to accept any liability towards the Third Party for any loss of production or damage to equipment belonging to the Third Parties as such oil field risk is generally seen as a risk which should be borne by the relevant field partners entitled to the oil, provided always that the operator carries out the services to the required standard of an operator.

Such insurance and liability clauses should clarify liability for damage to the Platform Owners' equipment, damage to the Third Parties' equipment, damage to equipment of other third parties, death or injury of employees and subcontractors, pollution and environmental damage as well as consequential loss, loss of production and reservoir damage.

Transfer of rights and obligations under the POSA

As the POSA is a key field agreement relating to the Third Parties' field (and also to the Platform Owners' field), the POSA will set out clearly how and when the benefit and burden of the POSA can be assigned. Typically, the POSA is part of a package of contractual arrangements relating to a field (whether the Platform

Owners' field or the Third Parties' field) and assignment of an interest under the relevant licence and JOA pertaining to a field should also trigger an assignment of rights and obligations under the relevant POSA.

Although, given the nature of the agreement, no issues of pre-emption rights arise, the parties on each side of the POSA are normally concerned to ensure that the counterparty is of adequate financial standing to perform their part of the bargain under the POSA. The assignment clause may therefore contain a financial capability test which is applied by existing parties to the POSA to any proposed contracting party.

Other legal boilerplate clauses

The POSA will also contain other provisions common to JOAs, eg a provision setting out the standard to which services are to be performed (usually that of a good prudent operator), force majeure, confidentiality, waiver and amendment, applicable law and jurisdiction, audit rights to ensure that tariffs are properly calculated, and measurement, metering, sampling and allocation is done correctly, notices and entire agreement clauses.

Other provisions?

Depending upon the fields to which the POSA relates, there may be other ancillary commercial agreements either entered into at the same time as the POSA or contained within the POSA itself. As an example, if the Third Parties' field primarily produces oil but some gas is produced as a by-product then the Third Parties may, as an alternative to trying to find an export route to bring that gas to shore, sell that gas offshore to the Platform Owners, either for use as fuel gas for the platform itself or for onward transportation and sale by the Platform Owners as part of a larger stream.

11.11 Facilities Management Agreements

Ordinarily, one of the licence holders would be appointed as operator of the platform and would itself engage staff and contractors in order to manage the platform. Until recently it was very rare that any contracting company could take over the role of operator or manager of the facilities as there were few, if any, contracting companies which were approved by the DTI as duty-holders for the purposes of ensuring health and safety compliance. Now that an increasing number of contracting companies have been approved by the DTI as potential duty-holders it has become possible for the party appointed as operator under the licence to delegate some management of the platform, pipelines and other subsea facilities to a duty-holder contracting company rather than handling all of those functions in-house.

Such delegation is achieved by a Facilities Management Agreement in terms of which the contractor company is appointed to manage the facilities and act as duty-holder.

The extent to which an operator chooses to delegate responsibility for platform management to such a contracting company will vary from case to case, however, typically, such a Facilities Management Agreement would appoint the contractor as duty-holder for the purposes of the safety case relating to the platform, place obligations on the contractor with respect to the provision of platform management services, personnel, compliance, management of the subcontracted supply chain, management of any pollution incidents, carrying appropriate operational insurances and perhaps also preparation of the facilities for decommissioning at the end of production.

Although much of the contractor's remuneration may be based on day-rates/fixed prices for performing large elements of the management service with specific rates for additional work requested by the platform owners, such total services contracts are quite well suited to a remuneration structure based on risk/reward. Management of the platform so as to optimise production, maximise uptime, minimise HSE risk, and ensure compliance can all be encouraged by a remuneration structure linked to those key factors, to ensure that the field is operated in accordance with good oil field practice. A remuneration structure geared solely to hours of effort spent by the contractor and his personnel does not encourage efficient production, a remuneration structure geared simply to maximising production may result in poor maintenance of the platform or a poor HSE record – a package of remuneration designed to encourage the contractor to outperform set targets in all of these areas helps to ensure alignment of interest with the platform owners and a safe, efficient operating environment.

11.12 Floating Production Storage and Offloading Vessels (FPSOs)

Platform Services can also be performed by FPSOs, although, by their nature, the range of services an FPSO can offer is more limited than those available from a fixed platform. One other critical difference is in the terms of ownership of an FPSO – a fixed platform is usually owned outright by the field owners or, occasionally, leased by them under a finance lease, whereas an FPSO, effectively a ship, is either owned or leased under a marine charter party. Chapter 17 contains a summary of a typical marine charter party.

— 12 —

RESERVOIR MANAGEMENT

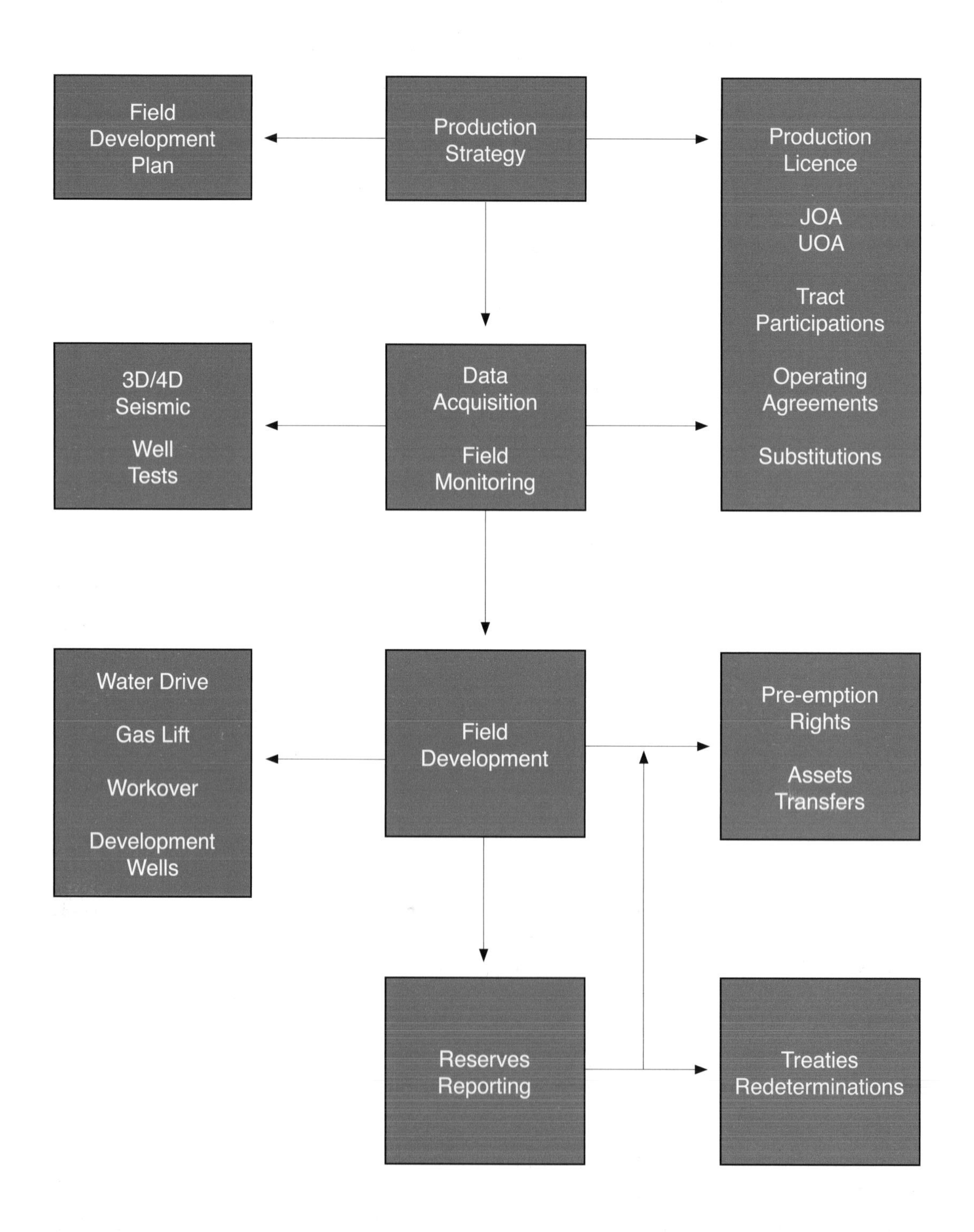

Field
Development
Plan
Production
Strategy
Production
Licence
JOA
UOA
Tract
Participations
Operating
Agreements
Substitutions
3D/4D
Seismic
Well
Tests
Data
Acquisition
Field
Monitoring
Water Drive
Gas Lift
Workover
Development
Wells
Field
Development
Pre-emption
Rights
Assets
Transfers
Reserves
Reporting
Treaties
Redeterminations

RESERVOIR MANAGEMENT

TECHNICAL

12.1 Introduction

Reservoir management is clearly important in the evaluation of the potential recovery of hydrocarbons following the exploration phase. A well designed reservoir management strategy will maximise recovery from the discovered and appraised reservoirs. Whilst the strategy will evolve significantly throughout the producing life of the field, a correct initial reservoir management strategy will do much to minimise project costs and maximise the benefit of new development wells and future workovers.[1] (See Chapter 6, section 6.6.)

Reservoirs remain in equilibrium until the start of the removal of oil and gas. All of the production profiles and performance have been based on static and dynamic (simulation) models which are untested for the field in question. Monitoring field performance to verify these projections and revise the models and projections if required, is critical to maximising recovery and value.

Whilst 3D seismic will give an accurate picture of the reservoir at any particular time, the superimposition of one time frame over another will show the changes that are taking place within the reservoir. This technique is known as 4D time-lapse technology which continues to improve, even allowing engineers to view reservoirs in immersive visualisation rooms based on the virtual reality interface.

As this technology advances, smaller field developments become increasingly attractive. The reservoir engineer can locate and understand the dynamics of small accumulations to allow the introduction of corrective actions. Accurate applications of secondary recovery techniques in harmony with new drilling and subsea technology, are all critical to the development of smaller accumulations of hydrocarbons.

12.2 Maximising recovery and value

Once the decision has been made to develop an oil or gas field, and large sums of money have been invested, the field clearly now needs to add value to the owner. The return on the investment comes in the form of gas and oil production over the life of the field. Typical producing lives of fields range from perhaps a few years for a small satellite field development linked to an existing larger platform or an FPSO (Floating Production Storage and Offtake) operated field, to half a century or more for some of the larger fields.

The choice of a reservoir management strategy commences with an assessment of the drive energy available in the reservoir. There is an infinite range of hydrocarbon molecular combinations possible, from viscous crude through gas condensate to dry gas. Generally, the more volatile the fluids are, the higher the natural recovery factor will be. This is due to a combination of the fluid viscosity (the natural resistance to flow), and the expansion factor (the ability of the fluid to expand as the reservoir is depleted).

Initially, most fields produce by natural depletion. That means, as oil or gas is produced, the pressure is allowed to drop as rocks and fluids expand to replace the emptied pore space. Gas fields are produced in this fashion until they are depleted. The high expansion factor of gas ensures that typically 50–80% of the initial gas in place is recovered in this way. Oil fields are a different matter. The available expansion energy in oil is limited and reliance on this alone would result in a recovery factor (see Chapter 5, section 5.3) of somewhere between 5 and 10%, slightly more if the oil is particularly rich in gas (solution gas drive or secondary gas cap).

Most oil fields, and particularly so in the North Sea, will benefit from water drive. In some fields, the water drive is a natural phenomenon, caused by a large body of water, the aquifer, expanding as the reservoir pressure is decreased. An artificial water drive, or water 'flood', is created by injecting water into the field to replace the oil produced. The benefit arises both from displacing oil by water towards the producing wells and from maintaining the pressure, hence the term 'pressure maintenance' is often used to describe the process. Recovery factors achievable from water drives are typically in the 30–50% range, depending on reservoir properties and shape.

In offshore developments, engineered water drive has become standard and in the North Sea many operators decided to apply the technique from the outset and platforms were designed accordingly. For water drive in a typical oil reservoir there are three factors which govern the oil recovery efficiency:

(i) the mobility ratio; (ii) heterogeneity of the formations; and (iii) gravity. When oil and water flow together the flow rate of each medium (at a given saturation) depends on the permeability-viscosity ratio, termed the mobility ratio.

The main method of designing and monitoring the performance of water floods is through the use of 3D and 3-phase reservoir simulation models. These models will be used to estimate the number of water injection wells required, along with the injection volumes and any modifications required to improve the performance of the system and hence recovery of hydrocarbons.

Two types of water flooding are considered by the reservoir engineers in locating the injection wells:

(a) *Peripheral flood* is where the injection is carried out around the boundaries of the oil and gas field reservoir – usually on very permeable and prolific reservoirs so that the pressure support is still able to be felt by the wells even in the centre of the field.

(b) *Pattern flood* is where the injection wells are located between the producing wells, often in fields that are less prolific and with poorer permeability, and thus need the injection wells to be much closer to each of the producers.

Whilst peripheral flood tends to delay water breakthrough into the producing wells – and even when this happens it is at the down-dip producers first – it tends not to deliver quite as high a recovery factor as for pattern flood.

On the upside, peripheral flood tends not to require such a high volume 'recycle' from the earlier pattern flood dynamics.

These issues have all to be considered in the design, and crucially in the ongoing monitoring of the 'flood progress' through time.

In most cases, the sweep efficiency is less than perfect and additional or replacement injection and/or producing wells are required to maximise the flood characteristics and production profile. This adds more requirements to designers of the platforms in the first place where often the reservoir knowledge is inadequate to make the informed decisions.

The quality of the water to be injected is as important as the quantity in a water flood and the water is normally treated before injection such that gas and solids are removed and a range of additives and corrosion inhibitors may be added. This is both to make the injected water compatible with the reservoir water and to reduce potential corrosion of the pumping facilities and the tubulars and valves, etc. in the wellbore.

In certain circumstances, polymers can be added to the injection water that can accelerate and/or increase the oil recovery. Further, for heavier crude oils hot water and/or steam injection is used in order to improve recovery. Other techniques include the injection of a miscible fluid or a range of surfactants, etc. These techniques, usually termed 'tertiary recovery', are less common in the UK North Sea and are therefore beyond the scope of this book.

Gas injection can be a viable alternative to water injection, but is less common in the North Sea due to the intrinsic value of the gas. In some larger fields, where the decision has been made to use gas injection to maximise oil recovery, the injected gas can be partially recovered at the end of field life through a final 'blowdown' phase.

As well as assisting in the flow of oil wells, gas can be injected into a reservoir for three main recovery purposes: (i) to displace and thus produce oil (gas drive); (ii) to provide a miscible flow; and (iii) to maintain pressure in a retrograde gas-condensate reservoir.

In the case of the gas drive, typically, gas can be injected into the gas cap and thus the gas displaces the underlying oil towards the production wells. The surface equipment for gas drive projects normally consists of the produced gas processing equipment for extraction of dry gas that may then be supplemented by gas from other reservoirs or fields.

Dry gas recycling is often used in gas-condensate reservoirs in order to maximise the amount of condensate produced. The aim is to maintain the reservoir pressure at a high level and thus minimise the deposition and loss of (retrograde) liquid condensate in the reservoir. The injected dry gas also displaces the wet gas towards the producing wells. There are two main types of recycling: (i) full recycling, in which all the separated produced gas is reinjected such that all the wet gas produced contains its maximum condensate yield; and (ii) partial recycling, which includes only partial gas reinjection such that the full pressure above the dew point is not maintained. As with water drive or gas drive the efficiency of any gas-recycling project depends upon mobility ratio, heterogeneity and gravity.

The majority of the North Sea oil installations have been commissioned with water injection facilities from day one (adding them later comes at great expense). Injecting water into the reservoir has the unwanted side-effect of also leading to increased water production. As water is heavier than oil, this in turn leads to reduced 'lift efficiency', ie the wells are flowing at lower rates than if there were only oil and gas flowing.

In order to improve the flow rates from the wells producing at high water-cuts, 'artificial lift' is implemented. In onshore environments, this typically takes the shape of the familiar beam-pumps, or 'nodding donkeys'. On space- and weight-constrained offshore installations, gas lift, and sometimes electrical or hydraulic pumps, are preferred. The lift installations are often, together with the water injection pumps, the largest consumers of energy on the installation and require a dedicated power supply, more often than not in the form of gas turbines utilising the locally produced gas. The economic cut-off for production from individual wells is often determined by the lifting costs (in terms of gas/ energy requirements).

Maximising production and recovery from the ageing field thus becomes a trade-off between finding new drainage points or intervals that can still produce relatively dry oil and cycling more water through the reservoir. In the constrained environment that offshore installations quickly become (well slot, lift gas, water injection and gross liquid capacity constraints), maximising production becomes a precarious optimisation routine and, with facilities having a limited life expectancy, a race against time.

If and when there is space capacity in the facilities and all reasonable development options have been exploited, it becomes possible to use the facilities as host facilities for other fields, also third party fields. This may significantly extend the economic life of a field. Some of these optimisations are carried out by daily experimentations, but for major changes, eg workovers or infill wells, the decisions are backed up by integrated reservoir, well, and sometimes facilities models.

12.3 Data acquisition and field monitoring

The initial development decision is based on the data acquired during the exploration and appraisal campaign. With the possible exception of well tests and some core flooding data, these data will be of a static nature: seismic data to reveal the size and shape of the reservoir, core and log data to reveal reservoir properties and initial saturations, and some fluid data. The field model that can be built from these data has to suffice for making the development decision, but any production forecast derived from it would have large error bars attached to it . The range of reserves for an undeveloped field should typically be 'base case' ± 50%.

During development drilling and initial production, an enormous amount of data is acquired, often of a different and more revealing nature than was available when the original development decision was made. The new data often throw an entirely new light on the field and, invariably, the field turns out to be more complicated than initially thought. The well performance data, in the form of rates and pressures, provide better indications of the internal reservoir architecture, or to put it more crudely, the internal 'plumbing' of the reservoir. Production logging tools show which intervals in the well are producing oil and which are producing gas or water. Dedicated observation wells are sometimes drilled with the sole objective of gathering data to better understand the field.

Permanent downhole monitoring of pressures in production and injection wells is becoming the norm.

Increasingly popular successive seismic surveys can sometimes reveal changes in the fluid and pressure distribution in reservoir that cannot directly be detected in wells. These are often called 4D seismic surveys, with the fourth dimension referring to the time dimension.

The incoming information is used regularly to update the models of the field. A good 'history matched' model of the field is one that is capable of reproducing all the historical production and pressure data. A model with a good 'history match' inspires enough confidence for its predictions to be relied on. Regularly, the underlying framework of the model, ie the understanding of the geology and internal reservoir architecture, has to be completely revised in order to explain the production performance.

12.4 Further development planning

The initial drilling campaign is typically designed to give sufficient production capacity to 'fill' the facilities, or to reach the plateau production. The locations for these wells are agreed upon and approved in the initial field development plan. Once production from the initial wells declines, additional wells are required to maintain the production levels.

The further development plans are reviewed and optimised on a regular basis, in order to maximise the operator's share of the remaining Net Present Value (NPV) of the field. When making further development decisions, the individual projects are not only screened against other activities in the field (see section 12.5 below), but also assessed against other viable projects in the corporate portfolio. Corporate objectives or constraints may override decisions on a field level (see section 12.7 below). In the case of multiple licence holders, there may be conflicts between companies who may have different commercial arrangements which lead to different optimal off-take scenarios, or different views on how to maximise the value of the field. The licence holders have regular operational, technical and commercial meetings, comparing notes and agreeing on further developments.

Given the different corporate portfolios of different operators, there may be very different views of the value in a particular licence. A large operator with a broad international portfolio, also in relatively low cost environments, may find it difficult to justify allocating capital and resources to ageing North Sea fields. Smaller and leaner operators may see significant opportunities in the same fields. This phenomenon drives the typical divestment and acquisition process whereby maturing fields change ownership, sometimes more than once.

When the facilities, in addition, are used as host to third-party fields, the ensuing commercial arrangements further complicate the reservoir management strategy. The DTI (or Norwegian Petroleum Directorate (NPD) in the Norwegian sector) maintains the interests of the public, with its stronger focus on maximising recovery rather than the owners' NPV. A 'fair-play policy' ensures that third party fields are given reasonable access to existing infrastructure.

12.5 Production optimisation

There are many ways to optimise and/or increase the production from a particular field. Often the techniques to be utilised rely on analysis of the routine reservoir and production monitoring data acquisition program (see section 12.3 above).

Initially, a field would typically produce dry oil and/or gas at the maximum design capacity. With the onset of decline, and in the case of a water flooded field, with the onset of water production, there is invariably room for optimisation. This may take the shape of improving the performance of the existing well stock, or the drilling of additional wells. On well slot constrained offshore facilities, old wells are often 're-used' by side-tracking them to more favourable locations.

As production from individual wells declines, the cause of the decline is investigated. It may be due to reservoir effects, or near wellbore effects, or problems with the well itself. Each of these will prescribe a different remedy.

Declining reservoir pressures, or increased water production, can be remedied by improving or altering the water injection process. This may require the drilling of alternate injection wells, the conversion of producers to injectors, or simply the isolation of water producing intervals in the producing well. The potential benefits of these actions are typically modelled in the dynamic field (simulation) model.

Near wellbore effects, or formation damage, is caused by a reduction of the inflow capacity of the well. This invariably happens in the life of a well, and it is monitored by regularly testing the well. When a significant decline in inflow performance is apparent, the causes are investigated. The inflow capacity may be remedied by a suitable stimulation technique. This may take the shape of pushing acid or a surfactant into the formation to clean out small rock particles that plug the pore throats near the well, or it may take the shape of fracturing the rock around the wellbore to bypass the damaged zone.

Sometimes the problem is within the well itself. With age, the tubulars may get worn out (eroded), or pumps and gas-lift equipment may require replacement. The production string may get constricted by the build-up of wax, paraffin or scale; the latter is typically the case with increasing production of injected water. Often the scale build-up can be removed or inhibited by the use of chemicals. Activities aimed at improving the performance of, or repairing, wells are typically called workovers.

With constrained lift gas capacity, gas lift optimisation becomes important. Lift gas is distributed to the producing wells with the maximum possible overall benefit. This would have to consider the total fluid production (oil and water) of each well and the opportunity cost of not using this gas elsewhere. Increases to the lift gas compression capacity late in field life are not uncommon. Alternatively, other lifting techniques, eg electrical submersible pumps, may be implemented in suitable candidate wells. This can require the expansion of the water handling facilities in the field.

Infill wells allow the targeting of undrained pockets of oil or gas in the reservoir. These are inferred from the dynamic field model, or sometimes indicated directly by 4D seismic. Secondary well targets may have been known from the onset of field development, but may have been put on hold while the limited number of wells drained more attractive targets. Changing economics may also allow new zones to be targeted which previously were deemed uneconomic.

Improved drilling techniques have been game changers in many fields. Longer and longer outsteps have allowed satellite structures to be drilled up which were unforeseen developments in the original plans. The advance of horizontal drilling techniques and/or the use of multilaterals have allowed previously marginal reservoirs to be produced at economic rates.

12.6 Enhanced recovery

Enhanced recovery, sometimes called tertiary recovery following on from natural depletion and secondary and/or water injection, is playing an increasing role globally, also in the North Sea. The objective of an enhanced recovery scheme is to improve the recovery factor over and above what is achievable by water and/or gas injection.

Many processes that are currently viable onshore, such as hot water, steam or polymer flooding, are not (yet) viable offshore due to facilities and well spacing constraints. However, as fields are reaching the ends of their lives, there is an increasing willingness to experiment with such processes.

The enhanced recovery process that has found most application in the North Sea is the miscible flood. In a miscible flood, a fluid, typically a rich gas, is injected into the reservoir at such high pressure that it physically mixes with the residual oil (ie perhaps after a water flood). Flooding agents comprise hydrocarbon and other gases, such as CO_2, which at the appropriate temperature and pressure are miscible with the oil, thus eliminating the surface tension between oil and gas and dramatically increasing the recovery factor. Typically, the injected fluid is selected in terms of the necessary physical/chemical requirements and the availability and cost of the fluid: the richer the gas the lower the pressure has to be.

In recent years, the injection of CO_2 has become increasingly attractive as an enhanced recovery technique, not least because of its beneficial environmental impact. Several large projects are in the study phase, both in Norway and in the UK. One disadvantage with CO_2 flooding is that CO_2 is a corrosive gas and may require a considerable investment in corrosion resistant wells and facilities.

Hybrid processes, such as simultaneous (SWAG) or alternating (WAG) injection of water and gas, sometimes above the miscibility pressure threshold, have already been implemented in a number of North Sea installations.

12.7 The role of reserves

In order to satisfy stakeholders, most companies are required to produce annual reserves reports. A company's reserves are nothing but an estimate of its share of the remaining economic production from its oil and gas fields, expressed in volume terms.

Reserves are classified according to the rules of various institutions. (See Chapter 5, legal section.) The most stringent rules are imposed by the Security and Exchange Commission for all companies that are listed in the US. For companies listed in the UK, the slightly less stringent guidelines agreed by the Society of Petroleum Engineers (SPE) and the World Petroleum Congress (WPC) in March 1997, and revised as recently as March 2007, are honoured. The Norwegian Petroleum Directorate (NPD) has its own system, based on the SPE/WPC classification, but more geared towards tracking resource maturity and the stage of development.

A key performance indicator for oil companies is their reserves replacement ratio, ie the degree to which their reserves base, which is being continuously depleted by production, is being maintained by maturing reserves, effectively implementing new field projects and developments and/or upgrading reserves in existing developments. This indicates how active or successful the company is in replenishing production. A related indicator is the ratio between proven reserves and annual production, effectively indicating how many years' worth of production the company still has in its reserves base.

Most companies will have their own in-house reserves classification system, allowing them to manage their project portfolio effectively whilst complying with the rules imposed by the regulating authorities. The resource and reserves classification system is typically limited to the project development framework outlined in Chapter 9.

In order to ensure that the reserves replacement ratio stays above unity, new projects are continuously entering the 'reserves pipeline', changing status from identified to planned, sanctioned, and finally implemented. Projects can be accelerated or slowed down depending on what other projects are in the corporate 'reserves pipeline'. Projects that are subject to this process can range from development of new fields, through infill drilling, to workovers and facilities improvement.

Key indicators, most importantly NPV, are used to rank projects throughout the corporate portfolio. Each project must therefore be well defined in terms of cost and yield. More often than not, a dynamic reservoir model will substantiate a project's yield, ie the incremental production profile.

Note

[1] A workover is a remedial action in an existing well, typically enhancing or restoring productivity.

RESERVOIR MANAGEMENT

LEGAL

12.8 Introduction

Once a field has reached the stage where it is producing (and perhaps continued exploration is in progress in the areas surrounding the field), the management of the rights to hydrocarbons can become a complex legal matter. This is specially the case where there are a large number of parties to a Joint Operating Agreement (JOA) and potentially it can be more complex where a reservoir straddles a number of blocks which are not in common ownership. This chapter considers the legal mechanisms which are used in the UKCS to deal with such matters and considers the JOA (which is usually the principal agreement regulating the rights and obligations of the parties under a licence). Consideration is then given to the often complex matter of reservoirs which straddle different licence blocks, why rights in respect of such structures might be unitised and the Unitisation and Unit Operating Agreement (UOA) which sets out the rights and obligations of parties in respect of structures which have been unitised ('unitised structures'). Ensuring that each party is legally able to exploit its rights under its licence where there are many parties holding rights to extract hydrocarbons from the same reservoir can be enormously time-consuming. It can prove to be a negotiating hurdle of some magnitude.

12.9 Reviewing the reservoir

There will be more knowledge about the reservoir and more data available to the reservoir team once exploration and appraisal wells have been drilled. Once this knowledge and data is available, the interest owners will be in a better position to understand the risks associated with development and production. At this stage the nature of some of the existing contractual documentation relating to the interest may have to be reconsidered to reflect the changes in reservoir modelling and assumptions of the Net Present Value (NPV) of petroleum in the field. Petroleum engineers, in conjunction with the other members of the multidisciplinary reservoir team, will be recalculating the reservoir flow patterns and determining the type of production facilities which may be needed to commission the field.

It may be that the parties have proceeded to this stage on the basis of a bidding agreement which does not cater for development and production or it may be the case (although it is very unusual) that a JOA was put in place at the time of exploration and appraisal but which does not deal with development and production issues. These documents may now need to be amended or replaced to deal with the development and production phase. Alternatively, and much more commonly, the JOA already in place may have provided for development and production issues from the time it was entered into. Later in this chapter we will have a quick look at the issues which a JOA will need to cover in the development and production phase.

Sometimes, reservoirs straddle international boundaries. In such a case treaties are in place between countries which aim to more effectively regulate those cross-boundary reservoirs and to deal with the fair sharing of petroleum between the relevant states. Such treaties exist between the UK and Norway and between the UK and the Netherlands. In February 2005, a new agreement was entered into by the Norwegian and UK Governments which set a framework for dealing with transboundary issues including such issues as pipelines, reservoirs and operations which traverse the boundary between the two countries. It also deals with certain health and safety issues.

12.10 JOA

A full analysis of the terms of a JOA has been given in Chapter 9 and readers should refer to that chapter for more detail of the issues involved in JOAs.

As mentioned above, in some cases the JOA agreed between the parties at the stage of exploration is not sufficient to deal with issues which are of relevance at the development stage. Usually the JOA agreed at the outset will be sufficient to cover development and production but in a few cases this is not the case and amendments are required to the original JOA as the field moves into the development and production phase. It may be that the parties bid jointly for licences with their relationship governed by a Joint Bidding Agreement. By the development and production state, any such Joint Bidding Agreement should be replaced with a fully termed JOA.

A JOA must cover certain key issues in connection with the development and exploration phase. It will require to contain provisions setting out offtake procedures for the physical lifting of hydrocarbons (although these could be dealt with separately in a lifting agreement), provisions which place obligations on the unit operator to provide statements of the amounts lifted and to make long and short-term forecasts of production.

The JOA would not normally deal with issues of transportation and processing. It would be up to each party to the JOA (or 'co-venturer') to enter into separate arrangements for transportation, processing, terminalling, etc. Such agreements would perhaps set out arrangements for the delivery of oil or gas from a delivery point near the platform facilities through pipelines to an onshore terminal. It is almost invariably the case that the co-venturers all enter the same transportation agreement, processing agreement, etc. rather than having separate agreements.

Until reasonably recently it was not normal practice to include detailed provisions in a JOA dealing with field abandonment. The JOA may simply have said that at some future point the parties would try to agree on provisions dealing with abandonment, or the JOA may have been completely silent on the issue. Nowadays, new JOAs usually contain detailed provisions dealing with field abandonment and the provision of security for decommissioning. People are very much aware of the joint and several liability under licences and the fact that even where a party ceases to be a licensee there is still the possibility of it being liable for the costs of decommissioning if the remaining licensees do not meet decommissioning costs at the time of decommissioning. The abandonment provisions in modern JOAs (and unit operating agreements (UOAs) (see below)) normally provide that the interest owners will be required to provide financial security for abandonment once a certain point in field life is reached. The JOA may state what forms of security will be acceptable and these may include an irrevocable standby letter of credit issued by a bank (or banks) which has a suitable credit rating. In some cases where the co-venturer has a financially robust holding company the JOA may provide that a parent company guarantee will suffice although parent company guarantees are generally viewed less favourably by the DTI and by counterparties.

There is clearly a cost in providing such security. For example, in the case of a company which is required to provide a letter of credit issued by its bank the bank will charge a utilisation fee for issuing the letter of credit. The existence of the letter of credit will also eat into the facilities available for drawdown by the company. One way of providing abandonment security which is becoming more popular is the use of a structure which utilises insurance. Very basically, rather than use its bank facility a company would pay a premium to an insurer for an insurance policy against the risk of it failing to pay its decommissioning costs, the insurer would then issue a guarantee to the company's bank and on the strength of the guarantee the bank would issue a letter of credit as security for the decommissioning obligations of the company. The cost to the company is less than the cost of utilising its bank facility for the issue of the letter of credit.

12.11 Default

If a party defaults in a payment due there are various ways that this can be dealt with in a JOA. The most regularly seen approach in JOAs (and UOAs) are provisions in terms of which if a party is in default:

(a) interest runs on the amount in default;
(b) the defaulting party ceases to have a right to take production during the period of default;
(c) the defaulting party loses the right to attend operating committee meetings and to vote during the default;
(d) if the default continues beyond a certain period then the other parties who are not in default can require that the interest of the party in default be forfeited to them (usually for no consideration); and
(e) even where there is forfeiture the defaulting party is still liable for the costs of abandonment where this occurs within a certain period of the forfeiture.

In JOAs covering development and production phases, it is possible (although highly unusual) that there will be less onerous default provisions in recognition of the fact that co-venturers have contributed substantial amounts of cash to get to that the point where the field is producing. 'Withered interest' provisions may be included whereby the defaulting party's percentage interest will 'wither' to a reduced percentage interest, based on a formula which is calculated based on the amount of cash defaulted and the period of the default.

In some JOAs, the default provisions may provide that after a period of time has expired without the default being remedied then the defaulting party is required to assign its interest to the remaining co-venturers for a payment, perhaps based on the written down value of the defaulter's share of assets under the JOA less the amount of the default and applicable interest. Another provision sometimes seen is a provision where the non-defaulters acquire the defaulter's interest in consideration of payment of the estimated net salvage value of the defaulter's interest in joint facilities (after taking into account decommissioning costs) less the total amount of default and interest. Due to the high cost of decommissioning, the use of such a mechanism could result in the defaulter being paid nothing.

There is always a risk that such clauses may be struck down as being penalties under English law. If such a default provision was successfully challenged then the clause may be unenforceable or equitable relief could be granted against the forfeiture.

By the time the field starts production (and hopefully well before then) the transportation arrangements required for the transport of hydrocarbons from the field to the shore must be in place. JOAs and UOAs do not deal with transportation in detail. They would normally provide no more than that the hydrocarbons will be made available for offtake by the interest owners.

12.12 Unitisation

As a result of drilling it may now be understood that the field or structure is not neatly located within one licence block but that it straddles more than one block. These blocks might be held by different parties. It may be necessary to negotiate and enter into a UOA with the holders of other blocks to allow the efficient exploitation of the reservoir. Under licence Model Clause 23 the Secretary of State has the power to give notice to the holders of licences which cover a common structure requiring them to work together on a unitary development of the field. A unitisation of a common structure can prevent wasteful drilling by parties in adjoining blocks into the same reservoir. It reduces the risk of practices such as those which became common in the United States in the early twentieth century where the holders of licences on neighbouring blocks would drill into the same common structure to extract oil from common reservoirs. This competition to get oil out of the common structure led to faster depletion of fields and at higher aggregate costs to the competing drillers.

Fields which have been unitised have a more complex legal structure than those which have not. There may be a JOA between licensees with an interest in a block which regulates the relationship between those parties in respect of that block. One usually finds that the original JOAs still exist in the background. This is important as the interest which a party has in a JOA is used to calculate the interest ('unit interest') which a party should have in a unitised structure.

Sometimes the unit structure does not occupy the whole of a block, and accordingly, a UOA may have been put in place to regulate the unit structure whilst the JOA remains in place to regulate that part of the block which is outwith the unit structure. (UOAs will be considered in some detail below.)

Often, at an early stage in the unitisation process, the parties interested in the respective blocks enter into an agreement in terms of which they agree to share data on the reservoir and to co-operate on a joint programme for appraisal, drilling and evaluation. Such an agreement is commonly called a 'Pre-Unitisation Agreement'. The Pre-Unitisation Agreement may give details of the interests which each party will initially hold in the unit structure.

12.13 Unitisation Agreement

As seen above a UOA may be entered into where a reservoir straddles two or more blocks. For example, a reservoir is found to straddle Block A and Block B. The parties holding Block A and the parties holding Block B may agree to jointly develop the common reservoir by unitising their interests to the extent that these relate to the common reservoir. This is a simple example with only two blocks involved but one can find examples where the reservoir is common to more than two blocks.

A UOA will include provisions analogous to those contained in a JOA (see Chapter 9 for full details).

The UOA will provide that all rights and interests of the parties in respect of the blocks in which the unit structure are located are unitised in accordance with the UOA insofar as those rights and interests relate to the common structure (the 'unit structure') and the petroleum in that structure ('unitised substances').

The UOA will provide that its purpose is the joint development and operation of the unit structure and the production, sharing and transportation of unitised substances. The UOA will normally provide that the UOA will prevail over any JOA relating to a block to the extent affecting the unit structure.

The agreement will then state the respective interests of the parties (their 'unit interests') . It is often difficult to establish what percentage interest the parties in each block should have in the unit structure on a unitisation. This is due to the fact that it is highly probable that at the stage of carrying out the unitisation there is no accurate information as to the quantity of hydrocarbons in the structure and exactly how much of these are in each block. As a result the parties initially set the interest of each block (or 'tract') based on the information then available to them. This is based on their estimate of STOOIP (stock tank oil originally in place). These 'tract participations' represent an estimate of the percentage of hydrocarbons in the reservoir on each separate block.

For example, say that there is a simple structure which straddles two blocks, Block A and Block B. Initial information suggests that 70% of the hydrocarbons are located in Block A and 30% are located in Block B. The tract participations would therefore initially be:

Block A	70%
Block B	30%.

Based on these tract participations it is then possible to calculate the initial unit interest of each party.

For example: The licensees with an interest in Block A are X Ltd and Y Ltd which each hold 50% under the JOA for Block A. The unit interests of each of X Ltd and Y Ltd would be 35%.

This is simply their participating interest in Block A (50%) multiplied by the tract participation of Block A (70%).

The UOA will usually (but not always) contain provisions for redetermination of the tract participations once further information becomes available in respect of the reservoir. Sometimes where the life of a field is expected to be short or where STOOIP can be estimated with a reasonable degree of accuracy at an early stage the UOA might not provide for redeterminations of tract participations and the unit interests would be fixed from the time of the UOA.

Following drilling there may be more knowledge of the STOOIP and of the proportion of hydrocarbons which lies in each block. The UOA can provide for a number of redeterminations of tract participations over a period of time as different stages in development of the field are reached. The UOA will provide that after a certain point the tract participations will be fixed and that there can be no further unit redeterminations. Whilst redeterminations are basically estimates, the final redetermination is final and binding on the holders of unit interests ('unit interest owners').

For example, the UOA may provide for three tract redeterminations over the life of the field. The first redetermination might occur shortly after the drilling of the development well, the second after further wells have been drilled and completed and the final redetermination when at least half the original oil and gas has been produced.

One of the jobs of the reservoir engineers is to negotiate these redeterminations. If there are to be redeterminations the process and 'rules' to be adopted in carrying out redeterminations are usually set out at length in the UOA. There will usually be a provision for an independent third party to provide an expert opinion or alternatively for arbitration in the case of disagreement over the redetermination. Disputes over redeterminations are not uncommon and there have been numerous examples where third party expert determinations have been required, with the expert's opinion normally being regarded as final and binding. The determinations themselves can run to thousands of pages.

Redeterminations have important commercial and legal consequences. Not only will the unit interests of the co-venturers change by reference to the new tract participations which result from the redetermination but also the UOA will usually provide that there will be adjustments between the unit interest owners to put the unit interest owners into the position they would have been in had the new unit interests always applied.

One of the effects of a redetermination is a retrospective change to entitlements to hydrocarbons produced from the reservoir.

Using our example above, assume that there is a tract redetermination. As a result of additional data now available it is determined that the relevant tract participations should be Block A: 60% and Block B: 40% rather than the 70/30 split originally provided for in the UOA. As seen previously, the unit interest of each of X Ltd and Y Ltd was initially 35%. Now their unit interests will each be 30% (ie 50% x 60%). X Ltd and Y Ltd have each lifted 35% of the production from the unit since it started to produce. As a result of the redetermination X Ltd and Y Ltd should each have lifted only 30% of production. X Ltd and Y Ltd have, therefore, both overlifted from the unit structure. The owners of Block B will have underlifted.

These underlift and overlift positions need to be addressed. The UOA will usually provide that following a redetermination the operator of the unit ('the unit operator') will provide the unit interest owners with a statement as to how much they have overlifted or underlifted. The UOA will provide for the phased redress of the lifting imbalance over a period of time, perhaps by giving unit interests owners which have underlifted a right to lift more than their unit interest share of hydrocarbons until such time as the imbalance has been addressed. There may also be provisions which deal with what is to happen if the lifting imbalance has not been dealt with by the time production from the reservoir ceases.

As well as adjustments to reflect overlift and underlift positions there will also have to be balancing payments between unit interest owners so that following the redetermination they have paid the correct amount of cash in respect of unit expenditure. In our example above, X Ltd and Y Ltd will have paid more unit expenditure than their new unit interests would require them to pay. They have each paid 35% of capital and operating expenditure. They should each have paid only 30%. The parties with an interest in Block B will have underpaid. The UOA will usually provide that the owners of Block B will require to make payments to address their underpayment position.

The UOA will contain provisions as regards lifting of unit substances. As with JOAs, the UOA will provide that unit interest owners in each block or tract will have the right to recover all of the produced and saved unitised substances which are allocated to it. All hydrocarbons produced and saved are allocated to the respective groups by the unit operator. Each unit interest owner has the right and obligation to take delivery of its entitlement to hydrocarbons produced and saved from the reservoir and is obliged to separately dispose of it. The unit operator is usually obliged to transport hydrocarbons through the unit infrastructure to the tie-in point to the export route.

As with a JOA, the UOA will provide that the unit operator has to notify the owners of the proposed annual production programme and proposed forward production programme. Such production programmes require to be approved by the Unit Operating Committee. There are also obligations on the unit operator to provide production reports, and information on the allocation of quantities of hydrocarbons.

A UOA, like a JOA, provides for an operating committee ('Unit Operating Committee'). The function of the Unit Operating Committee is basically the same as the function of the Joint Operating Committee under a JOA (see Chapter 9).

Each unit interest owner has a right to appoint a representative to the Unit Operating Committee. Usually each unit interest owner has a voting interest equal to its unit interest. As with a JOA the UOA will contain a voting mechanism for decisions of the Unit Operating Committee and a passmark will be set for routine decisions of the Unit Operating Committee. There may also be circumstances in which unanimity is required. For routine matters, the voting passmark to carry resolutions of the Unit Operating Committee might, for example, be two parties (with at least one from each block) having a combined interest of at least 75%.

As with a JOA, the UOA will identify the initial unit operator and will indicate the circumstances in which the unit operator can resign or be removed. Removal can normally take place on the vote of parties holding a certain aggregate percentage voting interest (for example, 85% excluding the operator and its affiliates) or immediately in the case of certain default or insolvency scenarios. The approval of the Unit Operating Committee and of the Secretary of State is required before any successor operator can be appointed.

The remainder of the UOA is largely like the terms of a JOA (see Chapter 9). For example, there will be clauses dealing with the authority and duties of the unit operator, the provision of information to unit interest owners, the process to be followed when contracting for goods and services, the status of the unit operator in contracting with third parties (ie that it acts as agent for the unit interest owners), rights of audit of the unit account, access to information such as all logs, well surveys, reports to any governmental authority and other reports relating to unit operations, cash call procedures, rights to use unit equipment in cases where it is not being used for unit operations, abandonment security provisions and financial capability issues in respect of proposed transfers of interest, etc.

As with a JOA, the UOA may contain sole risk provisions. These may provide that if it is proposed that a well is drilled as a unit operation but is not approved by the Unit Operating Committee as a unit operation then any unit interest owner has the right to have the well drilled at its sole risk and expense. The UOA may provide that the data obtained in drilling the sole risk well will be available to all the unit interest owners notwithstanding that they are not involved in the Sole Risk drilling. It may also provide that on drilling the sole risk well the Unit Operating Committee would decide whether a well should be completed as a production well. If the Unit Operating Committee votes for the well to be completed as a production well, then the well will be dealt with from that point forward as a unit well. If the Sole Risk well is to be plugged and abandoned then this is normally done at the cost of the unit interest owner carrying out the sole risk in accordance with the requirements of the Unit Operating Committee.

The provisions dealing with cost and accounting are much the same as the JOA with cash calls being made on unit interest owners in accordance with their unit interests. Default provisions in UOAs normally vary slightly from those in JOAs. In a UOA it is common to see default provisions in terms of which if a unit interest owner defaults in making a payment then rather than all other parties being required to contribute additional funds to cover the amount not paid by the defaulting party, the unit interest owners with an interest in the same block (the same tract) as the defaulting party are normally required to pay the amount in default. If they fail to do so then they too would be in default and the unit interest owners with an interest in the other block (tract) would require to pay the amount in default.

Another major difference between JOAs and UOAs can be seen in pre-emption provisions. If there are pre-emption provisions in a UOA they commonly provide that the interest which it is intended will be transferred is to be offered to the unit interest owners in the same tract as the proposing transferor. If the unit interest owners in that tract do not buy the interest then the interest is to be offered to unit interest owners in the other tract.

It may be that there is a much better understanding of the extent of the reservoir after several programmes of drilling. It may be necessary for an extension of the unit area into other parts of the blocks held by unit interest owners and there will be provisions in the UOA to deal with this. Should the reservoir extend into blocks which are licensed to other parties but which do not form part of the area covered by the UOA, then there may need to be a re-unitisation of the field to bring in the new participants and there would have to be re-negotiation of the UOA.

12.14 Submarine pipelines

The rules relating to authorisations for the construction and use of pipelines are set out in sections 15, 16 and 17 of the Petroleum Act 1998. A consent or authorisation is required from the Secretary of State for any construction or modification of a pipeline within UK territorial waters. The Secretary of State can order a notice of compulsory alteration of any pipeline or can order a modification to the pipeline. There are now in place measures to make the system of pipeline works authorisations more transparent and to reduce the regulation surrounding them. Guidelines have been issued by the DTI for completion of pipeline works authorisations. As is referred to in the previous chapter, the Secretary of State can require the pipeline to be transferred and to vest in it on termination of the authorisation.

12.15 Other Operating Agreements

As part of the process of taking a field onstream the co-venturers may have commissioned the building of pipelines, other delivery systems, an FPSO or even a terminal. Whilst the operation, development, production and management of the field may be regulated by the JOA or UOA, there may be separate operating arrangements in respect of such other facilities where these are to be used other than for joint operations. For example, if the parties have constructed a pipeline through which they wish to transport third party production then they may well enter into a Pipeline Operating Agreement. Perhaps the co-venturers have built an onshore terminal. The operation of that terminal will be regulated amongst the co-venturers via a Terminal Operating Agreement. Separate agreements will be put in place with non-owners in respect of the use of the system (eg Transportation and Processing Agreements).

The principles involved in such operating agreements will largely follow those in a JOA. The particular business function is run as an unincorporated joint venture. Some provisions similar to those which are found in JOAs or UOAs can be found in Pipeline Operating And Terminal Operating Agreements (eg percentage interests, operator, operating committee (usually termed a 'Management Committee' in such agreements)). Such agreements would also deal with things such as the use of capacity in the system, what is to happen in the case of restricted capacity in the system, ancillary provisions dealing with shrinkage of quantities of petroleum, suballocation, substitution and offtake regimes, admission of new users of the facilities, default provisions, etc.

Normally, in the case of a pipeline joint venture, each co-venturer will have the right to capacity in the pipeline up to its ownership interest share of available capacity. If participants want to use more than their ownership interests, they may have to pay for that entitlement. If they use less, then they can often grant others the right to utilise that capacity in exchange for a tariff payment. There may be plenty of spare capacity in the system which can be exploited by agreeing to transport third party production.

In extractive industries the costs involved in getting a valuable resource from its environment can be, and often is, prohibitively expensive. It is relatively unusual for one party on its own to be willing to commit the resource and to take the associated risk involved in underwriting an entire exploration to production programme. Clearly, being in a situation where all decisions can be taken alone without having to get involved in debates seems like an ideal situation. Such a situation, however, comes at the cost of having to carry *all* the risk and expense.

In many developments, there is more than one party involved and parties carry out joint projects which allow them to spread the risk. In such joint projects a substantial amount of effort can be required to document a system of rights and obligations acceptable to the co-venturers.

In this chapter JOAs, UOAs and other Operating Agreements which regulate the exploitation of assets in situations where there is more than one party to the project have been considered. These are essential tools which aim to balance the interests of co-venturers in such developments.

— 13 —

SUBSEA FACILITIES AND OPERATIONS

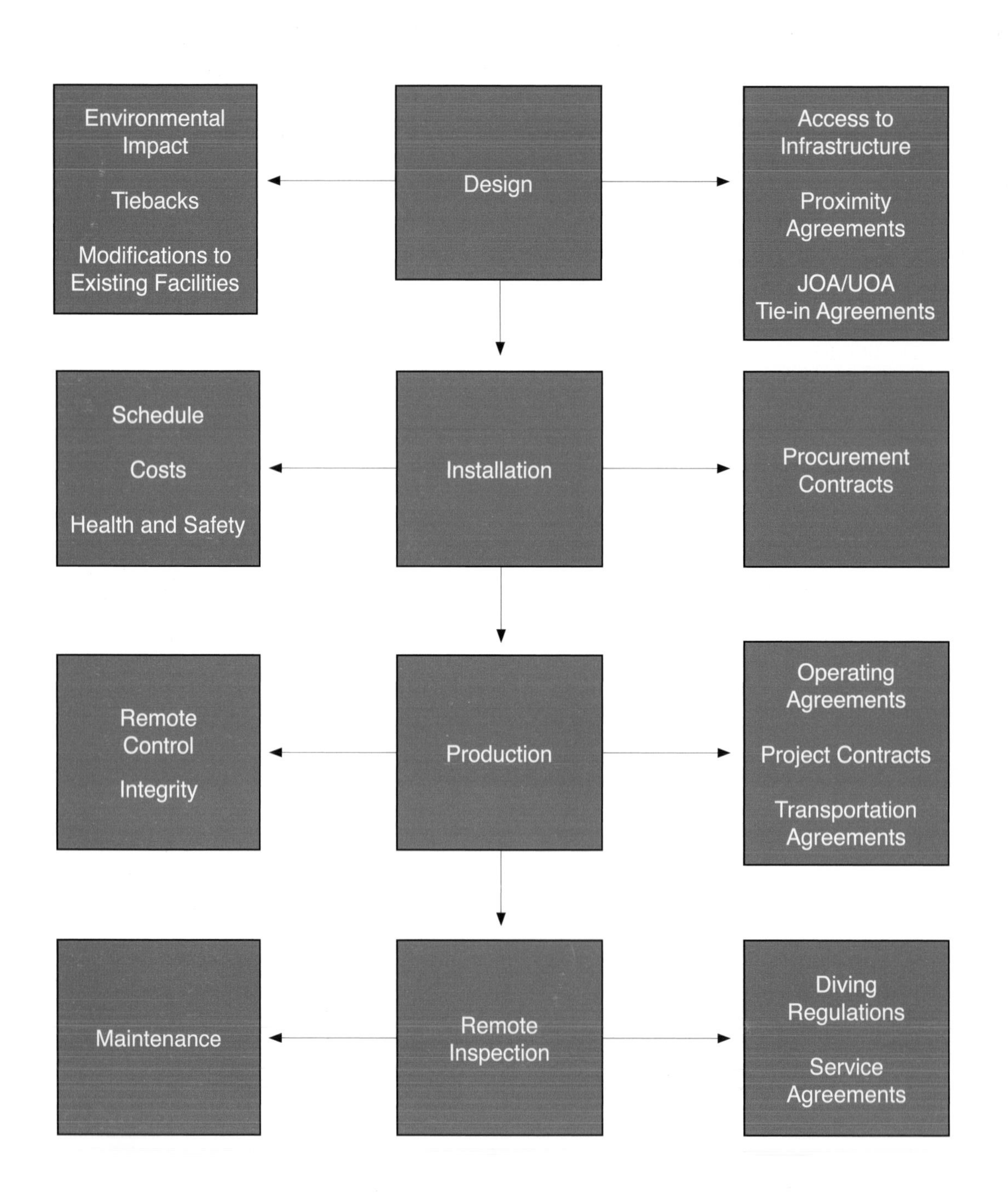
Environmental Impact
Tiebacks
Modifications to Existing Facilities
Design
Access to Infrastructure
Proximity Agreements
JOA/UOA
Tie-in Agreements
Schedule
Costs
Health and Safety
Installation
Procurement Contracts
Remote Control
Integrity
Production
Operating Agreements
Project Contracts
Transportation Agreements
Maintenance
Remote Inspection
Diving Regulations
Service Agreements

SUBSEA FACILITIES AND OPERATIONS

TECHNICAL

13.1 Introduction

After 25 years of production, the UK North Sea has yielded approximately 50% of its recoverable reserves. Like any other major oil-producing area, the remaining reserves will offer more challenges and will be more difficult to produce. Most of these reserves will be in smaller fields or in less accessible areas. The cost per barrel is unlikely to justify the installation of a fixed platform but oil and gas from these fields will be produced from a subsea wellhead either to an existing nearby platform or floating production facility. This may be moved from field to field to exploit these smaller reserves.

Subsea technology will therefore play an increasing role in extracting the remaining recoverable reserves from the UKCS and the continuing innovation in design and technology will continue to place the UK subsea sector in a lead role internationally for similar areas in the future.

Existing subsea production facilities and diving techniques for installation and repair are continuing to advance as operators are developing new and existing finds in deeper and more remote locations. The UK will most certainly be dependent on this new and emerging technology to continue to sustain the future of the UKCS.

13.2 UK offshore subsea development activities

Subsea engineering has become a widely accepted term which refers to the multidisciplinary activity covering the design, installation and operation of equipment and systems situated in the vicinity of the seabed for the purpose of hydrocarbon production. An underwater wellhead is installed on a well, drilled into a remote reservoir. The hydrocarbons coming out of that well, or wells, are then transported in pipelines back to a nearby fixed or floating facility, or to the shore, for processing. These pipelines are part of an extensive network of oil pipelines that also connect individual fields and transfer oil and gas to the mainland.

The UK has major pipeline links to Europe and there are also pipelines connecting Scotland to Northern Ireland and the Republic of Ireland.

Subsea wells were proposed as early as 1958 and in 1961 Shell announced the first subsea well completion in the Gulf of Mexico. The North Sea's first subsea completion was installed in the Norwegian sector, on Phillips' Ekofisk field as a tie-back to a jack-up drilling rig.

It is also interesting to note that the first UK oil field to go into production was based on early subsea technology. Hamilton Brothers' Argyll field was developed with subsea wells producing to a converted semi-submersible drilling rig and exported to shuttle tankers via a loading buoy.

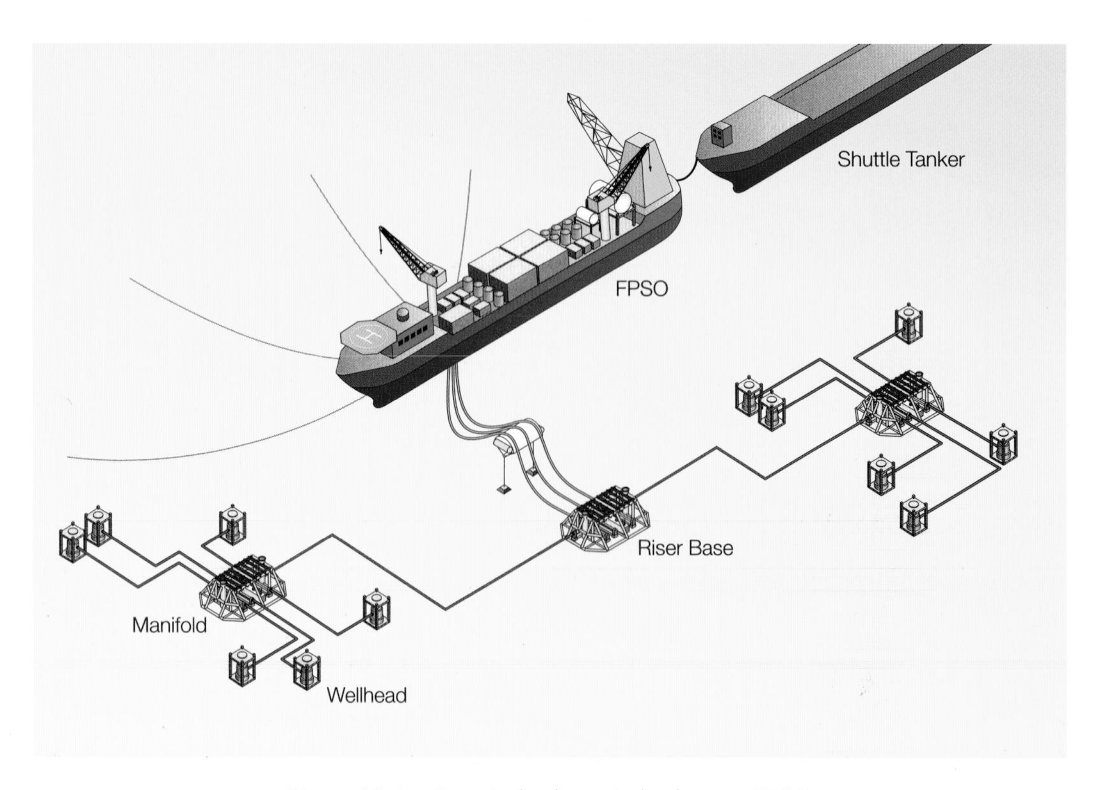

Figure 13–1 A typical subsea tie-back to an FPSO

Most North Sea developments for the next 20 years were based on the fixed platform concept, with large reservoirs being produced from directionally drilled wells from the host platform.

As exploration success in finding larger fields has declined, the trend is now towards smaller fields being developed with subsea wellheads tied back to host platforms for processing. This has allowed the subsea market within the UK offshore oil and gas industry to enjoy steady growth whilst taking up spare capacity in the substantial offshore infrastructure, and this is forecasted to continue.

The business has reached the point where it has the ability to install subsea completions in water depths in excess of 10,000 ft, extended developments to lateral spreads beyond 50 km, tie-back distances of over 100 km and well counts of over 70.

Once the basic development scheme has been agreed and the government given the go-ahead, the operator will often start awarding contracts for companies to execute the development project. The principal contracts concern the drilling of the wells, the design and fabrication of the host facility, the installation or modification of the host facility and the design, fabrication and installation of the subsea systems. The operator may elect to carry out some aspects of the work themselves, or contract direct with the companies to carry out specialist work. The decision on the break of the scope of work often depends on the time and resources that are available.

All oil and gas prospects go through a similar process, commencing with identification of the potential reservoir by interpreting seismic data, the acquisition of rights and permits from existing owners or the government; exploration drilling to ascertain if hydrocarbons actually exist in commercial quantities in the structure and then development engineering, construction and finally production. The scope for a subsea and pipeline contract usually runs from the wellhead to the tie-in flange on the host facility and can be awarded as a single contract.

13.3 Subsea production facilities

Since the early North Sea subsea installations in the early 1970s much has been learned to improve the design installation, and operation of subsea facilities to optimise capital and operating costs and decrease the need for subsea intervention. This is applicable to all subsea elements from the wellhead to the subsea connection of the host processing facility. Figure 13–1 shows a typical subsea arrangement for such production facilities and each component is described in more detail below.

Subsea satellite wells

A subsea satellite well consists of a subsea well and guide base or flow base, supporting a subsea tree, with individually connected flow lines and control umbilical.

Each system is installed individually and has its own independent foundations. Satellite wells can either be completed as a tree on a 'dumb' guide base (ie where the flow line is connected directly to the tree, and the guide base can be a simple drilling guide base); or as a tree on flow base (ie, as the tree lands and locks to the wellhead, flow loops from the tree production, and possibly annulus valve blocks, link into receptacles on the flow base). Flow lines and umbilicals are made up to the flow base, and the flow line does not need to be disturbed if the tree is removed.

Figure 13–2 Subsea wellhead installation

Daisy-chain

Daisy-chain subsea wells consist of two or more subsea satellite wells joined together by a common flow line (and possibly control umbilical). Valves on the flow bases of the daisy-chained wells allow co-mingling of the flow streams. Using daisy-chained wells allows combined use of infield flow lines by more than one well. As more subsea wells are needed, the attraction of daisy chains disappears as a manifold becomes more feasible.

Templates

Subsea template field layouts involve a structural frame that supports and protects a number of subsea wells together on the seabed. In areas of high fishing intensity, the template structure is ideal for deflecting trawl boards and dragged lines away from sensitive wellhead equipment. A key advantage of templates is that the subsea tree connects directly to the flow line and template pipework as it lands and locks onto the wellhead this effectively eliminates flowline connections needed between a subsea tree and cluster-style manifold.

Clusters

Clusters are single satellite wells arranged, at distances between 150 ft and 2–3 km, around a manifold assembly that collects, commingles and exports flow to the surface gathering facility. Cluster-style developments were originally

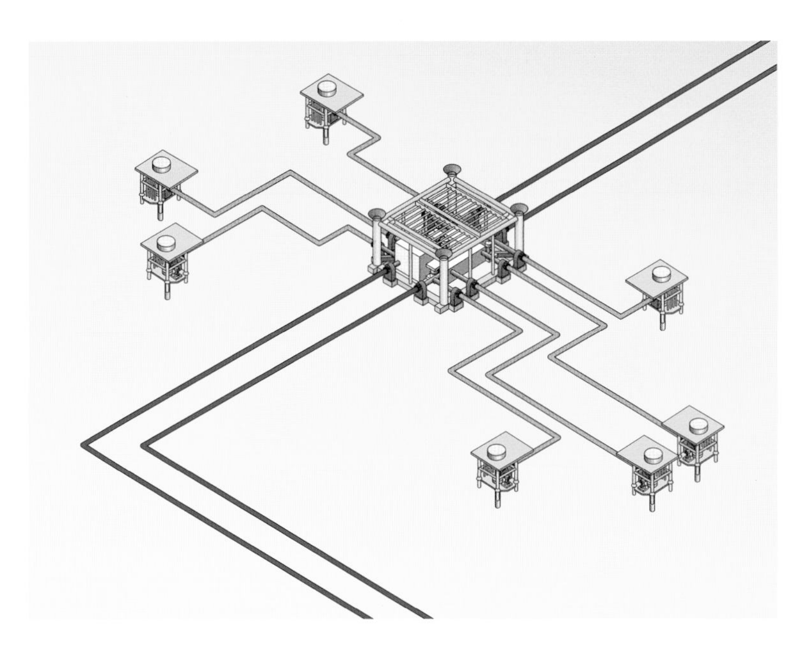

Figure 13–3 Cluster well and manifold

developed to counter-act the potential for damage from objects dropped at surface, which was increased if the wells were located close together within a template (Fig. 13–3).

Manifold foundations can be piles, gravity or skirts, depending on seabed conditions. The manifold structure also provides accommodation and protection from fishing gear interaction and dropped objects for the control system and other production equipment such as meters. The most recent deepwater manifold systems have included retrievable manifolds with remote diverless connections of intra-field flow lines, umbilicals and pipelines.

Control systems

In early subsea systems, equipment was operated by sending either a pulse of fluid or a flow of fluid to move a control mechanism. Such direct hydraulic systems are, however, limited by distance and, beyond about 5 km, problems arise from the dissipation of the fluid volume through expanding the umbilical hose to the point where the distant actuator does not register any signal. Further, the time taken for the signal to get to the actuator may be too long for the required operation. Over the years direct hydraulic control has been replaced by the multiplexed electro-hydraulic control systems in common use today. All-electric systems are now being developed for the next generation of control systems.

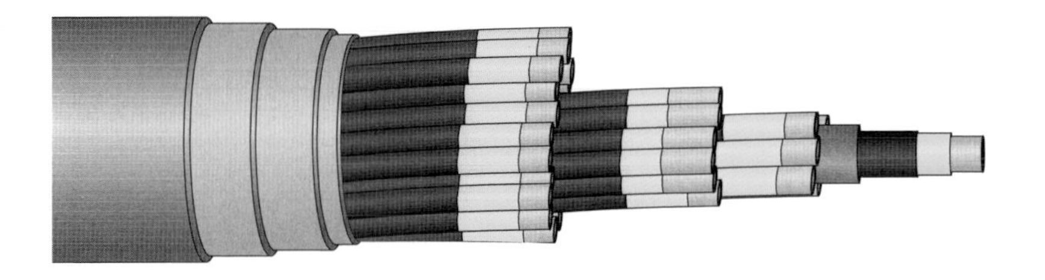

Figure 13–4 Armoured electro-hydraulic umbilical

Umbilicals

Umbilicals connect subsea equipment to their master control system on the host facility. Generally they consist of a set of helically wound tubes and cables (Fig. 13–4).

The tubes are used to transport hydraulic fluid for activating equipment such as valves and chemicals for dosing the production fluids, and can be made of either thermoplastic or steel.

The steel tubes are more resilient to the fluid and do not expand.

Risers

Risers carry the hydrocarbon flow from the seabed system to the surface facility and are similar in construction to pipelines. They have a number of alternative configurations depending on water depth and whether the host facility is fixed or floating. Fixed steel risers are a permanent structure attached to a platform. Where multiple lines are being brought onto the platform they can also be bundled, within a riser caisson.

For floating facilities and in deeper water the risers are suspended from the facility. They often hang as a catenary, in a long natural curve between the surface and seabed supported either by distributed buoyancy along their length or by a tethered mid-depth buoyancy 'arch' (Fig. 13–5). Catenary risers can be either rigid pipe or flexible construction.

13.4 Diving activities

The oil and gas industry is one of the largest employers of divers in UK waters and in most other parts of the world. Few of the marine contractors maintain a permanent diving workforce, so diving is usually subcontracted and appropriately qualified and experienced divers move from project to project.

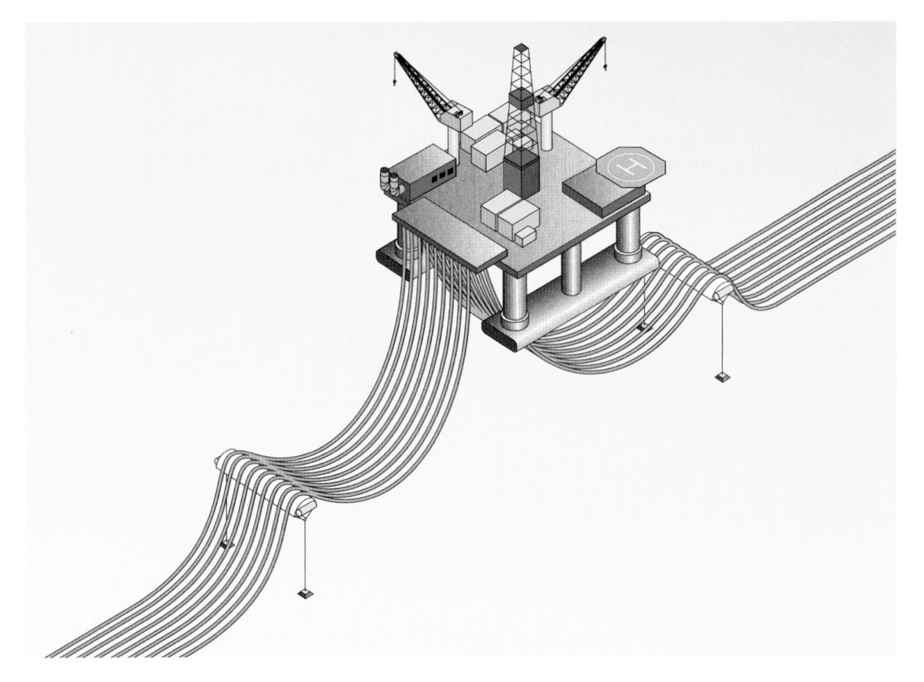

Figure 13–5 Catenary riser system

Offshore and deep diving commonly uses ‘exotic’ mixes of gas including helium-oxygen to overcome the narcotic effect of nitrogen under pressure. Commercial deployment of divers and day-to-day living is often done off diving support vessels (DSVs) using diving bells and compression chambers. Sophisticated suits with diver body and gas warming allow dives to depths exceeding 1000 ft. However, the divers usually work to depths of 150 or 300 ft, because approaching 600-plus ft the robot has the lower risk and better commercial return.

Many subsea construction tasks in the UK sector of the North Sea are still performed by divers, for the economic reasons mentioned above. A major characteristic of subsea developments in the North Sea is that infrastructure is installed on the continental shelf in water depths in excess of 150 ft where saturation diving techniques are used.

Saturation diving is a technique which allows divers to operate at these and greater depths for extended periods, as opposed to ‘bounce’ diving which involves frequent decompression. The term ‘saturation’ refers to the fact that, under these conditions, the diver’s body tissues have reached the maximum partial pressure of gas possible for that depth due to the diver being exposed to breathing gas at that pressure for prolonged periods. The significance of this is that once the tissues become saturated, the time to ascend from depth, to decompress safely, will not increase with further exposure.

The net result of this is that if divers are kept at seabed pressure, they can work for weeks at a time without the need for regular time-consuming and potentially risky staged recompression. During the period 'in-saturation', divers live and work at pressure, either on the seabed or in between shifts in a compression chamber on board a DSV or offshore platform. The diver's journey from the chamber to the work-site is made in a diving bell. The bell is mated to the chamber to allow safe, pressurised transfer of the diver to the bell before being lowered to the seabed and vice versa.

The work performed by divers in the field of subsea construction and intervention is rich and varied. From mating and bolting flanged joints between pipelines and wellheads, to actuating valves, many manual tasks are performed by or with the assistance of divers. Indeed, the contribution made by divers to the development of North Sea oil and gas cannot be overestimated.

As the industry has moved into developing fields in deeper waters, where diving is not feasible or simply not economic, the development of remote, diverless technologies has accelerated. It is now common practice to install complete subsea fields without the use of divers. Indeed, in the Norwegian sector of the North Sea, in similar water depths to the UK sector, the use of divers is prohibited and all work is carried out with remote technology. Despite these factors and an ageing diver workforce, the role of the diver in the North Sea is anticipated to be significant in the years to come.

13.5 Subsea intervention

Subsea technology has developed to such an extent that many of the tasks once carried out by the diver can be undertaken by an underwater robot either controlled from surface as a Remotely Operated Vehicle (ROV) or operating independently (Autonomous Underwater Vehicle (AUV)). The tasks for which ROVs hold the advantage are mostly inspections (particularly in areas difficult to access), followed by tasks connected to assembly of infrastructures and the recovery of objects. The use of ROVs is considered advantageous, even for some tasks that could be done by divers, because of the safety and economic advantages. ROVs obviously gain an advantage in cases where the project is engineered to be carried out by remote intervention.

Atmospheric Diving Suits (ADS)

An Atmospheric Diving Suit (ADS) encloses a man in normal, one-atmosphere pressure while allowing him to operate underwater. This also eliminates compression and decompression schedules and hyperbaric-induced health effects. Depth limits also extend beyond human physiological limits, but suit joints restrict the ADS to shallower depths than a Remote Operated Vehicle (ROV).

Like an ROV, an ADS is on a tether to provide launch and recovery, communications and power. Thrusters, powered through the tether, allow the otherwise too-heavy-to-swim system mid-water operational capability.

Remotely Operated Vehicles (ROVs)

An ROV is an underwater robot that allows the vehicle's operator to remain in a comfortable environment while the ROV performs the work underwater. ROVs come in all shapes and sizes. However, they all serve a single purpose – to provide a mobile platform that can transport the necessary tools to a subsea work-site. All ROVs employ the same basic building blocks, namely a buoyancy package, thruster package, onboard hydraulic or electrical power unit, control and telemetry system, vehicle lighting, and a video camera.

Figure 13–6 Work class ROV

Although the size, shape, and complexity of ROV systems may vary greatly, with these basic building blocks in place, any ROV can travel to a submerged work-site, manoeuvre within the water column, and deliver live video to a remote operator. An umbilical, or tether, carries power and command and control signals to the vehicle and the status and sensory data back to the operator. In larger systems, a subsea garage and Tether Management System (TMS) is often included (Fig. 13–6).

ROVs can vary in size from small vehicles fitted with one TV camera that are used for simple observation), up to complex work systems that can have several dexterous manipulators, video cameras, mechanical tools and other equipment. They are generally free flying, but some are bottom-founded on tracks.

The difference between a low-cost inspection ROV (often called a flying eyeball) and a large powerful work-class vehicle lies in the ability of the larger vehicle to support manipulator arms, special tool packages, and other peripheral equipment that enables the vehicle to do more than just have a look around. However, without the integration of manipulator arms and special tooling, there is little difference between the work class vehicle and the low-cost inspection vehicle.

Many small or 'flying eyeball' ROVs, some as small as a breadbox, are in use today. These vehicles are used primarily for inspection and observation tasks.

Work-class ROVs are electro-hydraulic vehicles ranging from 50 to 100 horsepower. Most carry a seven-function rate manipulator and a five-function grabber. These vehicles comprise the most widely used ROV class, which evolved from the early 'eyeball' systems that were used to observe divers working or to perform routine inspections. Typical tasks for this class are drilling support (where most are deployed), light construction support, pipeline inspection and general 'call out' work.

Heavy work-class vehicles are used for current deepwater operations to 10,000 ft and ranging from 100 to 250 horsepower. With new requirements to perform subsea tie-in operations on deepwater installations and to carry very large diverless intervention systems, this class of ROV is becoming increasingly large, powerful and capable of carrying and lifting large loads. These vehicles can weigh more than 10,000 lb and resemble a minivan in size. Units capable of operating in 10,000 ft depth are now commonplace, with at least one system capable of 20,000 ft. Cameras, lights, sonars and other sensors necessary to operate at great depths are readily available. Manipulators capable of lifting hundreds of pounds are commonly installed on these vehicles.

Autonomous Underwater Vehicles (AUVs)

For some specific applications, the limits of ROVs have now been reached and further advancement requires the employment of the embryonic technology

Figure 13–7 Autonomous Underwater Vehicle (© Bluefin Robotics Corporation)

of AUVs. An autonomous underwater vehicle (or AUV) is a self-propelled, unmanned underwater vehicle controlled by an onboard computer (Fig. 13–7). Freed of the constraints of an umbilical cable, AUVs are true robots designed to carry out specific pre-programmed tasks such as seabed survey without any communication with the surface.

Over the last decade, more than 40 different AUVs have been designed and many have been demonstrated. Yet, the technology has not fully matured. AUVs are now being ordered by commercial vehicle operators for deepwater seabed survey work.

AUVs are coming of age for maintenance, inspection and repair (IMR). They will ultimately be capable of working at full ocean depth for extended periods without resurfacing except for periodic maintenance. The snag is that their infrastructure is expensive to install and even more expensive to retrofit to existing fields. But once in place, the cost savings from these vehicles will be tremendous.

13.6 Hyperbaric welding

When building pressure-containing systems such as pipelines and subsea systems, a crucial part of the construction process is the ability to perform high-quality welded joints. In many instances of pipeline and subsea construction, onshore and offshore, welding is performed in a relatively controlled environment, for instance on the pipeline right-of-way or on the deck of a lay barge. There are, however, instances when the need arises to perform high-quality, high-strength welds subsea. This could be to join two separately laid pipelines together or perform a repair on a pipeline or structure.

So-called 'wet-welding' using water-proofed electrodes has been used in the past to facilitate underwater repairs of structures, but the welds produced are of low quality and low strength. There are also the inherent safety issues of using open-circuit voltages in water.

To meet the needs of the developing North Sea oil industry in the early 1970s, the technique of 'hyperbaric' or 'dry environment' welding was developed. Hyperbaric welding involves the use of an underwater, dry, pressurised 'habitat' in which diver-welders perform a weld in a carefully controlled environment. Since the early 1970s, hyperbaric welding has developed further and has been used many times to perform pipeline tie-in welds and hot-taps – a technique where branches are welded onto a pipeline system whilst it is in operation.

Performing welding at depth presents many challenges and the behaviour of gases and welding consumables and equipment is affected by the higher ambient pressure, just like the divers who are performing the work. Despite the challenges, being able to perform a high-quality weld to complete the construction of a large diameter, high-pressure pipeline can represent a much better option than using a diver-assembled flanged joint.

13.7 New and emerging technologies

Recently, hydrocarbon discoveries have been made in deep water and the necessary equipment for oil and gas production can only economically be installed directly on the seabed. Future developments will see processing or pumping equipment placed on the seabed close to the wellheads to assist the extraction of the hydrocarbons. Several development projects have taken place over the past decades, and now the first commercial installations have been put in place.

Subsea boosting

Boosting the pressure of fluids flowing from subsea wells has become a high priority. If fluids can be pumped at seabed level, additional production can be gained from ageing wells with declining pressure and new satellite wells can be located further away from the host, extending the reach to capture additional reserves within acceptable development economics.

Subsea separation

In mature fields with increasing water production, such production to the surface facility must be choked back, or the liquid handling capacity of the facility increased. Removing water from the wellstream at the seabed reduces the total flow to be lifted to the surface. This dramatically reduces the static head of the fluids in the riser, which facilitates higher production rates.

Subsea processing

Installing processing on the seabed offers significant cost-saving possibilities; individual fluids can be routed to different facilities where optimum topsides handling capacity exists, making it possible, for example, to maximise oil production without being constrained by gas coming from the same well. Separating oil, gas and water streams and boosting their pressure subsea would also enable gas and water reinjection at the wellhead without first transporting the products to the host platform.

Separation, reinjection of produced water and transportation of gas and oil over long distances requires heavy duty equipment such as water injection pumps, oil pumps, multiphase pumps, wet gas compressors and rotating separators being installed subsea. The systems need to be capable of being operated reliably and safely, with minimal intervention over periods of up to 20 years, which requires high levels of reliability and robustness.

ROVs and AUVs

The offshore oil and gas industry is relying on ROV and AUV technology to extend its reach to ever-greater depths where diving is too dangerous or costly. ROVs reach the deepest working depths, and there is every reason to believe that steady evolution will provide technical solutions that will allow them to work in even the deepest ocean trenches. Scientific research involving exploration of the ocean depths by autonomous vehicles is now possible, but the primary limitation is the power the AUV can carry. Rather than making quantum leaps to AUV technology, it is likely that ROV systems will evolve to hybrid systems.

SUBSEA FACILITIES AND OPERATIONS

LEGAL

13.8 Overview

The contractual framework for subsea facilities can be looked at as comprising two main elements. The first element deals with the contracts which govern design, procurement, construction, installation and commissioning of subsea equipment and systems and the provision of associated services. The contracts are commonly termed 'project contracts'. These involve the owner(s) of the interests in a field contracting for the provision of services, be they diving services, pipe laying, drilling, etc. The second element deals with contracts which govern operations, management and, ultimately, decommissioning. These agreements are commonly termed 'operational contracts'.

As with most aspects of the oil and gas industry, there is a raft of regulation and legislation governing subsea activities. In addition, there are a number of other users of the sea and many parties who are, whilst not users of the sea, interested parties. The interests of these parties should be taken into account when considering a development. Fishermen's groups and environmental agencies must be informed and consulted wherever there is a proposal for a new structure or activity to be undertaken on the seabed. It is also wise to consult with pressure groups. An Environmental Impact Statement is a key part of the consent process for much project work in the UKCS. Like most activities in a potentially dangerous industry, the health and safety of all people involved in a subsea project must be protected and work undertaken to ensure that a Safety Case has been properly executed and sanctioned by the relevant authority. Specific regulations as they pertain to divers are considered towards the end of this chapter.

Much of the activity in the subsea arena is undertaken by divers and often utilises technically complex and 'cutting-edge' tools, equipment, techniques and systems. The relationship between divers and the operators of facilities is critical.

As with virtually all aspects of work in the UKCS, there are many regulations and primary legislative provisions which govern operations, facilities and decommissioning. Many subsea contracts are of a complex nature due to the utilisation of new technologies and the requirement to construct and operate in varying water depths. There are many areas of potential risk in the subsea environment, and accounting for, and managing, these risks in contracts is crucial. At a practical level, to minimise risk, much of the preparatory assembly and construction work is prepared in modular form onshore and is then hooked up subsea, with the subsequent operations perhaps taking place remotely or via remotely operated vehicles (ROVs). The management, quantification and apportionment of risks is therefore a critical task and is an area which is covered comprehensively in all contracts.

13.9 Project and operating contracts

As indicated above, contracting arrangements for development and production in UKCS can generally be analysed in two parts – the 'project' part and the 'operation' part.

Project contracts are required at various stages pre-production and for the eventual extraction and treatment of gas and oil. The location and nature of a field may mean that agreements generically known as 'Tie-back' and 'Tie-in' Agreements are required. These types of agreements might be used where a field is too small to warrant full stand-alone development and where it is necessary to utilise third party infrastructure. In a tie-in scenario, a field owner might contract with an existing infrastructure owner with infrastructure in the vicinity of the field to provide for exploitation of the field via that existing infrastructure.

Where a new field lies close to a pre-existing developed field there may be issues involved where new pipelines or facilities are to run close to existing pipes and/or infrastructure (in which case a 'Proximity Agreement' may be required) or where pipelines require to cross existing pipelines (in which case a 'Crossing Agreement' will be required). In the pre-production phase of a project, agreements relating to the installation of the pipelines and facilities on site will be required. In a mature operating environment like the UKCS, there are many existing networks of pipelines and the location of these needs to be considered carefully when any subsea development is proposed.

In addition to other pre-production matters, there will be a need for operating contracts such as agreements for the transportation and delivery of oil and gas and also for the reception, treatment and processing of hydrocarbons. Contracts may be required with terminal owners, terminal operators and existing pipeline users.

The types of contracts mentioned above will form the 'backbone' of the overall contractual structure required to develop the field. However, in addition to those there will also be a series of contracts for services with specialists, for example, for the front-end engineering and design study (the 'FEED study') and contracts will have to be put in place with providers of equipment and services for the mobilisation, construction and installation of project equipment. These may include contracts for diving services, drilling, drill rigs, the provision of other subsea equipment, and contracts with engineering and diving companies which will physically install the facilities. Other contracts such as those for barge hire, cranes and other subsea related services may also be required.

The role of the operator of the facilities or project will now be considered, before discussing a number of the more typical agreements encountered when dealing with subsea developments.

13.10 The project operator

The role of a project operator is key. His function is to co-ordinate and manage all activities in respect of the project. Where there is more than one field owner it is administratively and logistically difficult if all owners get involved in all technical aspects of the project. Although decisions as to how to proceed will be made at the Joint Operating Committee level, and owners will have a say as to the overall approach to be taken using their vote at the meetings of the Joint Operating Committee, it would be almost impossible to deliver a project efficiently if all of the owners interfaced with the contractors. From a planning, management and delivery perspective it is important that there is one point of contact and therefore one organisation to project manage the preparation and installation of the facilities. The operator appointed will be one of the parties to the project contracts. It will be appointed to the position because of its expertise and technical resources.

In situations where agreements involve owners of existing fields (for example, in a scenario where a party wishes to develop a field (the new field) by tying it back to infrastructure situated on another field (the existing field)) the negotiations for the new field owners will usually be led by the operator of the new field (acting on behalf of the owners of the new field). The operator will be the operator under the applicable Joint Operating Agreement (JOA) or Unitisation and Unit Operating Agreement (UOA). The operator of the new field will negotiate with the operator of the existing field (which will be acting on behalf of the owners of the existing field). It may be that as well as the particular agreement which is being negotiated (eg a Tie-in Agreement) that there will need to be amendments to existing contracts to which the owners of the existing field are a party and these may need to be amended to allow the tie-in to occur. The operator of the existing field will co-ordinate this operation. Each operator will report back and consult with the owners of their respective fields.

For example, the operator of the new field will have authority under the relevant JOA or UOA to act as agent for the co-venturer(s) in the new field in commissioning FEED studies for the development of a subsea field, and thereafter for field development programme consent from the Secretary of State. Such development programmes will cover and set out the various functions to be performed and work needed to ensure delivery of production. This may, of course, involve subsea services and the operator will be required to mobilise and commission the subsea equipment and services in addition to carrying out the duties under the project and operating contracts detailed above.

Contracts which regulate the construction and use of pipelines are of particular interest when looking at subsea activities.

13.11 Tie-back and Tie-in Agreements

The UKCS has many different systems of pipelines some of which connect with other pipelines, platforms, terminals and refineries. As a new field is developed, it is often tied back to another platform or tied in to an existing pipeline. The notion of the tie-in or tie-back to existing structures is how these agreements derive their generic titles.

A tie-back arrangement might be used where the project economics of the development are not attractive enough to warrant developing the field on a stand-alone basis. An example might be where a small field is discovered near an existing producing field. The costs of putting in place the necessary infrastructure to allow development and transportation of production might be so great that the satellite would be uneconomic if developed on a stand-alone basis and, therefore, not be a viable project.

The new field might be held by one owner who will act as operator or several owners who will appoint one of their number as the operator. In some situations, the new field may be owned by a subsidiary of an owner and/or operator of the existing field and in order to avoid any conflict of interest if that party is operator of both fields it will be usual for one of the other co-venturers to take the lead in the negotiations in respect of one of the fields.

The only way to make the development of the field a commercially viable project may be to utilise third party facilities which exist nearby. The operators of the existing field might enter into a Construction and Tie-in Agreement in terms of which the operator of the new field will construct wellhead facilities and pipelines to link the satellite field to the existing facilities and tie these in to the existing facilities. The operator of the existing facilities may be obliged under the contract to carry out work to the existing facilities at the cost and risk of the owners of the new field to deal with any compatibility issues between the two systems or to provide for enhanced capacity within the existing system to allow for production from the new field.

In this instance, if there are a number of new fields these are often linked together (or 'tied in') before being tied back to the existing pipeline. The operator of the satellite field will then arrange construction of its own wellheads and satellite equipment which will produce oil or/and gas, build a short pipeline network to tie-in the smaller fields and subsequently tie-back the pipelines into neighbouring field facilities. The bulk of such work, which can be technically demanding, will involve subsea contractors.

The contracts documenting the tie-in and tie-back arrangements will set out the nature and type of the works which the operator of the new field is permitted to undertake, namely to construct a new pipeline which connects to the existing field pipelines. The contracts will provide that the operator of the new field will perform the field work in accordance with the scope of work set out in the agreements. They will also invariably provide that all work carried out under the agreement will have to be carried out by the operator to the standard of a reasonable and prudent operator which is the standard usually required in the industry. The operator of the new field will be responsible for ensuring the compatibility of all facilities and equipment which connect, tie into, or otherwise interface with the existing pipeline. Usually the contracts will contain provisions to ensure that there is consultation between the parties regarding design and engineering issues. It may be the case that the operator of the existing field will carry out the necessary work on the existing field facilities at the cost and risk of the operator of the new field in order to facilitate the tie-in of the new field pipeline. In such a scenario the operator of the existing field will normally be contractually obliged to liaise and consult with the operator of the new field during the testing of the compatibility of the facilities and equipment.

In complex, large-scale projects there may be many parties. Normally each 'user group' will appoint a representative to be a member of a 'user group committee'. Such groups will then undertake to use reasonable endeavours to obtain all permissions, authorisations and consents necessary for the performance of the new and existing field work. There will be mutual undertakings between the parties on standard procedures and safety matters and both the new field operator and existing field operator are likely to be contractually obliged to use all reasonable endeavours to provide for the receipt and transportation of the oil and/or gas and their re-delivery within the terms of a Transportation Agreement. The agreement will also set out the ownership of property; the new field owners will own all facilities and equipment to a certain connecting point and thereafter the existing field operators will own facilities and equipment downstream of that connecting point. The connecting point will be precisely defined, usually by reference to a pipeline connection identified using co-ordinates and/or pipe and junction reference numbers.

It is often common practice in construction projects for a certificate of mechanical completion to be issued by the new and existing field operators with a final completion of works letter and certificate issued at a later stage.

All such agreements should have clear terms regarding the payment of money for the costs of the work undertaken and will include standard provisions which will apply in the case of disputes as to sums due; for example, there is often a reference to an independent expert.

Given the potential risks involved in carrying out construction work offshore, the liability and indemnity regimes in contracts are of fundamental importance. The indemnity provisions in tie-in and tie-back contracts will usually provide that the operator and owners of the new field will indemnify the operator and owners of the existing field, against all physical loss of, or damage to, the facilities of the existing field, perhaps for any consequential loss they may suffer, and against claims from third parties arising in connection with the work carried out under the agreement.

As far as liability for the injury or death to employees is concerned, one is likely to see the usual UKCS 'hold harmless' provisions in terms of which each party is to indemnify the other party against expenses, liabilities, claims, etc. arising from the death of, or injury to, its own employees. For example, if company A and company B enter into a contract containing such a provision and B's employee is injured then it would be B which would be responsible for the economic cost of the claim. If B's employee sues A because of the injury and is awarded damages against A then A could require B to reimburse A (in terms of the indemnity) for the money paid to B's employee.

A problem arises in some cases. In our scenario above, should B be required to indemnify A if A was actually at fault? The whole point of the indemnity regime is to apportion risk and a clean 'hold harmless' provision would provide that B should indemnify A for death or injury to B's employees howsoever caused. In many contracts, however, the 'hold harmless' provisions are not as clear cut as this and there may be a carve-out from liability in cases where the loss arises due to certain actions or omissions of the indemnified party (in this case, A). In such a scenario, the contract may provide that B will not have to indemnify A for an injury to B's employees which arises where A is sufficiently to blame – for example, if A's actions constitute 'Wilful Misconduct' as defined in the contract. 'Wilful Misconduct' is usually defined very carefully in the contract and in most cases the definition requires there to be an intentional, conscious or reckless disregard by senior management personnel of good and prudent oil and gas field practice in disregard of avoidable and harmful consequences (but not errors of judgement or mistakes made in good faith). The result is that the exclusion from the straight 'hold harmless' regime may not often occur in practice. Nevertheless, if there is such a carve-out then it is a matter which should be considered when putting insurance in place.

In UKCS oil and gas contracts generally, given the substantial possible exposures and the problems involved in insuring unquantifiable losses of other parties, it is quite usual for contracting parties to seek to carve out liability for consequential loss which might be suffered by the other parties to the contract. Contracts will normally define 'Consequential Loss' in quite detailed terms, but in general terms it usually covers matters such as indirect or 'consequential' losses such as loss of production, loss of product, loss of revenue and loss of profit or anticipated profit. The contract will then normally provide that the parties will not be liable for the Consequential Losses of the other party howsoever caused. Although this is a very common provision, occasionally a party accepts liability for consequential loss of the other party to the contract, but even in that case there is normally a cap on the level of liability of the indemnifier.

Such agreements will also contain provisions on insurance, the treatment of data and confidential information as well as on assignment of the agreement to a third party, the terms of which may be onerous. Consent to assignment from an existing party to a new party will usually require the consent of the other parties (which might be stated must not be unreasonably withheld). Much of the detail of the actual workings of the project, its technical specifications and processes, will be set out in the schedules to the agreement. If there is an accounting procedures schedule, it will contain provisions which are likely to be similar to those found in the JOA and, again, will be extensive.

13.12 Proximity Agreements and Crossing Agreements

Understandably, in areas with a mature oil and gas industry it is common to find a large amount of existing infrastructure and subsea equipment on the seabed.

Where new discoveries are located in such mature areas, the complexities of planning facilities are fraught with challenges, not least of which is avoiding or interfacing with existing infrastructure.

If pipelines have to be put in place near one another, or if one is to cross the other, then it is important for the respective owners to agree the contractual arrangements which will apply in respect of the construction and operation of the new pipeline and to set out what is to happen if there is damage to the respective pipelines. Contracts which deal with such issues are called 'Proximity Agreements', in the case of contracts governing pipelines which are to run close to one another, and 'Crossing Agreements', in the case where one pipeline is to run across the other.

A new field may lie in close proximity to other producing fields. There may be a raft of pipelines in the vicinity, especially in the case of gas fields. Where the operator and owners of the new field wish to develop the new field, it may be necessary to seek permission and agreement from the owners of existing pipelines if any of their proposed new facilities are to cross or run alongside the existing pipelines.

A Proximity Agreement will detail the parties, the affected pipelines and the new pipeline which is to be laid near the existing pipeline. As with other contracts detailed previously, it will be the respective operators of the new and the existing field which will negotiate the terms of the Proximity Agreement in their capacity as agents on behalf of the co-venturers in their field. Due to the nature of the subsea terrain and the size and variety of pipelines, it is vital that the technical specification and details for the new construction and installation are clearly set out, including exact details of where the existing pipeline is, where the new pipeline is to be and specifying the proximity of the new pipeline to existing facilities (and where it will cross in the case of a proposed crossing). Issues arise such as: where will a new pipeline run? Will the new pipeline cross over the existing pipeline or run alongside? If the pipeline is to be near an existing pipeline how close will it be? These issues all need to be covered in detail in the contract.

What will be done and exactly how such work will be conducted will comprise a major element of the contract. Prior to commencement of construction, the consent of the existing facility operator/owners will be required. Consents will also be required from the DTI and other agencies regarding routing, construction methods and environmental impact issues. Therefore, the agreement must contain, or provide for the provision of, particulars regarding the route of the proposed pipeline, the design details, timing schedule and construction and installation procedures for the new facilities. The contract will also detail any consultation procedures which will be required throughout the works and for reports on progress.

Even after the other terms of the agreement have expired, certain provisions such as limits on liability, insurance and mutual 'hold harmless' provisions will normally survive and, therefore, continue to be enforceable by the parties. The parties will have to give consideration as to what is to happen as regards decommissioning. In particular, as discussed in Chapter 15 on decommissioning, the ongoing liabilities for interest owners can be onerous and of an extended nature. If the agreement (other than the indemnity regime, etc.) expires on the conclusion of the installation works, the issues on any subsequent decommissioning of either the new or the existing pipelines may be dealt with by way of a further agreement. Normally, such agreements provide that a pipeline owner requires to give a period of prior notice to the owner of the other pipeline before decommissioning or removal and that after such notice the parties will try to agree terms for removal including terms on which the decommissioning or removal will occur, arrangements for future surveys and other arrangements. It is usual that whichever party is the last to decommission will take responsibility for whatever parts of the other party's pipeline(s) or facilities could not be previously decommissioned due to any crossing or proximity issues.

The liability and indemnity regime will be crucial, as mentioned above. Pipeline Crossing Agreements are one of the types of contracts in the UKCS where there is usually no exclusion of liability for consequential losses. The owner of one pipeline (the crossing pipeline) will generally be responsible for the consequential losses of the owners of the other pipeline (the crossed pipeline) up to a certain amount. The cap on liability for consequential loss is usually set at a high level (tens of millions of pounds).

13.13 Installation Agreements

Installation Agreements are used between operators to outline the procedures for moving the newly fabricated facilities from their onshore construction site to their eventual subsea installation location. Such agreements may be included as part of a Tie-in or Tie-back Agreement, however, if it is a larger field which is being developed, with its own, self-contained facilities, the installation will be carried out as a separate process.

The obligations of any operators will be outlined within the agreement covering their role in co-ordinating any tie-in works with existing facilities, installation and connection of newly constructed pipelines and the subsequent running of the platform. While the operator will be responsible for the co-ordination, running and maintenance of the facilities, details will also need to be included in the agreement of the respective percentage ownership of the field, the facilities and the transfer points of ownership. As with the Tie-in and Tie-back Agreements, this will be by reference to co-ordinates, maps and pipeline or junction references.

In addition, the operators will be required to grant each other, and in some cases the owners, inspection rights. This ensures that each section of the installation, be it wellheads, pipelines or platform, can be reviewed by its adjacent section operator and guarantee co-ordination and smooth running of the facilities as a whole. Similarly, if any claims are made for damaged property the operator reports that a claim is being made against a party and there should be provisions in the agreement to entitle inspection of the damage claimed for. Moreover, the agreement will require provisions for the allocation of costs and reimbursement based on percentage levels of ownership.

13.14 Field Agreements

Once a field operator has finished design, procurement, installation and commissioning of equipment and services into the field, the field should then be ready to start producing. At this point, there may be new contracts which the operator will need to enter into as 'operating contracts' for operating the equipment and providing the services to the co-venturers and continue operations over the life of the field. Field Agreements are further analysed in Chapter 14. Many Field Agreements involve subsea operations relating to transportation, processing and, as mentioned above, the physical interfacing of pipelines to existing subsurface structures.

13.15 Operating Agreements

Some of the more substantive agreements encountered in the oil and gas industry are those which govern the operation of facilities, be they subsea or otherwise. Broadly, such Operating Agreements fall into two main types which are discussed in greater detail in Chapters 9 and 12. A JOA deals with the relationship, ownership rights, management and accounting principles. In the situation where different parties own interests in a field which straddles different blocks, there will normally be a requirement for the parties to enter a Unitisation and Unit Operating Agreement (UOA). By its nature, the UOA is a more complex document because of the potentially large numbers of parties and the mechanisms whereby attribution of assets are extracted from a field under joint ownership. To the extent that these types of Operating Agreements extend to the subsea arena, clearly, any programmes of works and commissioning of services required to ensure production, ongoing processing and ultimately decommissioning will be, to some extent, governed by these important agreements.

13.16 Operating Service Agreements

As mentioned previously, often, rather than developing a field on a stand-alone basis, fields are developed utilising tie-backs to existing third party infrastructure. It may be that a subsea development in Block A is tied back to a platform on Block B (the B platform). In such a scenario, production from A will be transported to the B platform where it will be processed and then transported from the B platform to its ultimate destination.

It may be that A is producing via B, that production from A is being processed on the B platform with water being removed, etc. There are a variety of different services which may be being provided. These are normally dealt with in a 'Production and Operating Services Agreements' or 'Processing and Operating Services Agreement' (POSA).

A POSA will contain provisions dealing with matters such as, exactly what services the services provider (sometimes referred to as 'Joint Services Operator') will be obliged to perform under the agreement, how oil and/or gas are to be delivered to the platform, how separation of production into different products is to occur, what the fees will be for the services provided, what the payment terms are and where the platform owner will redeliver the product to the operator of the field. Elements of POSAs are linked to the subsea arena. The process of delivering the gas or hydrocarbons to the platform from the wellhead will be a subsea operation. Treatment and processing will be less dependent on subsea services. Parties to the POSA will typically be the field owners and the operator of the platform. The three most important sets of provisions in the POSA govern financial/commercial issues, production issues and product issues.

One of the key provisions of the POSA is the pricing or tariff clause. The tariff is the amount payable by the owner of the product to the party which processes the hydrocarbons. This tariff is based on a set amount per unit of production (which is metered).

Normally, a POSA will provide that the operator of each field using the facilities will notify the operator of the facilities of the quantity and pressure of hydrocarbons which it is intended will be delivered into the system by its field group. For example, a notice might have to be given by a field operator to the facilities operator by 11.00am on a Friday indicating how much it will introduce into the system in the following week. Issues such as the allocation of production would normally be dealt with in a separate agreement between the users of fields in an Allocation Agreement and issues of liability between different field groups would usually be dealt with in a User Field Agreement.

The agreement will detail how the gas and/or oil will be processed and how it will be allocated (which, as stated above, might be dealt with in a separate

Allocation Agreement). Raw gas and/or crude oil are delivered to the platform for processing. The operator of the facilities will determine how best to separate out the various products contained within the hydrocarbons delivered to it for processing on the platform. Some of the final products which occur following processing are by-products of the process. The quality of the raw product delivered for processing may vary. It is the responsibility of the platform operator to oversee processing and to ensure that the processed product is allocated in accordance with the mechanism agreed between field groups (which is a complicated process usually involving testing of the product from each field and calculations of the calorific values of the hydrocarbons delivered from each group).

The agreement will set out the minimum quality of hydrocarbons which will be acceptable in the system. The agreement will also set out detailed specifications which must be met by hydrocarbons before they can be accepted in the system. Minimum standards are required to ensure that hydrocarbons do not enter the system which might be damaging to the system or which, if blended with hydrocarbons from other fields, might result in a product which does not meet buyer specifications. It is acknowleged that it is not always possible to meet such specifications, and therefore the agreement will also allow for the facilities operator to use its discretion whether or not to accept delivery of products which do not meet the entry specification. If lower specification hydrocarbons are accepted, the tariff may be amended to reflect the lower quality of the product. The agreement will generally also provide for the consequences for a field group if it delivers hydrocarbons into the system which do not meet the entry specification ('off specification' oil or gas) and where damage occurs to the system as a result.

The POSA might contain provisions which will apply if there is a 'shortfall' in the quantity of hydrocarbons delivered, or if too many hydrocarbons are delivered ('excess' oil or gas). Where there are such provisions there will also be provisions for 'make up' and 'carry forward'.

Overall, the POSA will (perhaps in conjunction with associated documents such as a User Fields Agreement and an Allocation Agreement) detail all the practical terms for the acceptance, processing and subsequent allocation of the gas from fields using the facilities. These contracts will be the main contracts relating to the commercial production from a field. There are elements of this type of agreement which feature in the subsea arena however such agreements are dealt with in more detail in Chapter 11.

13.17 Transportation Agreements

A Transportation Agreement will be entered into by the owners of the new field and the owners of the infrastructure through which the production from the new field is to be transported. The owners of the new field will have to pay a tariff to the owners of the transportation system. Many Transportation Agreements provide that the basis of the payments for use of the system can be changed by the owners of the transportation system from a tariff-based approach to a method which involves users paying a share of the costs of maintaining and operating the transportation facilities if the return to the owners of the transportation system under a tariff-based payment falls below an agreed level.

Hydrocarbons from a new field can only be transported in a pipeline if there is available capacity within the system to accommodate such production. There may be sufficient capacity in the pipeline to cater for the production from the new pipeline or, alternatively, the capacity in the pipeline system may need to be increased.

The existing users of the pipeline will already have allocation and co-mingling agreements in place which will contain detailed procedures regulating the allocation. If hydrocarbons from a new field are to flow through the system then the owners of that field will need to become parties to the existing allocation and co-mingling agreements.

A Transportation Agreement will be required to document the arrangements for the transportation of hydrocarbons in the system. Full details of transportation agreements are contained in Chapter 18.

13.18 Diving at Work Regulations

As mentioned above, the health and safety of those engaged in subsea work is of paramount concern to all those engaged in this aspect of the industry. In addition to the Health and Safety at Work, etc. Act 1974, which is the principal piece of legislation applying to all those who are engaged in the supply and procurement of subsea and diving services, there are specific regulations which govern the conduct of divers and associated contractors.

The Diving at Work Regulations 1997 (SI 1997 No 2776) ('the Regulations') came into force on 1 April 1998 and regulate diving (as defined in the Regulations) in all of its manifestations from diving instructors to those in the acting profession. The key element is the requirement for valid qualification of divers and the roles of the diving contractor, the diving project plan and the diving supervisor.

In relation to any diving project, there may be one person, and one person only, who is the diving contractor for that project. The diving contractor will be the employer of the diver or divers engaged in the diving project. The diving contractor is responsible for the planning, management and conduct of the diving project in a manner which protects the health and safety of all persons taking part in the diving project. There is an obligation on the diving contractor to supply certain details of the project and those involved in its execution to the Health and Safety Executive. In addition to the appointment of diving contractor, one person must be appointed to be the diving project supervisor, such project supervisor must be competent and where appropriate suitably qualified to perform the functions of supervisor. In addition to ensuring that the diving operation is carried out within the remit of the Regulations, the diving supervisor may not dive during the diving operation except where he is guiding or training persons in recreational diving, or diving in relation to educational, archaeological or scientific purposes.

Under the Regulations, divers must hold a current approved qualification and certificate of medical fitness. Every diver is required to maintain a daily log of their diving activities.

— 14 —

PIPELINES

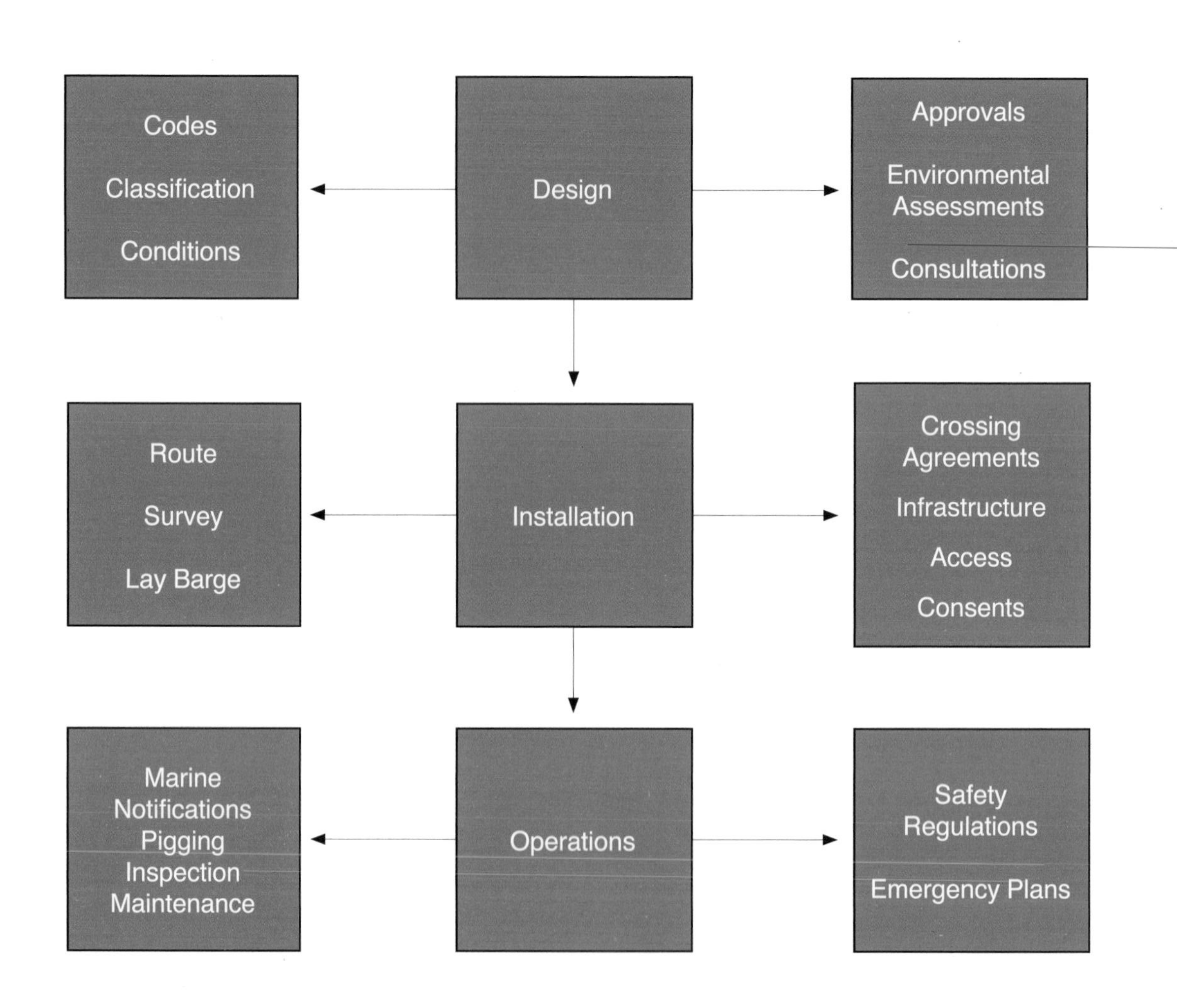
Codes
Classification
Conditions
Design
Approvals
Environmental Assessments
Consultations
Route
Survey
Lay Barge
Installation
Crossing Agreements
Infrastructure
Access
Consents
Marine Notifications
Pigging
Inspection
Maintenance
Operations
Safety Regulations
Emergency Plans

PIPELINES

TECHNICAL

14.1 Introduction

There are over 10,000 km of pipelines in use in UKCS offshore oil and gas production for carrying fluids from wells to facilities, platforms to onshore or offshore receiving loading terminals, and platforms to water or gas injection wells. These have been laid over the last 30 or more years as the infrastructure of the UK offshore industry has developed.

Each pipeline application has been considered for its current and future potential use, taking into consideration the exposure to internal or external damage. Any such instance is costly to repair, requiring the best levels of technology to be deployed in the frequently hostile waters of the North Sea. In addition to repair costs, any shutdown of a pipeline carries significant costs due to downtime of the associated production facility. It therefore follows that the initial design of the pipeline and route offers significant challenges to ensure full integrity throughout its lifecycle.

The route of any pipeline also needs to be made to eliminate risks through proximity and interference with other pipelines. Furthermore, other marine users can also add to the threat of damage from anchors and fishing equipment which are increasing in size and robustness.

Full pipeline design integrity is therefore essential to avoid significant loss of production or any possibilities of oil pollution. Unforeseen changes in transported fluids can also occur during the course of operations throughout the lifecycle of the pipeline and facilities. Internal inspection will provide invaluable information as to any changes to the internal surface of the pipeline which may also result in reduction of pipeline wall thickness.

Techniques are now becoming more available for pipeline internal and external protection, and repairs to the pipeline whilst still in operation. These are particularly useful for greater flexibility of use in the introduction of third party production which may not have been anticipated in the early design of the pipeline.

14.2 Types of pipeline

There are four general classifications of pipelines:

- Short small-diameter flowlines connect wells to platforms, or subsea manifolds, that often operate at high (reservoir) pressures.
- In-field pipelines are small to medium in diameter and gather production from subsea and surface facilities, and transport fluids between facilities. They can carry unprocessed or processed hydrocarbons or water oil, gas, condensate or two-phase flow.
- Large-diameter trunk lines handle the combined flow (oil or gas) as a common carrier from one or more platforms to shore. Booster pumps or compressors are provided at intermediate platforms for very long lines.
- Loading lines usually connect a production platform and an adjacent loading facility. The lines can be small or large diameter and carry liquid only.

The majority of pipelines are so-called 'rigid' pipelines. Steel is the most common material, but with harsher environments, high temperatures and pressures and aggressive fluids, high-strength steels and corrosion resistant alloys (CRA) are increasingly used. The whole pipeline can be made of CRA or alternatively the pipelines can have a CRA liner. Pipelines used for transporting water can have a plastic liner to mitigate the corrosion and erosion effects.

Smaller pipelines are trenched into the seabed and often covered with soil or rock for protection. Larger pipelines are laid on the surface and have a concrete coating to provide protection and stability. Pipelines are often insulated to reduce the loss of heat from the hydrocarbon fluids and improve flow performance. Pipe-in-pipe systems are used where very high insulation levels are required.

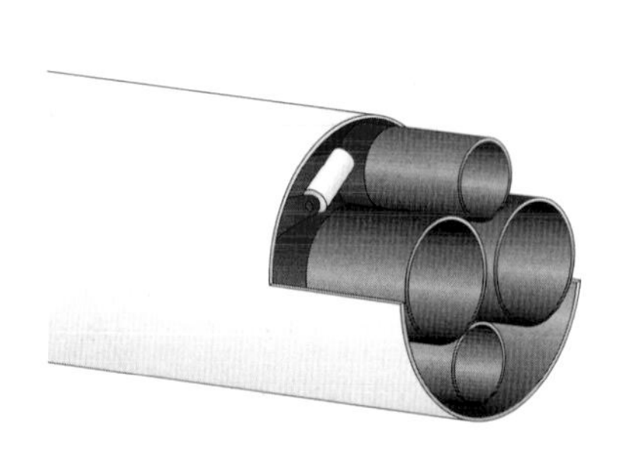

Figure 14–1 Pipeline bundle

Where several pipelines are required to connect facilities these can often be 'bundled' (Fig. 14–1). At its simplest this takes the form of piggybacking a small line onto a larger one. A 'rigid' bundle is where a large 'carrier' pipe is used to hold all the pipelines in a

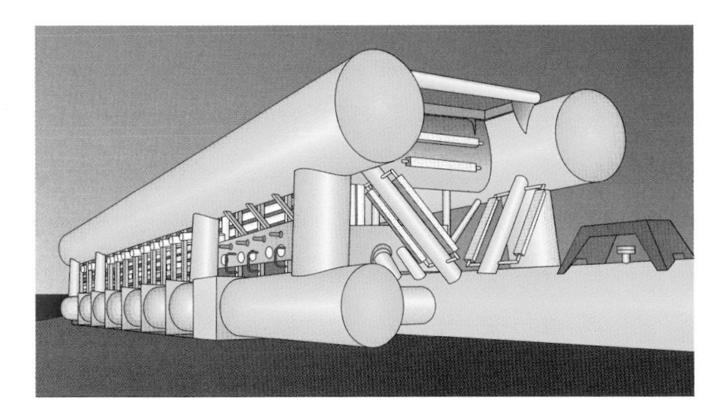

Figure 14–2 Bundle towhead/manifold

single structure. Bundles also provide insulation similar to the pipe-in-pipe system. The pipeline end structures such as manifolds or subsea isolation valves can be built into the bundle where they also act as tow or trailing heads for the installation (Fig. 14–2).

Flexible pipeline technology is of particular importance to the subsea business. A typical flexible pipe is made up of many concentric layers of plastic or spirally wound steel fibres, each performing a different function.

These structures combine great axial and pressure containment strength, with a high degree of bending flexibility: ideal properties for connecting floating production units to subsea production wells.

14.3 Pipeline design

Pipelines installed at any water depth must be designed such that the system maintains its integrity during installation and operation. The subsea environment is very demanding and pipeline equipment needs to meet oilfield operating conditions and design codes, maintain its integrity over a long period, withstand wave and current forces and be maintainable by diver or remotely operated vehicle. Together these provide the designers with enormous challenges.

Pipelines provide the means of flowing the oil or gas from the subsea well to the production facilities. The size of the line is based on this ability to flow the fluids. Flow assurance is the ability to produce fluids economically from the reservoir to a production facility, over the field life in any environment and is particularly critical over long-distance tie-back developments.

Production modelling provides guidelines to safe operational strategy development and the assessment of operational risks. After the pipeline has been sized based on the flow conditions and friction characteristics of the product being carried, the pipeline design work typically involves the evaluation of wave, current and bottom conditions along the pipeline route from which the selection of the pipe parameters can be made. This involves the evaluation of soil strengths under static and storm conditions and the identification of the bottom features to define any slope movement tendencies and limits of unstable areas. The pipeline route is selected to minimise forces on the pipeline from soil movements and to avoid any obstruction or hazards which may occur along the route.

Figure 14–3 Survey operation

Specifications of pipeline materials and weight are made so that the pipe can resist hydrodynamic forces and remain stable during its lifetime. It may be necessary to increase the pipe submerged weight significantly to withstand hydrodynamic forces on the seabed. This may require a large thickness of concrete coating on the pipe.

Design work typically involves the analysis of the pipeline under operating conditions including pressure effects, thermal expansion and storm loads on the pipeline. In deep water and for relatively large-diameter pipelines the design work also involves an analysis of the buckling characteristics of the pipe under various conditions.

During construction pipelines are often exposed to complex loading conditions. After it rests on the seabed the pipeline is exposed to the risk of damage due to wave (the effects of waves are felt well below the sea surface) and current conditions, soil instability, fishing trawls, anchor interference and other hazards. The designs must incorporate all these factors in an efficient, cost-effective system specification.

14.4 Pipeline installation methods

There are various methods for installing subsea systems but before the facilities can be designed or installed the location and route must be surveyed (Fig. 14–3).

Comprehensive, high-quality surveys are crucial to the planning and development of subsea pipelines, particularly at greater depths where both the complexity and the cost of the operation increase. Various features of the seabed topography, including sand waves, iceberg scars, pockmarks and boulders, impact placement of structures and route selection as does the seabed profile, or composition material (rock, sand, clay, etc.).

The most common method for large-diameter pipeline installation is the lay barge. There are different types of lay barge including box hulls, ship-shaped barge and semi-submersibles. The barges either employ an array of anchors which are placed, lifted and replaced in sequence in order to move the barge along the pipeline route, or have their own propulsion system enabling them to both move along the route and keep position in seas and currents (Fig. 14–4).

14.5 Marine and fisheries interface

There is an unavoidable interaction between the offshore oil and gas industry and other users of the sea. In particular there is a long-established relationship between the oil and gas operators and the fishing industry. This interaction covers the development of subsea and pipeline systems via the Pipeline Works

Figure 14–4 Pipelay barge

Authorisation (PWA) application and consultation process and the ongoing liaison which ensures any claims for compensation or safety matters are addressed promptly.

Although the impact of the oil and gas sector on North Sea fisheries has been well studied and reported over the years, from a subsea and pipeline perspective, the major issues relate to the safety implications of fishing interaction with subsea infrastructure. Under the Petroleum Act 1989 subsea infrastructure close to a wellhead can be deemed to lie within a 500 m safety exclusion zone. In addition, subsea equipment (such as wellheads and manifolds) is installed with protective structures which are designed to be over-trawlable, ie if trawl-gear is dragged across the facilities, it causes no damage to the infrastructure or the trawl gear.

Pipelines, on the other hand, cannot be protected by a safety zone along their length and hence a different approach is taken. Traditionally, all pipelines less than 16-inch diameter have been trenched below the seabed. Pipelines of 16-inch or above can be protected by concrete coatings if necessary and can be shown to be robust against potential damage from trawl gear when installed on the seabed. It has been suggested that pipelines are used as trawling routes by some fishermen, under the belief that pipelines attract fish. Although this has not been ratified scientifically,[1] it raises the need for the pipeline operators to ensure that spanning sections of pipelines on the seabed are minimised.

The need for the industry to address this issue was emphasised in 1997 when the Arbroath-based trawler, *Westhaven*, sank with the loss of four lives, after snagging its gear on a pipeline. Since then, the industry and the fishing industry have collaborated to develop the FISHSAFE system which raises an alarm on a trawler when it approaches oil-related infrastructure on the seabed.

In addition, the routine inspection of pipelines using ROVs identifies pipeline spans or other obstructions and these are then addressed if they pose an integrity problem to the pipeline or a safety risk to fishermen.

14.6 Pipeline integrity management

In addition to ensuring the pipeline meets its design requirements when it is first constructed, the pipeline designer seeks to ensure its integrity is maintained throughout its life. For example, internal and external corrosion are predictable phenomena and can be accommodated in the design by treating the transported product with corrosion inhibitors and utilising anti-corrosion coatings and cathodic protection systems for the external surface of the pipe.

In addition to corrosion, there is a range of threats to the integrity of a pipeline system over its design life. The list below categorises the major areas which may be of concern to the pipeline owner:

- internal metal loss (corrosion, erosion, etc.);
- external metal loss and damage (eg corrosion, fishing interaction, dropped anchors, etc.);
- metallurgical cracking anomalies;
- process upset (eg pressure spikes, water carry-over, etc.);
- extreme weather events (eg loop currents, internal waves, etc.);
- seismic events.

Unlike corrosion, which can be managed by careful design, some of these threats are not predictable and to design to mitigate for each and every threat would likely make all pipeline systems prohibitively expensive. Under the Pipeline Safety Regulations (SI 1996 No 825), however, the operator of a pipeline is obliged to '... ensure that a pipeline is maintained in an efficient state, in efficient working order and in good repair'. It is therefore incumbent on the operator to demonstrate it has in place a system to ensure the integrity of their pipeline systems is understood and managed.

To manage the integrity of pipeline systems, operators typically have in place a Pipeline Integrity Management System (PIMS). Modern PIMS are usually 'risk-based', ie the system relies on risk assessment and risk management techniques to manage the integrity of the operator's pipeline assets efficiently. Operation of a PIMS ensures the systems are in place to manage the integrity of pipeline assets effectively such that it can be demonstrated to the HSE and other regulators when necessary.

Techniques applied by pipeline operators to manage the long-term integrity of their pipeline systems are outlined below.

Internal and external corrosion management

As noted above, there is the potential for corrosion to take place both internally and externally to the pipe wall. Corrosion phenomena are well understood and, if the service conditions are accurately known, corrosion mechanisms can be managed at the design stage.

External to the pipeline, the steel pipe is in sea water, a naturally corrosive environment. Galvanic corrosion mechanisms in sea water are well understood and are readily mitigated by a combination of high-quality external coatings, backed up by a cathodic protection system. Cathodic protection (CP) can take the form of impressed current systems, which are mostly used for onshore environments, and sacrificial anode systems which are almost exclusively used on offshore pipelines. In simple terms, the sacrificial anode CP system works by creating an electrical circuit between the pipeline and an anode of either zinc or aluminium, such that the anode dissolves in the sea water in preference to the steel pipe.

Coatings applied to the outside of steel pipes are typically enamel- or epoxy-based and are extremely robust and effective in corrosion protection terms. Such coatings can remain effective for design lives of up to 30 years and beyond.

The internal surface of a pipeline may be susceptible to corrosion due to the corrosivity of the hydrocarbon fluids it is transporting. The most common form is carbonic corrosion due to the presence of carbon dioxide (CO_2) on the production stream.

Like external galvanic corrosion, CO_2 corrosion is well understood and it is possible to treat fluids with corrosion inhibitors before they enter the pipeline to reduce this and other corrosion mechanisms taking place. This can be relatively straightforward if the product is being treated when it leaves the well, eg on an offshore platform.

For flowlines connected to subsea wells where the 'raw' production fluid enters the pipeline, corrosion inhibitors can be injected via umbilicals from a host facility, or the pipeline is built using high-alloy, corrosion-resistant steels which are inherently resistant to corrosion.

Under the Pipeline Safety Regulations, the operator is responsible for understanding the corrosion mechanisms taking place inside and outside his pipeline and must carry out inspections and gather data to allow integrity to be assured.

Inspection and maintenance

The pipeline operator's primary data-gathering and integrity assurance strategy is built around his inspection and maintenance programme. With many thousands of kilometres of pipelines in the North Sea and around the world, the larger offshore pipeline operators have developed sophisticated Pipeline Integrity Management Systems (PIMS) which use risk techniques to internally and externally inspect their assets efficiently. These strategies ensure that inspections are performed at appropriate intervals such that the risk to the integrity of the pipeline is as low as is reasonably practicable.

External inspections are performed using acoustic inspection tools which are towed from survey vessels and ROVs. These tools detect so-called 'anomalies' which are classified under the PIMS and maintenance or interventions planned as necessary. Anomalies include anything which is found which is contrary to the as-built condition of the pipeline and include: dents, coating damage, buckles, etc. It is also not uncommon to encounter unexploded ordnance which is dealt with by the Navy.

Internal inspections are carried out using inspection tools or 'pigs' which are propelled through the pipeline. 'Intelligent Pigs' are sophisticated pieces of electronic equipment which can measure the pipeline wall thickness along the length of the pipeline and so detect dents and reductions in wall thickness due to unexpected corrosion or erosion.

Clearly, intervention and repair of a pipeline due to an internal anomaly are potentially very costly in terms of both the intervention itself and the inevitable loss of production. If internal anomalies are detected, they are usually carefully monitored and if possible steps taken to control the mechanisms causing the anomaly before physical intervention or repair is necessary.

Pigging

As noted above, so-called 'pigs' are devices which are propelled through the pipeline using the pressure drop along the pipeline. In addition to the inspection tools described above, pigs are used during pipeline pre-commissioning for cleaning, gauging and filling with water for testing; and during commissioning for control of dewatering and filling with product. In operation, it can be necessary to pig the pipeline to remove contaminants or liquids to maintain flow performance as part of the integrity management programme.

The use of the inspection tools described above can be carried out when the pipeline is first constructed to provide a benchmark survey against which future surveys are judged. Due to the cost and interruption to production which can arise during such an internal inspection programme, they are carefully planned using the risk criteria which are central to PIMS.

Leak detection

It is recognised that even when the integrity of pipeline assets is managed within a comprehensive integrity management system, it is not possible to eliminate all risks to the pipeline throughout its life. The environmental consequences of a loss of containment can be serious and therefore technology has been developed which can rapidly detect an unexpected pipeline leak and alert the pipeline operator.

The available technology can be categorised as hardware- and software-based systems. The most mature technologies with the greater track record are the software-based systems. These systems use validated analytical models of a pipeline to predict leaks based on detected changes in pressure, flow-rate or mass-balance. These systems are simple to implement in that they use measurements which are readily available and can detect small leaks over hundreds of kilometres.

Hardware-based techniques are much less mature in their development and application. These systems typically rely on hardware being installed or deployed along the pipeline, providing data which can detect a loss of containment. Examples are acoustic sensors, cable and fibre-optic-based sensors.

Leak detection technology is developing all the time as regulatory bodies increasingly demand that operators provide more objective evidence of the integrity of their systems.

14.7 Pipeline operations

Pipeline operations can be broadly divided between long-distance trunklines, carrying processed oil or gas to terminals for refining or onward distribution to consumers; and shorter pipelines, often referred to as ‘flowlines’, carrying unprocessed fluids typically from a subsea well to a host facility. In each case, the operating conditions of the pipeline represent the major input to its design.

Trunklines, which can be hundreds of kilometres in length, usually transport hydrocarbons from a number of producing fields, for a number of operating companies on a tariff basis. The processed or partially processed products carried in such systems are usually easy to manage in that the specification of the fluid that can be carried in the pipeline is set to ensure operations are predictable and long-term integrity is assured by matching the specification to the pipeline design. To gain capacity in such infrastructure, the operator of an oil or gas field must demonstrate to the pipeline owner that they can meet the required fluid specification.

For gas pipelines, the system is designed to operate at a certain temperature, pressure and composition which determines whether any liquid is present during normal operations. This enables the receiving terminal to determine the facilities required to receive the gas and any associated liquids. The pipeline operator is responsible for ongoing maintenance and carries out the necessary inspection and maintenance activities to ensure the long-term integrity of the system.

Shorter pipelines or flowlines, which can be longer but are usually less than 10 km long, carry unprocessed, often 'multiphase', products containing oil, gas and water in different proportions. For such pipelines which typically link subsea wells to host facilities, and where the produced fluids are completely unprocessed, a number of issues need to be managed.

In pipelines transporting gas, a major issue is the potential for the formation of hydrates if the temperature and pressure in the pipeline reach certain threshold criteria. Hydrates are an ice-like crystal formation which can form at a pipeline's operating pressure if the pipeline is shut in and the product is allowed to cool. In the extreme, hydrates could effectively block a pipeline system such that production could be interrupted for days or weeks while strategies to re-dissolve the hydrates are implemented.

Various strategies exist for preventing the formation of hydrates in the line, such as insulating the pipeline to keep the temperature up, depressurising the line out of the hydrate formation conditions or dosing the gas with methanol which prevents hydrates forming as the pipeline cools. Contingency strategies such as these are put in place during design of a subsea system.

In flowlines that carry predominantly oil, a major concern is the formation of wax in the pipeline as the temperature of the unprocessed fluid reduces. Some produced crude oil has a high proportion of wax present and as it enters a subsea system it must be either chemically treated or kept above the wax formation temperature until it reaches the host processing facility. Failure to manage the wax formation in the pipelines could lead to the pipeline becoming full of wax and effectively useless.

The requirement for chemicals and the host from which these will be provided can be a significant economic and logistic element of a field development plan.

It is important that the operation of a pipeline is managed carefully throughout its life to ensure it is operating within specification and that its integrity can be assured. Current instrumentation, communication and flow modelling technologies give the operators the real-time data they need to ensure they know what is going on in their system at all times.

Note

[1] CEFAS (2001) Technical Report TR 003, Technical report produced for Strategic Environmental Assessment – SEA2. North Sea Fish and Fisheries Data supplied by FRS August 2001.

PIPELINES

LEGAL

14.8 Introduction

As discussed, there are a variety of issues which impact on the decision as to whether to invest in the construction of a pipeline. Pipelines are expensive to build and it is unlikely that a decision will be made to build a dedicated pipeline where it is possible to utilise the pipeline infrastructure which may be nearby a prospective development. Where a discovery is large and the economics support a pipeline or where there is the likelihood of tariff income being generated in the pipeline through transportation agreements entered into with third party users, the decision may be taken to construct a pipeline. A major consideration is the security of supply issue. Having your own pipeline avoids the possibility of capacity priorities in third party infrastructure limiting production capabilities on a particular day.

The construction and operation of UK offshore pipelines[1] is regulated by Part III of the Petroleum Act 1998 ('the 1998 Act'). The original system of government authorisations was introduced by the Petroleum and Submarine Pipelines Act 1975 which formed the basis of Part III of the 1998 Act. In addition to the 1998 Act, offshore pipelines are subject to the Prevention of Oil Pollution Act 1971, the Coast Protection Act 1949, the Merchant Shipping (Oil Pollution Preparedness, Response and Co-operation Convention) Regulations 1998, the Offshore Petroleum Production and Pipeline (Assessment of Environmental Effects) Regulations 1999 and the Pipeline Safety Regulations 1996.[2] Pipeline Crossing Agreements and Proximity Agreements also contractually regulate the construction, maintenance and operation of pipelines between different field owners.

The legal framework regulating pipelines is complemented by a series of collaborations between industry and government. Facilitating access to existing infrastructure and encouraging co-operation between parties have been the main aims of the relevant codes of practice and standard contracts. The DTI have been very proactive in this area and have also published a broad array of guidance in relation to pipeline infrastructure.

14.19 Petroleum Act 1998

Written authorisation[3] from the Secretary of State is required before a controlled pipeline may be constructed or used, in, under or over any controlled waters, under section 14(1) of the 1998 Act.[4] The term 'pipeline' is defined in section 26(1) to mean 'a pipe or systems of pipes (excluding a drain or sewer) for the conveyance of any thing, together with any apparatus and works associated with such a pipe or system'.[5] Section 14(2) defines 'controlled waters' as the 'territorial sea adjacent to the United Kingdom and the sea in any area designated under section 1(7) of the Continental Shelf Act 1964' and a 'controlled pipeline' means 'so much of any pipeline as is in, under or over controlled waters'.[6]

14.10 Pipeline Works Authorisations

The ministerial functions under the 1998 Act are carried out by the Secretary of State for Trade and Industry. In particular, the Pipeline Consents and Approvals Team forming part of the Energy Resources and Development Unit, a division of the Department of Trade and Industry (DTI), is responsible for the administration of Pipeline Works Authorisations (PWAs) and consents to deposit materials on the seabed (DEPCON).[7]

Schedule 2 to the 1998 Act governs the PWA application procedure; PWAs cannot be issued to a person other than a body corporate.[8] Upon receipt of the application the Secretary of State makes an initial decision as to whether or not to consider the application. If the application is not rejected, the applicant must publish his proposal, including a map, and allow a period of 28 days for representations and objections to be made to the Secretary of State. A PWA may then be issued. Alternatively, the Secretary of State may come to the conclusion, perhaps as a consequence of third party representations, that the route or capacity of the pipeline, or a part of it, be adjusted for reasons such as navigational safety, fishing, or marine conservation. The applicant will be served with a notice of this opinion. The Secretary of State will grant the applicant the opportunity to be heard at a hearing and decide on the issuance of the PWA.

PWAs are generally provided for an unlimited duration; however, the Secretary of State may limit the period of the authorisation in special circumstances.[9] The Secretary of State may include in the PWA any terms which he deems appropriate. Some examples include:

- the route, design and capacity of the pipeline or part of it;[10]
- the persons or kinds of persons who are authorised to carry out the works or use the pipeline in question;
- the boundaries within which any works may be executed in pursuance of the authorisation;
- the steps to be taken to avoid or reduce interference by the pipeline with fishing or with other activities connected with the sea;
- the items that may be conveyed in the pipeline;
- where responsibility for damage attributable to the release or escape of anything from the pipeline lies;
- any transaction which relates to the pipeline for which the consent of the secretary of state is required;
- who may/may not acquire an interest in the pipeline;
- the method of operating the pipeline;
- information which must be provided in respect of the pipeline; and
- who will be operating the pipeline and who may/may not operate the pipeline.[11]

The DTI recommend that discussions with the DTI and HSE should be commenced at the earliest possible opportunity. A PWA should have been issued before construction of a pipeline or pipeline system begins. The process of obtaining a PWA should take approximately four months where there are no objections and where no Environmental Statement[12] is required.

A PWA will expire according to the express time limit contained within it, if the pipeline works have not begun within three years or if a term of the authorisation or compulsory notice issued by the Secretary of State is contravened.[13] When the authorisation ceases to be valid the controlled pipeline, by virtue of section 19, vests in the Secretary of State, free from encumbrances, but without prejudice to any rights conferred on third parties by section 17.[14] The Secretary of State may grant an authorisation for any pipeline which vests in him to any other person, upon terms that may include payment to be made to the Secretary of State for such transfer.

In addition to the PWA, all proposed pipeline construction works will require a DEPCON (written consent from the Secretary of State to deposit materials on the seabed). This consent is required before any permanent positioning of gravel, rock, concrete mattresses or protective pipeline covers on the seabed.

14.11 Compulsory powers

As the oil and gas reserves on the UKCS diminish, the ability to use the existing infrastructure in their exploitation becomes increasingly important. The investment required to build new infrastructure is substantial, and the sums involved become infeasible as the producing fields become smaller. As discussed by the DTI, conflict arises between the efficient use of resources, which requires no unnecessary duplication of infrastructure, and the wish for greater competition, which requires alternative pipeline systems to be available to producers. It is evident that there will be benefits for all parties if the development of small fields is made possible by existing infrastructure owners permitting access. The owners of the pipelines will gain supplementary income and production companies will avoid massive expenditure building new pipelines. Where a third party wishes to gain access to another party's pipeline structure, the industry code of practice developed by the UK Offshore Operators Association (UKOOA) and the DTI, the *Code of Practice on Access to Upstream Oil and Gas Infrastructure on the UK Continental Shelf*, should be followed in the first instance.[15] Initially, this involves a direct approach to the pipeline owner, making the request and, in particular, specifying the substance and quantity of production which is to be conveyed.

In the event that the negotiations are unsuccessful, the Secretary of State has the power to settle disputes.[16] Third parties can make an application to the Secretary of State under section 17F of the 1998 Act, and the Secretary of State may issue a notice to the pipeline owner ordering compulsory modifications to an existing or proposed controlled pipeline,[17] including changes to capacity, routing and third party rights of access to the pipeline. In considering whether to grant the notice, the Secretary of State will take into consideration the issues detailed in section 17F(8). These include, for example, the owners and all other users' reasonable current and future needs in respect of the transportation of petroleum and other technical considerations. Section 16 allows the Secretary of State to issue a notice instructing the owner of the pipeline to modify apparatus connected to the pipeline so that capacity may be increased or to install a junction in the pipeline to allow another pipeline to be connected; this application would normally be carried out in conjunction with an application under section 17F. The Secretary of State must hear representations from the owner or applicant and may not make a compulsory order unless satisfied that the third party use will not prejudice the efficient use of the pipeline, which the owner is entitled to expect. If the request is made by a third party for their benefit, the Secretary of State may include in the notice the sums, or method of determining the sums, which he determines appropriate to be paid to the owner by the applicant for the purpose of defraying the costs of making the modifications or securing connection to the pipeline or alternatively the tariffs imposed for use of the pipeline.

14.12 Enforcement

It is an offence under section 21 of the 1998 Act to construct or use a controlled pipeline without a PWA or to not comply with an order under section 16 or 17 to modify the capacity or route or allow third party access. Furthermore, it is an offence to knowingly or recklessly make a false statement to induce the Secretary of State to issue, terminate, or limit an authorisation. The corporate body can be penalised with a fine, if found guilty of the offence.

14.13 Pipeline Safety Regulations 1996

The 1998 Act does not contain specific provision in relation to pipeline safety. The Specialised Industries Gas and Pipelines Unit, which forms part of the Health and Safety Executive's Hazardous Industries Directorate, is responsible for enforcing health and safety law in respect of offshore pipelines through the powers vested in it by the Health and Safety at Work, etc. Act 1974. The Pipeline Safety Regulations 1996 (SI 1996 No 825), made under this Act, were created to ensure that pipelines are designed, constructed and operated safely.

14.14 Coast Protection Act 1949

The Coast Protection Act 1949 is concerned with navigational safety. When the DTI awards a PWA it will enclose a copy of the additional consent required under the Coast Protection Act 1949 for the construction of the pipeline. The DTI will arrange for this consent with the Department of Environment, Food and Rural Affairs on behalf of the body applying for the PWA. The consent specifies the appropriate conditions for the pipeline construction works to prevent them from endangering or obstructing navigation.

14.15 Prevention of Oil Pollution Act 1971

Under section 3 of the Prevention of Oil Pollution Act 1971, it is an offence to discharge any oil from a pipeline into the sea or any area designated under section 1(7) of the Continental Shelf Act 1964 unless special exemption is granted by the Secretary of State.

14.16 Merchant Shipping (Oil Pollution Preparedness, Response and Co-operation Convention) Regulations 1998

The Merchant Shipping (Oil Pollution Preparedness, Response and Co-operation Convention) Regulations (SI 1998 No 1056) require that operators of oil-handling facilities, which include pipelines, have an approved oil pollution emergency plan, where there is a risk of an oil pollution incident.

14.17 Offshore Petroleum Production and Pipeline (Assessment of Environmental Effects) Regulations 1999[18]

The oil industry and government are well aware of the potential environmental risks if offshore oil and gas production activities are not carried out appropriately. For example, releases of petroleum caused by damage to pipelines due to ship movements such as anchoring can be very damaging to the environment. This is always of concern but can be a particular problem where the area is used by endangered species or as breeding grounds for migratory species. The oil industry and government are keen to ensure that potential environmental hazards and the effect of proposed pipeline projects are identified and evaluated so that appropriate risk mitigation measures can be adopted.

Under the Offshore Petroleum Production and Pipeline (Assessment of Environmental Effects) Regulations 1999 the Secretary of State for Trade and Industry is obliged to consider information relating to the environment before it consents to various offshore oil and gas activities. Prior to certain activities, operators must carry out an Environmental Assessment. The conclusions must be presented in an Environmental Statement (ES) and submitted to the DTI in support of an application for offshore activity under the 1998 Act. The consent will only be granted if the Secretary of State is satisfied that there will be no major impact on the environment and that he has received sufficient information to allow him to make a decision on the matter.

The ES will be unnecessary in two situations:

- where it is considered that the proposed activity will not have a significant impact on the environment; and
- where consents are being sought in relation to an activity which has already been the subject of an ES under the Regulations.

A Petroleum Operation Notice (a PON 15) will be submitted in circumstances where it is considered that the activity will cause no significant impact on the environment.[19] The PON 15 provides a synopsis of the environmental impact of the proposed works, and will form the basis for the decision on whether an ES will be required or not. If the Secretary of State decides that the effect on the environment will be minimal, a Direction will be issued that an ES is not required and consent to the works will be granted.

The Secretary of State may refuse to grant consent following appraisal of the PON 15 or the ES, if the proposed activity is deemed detrimental to the environment. Alternatively, the consent may stipulate conditions aimed at alleviating the environmental impact of the developments. The Secretary of State may well grant an unconditional consent if the environmental impact of the works will be minimal.

14.18 Decommissioning

The decommissioning of offshore infrastructure on the UKCS is regulated by Part IV of the Petroleum Act 1998. To ensure safe decommissioning there are additional requirements under the Pipeline Safety Regulations 1996, which are administered by the Health and Safety Executive. The European OSPAR Decision 98/3 which relates to the disposal of disused offshore installations does not apply to pipelines. Furthermore, there are no international guidelines which relate to the decommissioning of disused pipelines.[20]

14.19 Code of Practice on Access to Upstream Oil and Gas Infrastructure on the UK Continental Shelf

In the early 1990s the UK Government believed that field development on the UKCS was being delayed by a lack of transparency between parties negotiating access to infrastructure. Furthermore, the existing statutory powers to secure access had never been exercised. The DTI recommended the creation of an industry-wide voluntary code of practice to expedite recovery on the UKCS.

The original code, published in January 1996, did not operate as desired; access to infrastructure was still not being easily obtained. In August 2004 a revised code was developed between the UK Offshore Operators Association (UKOOA), the Department of Trade and Industry and a range of interested parties.[21] The non-statutory code sets out principles and procedures to guide all those involved in negotiating third-party access to oil and gas infrastructure on the UKCS. It aims to facilitate the utilisation of infrastructure through the use of timely agreements for access on fair and reasonable terms. All owners and users of infrastructure are expected to endorse the Code and commit to its principles and procedures.

The overarching principles of the Code are:

- parties uphold infrastructure safety and integrity and protect the environment; and
- parties follow the Commercial Code of Practice.

The specific principles of the Infrastructure Code of Practice are:

- parties provide meaningful information to each other prior to and during commercial negotiations;
- parties support negotiated access in a timely manner;
- parties undertake to ultimately settle disputes with an automatic referral to the Secretary of State;
- parties resolve conflicts of interest;
- infrastructure owners provide transparent and non-discriminatory access;
- infrastructure owners provide tariffs and terms for unbundled services, where requested and practicable;
- parties seek to agree fair and reasonable tariffs and terms, where risks taken are reflected by rewards; and
- parties publish key, agreed commercial provisions.

The Code applies to all UK oil and gas pipeline infrastructure from wellhead to onshore processing facilities. All parties negotiating new contracts for access and services should follow the Code. It is also applicable to prospective users who request information on the ullage[22] of the pipeline systems, and the owners and capacity rights holders of the relevant infrastructure.

The Code does not provide standard terms or tariffs. The aim is to develop a culture of transparent and non-discriminatory negotiated access to infrastructure. It attempts to prevent the application of dissimilar conditions to equivalent transactions, without imposing fixed common prices for particular services, on account of the different risks and costs which may be involved. The Code states that tariffs and terms offered and agreed ought to be fair and reasonable, with risks taken being rewarded. Infrastructure owners should consider all legitimate requests for services, offering terms in good faith, with no preferential treatment to any specific company or group of companies. Open competition between pipeline systems seeking to deliver the prospective users' requirements should be a primary goal.

The provision of information is one of the main aims of the Code. It states that infrastructure owners should examine, maintain and review data delivery mechanisms so that prospective users can obtain an informed view of the infrastructure options in their area. Sufficient operational and ullage data should be available to enable the prospective user to undertake basic economic research. In particular, high-level infrastructure capacity information should be made publicly available via their company website and linked to the centralised website, the DEAL portal. More specific technical data should also be made publicly available on their website or on request for the purpose of determining the suitability of the infrastructure to meet a prospective user's transportation and processing requirements. At this stage owners are not required to publish data regarding tariffs, which was required under the previous code.

When prospective users enter into substantive discussions with infrastructure owners they become known as 'bona fide enquirers'. The bona fide enquirer and the owner/operator are to exchange information until they are in a position to conclude a commercial agreement. Liability for the accuracy and completeness of the data is not guaranteed at this stage, but will possibly be covered in the final commercial agreements.

The Code provides a flowchart (Fig. 14–5) which shows best practice for negotiations. The parties should at the outset agree a timetable which identifies the technical, operational, legal and commercial issues that will require resolution in order to reach a satisfactory commercial agreement. The Code states that it is unacceptable for either party to deliberately delay or speed up negotiations in an attempt to gain commercial advantage.

The 2004 Code introduced Automatic Referral Notices (ARNs). They are an attempt to stimulate the use of the compulsory powers under sections 15, 16 and 17 of the 1998 Act. The bona fide enquirer must detail in the agreed timetable when he intends to lodge the ARN.[23] Submission of the ARN creates an undertaking by the bona fide enquirer to apply for a notice from the Secretary of State to exercise his statutory powers. This obligation only arises if six months

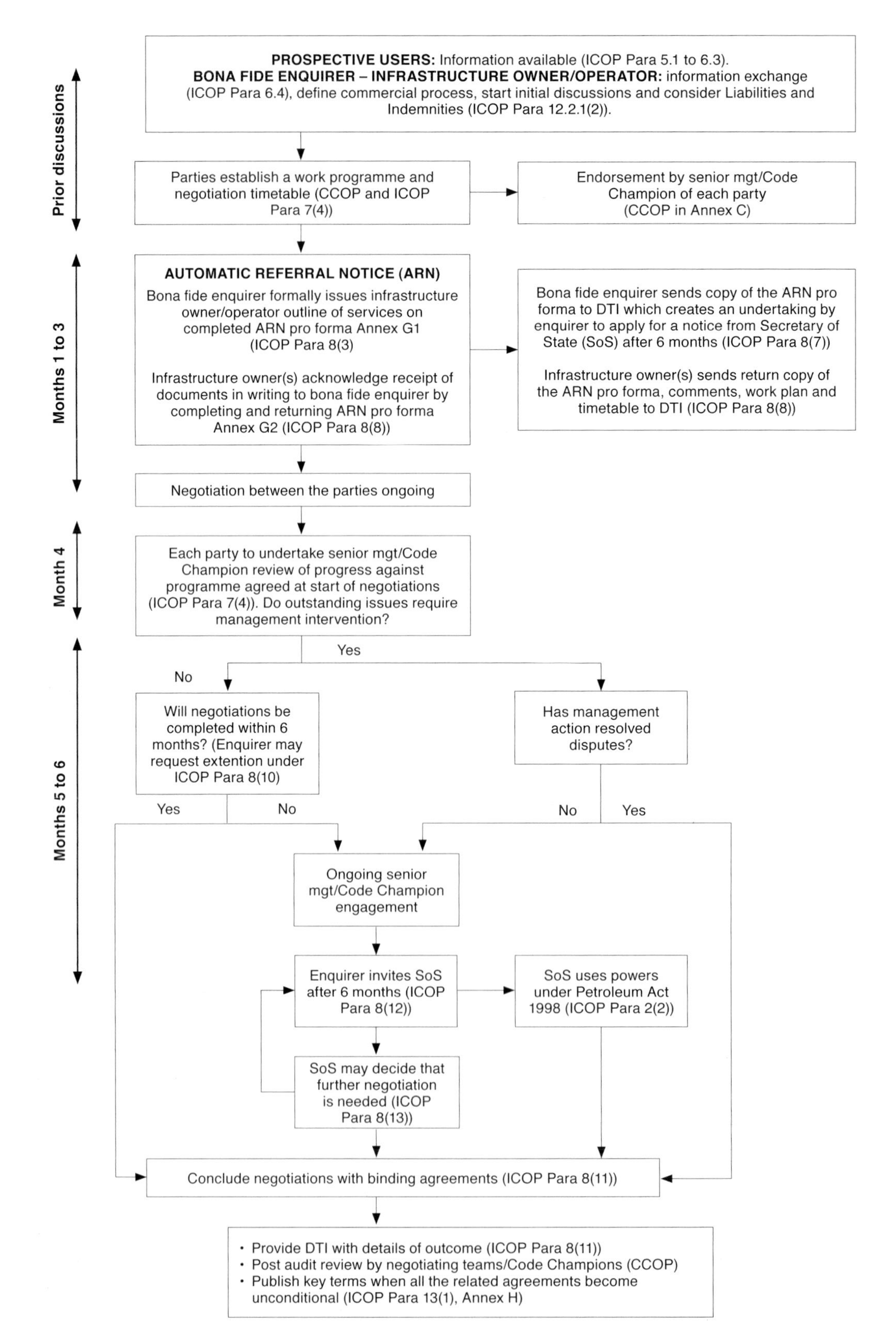

Figure 14–5 Flowchart of best practice for negotiations

have passed and satisfactory negotiations for access to infrastructure have not been concluded. However, the bona fide enquirer can make an independent application under the 1998 Act at any point during negotiations. ARNs are handled with a degree of flexibility; if the bona fide enquirer feels that an extension to the six-month period would facilitate agreement, he can request extra time. The bona fide enquirer's obligations to apply to the Secretary of State will cease if he no longer requires access to the infrastructure or negotiations end by way of a binding agreement.

There may be situations where there is a conflict of interest. For example, one party could be in negotiations as an infrastructure owner and as a bona fide enquirer. Alternatively, the party could have ownership interests in two pipeline systems competing to provide similar services. The conflicted party will frequently play no part in the discussions or elect at the outset in which capacity they are negotiating. This is simply a tool to prevent unfair prejudice in the negotiations; the party does not waive their rights and will sign the contracts in both capacities upon agreement.

In terms of the Code, infrastructure owners should offer services on an unbundled basis. This means that where it is practical and requested, distinctly separate components should be available for negotiation individually, with no attempt to gain leverage on another component. This may also be relevant where parts of the infrastructure chain which it is proposed to be used are in separate ownership.

The allocation of liabilities and indemnities will obviously form an important part of negotiations. In particular, the greater the risk the parties are willing to face, the higher the expected rewards. Parties should consider these issues early in negotiations, generally prior to the submission of the ARN. The two phases where liabilities will be an issue will generally be indemnified differently. During the tie-in or initial modification phase, the bona fide enquirer should indemnify the owners, after taking account of the future imposed tariffs and potential exposures, against liabilities and losses arising out of a tie-in or modification activity. The owners are encouraged by the Code to offer reasonable caps on their maximum liability exposure, taking into account their realistic exposure and the risk-reward balance of the overall transaction. Where it will be necessary for there to be a planned shutdown for the sole purpose of tie-in or modification, the parties are encouraged to quantify and pre-agree a reasonable level of liquidated damages to cover the losses from deferral of production. After completion of the tie-in phase, the Code recommends that, where possible, the parties adhere to the principle of mutual 'hold harmless' in relation to damage to property, personal injury to their respective employees and their respective contractors' employees, pollution and consequential loss, usually subject to exclusions for wilful misconduct.

Another principle of the Code is that infrastructure owners should publish a short summary of newly concluded Construction and Tie-in Agreements, transportation and processing agreements and operating service agreements within one month of these becoming unconditional. The Code outlines the specific information that should be included in the summary, which includes tariffs. The publication of these terms is intended to provide an indication of tariff levels and commercial terms to future potential users.

14.20 Infrastructure Code of Practice 2006 Review Report

UKOOA published a report on the effectiveness of the Code in September 2006. They reviewed the information available on operator websites, the Automatic Referral Notices received by the DTI and comments from parties seeking and providing access to infrastructure.

According to the report, operators have generally complied with the requirement to post technical information on their websites and most of the required data are available. The provision of information is expected to increase as a result of discussions following the review and full data provision is expected in the future. However, there has been reluctance by operators to publish the commercial details of completed deals on their websites. UKOOA attributes this to the lag between completion and deals becoming unconditional, and as such it may be several months before the contract summary can be made available.

There had been 38 ARN submissions between the Code's introduction and May 2006. Four deals have been concluded from these submissions.[24] The confusion surrounding the ARN process is one of the main issues which will need to be addressed as a result of the review. It is apparent that some deals have been negotiated without an ARN in place or the ARN has been submitted before an appropriate timetable has been agreed. Some operators have also been accused of being slow to enter into initial discussions and to respond to requests for services. It appears that ARNs have been used to stimulate negotiations, with the DTI eventually having to extend the ARN to fit with a more reasonable time scale. The DTI believe that the incorrect use of ARNs will decrease with experience and understanding of negotiating parties.

System providers and users have commented that demands for onerous indemnities have acted as stumbling blocks in some negotiations. Infrastructure owners have, in some instances, placed uncapped liabilities on the party seeking to gain access. Uncapped liabilities are uninsurable and so despite being able to agree an appropriate tariff the parties were unable to reach agreement. The Code specifically states the importance of the balance between risk and reward and this should prevent parties from placing unduly onerous burdens on the other party. Further problems may arise in situations where capacity owners are not signatories to the Code and do not follow its guidelines. Negotiation delays have also been caused by owners' divided rights in the infrastructure making competing bids to users for the same piece of infrastructure. The DTI envisaged this problem during the drafting of the Code but felt that it was too complex to address. Legislative changes have been mooted.

The review concluded that the Infrastructure Code of Practice requires no revision. It found that the Code is fit for purpose and is having a positive influence on processes and behaviours. Most problems that have been encountered thus far have been as a result of parties to the Code lacking experience in the workings of its provisions. It was thought that changes at this early stage would cause confusion within the industry. The review recommended industry-wide training sessions to publicise the Code and in turn improve current working practices. Further recommendations included DTI field groups taking a more proactive role in discussions regarding ARNs and Commercial Code of Practice Champions also playing a more supportive role.

14.21 Consideration of Applications for Resolution of Disputes over Third Party Access to Infrastructure: Guidance to Parties in Dispute

As mentioned previously, where parties fail to agree terms of third party access to upstream oil and gas pipelines, it is possible for an application to be made to the Secretary of State under the 1998 Act. The DTI have published a guidance note on this topic, *Consideration of Applications for Resolution of Disputes over Third Party Access to Infrastructure: Guidance to Parties in Dispute.* The guidance note describes how the Department would process such an application, the principles it would apply and the requirements and obligations of all parties. The procedure has not, as yet, been used in practice.

The DTI's aim is to promote a fair and transparent resolution procedure. It aims to facilitate the effective and quick processing of applications whilst avoiding unnecessary expense and maintaining commercial confidentiality. The guidance note contains a timetable setting out the stages involved in the application process and outlines the Department's intentions to process applications within 16 weeks. After the DTI obtain all the facts the most crucial element of the process will be setting an appropriate tariff, which is likely to be the main problem in the first instance. General examples of possible disputes and the DTI's proposed approach to the determination are provided. The DTI states that they understand that it is important to strike the correct balance between rewarding investment in infrastructure and preventing further development in the UKCS being stifled by imposing uneconomically high tariffs.

14.22 Standard Pipeline Crossing Agreements

In 1998, following a dramatic decrease in oil prices and surge in the cost base on the UKCS, the Oil and Gas Industry Task Force (OGITF) was established in an attempt to secure the long-term future of the oil and gas industry. It was a joint programme between the UK Government, oil and gas industry operators, contractors, suppliers, trade unions and other enterprises. The objective was to stimulate activity on the UKCS and reaffirm the UK's status as the optimum centre of oil and gas exploration, development, service and production in the world. PILOT was established in 2000 and has assumed responsibility from the OGITF for the continued improvement to the UK oil and gas industry's competitiveness and capabilities.

PILOT established the Progressing Partnership Working Group (PPWG) in 2001. Its remit was to maximise recovery of reserves on the UKCS by addressing commercial and other behavioural barriers in the industry. In conjunction with UKOOA, the PPWG has developed a range of standardised legal agreements, aimed at speeding up and streamlining commercial negotiations. They include a Joint Operating Agreement, a Sale and Purchase Agreement, a Pipeline Crossing Agreement and various others.[25]

The Pipeline Crossing Agreement (PCA) provides standard terms and conditions to govern the relationship between the owners of the pipeline that will be crossed ('crossed pipeline') and the owners of the pipeline that will be crossing ('crossing pipeline'). The agreement is entered into between the operators of the pipelines in their capacity as operators and as agents for the remaining owners of the pipelines.[26] The main provisions relate to liabilities and indemnities. In simple terms the owners of the crossing pipeline, grant indemnities and assume certain liabilities in respect of the pipeline which is being crossed. The owners of the crossed pipeline, in turn, consent to the laying of the crossing pipeline. There are also standard provisions relating to the obligations of the parties in connection with the installation of the crossing pipeline and the procedures for maintenance and repair.

According to the principle of privity of contract, when a contract is entered into between two parties, which confers a benefit on a third party, the third party cannot bring an action under the contract or have it enforced for him by one of the contracting parties. This principle has been eroded by the Contracts (Rights of Third Parties) Act 1999 ('the 1999 Act') which states that a third party may enforce a provision of a contract, in his own right, if it is expressly provided in the contract that the relevant term confers a benefit on him. This right can be expressly excluded by contract, and the standard form PCA does so in Clause 1.2(i). There are exceptions where third parties will be able to enforce the contract. Clauses 6 and 10, which relate to liabilities and indemnities, offer third parties relief from certain liabilities, will still be enforceable by these parties. The PCA contains a clause which states that the parties to the contract are permitted to rescind or vary the terms of the contract without the consent of third party beneficiaries. If this caveat was not in place, third party consent would be required under the 1999 Act.

Clause 2.2 specifies the standard at which the parties must exercise their respective rights and discharge their respective obligations – the standard of a reasonable and prudent operator. The 'reasonable and prudent operator' is defined in Clause 1.1 as 'a party seeking in good faith to perform its contractual obligations and, in so doing and in the general conduct of its undertaking, exercising that degree of skill, diligence, prudence and foresight which would reasonably and ordinarily be expected from a skilled and experienced operator engaged in the same or similar circumstances and complying with applicable law'. The inclusion of a performance standard indicates that parties may be held accountable if they fail to achieve acceptable standards under the PCA.

The procedure and conduct of the work is regulated by Clause 3 of the PCA. In short, the Crossing Pipeline owner has to:

- provide designs, drawings, timing schedules and procedures relating to the work for approval by the crossed pipeline operator;
- advise of the commencement date and completion date;
- obtain all necessary permits, certifications, and authorisations and comply with all applicable laws, rules, orders and regulations;
- prior to construction, carry out surveys of the crossed pipeline and the seabed along the proposed route within 200 metres of the proposed crossing point, for review by the crossed pipeline operator. The crossed pipeline operator will provide the crossing pipeline operator with such data, video recordings and information that it has, to assist the crossing pipeline operator to plan and perform the work;
- clean up the site if it has been littered with debris during the construction;
- carry out a survey of both pipelines within 200 metres of the crossing and report to the crossed pipeline operator upon completion; and
- carry out a review within 24 months of completion of the work and thereafter at intervals of not more than five years.

The requirements and specifications are adapted to suit the specific crossing.

The crossed pipeline operator under Clause 7 is authorised to have a representative closely liaising with the crossing pipeline operator during the construction works. The crossed pipeline operator has the ability to order suspension of the works, if they believe that the actions of the crossing pipeline operator are likely to cause or result in damage to the crossed pipeline, or are contrary to the terms of the PCA.

Clause 5 states that if the crossing pipeline owners decide to decommission the pipeline, or are required to by the regulatory authorities, the crossing pipeline operator shall inform the crossed pipeline operator and thereafter the parties shall use their best endeavours to decide upon terms for such work. The Clause works in the same way if the crossed pipeline owners decides to decommission.

Obviously one of the most contentious issues regarding the crossing of pipelines is risk allocation. It is likely that despite the standard terms included in the PCA there will be lengthy negotiations on the topic. There are certain standard mechanisms used in the industry for the allocation of risk which form the basis for Clause 6 of the PCA. The crossing pipeline owner is to indemnify and 'hold harmless' the crossed pipeline owner for loss or damage to the crossed pipeline and for damage to property, health or injury of any third party arising from the pipeline works.[27] The crossing pipeline owner will also indemnify and 'hold harmless' the crossed pipeline owners in respect of consequential loss. Due to the far reaching nature of consequential loss a definition is contained within the PCA. Parties frequently exclude or limit liability for consequential loss. Furthermore, the total liability of the crossing pipeline owners to the crossed pipeline owner, in respect of these obligations, is to be limited to an appropriate amount agreed between the parties in the circumstances.

It is worth noting that the parties will not be indemnified in the event there is wilful misconduct. The PCA defines 'wilful misconduct' as an intentional, conscious or reckless disregard by senior management personnel of good and prudent oil and gas field practice or of any of the terms of the PCA in disregard of avoidable and harmful consequences but shall not include any act, omission, error of judgment or mistake made in good faith in the exercise of any function, authority or discretion vested in, or exercisable by, such senior management personnel and which in the exercise of such good faith is justifiable by special circumstances including safeguarding of life, property or the environment and other emergencies.

Under Clause 6.3, the crossed pipeline owners and the crossing pipeline owners are to indemnify and 'hold harmless' the other party in respect of claims which relate to pollution and the health, injury or death of its own or its affiliates' employees. This obligation to indemnify is not subject to a financial limit.

An important part of the owner's risk management approach, in addition to agreeing appropriate terms in the PCA, is to properly insure. The PCA dictates that insurance must be obtained by the parties, to the extent of its liabilities under the liability clause. This may be through a reputable insurer or through self-insurance.

Any relief from liability, 'hold harmless', indemnity or benefits in favour of the crossed pipeline owners and the crossing pipeline owners in Clause 6 is extended to their directors, employees or agents in Clause 6.6. In addition, the relief extends to their respective affiliates, their affiliates' contractors and subcontractors and in turn their directors, employees or agents. As mentioned previously, the Contracts (Rights of Third Parties) Act 1999, which allows third parties to depart from the usual privity of contract position, applies in respect of any relief from liability, 'hold harmless', indemnity or benefit created in favour of the aforementioned parties by virtue of Clause 6.

The obligations of the parties shall be suspended to the extent that the party concerned is prevented from complying by force majeure under Clause 8. Force majeure is defined in the PCA as any event or circumstance which is beyond the reasonable control of a party, rendering them unable to fulfil their obligations under the agreement and in relation to which such party has exercised and is exercising the standard of a reasonable and prudent operator. A detailed procedure to be followed by the affected party is included.

The agreement was drafted to regulate the complex situation that arises when a pipeline crosses another pipeline. If the pipelines run in close proximity, but do not cross, the contract will have to be adjusted in accordance with the particular project.

Notes

1. Onshore pipelines are regulated by separate legislation.
2. As introduced by the Health and Safety Executive.
3. Known as a Pipeline Works Authorisation (PWA).
4. Except where construction of the controlled pipeline began on or after 1 January 1976.
5. 'Apparatus' and 'works' are defined in s 26(2) of the 1998 Act.
6. Where there is no initial or terminal point of a pipeline situated in the United Kingdom or controlled waters, the pipeline shall largely be disregarded for the purposes of Part III of the 1998 Act, except insofar as the Secretary of State may make provision in accordance with the jurisdiction of the United Kingdom under international law (s 24).
7. Comprehensive guidelines can be found on the DTI website at: www.og.dti.gov.uk/regulation/guidance, including what exactly should be contained within the application.
8. Section 15(2).
9. Section 15(4).
10. Where the PWA contains terms which vary the proposed capacity or route of the pipeline, the Secretary of State may serve a notice under s 15(6) to the concerned parties regarding compensation for the financial ramifications of the modification.

[11] Section 15(3).
[12] See the section on the Offshore Petroleum Production and Pipeline (Assessment of Environmental Effects) Regulations 1999 (SI 1999 No 360) below.
[13] Section 18.
[14] See section 14.11 below.
[15] See section 14.19 below.
[16] See section 14.21 below.
[17] Including pipelines in existence pre-1976.
[18] (SI 1999 No 360) as amended by the Offshore Petroleum Production and Pipe-lines (Assessment of Environmental Effects) (Amendment) Regulations 2007 (SI 2007 No 933). The DTI have produced guidance notes for industry on these Regulations: *Guidance Notes on the Offshore Petroleum Production and Pipelines (Assessment of Environmental Effects) Regulations 1999.*
[19] According to the DTI a PON 15 is fundamentally a 'mini ES' which is used for the environmental evaluation of smaller projects, eg drilling a well, constructing a small pipeline or adjustments to existing projects.
[20] See Chapter 15.
[21] The Code will be maintained by UKOOA, with the support of the DTI, to ensure it continues to serve the needs of infrastructure users and owners.
[22] Spare capacity of a pipeline.
[23] The point should not be more than six months prior to the target date for completion of the negotiations and will generally be when the bona fide enquirer feels he has sufficient information to complete negotiations within six months.
[24] Accounting for 12 ARNs, as one deal involved the submission of 9 ARNs.
[25] The full selection can be found at http://www.ukooa.co.uk/issues/stdagreements/index.htm
[26] Pipelines on the UKCS are generally owned by a consortium of companies, allowing the costs and risk to be divided between the companies.
[27] There are also specific clauses which relate to liabilities in respect of Additional Work as defined by the PCA.

— 15 —

DECOMMISSIONING

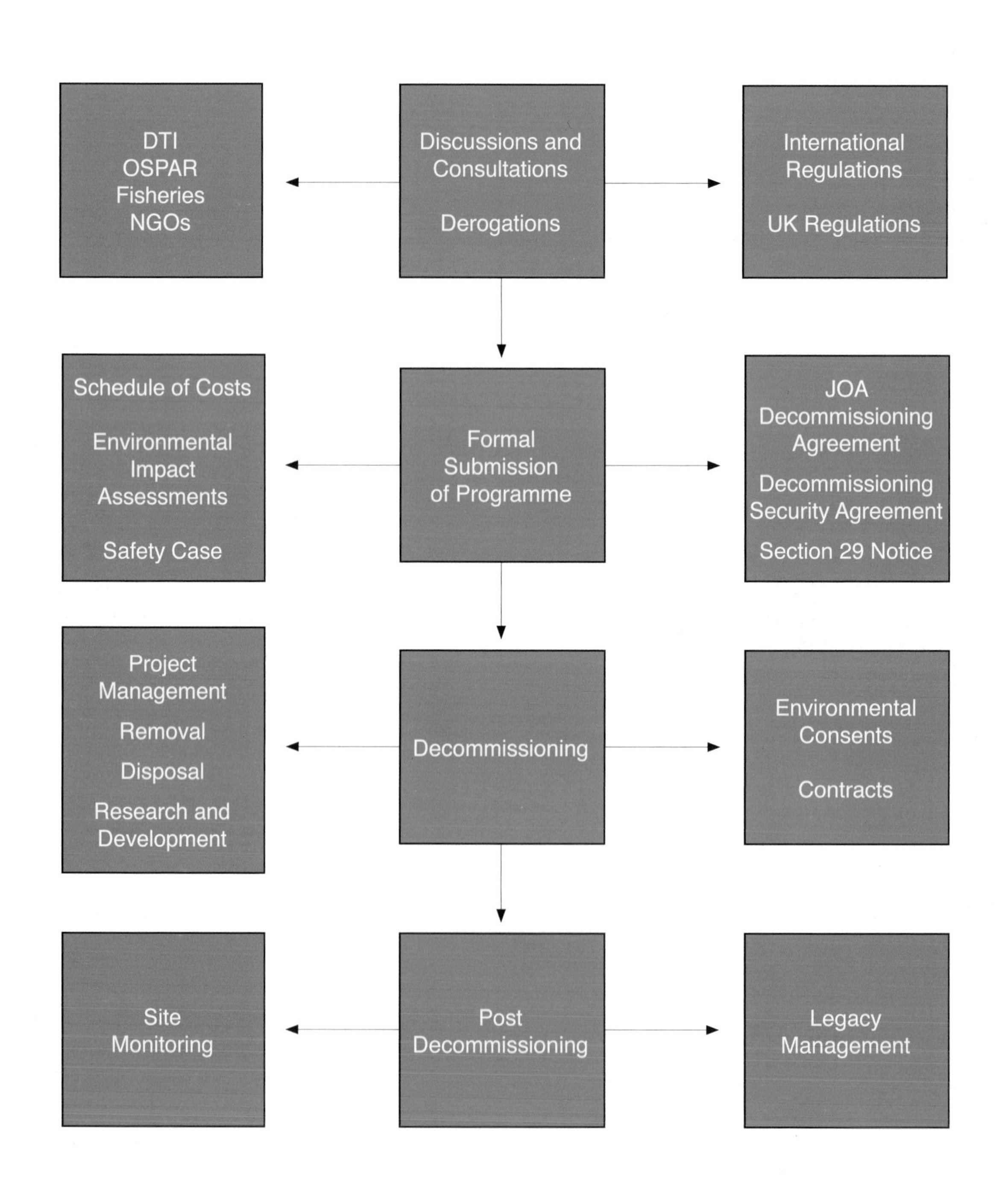
DTI
OSPAR
Fisheries
NGOs
Discussions and Consultations
Derogations
International Regulations
UK Regulations
Schedule of Costs
Environmental Impact Assessments
Safety Case
Formal Submission of Programme
JOA Decommissioning Agreement
Decommissioning Security Agreement
Section 29 Notice
Project Management
Removal
Disposal
Research and Development
Decommissioning
Environmental Consents
Contracts
Site Monitoring
Post Decommissioning
Legacy Management

DECOMMISSIONING

TECHNICAL

15.1 Introduction

As oil and gas installations reach the end of their productive life they have to be decommissioned. Decommissioning is the process by which options for the removal and disposal of structures are assessed; a plan of action is formulated by the operator, approved by government and then implemented. The overall timescale for this is several years, as it needs to take into account many diverse factors and involves many organisations. This chapter outlines the key elements which need to be considered.

In the UK, there are about 500 offshore oil and gas installations. The first decommissioning of a platform was in 1978. Since then about 30 structures have been removed or approved for removal. Nearly half of these are floating/ subsea structures and all removals to date have been to a clean seabed. However, approval has recently been given to North West Hutton and Frigg structures, which allow for partial removal, leaving a steel stump and the concrete substructure respectively. The decommissioning issue, therefore, will continue with the effective management of this legacy.

In the early 1990s, when the oil price dipped below $10 per barrel, the prospect of a significant increase in decommissioning activity fired predictions of over 50 installations and £1.5 billion in the 10 years to 2005. This aroused much speculation that a lucrative new business would result. However, studies showed that the economic activity from extending oil and gas developments is far more beneficial, and with the rise in oil prices and renewed interest in the UKCS, this has been the predominant investment focus. Decommissioning activity levels have turned out to be less than a third of those predicted and some field lives have been extended beyond 15 years. This also illustrates the uncertain nature of planning for contract service capacity into this market.

In 1995, approval for the deep-sea dumping of Brent Spar was famously reversed by the actions of Greenpeace. Public interest was aroused and international governmental policies were significantly adjusted. The legislative requirements of today have been shaped by the debates which followed.

15.2 Approvals process for decommissioning

International regulations

The process of decommissioning is very strictly regulated by international, regional and national legislation. These regulate both the removal of installations, primarily concerned with safety of navigation and other users of the sea, and disposal, primarily aimed at pollution prevention. There is a framework of international conventions which, in turn, influence national legislative requirements. The primary conventions are noted below:

- *UNCLOS.* The United Nations Convention on the Law of the Seas 1982 (UNCLOS) superseded the 1958 Geneva Convention and Article 60(3) permits the partial removal of structures provided that IMO (see below) criteria are met. This first came into force in 1994 and was ratified by the UK in 1997.
- *London (Dumping) Convention.* The 1972 London Convention (and the subsequent 1996 Protocol) made the provision of generic guidance for any wastes that can be dumped at sea. New guidelines were adopted in 2000, to specify different classes of waste, including platforms and other man-made waste.
- *IMO.* The International Maritime Organisation (IMO), headquartered in London, sets the standards and guidelines for the removal of offshore installations worldwide. The 1989 IMO Guidelines require the complete removal of all structures in water depths less than 100 m and weighing less than 4000 tonnes. Those in deeper waters can be partially removed, leaving a minimum 55 m of clear water for the safety of navigation. All structures installed after 1 January 1998 must be designed so as to be feasible for complete removal.

  Many of these IMO guidelines are superseded by OSPAR 98/3, but some remain relevant:

  - any disused installation, structure or part thereof, which projects above the sea (ie the topsides) should be adequately maintained;

- an unobstructed water column of at least 55 m must be provided above the remains of any partially removed installation, to ensure safety of navigation;
- the position, surveyed depth and dimensions of any installation not entirely removed should be indicated on nautical charts and any remains, where necessary, properly marked with aids to navigation;
- the person responsible for maintaining the aids to navigation and for monitoring the condition of any remaining material should be identified;
- it should be clear where liability lies for meeting any future claims for damages.

- *OSPAR*. In 1992 the Oslo and Paris Convention for the Protection of the Marine Environment of the North East Atlantic (OSPAR) was drawn up to replace the 1972 Oslo Convention on dumping from ships and the 1974 Paris Convention on discharges from land. There are 16 contracting parties, including the UK. Until June 1995, the OSPAR Convention permitted, under certain circumstances, the disposal at sea of parts or all of disused offshore installations; but this changed after the Brent Spar affair.

In July 1998, at the OSPAR Ministerial meeting in Sintra, Portugal, a new regulatory framework was drawn up which no longer permits disposal of offshore structures at sea (except for exceptional circumstances). Decision 98/3 came into force in February 1999 and requires:

- the topsides of all installations must be removed to shore;
- all substructures or jackets weighing less than 10,000 tonnes to be completely removed to shore for reuse, recycle or disposal on land;
- however, it provides, on a case-by-case basis, a mechanism of derogation where there may be practical difficulty in removing installations, ie the footings of large steel platforms weighing over 10,000 tonnes, the concrete gravity-based platform substructures; concrete anchor bases and other structures with significant damage or deterioration (which would prevent removal).

The decision for granting derogation lies with the UK Government, following technological justification and appropriate consultation with other OSPAR Contracting Parties. These rules are implemented in the UK through the Petroleum Act 1998. (They do not apply to pipelines.)

Every five years after 1999, in light of the experience of relevant research and the exchange of information, the OSPAR Commission shall review the criteria for future derogations. However, this was not changed in 2003. The next review is planned for 2008.

UK regulations and due process

The Petroleum Act 1998 regulates decommissioning of oil and gas installations and pipelines on the UKCS. Under the Act the relevant parties (operators and owners, as designated by the DTI through serving section 29 notices) are jointly and severally responsible for submitting an appropriate decommissioning programme to the Secretary of State within a specified time frame.

Under the Petroleum Act 1998 (which consolidated the Petroleum Act 1987) a decommissioning programme should contain an estimate of the cost of the measures proposed, specify the times within which those measures are to be taken and, where an installation or pipeline is to remain in position or be only partly removed, include provision for maintenance where necessary. It is recognised that, where appropriate, a decommissioning programme will deal with both removal and disposal of an installation or pipeline.

These programmes are available for public scrutiny and operators undertake a period of consultation to receive (and address) comments from other government departments/agencies, statutory consultees (ie fishing organisations, SFF and NFFO, and the JNCC), non-governmental organisations, members of the public and other bodies. Prior to submission, operators (on behalf of joint-venture owners) will need to undertake studies, verification inspections and option assessments to include as justification for the proposed decommissioning programme. It then passes through the following stages (Fig. 15–1).

Decommissioning process – main stages

A programme may deal with the decommissioning of all of the facilities located on a field or part of the facilities, including a single installation or pipeline. The precise content of a programme may vary according to the circumstances. However, the following sections are likely to be necessary in most cases:

1. Introduction;
2. Executive summary;
3. Background information;
4. Description of items to be decommissioned;
5. Inventory of materials;
6. Removal and disposal options;
7. Selected removal and disposal option;

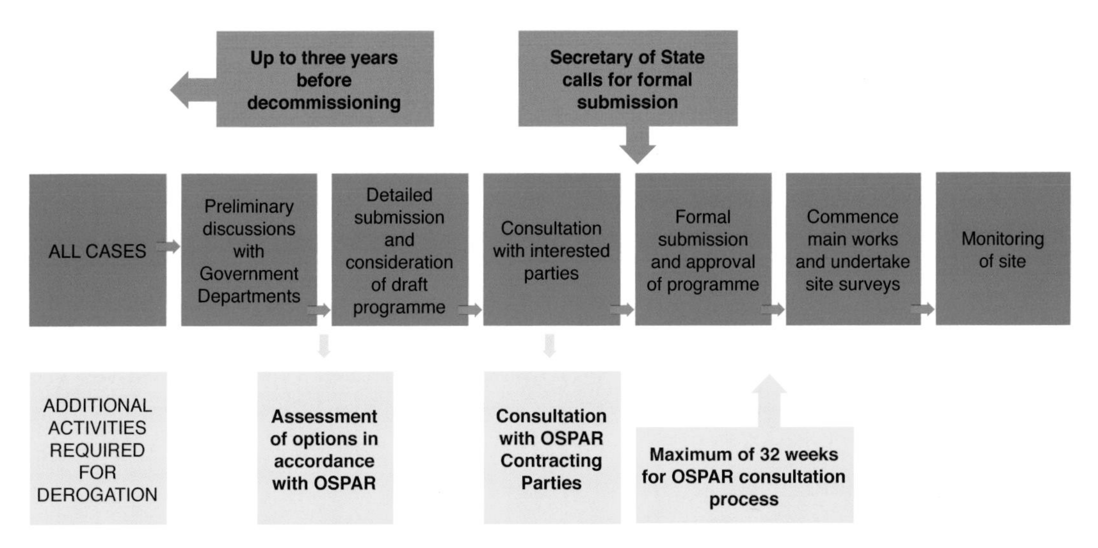

Figure 15–1 UK decommissioning process including derogation

8. Wells;
9. Drill cuttings;
10. Environmental impact assessment;
11. Interested party consultations;
12. Costs;
13. Schedule;
14. Project management and verification;
15. Debris clearance;
16. Pre- and Post-decommissioning monitoring and maintenance; and
17. Supporting studies.

In addition to approval of a decommissioning programme, the following will also need to be obtained as appropriate:

- confirmation that the requirements of the Coast Protection Act 1949 have been satisfied;
- acceptance of an Abandonment Safety Case under the Offshore Installations (Safety Case) Regulations 2005 (installations only);
- fulfilment of notification requirements to Health and Safety Executive (HSE) under regulation 22 of the Pipeline Safety Regulations 1996;
- any environmental consents or permits required during decommissioning activity; including Parts I and II of the Food and Environment Protection Act 1985
- approvals for the transboundary shipment of waste, including authorisation under the Radioactive Substances Act 1993; and
- approval of a well abandonment programme in accordance with the obligation contained in the petroleum production licence.

Where appropriate, consideration of the draft decommissioning programme will run in parallel with:

- consideration by DTI Licensing and Consent Unit Field Teams of any Cessation of Production (COP) Document; (the procedures for submitting an application for COP are set out in the DTI's 'Guidance Notes on Procedures for Regulating Offshore Oil and Gas Field Developments' which can be viewed on the DTI's Oil & Gas Website at http://www.og.dti.gov.uk/regulation/guidance/reg_offshore/index.htm);
- consideration by the HSE of the Abandonment Safety Case;
- consideration of any environmental permits or consents; and
- any onshore disposal consents or licences which may be necessary, including any transfrontier shipment of waste issues.

The following approach will be taken in considering the decommissioning of pipelines on the UKCS:

- decisions will be taken in the light of individual circumstances;
- the potential reuse of the pipeline in connection with further hydrocarbon developments or other projects (such as hydrocarbon storage or carbon sequestration) should be considered before decommissioning. If reuse is considered viable, suitable and sufficient maintenance of the pipeline must be detailed.
- all feasible decommissioning options should be considered and a comparative assessment made;

- any removal or partial removal of a pipeline should be performed in such a way as to cause no significant adverse effects upon the marine environment;
- any decision that a pipeline may be left in place should have regard to the likely deterioration of the material involved and its present and possible future effect on the marine environment; and
- account should be taken of other uses of the sea.

The DTI *Guidance Notes for Industry – Decommissioning of Offshore Installations and Pipelines under the Petroleum Act 1998* has been revised in 2006 to expand on issues such as risk assessment for derogation applications and financial liabilities under OSPAR 98/. It is found at: http://www.og.dti.gov.uk/regulation/guidance/decommission.htm

15.3 Technical perspective: scale of the challenge

Installations

There are over 600 offshore oil and gas installations in the North Sea, 470 of which are in UK waters. These include subsea equipment fixed to the ocean floor as well as platforms ranging from the smaller structures in the Southern North Sea to the enormous installations of the Northern North Sea built to withstand very harsh weather conditions in deep water. Many were built in the 1970s and were hailed as technological feats of engineering when they were installed. The industry now faces the equally challenging task of decommissioning them.

One of the main challenges is the many different types and designs of structure which means that there is no single tried and tested method for removal. Most of the structures were designed to suit particular development and field conditions. They range from small steel lattice-work structures, through to large heavy concrete or steel structures, including floating production and underwater (subsea) extraction systems. Figure 15–2 gives some idea of the diversity of shape and scale.

Offshore, as well as installations there are more than 10,000 km of pipelines, approximately 10,000 wells and many drill cuttings piles. Associated with these operations (and covered by the same legislation) are also 15 onshore terminals, which are covered by onshore planning and environmental legislation.

Under current regulatory requirements, over 90% of offshore structures will be completely removed from their marine sites and brought to shore for reuse, recycling or other disposal means. The rest, which comprise the very large and heavy steel or concrete installations, will be looked at on an individual basis to assess whether it is technically feasible and safe to remove them, bearing in mind

470 INSTALLATIONS

- **10% floating**
- **30% subsea**
- **50% small steel**
- **10% large steel or concrete (with a potential for derogations)**

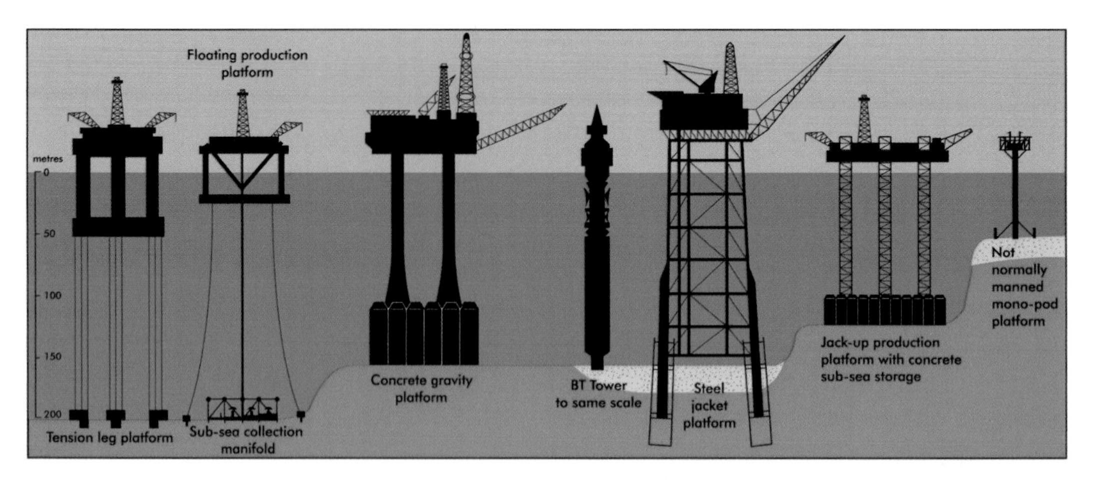

Figure 15–2 Size comparison of various types of offshore installations (Courtesy: Oil & Gas UK)

that there is a general presumption for total removal. If they are too difficult or dangerous to be removed to shore, an exceptional case for 'derogation' can be made.

It is difficult to predict the exact date of decommissioning for each structure. There are a number of reasons for this:

- the price of oil, which influences the time of economic cut-off;
- improved production and reservoir recovery methods;
- extending the uses of the infrastructure, eg for smaller satellite fields tied back into existing export systems; and
- alternative use of the structures, eg for gas storage or carbon sequestration.

The industry is actively pursuing ways to delay decommissioning and extend the productive life of existing infrastructure, so it can be used to recover the UK's remaining hydrocarbon resources to the maximum. This raises another challenge, that of an uncertain market place for decommissioning in which contractors have a difficulty in gearing up technology and workforce for an ever-changing activity plan. Figure 15–3 shows the DTI's current estimate of decommissioning dates.

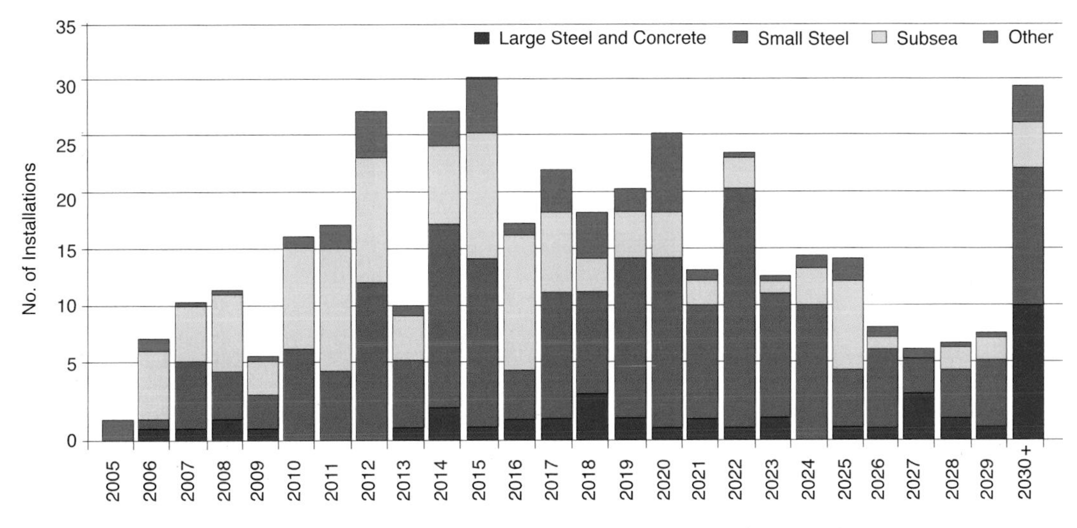

Figure 15–3 Estimated decommissioning dates

Estimates of the overall cost of decommissioning for the UK also vary widely, from £10 bn to £20 bn. The variables responsible for this range include:

- the inclusion of wells and pipelines;
- the level of removal, ie success in achieving derogations for installations (and final status for pipelines);
- cost estimation methods (new industry guidelines have recently been compiled).

A breakdown of overall UKCS costs is noted in Fig. 15–4:

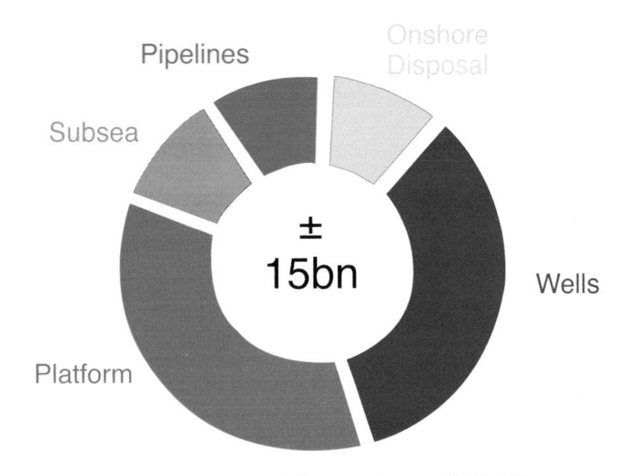

Figure 15–4 Breakdown of overall UKCS costs

Figure 15–5 Steel jacket removal for decommissioning (Courtesy: Oil & Gas UK)

Fixed platforms

Platforms can be designated as small or large (those in water depths of more than 300 ft, with jackets or substructures weighing more that 10,000 tonnes).

For small platforms, entire removal to shore is the only option. Figure 15–5 shows a process of decommissioning used in the Southern North Sea, where experience to date runs to more than a dozen fixed platforms having already been decommissioned, including all Esmond, Forbes and Gordon field structures and infield platforms in West Sole, Viking, Leman and Camelot.

For the large platforms, the topsides need to be removed to shore, but there may be options, under OSPAR 98/3 derogation, for part of the steel jackets and for concrete substructures. These include:

1. Complete removal.
2. Partial removal, leaving 55 m clear water column for navigational safety. The cut-off point would be so as to leave only the jacket footings or part of the jacket footings in place. In the case of North West Hutton (the only approval for a steel jacket to date), this was at the top of the 'bottle leg' footings.
3. Leave in place, for concrete gravity-based structures only, leaving appropriate navigation aids. The cut-off point is determined by the construction.

On the UKCS there are only 40 platforms which qualify to apply for derogation: 11 concrete and 31 steel. However, some of those will programme option 1 above, so the total number leaving structures on the seabed will be less than this. (It is unlikely that any new large platforms will be constructed in the UKCS after 2006 and all structures after 1 January 1998 have to be capable of total removal.)

The first derogations approved are for the Ekofisk tank (by Norway) and the three Frigg concrete structures which straddle the Norwegian/UK sector (by Norway and the UK jointly) (shortly to be followed by MCP01 within the UK sector) and North West Hutton in the UK sector. The latter, which received approval from the UK Government in the first half of 2006 to remove topsides and the steel jacket down to the bottle-leg footings, is programmed to be decommissioned between 2008 and 2009. It took three years to consult on the options and final plans for recycle or reuse of 97% of all materials (Fig. 15–6).

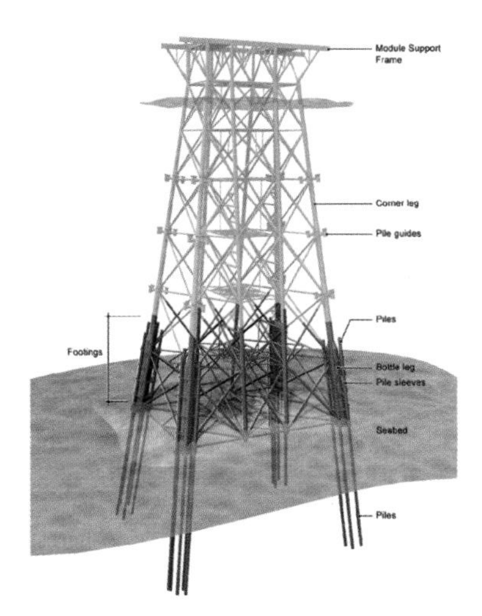

Figure 15–6 Components of North West Hutton steel jacket structure (© BP)

Floating and subsea

Many of the high-profile large structures being decommissioned in the UK sector have been unusual floating structures. These include:

- Brent Spar – a floating storage and off-loading column, originally approved in 1995 for removal to a deep seabed disposal site. This was reversed (following direct action by Greenpeace environmental activists) and later cut into segments to make the base of a ferry quay in Mekjarik, Norway, in 1999 (Fig. 15–7).
- Maureen – a unique steel gravity base platform (100,000 tonnes), which was floated free from the seabed and towed intact to Norway. Initially, full reuse options were considered, but eventually it too was recycled as a quay in Stord, Norway in 2001. As with Brent Spar, the draft required deep inshore waters to effect the subsequent deconstruction and disposal (Fig. 15–8).
- Hutton TLP – the first ever Tension Leg Platform (TLP), which was removed for reuse outside the UK, in 2002.

Fields with floating systems, especially Floating Production, Storage and Offloading vessels (FPSOs) tied into subsea manifolds lend themselves to reuse at the end of field life. To date, floating production platform Argyll

Figure 15–7 Brent Spar
(Courtesy: Shell)

Figure 15–8 Maureen platform
(Courtesy: ConocoPhillips)

(1992) and FPSOs Angus (1993), Emerald (1996), Donan (1998), Blenheim/ Bladon and Durward/Dauntless (both 2000) have been reused following field decommissioning.

Recently there has been an increasing use of subsea satellite developments tied back to existing fixed platforms, which makes decommissioning fairly straight forward for those fields.

Wells

Following a field Cessation of Production (COP), the decommissioning of production and injection wells is often the first phase of the overall programme. On platforms this requires the removal of conductors from the seabed to the platform deck, which can also have structural implications. On floating or subsea developments, it requires the removal of subsea wellheads to (approximately 5 metres) below the level of the surrounding seabed. After this time it is recommended that the fishermen check the seabed for over-trawlability and issue a clearance certificate, to preclude safety/compensation issues in the future.

From a separate perspective, the decommissioning of exploration wells is also an important issue. Remains on the seabed, especially in open water, can cause a hazard for fishermen. It is sometimes attractive to suspend discovery wells for future use in developments. However, there is no record of a well over six years old being so used, but there are many wells older than this remaining suspended. There is a rigorous tracking of well ownership and location, which is regularly communicated to fishing vessels to allow on-board plotters to be updated to help them avoid the hazards. In recognition of this, Oil & Gas UK, formerly United Kingdom Offshore Operators Association, UKOOA) since 1998 has also promoted a campaign of abandoning suspended wells, to reduce the seabed inventory. This involves the promotion of operator contributions to industry reduction targets, to lessen the hazard and maintain a good working relationship with the fishing industry.

The standards of safety required before wells can be left are of importance for all these cases. Oil & Gas UK provides a framework of good industry practice and regulatory requirements through its *Guidelines for the Suspension and Abandonment of Wells*, which is regularly updated to incorporate recent experience and learning (1995, with revisions in 2001 and 2005). The main issue is to ensure that effective barriers adequately isolate reservoir fluids both down hole and with the surface.

Pipelines

Pipeline decommissioning involves the pigging, flushing, filling and plugging of lines, followed by removal or abandonment in situ. However, the regulations relating to pipelines are currently controlled by national rather than international requirements. This, together with a low level of experience to date, means that the actions required will depend on a comparative assessment of the options available.

Pipelines can be laid on top of the seabed, trenched or buried and this may also influence the decommissioning programme required. In general, if the pipeline is of a small diameter (<12") it is likely that it will need to be removed or fully buried. This would apply to all in-field flowlines and control bundles. For larger trunk lines, the options depend on other factors and the practicality of removal, disposal, etc. There are a number of issues which influence these decisions and which need to be addressed, including overlapping/crossing pipelines, concrete mattresses, spans, seabed stability, etc.

Drill cuttings

Under some platforms there are large mounds of drill cuttings, deposited when the wells were drilled. In the main these only exist in Northern North Sea waters, where seabed currents are not strong enough to have dispersed them. These piles also contain drilling mud weighting material (barite) and hydrocarbons from when oil-based drilling muds were used. The composition, size and nature vary greatly, but some piles are over 10,000 tonnes.

Following studies for the industry (see OGP, UKOOA and OLF literature and websites) OSPAR agreed a recommendation (2006/5) which is being implemented in the UK. Piles must be characterised against specified thresholds to determine which action is necessary.

Consideration may be given to the options below:

- In situ, without treatment or capped using sand, gravel, concrete or aggregate/rocks. Some level of monitoring and/or maintenance might also be expected. There is also the possibility of introducing bacteria to accelerate bio-remediation. In the past, seabed dispersal has also been used, but it is unlikely that this would be acceptable in the future.

- Removal by pumping or dredging, with subsequent disposal by reinjection into a disposal well or into landfill. Platform footings may constrain access and handling of the materials can also be impractical. Also, the lifting of cuttings is likely, by dispersal, to broaden any onsite environmental impact and subsequent disposal, because of the sea water dilution effect, tends to magnify the problem.

Project management, engineering and safety

One of the challenges concerning decommissioning is that most North Sea structures were custom built for the particular field conditions, so decommissioning solutions will be equally as varied, with no readily tried and tested techniques. The work is non-productive so a key objective will be to find ways to reduce costs. The possibility of aggregating work over several structures, or scheduling to slack time, with flexible deadlines have been mooted as possible strategies. Developing new techniques or vessels to improve capabilities beyond straight deconstruction reverse-engineering processes may also raise possibilities.

However, with the continual change in field cessation of production and decommissioning timings, it is difficult for contractors/suppliers to understand and react to market signals. A key part of the way forward for industry therefore is to come to terms with this situation and be more lucid on operational plans, especially firm requirements and any flexibility, so the supply chain can respond effectively.

Issues which should be considered in the decommissioning programme include:

- Well killing, plugging, abandoning and surface structure removal operations can take place before the formal process decommissioning programme is complete.
- Clean-up, preparation and removal of topsides: hydrocarbons have to be removed and systems isolated, purged and cleaned before removal.
- Steel jacket removal: many deepwater structures were floated in place, not lifted with a crane-barge, and so may have to be removed in sections.
- In-field flow-line removal: especially difficult if adjacent fields are still producing.

- Clearance of all debris on the seabed, which may result from the current decommissioning operations (or even remain from earlier commissioning/ production operations) will need to be completed and checked.

There are a great many safety hazards which will need to be properly managed during the decommissioning programme implementation, including:

- Use of explosives, for underwater cutting; giving consideration to collateral damage to structures and their stability, divers, marine mammals, floating vessel damage.
- Ageing and corroding structures; suitability for decommissioning operations, unplanned eventualities arising from old/poor/incomplete records, etc.
- Dealing with contaminants needs careful consideration, especially low specific activity, LSA scale, polychlorinated biphenyls (PCBs), asbestos, etc.
- Lifting operations, especially heavy-lift or through water/air interface.
- Marine vessel interactions and sea-state/weather conditions.
- Personnel travel (helicopters) and accommodation/ maintenance of life-support on 'dead' platforms, etc.

Criteria to be considered in determining a solution

The DTI Guidelines state that the criteria used to determine the most appropriate decommissioning solutions need to take into account:

- local and international regulations (see section 15.2);
- impacts on the marine environment and other users of that environment;
- reuse and recycling opportunities; and
- cost, safety and the practical availability of technology.

Environment: when considering the environmental impacts of a given option it is necessary to assess the wider effects on the land, sea and air of the energy used, the emissions/discharges/waste streams generated and the effects they have on the marine flora, fauna and other users of the sea.

Reuse, recycling and disposal: apart from FPSOs the reuse of platforms or even process equipment has been non-existent to date. The reasons why this does not make economic sense in the North Sea include the lack of operational confidence in second-hand equipment in a high-cost environment, recertification issues, tax/duty anomalies and customisation mismatch. A more likely possibility exists of refurbishment and reuse into other areas, eg Hutton TLP in Russia and in usage for different requirements, eg Brent Spar and Maureen cut up to build quays. Failing that, most is brought to shore and recycled as scrap. There is always a proportion that will end as landfill, but this should be reduced to as low as practical and is usually less than 10% by weight.

Cost and safety: the onus is on the operator to find the most cost-effective option which does not compromise the safety of workers or the environment. At present, the cost for platforms is in the order of £30 million for a small Southern North Sea platform and £100–200 million for a large Northern North Sea platform.

Public opinion: the views and concerns of people outside the industry are important, overall in setting the climate for legislation but also individually through statutory and other consultees influencing regulatory approvals (see section 15.4).

Research and development

Research and development, R&D, takes place across the industry, with operators, major contractors, specialist suppliers, universities etc. and sometimes through programmes supported by government. R&D areas to date include the following:

- alternative removal methods, looking to develop new vessels attempting to remove topsides in one go or in the floating removal of jackets;
- underwater cutting – there have been a lot of advances here through the use of abrasive water-jets, diamond wire cutters and shaped explosive charges;
- drill cuttings removal; and
- lifting, back-loading and sea-fastening methods.

15.4 Business perspective: productive life and liability

Asset trading and the impact of decommissioning liabilities

The UK North Sea is a maturing province, but figures estimated in 2006 show that there could be between 16 and 27 bn boe yet to be recovered. Continuing success, in part, rides on the back of existing physical infrastructure and attracting new investment. With a high oil price, the viability of existing fields is extended, bringing with it a wider window of opportunity for smaller fields to get to market using this infrastructure. In recent years, this has provided an opportunity for new players, bringing significant investment to existing asset maintenance and integrity, as well as for new developments.

The DTI policy of maximising recovery through attracting investment from a diversity of companies is, to some extent, offset by the Petroleum Act 1998 which defines the liability on all these companies to effectively eliminate the risk to government of any default on decommissioning obligations. It is important that joint venture partners can cover their obligations and liabilities, but onerous responses to security needs can work against asset trading and subsequent investment.

The overall cost of decommissioning primarily falls on the current asset owners but the legislative mechanism for decommissioning obligations (section 29 of the Petroleum Act 1998) is separate from licence requirements (so that it can extend liabilities beyond the normal timescale for exploration and production licence operations).

Usually the liability passes with the licence transfer, but the DTI can require some parties to retain the liability, even though they have no further commercial arrangements with the licence. To manage this ongoing decommissioning liability (which is joint and several on all section 29 parties) existing parties often require securities from those coming in, if the deal includes taking on these liabilities.

To help in managing this situation, the industry in 2005/6 created a template Decommissioning Security Agreement (DSA) which sets up an agreed 'boilerplate' format, with options for negotiation. The initial driver was to streamline the process for companies needing to establish such agreements (either before production start-up tied to the Field Development Plans or upon transfer of the asset). It also gave increased confidence to the commercial arrangements (given the importance of controlling exposure to decommissioning liabilities) ie improvements in efficiency and effectiveness. Also, associated with this, in an attempt to get some consistency in the decommissioning cost estimates concerned with individual assets, a standard cost-estimating guideline has been created.

The template DSA, together with guidance notes on its usage and the relative benefits of its options (and the cost-estimating guide), is available from the Oil & Gas UK website www.oilandgas.org.uk. It is a stand-alone agreement, but should be linked to the Joint Operating Agreement (JOA) by the common terms and obligations. It allows inclusion of all section 29 parties (both those still as licensees and party to the JOA and others) and, if appropriate (by use of DTI recognised options), the Secretary of State.

It includes the use of a new Trust Fund concept, widely used in potential insolvency cases to provide a secure place for any liquidated guarantees due to default, until such time as they can be used for the decommissioning purpose they were set up for. It also tries to minimise the overlaps of different securities

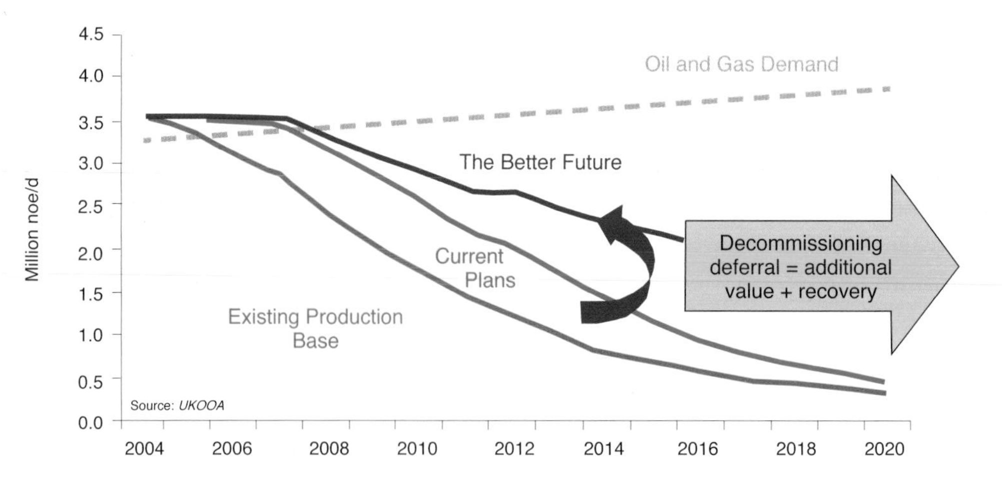

Figure 15–9 Future of the UKCS

due to different commercial arrangements and provides an option to adjust the 'safety factor' applied to calculations, to fit with the level of uncertainty in the cost estimation.

Currently, the only recognised forms of security guarantee in use are bank letters of credit or (for commercial arrangements involving strong companies only) parent company guarantees. This does not suit everyone and the industry is looking at alternatives to give a range of options. The workability of options is, however, strongly dependent on taxation treatment.

Reputation management: public consultation and confidence

As the decommissioning of redundant North Sea oil and gas installations becomes an increasingly important activity for operators in the UKCS, it has the potential to again attract significant interest from external audiences, particularly on environmental, social and economic impact issues.

Engaging with these interested parties is a critical element of achieving a successful outcome and although each decommissioning project will have different issues and drivers, operators' current and past experience of stakeholder dialogue can be analysed to find some common principles and methods.

Every decommissioning project involves consultation – with partners, regulators, and statutory consultees (in the UK this includes the fishing organisations, primarily Scottish Fishermen's Federation, SFF, and the National Federation of Fishermen's Organisations, NFFO, and the Joint Nature Conservation Council, JNCC).

The experience of recent years, however, suggests that in future, consultation will need to be much wider and take a rather different approach. It is therefore becoming common for some operators to now run more extensive stakeholder consultation programmes, especially when derogation is an option. Involving this wider spectrum of stakeholders makes sound business sense. Company reputation is an important commodity and identifying potential conflict and addressing it early is a sound strategy for protecting reputation.

It is only through dialogue that different sectors and interest groups can resolve the dilemmas associated with formulating a decommissioning programme, and this will enable a robust solution to be established and endorsed by the regulator. The DTI publishes guidelines on how stakeholder consultation should be included in the decommissioning programme formulation. These are found at http://www.og.dti.gov.uk/regulation/guidance.guidenote.htm and explain how a wide ranging stakeholder dialogue should precede statutory public consultation in certain cases. Oil & Gas UK has also developed guidelines on effective stakeholder dialogue, drawing from experiences at North West Hutton and Frigg (this can be found at http://www.oilandgas.org.uk).

Outline of a stakeholder dialogue process:

- identify and prioritise stakeholders;
- analyse and map stakeholder interests;
- define dialogue strategy;
- implement stakeholder engagement plan;
- analyse, evaluate and feed back into decommissioning programme.

Some of the key themes and issues which are consistently raised by stakeholders through dialogue on North Sea decommissioning are:

- the 'clean seabed' principle and no dumping of installations;
- concern over material left on the seabed being a hazard for fishermen;
- uncertainty about the long-term effects of leaving drill cuttings piles;
- alternative uses of equipment, as opposed to disposal solutions;
- concerns over potentially hazardous waste streams;
- UK employment and regional economic impact aspirations; and
- long-term legacy issues.

Decommissioning contracts

There has been much speculation in recent years about whether decommissioning will create a lucrative new part to the UK industry, with associated jobs. As the North Sea matures, technical project and operational support for developments will increasingly turn from construction and commissioning to decommissioning.

However, this is likely to sustain jobs rather than create more, with the overall numbers reducing as, compared with investment in productive developments, decommissioning is not so potent a force in the economy.

Decommissioning is a different market from installation and contractors may have to re-establish their credentials as demand builds and new technologies become available. There are also differing factors which need to be taken into account, particularly with respect to:

- project management;
- financing, risk management and contract regime;
- varying and extending activity completion times;
- cross-operator collaboration to co-ordinate/aggregate activities;
- duty-of-care responsibilities for disposals; and
- residual offshore liabilities and monitoring survey requirements.

Whilst deferral of decommissioning expenditure and continued production due to oil price rises is to be welcomed, the variability of timing estimates creates problems in establishing an effective market place for decommissioning operations. Contractors have difficulty in gearing up technology and workforce for an ever changing activity plan. A key part of the way forward for industry is to come to terms with this situation by being more lucid on operational plans, especially firm requirements and any flexibility, so that the supply chain can respond effectively.

As well as an uncertain market, there are a number of specific risks uniquely associated with decommissioning which will need to be appropriately accommodated in service contracts. These include:

- condition of the structures, facing unforeseen problems related to poor records or deterioration;
- preparations in the proximity of continuing production operations;
- differing standards for new contractors to the oil and gas industry;
- achieving new technical challenges, eg cutting, lifting or floatation;
- conditions of work, including handling hazards associated with metocean, weight/size, hydrocarbon, etc. as for normal operations, but also the presence of asbestos, PCBs, LSA scale, etc. and other conditions.

In recognition of this, the industry is developing LOGIC Standard Contracts *Specific Recommended Contractual Provisions with Guidance Notes for Decommissioning Projects at the UKCS* (for publication and use in 2007).

The diversity of contractor segments engaged in decommissioning, include:

- engineering design and project management contractors;
- clean-up and facilities preparation contractors;
- drilling contractors;
- subsea contractors;
- heavy-lift and transport barge contractors; and
- disposal and refurbishment contractors.

15.5 Public perspective: legacy management

Other users of the sea: fishing issues

Oil & Gas UK has had a long-term working relationship with fishing organisations, especially the Scottish Fishermen's Federation, SFF and the National Federation of Fishermen's Organisations, NFFO. There is constructive dialogue on ensuring that interactions between the two active users of the North Sea does not get acrimonious and, often, to provide mutually beneficial services. Discussions in recent years have been held to consider how best to manage the implications of any decommissioning legacy left on the seabed for the long term.

The oil and gas industry currently provides regularly updated information on all seabed inventories to the fishermen to help prevent interaction with their operations and a comprehensive compensation scheme to address where incidents do occur. What is needed is a means to extend this into the future and to cover decommissioned sites, where owners have completed their approved programme and moved on. There is great interest in setting up a Fisheries Legacy Trust Company which would address the long-term safety of fishermen and fulfil DTI requirements for a long-term management of the legacy (as the legislation requires owners to retain any residual liability in perpetuity).

Industry forums and other sources of information on decommissioning

Following the establishment of PILOT in 1999, a North Sea Decommissioning Forum was established, recognising the likelihood for substantive decommissioning activity with the low oil price of the day. Although this became subsequently defunct, some of the associated forums remain. There is a Decommissioning Technology Forum, DTF, and The Early Decommissioning, TEDs group. More recently, PILOT established a working group to address the issue of decommissioning securities affecting asset trading and investments. It is also aiming to promote and stimulate the decommissioning supply-chain capability.

The following website links to relevant information may be of assistance:

Regulatory bodies:

DTI Guidance: http://www.og.dti.gov.uk/regulation/guidance.guidenote.htm
OSPAR guidelines: http://www.ospar.org/
IMO: http://www.imo.org/
EU Commission, DG Environment:
http://www.europa.eu.int/comm/environment/index_en.htm/

Industry bodies:

Oil & Gas UK: http://www.oilandgas.org.uk/
PILOT: http://www.pilottaskforce.co.uk/index
OGP: http://www.ogp.org.uk/
OLF: http://www.olf.no/

Case Studies – some past decommissioning programmes

www.shell.com (section on Brent Redundant Facilities)
http://www.kerr-mcgee.com (information on Hutton TLP)
www.phillips66.com/maureen/decommprog/prog.htm
www.totalfinaelf.no/en/Activities/Field+decommissioning (section on Frigg)
www.bp.com (information on North West Hutton)
http://phillips.netpower.no (section on Ekofisk)

15.6 Conclusions

Public perception of the appropriateness of how the oil and gas industry applies itself to the decommissioning of structures at the end of productive life will influence the legislative requirements to which it is obliged to comply. This, in turn, drives the technical solutions available and the commercial consequences. The position today is a consequence of the issues of the past and it is important that the industry builds an improved licence to operate in the future from a robust and transparent response to external concerns that generates public confidence.

Because of variable commercial factors, especially oil price, the oil and gas business is dynamic and decommissioning plans are very fluid. Continued investment extends productive asset life, maintaining economic activity but continually adjusting decommissioning forecasts. This uncertainty adversely affects the market place which provides the contractor workforce and technological capability needed to deliver cost-effective decommissioning programmes.

Another challenge will be how well the industry manages any legacy issues resulting from its implemented decommissioning programmes. It is likely that most structures will be removed and the final 'footprint' will be small, but anything which remains needs to have a minimum impact on the environment and other users of the sea. Ideally the economic legacy resulting from this industry's successes and the management schemes put in place for any seabed residue will satisfy public expectations and leave a net positive legacy when the industry moves on from UK waters.

DECOMMISSIONING

LEGAL

15.7 Introduction

One of the most challenging and pressing issues facing the oil and gas industry is decommissioning and abandonment of offshore equipment and installations. The potential future expenditure involved is considerable and the technical and operational resources required will be extensive and, as this part of the chapter considers, compliance with international, regional and domestic legislation means that operators and related parties will require extensive advice and the co-operation of all those involved. Expenditure estimates for future removal of the 600 or so installations and pipelines in the North Sea is thought to be in the region of £10–20 billion. And, given the UK Government's current stance that the tax payer should not be burdened with any decommissioning and removal costs, it remains for the commercial participants in the North Sea to plan for, and regulate, these significant financial liabilities. There has been recent debate in the UK amongst industry organisations and participants that suggests that unless the Government addresses the future costs of decommissioning and considers introducing measures in the forthcoming Energy Bill (expected in the 2007–08 session of Parliament) that simplify and bolster decommissioning and security requirements, then investment in the North Sea may well suffer. Moreover, although currently a proportion of decommissioning costs can be offset against tax, the fiscal stance of government going forward will be a crucial factor. This part of the chapter is concerned with how legislation, both international and domestic, along with commercial contractual arrangements, addresses the matter of such decommissioning liabilities.

In the current political and commercial environment, the UKCS is a fairly dynamic region of the world for those in the oil and gas business. UK Government initiatives, in consultation with industry, have moved towards facilitating smaller operators/production companies to enter the market for mature assets and, in turn, this has affected the financial landscape regarding decommissioning liabilities and security. For new entrants and smaller existing businesses the prospect of assuming part of a field's decommissioning liability could deter entrants. In particular, the UKCS legislative framework, in seeking to insulate the tax payer from any burden, sets a 'joint and several'[1] liability obligation on parties which is extremely wide-ranging. The UKCS liability regime captures related parties that may well be further up the corporate structure from the licensee and, indeed, allows for an almost perpetual obligation for decommissioning costs to rest on all and any parties that may have at any time held a licence interest or have been associated with it. In the UK, the Secretary of State for Trade and Industry[2] has powers under legislation to regulate all such liabilities. As discussed below, efforts have recently been made to address certain vendor/purchaser concerns relating to the provision of security for historical decommissioning liabilities where assets are transacted.

Characteristic of such a liability regime are precisely drafted legal contracts that satisfy the parties' obligations under the legislation but also reflect and guarantee their respective work and financial and ownership obligations. In line with other developments in the legal contractual framework in the UKCS, a draft template for a Decommissioning Security Agreement[3] has recently been tabled and it is hoped that, as with the industry Master Deed[4] and standard format Joint Operating Agreements (JOAs)[5], it will become more efficient and indeed easier to document decommissioning arrangements. Clearly it is in all parties' interests to move toward standardised but flexible practice and procedure, notwithstanding the higher-level fiscal and policy considerations of government.

While some comparative work on decommissioning practice and procedure has been undertaken which looked at the UKCS and the Gulf of Mexico,[6] there is little recently written on the legal nexus that regulates the liabilities for removal and disposal of installations on the UKCS. As progress towards decommissioning of some of the North Sea's older installations quickens, government, industry groups, asset holders and the legal profession have been examining how best to develop existing structures and practices to suit the changing regulatory and financial environment but also to balance this with business investment aspirations.

Below, consideration is given to the three principal layers of legislation which regulate the decommissioning process in the UKCS and the ways in which liabilities for decommissioning are addressed in three key agreements: the Decommissioning Agreement itself (which details the content, planning and implementation of the decommissioning content); the JOA which sets out certain obligations relating to decommissioning for owners of joint property; and the Financial Security Agreement which is designed to ensure that each of the parties that has any financial liabilities for decommissioning holds or deposits adequate financial security to meet their respective obligations. One of the objectives of the new draft Decommissioning Security Agreement is to provide, in a standalone agreement, detailed contractual arrangements capable of surviving the termination of a JOA and thus making clear ongoing liabilities where cessation of production may leave residual material on the seabed.

Historically, as most of the development in the UKCS has been carried out by major oil companies with strong balance sheets and a wide portfolio of assets, companies tended not to put into place formal abandonment security agreements but rather to rely on the fact that each of them was clearly 'good for the money'. As the North Sea basin matures and an increasing number of smaller companies, some with only a single asset or a very small number of assets, come to own interests in the North Sea, there is less comfort available to their field partners that they will be able to meet their abandonment commitments when called upon to do so – simply, their balance sheets may not be strong enough to give their field partners comfort that they will be around in seven or ten years' time when a large decommissioning liability crystallises. To that extent, the risk of insolvency of field partners impacting on their other field partners has always been there; it is just that it has become greater, and more of an issue as smaller players come into the market. The development of an industry standard abandonment security agreement should result in greater certainty for all parties, including the Government, that all decommissioning liabilities have been effectively secured.

15.8 Overview of current legal structures

International

The 1958 Geneva Convention on the Continental Shelf[7] was the first international agreement which considered the decommissioning of offshore installations. This Convention recognised the need for international control over offshore installations and other devices to be constructed on the seabed, both during their operating life and after they ceased functioning. The 1958 Geneva Convention was superceded in 1997 when the UK ratified the 1982 United Nations Convention on the Law of the Sea (UNCLOS).[8] UNCLOS built upon the Geneva Convention and provided, in Article 60(3), for the adoption of further 'accepted international standards', to be set out by a 'competent international organisation'. Subsequently the International Maritime Organisation (IMO)[9] emerged as the competent international organisation which is based in London.

IMO devised 'generally accepted international standards' in the form of the 1989 IMO Guidelines to be adhered to by member governments when making decisions involving abandoned or disused offshore installations. In general, the IMO Guidelines provide instruction relating to the removal of installations in various water depths, the extent of removal required and any foreseeable interference the disused structures may have with other uses of the sea, principally protecting the fishing and shipping industries.

Regional

The second layer in the tripartite legislative and regulatory structure affecting UKCS decommissioning is the regional layer. The Oslo and Paris Convention on the Protection of the Marine Environment of the North East Atlantic (OSPAR)[10] was agreed in 1992 and sought to bring together the two earlier Paris and Oslo Conventions on dumping at sea and discharges into the sea from land. OSPAR is, therefore, the primary regional Convention on the dumping of offshore installations affecting the UKCS. It was, however, the decision taken at the OSPAR meeting in July of 1998 (Decision 98/3)[11] that largely provides for complete removal of topsides and subsea structures to the shore for recycling or disposal. The Decision allows for derogation from the main rule in certain circumstances on a case-by-case basis. Installations which may be eligible for consideration for derogation from Decision 98/3 are those weighing more than 10,000 tonnes the removal of which may be technically difficult or environmentally sensitive. Decisions for the grant of derogation lie with governments of the OSPAR contracting parties following a predetermined consultation process.

Domestic

The Department of Trade and Industry (DTI), acting through the Secretary of State, is the UK government department responsible for ensuring that the UK's obligations under international and regional legislation are met and that businesses operating on the UKCS comply with relevant domestic legislation. In fact, the exclusive right of searching, boring and for getting petroleum from the UKCS vests in Her Majesty the Queen, the Secretary of State being the authority which grants licences to the oil exploration companies. The body of domestic legislation which governs operations in the UKCS is largely enshrined in the Petroleum Act 1998 although, as will be seen below, there is a significant body of other primary and secondary legislation which is also relevant.

The Petroleum Act 1998[12] and Licence Model Clauses

The Petroleum Act 1998 is the primary legislation which controls the licensing and regulatory regime in the UKCS. Part IV of the Act sets out the requirements for the decommissioning process and gives effect to the obligations of the licensees under the licence which operates through a number of Model Clauses.[13] In order to assist the industry and in consultation with it, in August 2000, the DTI issued a set of Guidance Notes for Industry[14] setting out guidance for those engaged in preparing decommissioning programmes (it is a requirement under both the licence and the Act that the licensee submits a fully costed decommissioning plan to the DTI for approval). This guidance is updated from time to time, most recently in February 2006. A decommissioning programme approved by the Secretary confers an obligation on the persons who submitted the programme to ensure that it is carried out. The submitting party or parties must prove to the Secretary of State that they are capable of carrying out the decommissioning programme and, should they not be able to, then the Secretary of State ultimately has the right to commission the work and recover the cost from the parties. It is this area of the domestic legislation which largely gives rise to the matter of decommissioning security and how the costs of decommissioning are to be met.

The interaction between the Act and the licensing regime hinges on section 29(1) of the Act and on Model Clause 19 of the current standard offshore production licence. It is principally the exploration and production licences which give rise to the underlying obligations for abandonment and decommissioning of offshore installations and the requirement to submit fully costed decommissioning programmes to the DTI. The DTI has utilised a standard licence format for some time using Model Clauses, a number of which set out the obligations of the licensee with regard to abandonment.

It should be pointed out, however, that since the First Licensing Round over 40 years ago, successive governments have amended and updated the Model Clauses. This is important in the context of commercial transactions involving the transfer of Licence Interests because where, for example, a new JOA is to be created and will be based on the 20th Round standard form, then the references to Licence Model Clauses will not apply. For example, where a Licence Interest is being transferred relating to a Licence granted in 1964, the Model Clauses that will apply to that Licence will not be the Current Model Clauses. One must return to the statutory instrument which created the Current Model Clauses and which incorporates all previous Model Clauses to be sure of applying the correct references. The Petroleum (Current Model Clauses) Order (SI 1999 No 160) contains the full set of Model Clauses as incorporated into the Petroleum Act 1998.

The two most relevant current Model Clauses in relation to decommissioning are Model Clauses 19 and 31.

Model Clause 19

Model Clause 19 governs the licensee's obligations regarding abandonment. The licensee may not abandon any well without the consent in writing of the

Minister (Secretary of State) and must ensure compliance with any conditions under which the Minister's consent is granted. Simply put, once the Secretary has granted his consent for an abandonment based on a fully costed abandonment programme, the licensee is obliged to carry out the programme. Model Clause 19.5 states that the plugging of any well must be done in accordance with the specifications approved by the Minister and works carried out are required to be done in an efficient and workmanlike manner. There is an obligation on the licensee to ensure that any well which is the subject of a licence is plugged and sealed. Any materials such as fixtures and casings left in situ following completion of a decommissioning programme are deemed to be property of the Minister although the ongoing environmental liability is likely to rest with the parties. It is clear therefore, that once granted a licence the responsibility for ensuring a site is decommissioned in compliance with an approved programme lies with the licensee who has submitted it. However, as discussed below, the net of obligation in this regard may extend far and wide.

Model Clause 31

Under Model Clause 31, the licensee is obliged to keep accurate records of any well plugging or abandonment undertaken and to furnish such information to the Minister when required to do so. Should the licensee fail to perform any obligations under the terms of the licence, then the Minister has the power to step in and cause the works to be undertaken at the cost of the licensee. Failure to perform any of the licence obligations also gives the Minister the right to revoke the licence.

Under section 31(5) of the Act the Secretary has the power to withdraw a section 29 notice where a party transfers its interest under the licence and he is satisfied that the residual and ongoing financial obligations of the remaining licensees are secured. In certain cases where, as a result of a transfer, there is only one licensee, the Secretary has the powers to require that the transferor (the party selling part or all of its interests) remain liable for the performance of the remaining licensee's decommissioning liabilities (again, this is an issue which is addressed in the new draft Decommissioning Security Agreement). The broad thrust of the legislation is to ensure that there will always be a party who has the financial ability to secure completion of the decommissioning programme. It is in the area of licence interest transfers and related residual and ongoing decommissioning liabilities that gives rise to the need for decommissioning security arrangements and which has given the industry certain cause for concern.

Section 29(1)

A section 29 notice can be served on any person responsible for the management of the installation which is the subject of the licence (normally the operator);

any person who is a licensee or party to a JOA, giving him similar rights to explore for or lift petroleum; or any other person who owns an interest in the installation otherwise than as security for a loan. This final element ensures that where lending institutions have taken security over a company's assets and in effect 'owns' an interest in the asset which is subject to a section 29 notice, the institution does not attract any liability for its decommissioning. In addition, the Secretary of State can, under section 34 of the Act, serve section 29 notices on any persons who are 'associated' with a company which has, at any time held a licence interest. These are wide-ranging powers and effectively mean that any person who has been associated with an offshore installation can be liable for its decommissioning. As mentioned above, the 'joint and several' nature of the liability under the Act means that where one party to a decommissioning agreement and associated abandonment security agreement defaults, then the remaining parties are liable for the defaulting parties proportion of such decommissioning liability. It is this wide-ranging effect which gives prospective new entrants to the UKCS the greatest concern and which any vendor of interests wants to secure against in relation to future decommissioning liabilities.

The effect of service of a section 29 notice is that each person on whom it is served becomes obliged to submit an abandonment programme to the Secretary of State and, upon submission of that programme, each person who submits the programme becomes obliged to implement the programme, irrespective of whether or not, at the time at which the abandonment programme falls to be implemented, they still have any economic interest in the installation, the licence, JOA or other related contract.

Thus the primary obligation on licensees arises from the time that the licence is granted. The Minister has all the necessary powers to ensure that the liability for decommissioning is secured to his satisfaction. Notwithstanding the provisions in the licence and the powers of the Minister, there are a number of other legislative measures with which UKCS operatives are required to comply.

Coast Protection Act 1949[15]

The Coast Protection Act 1949 deals largely with safety of navigation and requires that before any installation or pipeline can be built on the seabed, the consent of the Secretary of State is required. There is a standard form of decommissioning obligation under this Act; however, a satisfactorily completed decommissioning programme as submitted under the terms of the 1998 Act would satisfy this obligation.

Food and Environment Protection Act 1985[16]

While this piece of legislation captures deposits of substances or articles on or under the seabed within UK controlled waters, a number of exceptions exist within this Act's Schedule which largely exempt oil and gas exploration activities as these are caught under the 1998 Act.

Environmental Protection Act 1990[17] and the Waste Management Licensing Regulations 1994[18]

These two items of legislation reflect, in domestic legislation, the requirements of the EC Framework Directive on Waste and relate largely to 'controlled waste' which is regulated under licence. Under this and associated control of pollution legislation, registration with the Environment Agency is required.

Pollution Prevention and Control Act 1999[19]

This legislation, as it relates to the oil and gas industry, is concerned largely with the removal of metallic items during the decommissioning process. Authorisation to carry out removal of metallic substances is required under this Act.

Special Waste Regulations 1996[20]

Certain types of waste can be designated 'special wastes' as set out under these regulations. There is a requirement to inform the relevant government agency prior to any proposed movement of special waste.

Transfrontier Shipment of Waste Regulations 1994[21]

Another enabling piece of legislation, these regulations provide that EC Regulation 259/93[22] which controls the international movement of waste is given effect under UK law. In particular, these regulations affect the decommissioning of offshore installations where any waste may be transported across international boundaries.

Radioactive Substances Act 1993[23]

This Act applies to offshore installations and particularly where planning of routes for the removal of waste is considered. Application should be made to the relevant authority to identify whether or not authorisation is required. It is likely that any proposed new route for the removal of waste would require an application for authorisation.

Transfrontier Shipment of Radioactive Waste Regulations 1993[24]

This legislation would affect offshore installations where any radioactive waste may be evident and where, after decommissioning, such waste was to be shipped to a State outside the EU. Approval to ship such waste is granted by the relevant regulatory body, either the Environment Agency[25] or, in the case of Scotland, SEPA.[26]

Dangerous Substances in Harbour Areas Regulations 1987[27]
The control of all classes of dangerous substances, including the carriage, loading, unloading and storage of such substances in harbour and port areas, is regulated through this legislation.

Water Resources Act 1991[28]
It is an offence both in Scotland and in England and Wales to cause or knowingly permit any poisonous, noxious or polluting material to enter controlled waters. Controlled waters are waters 3 miles from the defined baseline both in England and Wales and in Scotland.

Health and Safety at Work, etc. Act 1974[29]
For every proposed decommissioning of an offshore installation, a Safety Case is required to be submitted to and accepted by the HSE. Safety Cases must be submitted to the HSE at least six months before any decommissioning operations commence. All works including those covering the dismantling of pipelines and installations are subject to the provisions of the Health and Safety at Work, etc. Act 1974. There are a number of other specific pieces of legislation that cover well, pipeline and installations. The Offshore Installations (Safety Case) Regulations 2005 came into effect in April of 2006 and are aimed at simplifying procedures and aligning the various separate pieces of legislation into a more cohesive body of regulations and statutes.

Export controls[30]
Where any parts of decommissioned installations are considered to be potentially 'dual-use', that is parts that may be used in other ways, particularly military uses, an export licence may be required. Largely, there is a list of exceptions to the requirement for an export licence. The Export Control Organisation of the DTI is the authority with responsibility for assessing whether the export of oil and gas installations for reuse outside the UK requires a licence.

15.9 Decommissioning under the Joint Operating Agreement (JOA)

In addition to the statutory framework which controls decommissioning, the individual contractual arrangements between parties govern liabilities and obligations under a number of commonly utilised legal contracts. The three main contracts that are encountered are the Joint Operating Agreement (JOA), the Decommissioning Agreement and the Financial Security Agreement or Decommissioning Security Agreement. One of the most critical provisions of these contractual arrangements relates to the decommissioning programme and budget and the fundamental issue of how the parties' costs will be provided for and secured. It should be noted that such liabilities can run to many tens if not hundreds of millions of pounds and the actual completion of decommissioning of infrastructure may be 10 to 20 years away. It is, therefore, quite common for assets to have changed hands many times before decommissioning actually takes place. As noted above, it is a requirement under legislation to submit to the Secretary a fully costed decommissioning programme and it is how the parties manage their obligations under that programme that is a common element in these three agreements. Usually it is the operator, for the time being, who is in control of the decommissioning process and information flow along with any appointed joint committee. These bodies have the main responsibilities and obligations under the JOA in relation to decommissioning. It should also be noted that even after a party no longer has an interest under a licence, it may retain decommissioning obligations and liabilities.

As the title suggests, the JOA governs the rights and obligations of those parties who have an interest in the licence. It is further worth reminding ourselves that under legislation and the JOA, the liabilities in relation to decommissioning are joint and several which means that even if there is a defaulting party which may be unable to meet its financial liabilities under the agreement, the non-defaulting parties must share that defaulting party's percentage element of decommissioning cost.

The main elements of the decommissioning obligations under the JOA regulate the decommissioning budget, the decommissioning plan and the decommissioning programme. Under the UKOOA 20th Round industry standard JOA the operator is responsible for preparing the plan, programme and budget when it calculates that 50% of the recoverable reserves of the field have been produced, or earlier if the joint operating committee so decides. The operator draws up the decommissioning plan in consultation and is responsible for ensuring that all parties' obligations under legislation are complied with. The decommissioning plan will normally cover the following aspects:

- a geological/reservoir review of the field;
- the costs of the final decommissioning obligations of the parties;
- an estimate of the date on which the cumulative net cash flow from production will equal 150% of the costs of final decommissioning obligations;
- the salvage value of any jointly owned property which is the subject of the decommissioning; and
- among other elements, consideration of the plugging of wells, removal of structures and pipelines.

The members of the Joint Operating Committee, having had an opportunity to review the proposed decommissioning plan and budget will grant the operator the authority to proceed with the expenditure required to carry out the plan.

In circumstances where one party wishes to assign (that is sell or pass) its interest under a licence and JOA, it is a normal requirement that the party who joins the licence provide acceptable security in respect of the cost of final decommissioning attributable as a percentage share equal to the joining party's interest acquired under the licence. Under the standard form 20th Round JOA, it is a condition precedent to any assignment that such acceptable security is put in place. There is an obligation on the party who is providing the security in such circumstances to inform the Joint Operating Committee of any material adverse change in any matter relating to its business which may impact on the reliability and enforceability of any such security.

Thus the responsibility for managing the programme, budget and plans for decommissioning usually rests with the operator and that through the Joint Operating Committee, among other things, expenditure is authorised. The JOA also contains provisions which regulate the change in ownership of interests in relation to decommissioning liabilities and imposes obligations on parties leaving the licence to ensure that any new participant provides acceptable security for its percentage share of any decommissioning costs. In addition to the JOA, it is normal practice to have in place a separate Decommissioning Agreement which details the actual process for the final decommissioning of the asset.

15.10 Decommissioning Agreements

While the JOA documents the relationship between licence participants and their resulting joint property, the Decommissioning Agreement details the actual process, timing and cost apportionment of the decommissioning programme as submitted to the Secretary. It should be noted that the Decommissioning Agreement is not the abandonment programme as submitted to the Secretary of State under a section 29 notice but rather the document regulating the final decommissioning process including, among other things, the critical accounting procedure. It is not uncommon to see parties to Decommissioning Agreements that no longer have any interest in the asset. Here, the issue of residual liability is evident in which all asset owners past and present may remain liable until such times as decommissioning has been fully effected. This aspect of the maturing UKCS is particularly relevant where there is a buoyant market for assets and in a climate where small businesses are entering the market for those assets. Many of these smaller companies may not have the financial reserves to take on full decommissioning costs and, very often, the bigger oil companies, due to their section 29 notices not having been withdrawn by the Secretary, will remain part of any decommissioning financial structure. The Secretary has powers under legislation to withdraw a section 29 notice and in taking applications for withdrawal into account, the Secretary's overarching concern is to ensure that the asset will be fully decommissioned in accordance with the abandonment programme and at zero cost to the taxpayer.

Generally the decommissioning agreement will sanction the procurement of a 'baseline' survey of the infrastructure to be decommissioned which will be administered by the operator on behalf of the participants. The baseline survey is a full survey of the infrastructure to be decommissioned and would normally be carried out by an independent third party. The detailed scope of any survey would also be annexed to the decommissioning agreement itself. The baseline survey forms the basis on which costs are assessed and works planned.

As with many agreements where joint property, rights and obligations are involved, there will be a joint committee, namely the decommissioning committee, which oversees the budgetary process and agrees the decommissioning programme. The decommissioning committee will have some of the following duties:

- initiating discussions with the Secretary of State;
- preparing the draft decommissioning programme for approval by each of the parties and for submission to the Secretary of State;
- reviewing and revising the decommissioning programme;
- preparing and securing approval of an abandonment safety case;
- overseeing the management, implementation and operation of the decommissioning programme;
- reporting to the parties on the status of any works;
- the provision of reports, data and information to the parties; and
- engaging such advisors as required to carry out the works.

Normally, the committee would have a member from each of the parties and the operator would usually hold the chair, each party having one vote. The agreements also have mechanisms for regulating actions leading up to decommissioning and from the date of cessation of production. Generally, there will be provisions relating to the expenditure of joint funds and certain approval mechanisms are required where large sums are being drawn upon.

As is normal in the UKCS, the parties agree to keep the other parties indemnified for any claim by, or liability to, any non-party. The operator, who shoulders the greatest responsibility under the agreement, is generally not held liable for any loss, etc., which results from its performance of any decommissioning duties except where there has been wilful misconduct. Each party, as required by the decommissioning committee, would normally be required to have in place all the necessary insurances at all relevant times.

Where assets are covered by JOAs it would be normal for the terms of a separate Decommissioning Agreement to override those of the JOA on matters of decommissioning. The parties would also usually execute an agreement which manages the provision of security for the relevant percentage of the decommissioning costs. The financial security agreement is a critical element of the decommissioning process and a PILOT working group has recently commissioned a template Decommissioning Security Agreement which should make the issue of security provision a clearer and more effective process for all participants.

15.11 Decommissioning Security Agreements (DSAs)

The new template DSA is designed to be entered into by all parties to a JOA and should either replace or supplement any existing provisions in a JOA regarding security for decommissioning. While the agreement has not been drafted specifically in relation to the sale and purchase of licence interests, it will be utilised to regulate the security requirements of those who are coming off a licence but who have some ongoing liability for decommissioning costs (for example where a section 29 notice has not been withdrawn). The provision of such security is to the benefit of the selling party to ensure that any ongoing liability is adequately funded.

It has been common in the past that the incoming party is required to provide security to more than one party to the JOA thus having to provide double security. The new template DSA, in tackling the issue of ongoing liabilities for decommissioning, introduces the concept of second- and third-tier participants. These concepts contemplate the situation where a former owner of an interest remains liable and has not had their section 29 notice withdrawn. The new template agreement allows such parties to become a party to the DSA without the obligation to provide any security under it. The DSA also allows for those parties who have had their section 29 notices withdrawn, and who find themselves with some financial liability for decommissioning the installation, to have limited rights under the DSA. This is achieved through specific drafting in the DSA which allows a non-party to the DSA certain limited rights under the Contracts (Rights of Third Parties) Act 1999. The template DSA contemplates the case where such entity, which finds itself liable but not party to any decommissioning security arrangements, has access to the security granted under the DSA and to draw upon such security.

As there is some variety regarding the treatment of decommissioning in JOAs, the standalone DSA is designed to survive the termination of a JOA. However, where the DSA is entered into in conjunction with a JOA or a UOA then some interaction between the provisions of such agreements will result.

In essence, the DSA provides for a decommissioning security fund of a certain size which, over time, will grow to cover the estimated costs of abandonment some years later. It is normal for the fund to be controlled and administered by the security trustee under a trust deed. The operator of the asset will be the trustee on behalf of itself and the other beneficiaries, the beneficiaries being all those parties to the decommissioning security agreement.

The calculation of the size of the fund of money required to cover the decommissioning liability is usually linked to the concept known as Net Present Value (NPV). This refers, in this case, to the NPV of the petroleum remaining to be produced and the NPV of the likely costs of abandonment. In essence, whenever the NPV of the likely abandonment cost is equal to or greater than the NPV of the net revenues likely to be received from the sale of petroleum from the field, a requirement to put up security arises so that at least the difference between the positive NPV of the income stream and the higher negative NPV of the abandonment cost is covered by security. In this way, as production declines to cessation of production, the amount of security increases so that at cessation of production, the DSA is fully funded. The inputs into this valuation formula are usually retested every year based upon the operator's estimates for future production, opex and abandonment costs, the application of an appropriate discount rate and with provision for reference to an independent expert should the parties be unable to agree the amounts of security required.

15.12 Types of security

Cash is obviously the best form of security. In the event that the parties choose to use cash, then the cash is usually held in a trust account, ideally by an independent trustee company but sometimes by one of the other parties to the JOA. That cash remains in the trust account until abandonment costs are incurred and then the cash held in that account can be applied in meeting the relevant party's share of abandonment costs.

Alternatively, letters of credit are a common form of acceptable security, provided that the issuer meets an acceptable credit rating. Letters of credit, although more efficient from the point of view of utilisation of cash resources and bank facilities and ultimately cheaper than locking up real cash, are more expensive to administer as, typically, they require to be renewed every year. If a party fails to renew a letter of credit or fails to meet a cash call for abandonment costs under the JOA, then that constitutes a default, the letter of credit can be called, and the resulting cash placed in a trust account.

In certain cases, particularly involving substantial companies or groups, the party which is securing its obligations may seek to negotiate a position whereby a parent company guarantee is acceptable security, provided that the parent company maintains a particular credit rating. Should the credit rating drop below that level, then the securing party would be obliged to put up cash or a letter of credit from an acceptable financial institution.

Trust mechanisms

Any form of security or cash put up as abandonment security should be held in trust for all of the field partners for the express purpose of meeting the abandonment obligations of the party creating the trust fund. No party should hold its own trust fund (if it does so there is a risk that there may be some confusion as to whether the funds it holds are truly held in trust or are caught by that party's bank's security arrangements, if any). Typically, the operator might act as trustee for all of the security put up by the remaining parties and the non-operator with the next largest participating interest would act as trustee to hold the security put up by the operator. The parties may prefer to use independent trustee companies and there are a number of commercial entities who can perform that service.

Insurance-based security

For a small company which does not have sufficient head room in its bank facilities to cover all abandonment letters of credit and its own working capital requirements, this means raising equity funding from shareholders in order to capitalise the company properly. Equity funding, as suggested elsewhere in this book, may be in certain cases a more expensive source of capital.

There are some partial solutions to this being offered by the insurance industry whereby a bank issues a letter of credit to meet the requirements of the DSA and, rather than that letter of credit being drawn on the borrower's bank facility and therefore utilising working capital, the bank in turn looks to an insurance policy underwritten by an insurance company to pay out in the event that the insured event (ie the calling of the letter of credit) occurs. The insurance company in turn takes a back-to-back indemnity from the borrower, but ranking only as an ordinary creditor, unsecured and behind the bank. In opting for this form of security, and capitalising on the strength of its unsecured balance sheet, a company can minimise the cost of putting up a letter of credit security under an DSA, dispense with the need to utilise its bank facilities or seek fresh cash from shareholders.

15.13 Decommissioning of pipelines

There is very little experience in the UKCS of decommissioning of pipelines and subsea equipment and, while the Government provides certain guidance, it is a largely untested area both in the terms of process and the legal structures governing such infrastructure. The obligations placed on participant states under the OSPAR Decision 98/3 and largely given effect in the UK through the Petroleum Act, as noted above, do not apply to the decommissioning of pipelines; neither are there any international guidelines which specifically address the matter.

Estimates suggest that there are around 10,000 km of pipelines in the North Sea, resulting in material to be 'disposed' of that is estimated at twice the weight of all other infrastructure on the UKCS. The long-term importance of the control of pipeline decommissioning is therefore crucial to the environment. Given the nature of the pipeline and its functions, it is a quite different task to the abandonment of jackets or platforms. In particular, the substances that are used in pipelines aside from the crude hydrocarbons themselves can be – and many are – highly toxic and may even include radioactive elements. Consequently, there is a raft of statutory instruments which would need to be considered when pipeline decommissioning arises as discussed at section 15.8.

The decommissioning of pipelines will largely follow a similar process to that of abandonment of other infrastructure. Individual cases require to be submitted to the Secretary for consideration and here the DTI adopts a comparative methodology and seeks to look at a number of decommissioning options for individual pipelines or pipeline systems. Whereas platforms or other infrastructure and the associated decommissioning liability extend to licensees and to others, it is to the pipeline owners that the DTI will seek to attach decommissioning liability. As we have suggested, all options will be examined in regard to pipeline decommissioning and ultimately the solution may be to leave the pipeline in place, which raises the matter of ownership of the abandoned material. This issue of ownership is critical, as materials left on the seabed, even after extensive consultation and review of options, will inevitably degrade over the long term and the obligation to monitor, maintain and take any remedial action necessary lies with the owner. This perpetual obligation, by its nature is likely to be economically uncertain. Complete removal, despite obvious costs implications may be the only certain way to rid businesses of ongoing liability in the long run.

The comparative assessment approach, captured to some extent by the 12th Report by the Royal Commission on Environmental Pollution, 1988,[31] opts for applying the rule that whatever method of decommissioning is applied, it should be the best practicable environmental option (or BPEO). The Royal Commission defined BPEO as: 'A BPEO is the outcome of a systematic consultative and decision making procedure which emphasises the protection and conservation of the environment across land, air and water. The BPEO procedure establishes, for a given set of objectives, the option that provides the most benefit, or least damage, to the environment as a whole at an acceptable cost in the long term as well as in the short term.'

This would appear to be a sound and flexible approach to the problem of abandonment and decommissioning more generally and links into the legislation which regulates the conduct of businesses in relation to health and safety, a further key area affecting all decommissioning and abandonment.

The Health and Safety Executive administers the Health and Safety at Work, etc. Act 1974 and a number of associated regulations applying to offshore industries. There are specific items of secondary legislation which apply to pipeline safety and to well design and construction, all of which must be considered when the issue of decommissioning pipelines arises. Just as the environment itself is given high priority, naturally so too is the health and safety of users of the sea and oil industry workers themselves.

15.14 General

Decommissioning and abandonment of the infrastructure used in the UKCS, both on the seabed and above it, are controlled by layers of legislation ranging from international and regional treaties and obligations to the micro-detailed contents of the abandonment programme submitted to the Secretary of State. This body of legislation licences the areas of the North Sea from which hydrocarbons may be extracted or explored for but also stipulates the critical responsibilities for eventual cessation of production and abandonment of the area.

The UK Government's policy to date has been to ensure that the costs and liabilities for the removal of infrastructure from the UKCS lie fully with the businesses that have been involved with the production and processing of hydrocarbons. The powers vested in the Secretary of State to ensure that businesses very carefully plan, design, cost and execute abandonment programmes is enshrined largely in the Petroleum Act 1998. Through a section 29 notice, the Secretary obliges those served with such notice to ensure that the operationalisation of any plans to abandon are fully funded and executed. The joint and several nature of the liability for decommissioning in the North Sea means that where a party who is obliged to fund its percentage share of the cost of such decommissioning fails to do so, then all other parties are thereafter liable for the defaulting party's share of that cost.

In an economic climate where smaller businesses are encouraged and the fiscal and licensing regime makes that a viable proposition, then the trading of mature assets is commonplace. However, a party coming on to a licence will often have to procure that it can fund its percentage share of any decommissioning liability and the seller of an interest wants to be sure that it is 'secured' financially once he comes off the licence for any ongoing liability. The Secretary may withdraw the section 29 notice where he is satisfied that certain obligations have been met or are adequately replaced but there is, with the UKCS regime, a lingering liability that means any person who has been associated with an asset in the UKCS may still have some residual decommissioning liability.

The management of these arrangements is governed at the contractual level by three principal agreements: the JOA, the Decommissioning Agreement and the DSA. While there is some overlap between these contracts, they are a crucial stage in managing the rights and obligations of all parties to any joint or solely owned property. The industry, government and others have moved towards standardisation of contractual forms which means that transaction costs should be less and that transparent arrangements are in use. While the UKCS has been largely developed both as a matter of technology, process and form by the great multinational oil giants, and as the zenith of production in the North Sea is reached and passed, these forms and processes are being adapted to allow the smaller companies to rise to the challenge of hydrocarbon extraction and discovery. The legal structures considered in this chapter have evolved and continue to evolve with the help of those interested parties.

Notes

1. If two or more parties enter into an obligation, their liability for its breach can be enforced against them all by a joint action against any of them by individual action.
2. See DTI oil and gas website at: www.og.dti.gov.uk
3. The draft template DSA can be viewed at the UKOOA website: www.oiland gas.org.uk
4. The Master Deed can be viewed at www.masterdeed.com, a site administered by LOGIC.
5. The UKOAA 20th Round template JOA can be viewed at www.ukooa.co.uk/issues/stdagreements/worddocs/joint%20operating/%20agreement/%20final.doc
6. See Proceedings of the 14th International Offshore and Polar Engineering Conference, May 2004.
7. The text of the Treaty can be viewed at www.untreaty.un.org
8. The text of the UNCLOS convention can be viewed at www.un.org
9. The IMO website is at www.imo.org
10. The OSPAR website is at www.ospar.org
11. The OSPAR 98/3 Decision can be viewed at www.ospar.org
12. The full text of the Petroleum Act can be seen at www.opsi.gov.uk/acts/acts1998/19980017.htm

[13] The full set of current Model Clauses can be viewed at www.opsi.gov.uk/si/si1999/99016024.htm

[14] The Guidance Notes can be viewed at www.og.dti.gov.uk/regulation/guidance/decommission.htm

[15] Reference to s 34 of the Coast Protection Act can be found at www.mceu.gov.uk/MCEU_LOCAL/FEPA/CPA.htm

[16] The text of this Act can be viewed at www.mceu.gov.uk/MCEU_LOCAL/FEPA/FPEA-ACT.htm

[17] The text of this Act can be viewed at www.opsi.gov.uk/acts/acts1990/Ukpga_19900043_en_1.htm

[18] (SI 1994 No 1056). The text of these Regulations can be viewed at www.opsi.gov.uk/si/si1994/Uksi_19941056_en_1.htm

[19] The text of this Act can be viewed at www.opsi.gov.uk/ACTS/acts1999/19990024.htm

[20] (SI 1996 No 972). The text of these Regulations can be viewed at www.opsi.gov.uk/SI/si1996/Uksi_19960972_en_1.htm

[21] (SI 1994 No 1994). The text of these Regulations can be viewed at www.opsi.gov.uk/si/si1994/Uksi_19941137_en_1.htm

[22] The text of these Regulations can be viewed at www.eur-lex.europa.eu/LexUriServ/LexUriServ.do?uri=CELEX:31993R0259:EN:NOT

[23] The text of this Act can be viewed at www.opsi.gov.uk/ACTS/acts1993/Ukpga_19930012_en_1.htm

[24] (SI 1993 No 1137). The text of these Regulations can be viewed at www.opsi.gov.uk/SI/si1993/Uksi_19933031_en_1.htm

[25] The Environment Agency website is at www.environment-agency.gov.uk

[26] The Scottish Environmental Protection Agency website is at www.sepa.org.uk

[27] (SI 1987 No 37). The text of these Regulations can be viewed at www.opsi.gov.uk/si/si1987/Uksi_19870037_en_1.htm

[28] The text of this Act can be viewed at www.opsi.gov.uk/si/si1991/Ukpga_19910057_en_1.htm

[29] The text of this Act can be viewed at www.healthandsafety.co.uk/hswa.htm

[30] The DTI Export Control Organisation website is at www.dti.gov.uk/europeandtrade/strategic-export-control/index.htm

[31] The Royal Commission on Environmental Pollution website is at www.rcep.org.uk

— 16 —

ENVIRONMENTAL MANAGEMENT

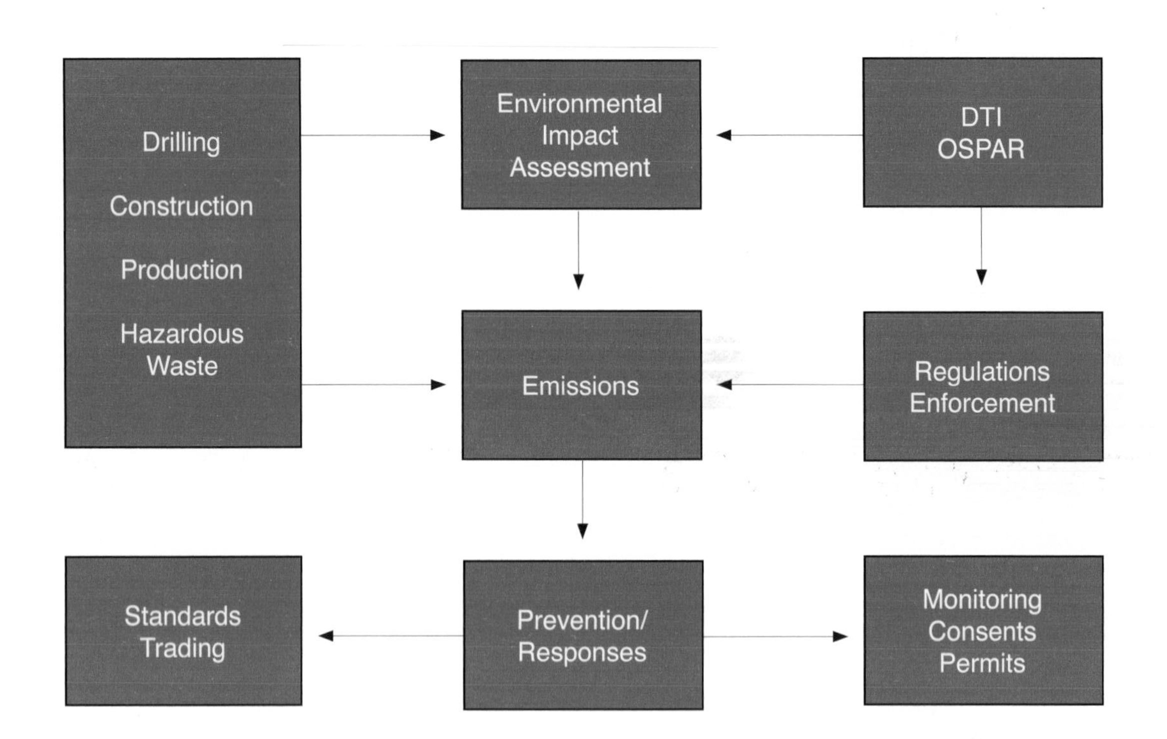

Drilling
Construction
Production
Hazardous Waste
Environmental Impact Assessment
DTI
OSPAR
Emissions
Regulations Enforcement
Standards Trading
Prevention/ Responses
Monitoring Consents Permits

ENVIRONMENTAL MANAGEMENT

TECHNICAL

16.1 Introduction

In the early days of UKCS exploration and production, environmental management requirements were mandated either via licence conditions or through a small number of issue-specific regulations. The environmental management focus was consequently on a limited range of narrowly focused issues, eg application of best practice in relation to spill response, limiting oil in produced water content to '40 ppm', etc.

Over time, the range of environmental impacts that licensees have had to address has steadily increased, as has the severity of the technical standards to be achieved. In the main, these changes derive from four sources:

- Some are driven by 'regional regulation'. In relation to UKCS operations, the two main sources of regional environmental regulation are the EU and the OSPAR regional seas convention (the Convention for the Protection of the Marine Environment of the North-East Atlantic).
- Voluntary, industry-led environmental management initiatives. For example, in 1979, the UK offshore industry developed the first chemical discharge monitoring framework, upon which subsequent regulations were built.
- Environmental accidents and incidents not necessarily related to the UK oil industry. For example, much of the industry best practice in relation to oil spill prevention and response had been driven by international shipping-related oil spill incidents.

- Campaigns led by environmental non-governmental organisations, some of which are described below.

At the present time, the UK offshore environmental regulatory regime is going through a process of rapid evolution in much the same way as the offshore safety regime developed in the mid-1990s. However, the environmental regime has some differences when compared to health and safety regulation. Whereas health and safety regulations provide a common framework for assessing and balancing the various kinds of health and safety risks on a particular installation, different, relatively unconnected, permitting processes exist for the various types of offshore environmental discharge.

16.2 Non-Governmental Organisations

Greenpeace is prominent amongst Environmental Non-Governmental Organisations (ENGOs) in campaigning for an end to North Sea oil and gas exploration. The grounds for these various campaigns have been a combination of the direct environmental impact of exploration and production operations, as well as emphasising the consequences for climate change of continued use of fossil fuels.

One of the first of these public campaigns was launched in 1992 when Greenpeace sought to prevent exploration drilling in block 107/1 off the coast of North Wales. Here the campaign focused on the likely environmental impact of oil production operations on a sensitive coastal environment.

Some five years later Greenpeace activists sought to prevent the MODU 'Stena Dee' moving towards its intended destination at BP's Foinaven field in the West of Shetland basin. Here the objective was to seek political and public support for a campaign to prevent climate change by halting oil exploration and investing in solar power. On the back of such a newsworthy action, Greenpeace pursued a series of political strategies (early day motions, party conference lobbying, etc.) calling for the redirection of fossil fuel investment to sustainable energy technologies.

These UK-based campaigns should be seen in the context of Greenpeace's global campaign to prevent new reserves of oil being opened up.

Perhaps Greenpeace's most notable oil industry campaign was in relation to the decommissioning of the Brent Spar (Fig. 16–1). Following extensive impact assessment work on a variety of disposal options, the UK Government granted the facility's owners, Shell, a licence to dispose the storage and loading facility at a designated deepwater site in 1995.

Greenpeace activists, however, boarded the facility and used the press coverage to promote on-land decommissioning as an alternative disposal option. The results of the analysis of samples taken by Greenpeace during the occupation was used to claim that there were up to 5000 tonnes of oil still on the Brent Spar. Greenpeace were subsequently forced to admit that this claim was in error. By the time that the mistake had been admitted, however, secondary actions obliged both the UK Government and Shell to reverse its decision regarding deepwater disposal. For example, in Germany, some Shell petrol stations reported significant loss in income as protestors encouraged boycotts. Later in the year the regional oceans regulatory body OSPAR agreed on a moratorium leading to a ban on the dumping of installations at sea. In the event, the Brent Spar installation was towed to Erfjord in Norway. In November 1997, the British–Norwegian consortium Wood–GMC began the onshore decommissioning of the Brent Spar.

Figure 16–1 Greenpeace activists approaching Brent Spar (David Sims © Greenpeace)

16.3 Oil spill prevention and response

The model clauses incorporated into all offshore production licences require that licensees prevent the escape of petroleum into the sea and report spills to the DTI. By convention, these reports also include temporary increases in routine oil discharge caused by process upsets (eg produced water-related sheens).

This operator spill reporting requirement is backed up by aerial and satellite surveillance of the marine environment. Since 1986, the UK Government has carried out unannounced surveillance flights over offshore installations in accordance with international obligations under the Bonn Agreement.

With regard to spill response planning, offshore licensees are required to show that they have funds available to discharge liability for damage caused by pollution. In addition, since the UK is a signatory to an international convention on oil pollution prevention and response planning, licensees are required to ensure that all offshore activities are subject to a government-approved Oil Spill Contingency Plan (OSCP).

In 1999, the Donaldson Report, following the grounding of the 'Sea Empress' at Milford Haven, made a number of recommendations in relation to spill response planning which were subsequently enacted in UK oil industry regulations. These regulations require that a single representative be authorised to act on behalf of the Secretary of State for Trade and Industry (the so-called Secretary of State's Representative (SOSREP)) whose role is to monitor and, if necessary, intervene to protect the environment in the event of a threatened or actual pollution incident.

16.4 Drilling-related emissions

The most significant potential marine discharge from drilling operations relates to drilling muds and cuttings. On the drilling rig, the mud and cuttings are separated in a range of solids control equipment before the cuttings are subject to disposal. The achievable solids concentration in the solids control equipment discharge has increased in recent years as separation technology has improved. Even after treatment, however, cuttings are still contaminated with residual amounts of drilling mud.

Until the late 1990s, the discharge of oil-based mud (OBM) contaminated cuttings constituted a relatively large proportion of the marine oil discharge from the oil industry. For example, in 1993, nearly 4600 tonnes of oil on drill cuttings was discharged to the North Sea compared with 4200 tonnes associated with produced water, and 1.2 tonnes associated with oil spillage.

Over the last few years, progressive changes to environmental regulations have been aimed at limiting the amount and type of oil discharged to the marine environment in association with drill cuttings. OSPAR Decision 2000/3 came into effect in 2001 and effectively eliminated the marine discharge of all so-called Organic Phase Fluids (OPF–OBM, synthetic based drilling fluids (SBM), etc.) either as 'whole mud' or as cuttings contaminated with these fluids. OPF-contaminated cuttings must either be reinjected or returned to shore for treatment and disposal. By the same token, any contamination of cuttings by hydrocarbons from the reservoir requires a permit if being discharged overboard or reinjected.

For non-OPF systems, the regulation of discharge of cuttings to the marine environment is linked to the chemical content of the associated mud. A mechanism for control of offshore chemical discharge in the UKCS was first introduced by the industry on a voluntary basis in 1979. This original framework has been subject to progressive amendment through the work of OSPAR. A harmonised framework was finally established, and associated UK regulations put in place, via the Offshore Chemicals Regulations (OCR) 2002.

Under these Regulations, offshore operators need to apply for permits to cover both the use and discharge of chemicals via the Petroleum Operations Notice 15 (PON15) process. Permit applications require a combination of operational data (well information, etc.), environmental data (site-specific marine mammal and fish vulnerability, etc.) and, in the case of each chemical to be used, a quantified environmental risk assessment based on a mandated risk assessment protocol.

16.5 Production-related emissions

Like drilling rig owners, production operators have to ensure effective oil spill prevention and response in the same way as described above. By the same token, a similar permitting process exists for production chemical use and discharge as exists in relation to drilling mud. There are other discharges, however, which relate specifically to production operations. The main discharges are oil-in-produced water and atmospheric emissions.

At the present time, regulation of oil-in-produced water is in the process of transition. Historically, operators were given an exemption to discharge produced water to the sea provided a specified oil-in-water content was achieved. Oil content of produced water is now regulated under a permit granted under the Offshore Petroleum Activities (Oil Pollution Prevention and Control) Regulations (OPPC) 2005. OPPC requires more details with regard to discharge management plans including field-life forecasts of emissions and detailed measurement and reporting plans. The regulations also require reductions in oil discharges associated with produced water via an emissions trading framework.

As with oil-in-produced water discharges to the marine environment, offshore atmospheric emissions are controlled by a series of regulations/permitting frameworks each addressing specific pollutants or particular sources of emissions. The three main permitting frameworks in relation to offshore atmospheric emissions are as follows:

- Licensees are required to apply for annual consents to flare or vent gas. The main purpose of this requirement is to ensure that associated gas is conserved where possible by avoiding unnecessary wastage and that climate change-related emissions (CO_2 and methane) are reduced as far as possible.
- Diesel engines, gas turbines, inert gas generators and other such equipment are termed 'combustion plant', and, along with flaring and venting, are the major offshore contributors to the emission of CO_2. During 2001, a number of UK oil and gas companies were involved in setting up a voluntary UK emissions trading scheme for greenhouse gases. UK ETS is now absorbed within a larger mandatory EU Emissions Trading Scheme (EU ETS), which commenced at the beginning of 2005. EU ETS applies to any installation that has an aggregate of more than 20 Megawatts Thermal (Mw(th)) of fuel input to the various combustion plant in operation.
- Combustion plant also gives rise to other atmospheric emissions; regional pollutants such as the acid gases (SO_x, NO_x) as well as smog precursors such as CO, Unburnt Hydrocarbons (UHC) & Smoke/Particulates. These are now subject to regulation under a third permitting framework – the Offshore Combustion Installation Regulations (OCIR) 2001. The Regulations apply to any oil/gas-producing platform, which has combustion plant which in total exceed 50 MW(th) of fuel input.

Although these emissions are managed under separate permitting frameworks with different emissions thresholds, there are a number of common elements in relation to the environmental management requirements of these three schemes. The regulations generally require that operators demonstrate that they are using defined Best Available Techniques (BAT) to reduce pollutant emissions. For qualifying installations, operators are also required to calculate or measure emissions according to an agreed and verifiable site-specific measurement and reporting plan and to demonstrate that emissions are consistent with permit levels or emissions credits held at the end of each reporting cycle.

16.6 Sources and handling of waste

Unlike most other UKCS environmental management requirements, the management of wastes returned to shore is regulated by the Environment Agency (EA) in England and Wales and the Scottish Environmental Protection Agency (SEPA) in Scotland. EA/SEPA regulates waste transport and disposal through a system of licences and formal documentation trails, particularly in relation to hazardous wastes.

Industrial waste regulated in this fashion is termed 'controlled waste'. Under this heading, certain types of waste are categorised as hazardous by virtue of their toxicity, corrosivity or flammability. More recently the European Commission has revised waste definitions to increase the numbers of hazardous waste categories (for example, used fluorescent light tubes). Waste categories are now subject to Europe-wide definition (The European Waste Catalogue – EWC). Any producer of waste has a duty of care which involves correct labelling of the waste and ensuring that properly licensed carriers are collecting the waste and that it is going to an appropriate disposal site.

Unlike household waste disposal, industrial and commercial waste disposal is not free of charge. Recent European regulations have limited the number of locations where hazardous wastes can be disposed. This has had the effect of significantly increasing the cost of waste disposal in recent years. The consequence of this for the offshore oil industry (as well as onshore industry) is an increased focus on the need to reduce the amounts of waste (particularly hazardous wastes) that are being disposed of to landfill. There are typically four ways that this can be done.

- Operators can reduce the amounts of waste arising from a particular activity. For example, some operators are purchasing consumables in bulk in order to reduce the amounts of packaging to be disposed of.
- Operators can re-use materials where possible. For example, some operators reuse pallets and wooden packaging as a means of reducing waste.
- Operators can recycle. Many of the strategies for household recycling with which we are all familiar are equally valid for offshore operations.
- There is also an opportunity to recover resources from the waste. Some operators have discovered that certain wastes can be used to supplement fuels. This recovers energy from the waste and reduces disposal costs.

One way that operators can identify waste reduction, reuse, recycling and recovery opportunities is through formal waste assessments and audits. Once initiated, it is rare for such assessments not to identify improvement opportunities and associated cost savings.

16.7 Environmental impact assessment

In relation to offshore operations, environmental impacts are assessed at two levels: strategic impact assessments are carried out in relation to offshore licensing; and activity-related impact assessment is carried out in relation to certain types of specific operations.

Environmental implications of offshore oil and gas licensing are addressed through a process of Strategic Environmental Assessment (SEA). In this context, SEA is a formal process of appraisal of the likely environmental consequences of offering particular areas of the UKCS for oil and gas exploration. Although a formal SEA framework was introduced into UK law in 2004, the DTI had already adopted the process as early as 1999 in relation to offshore licensing.

An official SEA website has been established to act as a clearing-house for the substantial amounts of information compiled through the SEA process (www.offshore-sea.org.uk). This includes data on fishery sensitivities, bird and marine fauna populations and the existence of environmentally significant seabed features. This information provides the primary resource for potential operators when they are making license applications. The information also provides a basis for developing site-specific environmental management plans during the exploration phase (seismic, etc.).

The need for formal environmental assessments (EIA) of offshore projects is driven by European directives. Regulations require that any operator who wishes to drill a well, construct a pipeline or develop a field has to formally assess the environmental impact of their plans.

For major projects, there is a mandatory requirement to carry out an environmental assessment (EA) and to prepare an environmental statement (ES). Major projects are deemed to be those that meet the following criteria:

- where production will be greater than 500 tonnes of oil (approximately 3,750bopd) or 500,000 m^3 of gas per day; and
- where pipelines will be greater than 800 mm in diameter and 40 km long.

For drilling operations and smaller development and pipeline projects, where an operator believes that impacts are not significant, they are allowed to seek a direction that a full EA/ES is not required. Under these circumstances, an operator prepares a screening assessment for approval.

Where a full EA/ES is needed, the process is in line with international good practice for impact assessment: the proposed activity is characterised, a description of the receiving environment is compiled, alternatives are considered, impacts are assessed (including cumulative impacts) mitigation plans are put in place, and proposals are subject to stakeholder consultation. The DTI has committed to turn around formal EA/ESs in eight weeks.

ENVIRONMENTAL MANAGEMENT

LEGAL

16.8 Introduction

It will have become obvious from the preceding part of this chapter that there is a raft of regulatory provisions governing the environmental aspects of offshore oil- and gas-related activities. Much of the domestic legislation (in the form of either Acts of Parliament or Regulations) has been driven by obligations owed by the UK under the terms of international treaties and EU law. The UK may perhaps find itself at a disadvantage to other states who are party to international treaties or the EU as environmental legislation becomes more developed given the size and significance of the UK oil and gas industry compared with that of some other EU countries. On the coal face, so to speak, much of the regulation is applied and enforced by means of licences, permits and consents granted by the Secretary of State for Trade and Industry ('the Secretary') through the Department for Trade and Industry (DTI).

16.9 Attitude towards environmental regulations

Both the exploration for, and production of, oil and gas has an effect on the environment and can cause damage to it. When oil was first discovered in the North Sea, environmental issues were overlooked in the rush to develop and invest, partly because of a lack of scientific understanding of the environmental consequences. Even when specific legislation was introduced to protect the environment, in the form of the Prevention of Oil Pollution Act 1971, the technology at that time was not sufficiently advanced to meet the standards set, leading to a practice of exemptions being granted.

A greater awareness of the damage that can be caused, coupled with media and public concern over environmental issues, has, however, played a significant role in changing attitudes towards the environment by exerting pressure upon the Government and the industry to adopt more environmentally friendly practices.

An example of this is the concept of 'corporate social responsibility' which has led to the industry adopting and promoting socially and environmentally friendly working practices. In the past, health and safety has been the subject of much more public and industry focus than environmental matters and a culture of safety developed as a result (as discussed elsewhere in this work). Environmental concerns are now evolving in a similar way, and indeed the International Association of Oil and Gas Producers (OGP) report, that there is a culture of responsible oil and gas operations.

A similar view is expressed by the industry body UKOOA which states that 'Environmental Management, as part of the commitment to sustainability, is today a fully integrated part of the oil business'.[1] This commitment is reflected by the adoption by UKOOA member companies of guidelines relating to environmental management systems, auditing and training procedures. Another indication of a change in industry attitude is the frequent consultation that oil and gas producers enter into with government, conservation agencies and the public with a view to identifying environmental concerns and establishing controls to deal with these. Perhaps, however, the greatest indicator of the industry's commitment is the investment it is making in new technologies to not only meet, but where possible exceed, compliance with environmental standards. For example, with regard to the problem of drilling muds and cuttings, the industry has invested heavily in new technology to realise a change of approach involving a commitment by UK operators of some £50 million a year in additional costs.

The change in government attitude is perhaps best reflected by the introduction of the Offshore Petroleum Activities (Oil Pollution Prevention and Control) Regulations 2005. These not only mark a move from a scheme of exemptions to a permitting scheme but also introduce wider powers for environmental inspectors to monitor and investigate oil discharges and pollution.

This change of attitude has resulted in an increase in co-operation. In 1999, the DTI founded the UK Offshore Forum in order to bring together the Government, offshore oil and gas industry and environmental groups. The aim of this move was to build a greater, shared understanding of offshore environmental issues and to provide face-to-face dialogue on key issues such as environmental research, sustainable energy development, environmental concerns, the progress of Strategic Environmental Assessments (SEAs) and any new or impending legislation.

These changes in attitude, coupled with technological advances, do appear to be having a positive effect. UKOOA's Third Environment Report in October 2000 indicated that although oil and gas production was at a record high, all offshore emissions decreased, oil spills declined and oil in produced water had been reduced to half the legally permitted maximum. The challenges of an ageing infrastructure and increasing costs as available oil and gas reserves decline, however, mean that, even with the best of intentions, compliance remains an issue for the industry and government alike.

16.10 Framework of environmental legislation

As stated above, some of the environmental framework originates from outwith the UK and this has developed as a result of the UK's participation in international treaties and the EU.

At an international level, the Convention for the Protection of the Marine Environment of the North-East Atlantic 1992 (the 'OSPAR Convention') is an international treaty in respect of preventing and eliminating pollution of the marine environment in the North-East Atlantic. The OSPAR Convention combines and updates two older international treaties: the Convention for the Prevention of Marine Pollution by Dumping from Ships and Aircraft 1972 (known as the Oslo Convention) and the Convention for the Prevention of Marine Pollution from Land-Based Sources 1974 (known as the Paris Convention). It should be noted, however, that the OSPAR Convention does not supercede decisions, recommendations and all other agreements adopted under the Oslo Convention or Paris Convention, which therefore remain binding on Member States unless terminated by new measures adopted under the OSPAR Convention.

The OSPAR Convention consists of a series of provisions that require the application of:

(i) *The Precautionary Principle.* This means that where there are threats of serious or irreversible environmental damage, lack of full scientific certainty shall not be used as a reason for postponing cost-effective measures to prevent environmental degradation.

(ii) *The 'Polluter Pays' Principle.* This recognises that the polluter should pay for any environmental damage created, and that the burden of proof in demonstrating that a particular technology, practice or product is safe should lie with the developer, not the general public.

(iii) *Best Available Techniques.* This is defined as 'the most effective and advanced stage in the development of activities and their methods of operation which indicates the practicable suitability of particular techniques for providing the basis for emission limit values designed to prevent, and where that is not practicable, generally to reduce the emissions and the impact on the environment as a whole'.

(iv) *Best Environmental Practice.* This is the application of the most appropriate combination of environmental control measures and strategies that involves inter alia the consideration of a number of issues including the development of codes of good environmental practice, public access to information, recycling recovery and reuse of resources and waste and continual monitoring and reassessment of what constitutes Best Environmental Practice.

The work carried out under the OSPAR Convention is managed by the OSPAR Commission. The OSPAR Commission is made up of representatives of the states who are party to the OSPAR Convention, namely Belgium, Denmark, Finland, France, Germany, Iceland, Ireland, Luxembourg, the Netherlands, Norway, Portugal, Spain, Sweden, Switzerland, the UK and the EU, represented by the European Commission. There is also provision in the OSPAR Convention for the participation of observers, including non-governmental organisations, in the work of the OSPAR Commission. The OSPAR Convention provides for the OSPAR Commission to adopt binding decisions. In order for a resolution to be accepted by the OSPAR Commission a vote requiring a three-quarters majority of all Member States is required. Once a resolution is passed it is legally binding on the Member States, however the detailed implementation of OSPAR resolutions is governed by national laws and EU Directives.

The OSPAR Commission has adopted specific strategies in the following areas: protection and conservation of ecosystems and biological diversity; hazardous substances; radioactive substances; eutrophication; environmental goals and management mechanisms for offshore activities; and the offshore oil and gas strategy (these are generally referred to as the 'Offshore Activities Strategy').

At a European level, the EU's role in environmental matters relies on Article 249 of the Treaty of Amsterdam in 1997 which empowers the European Council and Commission to make Regulations, issue Directives, make recommendations or deliver opinions on European environmental policy.

Where the EU issues a Directive, the UK Government is obliged to implement Regulations to give effect to that Directive. It is the UK Regulations with which operators will require to be familiar but the terms of the underlying EU Directive cannot be ignored as they will be of importance in interpreting the

UK Regulations. In addition, UK Regulations can potentially be challenged as not adequately giving effect to the EU Directive.

An example of such a challenge is the success of Greenpeace in 1999 in asserting that the Habitats Directive (Council Directive 92/43/EEC) had not been properly implemented by the domestic legislation as it did not extend to the UKCS and the waters above (*R v Secretary of State for Trade and Industry ex parte Greenpeace Ltd* [2000] Env LR 221). Greenpeace brought this challenge as a result of the DTI's decision to grant licences in the 19th Licensing Round to companies seeking to search and bore for oil in the area to the north and west of the Hebrides, Orkney and Shetland.

As a result of the decision, the Government introduced the Offshore Petroleum Activities (Conservation of Habitats) Regulations 2001 (SI 2001 No 1754) in order to apply the Habitats Directive and Wild Birds Directive in relation to oil and gas operations wholly or partly in the UKCS and superjacent waters outside territorial waters. The effect on the UK oil and gas industry was that the licensing process was significantly delayed, although it did not prevent the eventual award of licences in the 19th Licensing Round after the Habitats Directive had been successfully implemented. This example is illustrative both of the effect of EU Directives in terms of domestic legislation, and also of the potential influence of non-governmental organisations.

16.11 Need for legal input

It is beyond the scope of this commentary to examine the regulatory framework in detail; suffice to say that the various regulations cover all aspects of offshore oil and gas production from the exploratory stage, through production and transport, to decommissioning and abandonment. Given the increasing importance of environmental regulations and the attitude of both the DTI and the industry towards them, most businesses will be aware of the specific legal requirements of the regulations. Legal input may, nevertheless, be required in ensuring compliance with the regulations and in dealing with the negotiation and documentation of contractual arrangements between parties involved in the exploration, production and transportation process. This commentary on the legal aspect of environmental regulation is therefore divided into two parts: (a) compliance with regulations; and (b) individual contractual arrangements.

16.12 Enforcement through licensing and consents

The Regulations impose obligations not only on companies wishing to undertake oil and gas related activities but also on the Secretary of State. For example, the Offshore Petroleum Activities (Conservation of Habitats) Regulations 2001

(SI 2001 No 1754) provide that the Secretary must exercise his functions in such a way as to ensure that UK oil and gas activities are carried out in a manner consistent with the provisions of the EU Directives (which these Regulations bring in to effect).

One of the duties imposed on the Secretary and carried out by the DTI, is to consider licence applications in light of environmental considerations. In this way the licensing regime can be invoked to protect the environment.

The first way in which licensing can contribute to the enforcement of environmental regulations is through the application process. The DTI's website states that it is 'essential that any new operator in the North Sea demonstrates that he is aware of the environmental requirements, has and applies in practice a comprehensive environmental management system and is in a position to carry out a formal Environmental Statement if and when required'. In granting a licence the DTI also consider whether the operator can demonstrate a proven track record of environmental awareness.

Second, the exploitation of resources and the way production is carried out is largely governed by the terms of the production licence. Every licence incorporates Model Clauses. Although none of the Model Clauses is specifically directed at the control of pollution, it is believed that some of the clauses are sufficiently wide so as to be capable of being invoked by the regulator if there were to be damage or a risk to the environment. For example, the Model Clauses require operations to be carried out in a proper and workmanlike manner and in accordance with methods of practice customarily used in good oil field practice. It is believed these Model Clauses are flexible enough to impose the need to comply with all environmental regulations. DTI guidance makes it clear that good oil field practices should take proper account of environmental issues. In addition to the Model Clauses, the Secretary also has the power to attach specific conditions to a licence to control oil and gas related activity.

In addition to conditions contained in the licence, there will be further conditions attached to the consents and permits the Secretary grants under the provisions of the various regulations which require consents and permits in respect of surveying, exploration, drilling, production, flaring, discharge and other related activities. These conditions can include terms relating to monitoring and reporting, giving the DTI the means to check up on compliance and ensuring they will be aware of any pollution incidents.

16.13 Enforcement of the environmental regulations

The Department of Trade and Industry Oil and Gas Directorate is the government department responsible for licensing, exploration, enforcement and regulating development of the UK's oil and gas resources and is the principal point of contact for operators. The Offshore Environment Unit has responsibility for environmental regulation of the UKCS and is based in Aberdeen. The unit is made up of four sections: the Environment Operations Unit; the Environment Policy Unit; the Policy Development Unit; and the Decommissioning Unit. In terms of enforcement, operators are most likely to encounter the Environment Operations Unit as it is the unit responsible for ensuring implementation of environmental legislation through offshore inspection and the promotion of compliance. Operators may, from time to time, also encounter other regulatory bodies such as the Environment Agency (England and Wales), the Scottish Environment Protection Agency (SEPA), the Department for Environment, Food and Rural Affairs (England and Wales) (DEFRA), the Scottish Executive Environment and Rural Affairs Department (SEERAD), the Fisheries Research Service (Scotland) and the Centre for Environment, Fisheries and Environmental Science (England and Wales).

It is open to these regulatory agencies, specifically the DTI, to enforce environmental regulation through informal enforcement methods and/or formal, direct action, enforcement procedures. Operators should be aware that use of informal enforcement procedures can be followed by formal enforcement action where the regulator considers it necessary. The regulatory authorities possess broad discretionary powers as to the type of enforcement action they can undertake.

Examples of informal enforcement procedures undertaken by the regulatory agencies against operators include regular site inspections, aerial surveillance and testing of samples. It is open to the regulator to increase the frequency of these steps as a response to previous pollution incidents.

Informal enforcement action can also include regular consultations with operators and third party stakeholders and the negotiation of informal agreements and undertakings between the regulator and operator. During such consultations and negotiations, it is necessary to be aware that it may be difficult for the operator to prove and/or enforce the terms of any informal agreement at a later date.

Informal discussions and agreements can play an important role in reducing potential liability in the event of a pollution incident occurring, and it is therefore important that during any informal enforcement procedures an open dialogue is maintained with the regulator. In addition, in some situations informal action could negate the need for formal action to be taken. For example, the risk of the regulator undertaking formal legal action resulting in prosecution and/or financial penalties can be substantially reduced through unqualified co-operation and swift remedial action.

There is a risk, however, for the polluter in entering into informal discussions. During the course of such discussions, the operator is likely to make admissions about breaches of the environmental Regulations, and these admissions can be relied upon if there is subsequently a prosecution. Thus, it is possible for informal action to lead to formal enforcement measures. An example of this is where a formal caution is given as a result of the informal discussions. The formal nature of this caution means that, although there is no prosecution at that time, should there be a successful prosecution for a future breach the caution can be taken into account for the purposes of sentencing.

Where serious or repeated breaches of environmental Regulations by an operator have taken place, formal direct action enforcement procedures may be pursued. The action taken and sanctions imposed will depend on the nature and seriousness of the breach and the regulatory provision governing it. It is, however, possible to identify a number of different enforcement mechanisms.

The most serious of these are criminal sanctions. Most environmental offences are strict liability offences. Where an offence is one of strict liability, all that needs to be proven to secure a conviction is that an act or omission in breach of the relevant Regulation occurred (for example, that there was in fact an unauthorised discharge of chemicals into the sea). It is not necessary for the prosecution to identify or prove mens rea, ie that there was actual intent, negligence or recklessness on behalf of the polluter in regard to the offence. Bearing this in mind, it may be prudent for the polluter to consider whether lodging a guilty plea at an early stage in the proceedings will be in its best interests where the offence is one of strict liability. If it is likely to be proved that a breach of the regulations occurred, such a plea could potentially avoid an expensive and time-consuming prosecution and may also mitigate any financial penalty or other sentence imposed. Criminal sanctions may fall upon individuals in the polluting organisation, depending on the materiality and extent of the offence, the level of individual involvement and the extent of the environmental damage caused.

The most common types of formal enforcement procedures are 'Enforcement Notices' and 'Prohibition Notices'. A Prohibition Notice is a pre-emptory measure taken by the Secretary to prevent an activity that involves an imminent risk of serious pollution to the environment. The notice empowers the regulatory agency to insist upon any action that is considered appropriate to avoid or minimise the risk, including the cessation of activity and the suspension of the operator's permit. A Prohibition Notice shall: state the DTI's opinion; specify the risk involved in the operation of the installation; specify the steps that must be taken to remove the risk and the period within which such steps must be taken; and direct that the permit shall, until the notice is withdrawn, wholly or to the extent specified in the notice, prevent the facility from operating. A prohibition order may have a serious effect upon the day-to-day operation of an installation, as it has the potential to shut down or seriously restrict operations until action has been taken to remove or to control the pollution risk. Proposed Prohibition

Notices will be discussed wherever possible with relevant offshore or onshore personnel, such as the offshore installation manager prior to issue. At such times having a good dialogue with the regulator can be of particular importance.

Enforcement Notices, by contrast, can be pre-emptory or retrospective. An Enforcement Notice will compel the operator to take action to prevent or resolve a breach of the Regulations. Offshore Environment Inspectors and the Secretary can issue Enforcement Notices in the following circumstances: (a) when there has been a breach of regulations; (b) there is an ongoing breach of regulations; or (c) there is a likelihood that a breach of the regulations will occur. The Notice, shall set out the nature of the contravention or potential contravention, and the action required to remedy the situation. If the required action is not taken by the date stipulated in the Notice, the Secretary has the power to take action and to recover the costs from the permit holder served with the Enforcement Notice.

Given the regulator's powers to take remedial action and recover the cost of doing so from the polluter, it can be better to take remedial action on a voluntary basis so as to retain control of the work (and cost thereof) and also to gain credit for doing so.

Perhaps a less obvious, but no less effective, means of enforcement available to regulators is the power to revoke any pollution consent or vary the terms of it. In addition, much of the environmental legislation provides ancillary enforcement powers relating to the collection of information, entry, search and seizure.

16.14 The OPPC Regulations – a case study

Recently, progress has been made towards concentrating the regulatory requirements in industry-specific regulation rather than relying on a raft of non-specific legislation. While it is outwith the scope of this work to examine all the regulatory requirements, it is helpful to consider the most significant example of this trend which was the introduction of the Offshore Petroleum Activities (Oil Pollution Prevention and Control) Regulations 2005 ('OPPC Regulations'). As discussed previously in this chapter, these regulations phase out the system of exemptions for certain oil discharges which existed under the Prevention of Oil Pollution Act 1971 and replace it with a system of permits. The parties which operate offshore facilities (operators) must now apply for a permit (which may be lifetime or project-specific) to allow the discharge of controlled amounts of oil into the marine environment. A permit granted may contain conditions as to the amount, frequency and location of the discharge along with provisions regarding pollution control and monitoring. Permits may only be assigned to another operator with the consent of the Secretary.

Contravention of the OPPC Regulations is dealt with in the first instance by use of Enforcement Notices or Prohibition Notices. Enforcement Notices may require the operator to take steps to remedy any pollution caused by contravention of the Regulations.

Discharge of oil without a permit, or failure to comply with the terms of the permit or of a Notice, is an offence and the OPPC Regulations make provision for individuals (eg managers, directors, etc.) as well as bodies corporate to be guilty of the offence and subject, if found guilty, to an unlimited fine. Many of the offences created by the OPPC Regulations (and in particular the offence of discharging oil other than in accordance with the terms of a permit) are strict liability offences. This means that it is not necessary for there to have been the intention to discharge oil. The mere fact that oil has been discharged without a permit leads to an offence being committed.

The OPPC Regulations give rise to a trading scheme (the Dispersed Oil in Produced Water Trading Scheme) whereby individual installations are allocated allowances in respect of the dispersed oil in produced water which they may discharge. Permit holders must, on an annual basis, surrender allowances in respect of actual discharges made. If an operator has insufficient allowances to cover the discharges which have been made the operator's options are either to procure more allowances (from other operators) under the trading scheme or be subject to a civil penalty of £280 per kg of dispersed oil in produced water that is discharged in excess of allowances surrendered.

The scheme commenced on 1 January 2006 and it is envisaged that it will operate on similar principles to the Carbon Emission Trading Scheme. Trading agreements between permit holders is another area in which legal advice may be required.

16.15 Individual contractual arrangements

In addition to compliance with regulations, licence or permit conditions, (which may apply to all parties to a venture or to the operator of an installation only), parties involved in oil and gas activities will usually be bound by obligations arising from, and receive the benefit of, individual contractual provisions. It is in the parties' best interests to negotiate on, and agree, contractual provisions on obligations and liabilities because, in common with health and safety matters, the legal responsibility for offshore environmental protection lies with all parties to a venture. This is a particularly important consideration for an operator. The operator will usually be the permit holder for an installation and will be conducting operations for, and on behalf of, the other joint venturers. As such, the operator will look to contractual terms to ensure that any costs incurred are met in agreed proportions by the co-venturers.

The contractual arrangement between the operator and the co-venturers is usually contained in a JOA or a UOA. One of the main principles of such agreements is that the parties to the agreement contribute to the costs of operations in accordance with the extent of their interests in the project. In general, unless the operator has acted by wilful misconduct or has failed to arrange insurance, costs are allocated between the parties. Such costs usually include emergency expenditure incurred by the operator to prevent or limit a pollution incident.

Most operating agreements also contain specific 'OPOL' provisions. The Offshore Pollution Liability Agreement (known as OPOL) is an agreement developed by the oil industry to facilitate the settlement of claims for pollution damage and remedial costs in the event of spillage or escape of oil from an offshore installation.

Under the OPOL scheme, operators agree to accept strict liability for pollution damage and remedial costs up to US $120 million per incident. There are a few exceptions to the acceptance of liability, eg natural disasters etc. Parties to the scheme have to establish financial capability to meet claims and this may be done by means of insurance, bonds of surety or guarantees. The parties also agree to what is, in effect, a mutual guarantee of each other's obligations under the scheme.

The provisions of OPOL are usually reflected in the operating agreements whereby parties to the agreement agree: (a) that OPOL costs are to be met from the joint account; and (b) that parties provide evidence of their own capability to meet any obligations under OPOL and the operating agreement.

Where the OPOL scheme has been applied to a licence this will ensure that the licensees comply with the Model Clause provisions which require licensees to have sufficient funds available to deal with pollution. It is important to note, however, that acceptance of strict liability under the OPOL scheme does not change the basis of actual legal liability in law but simply provides an expedient method of settling claims.

The other main area in which companies may seek to allocate risk in respect of environmental costs is in their dealings with parties outwith the joint venture (eg contractors or other parties working in proximity to an installation).

Contracts for the provision of oil- and gas-related services often utilise model contract documents. In particular, LOGIC, an industry-funded organisation, has developed standard contracts for the UK Offshore Oil and Gas Industry, commonly known as CRINE contracts. Such contracts usually address the issue of liability for various types of claims directly by granting indemnities and, therefore, allocating risk. The indemnity provisions may include specific references to environmental liability. For example, the CRINE Standard Contract for Well Services provides that, in general, the company employing the contractor to provide the well services shall indemnify the contractor against claims arising from pollution or contamination. There are specific and detailed exceptions to this general indemnity but the point is that parties can negotiate and agree to allocate risk as they see fit. The standard contract further provides that any exclusion or limitation of liability under the contract excludes/limits liability not only under the contract but also at law. This means that the parties signing such a contract cannot, as between themselves, look to the law of tort (England) or delict (Scotland) as a basis of liability for a further claim.

Other types of contract where environmental liability may be directly addressed include Construction Agreements and Pipeline Crossing Agreements. The parties may decide to allocate risk in respect of pollution claims and may also provide for environmental surveys, analysis or monitoring to be carried out prior to, during and after the construction work. Such agreements may also include a clause requiring the parties to obtain and maintain appropriate insurance in respect of environmental claims.

16.16 The Future

The DTI have recently introduced a more transparent consultation process for future wide-scale licensing of the UKCS for oil and gas exploration and production in the form of Strategic Environmental Assessments (SEAs). SEAs are a process for predicting and evaluating the environmental implications of a plan in order to identify areas of concern and establish best environmental practice. They play an important role in the DTI's decision-making process in deciding whether to award a licence. SEAs are conducted at a strategic level, considering an entire region as a whole. This can be contrasted with an Environmental Impact Assessment (EIA) which considers only the environment in the immediate vicinity of a development. The SEA process is a more comprehensive analysis of the environmental impact of a development and seeks to include a greater number of parties that have a vested interest in the area. The parties involved in the consultation process include the general public, non-governmental organisations (NGOs) (such as the Royal Society for the Protection of Birds and the Worldwide Fund for Nature (WWF)), local authorities, government agencies (eg the Joint Nature Conservation Committee), experts in the field (universities, commercial consultants, etc.) and the industries wishing to undertake the development. One of the steps taken by the DTI to make sure this is a transparent and inclusive process has been the creation of a dedicated internet site (http://www.offshore-sea.org.uk) that invites any person with 'a useful contribution to make' to become involved in the SEA consultation process and allows the public to follow the consultation process.

The EIA regime has also undergone development, with the result that a mandatory EIA is required for the extension of any offshore developments, where the increase in production exceeds the thresholds of either 500 tonnes of oil or 500,000 cubic metres of gas per day and/or to the extension of an existing pipeline where that extension is 40 km or more in length and of a diameter of 800 millimetres or more.

In addition, public pressure to improve environmental standards is likely to continue to grow as the process becomes more transparent through the recent implementation of the Public Participation Directive 2003/35/EC, which implements the 1998 Aarhus Convention. This gives increased public access to environmental information and greater public participation in the environmental decision-making process. The provisions of the Public Participation Directive include requirements that all applications under the relevant regulations must be subject to public notice, the public must be able to express opinions before any decisions are made and that account must be taken of the results of public consultations when making decisions and a report published providing the basis for any decision. It is for the government to identify the 'public' entitled to participate. There are no set time periods for this consultation process – rather, the Government must give the public adequate time to participate at all stages.

The intention is that in the future there will be greater environmental awareness through a more informed and comprehensive consultation process.

Note

1 http://www.pilotsharefair.com/education/storyofoil/sustainability-03.cfm

— 17 —

MATERIALS AND LOGISTICS

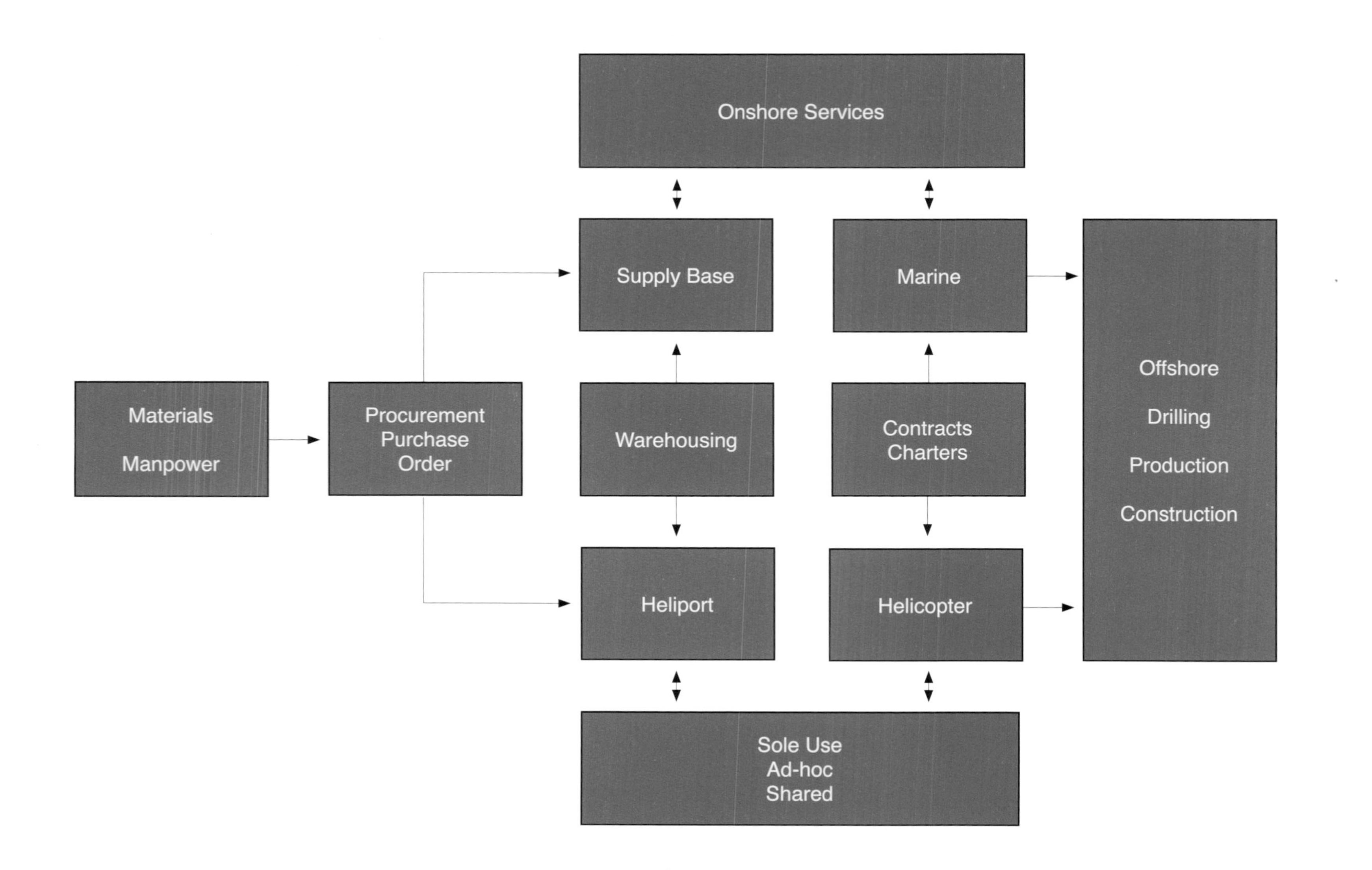
Onshore Services
Materials
Manpower
Procurement
Purchase
Order
Supply Base
Warehousing
Heliport
Marine
Contracts
Charters
Helicopter
Offshore
Drilling
Production
Construction
Sole Use
Ad-hoc
Shared

MATERIALS AND LOGISTICS

TECHNICAL

17.1 Introduction

At any stage of an oil and gas field development, the timely and effective movement of materials, equipment and manpower is vital to the successful execution of the operator's planned work programme. If not managed properly, costly overruns and delays could adversely affect project economics and ultimately lead to significant loss of profit and production and, in extreme cases, even project abandonment.

Each phase of the field development requires careful planning and scoping for what materials and supplies are to be procured, when they are needed and to what exact location they are to be delivered. Consideration as to what quantities are practical and necessary to ship offshore must also be continually identified and planned. Although a helicopter is capable of carrying cargo up to a certain physical size or weight limit, this type of transportation is more suited to the movement of manpower to and from the offshore facilities.

Marine transportation is by far the most common, effective and efficient way to transport supplies to offshore oil and gas fields. Rigs or production units based hundred of miles from the shore need a constant flow of materials and supplies to their location to ensure continuity of operations. The timely back-load of used or waste material from the location to shore is also crucial as space is always at a premium offshore.

This chapter describes the types of marine and aviation transportation needed to maintain uninterrupted offshore operations and the essential onshore support to ensure the efficient movement of manpower, materials and equipment to be in the right place at the right time often in hostile and unpredictable offshore sea and weather conditions.

17.2 Materials and supply to offshore operations

Any stage in the lifecycle of an offshore development will determine the material and supply chain activities that will be required on a day-to-day basis. During drilling operations the rig will require to be supplied with materials specific to drilling of wells, eg conductor pipe, well casings, drill bits, downhole tools, mud and other well fluids.

Drilling is a costly operation where delays are expensive hence the right materials need to be at the drilling site as is required by the drilling programme. This will be drawn up by the drilling team and should specify in detail what materials and supplies are required for each section of the hole. The bottom hole assembly components and drill types along with mud selections and casing specifications with their cement slurry designs all need to get to the well site on time and in the right order.

After the well has been drilled and tested and a discovery deemed commercial, the construction and development phase of the project will follow. During this time the materials and supply activities will centre on the physical construction of the offshore platform, pipelines or a subsea facility if a tie-back to an existing structure is required.

Platform installation, hook-up and commissioning activities will require the structural hardware of the project to be manufactured onshore and transported by vessel or barge to the offshore location for assembly and installation. Modular decks will be installed on top of the platform legs (or jacket as it is commonly known). The modular structures will house production plant, utilities provision, hydrocarbon processing equipment, platform drilling modules, accommodation and helideck facilities, as well as craneage and hydrocarbon exporting and many other facilities.

The successful management of all supply chain activities during platform construction is crucial to the timing and success of the development. The need to co-ordinate the supply of materials, consumables, modules, structures, etc. from a vast number of suppliers, contractors and specialist offshore construction experts together with their transportation, installation, hook-up and commissioning activities makes for a complex series of parallel activities which require detailed planning, and micro management. Development wells will also require to be drilled, therefore similar activity and material supply as in the exploration drilling phase will continue post-construction.

Once an offshore installation is producing hydrocarbons, the level of activity around materials supply and logistical support should reduce to normal 'routine operations'. By this stage, sufficient wells have been drilled and the construction and hook-up activities complete for the early stages of production.

During routine production operations material requirements will be centred on planned maintenance activities, production plant operational needs and the routine activities of the platform. Logistical supply by vessel will normally follow a planned routine (unless, of course, an emergency arises) and it is usual for platforms to be visited by a supply vessel on a weekly basis, sometimes more or less frequently. Supply boats will carry maintenance spares, diesel for fuel, production chemicals and of course supplies to keep the onboard crews well fed and comfortable. Each platform's requirements will vary but equipment and material supply during production operations should be more routine than during drilling or construction phases.

Such activities will increase dramatically when summer campaign maintenance requirements necessitate the platform to be shut down for a predetermined period of maybe weeks or months. Concentrated efforts in completing a set of maintenance activities will again mean that the management of the supply chain will be crucial in restoring the integrity of the platform and the resumption of hydrocarbon production.

17.3 Shore-based material support facilities

All material and logistics support required offshore during the various phases of a project require extensive onshore support. The operator or his nominated contractor will have an appropriate organisation in place to co-ordinate all material procurement and storage activities and timely transport of materials and supply from its onshore holding point to its final offshore location.

Supply bases

Once orders for materials and supplies are placed it is normal practice for the material to be delivered to a central storage location either for immediate supply offshore or for replenishment of stocked items that are held and stored onshore. These stocked items may have significant lead times for delivery or they may be critical-path items that could require to be shipped at very short notice offshore should an unplanned failure occur that may detrimentally affect offshore operations and production. This can be costly if not managed properly. As the majority of material will be shipped by vessel it is natural that the central storage bases that support the offshore operations are located at key ports along the UK coastline.

Since the first oil companies arrived in the UKCS in the 1960s, various ports, mainly along the east coast, have served the industry. There were no dedicated facilities and oil companies and drilling contractors used the facilities that were available. In Scotland port authorities from Lerwick, Peterhead, Aberdeen,

Figure 17–1 Supply base quayside

Montrose, Dundee and Leith attempted to establish their port as the one of choice for inward development.

Some oil companies also established their own port facilities when it became apparent that the North Sea had a significant future. BP set up a dedicated facility in Dundee, and Shell chose Aberdeen. In England, on the west coast, Heysham was, and still is, used as the main support base for the Morecambe gas fields. Liverpool was used briefly to support Liverpool Bay activities but has now closed and activity is consolidated at Heysham.

The Southern North Sea gas fields have been supported from Humberside, Hull/Grimsby, Great Yarmouth and Lowestoft. Shell constructed its own dedicated facility in Lowestoft which has also now closed following outsource to a contractor operated facility. Newcastle, Blyth and Teesside have also featured as onshore support bases mainly supporting the construction phases.

As operating costs increased and oil prices fell, the spiralling cost of materials supply and logistics needed to be better managed. Consolidation for better efficiencies and lower operating costs meant that the number of onshore supply bases was reduced. The majority of oil and gas operators also decided that it was not their core business to own and operate onshore materials and supply bases.

This has led to a reduction in the number of supply bases over the years to now five main locations in the UK. Heysham still supports the Irish sea fields, Lerwick, Peterhead and Aberdeen the Northern and Central North Sea fields and Great Yarmouth the Southern North Sea gas fields.

The oil and gas operators recognised the need for collaboration to reduce their costs by contracting out the operation of onshore support bases to specialist companies who have evolved over the past 20 or so years into logistics and supply chain management specialists. The operators can now place either singular or consortium-based contracts with such contractors who can offer a complete range of services. This has resulted in greater efficiency and means the specialist contractor can concentrate efforts in ensuring that support is tailored to the individual clients on an 'as required' basis.

Shared services

As well as consolidation in the numbers of bases and logistics service contractors, there have been concentrated efforts in elimination of waste and inefficiency in other aspects of the supply chain. For example, sharing of facilities, stock, and transportation arrangements have all helped to reduce costs whilst also maintaining adequate financial returns for the logistics contractors.

It has also been recognised that co-operation between neighbouring operators can provide benefits. Industry-wide discussions on actions for effective provisions of logistics and supply chain support has lead to the North Sea becoming a global benchmark for provision of logistics and supply chain services to the offshore industry.

Supply base operations

Space alongside the quay is expensive, so as well as having facilities at the dockside most supply base contractors will also have extensive storage space (both warehousing and open storage) away from the quay on a nearby, less expensive, industrial estate, usually close to good road links.

At the quayside, proper berthing for the marine vessels that support the offshore activity is crucial. The harbour may have to be dredged regularly to ensure enough tidal draft is available to cope with the larger supply vessels that are utilised. Laydown areas at the quayside are also required for mobile cranes and forklift trucks to operate loading and unloading articulated trucks and the supply vessels at the quayside (Fig. 17–1).

Most material and supply is containerised at the main warehousing facility, typically away from the quayside. The operator will normally contract out the whole operation, which would include storage of stock in the warehouse, provision of open yard space for large bulky non-perishable items such as carbon steel well casing pipes, office space for the supply chain team, computerised stock systems, craneage and fork lift operations, movement of cargo baskets and containers and road transportation to uplift and deliver the vast range of items required to run the offshore operation.

In addition to storage for stock items and lay down areas for cargo baskets and containers, the supply base will also house purpose built tankage used to store specialised chemicals, drilling mud and brine, fuel and water. These all need to be transferred by bulk hose from the quayside storage tanks into the hold tanks of the supply vessels. The process is then reversed with the bulk chemicals or mud being pumped from the vessel tanks into appropriate tanks on the rig or platform.

Drinking water may also be required to be transferred by offshore supply vessel. This is termed 'potable water' but this practice is becoming less common. Modern equipment to extract salt from sea water to make it safe and drinkable has been developed and installed offshore.

Supply chain

Some operators have contracted out all procurement and supply chain activities. Now teams of specialist buyers, expeditors, materials administrators and logistics movement staff provide a 'cradle to grave' service as part of the whole supply chain effort.

The co-ordination of material movement is vital to ensuring the right items are in the right place at the right time. Sophisticated software has been developed to list all required parts in the form of a catalogue and the required stock levels both at supply base locations and on the offshore locations are recorded and set.

Purchasing activity follows and the stock material stored at the base. Material requirements and demands are raised and satisfied either from stock or from a direct purchase order. Once the buyer has completed the material order, an expeditor will monitor progress to ensure timely delivery. Meanwhile, the materials co-ordinators are preparing the cargo list and manifests, arranging uplifts from suppliers or from stock at the warehouse and co-ordinating with the logistics team to make sure the material gets to its destination on time and in useable condition. This is not a one-way process. Whilst materials are arriving on location, a vast array of materials and equipment must be back-loaded and sent onshore, such as items requiring repair or to be scrapped. An army of articulated trucks will meet the incoming vessel at the quayside and once loaded will deliver the back-loaded cargo to the appropriate manufacturers, suppliers and vendors. Waste and scrap will be disposed by specialist and licensed contractors. The vessel, now empty of its return cargo, awaits its next load as the processing of outgoing supply starts again.

17.4 Marine operations

For the support of drilling construction and production operations offshore, various types of vessel have been developed to meet the required operations profile that each phase of field life demand. There are five main functional classifications of vessels.

Figure 17–2 Platform supply vessel

Platform supply vessels (PSVs)

These support all offshore activity and are specifically designed and built with cargo-handling capability in mind. Deck space is important, as is tankage below deck for transportation of water, fuel, chemicals, drilling fluids and muds. The deck space will be used to transport containers and cargo baskets. PSVs range in size from approximately 150 ft to 200 ft. However, larger PSVs up to 275 ft in length are in operation where their improved capacity can be used efficiently on larger-scale projects (Fig. 17–2).

Anchor handling, towing and supply vessels (AHTS)

These have flexibility in the drilling phase. These vessels are used to set anchors for the rigs and also tow the rigs from location to location. When not performing rig support duties, they will be used in limited supply roles. They have shorter decks and specialised towing winches. The Brake Horse Power capacity determines the vessel classification with smaller vessels less then 10,000 BHP. The most powerful AHTS working in the North Sea can have up to 25,000 BHP (Fig. 17–3).

Figure 17–3 Anchor handling vessel

Construction support vessels

An array of vessel types are used in the construction phase, from pipe lay barges supported by pipe carrier supply boats, to dive support vessels to crane barges capable of lifting complete modules. All of them will be required at some phase of field life. The use of propulsion thrusters is common, with most vessels having the capability to be 'dynamically positioned' and held on station as construction work proceeds.

Standby rescue vessels

These perform offshore location safety patrol duties. In the early days of the

Figure 17–4 Standby rescue vessel

North Sea, they would have been converted trawlers. Now state-of-the-art purpose-built vessels with readily deployable fast rescue craft are common. These vessels remain on station at the offshore location and will be called upon if any emergency situations arise. Most have fire-fighting capability on board (Fig. 17–4).

These vessels will also have casualty reception facilities and sophisticated medical equipment on board. Some crew members will also be paramedic-trained.

Oil tankers

Some oil fields require shuttle tankers to be on charter to transport the produced oil directly from the field via purpose-built mooring systems to refineries onshore. Where hydrocarbons have been transported via pipeline to an onshore oil terminal or refineries, the oil tanker will berth at the onshore location and take on board its oil cargo for onwards transportation to various worldwide markets.

17.5 Helicopter operations

In the UK sector of the North Sea the helicopter has been a critical asset that has been used to transport men, women, freight and specialised equipment by air quickly and effectively to and from offshore locations. Bristow Helicopters commenced its North Sea operations on 17 February 1965 when it flew a long-nose Whirlwind (G-APWN) from Sunderland's Unsworth Airfield to Amoco's Mr Cap, a three-legged jack-up drilling rig, 145 miles out on the Dogger Bank. Development gained pace and by the early 1970s Aberdeen in the North East of Scotland and North Denes near Great Yarmouth, Norfolk had both been established as the main logistical hubs for helicopter operations.

The Whirlwind, together with the 14-seat Wessex 60, were eventually phased out and the Sikorsky S61N, together with the Super Puma 330J, became helicopters in regular use in the North Sea. In 1982, 35 Eurocopter AS332L helicopters known as the 'Tiger' were purchased by Bristow. The £100 million order was the largest civilian order for helicopters at that time.

The Bristow 'Tiger', a 19-seat aircraft, was put to work in the Central and Northern North Sea, with Aberdeen as its main base of operations. Although not having the payload or range of the Tiger, the reliable S61N was still in demand. Its large, high cabin was a feature that the passengers favoured. With longer distances and larger numbers of passengers to transport, the S61N and Tiger aircraft were based in Aberdeen and Shetland, with the medium 12-seat Sikorsky S76 being deployed in North Denes supporting the smaller, closer-to-shore platforms in the Southern gas sector.

As well as regular crew change duties, the helicopter was, and still is, deployed in various ancillary roles to support the offshore industry. Interfield 'shuttling' was common during peak construction and maintenance activities. Here, a medium helicopter, typically a Bell 212 or a Sikorsky S76, was based offshore and 'fed' by the larger aircraft. Crew are 'shuttled' between nearby offshore locations to and from work each day and return to the main installation or flotel (accommodation barge) at night.

The helicopter is also used for cargo transfer where all the seats can be removed and special freight-carrying rails installed. They can be used to get a vital piece of equipment, tool or component to its destination quickly and effectively, with the objective of eliminating expensive rig or platform downtime and providing a cost-effective solution to the alternative of sending that key component by boat. A typical flight to a Central North Sea location will take around one hour 15 minutes from Dyce in Aberdeen; a vessel departing Aberdeen port may take 14–18 hours' sailing time – expensive if offshore operations are delayed.

Another common activity where the helicopter is deployed is heavy-lift duties using a cargo hook and specialised lifting strops. Typically, flare tips can be installed or changed using this method of cargo lift. Difficult installations of modules dependent on weight can be 'slotted into place' from above using underslung procedures; the limit on lifting operations is around the 3.8 tonne mark.

Although activity today is not as intense as it was in the early 1980s, the North Sea is still one of the busiest oil and gas provinces in the world, with three main helicopter providers (Bristow, CHC (a Canadian-based company) and Bond Offshore Helicopters) providing safe, professional and reliable services to the oil and gas operators and contractors.

Advances in technology have meant that a new generation of helicopters is being deployed, with the latest Sikorsky S92 and Eurocopter's third-generation Super Puma, the EC 225 (Fig. 17–5), now making their mark as the larger twin-engine helicopters of choice. In the Southern sector, where flight distances are shorter, Eurocopter's EC 155 and Agusta's AB 139 are coming into service.

The harsh environment of the North Sea means that safety precautions are taken very seriously. Helicopters are designed to float in the event of a ditching, with substantial flotation gear deployable as the aircraft touches the water: a rare event, but it has happened. Life rafts are also on board. The need for fast evacuation is also designed into the helicopter, with push-out windows and jettisonable doors to ensure that passengers and crew can exit the helicopter and are fully trained to do so.

Figure 17–5 Eurocopter EC 225 over deck

Approved training schools with dedicated survival training programmes use mock-up helicopter cabins and pools to simulate a ditching and helicopter roll-over. Every pilot and offshore worker undergoes this training at predetermined periodic intervals and must gain their 'survival' certificate to work offshore. As well as survival training, each passenger has to watch and listen to a safety briefing pre-flight. This is presented in DVD format at the heliport and summarises key safety messages in case of an incident whilst travelling in the helicopter. Emergency exits, life raft deployment and lifejacket instructions are all explained and highlighted.

As well as extensive survival training, each passenger travelling over water must wear a survival suit designed to keep body temperature at a survivable level in the event of the individual finding themselves in the cold waters of the North Sea. Each passenger is also provided with a lifejacket which may have a re-breather device incorporated which will provide an extra few minutes of air should an individual find themselves underwater. Personal Locator Beacons are also carried by the passengers for ease of location in an emergency.

17.6 UK helicopter bases and heliports

Today there are six main helicopter support bases in the UK. In the far north of Shetland, at Scatsta near Sullom Voe, fixed-wing feeder planes bring the offshore workers from Aberdeen for onward transportation to the east and west of Shetland oil fields.

Figure 17–6 Bristow's Aberdeen heliport line up

At Aberdeen, still the world's busiest heliport, there are three operators, Bristow (Fig. 17–6), CHC and Bond Offshore Helicopters. Over 40 large helicopters ferry offshore crew to and from the Central and Northern oil fields. Over 400 flights a week are undertaken, with an average round trip time of 3½ hours. The Southern gas fields are supported from Humberside (CHC), North Denes (CHC) and Norwich (Bristow), with medium helicopters such as the Sikorsky S76 and Eurocopter's Dauphin 365N. The gas and oil fields of Morecombe and Liverpool Bay are supported from Blackpool Airport by CHC.

17.7 Contracts and procurement

All the activity in material supply, storage and movement, the chartering of vessels and helicopters and the manpower required to undertake such activity require a legal and commercial framework for their provision.

Materials and supply base services

The oil and gas field operators have mainly contracted out purchasing and supply base activities and have entered into contracts for the provision of services and/or supply of materials.

In most cases, materials and supplies will be procured by a buyer in either the operator's organisation or the supply chain contractor's team. The buyer places the order for the material with a manufacturer, supplier, agent or vendor. This may be a direct single purchase or could form a call-off from a blanket order where terms, conditions and prices have been previously agreed. This form of contract for supply is commonly termed the purchase order.

As well as material supply, service contracts will be placed by the operator for all of the associated supply chain activities. This would typically be one contract for all services that the supply chain contractor provides and would include a services list from which the operator would agree its required scope; for example: '20,000 feet of secure warehousing, 2 berths at the quayside, 10 acres of open storage at the pipeyard, a supply chain team of 2 buyers and expeditor, 2 materials and logistics experts. Craneage fork lifts and trucking as required'.

A set of terms and conditions specific to these activities will be agreed and a schedule of agreed prices, normally fixed on an annual basis, will be set. Needless to say, these contracts can be of significant value and are normally awarded for between 5 and 10 years by the major operators.

Smaller independents or new entrants will contract on a well-by-well or project-by-project basis and will call from the list of available services for its specific needs and timescale only. In recent years the operators have sought efficiencies from the supply base contractors. The result has been a move away from schedule of rate contracts whereby the contractor was paid by the day, hour, square metre, etc. to payment by tonne moved or lift completed. This has put the risk of operations squarely on the shoulders of the contractors and has been partially responsible for the markets consolidation. Those contractors who have successfully adapted have become more efficient by helping the operators drive cost down and have increased their own market share.

Marine vessel charters

The chartering of marine vessels is a much specialised area and expert advice and help should be sought when chartering any vessel. Specific terms and conditions are included in the vessel charter that cover all eventualities in what can be a hazardous venture. Loss of vessel, loss of cargo, pollution incidents, etc. requires to be addressed, as the area of marine liability is complex.

When requiring to charter a vessel it is common to engage a ship broker who will source the vessel to meet the charterer's specific requirements. For instance, there may be a need to transport a certain volume of mud or brine which needs tankage capacity that suits or to have a vessel that has its own deck crane.

The ship broker will have detailed specifications of all vessels and their availability for charter. The charter party terms will normally have been agreed with the ship owners via the broker prior to taking the vessel. This will allow a speedy response when a short-notice vessel is required. It is also standard practice for longer-term work to charter vessels for a stated term, eg annually or to match the length of the supply base contract.

Vessels are normally chartered on a cost-per-day rate although there have been cases where an all-in rate for supply base operations including vessels has been agreed. The ship broker will be paid a commission by the ship owner for arranging the charter of his vessel. The market for vessels is very much supply and demand driven, hence day-rates can fluctuate vastly, dependent on who needs what and what is available in port. There has, therefore, been a trend to fix longer-term charters at agreed rates if demand is predictable.

By coupling demand with other operators, vessel utilisation can be planned and a longer-term arrangement agreed. This gives the vessel operator a guaranteed contract and normally leads to a more competitive rate for the operator and his consortium members.

Helicopter contracts

The main client base for all the helicopter operators is the oil and gas operating companies, drilling contractors and now, more recently, the major production and maintenance contracting companies. With the level of investment required and complexity of providing the service, contracts are mainly long-term.

Contracts are normally awarded by competitive tendering. Although price is important, client companies also evaluate quality and safety systems, aircraft types on offer, service levels proposed, flexibility and ability to provide a complete logistical service package to include ancillary services such as freight management, survival equipment provision and offshore fuel systems management.

Although there is an industry-standard format, each client company tends to issue its own form of contract, due to the complex nature of liabilities and indemnities surrounding the carriage of people by air and its associated risks. Long-term contracts give the client company access to the helicopter during the hours of airport opening and it is common for the client to contract on a 'sole-use' basis.

This normally means a fixed monthly fee is paid to reserve the helicopter and crew and thereafter an hourly rate is paid for each hour or part-hour that the client company uses. If a client does not have the volume of flying to justify a 'sole-use' contract, another means to access on a guaranteed basis is to contract for a share of a helicopter with perhaps one or two other clients who also cannot economically justify a sole-use arrangement. This type of contract is termed 'shared or part-use' and the client only pays for hours used.

The third method of contracting for a helicopter is by 'ad hoc' contract where no guarantee of work is given. Conversely the helicopter company is also not obliged to provide a service but will do so subject to availability. Ad hoc contracts carry a premium in the charge as all the risk is with the helicopter operator.

As the UKCS has matured as a region and continual pressure has been applied to operating costs, especially in times of low oil price, client companies have looked to become more efficient and cost-effective. Efficiencies in operating have been made by putting in place a flightshare scheme whereby client companies can share the helicopters that they have on contract.

Spare seats can be offered to participating clients if it makes sense from a geographical and route perspective. Charging arrangements are agreed in advance as are contractual terms especially in the area of insurance, liabilities and indemnities. It is now a proven and effective system with sharing taking place as a part of day-to-day business. With the upturn in activity and high utilisation of helicopters the flightshare scheme provides an alternative whereby spare seats can be sold to eliminate waste and ensure people can get offshore when needed.

MATERIALS AND LOGISTICS

LEGAL

17.8 Introduction

This section outlines some of the key aspects of contracts required for shore-based operations, the provision of vessels for offshore work and the supply of helicopters for offshore transportation.

17.9 Shore-based support contracts

Shore-based logistics/support operations discussed in this chapter cover such services as the provision of warehousing, transportation and goods handling, the provision of quayside services, loading/unloading and provisioning of vessels and the provision of all equipment and manpower relative to those services.

Ordinarily, an oilfield operator will contract with a single logistics company for the provision of all of the foregoing services, usually on a contract granted for a period of some years. Such contracts tend to be granted for long periods of time because: (a) the operator will wish to integrate its day-to-day operations, annual maintenance schedules and longer-term field projects with a single logistics company for ease of operation; and (b) the logistics company may require to invest significant capital in recruiting staff, procuring warehousing space and equipment and the stability of a long-term contract allows the logistics company to make such capital commitment with some confidence that the investment will be worthwhile.

In preparing any onshore logistics contract, the following issues will require consideration:

(a) Employees

The award of a contract to provide logistics support may, in certain circumstances, amount to the transfer of an undertaking within the meaning of the Transfer of Undertakings (Protection of Employment) Regulations 2006 (SI 2006 No 246) ('TUPE'). The effect of the contract award being regarded as a TUPE transfer is that all employees of any contractor who previously held a contract may be entitled to regard their employment as being transferred to the new contractor. Similarly, if logistics until that date have been handled internally by the operator then it is possible that employees of the operator may have their employment transferred automatically to the contractor to whom the logistics function is outsourced. This can have serious implications for the service provider and the operator as both will require to carry out some level of consultation with affected employees. The new employer will also require to honour all terms of engagement of the employees (or offer to match them in economic terms) and continuity of service of the relevant employees for the purpose of determining their rights under relevant employment legislation (for example, not to be unfairly dismissed or to entitlement to a redundancy payment) and is reckoned so as to include the period of employment with the previous contractor/operator.

It is important to determine whether or not the award of the contract would amount to a TUPE transfer and, if so, what is to happen to any affected employees. It is particularly relevant in the context of drafting clauses relating to indemnification and termination payments where the costs of failing to comply with TUPE, or dismissing employees at the time of a transfer, can be substantial.

(b) Remuneration

As logistics contracts can be granted for a number of years, it is important from the contractor's perspective that there is some mechanism for escalation of the contract rates, usually by reference to an index such as the Retail Prices Index.

As the amount of logistical support required over the life of the contract is likely to vary, depending upon the demands of the operator, the season, whether major construction projects are ongoing offshore, whether maintenance projects are in hand and so forth, the remuneration for the contractor tends to vary according to the volume of services used. For example, the contract may specify a fixed rate for every delivery, vessel turnaround, process into or transfer out of a warehouse, delivery or other service and may include the equivalent of a rental charge per square metre for every square metre of warehouse storage space used in the provision of the logistics contract.

Given that such contracts tend to be granted for a long period of time, if the operator wishes to terminate such a contract earlier than the anticipated contract period there may be some element of liquidated (ie pre-agreed) damages payable to the contractor to compensate it for the heavy capital investment it will have had to make in equipment and premises (save where the contractor is at fault in some way and that leads to termination).

(c) Specific contractor obligations

A contract for logistics support will contain many of the provisions found in offshore and onshore services contracts generally and may well be based on the CRINE Standard Contract. As such, it will cover the usual matters such as insurance, scope of work, liability and indemnification, dispute resolution, intellectual property rights and so forth. With respect to logistics, there are additional obligations which may be imposed upon the contractor as follows:

(i) Customs procedures and compliance

The shipment of goods in and out of the UK, and indeed in and out of the European Union, gives rise to a raft of compliance issues relating to VAT, duty and customs procedures generally. Goods identified for onward shipment outside of the EU, may qualify for Inward Processing Relief, Outward Processing Relief and Return Goods Relief and it would normally be the responsibility of the contractor to undertake import, export and re-import work in such a way as to enable maximum advantage to be taken of HM Revenue and Customs and Excise procedures and in order to minimise the VAT and any Customs duties liabilities of the operator.

(ii) Location of work and standard of facilities

The operator may have specific requirements with respect to where onshore logistics and quayside support should be provided. For example, the operator may have a long-term charter of a supply vessel operated out of a particular harbour and with a requirement to berth at a particular quay for technical reasons. In that event, the contract may well specify a particular quay at which vessel turnaround facilities will be provided by the contractor. The operator may also be concerned to ensure that the storage facilities of the contractor are of a good standard, not just for operational reasons, to ensure that the warehousing facilities are fit for purpose and as close as possible to the point of use (so as to minimise transport costs), but also for reputational reasons – certain of the goods being stored may be identified with the operator's logo and name and it is appropriate that those goods are kept in the right circumstances and in compliance with all relevant laws concerning health and safety and the protection of the environment. The contract, therefore, may specify precisely which warehousing facilities are to be used and may set out particular upgrade requirements if the warehousing facilities in existence do not meet the requirements of the operator.

(iii) HSE – Health, safety and environmental compliance

The operator will be concerned to ensure that all logistics services are carried out in compliance with all appropriate standards and regulations. These would extend to cover compliance with waste disposal regulations (for the handling of waste brought back to shore) and the handling of dangerous goods (for example, certain radioactive materials are required for offshore testing purposes and these require to be handled in accordance with all rules applying to radioactive materials). The operator will be concerned to ensure that the contractor complies with all relevant provisions of the Health and Safety at Work, etc. Act 1974 and all related regulations concerning health and safety at work. Although, strictly, liability for any accident occurring at work would probably rest with the contractor, from a reputational perspective operators are concerned to ensure that they have as few man-days as possible lost to accidents at work and, ideally, none at all. This 'health and safety conscious culture' extends not just within the operator's own organisation but very often into the supply chain, and particularly the logistics part of the supply chain where individuals can be exposed to handling dangerous materials or to risk of accident.

Similarly, compliance with the operator's policies on drug abuse and control quite often forms part of the logistics contract.

Although not suitable for all circumstances, the CRINE Standard Contract for the provision of services (on and offshore) is quite comprehensive and its terms cover most, if not all, of the legal issues which are likely to require to be addressed in the context of shore-based operations. These next two sections highlight some of the key legal provisions of the CRINE Standard Contract relating to (A) liability and indemnification and (B) dispute resolution, as those provisions are the ones which tend to cause most legal debate in the negotiation, the remaining provisions being largely mechanical and 'non-legal'. Many of the provisions discussed are relevant to other contracts, from purchase orders to EPIC contracts.

(A) Liability and indemnification

With respect to the liability and indemnity regime, CRINE adopts a quite typical mutual 'hold harmless' position in terms of which the contractor indemnifies the operator in respect of any expenses and liabilities relating to loss of, or damage to, the property of the contractor group, personal injury and death of any person employed by the contractor group and third party personal injury and death ('third party' in this context meaning any party which does not form part of the contractor group or the operator group). The operator gives reciprocal indemnities to the contractor in respect of similar loss, damage or injury suffered by the operator group. It is worth noting that it is not sufficient for the parties simply to give each other a release of any such claims without also including an indemnity in respect of liability. A release of claims by, say, the operator would not give comfort to the contractor in respect of third party claims brought by affiliates of the operator or the operator's employees or co-venturers – in order to be protected against such third party action, the contractor would require an express indemnity from the operator. It is not practical to obtain releases from all such third parties and therefore the potential for such third party claims being raised against the contractor remains – the risk is simply offset by the existence of an indemnity for such claims being granted by the operator.

One aspect occasionally overlooked is to ensure that where indemnities are being given that they are actually worth something – an indemnity in respect of third party claims from a party which is itself worthless is no real protection and, ultimately, leaves the contractor or operator open to claims without the benefit of a worthwhile indemnity. It is for this credit risk reason that there are often express insurance obligations placed – usually on the contractor – detailing the amount of insurance cover to be carried by the contractor for the liabilities being assumed by the contractor. In this way, the operator is given some assurance that the indemnity from the contractor is worth having. It is unusual to find reciprocal obligations to insure on the operator – in the normal course, the operator is usually a much larger company, with a stronger financial covenant, and therefore issues of whether they are or are not insured do not arise. In that event, the contractor is relying solely on the operator's balance sheet to back the operator's indemnities.

Following the mutual 'hold harmless' theme, each party to the contract normally grants an indemnity to the other in respect of consequential loss suffered by it and its affiliates – in effect, the operator accepts the risk of its own consequential losses and the contractor accepts responsibility for the contractor's own consequential losses. Without this, a contractor would be exposed to liability for, say, loss or delay of production if his particular nut or bolt did not arrive at the platform on time. The exposure to consequential loss claims would far outweigh any commercial benefit to the contractor in entering into the contract in the first place. There may occasionally be agreed exceptions to this in the form of liquidated damages where the operator may insist that, if delay occurs or some consequential loss is suffered by the operator, the contractor agrees to pay pre-agreed damages as partial compensation for that loss – perhaps a fixed rate for every day's delay in completion of the project up to a maximum amount.

The CRINE Standard Contract also contemplates the inclusion of financial limits on the contractor's cumulative liability under the contract in respect of defective performance or faulty workmanship, albeit those financial limits would not apply to the express indemnities and mutual 'hold harmless' provisions.

(B) Dispute resolution

The CRINE Standard Contract also makes provision for a dispute resolution mechanism. In the standard form, this envisages an escalation procedure whereby disputes are referred to increasingly senior levels of staff in the contractor and operator companies, followed by the possibility of alternative dispute resolution, if the parties agree, failing which either party may take the dispute to court. Occasionally, CRINE may be amended to provide for arbitration of commercial disputes and it is not that unusual to see arbitration clauses providing for arbitration at the International Chamber of Commerce.

Although arbitration can sound attractive, when compared to a court action, arbitration may be much more protracted and no less expensive than simply proceeding to court. Courts also have the advantage that they can effectively impose a timetable on the parties for resolution of their dispute and make effective legally binding orders for payment or delivery of assets at the end of the process – arbitration often suffers because of the inability of the arbiter to force the parties speedily through the arbitration process. Usually one party or the other sees delay as being in its interests. In one case which went to arbitration, concerning a partnership dispute, the arbitration was proceeding merrily into its tenth year with no signs of a resolution – court actions, however slow, are usually faster than this.

Alternative dispute resolution differs from arbitration in that it tends to be non-contractual and proceeds on the basis that the parties might be willing to reach some form of compromise provided that the independent expert selected by them reaches a conclusion that they should do so. This form of negotiated settlement can be quite attractive and certainly is not really an option in open court where both parties are asserting that 'their' position is right. For most commercial disputes, some attempt at informal settlement (whether by formal alternative dispute resolution involving a third party expert or by mediation between the parties' lawyers) is always advisable before jumping into court. It is noticeable that, since the CRINE contracts have come into general use, not only is there far less legal time spent involved in negotiating such contracts but the likelihood of a dispute ending up in court as a result of the contracts has reduced. There may be a number of reasons for this but perhaps the most convincing one is that as CRINE is intended to be quite well balanced as between the contractor and operator, and as such the outcome of the contract, given its normal interpretation, is generally seen as 'fair' – where contracts are unfair then there is greater scope for protracted negotiation, dispute and, ultimately, litigation.

17.10 Marine charters

Many different kinds of vessel are used in the offshore oil and gas industry in the UKCS. They range from small remotely operated vehicles (ROVs) designed for subsurface survey and maintenance work, through safety standby and supply vessels to tankers. This chapter focuses on offshore service vessels – those which are used to transport equipment and supplies offshore either for specific construction projects or for normal course operations.

One of the most common standard form charter parties used for the hire of offshore service vessels is the Supplytime 89 standard charter party produced by The Baltic and International Maritime Council (BIMCO). The remainder of this section summarises some of the key terms of the BIMCO Supplytime 89 charter party – corresponding provisions would be expected to be found in most typical charter parties.

The BIMCO Supplytime 89 form of charter party is suitable where a specific vessel is to be chartered for a set period of time. It comprises a pre-printed section of some 36 standard clauses covering provisions which will be common to most time charters, including certain clauses offering alternatives for the parties to select, for example, dealing with the place of arbitration of any disputes. It also contains a 'fill in the blanks' form allowing the parties to a charter party to set out the details specific to their contract, for example, the identity of the vessel, the names of the owners of the vessel and the charterers, time of hire and so forth. Where additional clauses specific to a particular charter party are required these can also be annexed to the standard form, for example, provisions relating to specific insurance requirements. A charter party such as this might be used where, for example, a large offshore construction project is underway and one of the main contractors requires the use of a supply vessel perhaps to deliver multiple cargos of construction materials to the offshore site. The time charter might also be used where, say, inspection and survey services are to be performed, perhaps using ROV to be deployed from the chartered vessel.

The following key clauses are worth mentioning.

1. Delivery and redelivery

Vessels are ordinarily chartered on a fixed day-rate, with certain specified additional costs being for the cost of the charterer. The charter party will set out the definition of when the vessel is delivered (usually by reference to a specific port of delivery) at which point the obligation of the charterers to pay the day rate hire commences. In order for the charter to commence, the vessel must usually meet a specific description and classification, an independent surveyor may be required to check the vessel to ensure that it comes up to specification and ordinarily it must be delivered free of cargo and with clean tanks ready to carry out the charterer's project. Fuels and lubricants used in a charter are generally for the cost of the charterer and, therefore, the charter party will normally make some provision for the valuation of or quantification of bunkers (ie fuel and lubricants) at the time of delivery and again at the time of redelivery so the quantity of fuel and lubricants used in the period of charter can be calculated and invoiced to the charterer. The charter party may include fixed sums for mobilisation and demobilisation of the vessel at the commencement and end of the period of hire.

2. Use of the vessel during the period of hire

Generally, the charterer is free to specify the route and sailing schedule of the vessel during the period of hire and set out any schedule appropriate to the transportation of cargo or performance of services offshore. The vessel, however, remains under the control of the master, who will be an employee of the owners. There are certain exceptions to this; for example, the owners are not normally obliged to sail their vessel into areas affected by ice or to follow an icebreaker as this would expose the vessel to an increased risk of damage or loss. If ice operations are required by the charterer then this is usually done by agreement with the owners in return for increased charter rates and the additional costs of any extra insurance being met by the charterer. There are also restrictions on the charterer using the vessel in any area which may be affected by piracy, wars (whether declared or not) and bringing it into any port where there may be risks of disease to the master and crew. Although this latter restriction is unlikely to be relevant in the context of UKCS operations, it can be of particular significance if the vessel is required to operate in, say, West Africa.

3. Obligations of the owners and charterers

Certain basic running costs of the vessel, such as provisions for crew, wages, insurance of the vessel, dues and charges directly related to the vessel's flag and/or registration and all maintenance and repair of the vessel's hull, machinery and equipment, are generally met by the owners. Charterers tend to pick up the costs of consumables such as fuel, lubricants, water, fire-fighting foam and so forth and other out-of-pocket costs of operating the vessel on that particular voyage for which it has been chartered, eg pilotage, launch hire, tug assistance, canal, dock, harbour, tonnage and other dues and security costs. Items such as Customs duties and the costs of obtaining any permits and payment of any import duties are ordinarily also for the account of the charterer.

4. Suspension of hire

The day-rate is ordinarily payable for any period of 24 hours or part thereof during which the vessel is on hire, ie the entire period between delivery of the vessel and redelivery at the end of charter. There are certain exceptions to this where the vessel may be 'off-hire' and, accordingly, hire is not payable – this can occur where, for example, there is a deficiency of crew or of the owner's stores, strike by any of the master, officers and crew, breakdown of machinery, damage to the vessel or any other cause preventing the vessel from working, unless the cause is due to the fault or neglect of the charterers themselves.

5. Liabilities and indemnities

In common with many other supply chain contracts, a typical time charter will normally contain mutual 'hold harmless' provisions. Generally, liability for loss of, or damage to, the property of the owners or of their contractors, including the vessel, or for personal injury or death of the employees of the owners or contractors falls on the owners, irrespective of whether it is wholly or partially as a result of the negligence of the charterers. Specific indemnities to that effect are normally included by the owners for the benefit of the charterers. Similarly, the charterers normally accept liability for any cargo being carried at the request of the charterers (whether or not owned by the charters) and for any death of, or personal injury to, the employees of the charterers or their contractors (again, irrespective of any negligence on the part of the owners or their employees or agents). Similar indemnities to that effect are included by the charterer in favour of the owners.

Liability for consequential loss, including loss of use, loss of profits, shut-in or loss of production is generally excluded by both parties.

6. Pollution

Generally, the owners accept liability for (and indemnify the charterers in respect of) all liabilities for pollution damage and the cost of the clean-up arising from acts or omissions of the owners or their personnel which cause or allow discharge, spills or leaks from the vessel, but not from any cargo carried on the vessel. All other pollution liabilities (for example, in respect of pollution caused by the cargo carried on the vessel or if the vessel in the course of its operations causes damage to, say, a pipeline, the pollution resulting from that pipeline damage) is for the account of the charterers who give appropriate indemnification to the owners.

7. Insurance

Given the scope for substantial property damage, loss of life and/or pollution resulting from the operation of offshore supply vessels, clauses relating to liability and indemnification in respect of these matters should be reviewed by each party's insurers and adequate insurance put in place. Few parties will wish to accept the liabilities imposed by the charter party (either the owners or the charterer) without most, if not all, of those liabilities being the subject of some insurance cover. Annex B to the BIMCO standard form allows the parties to detail specific insurance covers and levels to be maintained by each party and this can form a useful checklist to ensure that all insurable risks resting with a particular party are the subject of insurance carried by that party. It is not just in the interests of the party liable to ensure that its liability is covered but also in the interests of the party relying on indemnification from the liable party. An indemnity from a charterer may only be as good as the charterer's insurance cover and therefore it is in the interests of the owners to check that the charterer has appropriate insurance cover in place and vice versa. In the event that an insured liability arises and the insurers of, say, the charterer pay out under the insurance policy, as a matter of general insurance law, rights of subrogation ordinarily arise in favour of the charterer's insurer. The effect of subrogation rights is that the insurers step into the shoes of the insured party (the charterer) and if, say, the owners had been negligent in some way then it may be possible for the insurers to pursue the owners for damages in negligence – obviously, the existence of any such claim rather defeats the purpose of the charter party placing liability on the insured party in the first place. As a consequence, the charter party will provide for waivers of subrogation to be obtained, ie in the above example the charterer's insurance company would be asked by the charterer not just to insure the charterer but also to waive any claims which the insurers might have against the owners of the vessel, their employees and agents to ensure that the indemnities to be given by the charterer are not rendered worthless by a claim being made against the owner. As an alternative to waivers of subrogation rights, in respect of certain categories of cover, each party may asked to be named as a co-insurer of the other so that in that event either party may be able to claim under the insurance cover in respect of loss which it has sustained.

8. Saving of life and salvage

Recognising the circumstances in which vessels often operate, the charter party permits the Master of the vessel to deviate from the charterer's instructions where necessary to save life and, in that event, the vessel is not regarded as being 'off-hire' where it is on such a mercy mission. Opportunities to carry out salvage operations may arise and in that event, with the charterer's consent, the vessel is normally at liberty to undertake salvage operations, with the benefit of any such salvage operation being shared equally between the owners and the charterers, after deducting the Master's, officers' and crew's share of the legal expenses and other costs of the salvage.

9. Sublet and assignment

The charterer is ordinarily permitted to grant sub-charters of the vessel to third parties, subject to the owner's prior approval, not to be unreasonably withheld. This flexibility can be particularly useful in a long-term charter – generally, the longer the period of hire committed to by the charterer, the lower the day-rate. This is attractive provided the charterer continues to have a long-term requirement for the use of the vessel. If a vessel is chartered for, say, a three-year period in anticipation of the charterer having three years of offshore projects requiring such vessel but market conditions or commercial opportunities turn out such that the charterer does not require the vessel for the whole of that period, there is normally no provision allowing the charterer to cancel the charter party early or put the vessel 'off-hire'. In that event, the risk of the vessel standing idle would be entirely for the account of the charterer. Some running costs of the vessel can be saved in that event as, ordinarily, the charter party will allow the charterer to have the vessel lay up, at which point reductions can be made in the number of crew and their costs, fuel and so forth. The ability of the charterer to sub-charter the vessel in those circumstances can be critical to managing that risk.

10. Termination

Normally the charter party operates for a fixed period of time, with no ability to terminate early. However, the charter party can contain provisions allowing the charterer to terminate the charter earlier than expected, usually on payment of some termination charge and on notice. Costs of demobilisation of the vessel are normally fixed and agreed in advance and payable by the charterer at the end of the hire. Termination for cause is permitted under the BIMCO standard form on the grounds which one would expect, eg requisition of the vessel by government authorities, bankruptcy of either party, actual or constructive loss of the vessel, breakdown of the vessel for an extensive period rendering it unable to perform operations, default under the charter party or the occurrence of a force majeure event lasting for more than 15 consecutive days.

11. Wreck removal

In the event that the vessel sinks and becomes a wreck and an obstruction to navigation, and has to be removed upon request by any compulsory law or authority, the costs of such removal is normally for the account of the owners.

12. Dispute resolution

It is most common for any disputes arising out of a charter party to be settled by arbitration. The BIMCO standard form contemplates two principal alternatives – arbitration in London or arbitration in New York. If the parties wish to opt for arbitration in some other location, they may do so. Equally, they may simply delete all the arbitration provisions with any dispute being resolved by negotiation or, ultimately, in court. Given the scope for the vessel operating internationally, even within the UKCS, a choice of law clause and, if court proceedings are a possibility, a submission by each of the parties to the jurisdiction of a particular court are useful provisions to include.

In addition to the standard clauses commented on above, there may be a requirement for specific contractual provisions to be included in any given charter party, depending upon the circumstances of the charter. For example, where a vessel is being chartered by an operator on behalf of a number of owners of an oil field the mutual 'hold harmless' and liability provisions would require amendment to ensure that the operators co-venturers and their affiliate companies are held harmless to the same extent as the operator as charterer – the BIMCO standard format does not automatically provide for mutual 'hold harmless' provisions to extend across the co-venturer group.

17.11 Helicopter contracts

The supply of helicopter services and the related personnel, equipment and materials is typically governed by a Master Services Agreement between the operator of one or more oil fields and a helicopter company. The agreement can be a short term ad hoc agreement providing for a limited number of helicopter flights on agreed specified dates or, more commonly, in the form of a call-off contract whereby standard terms and conditions are agreed between the operator and the helicopter company for the provision of helicopter services over a period of some years with the precise numbers and dates of flights being called off under that master contract as required.

A contract for the provision of helicopter services shares many terms which are common to service contracts generally in the UKCS. There are, however, some peculiarities of helicopter contracts which are worth mentioning.

(a) Regulatory compliance

There should be obligations on the contractor to ensure that all helicopters provided and services carried out are in compliance with UK Civil Aviation Authority and other regulatory and governmental requirements. Operation of the helicopter in compliance with all safety regulations should be the responsibility of the contractor.

(b) Liability and indemnity regime

Typically, Master Services Agreements would incorporate mutual 'hold harmless' provisions. These would take the form of the following:

- An indemnity by the contractor to the operator, its co-venturers and their affiliates in respect of any loss of, or damage to, the property and equipment of the contractor and its subcontractors and affiliates, eg loss or destruction of the helicopter. The contractor would also indemnify the operator, co-venturers and affiliates in respect of any loss relating to death or injury of any personnel of the contractor, its subcontractors and affiliates. These indemnities would apply irrespective of any negligence or breach of duty (statutory or otherwise) on the part of the operator.
- There would be corresponding indemnities from the operator in respect of damage or loss to the equipment of the operator, its co-venturers and their affiliates and death or injury to their respective personnel, again whether or not contributed to by the negligence or breach of duty of the contractor.
- In common with other UKCS Service Agreements, there would normally be an express exclusion of liability for consequential loss suffered by either party.
- Liability of the contractor to other third party contractors may be addressed if the contractor and those other third parties are already party to the Industry Mutual Hold Harmless Agreement (IMHH) promoted by UKOOA. Where the contractor and any relevant third parties are not party to the IMHH then the contractor would be well advised to seek similar mutual 'hold harmless' arrangements on a case-by-case basis with any contractors whose personnel the helicopter company is transporting. The operator may use the helicopter service not just for the operator's personnel but for those of third party contractors and therefore it is essential to consider this mutual 'hold harmless' arrangement.

(c) Insurance

In the context of indemnification, there is normally an obligation on the helicopter company to provide adequate insurance in respect of its potential liabilities under the indemnities. This would cover at least the cost of damage to, or destruction of, the helicopter, with some level of personal injury/third party liability cover sufficient to provide insurance in the event of death or injury of the helicopter company's own personnel and those of its subcontractors and affiliates. The operator should insure its own personnel and should ensure its subcontractors whose personnel may use the helicopter service are the subject of adequate insurance cover by the relevant employer.

(d) Client obligations

Unlike most service contracts where the obligations tend to be placed solely on the contractor to satisfy himself as to the method of work and with respect to the carrying out of the work, in the context of the provision of helicopter services there would ordinarily be quite extensive obligations on the operator. These may include, for example, an obligation to provide messing, accommodation and medical facilities for the contractor's personnel while they are on any offshore installation, to provide landing deck area and flight deck facilities, provide and maintain refuelling and ground power supply on the offshore installation, provide storage facilities for the spare parts which may be required offshore by the helicopter, provide adequate fire-fighting equipment and generally provide such other support facilities as may be required offshore for the operation of the helicopter. These would normally be provided free of charge to the contractor as part of the operator's normal costs of running its platform.

(e) **Clauses peculiar to helicopter contracts**

The Master Services Agreement would make provision setting out who is responsible for boarding card services and ticketing and set out responsibilities and time lines for the delivery of freight and mail to the contractor sufficiently ahead of helicopter departure times to ensure they can be loaded safely. Provision would also be made for supply of protective clothing and safety equipment to the helicopter crew and passengers.

As helicopters may be called upon to attend offshore disasters or medical emergencies, the Master Services Agreement normally contains a priorities order for helicopter operations which may permit the helicopter operator to delay the provision of helicopter services to the operator where necessary to lend assistance in the case of disaster or medical emergency.

— 18 —

EXPORT AND TRANSPORTATION

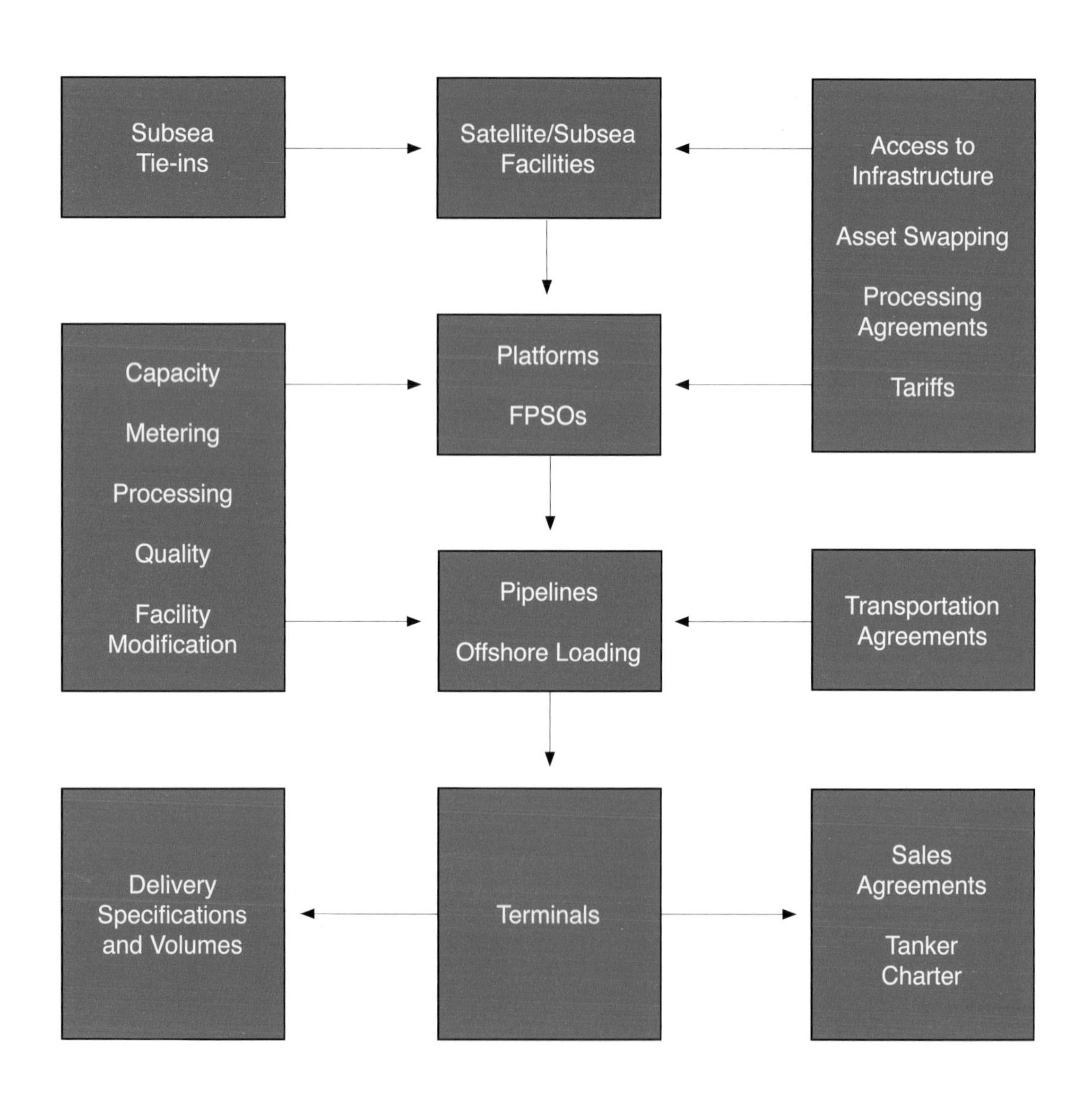
Subsea
Tie-ins
Satellite/Subsea
Facilities
Access to
Infrastructure
Asset Swapping
Processing
Agreements
Tariffs
Capacity
Metering
Processing
Quality
Facility
Modification
Platforms
FPSOs
Pipelines
Offshore Loading
Transportation
Agreements
Delivery
Specifications
and Volumes
Terminals
Sales
Agreements
Tanker
Charter

EXPORT AND TRANSPORTATION

TECHNICAL

18.1 Introduction

Gas and oil exploration has led to a significant infrastructure of production facilities linked by pipelines for export to oil and gas terminals around the coast of the UK. The earlier, larger gas and oil fields justified the laying of dedicated pipelines owned and operated by the major field producers.

Concurrent with the depletion of these larger fields, the smaller fields, discovered later, can now be linked to either platforms with excess processing capacity or directly to the nearest pipeline system providing that the oil or gas can be co-mingled without adversely affecting the host system and products.

With increasing oil prices, there continues to be an economic justification to develop and bring on stream much smaller fields which would not have been economically or technically possible some years ago. Subsea developments tied into the existing platform and pipeline network infrastructure are enabling new entrant operators to further exploit the remaining reserves (proven and unproven) estimated at around 40% of the total North Sea oil and gas reserves.

Selective trading between field owners is now also enabling more effective geographical control of ownership and operatorship of these smaller oil and gas accumulations. This simplifies the financial and technical approval process to help optimise field life and production whilst lowering operating costs.

This chapter describes the way in which the UK offshore industry is using its offshore infrastructure to allow the window of opportunity for smaller field developments and to maximise depletion of proven and future oil and gas reserves.

18.2 Southern North Sea gas fields

The first UK offshore hydrocarbon discoveries were made in the Southern North Sea. These were, predictably, gas discoveries as an extension of the successful gas exploration and production operations offshore in the Dutch sector of the North Sea.

Gas fields were discovered off the south-east coast of England by companies such as BP, Shell, Amoco, Conoco and Phillips and were of suitable-size reservoirs and under sufficient pressures to justify the development of gas terminals to process the gas before sales to the Gas Council (the then UK domestic and industrial supplier).

Transportation was by pipeline from the early platforms approximately 30 miles offshore. Britain's dwindling supply of gas from burning coal was now being replaced by gas delivered by pipeline from North Sea platforms. This was hailed as the start of one of Britain's greatest industrial success stories of the 20th century.

Based on reservoir predictions, long-term gas sales contracts were developed with the Gas Council who were responsible for the distribution of this new form of energy via the existing towns gas network. The oil companies had the advantage of agreeing long-term gas sales contracts for the life of the fields before final commitment to the capital expense required to build the offshore facilities and lay the pipelines to transport the gas under its own pressure to the onshore terminals for processing to gas sales specifications.

These contracts took into consideration periods of maintenance and seasonal predicted swings in temperature and subsequent demand. Gas was delivered on a daily nomination basis with agreed penalties for shortfall which would also reflect on the agreed annual contractual quantities to be sold the following year.

The oil companies owned and operated the facilities and pipelines up to the sales point. Opportunities therefore existed for the oil companies to enter into risk-sharing arrangements amongst themselves to ensure that the daily nominations from the Gas Council were met.

Ideally, the majority of gas processing takes place onshore to reduce operating costs in manpower and logistics. Gas flowing from high-pressure reservoirs with minimal corrosive elements requires only basic platform liquid knock-out facilities. Pipelines can be operated in a 'wet' mode, transporting the residual produced water and condensate for separation at the onshore terminal.

Operating high-pressure 'wet' pipelines can present difficulties in the formation of hydrates. These substances are similar in appearance to frozen snow which forms on the pipeline wall under certain gas pressures and composition. Once formed, hydrates can rapidly build to block the flow through the pipeline and then can only be removed by depressurisation.

This highly undesirable occurrence can be prevented by the injection of methanol or mono-ethylene glycol to absorb the water. Injection rates are calculated to accommodate gas flow rates and water content (BS&W). The wet mono-ethylene glycol or methanol is recovered and processed to remove the water at the terminal ready to be returned offshore either by a small 'piggy-back' line attached to the main gas pipeline or by containers transported offshore by supply vessel.

A further problem in the operation of wet gas pipelines is liquid drop-out in the pipeline due to reduction in flow rate. This can be more common during lower summer nominations. Higher flow rates can have the effect of sweeping the pipeline clear of any liquid accumulations. Predictions are therefore made by the pipeline operators to ensure appropriate flow rates to meet required nominations whilst ensuring a smooth flow of liquids to the terminal for separation and processing.

Further pipeline clearance can also be accommodated by the frequent launch from the platform of gauged polyurethane pig balls sized to clear the line of any residual liquid accumulation. Large slugs of liquid are received at the pipeline inlet to the gas terminal by a slug catcher specifically designed to act in the same way as a large gas liquid separation vessel.

Offshore gas processing facilities will vary depending on the reservoir gas composition that may produce harmful corrosive effects on the pipeline. The presence of such elements may require treatment offshore with a resultant transportation of dry gas through to the appropriate terminal. Such elements as hydrogen sulphide or carbon dioxide will be highly corrosive when combined with produced water from the reservoir and therefore the gas must be dehydrated at the platform before transportation via the pipeline.

Co-operation between terminal and pipeline operators can do much to smooth the operation of gas pipelines to accommodate swings in gas nomination demand. These variations could endanger meeting individual gas sales commitments. Adjacent terminal operators may have processing agreements to allow swings in flow due to operating difficulties during the nomination period. This is known as process aid and can be paid back during future nomination periods.

A more serious occurrence may be the inability to meet gas delivery due to reservoir restrictions. Mutual aid agreements to enable gas sales commitments can be made between operators importing gas at the same terminal complex. The applicable charges may be more palatable than the penalties inccurred due to the inability to meet gas sales commitments.

As reservoir pressures have fallen due to depletion, there has been the need to install offshore compression facilities. These are designed to maintain sufficient pressure to ensure that flow differentials across pipelines and onshore processing terminals are operated to meet gas sales delivery pressures consistent with the delivery needs at the sales point. This has required forward design for the early production stages to ensure minimal disruption at the modification stages for commissioning of the compression facilities.

18.3 Northern and Central North Sea production

With the establishment of the UK offshore oil and gas exploration and production industry and the arrival of the major international oil companies, enthusiasm for exploration in the deeper waters of the Northern North Sea began in the early 1970s. Major oil fields such as Brent and Forties with reserves estimated in billions of barrels of oil were discovered alongside smaller fields such as Shell's Auk field and Hamilton Brothers' Argyll field.

Whilst economics were well in favour of laying large pipelines for the major discoveries, the economics were not as favourable for the smaller discoveries. For such developments, offshore loading of oil to be exported by tanker was a solution. Various designs of floating production facilities were used, linked to tanker-loading buoys.

Although this concept was ideal for early production, such operations were weather dependent and required close co-ordination with the marine tanker operations to maximise offtake. In some cases, a permanent tanker storage facility provided a buffer to delays and weather.

Meanwhile, oil pipelines were being constructed from the major oil fields, but return on exploration and capital investment was also brought forward in some cases by early export to offshore loading facilities such as Shell's Brent Spar. Concrete gravity structures also incorporated buffer storage to allow for interruptions or delays in offshore loading.

Early oil production was at the cost of the economic disposal of the associated gas where, ideally, it could be re-injected to assist reservoir pressure maintenance or utilised as fuel for power generation. With no other options, the associated gas was flared at significant energy waste. This inevitably led to government flaring restrictions in the late 1970s which sharply focused the oil companies on more economic gas disposal, either as a secondary reservoir recovery technique or for gas sales via pipeline. Projects such as the FLAGS pipeline to St Fergus gas terminal now play a major role in the North Sea infrastructure.

18.4 Oil pipeline infrastructure and operations

As fields were discovered in the Northern and Central North Sea, various parameters were considered regarding the best options to export the oil to shore terminals and ultimately to be sold at prevailing oil prices throughout the world.

Whilst larger fields would have robust economics to justify the laying of dedicated pipelines, smaller field developments would consider options to utilise the existing or developing infrastructure. This has involved complex processing and transportation agreements between field operators to ensure minimum interruption of production to third party users of the existing infrastructure.

The escalation of the Piper Alpha disaster was a result of the continuous flow of oil from a neighbouring platform utilising the export pipeline infrastructure. The subsequent recommendations following the fatal accident inquiry resulted in the installation of fail-safe pipeline isolation valves both on the seabed and incoming platform pipeline riser. Estimations have shown that this was accomplished at a cost in excess of £5 billion, without taking into consideration the deferred oil production costs.

Oil is treated on the offshore production facility to remove any gas, associated gas, or produced water. It is also treated for any potential corrosive elements. It is, therefore, critical to ensure any third party use of the pipeline or production facilities is compatible with the host platform operations and handling. Frequent sampling programs and metering procedures are all part of the established agreements.

The composition of oil in pipelines can vary and requires close monitoring to reduce the possibilities of interruption to flow. Typical problems can be as a result of excessive water input which can cause emulsions difficult to separate at the receiving terminal.

Other problems can emerge due to deposition of free water at low spots in the pipeline which have the potential to create localised corrosion and ultimately pipe-line leakage and failure. At best, such incidents can create export interruptions and deferred production. At worst, potential environmental incidents can result.

Under certain temperatures and pressures, waxing can also occur. This is a solid substance deposited from the oil and can line or completely block the pipeline. Once formed, waxing can be difficult to locate and remove in subsea pipelines.

In developing a pipeline infrastructure for multifield operations with third-party ownership, system integrity monitoring is clearly essential to maintain the infrastructure throughout the life of the agreement. Changes in oil composition from any third party user can have transportation implications for all other users, hence the need for frequent sampling and reporting procedures.

18.5 Satellite field developments

During the early life of the North Sea, large field developments were considered essential to ensure an adequate return on the huge capital investment in the construction, load-out and commissioning of the production facilities, drilling the production wells and laying the pipeline for export of the crude oil or gas (or both in some cases). Much of this was done at a time of oil prices in the region of $40 per barrel in the early 1970s. The size of the reservoir and comparatively stable political climate made North Sea projects competitive with other oil-producing areas around the world.

In spite of periods of low capital expenditure on exploration, and project developments during periods of falling oil prices, the UK North Sea has enjoyed a significant infrastructure development of offshore facilities and pipelines. Statistics show an infrastructure of some 200 offshore platforms and over 10,000 km of pipelines interconnecting facilities and onshore terminals. There is nowhere in the UK sector of the North Sea that is more than 50 km from this existing infrastructure.

18.6 Asset swapping and trading

As production has declined from some of the larger fields, profit levels for these developments have also declined for some of the major international oil companies. This has given opportunities for new, smaller operators with expertise to continue to produce such fields more profitably. There has, therefore, been a significant change of ownership and operatorships of some of the older fields and platforms.

Furthermore, processing capacity and pipeline capacity has become available to accommodate production from small subsea field developments This may be as simple as single subsea wells tied back to an existing platform or appropriate infrastructure.

Higher oil prices, together with improved technology to identify and develop smaller fields, has provided encouragement to the rapidly increasing number of smaller oil companies to develop such fields.

Not surprisingly, the original major operators have been selective in such trading, in some cases withholding lower operating cost fields to harvest the production, and maintaining ownership of the pipeline infrastructure for the tariffing opportunities.

Changes in ownership of platforms have not only taken place for operating cost reduction but for strategic positioning relative to other potential producing assets.

Asset swapping and trading is now becoming more common to allow facilities operators the autonomy to make economic decisions without the burden of multipartnerships, each with different short- and long-term agendas.

18.7 New and future developments

More recently, developments have included ownership of different fields and platforms linked together with interconnecting pipeline systems for oil and gas transportation to respective processing terminals. A typical example in the Northern area of the North Sea is the Elgin/Franklin project which includes the existing BP Forties liquid pipeline system to Kinneil and the SEAL (Shearwater Elgin Area Line) to the Bacton gas terminal. It is anticipated that production from these systems will continue to at least 2022 but will also provide infrastructure for new smaller developments as system capacity becomes available.

A further example is the Central Area Transmission System (CATS) operated by BP which transports and treats gas for more than 20 facilities and field owners, including most of the major North Sea gas producers. The pipeline, linking many small gas production platforms and facilities, comes ashore at Cotham Sands and then runs a further 5 miles below ground to the CATS terminal at Seal Sands at Teesside.

With fewer major fields now being discovered in the UK North Sea, the remaining estimated 15 billion barrels of oil equivalent (proven and undiscovered) reserves will be produced from small fields, linked by satellite facilities or subsea wells relying on the existing infrastructure for processing and transportation to the existing onshore oil and gas terminals.

EXPORT AND TRANSPORTATION

LEGAL

18.8 Introduction

Finding an oil or gas field is only one part (albeit a very important part) of a successful development. A field will be worthless if there is no way of getting production from the field to market.

The cost of laying pipelines is high (some say $1 m per km) and a discovery would have to be very large to justify the costs of building a dedicated export system. The field may be hundreds of miles from shore. Historically, some fields were discovered in the UKCS which were large enough to make it commercially viable to build a dedicated export route for production. Today, discoveries tend to be much smaller and it is not usually commercially viable to construct dedicated transportation and processing facilities. It is much more common for a field to be developed with production being exported by tying into a nearby transportation system owned by one or more third parties. It may be that the owners of the system originally built the pipeline to export production from a field or fields which are now in decline and as a result of which there is spare capacity within the system. If such capacity is available in a nearby system the field owner could enter into arrangements in terms of which the field owner agrees to deliver its production to the transportation system and the system owner agrees to transport production from the field to a specified delivery point in exchange for tariff payments.

Transportation systems are often owned by more than one party, with one of the owners being the operator of the system. Although pipeline owners or Transporters are referred to below, this should be taken as meaning the consortium of owners of the system. In practice, Transportation Agreements often deal with processing of the product but this section deals solely with the transportation aspects.

18.9 Transportation Agreements

Transportation and Processing Agreements, although voluminous documents, deal with certain common issues and the following is a non-exhaustive list of some of the key issues.

Duration

When will the Transportation Agreements start and when will they end? The Transporter will need to be kept appraised of when the field is likely to come on stream.

Transportation Agreements are often for the life of the relevant field and so provide that the agreement can be terminated on the run-down or permanent cessation of the field. There will be other usual termination events such as the failure by the field owners to pay the tariff or other sums due under the agreement. The agreement might also give the field owner the right to have production transported using an alternate route or to terminate the Transportation Agreement where the system owner fails to transport the production.

There will usually be provisions to the effect that the system owner may abandon the transportation system on giving a period of written notice to the field owners. Such provisions are typically qualified by a requirement on the parties to hold 'good faith' discussions as to how the field owner can maintain its export route, including the possibility of the field owners (perhaps with others) assuming ownership and/or operatorship of the system.

Where from and where to?

It may seem obvious but it is crucial that the contract is clear exactly from where the product is to be transported (the 'Entry Point') and to where it is to be delivered (the 'Redelivery Point'). This requires to be defined very carefully and is usually referred to as being at a particular point on a piece of infrastructure – for example at a specific flange or weld. It is essential for the buyer to ensure that it has access to the product at the place specified for delivery.

It may not be possible to find a Transporter who can take the product all the way to its required destination. As a result it may be necessary to enter into transportation arrangements with more than one Transporter, with one transporting it through its system and then delivering it to the system of a second Transporter for onwards transmission.

Capacity rights

A pipeline can only transport a certain amount of production at one time. It will have a finite capacity at any one time. The Transportation Agreement will state how much production (whether gas or oil) the field owner (who is known as the 'Shipper') is entitled to transport through the pipeline – ie the capacity reserved for the Shipper up to which the Shipper can nominate for delivery on each day.

The capacity may be stated by reference to a profile based on what the Shipper expects to produce from the field over its field life. A Shipper will not need a constant capacity over the life of the field, as the volume produced will vary over field life. When the field enters the decline phase the Shipper will need less capacity in the system year on year. There may be provisions in the agreement to the effect that the Shipper can reduce the capacity which it reserves in the system but usually if it does so the agreement will provide that the Shipper cannot increase the reserved capacity in the following year without the consent of the Transporter. The reason is simply because the Shipper may wish to try to find someone else willing to take up the spare capacity in the system and should be able to do so without the risk of finding that in the next year the Shipper wants to utilise some of the capacity which it did not use in the preceding year.

The agreement will detail exactly how and when a Shipper is to notify the Transporter of the quantities which the Shipper intends to send for transportation through the system on a given day – the 'Nomination Procedure'. This usually involves giving an indicative nomination followed by more specific nominations in respect of a day nearer the date on which transportation is to occur. There is usually the right for the Shipper to request that the Transporter transport more than the contractual maximum and for the Transporter to use reasonable endeavours to do so.

The agreement will also contain details about what is to happen if there are problems with the system which mean that the Transporter is unable to transport production from all of the fields which wish to use the system on a particular day or days. Transportation Agreements often provide that the capacity rights of the various Transporters using the system will be abated during the period of the capacity restriction. Sometimes the Transporter will have contractual arrangements in place which give priority to certain Shippers. When negotiating a contract it is important to establish the pecking order: will your production be shut in if there is a capacity restriction or is there some equitable basis for dealing with the situation?

Tariff and 'send or pay'

A transportation system is an asset of its owners. Substantial amounts of cash can be generated by the efficient exploitation of a transportation system. Third party production can be transported in exchange for a tariff. The tariff is usually calculated as an amount per unit transported and is usually subject to escalation provisions.

There are sometimes provisions which will allow the basis of the tariff to be changed. For example, there are some pipelines where the Transportation Agreements provide that at the election of the Transporter the tariff level can be reduced and the Shipper can be required to take on responsibility for part of the costs of maintaining and operating the system (often with a right for the Shipper to terminate the agreement if it does not agree to the costs).

A Transporter will not want to see a situation where a Shipper has a contractual right to capacity but does not use that capacity. The fact that the Shipper has the right to that capacity means that the Transporter cannot let someone else have the capacity right. For that reason Transportation Agreements usually contain 'send or pay' provisions. Basically, send or pay provisions provide that if the Shipper fails to transport (or 'send' for transportation) in a given year a certain quantity of product (usually expressed as a percentage of the delivery capacity reserved by the Shipper) then the Shipper has to pay a tariff on the difference between the 'send or pay' quantity and the quantity which was actually transported by the Shipper in the contract year.

For example, X reserves 100 units of capacity for a year (Year 1). The 'send or pay' percentage is set at 75% of reserved capacity. X sends only 70 units in the year. X has sent five units less than the 'send or pay' amount and so X has to make a 'send or pay' payment equal to the tariff per unit multiplied by five.

Where there are 'send or pay' provisions there are usually 'make up' and 'carry forward' provisions in terms of which the Shipper can, in certain circumstances, have production transported in subsequent years up to the amount of the difference between the 'send or pay' quantity and the quantity actually transported in previous years. Transportation Agreements normally provide that if there are 'make up' or 'carry forward' provisions these must be utilised within a set period of time or the right to utilise them is lost.

For example, in the scenario above it may be that the contract allows the Shipper to carry forward the five units to the next year. Once the Shipper sends the 'send or pay' amount in respect of Year 2 the Shipper may be entitled to send five units carried forward from Year 1 free of tariff as 'make up gas'.

Quality

Each transportation system has specific quality criteria which must be met for entry. There will be provisions in the Transportation Agreement which will state what will happen if production is introduced into the system which does not meet the system's quality requirements (off specification or 'Off Spec' production). Production which does not meet the system's quality requirement may be corrosive or otherwise damaging to the system and the system can be costly to repair. The situation can be made more complex by the fact that usually the product being transported is not the product from one field but is rather product which is mixed or 'co-mingled' with production from other fields. Production which is introduced into the system which does not meet the specification could have the effect of taking the quality of the co-mingled stream below that required under the contracts for the purchase of the product.

A Transporter will usually have a provision in its Transportation Agreements to the effect that it is entitled to refuse to accept delivery of product which does not meet the relevant entry specification until the issue is resolved. There will normally also be provisions to the effect that if a Shipper introduces product into the system which is Off Spec then that Shipper has to bear the costs of cleaning out and repairing the system where this is necessary because of the delivery (with the liability usually being capped).

Maintenance

The agreement will deal with a variety of operational issues such as the co-ordination of maintenance and shutdowns between the Shipper and the Transporter. The parties will be keen to ensure that they try to co-ordinate the periods of planned downtime in the system and the fields so as to minimise disruption.

Liabilities

The agreement will deal with what is to happen if something goes wrong under the contract. It will set out the level of liability of the Shipper and the Transporter.

It is common to find standard 'hold harmless' provisions in such contracts in terms of which each party is to hold the other harmless in respect of physical injury or death of its own employees, against loss or damage to its own property and facilities and against third party claims and actions.

The more problematic issue is what is to happen if the Shipper suffers a loss as a result of a failure by the Transporter to deliver (for example, in the form of penalties for shortfall in deliveries under a Product Sales Agreement). In a gas sales contract it may be that there are provisions to the effect that if the seller fails to deliver on a certain day, the seller faces some financial penalty. Generally, the Transporter will not want to expose itself to claims for the loss suffered by the Shipper and, given the generally stronger bargaining position of Transporters it is quite common for Transporters to exclude liability for its breach other than where there has been wilful misconduct on the part of the Transporter, and even then liability would be subject to a cap.

18.10 Access to infrastructure

A field owner will not be able to develop a field unless satisfactory transportation arrangements are in place. Modern oil and gas companies (and in particular new entrants to the UKCS) are often prepared to consider developing fields which historically might not have been developed as the returns on the capital investment would not have been seen as high enough. Oil and gas companies used to pay less attention to such marginal or stranded assets and to focus more on assets which were easier to exploit. For new entrants, making money on developing these assets is dependent upon a large number of factors. These include negotiating reasonable terms for exporting the product and being in a position to develop the fields quickly rather than have them lying fallow for a long period.

The level of tariff and the other terms on offer by potential Transporters will have a great impact on the financial viability of the project. Will the development return an acceptable level of return to the field owners, taking account of the level of tariff and other provisions on offer? It could be that the tariff being requested could push the project into being uneconomic. Can a deal be agreed and documented quickly enough for the field owner to develop the field in line with its plan? If there is a delay in agreeing terms this could push the development back and it is not beyond the realms of possibility that the development is pushed back a year. In ideal scenarios there may be more than one system in the vicinity which could be used and it could be possible to have a discussion with more than one system owner about transportation.

The interests of field owners and Transporters have to be reconciled. The transportation system owner will understandably be keen to make as much as they can from the exploitation of their infrastructure but, historically, there have been claims that transportation owners have been looking for more than is fair.

There has been legislation in place for a long time, giving the right to apply to the Secretary of State for access to third party infrastructure. The Secretary of State has powers under the Petroleum Act 1998, the Pipelines Act 1962 and the Gas Act 1995 to settle disputes relating to access to infrastructure.

Until recently there was no clear guidance on the criteria which the Secretary of State would use in exercising his powers to order third party access. As far as the authors are aware, this power was never exercised in practice. Rather than agreeing detailed provisions governing when the Secretary of State would exercise his powers, the oil and gas industry and government agreed a voluntary code of practice. The latest one is the 'Code of Practice on Access to Upstream Oil and Gas Infrastructure on the UK Continental Shelf' (August 2004) which was developed by UKOOA in consultation with the DTI and others.

The Code sets out principles and procedures to guide all those involved in negotiating third party access to oil and gas infrastructure on the UKCS. One of its stated purposes is to 'facilitate the utilisation of infrastructure for the development of remaining UKCS reserves through timely agreement for access on fair and reasonable terms, where risks taken are reflected by rewards'.[1]

The DTI have issued guidance on how they envisage that the powers of the Secretary of State would be utilised (Consideration of Applications for Resolution of Disputes over Third Party Access to Infrastructure: Guidance to Parties in Dispute) and the hope is that by publishing the guidance parties will be able to gauge the factors which the DTI would consider if asked to determine the matter and so to agree a position without having to go to the DTI.

In basic terms the Code:

- applies to all UK oil and gas infrastructure from wellhead to receiving terminals;
- applies inter alia to parties negotiating new contracts for access to infrastructure, to infrastructure owners who may be approached by prospective users requesting information and to prospective users of the system;
- provides for parties to provide meaningful information to one another prior to and during negotiations;
- provides that parties are to support negotiated access in a timely manner and undertake to settle disputes by way of an automatic referral to the Secretary of State;
- provides that infrastructure owners are to provide transparent and non-discriminatory access;
- provides that parties are to seek to agree fair and reasonable terms where risks taken are reflected by rewards; and
- provides that parties agree to publish key agreed commercial provisions.

The Code also sets a timetable for negotiations on transportation agreements. Once a party seeking access (a 'bona fide enquirer') has enough information so as to believe that it would be possible to negotiate access within six months, the bona fide enquirer is to submit a notice to the Secretary of State to exercise statutory powers regarding access to infrastructure if satisfactory negotiations have not been concluded within six months of submission of the notice. A Form of Notice is given in Annex G of the Code.

It is possible that negotiations could fail notwithstanding the existence of the Code and in such circumstances the DTI have to decide whether the Secretary of State should use the power to allow third party access. If the DTI are asked to exercise the Secretary of State's powers then the criteria used to determine the matter would be as set out in the guidance note mentioned above. If a referral is made, the DTI would then gather information and try to reach a decision within 16 weeks. The aim of the DTI would be to set an appropriate tariff.

In the past there has been great reluctance to make applications to the DTI for determinations on access, as companies do not want to earn a reputation as being difficult within the industry. The new automatic referral procedure takes away this problem, to a large extent. Given the DTI's interests in ensuring that as much of the UK's oil and gas reserves as possible are developed, it is understandable that the DTI are willing to take a much more active role in trying to secure access for those wishing to develop fields.

18.11 Transportation of crude oil to the terminal and the operation of an oil terminal

Oil pipeline into oil terminal

If oil is not being exported by tanker from the oil field then it will be exported through the pipeline system directly to the terminal. The owners of the pipeline may have complete ownership of not only a pipeline system but also an offshore platform system feeding into the oil terminal. They may have agreed to construct, design and build the offshore facilities which feed into the pipeline and the pipeline system under a Construction Agreement. There will then be an Operating Agreement for the system which will be generally operated and managed through a management committee with delegated powers to an operator. It is the management committee that will receive all programmes and budgets, modify or approve such programmes and budgets, establish all general policies and decide on any major revision or installation to the system. The management committee will also appoint subcommittees who decide upon the sale or write-off of assets over a certain amount.

The operator will be appointed by the owners to act as agent for all the owners in connection with the pipeline system and the terminal matters which relate to the pipeline system. As under a JOA, the operator must conduct all system operations with the diligence customarily exercised by a reasonable and prudent operator. The operator can procure all facilities, materials and services required for system operations and has authority to spend up to a given amount. This authority can be removed if there is a material breach of its obligations under the agreement or it may resign.

Like the gas pipeline system, there will be throughput forecasts which will be based primarily on the provisional field forecasts provided to the oil terminal owners. The operator then prepares annual programmes and budgets for the systems operations and any partial system decommissioning. There will also be included details of tariff income attributable to each Tariff Agreement.

Each owner is then entitled to utilise its own monthly capacity entitlement; it may be able to use capacity which other owners are not using. There will be standards set for acceptable quality of crude oil into the system and provisions made for sampling and measuring the oil. The crude oil must enter the system at a given input pressure and comply with relevant regulations. If the crude oil delivered into the system is not at a given true vapour pressure and/or there is bottom sediment and water content which is greater than a certain percentage (this is often given to be not more than 2%) then the crude oil can be rejected by the operator. If the crude oil does not meet the specification it can be treated through the facilities and compensation may need to be paid by the field owners for that treatment. The system owners would normally have a measuring system with a low-pressure control system and a radio telemetry link.

There may be a requirement to have a certain amount of dead stock in the system, based on share ownership or equity ownership. There are normally further provisions dealing with sleeping owners (those who are no longer producing). Moreover, provisions dealing with the delivery of quantities of oil into the system by the owners will be included. As in JOAs or UOAs, there are accounting procedures agreed and set out within the agreement dealing with operating costs, extraordinary costs, insurance and other relevant capex and opex costs, including any partial system decommissioning costs. If an owner uses more than its entitlement, it may have to pay usage charges.

There will then be default provisions whereby a defaulter might lose his rights to tariff income but still be responsible for costs until the overdue payments are paid. In addition, there will be complicated provisions dealing with capacity and priority of certain fields over other fields.

Certain liabilities, such as those which might be found in a JOA, are normally only several rather than joint and several. Insurance is normally taken out by the operator in joint names. It may be that the system owners have also entered into liability agreements with other pipeline owners. Such arrangements are referred to as Pipeline User Liability Agreements.

Income is earned by the owners of the system charging tariffs. The general principle is that no owner will pay a tariff for its defined entitlement whereas third party users are charged tariffs which may be on a fixed variable or combination of tariff charging. The operator will have to find a balance between the amount of capacity used by owners themselves and third party tariff production.

There are then provisions dealing with the sale of an equity owner's interest. Normally, a third party buying into the system would need to demonstrate financial capability to the other owners. Decommissioning of the pipeline system and offshore facilities may be a very expensive and costly process. Owners might be required to provide security for their proportion of decommissioning costs in certain circumstances.

18.12 Transportation of gas – from field to terminal

Transportation Agreement

Transportation of gas will normally be through a Transportation Agreement between the field owners and the owners of gas pipeline structures which lead into a gas terminal. The gas will normally be transported through an offshore facility to the gas terminal and will be processed and redelivered as specification gas and/or specification condensate ready for sale to the market.

In the Transportation Agreement, it may be agreed that the gas is exported through a trunk line gas pipeline system which could be from a gas gathering platform to an onshore delivery point through a specified pipeline. The onshore delivery point may be the upstream flange of the pipeline emergency shutdown, located immediately upstream at the pig receiver where the pipeline system joins the gas terminal.

There will be a period in which the Transportation Agreement is live, which is normally from an Effective Date, of which prior notice is given, to an end date. The Transportation Agreement may recite that the parties have entered into a Tie-in Agreement to tie in the gas field satellite facilities into the export transportation pipeline. Undertakings will be given to procure the design, construction, installation, commissioning, repair, replacement and maintenance of certain satellite facilities to a standard of a reasonable and prudent operator and to ensure that they are compatible with other offshore facilities in which they feed the hydrocarbons. Further undertakings will be given that the construction works will have been completed before the services to be provided within the transport pipeline commence.

The Transportation Agreement will then set out the services and performance standards for those services. These will include accepting the gas, transporting it from the offshore delivery point to the onshore delivery point, compressing it through an offshore facility if necessary, performing functions and obligations in connection with other agreements, separating, metering, treating and processing the gas at the gas terminal (whether by way of a single or co-mingled stream at the redelivery point). In addition, the agreement is likely to set out standards for transporting the condensate from the gas terminal through pipeline systems in the terminal for redelivery at the redelivery point, undertaking gas production control services by remote telemetric control at the gas terminal, providing methanol corrosion inhibitor or chemicals and consumables and where necessary providing hydraulic fluids. The owners of the pipeline are, therefore, undertaking to the satellite owners to provide those services or procure the provision of the services all the way from accepting gas into its pipeline through to the terminal and back out for redelivery.

There is then a system of notification to the satellite owners of available capacity in the system and there are the normal provisions dealing with shutdowns at the terminal or in the pipeline and the associated liabilities and costs. If the satellite owners require additional capacity, then they may notify pipeline owners that they require such greater capacity and will meet the associated capital costs and operating costs.

There will be provisions dealing with capacity rights and there will be an agreed profile for the satellite field. Maximum capacity rights from the offshore facilities to the terminal will also be granted and are made available to the field owners. The gas will be divided into specification gas, which meets requirements set out in the agreement, and off-specification gas, which falls outside those requirements. Such Off Spec gas may need to be reprocessed in order to be accepted through the pipeline system and gas terminal or may need to be dealt with in some other way.

The field owners must notify the pipeline operator, who in turn notifies the terminal operator, of the expected amount of gas being delivered through the system over a given number of years. There will be a complicated system of procedures which deal with either the overproduction or the underproduction of gas, based on the original set of profiles. If there is an overproduction of gas it may be necessary to increase capacity either by taking capacity from other users of the system and paying a further tariff or by redeveloping the system to accept more gas. This information will also be provided to the gas terminal operator so it can determine how much gas it can process and redeliver. If there is too little gas being produced, this may lead to an economic termination of the Transportation Agreement.

The field owners have to undertake that they will deliver specification gas as determined in the agreement. If the produced gas is not specification gas, the pipeline owners and gas terminal may refuse to take it. There will then be provisions dealing with routine shutdowns for maintenance of the pipeline system and gas terminal and priorities for transportation and processing capacity.

The field owners pay a tariff to the owners of the pipeline for using the pipeline system. This tariff is reviewed from time to time over the duration of the agreement. The owners of the pipeline system will calculate the 'send or pay' tariff for the services they provide to the field owners. Payments have to be based on minimum tariff payments if insufficient gas is being produced in a contract year. In such an event there are further provisions for carrying forward unitised capacity in the previous year and a making up capacity. The tariff may include tariffs and costs of transporting gas and reprocessing it for redelivery at the redelivery point in the gas terminal itself. The pipeline owners will then pay a tariff themselves to the gas terminal for transporting and processing through the gas terminal the field owner's gas.

The carry forward is the amount of specification gas in excess of the relevant daily maximum capacity in the system for that field for that year. The relevant over usage is then reduced to the minimum payment in any subsequent contract year. There are usually also 'make up' provisions.

In addition, the normal provisions dealing with risk and property and liabilities and indemnities are included. The risk and property in the field gas and condensate remains with the field owners. There are often complicated sets of 'hold harmless' indemnity clauses, clauses dealing with exclusion of certain liabilities and caps where liability is limited to predetermined monetary values. Any sale by either the pipeline owners or field owners of their respective interests will require new parties to adhere to the Transportation Agreement and other associated agreements. If the field owners wish to sell to a prospective new owner, the new owner will normally have to demonstrate some degree of financial capacity to the pipeline owners.

In the event that there is not enough usage in the system to meet the project's costs, it is often the case that an economic termination notice could be served on the pipeline owners to terminate the agreement. Such a termination is normally based on the fact that the gross revenues do not cover project costs during a given period. In such an event, the figures may be audited by an international firm of accountants.

There will also be a general right by both parties to audit the books of the other. The figures used can be certified by an independent firm of international accountants to determine any difference between the parties. In terms of other disputes, the parties may refer the matter for determination by an expert selected by the Institute of Petroleum.

There are also further provisions specifying the capacity of the offshore facilities owned by owners of the pipeline system, and complicated provisions for redetermining the tariff in the event of certain matters occurring.

18.13 Transportation of gas – agreement for reception, treatment, processing and redelivery of gas into and out of gas terminal

The owners of the pipeline system will have to negotiate with the terminal operators to enable modifications to the terminal in order to accept the new specification gas and condensate through to the redelivery point. Moreover, an agreement to receive, treat and process the new specification of gas at the gas terminal will be required. The provisions of the agreement between the terminal owners and the operator of the pipeline system will reflect certain provisions in the Transportation Agreement but will also encompass all the other Transportation Agreements that the terminal owners have entered into with other pipeline owners and other field owners. The starting point is that there will have to be a Construction Agreement between the terminal owners, the terminal operator and the owners of the pipeline system in order to modify the terminal.

The gas terminal owners will undertake to modify and develop their gas terminal to receive the new specification gas and will design the terminal works based on a statement requirement from the pipeline owners and draw up a basis of design. The terminal operator will act as a reasonable and prudent operator (which is often a defined term). There will be provisions for placing contracts, providing cost estimates and regular contract meetings. While the terminal operator may initially pay for the capital costs, it will reclaim these from the pipeline owners by way of tariffs over the course of the agreement. All the modifications to the terminal will be the property of the terminal owners.

In the processing agreement between the pipeline owners/operators and terminal owners and operator, the terminal owners will state that they will accept specification gas which conforms to a pre-defined specification set out in the agreement. However, they are in a position to refuse gas which does not conform to those standards. They will provide services which might include receiving specification gas at a delivery point, separation, metering, treating and processing specification gas and redelivering uniform rates as part of the single or co-mingled stream at the redelivery point. The delivery point means the upstream flange of a pipeline emergency shutdown valve located immediately upstream of the pig receiver where the pipeline joins the terminal facilities. The redelivery point may be where the specification gas or condensate is exported from the terminal into another pipeline which then crosses the boundary fence at the gas terminal. The services to be provided by the terminal operator will also include transportation of gas and condensate to the delivery point, carrying out obligations on behalf of the pipeline owners under other agreements, undertaking gas production control services, providing methanol and corrosion inhibitors, assuring integrated safety and providing for emergency shutdown procedures.

The pipeline owner will undertake to procure the design, construction, installation, tie-in operation, maintenance, repair, replacement and removal of any new offshore facilities required to process gas before it reaches the gas terminal. The facilities in the gas terminal must be fully comparable with those of the offshore facilities to ensure the acceptability of specification gas.

The agreement will subsequently deal with capacity rights and the production of information, priority rights as between the pipeline owners, and control procedures. There will be further provisions dealing with suspension of services where no liability is incurred by the terminal owners. The agreement will set out the gas specification for gas to be delivered at the delivery point and gas to be delivered at the redelivery point. There will then be complicated provisions dealing with the payment of tariff and adjustments to the tariff during the term of the agreement which have been made at review dates.

There will be further provisions dealing with 'send or pay'. These are based on the pipeline owners agreeing to procure the payment to the terminal owners of a minimum tariff payment. Further provisions dealing with carry forward and make up are also included.

As in the Transportation Agreement, there will be provisions dealing with tariff re-openers in the event that gross revenues are not meeting a proportion of project costs of the terminal owners. There will also be a re-opener when the aggregate amount of the tariff payable for the contract year for the services provided by the terminal operator (which is likely to be the projected costs) are greater than a proportion of the gross field revenues during that particular year.

Note

[1] Code of Practice on Access to Upstream Oil and Gas Infrastructure on the UK Continental Shelf, August 2004.

— 19 —

CRUDE OIL TERMINALS

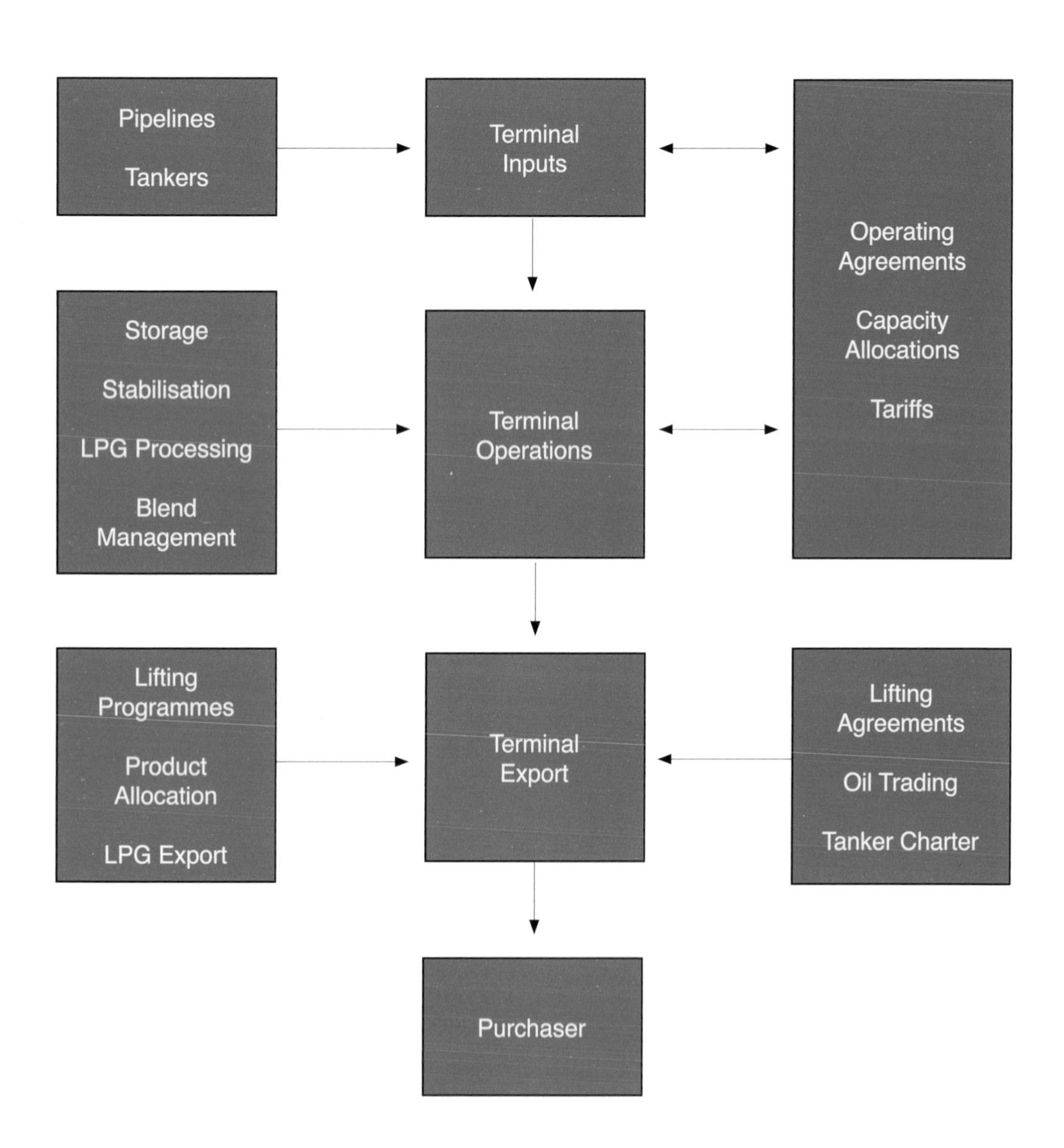
Pipelines
Tankers
Terminal Inputs
Operating Agreements
Capacity Allocations
Tariffs
Storage
Stabilisation
LPG Processing
Blend Management
Terminal Operations
Lifting Programmes
Product Allocation
LPG Export
Terminal Export
Lifting Agreements
Oil Trading
Tanker Charter
Purchaser

CRUDE OIL TERMINALS

TECHNICAL

19.1 Introduction

This chapter describes how a crude oil terminal receiving crude oils from different producing fields in the North Sea functions. There are four crude oil terminals in the UK whose basic statistics are summarised in section 19.4 of this chapter.

All receive crude oils via pipeline systems from the North Sea and co-mingle these crude oils together to produce a blend of reasonably consistent quality for loading into tankers for transportation to the end-user. These are typically refineries in the UK and elsewhere.

The owners of each field delivering its crude oil to the terminal are entitled to a share of the resultant blend determined from the quantity and quality of the crude oil from the contributing field.

The four terminals are:

- Flotta Terminal in the Orkneys, receiving crude oil via the Flotta pipeline;
- Sullom Voe Terminal in the Shetlands, receiving crude from both east and west of Shetland via pipelines and shuttle tanker;
- Forties Terminal, located at Kerse of Kinneil on the Firth of Forth, receiving crude oil via the Forties pipeline; and
- Seal Sands Terminal, located on the Tees estuary near Teesside, operated by ConocoPhillips and receiving crude oil primarily from Norwegian fields via the Ekofisk pipeline.

Each terminal produces its individual blend (Flotta, Brent, Forties and Ekofisk) which are internationally known crude oil blends and are all quoted and traded in the crude oil market. Some 70% of 2005 (based on DTI statistics) UKCS crude production is transported via these terminals, enabling the development of many smaller fields which can thereby sell their crude at premium prices.

The term 'crude oil terminal' may also be loosely used to describe the storage facilities at an oil refinery to receive, by tanker, crude oils prior to refining them or storage terminals where crude oils and petroleum products are stored pending onward transportation. Such facilities are not discussed here.

19.2 Terminal activities

To receive crude oils via a pipeline, blend and store them and load them onto tankers sounds a relatively simple operation. The activities involved, however, are somewhat complex and can be categorised as follows:

- receive crude oils from a number of field sources into a pipeline, ensuring that each crude oil input meets the requisite specification;
- regulate pipeline operation and receive the 'live' co-mingled crude oil stream into the terminal and separate it into 'stabilised crude oil' (SCO) and 'raw gas';
- process the raw gas into fuel gas for use by the terminal, LPG products and condensate;
- store the SCO and LPG – the condensate is usually blended back into the SCO;
- manage the crude oil blend to maintain reasonably consistent quality;
- manage tanker liftings to ensure that crude blend and LPG product offtake occurs without delays to tanker movements and interruption to input field production, whilst ensuring that stored quantities remain within maximum and minimum operational limits;
- operate and maintain all the facilities, including monitoring incoming pipeline operation, the provision of necessary utilities (fuel, electricity and water) and the disposal in an environmentally safe manner of any potentially polluting streams;
- allocate to each input field owner ('terminal users') an equitable share of crude oil blend and other products;
- allocate the costs of terminal operation to the terminal users and others in an equitable manner in accordance with the relevant agreements between terminal users; and

- administer all of the above in accordance with the contractual arrangements controlling the operation of the terminal, the rights and obligations of the terminal operator and terminal users.

Each terminal is operated by a single company on behalf of the terminal owners and the users. In all cases the operating company is the company (or its successor) which first established the terminal and associated pipeline(s) to receive crude oil produced from fields which they operated on behalf of themselves and their partners:

- BP for the Forties Terminal, receiving crude initially from the Forties field;
- BP for Sullom Voe, where the initial users were Shell/Esso with Brent production and BP operating the Ninian and Magnus fields;
- Talisman who took over Occidental's operation of the Flotta Terminal and the Piper and Claymore fields; and
- ConocoPhillips for Seal Sands, initially receiving crude oil from the Phillips-operated Ekofisk Area fields.

As additional fields have been discovered, where practical and economic, they have been connected to the pipelines feeding the terminals utilising spare and/or expanded capacity. This is accomplished under relatively standard contractual provisions appropriate to the individual pipeline system/terminal whereby the field owners have become pipeline/terminal users.

Such third party access has been driven not only by commercial logic but also by governmental regulation. This has been supplemented by industry codes of practise to maximise the use of infrastructure and to enhance the economic development of smaller fields.

19.3 Terminal operations

The purpose of an onshore oil terminal, as described in the previous section, is to receive crude oil from offshore fields, stabilise it and load it into tankers. Throughout these operations, each terminal user will receive an entitlement to a quantity of crude blend available for loading equivalent to the quantity of their crude inputs to the terminal. This is achieved through the operations as described below.

Pipeline inputs

The pipeline input from a field typically comprises a combination of crude oil together with dissolved gases (methane, ethane, propane and butane) and water produced from the field. Offshore separation of the hydrocarbons produced from a field into gaseous and liquid streams with bulk removal of produced water is standard practice. However, any further separation offshore would be impractical, requiring much additional equipment and pipelines to transport the different resultant products.

Thus, offshore separation is 'rough-cut' and pipeline liquids are significantly above atmospheric pressure to contain these dissolved gases whilst pipeline gas often contains significant quantities of lighter liquid hydrocarbons. The liquid stream nevertheless has to meet certain specifications designed to protect pipeline operation, to ensure that the terminal can process and treat these liquids and to protect the quality of the final crude oil blend. Critical specifications include:

- maximum vapour pressure, typically 9–11 bar above atmospheric pressure, and specified maximum pumping pressures to be within pipeline operational limits;
- maximum crude acidity, mercaptan, heavy metals and carbonyl sulphide limits to protect crude and LPG quality;
- maximum carbon dioxide and hydrogen sulphide to limit corrosion and to be within terminal processing/crude quality limits;
- maximum water (typically 2%) and salt contents to limit corrosion and to be within terminal processing/crude quality limits;
- maximum viscosity/pourpoint limits to ensure acceptable flow properties within the pipeline; and
- constraints on emulsion forming tendencies and on other additives which arise from offshore operations to protect crude quality and terminal operability, especially water treatment.

Quantities of input liquids from each input field will have been metered and sampled to ensure that they meet critical specifications. The resultant data are transmitted electronically to the terminal for monitoring and input into the procedures for allocating crude and other terminal products between input fields.

Operational data and instructions will also pass between the input field and the terminal to monitor pipeline operations such as flowrates, detection of leaks through pressure monitoring and acceptance or not of input liquids in the event they fail to meet specifications or in the event of a need to curtail inputs to the pipeline.

Stabilisation of pipeline liquids

The pipeline liquids are received into the terminal with high vapour pressure due to the dissolved gases. The liquids are metered, analysed and separated into raw gas and SCO (stabilised crude oil) by reduction in pressure such that the raw gas constituents are vapourised and separated from the then stabilised crude oil.

The resultant SCO has to have a vapour pressure significantly below atmospheric pressure to ensure that it can safely be transported by tanker in all climatic conditions. The maximum limit is a vapour pressure of about 11 psia where atmospheric pressure is 15 psia.

The vapour pressure of the SCO immediately following separation may well be below this limit and some condensate and butane can be recombined with the crude oil in the terminal to bring the crude blend vapour pressure up to this limit. The production water with usually high salt content is separated out so that the crude blend water content (referred to as BS&W content) is less than the industry norm of 0.5%. For the UK terminals the BS&W content is usually about half this value. The separated water is treated in the terminal to remove oil prior to disposal.

The raw gas is further processed to separate the methane and in some cases the ethane to be used in the terminal as fuel gas to generate power and raise steam for heating. Some terminals separate an ethane product for petrochemical use. The rest of the raw gas is further separated into condensate, propane and butane products. The latter are stored under pressure for loading into pressurised LPG tankers. The condensate consisting of predominately pentanes and similar to very light naphtha may be recombined with the crude or stored and made available as a separate product for tanker loading.

Storage and blend management

Storage of the crude blend and other products serves a number of functions:

- accumulation of sufficient quantities to be able to load tankers, in the case of some terminals up to 3 million barrels at a time, although most cargoes of SCO are usually smaller at around 500,000 to 1,000,000 barrels;
- a 'buffer' between production and offtake, ensuring that if tanker offtake is interrupted then receipt of pipeline liquids can continue – this avoids interruption to input field production and vice versa in the event that input field production is interrupted or reduced, although obviously storage capacity is limited and therefore there is a limit to the length of interruptions that can be tolerated; and
- although crude blend quality is primarily controlled by input field specifications, some control can be achieved to ensure consistent quality

by secondary blending within tankage. This can be required if an input field of significantly different quality is shut in for a period of time. Minor variations in crude blend quality at the terminal due to variations in individual input field production rates are effectively ironed out by the much larger quantity held in storage relative to the daily pipeline deliveries.

Management of storage by the terminal operator is a continuous juggling act to ensure that there is always enough crude blend in storage ready to meet the tanker lifting programme whilst allowing enough spare storage or 'ullage' to always accommodate aggregate field production.

If storage becomes full or reaches 'tank-tops' then no more pipeline liquids can be accepted and input fields will have to be shut in or curtailed. At the same time the terminal operator has to keep track of each terminal user's entitlement to crude blend in storage. Each tanker lifting is on behalf of a user who can aggregate all their entitlements from different input fields for lifting.

To optimise the use of available storage and to allow individual users to match their entitlements to intermittent tanker liftings, which can be growing on a continuous daily basis, the terminal operator/terminal procedures will allow an individual user to 'overlift' or 'underlift' their aggregate entitlement.

Overlifting is where a user borrows crude blend from the other users so that the user can schedule a lifting of more than their then current entitlement, usually to make up a minimum cargo size and/or to take advantage of market conditions. The overlift is then paid back from the user's future production delivered into the terminal.

Underlifting is the reverse where a user has not lifted their entitlement in storage so as to accumulate sufficient entitlement for a minimum cargo size, probably taking into account potential overlift, and/or because they are waiting for prices to increase.

Obviously there is a limit to how much a user can overlift/underlift without causing operational difficulties. Whilst a smaller user's overlift/underlift position can usually be equivalent to a couple of months' production, for a user with large entitlements it would be much less. In any case overlift/underlift is usually allowable at the terminal operator's discretion.

Such storage management applies not only to crude blend but also to each of the other products exported from the terminal. Even though these quantities involved are much smaller, this also applies to storage. If any product reaches tank-tops then input field production may be curtailed.

If a user fails to make a scheduled lifting and causes storage to reach tank-tops then the quantity that would have been sold may be sold by the terminal operator and/or the field(s) in which the user has interest may be curtailed.

Lifting programmes

Every terminal will produce on a rolling monthly basis a lifting programme scheduling a month's liftings of crude blend and other products, with a separate lifting programme for each product. The development of the lifting programme is a cycle of notifications and nominations culminating in a fixed programme of tanker arrivals.

Typically, this will start some two months prior to the month of lifting by the terminal operator notifying each user of its anticipated product availability, derived from each field in which it has an interest. The availability is made up of that user's current stock plus its anticipated share of production from the fields in which it has an interest to the end of the lifting month. This would be less any liftings already scheduled for that user in the meantime plus adjustments for changes in previously notified field production rates.

The individual input field operators notify the terminal operator of forecast field production rates on a monthly basis. The user, or their product buyer, will then notify the terminal operator of the lifting dates and quantities required and incorporate any desired overlift or underlift. The terminal operator then reverts to all users, either confirming acceptance of the desired dates and quantities or suggesting alternatives. The relevant users then accept or may request alternative dates and/or quantities. This process may go through two or three iterations until a programme is fixed. Where two or more users request the same lifting date range, priority is given to the most underlifted user.

About two weeks prior to a lifting the user or its buyer has to notify the details of the tanker scheduled to make lifting for the terminal operator to approve the tanker as meeting terminal standards. If this is not acceptable an alternative tanker has to be proposed.

The terminal operator may accept further changes in lifting dates and/or quantities to the programme but only at its discretion. The tanker will then have a window of two or three days in which it has to arrive. Once the tanker has arrived it will notify the terminal of its readiness to load. If this is within its loading window the terminal will accept and load the tanker with the specified quantity usually within operational tolerance.

Should the tanker be delayed berthing or take longer than the specified time to load due to the terminal's fault then the terminal will pay demurrage (compensation roughly equivalent to the tanker day-rate). If the tanker cannot load within the specified time then the tanker will compensate the terminal for berth occupancy.

Product allocation

The first stage of product allocation is based on the metered quantity of pipeline liquids input from a field over the allocation period of usually a month. This is converted into tons and the composition of those liquids determined as stabilised crude oil (SCO) and raw gas. The raw gas in turn is broken down into methane/ ethane, propane, butane and condensate. These determinations are done on a dry basis, typically using a process simulation model.

The input quantity of SCO is then converted from tonnes into barrels, based on the density of the crude blend being produced from the terminal. Each field owner will initially be allocated barrels of crude blend and tonnes of other products equivalent to the quantity input from the field multiplied by their equity interest. The allocated quantities will be adjusted as part of this procedure, to take account of fuel and flare usage, stock changes and any losses.

The second stage of SCO allocation is to adjust each owner's field entitlement for the value of the field crude relative to the value of the blend. In this way they become entitled to a quantity of SCO equivalent in value to their share of the input field crude.

Differing mechanisms are used, depending to some extent on whether the crude qualities from the input fields vary significantly from the blend quality. The most common form is to undertake assays of monthly samples from each of the input crudes to determine the crude yield of primary products such as naphtha, kerosene, gas oil and fuel oil. The input crude value is then determined by summing the percentage yield multiplied by the values of each of these products, adjusted for gas oil density, fuel oil sulphur content and possibly fuel oil viscosity. The product values used would be the average of the published quotes for each product for the month in question.

The resultant value for an input crude would then be compared with the value derived in a similar manner for the blend. The entitlement for each owner of the input field would be the quantity of blend determined from the first phase allocation adjusted according to the ratio of the value of the input crude to the value of the blend. Thus, if the value of the input crude was 1.02 time the value of the blend, the barrels of blend allocated pursuant to the first phase allocation would be multiplied by 1.02 and vice versa if the input value was less than that of the blend. The procedure is undertaken in such a way to ensure that all the blend barrels produced in a month are allocated equitably.

Terminal management and cost allocation

Terminal management varies largely depending on the contractual rights of the users vis-à-vis the terminal owners. In one case the terminal is operated effectively as a joint venture between the users. The terminal operator undertakes the operation of the terminal in accordance with a remit agreed between the users' representatives in accordance with the relevant contractual structure.

More common is where the users pay tariffs for the use of the terminal in accordance with an established contractual structure. This sets out the services to be performed for the user by the terminal. In the latter case (except where contractually specified) the users would pay a tariff and/or possibly a pro rata share of some operating costs. In the joint venture format the users would share on the basis of established formulae all operating costs for the terminal.

19.4 UK terminals

Flotta

The terminal occupies about one-sixth of Flotta Island in the Orkneys and was commissioned in 1977 by Occidental initially to process crude oil from the Piper and Claymore fields fed to the terminal via a 30" pipeline. Since then the number of fields (Fig. 19–1) input to the Flotta pipeline has grown. However, since the production from the input fields has declined the quantity of crude oil treated by the terminal has dropped from its peak of around 350,000 barrels/day and in 2006 production of Flotta blend was around 100,000 barrels/day.

In 2000, Talisman became the major shareholder in both the terminal and a number of the input fields and became terminal operator. The terminal has a current capacity of 375,000 Bbls/day and 6000 Bbls/day LPG and produces just Flotta blend and propane. Butane quantities are such that they are absorbed into the Flotta blend and ethane is used as fuel gas.

Although it has only one jetty, the terminal can additionally receive and load additional larger tankers via a single point mooring in the Pentland Firth connected to the terminal via a subsea pipeline. The terminal also receives crude oil from the Foinaven field via shuttle tankers for transhipment to conventional tankers. Third party terminal users pay tariffs to the owners, based primarily on throughput.

Forties

The Forties 'terminal' (Fig. 19–2) is in reality a combination of facilities known as the Forties Pipeline System, owned 100% by BP. It comprises the pipeline from the Forties field landing at Cruden Bay (between Aberdeen and Peterhead) from where it continues 132 miles overland to the Kerse of Kinneil stabilisation and separation facilities adjacent to the BP refinery at Grangemouth.

Forties blend can be pumped some 12 miles to the Dalmeny Tank Farm for pipeline transportation to the loading facilities at Hound Point in the Firth of Forth. Alternatively, Forties blend can be pumped directly to the Grangemouth refinery. The LPG products from Kerse of Kinneil can be loaded at Grangemouth docks or exported by pipeline.

Originally commissioned in 1975 to receive crude oil from the BP-operated Forties field, the Forties Pipeline (the original 32" pipeline to Cruden Bay was replaced in 1991 with a new 36" pipeline) has a nominal capacity of 1 million

PRODUCTS	INPUT PIPELINE
FLOTTA BLEND PROPANE	FLOTTA 30" DIAMETER
STORAGE	**INPUT FIELDS**
CRUDE 2 × 1.0 MMB FOINAVEN CRUDE 2 × 1.0 MMB PROPANE 100 MB **JETTIES** 1 – CRUDE + LPG 150 MTONS MAX 80 MB/HR CRUDE 10 MB/HR LPG SPM – CRUDE 200 MTONS MAX 50 MB/HR	CHANTER CLAYMORE GALLEY HIGHLANDER IVANHOE MACCULLOCH PETRONELLA PIPER RENEE ROB ROY RUBIE SALTIRE SCAPA TARTAN

ANCILLARY SERVICES
(1) RECEIPT AND TRANSHIPMENT OF OFFSHORE LOADED CRUDES ON A SEGREGATED BASIS
(2) MOTHBALLED CRUDE/LPG TREATMENT FACILITIES OF 150 MBD CAPACITY
(3) PROVISION OF ELECTRICITY TO ORKNEY ISLES

Figure 19–1 Flotta Terminal details

barrels per day and now receives crude oil from 55 input fields. Peak throughput of 950,000 barrels/day was in 1995 and in 2005 was some 700,000 barrels/day.

In addition, the facilities at Kerse of Kinneil receive and separate some of the natural gas liquids (NGLs being a mix of methane, ethane, propane, butane and condensate) produced from the gas terminals at St Fergus. The ethane and some of the other LPG products are used in the Grangemouth refinery and petrochemicals complex whilst the remaining propane and butane products are exported via LPG tankers.

Third party users pay BP throughput-based tariffs. These cover the transportation (from the input field tie-in point to the Forties Pipeline), processing and tanker loading services provided by the Forties Pipeline System. Those users whose NGLs from the St Fergus gas terminals are processed at Kerse of Kinneil also pay tariffs for the services provided.

Seal Sands

The Seal Sands Terminal at Teesside is operated by ConocoPhillips on behalf of its owners and was commissioned in 1975 to receive pipeline liquids from the Ekofisk Area (Fig. 19–3). These were transported via the 24" Norpipe pipeline from the Ekofisk Centre in the Norwegian North Sea. In view of the depth of the Norwegian Trench lying between the Ekofisk Area and the Norwegian coast, it was not feasible to lay a pipeline from Ekofisk to Norway and pursuant to a UK–Norway treaty it was agreed to construct a pipeline to Teesside and the terminal at Seal Sands.

The terminal receives and processes pipeline liquids from the Norwegian fields in addition to the original 8 fields in the Ekofisk Area and also from 11 fields in the UKCS. The NGL processing facilities also process NGLs generated by gas treatment at the CATS Teesside gas terminal.

Third-party users pay throughput-based tariffs covering the transportation, processing and tanker loading services provided as do those CATS (Central Area Transmission System) gas pipeline users whose NGLs are processed at Seal Sands.

Sullom Voe

The Sullom Voe terminal (Fig. 19–4) was started up in 1978, with crude oil flowing down the 36" Brent pipeline from Brent, Dunlin and Thistle fields. Later that year, crude oil deliveries to the terminal commenced via the Ninian 36" pipeline, with a nominal 1 million barrels/day capacity. This was originally from the Ninian and Heather fields, then the Magnus field in 1983.

Production of propane and butane did not start until 1982. Peak terminal daily throughput in January 1985 was 1,503,000 barrels/day. Throughput in 2005 was estimated at just under 300,000 barrels/day.

PRODUCTS	INPUT PIPELINE	CAPACITY
FORTIES BLEND PROPANE BUTANE	FORTIES – 36"	1.15 MMBD
	INPUT FIELDS	**INPUT FIELDS**
STORAGE	ANDREW/CYRUS ARBROATH ARKWRIGHT ARMADA BALMORAL/GLAMIS BEINN BEAULY BIRCH BRAE E BRAE W BRAE BRAEMAR BRECHIN BRITANNIA BRUCE BUCHAN BYGVE CALEDONIA ELGIN/FRANKLIN ERSKINE ETAP EVEREST FARRAGON	FORTIES HANNAY HEIMDAL HOWE HULDRA KEITH KINGFISHER LARCH LOMOND MILLER MONTROSE NELSON SCOTT SCOTER SW SEYMOUR SHEARWATER SKIRNE SYCAMORE TELFORD THELMA TIFFANY TONI VALE
CRUDE 8 × 500 MMB PROPANE 10,300 TONS BUTANE 9700 TONS		
JETTIES		
2 × CRUDE 16,000 M3/HR 1 × LPG		

ANCILLARY SERVICES
(1) RECEIPT AND TRANSHIPMENT OF NGLs EX ST FERGUS GAS TERMINALS
(2) DIRECT PIPELINE TRANSPORT OF FORTIES BLEND AND NGLs TO GRANGEMOUTH REFINERY AND COMPLEX (150 MBD CAPACITY)

Figure 19–2 Forties system details

The terminal also receives crude oil from operated fields west of Shetland as follows:

- *West of Shetland, Schiehallion Transhipment*

  Schiehallion field located 160 km west of Shetland, is being developed to recover oil reserves of some 340 million barrels of oil. The oil flows from the reservoir beneath the seabed into a Floating Production Storage and Offloading facility (FPSO). The FPSO has a storage capacity of 950,000 barrels of oil.

  Every 7–8 days the *Loch Rannoch*, a dedicated shuttle tanker, receives approximately 750,000 barrels of oil from the FPSO and travels to Sullom Voe terminal. Oil is offloaded at jetty 3, which has been dedicated to handle Schiehallion oil and stored in four of the terminal's existing crude oil storage tanks. All pipework containing Schiehallion oil has been electrically heat traced and insulated in order to maintain the oil at a temperature of above 40°C. Export tankers arrive at jetty 3 approximately every 7–10 days to ship the oil from the terminal.

- *Magnus Enhanced Oil Recovery*

  Two 20" diameter gas pipelines, one running from Schiehallion/Foinaven to SVT (190 km) and one from SVT to Magnus (210 km).

  Gas arriving from west of Shetland at dedicated reception facility at Sullom Voe Terminal is dried and H_2S removed. Some fuel gas is extracted to use as back up for power to the power station. The remaining gas is then transported by pipeline to Magnus where it is reinjected into the oil reservoir.

  With effect from 4Q 2002, some of the propane and butane from east of Shetland (received from Brent and Ninian pipelines) may be mixed with the west of Shetland gas and transported in the same way.

- *Clair Facilities*

  A new 22" oil pipeline has been laid between the Clair field, west of Shetland, and Sullom Voe terminal. Reception facilities were constructed at the terminal, include a pig receiver. Oil from Clair field, which came on stream in 2005, is stored in two of the terminal's existing crude oil storage tanks prior to loading onto export tankers from jetties 1 and/or 2. Clair gas will be imported to the terminal via the existing (Magnus EOR) gas pipeline along with gas from the other west of Shetland oil fields.

The terminal is operated on a joint venture basis, with BP as terminal operator, subject to overall control by a users' management committee. Operating costs are shared between users on a throughput-related basis.

PRODUCTS	INPUT PIPELINE	CAPACITY
EKOFISK BLEND ETHANE PROPANE ISO-BUTANE NORMAL BUTANE	EKOFISK 34" DIAMETER 220 MILES	890,000 BARRELS
	INPUT FIELDS	**INPUT FIELDS**
STORAGE CRUDE 10 x 750 M BBLS LPG NOT AVAILABLE **JETTIES** 1 × CRUDE + LPG 3 × CRUDE 3 × LPG	AUK* CLYDE* CURLEW* EKOFISK ELDFISK EMBLA FULMAR* GANNET* GYDA HOD JADE* JANICE* JOANNE* JUDY* LEVEN* ORION* TAMBAR	TOR ULA VALHALL

ANCILLARY SERVICES

(1) RECEIPT AND PROCESSING OF NGLs EX CATS GAS TERMINALS

(2) DIRECT PIPELINE TRANSPORT OF EKOFISK BLEND AND LPG TO THE PETROPLUS REFINERY AND TEESSIDE CHEMICALS COMPANIES

* UKCS fields

Figure 19–3 Seal Sands Terminal details

Figure 19–4 Sullom Voe Terminal (© BP Exploration Operating Company Limited)

PRODUCTS	INPUT PIPELINE	INPUT PIPELINE
BRENT BLEND PROPANE BUTANE	BRENT – 36" 1 MMBD CAPACITY	NINIAN – 36" 875 MBD CAPACITY
STORAGE	**INPUT FIELDS**	**INPUT FIELDS**
10 × 80,000 TONS FOR BRENT BLEND 4 × 80,000 TONS FOR SCHIEHALLION 2 × 80,000 TONS FOR CLAIR 4 × 20,000 TONS FOR LPG **JETTIES** 1 – CRUDE + LPG 2 – CRUDE 3 – CRUDE IMPORT/EXPORT 4 – CRUDE RETIRED SPARE	BRENT DON THISTLE MURCHISON OSPREY DUNLIN MERLIN N W HUTTON HUTTON PELICAN N CORMORANT CORMORANT S TERN HUDSON DON SW DEVON Q WEST PLAYFAIR OTTER BARNACLE EIDER KESTREL PENGUIN DUNLIN SW PLO37D	NINIAN MAGNUS S MAGNUS STRATHSPEY ALWYN DUNBAR LYELL HEATHER BROOM COLUMBA E COLUMBA BD ALWYN

ANCILLARY SERVICES

(1) RECEIPT AND TRANSHIPMENT OF OFFSHORE LOADED CRUDES ON A SEGREGATED BASIS

(2) RECEIPT AND TRANSHIPMENT OF PIPELINE DELIVERED CRUDE ON A SEGREGATED BASIS

(3) TREATMENT OF WEST OF SHETLANDS GAS AND ITS ONWARD DELIVERY TO MAGNUS

(4) PROVISION OF ELECTRICITY TO SHETLAND ISLES

Figure 19–5 Sullom Voe Terminal details

CRUDE OIL TERMINALS

LEGAL

19.5 The oil terminal

Construction and operating of an oil terminal

The terminals, whether gas terminals or oil terminals, require substantial capital expenditure and are therefore large-scale construction projects with huge capex costs which have to be repaid together with the cost of capital to the financiers of the project.

Many of the same principles which apply to the construction of a terminal will also apply to the redevelopment or upgrading of an oil or gas terminal. Over the next few years many terminals in the UK and throughout the world will need to be redeveloped, upgraded or newly constructed to meet new demands.

In order to effect this, large oil companies and syndicates of financial institutions would normally project manage the finance for the development. The project financing documentation will be substantial and is typically negotiated over a long period of time.

At the start of the project, a whole range of new facilities will need to be designed and procurement contracts put in place, together with mobilisation of teams of contractors and subcontractors to construct and build the terminal. There will be negotiations with the land owners, the relevant port harbour authority and local authorities (since the terminal owners will need either to acquire the land or to lease it on a long lease) and they will also need to enter into arrangements for creating or developing a port and harbour. In addition, negotiations will be necessary with regard to the facilities which are required, including jetty, berth and docking areas. In order to obtain planning approval and building warrants for such a large-scale project, applications will need to be put to the local authority and authorities responsible for ports and harbours. Negotiations may need to take place not only at a local level but also at a national level in terms of planning and there will need to be Environmental Impact Assessments Reports together with Health and Safety Reports and negotiations with different government departments and related agencies.

It may be the case that the participants in the project enter into a Shareholders Agreement or Participation Agreement to provide for the ownership of the terminal and the allocation of liabilities and costs. This would be normal in any large-scale project of this nature. There may be separate agreements for port and harbour areas for the operation and running of those harbours as well as the design and construction. Each of those agreements may also have the local land owner or local authority as a party.

In order to commission the terminal it will be necessary to provide supplies of power to operate it. There will, therefore, be a Utility Supply Agreement to provide utility services. In addition, a Power Purchase Agreement with the local power station may be necessary, together with any modification or reconstruction required to the power station in order to provide sufficient energy to the terminal over the period of time the terminal is operating.

There would also be a lease or acquisition of the land in which the terminal operator takes occupancy for the duration of the Terminal Agreement; if this is a lease then complicated provisions on duration, subjects, permitted use, rent, repair, irritancy and forfeiture would need to be negotiated.

Further utilities may need to be provided to the terminal owners which may include, for instance, water and gas. As there could be substantial liabilities and consequential losses for a shutdown of the terminal, providers of power and other utilities to the terminal will want to exclude their liability and consequential losses. As a result, there will be agreements and clauses dealing with indemnities and exclusion of certain liabilities. Normally there would be reciprocal 'hold harmless' indemnities subject to loan indemnities being given for the wilful misconduct of the party that was liable.

Terminal Operating Agreement

On the commissioning of a terminal, there would normally have to be an Operating Agreement in place. This governs both the future operation of the terminal while it is providing services and the decommissioning of the terminal after its life end. The Operating Agreement will need to dovetail into the Pipeline Agreements which are feeding hydrocarbons into it so that, for instance, the capacity restrictions and entitlements of the pipeline users feeding into the terminal match that of the overall capacity of the terminal to process and redeliver those hydrocarbons.

An oil terminal will be designed to collect, for instance, oil from a number of different fields, to take oil at a given specification and then to reprocess the oil ready for redelivery into tankers from a particular jetty in the harbour facilities of the terminal. As there is so much liquid passing through the terminal, the terminal operator has to manage the delivery of oil through the pipelines with large oil tankers coming in and out of the jetties and berthing facility on a 24-hour basis. The operation of the terminal will then need to match the individual requirements under oil sale contracts for nomination of vessels, complying with the rules and regulations for that terminal in coming into its harbour facility, for providing a notice of readiness to take oil for loading and then travelling out of the harbour facilities to the open sea. Normally, notice has to be given of an oil tanker approaching the terminal, with a further six hours' notice of readiness to take oil and a three-day time period to load the oil and leave.

The Operating Agreement of the terminal will not only contain provisions for dealing with terminal equity but will also cover the management of the terminal through a management committee made up of the owners of the terminal. Like the agreements dealing with JOAs, UOAs and Pipeline Agreements, the management committee will revise and approve operating programmes, budgets and AFEs, approve certain contracts, approve disposal of certain high-value surplus joint property, the appointment or termination of the operator of the terminal and decisions relating to the terminal's decommissioning. There will be a complicated system of voting on resolutions in connection with tariffs, budgets, decommissioning and amendments to the Terminal Agreement and arrangements which the terminal operator has entered into with other parties. That particular terminal may deal with a particular type of oil and any change to the allocation system of that particular oil may also need to be voted on.

The Operating Agreement will deal with the appointment of the terminal operator and its authorities and duties. These will normally include preparing and implementing operating programmes, operating budgets, business plans, AFEs and reporting generally to terminal owners on operations and negotiating and monitoring agreements which the terminal owners have entered into. It will also crucially operate the joint account and negotiate Tariff Agreements.

There would be the normal provisions for providing forecasting, plans, programmes and budgets, providing access rights for the owners and rights of access to the books and records of the terminal. There would then be the complicated provisions dealing with the liability and mutual 'hold harmless' indemnities together with the arrangement of insurances and dealing with threatened or pending or actual litigation.

The terminal may have the capacity of dealing with only one type of gas or gas condensate, or one type of crude oil or it may have the capacity to deal with, for instance, one type of crude oil and a derivative of that. Each owner will be allocated a capacity entitlement for processing its oil through the terminal and any excess over that capacity would normally attract an excess user's charge. The owners of the pipeline systems connected to the terminal may well also be the owners of the terminal and, therefore, they will be likely to undertake to provide the oil through the pipeline systems to the terminal. Like the pipeline system, there may be a requirement for a time vapour pressure and a bottom sediment and water content which is not greater than a given percentage; the oil will be referred to as stabilised crude oil (SCO).

There will be provisions dealing with the type of oil which will be accepted or type of gas accepted and that which is not acceptable. Some terminals will require the owner of the terminal to provide dead stock. Furthermore, there will be provisions dealing with underlifting and overlifting and entitlement capacity. One of the most difficult problems is dealing with capacity restriction where there may be a partial shutdown of the terminal. The terminal operator will then have to notify all the pipeline operators and arrange for an orderly reduction of throughput. Without this, a catastrophe could build up in the pipeline systems. In the event of any capacity restrictions, restrictions covering field groups utilising any pipeline are governed by the provision of the relevant Pipeline Operating Agreement. It is the terminal operator who will then have to determine the maximum production input rate into the terminal and there will be knock-on consequences for tariffs. Capacity restrictions may be caused by, for instance, lack of storage space for required maintenance.

There will be complicated accounting procedures for capex and opex costs charged to a joint account, with special consideration given to extraordinary costs. Furthermore, there will be provisions dealing with default and payment by the owner.

Normally no tariff is paid by an equity owner of the terminal but tariffs are paid by third parties wishing to process and deliver hydrocarbons processed and redelivered through the terminal based on each service used. Again, tariffs may be based on fixed or variable tariffs or a combination of both. As in Pipeline Operating Agreements, there may be a system of elections for allocating tariffs. The tariff income to be provided by the users of the terminal will go to pay the project capital expenditure, financing costs, other capital expenditure and operating costs. In the event that there is not sufficient tariff income, it may be that the terminal will have to serve economic termination notices on the pipeline users or renegotiate the tariffs to cover costs.

There will be provisions dealing with decommissioning given the very substantial costs involved. Where necessary, this will involve placing money into trust funds. As equity ownership in the terminal represents a substantial investment and liability, any party wishing to buy into equity ownership will need to demonstrate financial capability and technical capability to the other terminal owners. Only once this condition has been satisfied will the existing equity owners agree to the investment of the prospective new owner.

19.6 Lifting and oil trading

Introduction

This section looks at the commercial and legal aspects of nominating and lifting oil, the sale of the oil under a contract of sale and the trading of futures, options and swaps in oil.

The process of looking at the disposal of oil starts with licence controls and the Operating Agreement under which the oil is won and saved. The model clauses for Production Licences granted under the Petroleum (Production) Act 1934 used to require that crude oil or products were to be sold for consumption only in Great Britain or in Northern Ireland. This was the position under the Seaward Production Licences granted prior to 30 June 1995, however, Model Clause 30 has now been omitted by virtue of the Petroleum (Production) (Seaward Areas) (Amendment) Regulations 1995 (SI 1995 No 1435). There are now few restrictions on the sale or export of crude oil once landed. Nevertheless, there are informal letters of assurance between the UK Government and certain oil companies in relation to the supply of petroleum products in an emergency.

The Operating Agreement will state that the co-venturers have an entitlement to a share of production and that they are required to lift and dispose of their share once delivered. Much of the crude oil in the North Sea will be disposed of by using term, spot or forward contracts. This chapter focuses largely on forward contracts, although some attention will also be paid to term contracts.

In order for the crude oil to be available for lifting it must first be nominated by a co-venturer, which is often done in terms of a Lifting Agreement, as described below.

Lifting Agreement

A Lifting Agreement may often be put in place between the co-venturers to establish procedures for the lifting of a particular blend at a nominated point in the terminal. The oil may have been transported by virtue of a Transportation Agreement through different platforms and facilities; it might have been processed through a platform facility and then further piped through subsea pipeline or tanker to an onshore terminal. The co-venturers would then enter into a Transportation Agreement for the transportation of their oil on their particular block and the delivery of that oil in a stabilised form at the terminal.

An operator will be nominated by the co-venturers to operate and administer the Lifting Procedures.

The Lifting Procedures govern the nomination of lifting of each co-venturer's 'substance entitlement percentage' of the production, which is adjusted in accordance with the allocation procedures in the Transportation Agreement and made available at the terminal. The parties agree to comply with the Lifting Procedures and the operator is authorised to alter, amend or supplement the Lifting Procedures to reflect any changes in the Transportation Agreement imposed by the operator of the terminal. The primary purpose of the Lifting Procedures is to permit the operator to discharge its duties and obligations under the Transportation Agreement. Each party then indemnifies the operator for all the costs and expenses which it incurs as a result of claims being made by the operator under the Transportation Agreement. The operator of the terminal will have the right to suspend, reduce and accept delivery of oil from the field, to revise tank ship nomination and to administer regulations imposed on it.

Under the procedures, the operator notifies each 'Lifter' (ie each party taking oil) of its substance entitlement available for delivery and each Lifter will nominate and lift its substance entitlement in order to keep its storage account in balance, subject to the Lifter being allowed to lift more (over lift) or less (under lift) than their substance entitlement as long as their over lift or under lift complies with the provisions of the Lifting Procedures and any requirements under the Transportation Agreement.

In this part of the nominating procedures, the operator advises each Lifter of its substance entitlement available for delivery at the terminal in advance, together with its substance entitlement available for delivery for subsequent months. The Lifter then advises the operator of how much oil it wishes to lift during the forthcoming months, together with the day on which it wishes to lift. The Lifter also has to name the tank ship to be used (normally four working days prior to expected date of arrival), the amount of barrels to be loaded, the expected date of arrival at the terminal, the length of the tank ship and its estimated sailing draught for completion of loading and lifting of any other oil at that terminal at the same time. The operator then advises the terminal operator of the offtake programme for the relevant block. The terminal operator will notify the operator should it wish it to take additional oil. Alternatively, the terminal operator may state it wishes the Lifters to take less oil. There are then revised nominations and a revised offtake programme is worked out between the operator and the terminal operator. The final offtake programme normally states a three-day date range for the purposes of calculation of demurrage payable to the terminal operator in the event of late lifting.

A few working days before the Lifter's tank ship arrives at the terminal, the Lifter must inform the operator of its final nomination which will include name of tank ship, quantity to be loaded, destination, details of tank ship, confirmation that the tank ship is owned or demise chartered by a member of ITOPF (International Tanker Owners Pollution Federation) and that the cargo owner will be a party to CRISTAL (Contract Regarding a Supplement to Tanker Liability of Oil Pollution). In addition, the nomination will state that the Lifter will have the necessary documentation, which will normally include Bills of Lading, combined certificates of quantity, quality and origin, master receipt for samples and documents, transmittal letter and timesheet and ullage report. They will also have to inform the operator if an independent inspector is required to witness loading at the terminal. The tank ship nominated by the Lifter is subject to investigation by the terminal operator and must be capable of receiving a full cargo in not more than the specified hours. If the terminal operator requires the tank ship to be replaced then the Lifter can nominate another tank ship. Shortly before the tank ship arrives, the Lifter has to state the ETA or its departure from a previous port. They also have to confirm the 24-hour ETA before arrival, then issue a Notice of Readiness (NOR) together with pre-arrival information which will include details on the tank ship and the cargo. There is then normally a three-day loading date range in which the tanker must load the cargo. In the event there is a default by a Lifter, the operator can ask whether other Lifters are prepared to lift that default Lifter's entitlement with the sale of proceeds going to the defaulting Lifter less costs of the operator.

Furthermore, loading conditions for the tank ship are normally set out in the Transportation Agreement. The Lifter's tank ship normally has to locate its berth as soon as the loading arm has been disconnected, with demurrage payable to the terminal operator upon failure to do so. This cost would then be passed on to the actual Lifter.

Disposal of crude oil

Introduction

Consideration will now be given to the disposal of crude oil or its products and the different types of arrangements and contracts that may be put in place. The subject is substantial in its own right and as such it is only possible to give an overall summary in this chapter of these arrangements. Crude oil may generally be disposed of using term, spot or forward contracts. The most common method is by using a forward contract which would be subject to a major operator's standard terms and conditions.

A term contract may be for a short term or the life of the field and may be entered into between the producers or co-venturers in the field and a nominated buyer. It is possible the contract could stipulate a particular vessel to be used for the liftings or such other nominated vessel, while also stating the quality of oil and the place of loading. In the event that the quality of oil is outside the agreed cargo specification tolerance the buyer will be protected where he has reserved a right to negotiate a new price for the oil claimed. In addition, the contract would stipulate the cargo specification and agreed tolerance, going on to set out the estimated daily rate of production in barrels and state that no less than a minimum quantity of barrels could be lifted at any one time. Production forecasts would be produced by the seller to the buyer. Payment might then be on a net out-turn quantity determined by an independent inspector. The gross out-turn volume is measured by shore receipt less bottoms, sediment and water (BS&W) as determined by the sum obtained during discharge of the cargo.

In an out-turn contract the buyer nominates the terminal of discharge for the period before the three-day lifting period. It is common practice for there to be only one representation and warranty by the seller at the time of delivery of the cargo. Typically, the seller will warrant that at the time the oil is delivered the seller has a right to sell the oil and has an unencumbered title to it. In addition, the quantity of oil is determined by an independent inspector at the discharge point, while the risk and title to the oil transfer to the buyer who passes to the seller's vessels a permanent hose connection at the place of delivery. As a result, any loss or damage to the oil during discharge is borne by the buyers unless such loss is caused by the seller's vessel, officers or crew.

As the seller nominates the vessel it is his responsibility to ensure that the vessel carries on board a valid certificate of insurance as set out in the Civil Liability Convention for Oil Pollution Damage 1969 and International Convention on Civil Liability for Oil Pollution Damage 1992 and the vessel has in place insurance cover for oil pollution under the rules of international P & I Clubs. It would then be normal to exclude the UN Convention on Contracts for the International Sale of Goods (1980) and any liability between the parties for indirect, special or consequential damages. The clause may then go on to incorporate, for instance, Shell International Trading Company General Terms and Conditions of Sale of Crude Oil delivered out-turn (non-USA/US territories) dated 1 March 1994 with amendments dated 25 November 1999.

Forward contracts

Forward contracts will often take place on a CIF (Cost, Insurance and Freight) basis or FOB (Free On Board) basis. It may be useful to illustrate the context in which each of these types of contract is utilised. As an example, a co-venturer may enter into a sale contract for the sale of crude oil on FOB terms. In other words, the co-venturer sells to the buyer free of expense, in bulk, free on board the vessel, with the vessel to be nominated and provided by the buyer at the designated loading port as agreed. That buyer may be selling on the crude oil to an end user on CIF terms. The cost, insurance and freight would then be paid for by seller number (2) who would be responsible for supplying the ship, providing the insurance at his expense to the discharge port as designated by the buyer as a result. In the event that the buyer arranges for insurance then this will be a 'C and F sale'.

Under such an arrangement, where an FOB contract is used (which is normal for a co-venturer) it would be the buyer who must ensure the arrival of the ship at the port where the cargo is loaded and it is he who is to take delivery of the cargo. In contrast, under a CIF contract, seller number (2) would arrange for a contract of carriage where the goods were to be transported to buyer number (2)'s nominated discharge port. In this example, therefore, you might find the original buyer buying on FOB terms and selling on CIF terms while also arranging for a charter party in which that ship owner undertakes to go to the load port to take the cargo and then to ship it to the discharge port.

In order to finance this operation, the buyer may have approached its bank to open a letter of credit in favour of the seller. This letter of credit might be an irrevocable standby letter of credit payable on the presentation of specified documents and is likely to include Bills of Lading, certificates of origin and certificates of inspection, quality and quantity. The buyer may go further in establishing a letter of credit facility with the bank in order to open a number of letters of credit. The buyer's bank will subsequently open the letter of credit and advise the trader or the bank nominated by the trader that credit has been opened and confirm the letter of credit. The buyer's bank will then notify the sellers that credit has been opened and if required to do so will add its confirmation to the letter of credit. Such confirmation creates a personal liability to pay the seller against conforming documents which otherwise does not arise.

There may be several buyers and sellers in a chain which is sometimes known as a 'daisy chain'. This occurs due to the fact that transactions are often carried out without the contemplation of any actual delivery of cargo. A transaction may be classed as a 'wet' deal, in which a cargo of oil actually changes hands, or alternatively as a 'paper' or 'dry' deal, where the sale and purchase on a claim of cargo of oil in a future month are contracted for. The wet deal happens when the cargo changes hands in port and there will be other contracts in place, for instance, the employment of local agents by the seller and buyer and the appointment of independent inspectors to inspect the cargo. When the cargo has been loaded under an FOB contract the ship will generally issue a Bill of Lading to the seller number (1) which is referred to as 'ship' and then the ship will travel to the discharge port under the CIF contract.

Bill of Lading

The Bill of Lading is a document issued by, or on behalf of, a carrier of goods by sea to the person (ie the shipper) whom he has contracted for the carriage of goods. It is widely accepted that the Bill of Lading has three central functions. First, it operates as a receipt. In other words, the Bill of Lading provides evidence that the goods described in it have been received by the carrier or actual ship. Second, it is a contractual document which evidences a contract of carriage, providing a means for the transfer of rights under that contract. Finally, it is also a document of title to goods both in common law and in statutory law. The Bill of Lading can also be transferred by endorsement from the shipper to the buyer until it is finally transferred at the end to the receiver. The receiver uses this as evidence to take physical delivery of the goods.

There are different types of Bills which can be distinguished by the manner in which they indicate to whom the cargo is to be delivered at destination. These categories comprise Bearer Bills, Order Bills and Straight Consigned or Seaway Bills (known as 'non negotiable Bills'). A Bearer Bill does not detail a name of the person to whom the goods are to be delivered, rather being made out to 'bearer' when the oil is delivered, while an Order Bill provides the delivery of goods to be made to the order of a person named in the Bill. Both Bearer Bills and Order Bills are capable of transfer by way of endorsement. However, a Straight Bill or Seaway Bill is non-negotiable and cannot be transferred by endorsement or delivery. A 'shipped' Bill of Lading is one which states that the goods have been shipped by putting them on board the carrying ship and it might also state the date of shipment, whereas a 'received Bill of Lading' is a document which states that the goods specified in it have been received and are intended to be shipped on that ship. It is important to note that the Bill of Lading may not be issued until after the ship has sailed.

The Bill of Lading is not a contract of carriage itself but evidence of its terms. As a result, if there is a conflict between the Bill of Lading and the charter party, then the charter party will normally prevail as the original contract of carriage. It should be noted that the Bill of Lading which is a Bearer or an Order Bill is a document of title and gives the possessor constructive possession of goods; however, a Straight Bill is not a document of title and does not operate as a transfer of constructive possession of the goods. However, section 2(1)(a) of the Carriage of Goods by Sea Act 1992 states that 'a person who becomes the lawful holder of the Bill of Lading shall (by virtue of becoming holder of the Bill or, as the case may be the person to whom delivery is to be made) have transferred to and vested in him all rights of suit under the Contract of Carriage as if he had been a party to that Contract'.

As an example, the ship owner delivers the cargo to the lawful holder of the Bill of Lading which is presented to him at the delivery port. What might happen is that while the ship is sailing to the discharge port, the seller would approach his bank and produce the documents of title described in a letter of credit. If the documents of title correspond to the documents stated in the letter of credit, then the bank will forward them to the original seller's bank in order to arrange for payment under the open letter of credit. The buyer's bank will then forward the documents to the buyer against payment of security for payment; such security for payment will have been agreed in advance. The buyer will then be able to tender the Bill of Lading to the Master of the ship and the Master of the ship will deliver the oil cargo to the buyer.

However, there will be a number of traders creating a chain or daisy chain between the original seller and the final buyer. There are two forms of Brent crude which are the transaction-dated cargo deal and the fifteen-day Brent deal. The dated cargo deal relates to specific cargo of Brent crude which will be delivered within the specified three-day range at a price to be agreed at the time of the contract. There is also a fifteen-day Brent deal for sale of the cargo to be delivered on a date of delivery in which the seller gives the buyer fifteen clear days' notice of the first day of the three-day loading day range. In the fifteen-day market the chain can be booked out, which means the length of the daisy chain can be reduced. If the buyers and sellers appear more than once in a chain, then that part of the chain can be booked out which is done by a set procedure.

Contract for sale of oil

There are a number of different standard general terms and conditions for the sale of oil produced by major oil companies. The most commonly used for a specific contract are those produced by Shell and BP. In such a transaction, there will be two parts to the contract: the first on the standard general terms and conditions, described in more detail below, with the second part consisting of a short telex.

The telex would include specific details and particulars of the transaction such as the name and address of the seller and buyer, the cargo of Brent crude oil on fifteen-day terms for a given month at a specific price and the terms of payment. Moreover, details of persons and addresses to contact in terms of notices and a warranty from each party that by entering into the Agreement they are not in contravention of the Financial Services and Markets Act 2000 could also form part of the telex. There may be a further statement that each party is capable of entering into the agreement and taking delivery of the cargo, as well as a governing law clause, jurisdiction clause and arbitration clause.

The general terms and conditions of trade used in any transaction are dependant on the type of sale contract to be put in place. Variants include FOB,

CIF, CFR Out-turn, CIF Out-turn, Ex Ship, Ex Tank, In Situ and FIP Variation. This chapter will review the FOB and CIF sale contracts.

FOB sale contracts

Taking, as an example, the Shell International General Terms and Conditions of Sale of crude oil, FOB, the contract will state that the quality of oil is that supplied at the time and place of loading unless specifications are prescribed elsewhere in the agreement. All other obligations in respect of quality of oil and all statutory and other conditions and warranties in respect to description, merchantability or quality of oil or its fitness are excluded. The contract goes on to state that the oil is supplied by the sellers to the buyers free of expense, in bulk, free on board vessels to be provided by or procured by the buyer at a loading port to be agreed. The quantity and quality of oil in each cargo is to be determined 'by measurement, sampling and testing in the manner customary at the loading port and shall include testing that enables the net quantity to be calculated'. The sellers are to advise the buyer of the quantity and quality recorded in the certificate. The buyer is allowed to appoint a representative to assist in the supervision and inspection of each cargo and if there is a difference, this would be settled by an expert. The whole costs incurred by the buyer and any delays because of the inspection resulting in demurrage in the loading port are for the sole account of the buyers.

The risk and property in the oil supplied are to pass to the buyers at the loading port as the oil passes the loading vessel's permanent hose connection. The loss of or damage to oil during mooring, unless caused by the vessel or the crew, are for the account of the buyers.

Payment is to be made on presentation of a full set of clean original Bills of Lading and an invoice from the seller within 30 days after the Bill of Lading date. All payments are to be made free of all charges and without asserting at the time for payment any set-off, counterclaim or right to withhold whatsoever.

It is often the case that a seller does not have the documentation to present to the buyer (for instance, the Bills of Lading) within that period of time. The seller would then offer a letter of indemnity offering to indemnify the buyer against loss of documents of title (see below for discussion of letter for indemnities). Equally, the seller may require an irrevocable letter of credit to be opened or some other form of security from the buyer as security for payment. All taxes, duties and other liabilities in respect of the oil sold at the loading port are to the account of the seller other than Value Added Tax, or other taxes on goods and services.

Under the Shell Terms and Conditions for FOB the buyers have 14 days before the first day of the agreed loading date range to notify the sellers by telex with their name and summer deadweight tonnage of the vessel to be used and the expected date of the vessel's arrival at loading port. The sellers then have to accept or reject a nomination of the vessel within two working days. The buyers' nomination must comply with the loading port authority requirements. There is then the provision for the buyers to nominate a substitute vessel which is similar to the original vessel; such subnomination of substitutions can often be the cause of dispute. Further, a warranty as to the compliance of the vessel with restrictions at the loading port is then required.

The contract goes on to state the loading conditions. One of the main conditions is that the seller provides, free of charge, a berth or berths in which the vessel can safely unload. Additionally, the seller is required to provide and maintain in good working order all necessary flexible hoses, connections, pipelines, tanker facility and other accommodation for the loading of the vessel. There is a specific time for the loading of each cargo which is '36 running hours', in which Sundays and holidays are included. Laytime ceases on disconnection of cargo hoses and on completion of loading. While there are exceptions to which time does not count against laytime, demurrage is paid if time is lost outside the 36 hours and the cargo is not loaded within that time if it does not fall within the exceptions. The sellers have to pay to the buyers demurrage for all such excess time at an agreed rate.

There are, then, standard clauses on pollution compensation in which both parties ensure that all cargos under the agreement are covered to the fullest extent by voluntary schemes providing compensation for pollution incidents. Further clauses may cover force majeure, governing law (which in this case is English law), and dispute resolution and there may also be a statement to the effect that the UN Convention on contracts for the International Sale of Goods (1980) is not to apply.

Finally, in the limitation of liability, no claim in respect of shortage in quantity or defect in the quality of oil can be made against the sellers unless: (i) notice in writing is received by the sellers within 45 days from the date of the Bill of Lading; and (ii) a fully documented claim is to be received by the sellers within 60 days after the date of the Bill of Lading. The seller's liability is restricted to what it can recover in costs, losses or damages from its suppliers. In terms of any other failure to supply or of delay, the buyer is entitled to cost, losses and damages not exceeding the agreed selling price of the oil.

BP terms and conditions

BP Oil International Ltd's general terms and conditions for sales and purchase of crude oil include all terms and conditions for different types of sale of oil contracts so that the relevant section is incorporated. Essentially, the terms and conditions are not dissimilar to those of Shell's.

Subcontracts – delivery

It is crucial that the delivery provisions in FOB contracts are drafted carefully, as it is often this point which gives rise to dispute. The traditional concept of delivery under an FOB contract will be contrasted with what often occurs in practice. Subsequently, some of the typical areas of dispute will be considered.

The buyer of goods generally undertakes to arrange the contract of carriage and ensure the vessel arrives at loading port in time to allow loading within the specified period, whereas the seller is to provide the goods for loading on the ship. Therefore, it is the buyer who has the option of when during the delivery period his ship is to arrive, although the oil trade operates differently.

This can be seen in regard to the standardised forward markets for Brent, where the availability of cargoes is regulated by the Brent system controller. Lifting is supervised to prevent congestion and ensure the steady delivery of oil. The Brent contract therefore ensures that it is the seller who is to identify when, within the month, the buyer's ship is to arrive. He is to nominate a three-day layday range within the month during which the ship is to arrive, with this nomination to be given 15 days in advance of the first day of the range. It is the buyer who is then obliged to make sure the ship is in place during the specified period, incurring penalties under the contract if it is not.

One point to note when considering the drafting of the delivery clause is the extent of the obligation of the buyer. Does the ship merely have to tender Notice of Readiness (NOR) or is it necessary to tender NOR, await a berth and complete loading? Where the specified period for loading is a short one, the latter may be impossible to carry out in such a period. As a result, it is likely that the shorter the delivery period, the more likely the obligation will only extend the tendering of a NOR. Contractual wording to clearly specify what the buyer must do during the delivery period is certainly preferable.

Subcontracts – nomination substitution of vessel – CIF contracts

Most contracts require the seller to state the name of the vessel to be employed under the contract a specified number of days prior to her arrival at the port of discharge. In addition, it is common practice for the seller to reserve the right to substitute the nominated vessel. Where such foresight is not displayed by the buyer, the question of whether such a right of substitution may arise nonetheless must be dealt with. All that can be said in this regard is that the extent of any right to substitute which is not expressly included in the contract is unclear, and it would certainly be safer for the seller to incorporate such a right into the contract.

When a vessel is first nominated by the seller it is usually a named vessel 'or substitute'. There has been some debate as to the merits of the inclusion of 'or substitute' where no right of substitution exists under the contract. It has been suggested that such a nomination would be defective and therefore either invalid or a breach of contract.[1]

A final question to be considered in relation to substitution is the duration of the right, assuming it is permitted by the contract, of course. In other words, at what point could the right be lost? In the case of the *Ballenita* the contract expressly provided for a right of substitution and the nomination was made for the 'BP ENERGY or sub'. A substitution was made after the vessel had arrived and tendered its NOR, with the buyers claiming this was too late and that the sellers were in repudiatory breach. This argument was rejected as it was held that the right of substitution was exercisable at any time up to commencement of discharge. Nevertheless, the duration of the right would have to be judged on the facts and wording of the contract in each case.

Subcontracts – nomination substitution of vessel – FOB contracts

Similar issues arise, but to a lesser extent, under FOB contracts. Under a CIF contract the seller may be allocating a specific cargo (already on board the ship) when he nominates the ship. Clearly, this is not a problem which arises in FOB contracts. It is clear the buyer does not have to commit to a specific vessel and will usually provide details of such only for the convenience of the seller. It follows logically that the buyer is capable of changing his initial nomination, unless express wording provides otherwise. In practice, it is often the case that specific requirements regarding nomination are made and it remains open to the parties to agree that this nomination should be irrevocable.

Subcontract – risk

The risk of loss or damage will generally pass to the buyer at the port of loading. This is the case under both FOB and CIF contracts, although exceptions are considered below. Nevertheless, where the contract can be properly construed as an 'out-turn' or delivered contract (where the seller is committed to physical delivery of the goods which, at the time of discharge, will conform to the contract description) risk remains with the seller. Furthermore, where goods have been sold afloat risk is held to have passed 'as from' shipment, even if the sale contract has not been entered into by that point.

Risk is often separated from property, so that risk could pass in part of a bulk shipment before property has passed. Conversely, risk does not necessarily have to pass upon transfer of ownership. The provisions of the law are, of course, subject to the intentions of the parties. Express contractual provisions as to risk or even indications of intention can take effect to govern the passing of risk. For example, where the buyer of part of a bulk receives the benefit of insurance with the delivery order, the intention that risk is to pass to him is inferred.

Risk – CIF contracts

As explained above, risk generally passes on shipment or as from shipment. In other words, the buyer becomes liable for the risk of loss to, or contamination of, the oil when the oil is loaded on the vessel. Where goods are sold and then shipped, risk passes on shipment. Alternatively, where they are sold afloat, the risk is deemed to have passed as from the time of shipment. A distinction is to be drawn between the treatment of risk of deterioration and the risk of total loss in this regard. Where the goods are sold and shipped on CIF terms, risk passes to the buyer on shipment and so he bears the cost of both deterioration and loss. However, where the goods are shipped with a total loss or deterioration occurring before sale, only the risk of deterioration is with the buyer. In other words, the risk passes with retrospective effect with the buyer liable for any deterioration which has occurred before the contract was made. On the other hand, risk of total loss remains with the seller where a total loss occurs before sale.

Risk – FOB contracts

Generally, risk remains with the seller until shipment of the goods. This rule applies where the sale is of specific goods, where the goods were originally unascertained and such goods were appropriated to the contract on or before shipment. Risk may pass on shipment despite no passing of property where the seller reserves a right of disposal or because the goods form an undifferentiated part of a larger bulk and have not been paid for.

Nevertheless, exceptions exist to the general rule stated above. Risk may remain with an FOB seller after shipment in a number of cases. For example, the risk of deterioration will remain with the seller where he is in breach of his implied undertaking that the goods can endure normal transit. On the other hand, the situation may arise where risk passes to the buyer before shipment. One such situation would be where deterioration of the goods occurs where delivery has been delayed by the buyer's fault.

Subcontract – ownership

Under the Sale of Goods Act 1979 the passing of property occurs when the parties intend for it to pass. Therefore, where the FOB contract is for the sale of specific goods, the property may pass as soon as the contract is made. Nevertheless, property in unascertained goods (ie generic goods sold by description) cannot pass until they are in a deliverable state and are unconditionally appropriated to the contract.[2] Consequently, where the seller ships two unsegregated parcels of oil on a vessel to two different buyers, ownership remains with the seller throughout the voyage and until separation at destination.

The intention of the parties will usually be displayed by provision in the contract for when ownership is to pass. However, the rules of the Sale of Goods

Act are used to determine the presumed intentions of the parties where the contract remains silent on such matters. In general, it can be said that property passes on delivery unless the seller reserves the right of disposal. On the other hand, where the seller takes the Bill of Lading in his own name or retains possession of it for security purposes, this may point towards an intention to retain ownership.

Under classic CIF terms, ownership passes on the tendering of documents and payment, usually during the voyage. In many cases, however, payment is not due until after discharge. Here, it is likely any court would hold that ownership was to pass on discharge as the contract will expressly contemplate that the seller is to lose property in the goods before payment is made.

The difference under an FOB contract is that when goods are loaded onto the ship they are passed to a carrier who has a contract with the buyer as opposed to the seller. This eliminates the problem of establishing whether the seller intends to allocate the particular cargo to the contract. Despite this, it is still likely to be found that property does not pass on loading where the seller takes the Bill of Lading in his own name.

CIF sale contracts

In a CIF contract the seller arranges to sell the goods at an inclusive price covering the cost of goods, insurance and freight. The seller will have shipped or bought afloat goods in accordance with the contract and must tender to the buyer the proper shipping documents. If he does this he will not be in breach of the contract despite the fact that the goods may have been lost before such tender. The seller is under a negative duty not to prevent the goods from being delivered to the buyer at the agreed destination by diverting them somewhere else or ordering the carrier not to deliver. However, if there is an obligation on the seller to deliver goods at an agreed destination or to discharge them at such a point, this cannot be properly construed as a CIF contract and may be more accurately classified as a form of Out-turn contract or Ex Ship.

In the event that the seller cannot tender the documents, he can offer a Letter of Indemnity and guarantee against missing documents. Therefore, the duty of the seller under a CIF contract would be to ship the goods according to the contract, to procure and prepare proper shipping documents and tender those documents to the buyer or as the buyer directs. In terms of oil which is non-generic, where the seller cannot supply the goods he must buy goods already afloat and appropriate them to the contract accordingly.

The Bill of Lading is in transferable form, provides continuous documentary cover and states that the goods have been shipped. Moreover, it provides for carriage of goods to the agreed destination, states that it is issued 'on shipment', covers goods sold and no others, is valid and effective and is clean.

The insurance will be a policy of insurance and not a certificate of insurance and the invoice should cover the cost of goods, insurance and freight. The buyer for his part is only bound to pay against documents which meet the requirements of the contract. The buyer acquires his rights under the contract of carriage by being a lawful holder of the Bill of Lading which will be endorsed over by operation of the Carriage of Goods by Sea Act 1992.

The BP General Terms and Conditions for CIF deliveries state the conditions as to measurement and quantity of the taking of samples for the purpose of compliance of the crude oil with grade and quantity provisions of the Special Provisions. The buyer, where for instance the loading terminal is operated by the seller, has the right to appoint an independent inspector at the loading terminal. On the other hand, where the loading terminal is not operated by the seller, both parties hold such a right. The risk under the contract in crude oil delivered passes to the buyer as the crude oil passes the vessel's permanent hose connection at the loading terminal or, where it is a delivery of part of a cargo designed for receivers other than the buyer, when the crude oil passes the vessel's permanent hose connection at the discharge port. In terms of insurance, the seller undertakes to procure and pay for insurance against marine risks to the full value of the shipment plus 10%, with the insurance cover extending from shore tank at the loading terminal to shore tank at the discharge port.

It is important to determine what insurances to cover because the standard terms do not cover against the possibility of war, strikes, riots, civil commotions or risks in respect of the delivery of crude oil. In addition, the standard terms provide that the seller is required to provide insurance in accordance with the provisions of a standard Lloyd's Marine Insurance Policy subject to Bulk Oil Clauses SP 13C. Under a CIF contract, the seller may arrange shipment under Bills of Lading which incorporate any charter party conditions which are normal for such vessels. The seller is to pay for freight and demurrage subject to certain exceptions.

There are provisions dealing with the nomination of vessels whereby the seller gives the buyer a Notice of Nomination eight days prior to the first day of the Loading Terminal Laydays of the vessel. The notice is to specify details of the vessel, amount to be loaded, the estimated time of arrival, Discharge Port and other details. Within a day of this nomination the buyer is to notify the seller of the final Discharge Port and full written instructions regarding particulars and destination of the Bills of Lading and other relevant documentation. Nevertheless, the seller has a right to nominate another vessel by giving not less than three clear days before last day of the Loading Terminal Laydays with certain restrictive rights for the buyer to reject the vessel. There are also further provisions dealing with the regulations of the loading terminal or discharge, alternative discharge and liability.

On the arrival of the vessel, the seller has to arrange for its vessel to report to the buyer or its representative at the discharge port, with the buyer having to arrange for a berth free of charge. There are then detailed provisions dealing with shifting and lightening. The time permitted under the BP standard terms for discharge of the crude oil is '36 running hours'. This time begins to run six hours from the tendering of NOR and should end upon the disconnection of the discharging hoses. Finally, there are then provisions dealing with damages for delay and crude oil washing, before additional provisions for offshore loaded North Sea Atlantic crude oil are detailed.

CIF contract – delivery

It is necessary to look at the separate stages of delivery to understand the duties of the seller under a CIF contract. Delivery is said to consist of a 'provisional delivery' on shipment, a 'symbolical delivery' on tender of documents and a complete delivery of the cargo when it is handed over to buyer. The nature of the seller's duties extends only to the first two of these three, with the seller not concerned with the goods in transit. Any failure of the goods to be delivered will allow the buyer a remedy against only the carrier or insurer and not the seller, provided seller has both shipped proper goods and tendered proper documents.

However, that is not to say that the seller has no obligations in relation to the final element of delivery, namely complete delivery of the cargo. Rather, the seller is under no positive obligation in this regard. Nevertheless, the seller is under the duty not to interfere with the contract of carriage so as to prevent the buyer from receiving the goods at the agreed destination. So if the seller orders the carrier to deliver to a port other than the agreed destination in the contract of sale he may be in breach of this obligation.

A further aspect of delivery dealt with in the contract is the time at which it is deemed to have been made. It is clear the effects of such provisions are dependant on the wording used in each case. Many delivery clauses depart from traditional CIF terms, providing for delivery within a certain period at the discharge port rather than the loading port. For example, the wording may state: 'Delivery: CIF one safe port ..., within 10–20 March 2006. Dates to be narrowed to 5 days by 5th March 2006 ...'.

Despite the wording of such a clause, the Courts have shown a willingness to adopt the traditional interpretation of delivery in CIF contracts. The rationale for overlooking the express terms of the contract to preserve this interpretation has been given as the fact that the phrase 'CIF' has an established and certain meaning in itself and that as a result the other terms of the contract should be construed in this light where at all possible. The result is that clauses such as the one above have been interpreted to mean that the seller must deliver the oil to a vessel which is expected to arrive at the discharge port within the specified period. In other words, the obligation under such contractual wording is not an absolute one. If the vessel is expected to arrive within that period but fails to do so, the seller is not in breach of contract. However, the decision of the court in 'The "Jambur"'[3] shows each case will turn on its own facts as here it was held a seller was in breach for failure to deliver at the discharge port within the specified time period. It is apparent that to impose on the seller an absolute obligation to arrive within specified dates, clear words must be used to that effect.

Letter of Indemnity

The necessity for the use of Letters of Indemnity (LOI) has arisen due to the peculiarities of the nature of shipping oil, where tankers have a faster loading and discharge rate than dry cargo ships. The fact that voyages are often short while the chain of transactions are relatively long, coupled with consideration that the processing of the loading documents can take a substantial amount of time means the documents which must be tendered[4] to the buyer can take months to reach their intended final recipient. Consequently, the Bills of Lading and other documents may not be available when the receiver wishes to take delivery or where the seller looks for payment of the price. As a result, the parties may agree in the charter party and contracts for sale for the use of an LOI, the effect of which is discussed below. In broad terms, once the letters are in place the shipowner can deliver cargo to the buyer who, in turn, makes payment. Upon the eventual arrival of the shipping documents through the chain of transactions, each LOI is cancelled.

Letter of indemnity given to the shipowner

Where the shipowner delivers the cargo to the lawful holder of the Bill of Lading he will be protected against claims of misdelivery. Otherwise, he may face claims for damages from the true owner of the goods or the lawful holder of the Bill. Consequently, the shipowner is not generally obliged to deliver without a Bill of Lading, although he may often agree to deliver against an indemnity. This measure does not absolve him of his liability to the true owner/holder of the Bill of Lading, rather aiming to provide compensation to the carrier for incurring that liability in the first place.

LOI's given to shipowners tend to be drafted widely and follow a standard layout. The possible need for the indemnity to be backed by a bank and the effect of any financial or time limits on the shipowners' liability should be considered carefully before entering the transaction.

Seller's Letter of Indemnity

It may be agreed that payment is to be made against a seller's LOI. A general structure is followed by the standardised forms used by the major companies, although precise wording varies. Some of the typical provisions are considered below:

- the consideration paid by the buyer is payment of the purchase price;
- the seller will warrant that he has the right to sell the goods and has title to them, that goods are and will remain free of charges or encumbrances and that the buyer will enjoy quiet possession;
- the seller will then agree to indemnify the buyer against any claims, losses, costs or damages incurred as a consequence of breach by the seller of warranties; and
- the seller undertakes to deliver shipping documents to the buyer as soon as possible, and that the indemnity is to become null and void upon such presentation.

The indemnity should be drafted to cover the consequences of the seller's failure to pass good title or to have the shipping documents available. For example, where the true owner of the goods is a third party who aims either to claim the goods back or to sue the buyer in conversion, the LOI should provide a basis for this. If there has been a clear breach of the seller's warranty of title an action under the LOI should be available. It must also be noted that the use of an LOI means that the buyer will not have a Bill of Lading in his possession. As a result, this may affect his right to sue the carrier in respect of loss or damage to goods.

Claims under contract must be made within the legal time limits, although some LOI's provide for an even shorter period, such as 12 months. Where no such provision is made, the difficult question of when time is to run from may arise. This problem can be compounded by the fact that any claim against the carrier or claim by the carrier against the receiver may be governed by different foreign laws, resulting in the potential for different time limits and rules applying to these claims. In some cases, time may not begin to run until the buyer's loss is suffered or his liability to a third party is established.

The LOI will often provide that it is to become null and void once the shipping documents are tendered or for the LOI itself to be physically returned itself to the carrier to effect cancellation.

19.7 Chartering tankers

Charter parties

Introduction

A charter party is the contract which governs the relationship between the two parties involved in the chartering of a tanker. A charter party can be classified as either demise or not amounting to demise. The former involves the charterer taking over possession of the boat, with the master and crew in effect his servants, whereas the latter involves possession of the vessel remaining with the owner through his master and crew. Charter parties by demise will not be covered in this chapter, while those not by demise are considered below. Such agreements can themselves be generally classified as either time charters or voyage charters.

Although these are two distinct forms of charter, most of the principles contained within them are common to both forms of contract and will consequently be looked at together. Developments in practice have also obscured the distinction between time and voyage charters.[5] On the one hand, a time charter allows for the vessel to be at the disposal of the charterer for a specific period of time, with the shipowner's payment of 'hire' calculated at a monthly rate on the tonnage of the ship. In contrast, a voyage charter specifies that the cargo is to be carried on a certain voyage or voyages, with the freight payable either on the quantity of cargo shipped or in an agreed lump sum. Hybrid species have also evolved, such as provision for as many voyages as can be performed within a specified period.

Below is a consideration of some preliminary issues before the typical terms of a charter party are looked at.

The contract

There is no one statutory or standard form of contract and the general principles of contract law determine whether a binding charter has been made, although *pro forma* agreements can be tailored to suit the demands of the parties. Agreement on the essential terms by the owners and charterers is sufficient evidence of contract, and it is generally these two named parties whose relationship is governed under the contract, although the use of brokers as agents may extend the right to sue or be sued beyond the listed parties.

Nature of the contractual terms

Scrutton classifies contractual terms as falling within one of three categories, namely 'conditions', 'warranties' and 'innominate or indeterminate terms'. It will be useful to consider the nature of each of these before looking at the substance of the charter.

Any breach of a condition allows the 'innocent' party the option of being released from any further obligation under the agreement, in addition to a claim for damages. In contrast, any breach of a warranty, regardless of the seriousness of the breach, results in only the right to recover damages from the other party. With regard to the final category, the right to be discharged from one's contractual obligations only arises where the breach of the other party is sufficiently serious to go to the root of the contract.[6]

The terms

In this chapter, the basis for the consideration of the typical terms of a charter party are the Shelltime 4 form ('SHELLTIME 4'), the New York Produce Exchange form ('NYPE 93') as well as the use of other time charter parties. The Shelltime 4 and NYPE 93 are commonly used in the oil industry. The terms of the central clauses shall be considered in turn.

Description

The Shelltime 4 form provides:

> 'At the date of the delivery of the vessel under this charter
> (a) she shall be classed ... (eg +1A1 Tanker for Oil ESP, Inert, EO);
> (b) she shall be in every way fit to carry crude petroleum and/or its products;
> (c) she shall be tight, staunch, strong, in good order and condition, and in every way fit for the service, with her machinery, boilers, hull and other equipment ... in a good and efficient state;
> (d) her tanks, valves and pipelines shall be oil-tight;
> (e) she shall be in every way fit for burning at sea ... (and) in port ...'[7]

The descriptive details of the vessel are to be accurate at the time the charter is entered into. Where there has been a divergence from the agreed description, any negligible differences will be disregarded. However, for any misdescription above the *'de minimis'* threshold, the question of which remedies are open to the charterer arises. Either delivery may be refused or delivery must be accepted with only a claim in damages for any loss suffered. The availability of the former remedy appears to be dependent upon the seriousness of the misdescription.

The charterer cannot be compelled to accept delivery of a ship other than the named ship, even if an alternative is of identical characteristics. Nevertheless, the parties may agree to a substitution of the originally named ship, and may agree this can be made at any time, whether before delivery, during the charter period or after the loss of the vessel. Where the ship is sold during the charter, the original owners remain responsible to perform their obligations under the charter and are not in breach of the charter as a result.

Obligations of seaworthiness

An absolute undertaking of seaworthiness will typically form part of the description; however, where such a provision is absent it will be implied in any case. Typically, the clause may state: 'with hull, machinery and equipment in a thoroughly efficient state' and may in addition provide that the ship is to be 'tight, staunch, strong and in every way fitted for the service'. Such wording is used in the Shelltime 4 form.[8]

Although it is clear these undertakings are not continuing obligations and apply only to the state of the ship when the charter is entered into, they will usually be replaced by the lesser undertaking that due diligence to make the ship seaworthy is to be exercised at the beginning of each voyage under the charter, provided that the Hague–Visby rules have been incorporated. The duty to maintain the ship in a thorough and efficient state throughout the duration of the charter is a wholly independent obligation and is dealt with below.[9]

The seaworthiness obligations are not conditions of the contract, and breach of them would not in all likeliness allow the charterer the opportunity to terminate in the case of a breach of a minor nature. However, the charterers will not be obliged to accept delivery of an unseaworthy vessel. In addition to the cancelling clause in the charter, there is the common law right to discharge where, at delivery, the ship is unseaworthy and cannot be made seaworthy within a given period of time under the terms of the charter, the charter will be taken as frustrated and at an end.

Oil company approvals

There will usually be an additional clause describing the ship as having to meet certain oil company approvals. These approvals may be treated as conditions by which the entire contract is to be treated as discharged where these are not held.

Shipboard personnel and their duties

The charter will provide for detailed requirements as to the efficiency and competency of the crew at the date of delivery. These obligations are absolute in nature. A second limb of the clause will 'guarantee' the performance levels of the crew throughout the service of the charter. This will typically involve a duty to 'prosecute all duties with utmost despatch', to 'render all customary assistance' and to 'load and discharge cargo as rapidly as possible when required by Charterers'.

There will often be more specific requirements, in relation to the qualifications of the crew (such as certificates of competence and/or training requirements), and the carrying out of test drills and simulations. There may be a stipulation for the need for sufficient personnel with a good working knowledge of the English language to enable cargo operations at loading and discharge places to be carried out efficiently and safely and to enable communications to be carried out quickly and efficiently.

Detailed description – performance and speed

This clause sets out the required capabilities of the ship. For example, it could be stated that: 'Owners guarantee that the speed and consumption of the Vessel shall be as follows: In moderate weather up to and including BFT5 and Douglas sea state 4; Below figure to be used for C/P purposes: Service speed loaded abt 13 knots with consumption of abt 43 MT HFO/day for main engine, etc.'

Although express mention may be given of the conditions to which the performance criteria are to apply, the warranted speed and consumption rates are to be taken to relate to good weather conditions.[10] It is important to note that case law has made clear that the warranties apply only initially at the date of charter and do not continue throughout the period of the charter. Nevertheless, there is scope for an additional cause of action on the grounds of a breach of general obligation typically inserted in time charterparties to maintain the vessel in an efficient and fit state.

The consequences of a misdescription of the performance of the vessel can usually only be compensated for by way of a claim in damages, although a serious discrepancy which is fundamental to the charter may on occasion allow the charterer to treat it as discharged. The availability of this remedy is dependent upon the nature and consequences of the breach.

The use of 'about' in speed and consumption rates has typically been interpreted as allowing a margin of half a knot on speed and 5% on consumption rates. However, the leniency afforded by the inclusion of 'about' will be decided upon the facts of each case, depending on factors such as the size and nature of the particular vessel in question and it is not a matter of law.[11]

If a statement is given that the speed and consumption considerations are 'without guarantee', the provision does not even amount to a contractual warranty. It amounts only to a representation that the statement is given in good faith.

The Shelltime 4 form excludes the consideration of 'Adverse Weather Periods' where safety reasons demand the speed of the vessel is reduced. Provision is also made for an adjustment of the penalty to be made as a result of Adverse Weather Periods, which are defined as being '(i) any periods during which reduction of speed is necessary for safety in congested waters or in poor visibility (ii) any days, noon to noon, when winds exceed force 8 on the Beaufort Scale for more than 12 hours'.

Duty to maintain

The Shelltime 4 form provides: 'Throughout the charter service Owners shall, whenever the passage of time, wear and tear or any event requires steps to be taken to maintain or restore the conditions stipulated in Clauses 1 and 2(a), exercise due diligence so to maintain or restore the vessel.'[12]

In contrast to the clauses relating to the description of the vessel, the duty to maintain is limited to the exercise of due diligence rather than applying absolutely. Moreover, the clause applies only to deficiencies arising after delivery. In addition, such a clause will typically allow for a reduction in hire in relation to any deficiencies relating to the description of the vessel or its personnel, as is the case in the Shelltime 4 form.

Period trading limits

The Shelltime 4 form provides: 'Owners agree to let and Charterers agree to hire the vessel for a period of ... commencing from the time and date of delivery of the vessel, for the purpose of carrying all lawful merchandise including in particular ... in any part of the world, as Charterers shall direct subject to the limits of the current British Institute Warranties and any subsequent amendments thereof ...'. 'Charterers shall use due diligence to ensure that the vessel is only employed between and at safe places ... where she can safely lie always afloat.'[13] The time from which hire begins to become payable is delivery of the vessel, although this simply means putting it and its crew at the disposal of the charterer.

Although the charterers are limited to where they can trade, this restriction may be relaxed to enable them to trade in any part of the world provided that the owners consent and the charterers pay an additional premium. A general consent to trade beyond the charter's limits will not curtail the safe ports requirement, although consent to a specific port may do so.[14]

The due diligence condition on safe ports is less exacting a standard than is required in most dry cargo time charters,[15] which typically provide for the vessel to be employed 'between safe ports and safe places'. The port is to be safe at the time the order is given. In addition, the charterers will not be liable for damage unrelated to the characteristics of the port in question, for example where the damage is caused by an unforeseeable and exceptional storm.

Cancelling clause

The Shelltime 4 form provides: 'The vessel shall not be delivered to the charterer before ... and Charterers shall have the option of cancelling this charter if the vessel is not ready and at their disposal on or before ...'.[16]

If the ship is not ready (in accordance with prescribed description) on the date specified in this clause, an entitlement is provided for the charterer to cancel. It must be noted that the applicability of the right to cancel is not dependant on the fault or otherwise of the owner. Rather, the right arises automatically upon failure to put the vessel at the charterer's disposal and is to be distinguished from the separate issue of a discharge of obligations resulting from a breach of contract.

Rate and payment of hire

Typically, the charter will provide for a daily rate (and pro rata for any part of a day) to be payable from the date of delivery until date of redelivery. When drafting the clause it is advisable to include a term stating that both times are in local time, to avoid difficulties of interpretation.

The charterer is liable to pay hire throughout the whole of the period contracted. This basic starting point may only be departed from in one of three circumstances. Where the charter is frustrated or where the owner fails to provide the services agreed, liability ceases. In addition, such suspension of liability may be expressly provided for in the contract. Most typically, this would take the form of an off-hire clause (discussed below).

Express provision may also be made allowing the charterer to make certain deductions from hire, such as master's disbursements, although such allowances do not compromise the right to equitable set-off in other circumstances.[17] These deductions are based on the proposition that it is only fair that a charterer should be able to recoup himself by making a deduction from the following month's hire to compensate himself for the loss of use for those days equivalent to the loss of hire for those days. The claims must arise out of the same transaction or one linked closely with it. It has been decided this encompasses, for example, breach of a speed warranty but would not cover loss or damage to cargo.[18]

Payment is usually made monthly in advance, calculated at a rate per calendar month and at the same rate for any part of a month until redelivery. The owner is under an implied obligation to repay any hire paid in excess of what is actually due upon redelivery before the end of the month.

Cargo space

'The whole reach, burthen and decks of the Vessel and any passenger accommodation shall be at Charterer's disposal, reserving only proper and efficient space for the vessel's master, officers, crew ... provided that the weight of stores on board shall not, unless specifically agreed, exceed [ ] tonnes at any time during the charter period.'[19] Where the space available to the charterers is less than agreed a claim to a reduction in hire could be available under the duty to maintain clause in addition to the potential claim under breach of contract.

Pumping

The Shelltime 4 form does not provide for the owners to give any guarantee as to the efficacy of the pumping equipment. However, it may be that the charterer wishes to ensure a certain level of performance. As a result, a clause may be inserted, for example, to guarantee the equipment shall be able to discharge a full cargo of crude oil at say sp. Gr. 0.887 in 24 hours, excluding stripping against a back pressure of 100PSI at the Vessel's manifold.

Bills of Lading

The Shelltime 4 form provides: 'The master (although appointed by Owners) shall be under the orders and direction of Charterers as regards employment of the vessel, agency and other arrangements, and shall sign bills of lading as Charterers of their agents may direct and without prejudice to this charter. Charterers hereby indemnify owners against all consequences or liabilities that may arise

(i) from signing bills of lading in accordance with the directions of the charterer or to their agents ...'[20]

This clause will generally stipulate that the master shall be under the orders and direction of the charterers with regard to the employment of the vessel and shall sign Bills of Lading as the charterers or their agents may direct. In return, the charterers indemnify the owners against liabilities which may arise from signing Bills of Lading at the direction of the charterer. The fact that the master is under directions of the charterers does not mean the master must comply immediately with such orders.

Although, typically, an express indemnity is provided for, where the contract is silent on such a matter an indemnity will usually be implied in favour of the owners against any liabilities or losses arising from the carrying out of the charterers orders. Nevertheless, it is clear that no such indemnity would be implied where its effects are contrary to the stated terms of the contract. Moreover, the implication of an obligation to indemnify is not automatic, with best practice for any owner to insist on an express inclusion of the term.

Bunkers

In general, the charterers are to accept and pay for all bunkers on board at the time of delivery, with a reciprocal obligation on the owners to pay for all bunkers remaining on redelivery. Prices in each case are based on the current market prices at the port of delivery or redelivery, as applicable. As the charterer is supplying and paying for the fuel, they are taken as owner of the bunkers and therefore carry the consequential risk of loss or damage during the voyage.

Final voyage

Before considering the content of such a clause it is necessary to state that where the final voyage of a ship exceeds the charter period, the charterer is in breach, regardless of the merits or otherwise of his making of the order. In other words, the fact that the charterer could have reasonably expected to make redelivery in time after the final voyage will not prevent him being in breach of the contract.

As a result, a clause may be included to govern the situation where redelivery has not taken place by the end of the charter period. The judgment in *The World Symphony*[21] case is instructive in this area, holding that a charter with a specific margin will have no further implied margin and a charter for a fixed time will have a small margin implied. Further, it was held that a 'last voyage' clause will typically protect the charterer where he orders a final voyage which can be reasonably expected to arrive for redelivery in time, but without fault on his part, if redelivery becomes impossible.

Loss of vessel

The Shelltime 4 form provides: 'Should the vessel be lost, this charter shall terminate and hire shall cease at noon on the day of her loss; should the vessel be a constructive total loss, this charter shall terminate and hire shall cease at noon on the day on which the vessel's underwriters agree that the vessel is a constructive total loss; should the vessel be missing, this charter shall terminate and hire shall cease at noon on the day on which she was last heard of. Any hire paid in advance and not earned shall be returned to Charterers and Owners shall reimburse Charterers for the value of the estimated quantity of bunkers on board ...'.[22]

The result of the loss of a ship is dependent upon the circumstances surrounding its loss, and may lead to the contract being frustrated. This is likely to occur where the total loss or commercial destruction of the vessel is not caused by the breach of either party. The clause above also provides for prepaid hire to be reimbursed to the extent it has not been earned.

Off-hire

It is usual for provision to be made that hire may be withheld, or reduced in a rate pro rata to the level of deficiency of the ship, in a number of specified circumstances. As a primary point it must be noted that the occurrence of an off-hire event does not necessarily constitute a breach of contract, with the two concepts wholly independent of each other. The off-hire clause simply provides a departure from the principle that hire is payable throughout the duration of the charter and the outcome may differ from a claim in damages for a breach of contract. The clause may be generally along lines of the example below, taken from NYPE 93: 'In the event of loss of time from deficiency and/or default and/or strike of officers or crew, or deficiency of stores, fire, breakdown of, or damages to hull, machinery or equipment, grounding, detention by the arrest of the vessel or detention by average accidents to the vessel or cargo unless resulting from the inherent vice, quality or defect of the cargo ... or by any other similar cause preventing the full working of the vessel, the payment of hire and overtime, if any, shall cease for the time thereby lost.'[23]

The occurrence of an event listed in the off-hire clause will not in itself permit a suspension of hire. Rather, there must be a resultant loss of time. To illustrate, where a ship departs on a voyage in an unseaworthy state, it is not the case that there is an interruption in hire until the defect is remedied. Rather, hire is not paid in accordance with any loss of time.

A distinction must be drawn between 'net loss of time' and 'period' off-hire clauses. The wording of the latter demonstrates that the off-hire period commences on one event and ends with another, ie once prevention of full working of the vessel is overcome. In contrast, the NYPE 93 form intends that the net overall loss consequent on the event is deducted from hire, with no reference to the time at which full working is resumed.

Nevertheless, hire begins again once the ship is fully efficient and not once she has reached the same position as when the off-hire event occurred. Therefore, the risk remains with the charterer that they could foreseeably have to pay twice for a part of the voyage where, for example, the ship has had to return for repairs.

The continuing obligations of the charterer are not compromised by the fact that an event listed in the off-hire clause has occurred. Consequently, they remain liable for the payment for bunkers consumed unless the contrary is expressly provided for. It should be noted that the NYPE 93 form does in fact provide for such an exclusion from liability to provide bunkers, however, the other obligations of the charterer would continue in full force and effect.

Salvage

Generally, a clause will provide for the costs of an attempt to salve property or save life to be shared equally by the owner and charterer. However, the charterer should not assume any liability for the costs of any damages to the vessel incurred as a result or of any delictual liability to third parties.

Lien

The clause may state: 'Owners shall have a lien upon all cargoes and all freights, sub-freights and demurrage for any amounts due under this charter: and Charterers shall have a lien on the vessel for all monies paid in advance and not earned, and for all claims for damages arising from any breach by Owners of this charter.'[24]

A possessory lien in favour of the owner is typically provided for over goods not belonging to him until amounts owed to him are satisfied. Such a clause would provide a personal right to the owner, enforceable against the charterer. The question arises as to how cargo which is not owned by the charterer is to be treated. In other words, is such cargo subject to the lien?

A conflict may arise between the need to provide a remedy to the owner and the need for protection of an 'innocent' third party holder of a Bill of Lading who believes he has the right to immediate delivery of their cargoes. Such a problem would not occur where the lien is incorporated into the Bill of Lading, as the holder of the Bill of Lading would have prior notice of the possibility of their cargo being held. However, where this is not the case, the outcome is to be determined by interpretation of the particular lien clause. The courts have adopted contrasting views depending on the facts of each case, willing to hold that lien for unpaid charterhire was not exercisable over such cargo, while taking the opposing view where the right of lien was over 'all' cargoes. With regards the latter, it has been held that the right could be exercised on any cargo irrespective of who owns it.[25]

Lien on sub-freights

This lien is enforced by timely interception of the targeted monies before they have been paid to the time charterer.[26] In contrast to the situation above, such a lien is not possessory in nature. Rather, a notice is sent to the party due to pay the freight, dispatched so as to reach him before he has paid monies over to the charterer.

Outbreak of war

A charter party will make provision for cancellation where an outbreak of war does not permit performance of obligations under the charter. For example: 'If war or hostilities break out between any two or more of the following countries: USA, USSR, PRC, UK, Netherlands – both Owners and Charterers shall have the right to cancel this charter.'[27]

The courts have held that this right to cancel must be exercised within a reasonable time from the outbreak of war. Additional clauses are typically included to deal with additional war expenses and for war risks.

Clauses to be incorporated into Bills of Lading

Clause paramount

A clause paramount does not incorporate the Hague or Hague–Visby rules into the charter itself, but rather ensures the charterers shall procure that the clause will be contained in all Bills of Lading issued pursuant to it. Failure to do so will constitute a breach by the charterer.

Both to blame

Again, this clause requires that the charterer shall procure that all Bills of Lading issued under the charter shall contain the Both to Blame Collision clause rather than making the clause part of the charter itself. The inclusion of the clause in the charter allows the owner an indemnity where the charterer fails to include the collision clause and a loss is incurred from which the owner should have been protected.

New Jason clause

Similarly, a Jason clause must be incorporated into all Bills of Lading with the same protections afforded to owner as above upon failure of charterer to do so, if so provided for in the charter party.

TOVALOP

With TOVALOP (Tanker Owners Voluntary Agreement Concerning Liability for Oil Pollution) no longer relevant, an alternative condition for inclusion in the charter party is the International Tanker Owners Pollution Federation Clause, which provides as follows:

'Owners warrant that the vessel is now and throughout the duration of the charter will be (i) owned or demise chartered by a member of the International Tanker Owners Pollution Federation Limited and (ii) entered in the following Protection and Indemnity (P & I) Club …'.

Notes

1 Lecture on 'Oil Trading' by John Bassindale, Clifford Chance, London, p 8 of transcript.
2 Sale of Goods Act 1979, s 18.
3 *CEP Interagra SA* v *Select Energy Trading G.m.b.H.*, *The Jambur*, LMLN 289. QBD 14 November 1990.
4 Such documents include invoices, Bills of Lading, certificates of origin, quantity, quality, inspection, etc.
5 Boyd, Burrows and Foxton, *Scrutton on Charterparties* (20th edn, 1996), p 64.
6 Boyd, Burrows and Foxton, *Scrutton on Charterparties* (20th edn, 1996), p 88.
7 Clause 1, Shelltime 4.
8 Clause 1(c), Shelltime 4.
9 See the 'Duty to Maintain' below.
10 See Hill, *Maritime Law* (6th edn), 2003), p 174.
11 See Hill, *Maritime Law* (6th edn), 2003), pp 174–175 for discussion of case law on this matter.

[12] Clause 3, Shelltime 4.
[13] Clause 4, Shelltime 4.
[14] Wilford, Coghlin and Kimball, *Time Charters* (5th edn, 2003), p 650.
[15] Wilford, Coghlin and Kimball, *Time Charters* (5th edn, 2003), p 650.
[16] Clause 5, Shelltime 4.
[17] The right to equitable set-off is not applicable to a claim for freight.
[18] For further discussion and review of relevant case law, see Hill, *Maritime Law* (6th edn, 2003), p 185.
[19] Clause 10, Shelltime 4.
[20] Clause 13, Shelltime 4.
[21] [1991] 2 Lloyd's Rep. 251.
[22] Clause 20, Shelltime 4.
[23] Clause 17, NYPE 93.
[24] Clause 26, Shelltime 4.
[25] See, for example, *The Aegnoussiotis* [1977] 1 Lloyd's Rep. 268 in contrast to *The Agios Giorgis* [1976] 2 Lloyd's Rep. 192.
[26] Hill, *Maritime Law* (6th edn, 2003) p 191.
[27] Clause 33, Shelltime 4.

— 20 —

GAS TERMINALS AND SALES AGREEMENTS

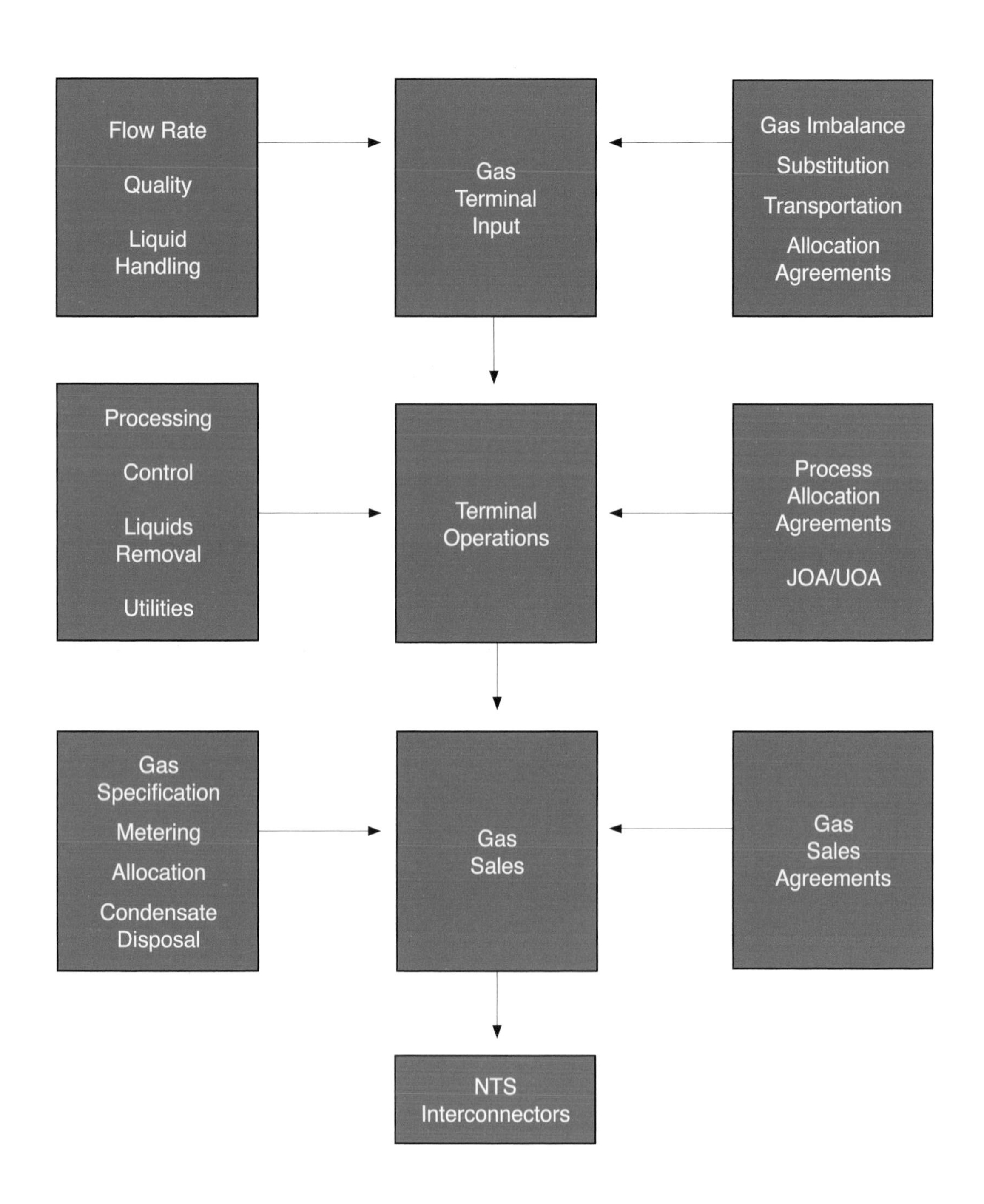

Flow Rate
Quality
Liquid Handling
Gas Terminal Input
Gas Imbalance
Substitution
Transportation
Allocation Agreements
Processing
Control
Liquids Removal
Utilities
Terminal Operations
Process Allocation Agreements
JOA/UOA
Gas Specification
Metering
Allocation
Condensate Disposal
Gas Sales
Gas Sales Agreements
NTS Interconnectors

GAS TERMINALS AND SALES AGREEMENTS

TECHNICAL

20.1 Introduction

Gas was first discovered in the Southern North Sea in the mid-1960s, at a time when Britain's energy supplies were depleting. Over the last 40 years an infrastructure of offshore platforms, subsea pipelines and terminals has been installed which made Britain self-supporting in its natural gas supplies for many years until it became a net gas importer in 2004. This chapter will describe this infrastructure, and the processing of this gas for sales and delivery to domestic and industrial users.

Gas is delivered to the seven reception points (called beach terminals) by gas producers operating offshore facilities from over 100 fields beneath the sea around the British Isles. Most of these onshore locations consist of a number of separately operated plants sited adjacent to each other.

All the processing terminals receive a co-mingled feed gas supply from a number of offshore platforms via a subsea pipeline network. In some cases, this co-mingled feed is received together with water and hydrocarbon liquids.

The function of the gas terminal is to process this feedstock to provide sales-quality gas and liquid hydrocarbon by-products such as propane, butane and natural gas liquids or condensate. The treatment process also includes checking the quality of the products to meet the safety requirements and measuring the calorific value of the sales gas (the amount of energy contained in the gas).

The gas is shipped to the customers (domestic and industrial users) via the National Gas Grid (NGG, that part of National Grid plc formerly known as TRANSCO) operated National Transmission System (NTS) and eight

Distribution Networks (four of which are owned by NGG and four by mixed investor groups). In addition, there are some cases where supplies go direct to power stations have dedicated onshore pipelines. The entire total system consists of a network in the region of 275,000 km of iron, steel and polyethylene mains pipeline. The liquid by-products are stored and shipped as fuel or as petrochemical feedstocks.

The terminals are also required to treat and dispose of all waste streams such as the water that is extracted from the reservoir along with the gas.

In addition to the gas processing terminals, there are three facilities that enable sales-quality gas to be imported from gas pipelines from Holland, Belgium and Norway through reception facilities located at the Easington and Bacton gas terminals. One of these facilities, the Bacton to Zeebrugge Interconnector, also allows gas from the UK to be exported to the Continent. Furthermore, a recently commissioned re-gasification terminal at the Isle of Grain allows liquefied natural gas (LNG) to be delivered by sea.

20.2 UK gas terminals

There are a total of seven UK gas terminal locations (Fig. 20–1):

- St Fergus;
- Bacton;
- Easington/Dimlington;
- Point of Ayr;
- Barrow-in-Furness;
- Theddlethorpe; and
- Teesside (Seal Sands).

St Fergus

The St Fergus gas terminal is a complex of four sites located some 60 km north of Aberdeen on Scotland's north-east coast. The complex comprises:

- The Total E&P UK-operated facilities that receive gas through the Miller, Vesterled (which transports up to 13 bcf of gas from the Norwegian Continental Shelf) and Frigg pipelines.
- The Shell-operated site that receives fluids via the Far North Liquids and Gas System (FLAGS), Fulmar and Goldeneye pipelines. From October 2007 FLAGS will carry an increasing amount of Norwegian wet gas via a connecting pipeline.

Figure 20–1 UK map showing location of gas terminals

- The Exxon Mobil-operated SAGE terminal that receives gas via the Scottish Area Gas Evacuation Area (SAGE) pipeline, the Britannia pipeline and the Atlantic and Cromarty pipeline.
- The NGG-operated terminal which receives the sales-quality gas from the Total, Shell and Exxon Mobil sites compresses it into the NTS for distribution within the UK.

The Total site became operational in 1977, to receive lean gas through the Norwegian Frigg line (subsequently modified in 2001 to become the Vesterled system) as well as rich gas from the British Frigg pipeline. Today, it receives natural gas from some 20 fields, supplying up to 15% of the UK's gas.

The terminal receives gas transported through the Frigg Transportation System from the TOTAL-operated Alwyn North, Dunbar, Ellon, Grant, Nuggets and Frigg fields, and from non-operated fields including Bruce, Captain, Ross, Blake, Buzzard and the fields that make up the Flotta Catchment Area (FCA).

The Miller facilities are located within the Total site and are entirely separate from the Frigg Transportation System facilities. On arrival at the terminal, the gas from the Miller field is heated and depressurised and then exported to the Peterhead power station along a buried landline.

The Shell UK Exploration and Production-operated terminal processes gas for the FLAGS and the Fulmar Gas pipelines. The FLAGS facilities commenced operation in 1982, followed by first gas through the Fulmar facility in 1986. The plant capacity is approximately 800 MMscfd for the FLAGS system and 100 MMscfd for the Fulmar system. In 2002 production commenced through the Goldeneye facilities. This consisted of a dedicated pipeline and processing facilities (capacity 300 MMscfd wet gas and 10 mbpd (thousand barrels per day), condensate) within the Shell Site to directly treat the gas, water and condensate produced from the Goldeneye offshore wells.

The SAGE plant capacity is 1900 MMscfd with 5,300 tonnes/day of condensate production and 2500 tonnes/day CO_2 (carbon dioxide) removal. The plant commenced operation in 1992 with two identical trains (each designed to handle 575 MMscfd) to receive gas from the 1100 MMscfd-capacity SAGE pipeline. In 1998 the plant capacity was expanded by the addition of a third 840 MMscfd train to receive gas from the Britannia pipeline. In 2006 production commenced from the 232 MMscfd-capacity Atlantic Cromarty pipeline. The gas from all sites is metered and exported to NGG.

The hydrocarbon condensate, which has been separated during the gas treatment process on all three sites, is then sent either 24 km along the coast to join BP's Forties Pipeline System at Cruden Bay or to Mossmorran via the Shell condensate export line. Ethane, Propane, Butane and Natural Gas Liquid (NGL) products are then separated at the Shell-operated Fife NGL

Figure 20–2 Aerial view of Bacton gas terminal

plant or the BP-operated Kinneil Oil Terminal. These products are either used as feedstocks to the adjacent Fife Ethylene Plant or Grangemouth refinery or stored and exported by sea.

Bacton

Bacton (Fig 20–2) is located on the Norfolk coast and is one of the largest gas terminal complexes in the UK, supplying approximately 30% of the UK demand. It is a complex of a number of gas terminals, built over the last 35 years, that receives gas from offshore fields, processes it and transmits it into the NTS for use throughout the UK.

Gas lands onshore at the four producer terminals from the Southern North Sea and from the Shearwater Elgin Area Line (SEAL) and is then distributed to UK customers via the National Grid, or to Belgium via the Interconnector system (export capacity 2000 MMscfd) which is also located at Bacton. When in reverse flow mode (capacity 2400 MMscfd increasing to 2550 MMscfd later in 2007), the Interconnector Bacton Terminal is used to import gas into the UK.

The four producer terminals are:

- The Tullow Oil (ex BP)-operated plant that processes gas from Thames, Lancelot (LAPS) and Hewett areas. The Hewett plant commenced production in 1969, with the LAPS plant starting in 1998. The maximum possible capacity of the total site is 1200 MMscfd, although this is currently limited to 800 MMscfd.
- The Perenco (ex ConocoPhillips)-operated site that processes gas via the system known as the East Anglia Gas and Liquids Evacuation System (EAGLES) including the Indefatigable, East Leman, Davy, Trent, Tyne and Waveney fields. Production started in 1995 and the plant capacity is 500 MMscfd.
- The 1750 MMscfd capacity Shell plant that processes gas from Leman and Sean fields and the SPOTS system.
- The Shearwater / Elgin/Franklin system (SEAL). Production commenced in 2000 at a capacity of 1100 MMscfd. The SEAL system feeds the Interconnector via the SILK pipeline (SEAL-Interconnector Link) bypassing the NTS. However, SILK has been little used in recent years.

Condensate is exported to the Condensate Disposal System (CDS) via a pumping station and piped to a nearby rail terminal. The CDS is operated by the British Pipeline Agency.

A fifth terminal has commenced operation in December 2006 to heat and control the gas flow from Holland via the Balgzand Bacton Line (BBL).

Easington/Dimlington

The Easington and Dimlington terminals are located close to each other on the Yorkshire coast, to the north of Easington village. There are three separate terminals: the BP-operated Dimlington and Easington terminals and the Centrica-operated Easington terminal. All treated gas is routed through the Centrica site where it is metered and routed to the NTS. Stabilised condensate is piped via the BP Dimlington site to either BP's Saltend facility near Hull or to a storage facilty near Immingham where it is shipped for use in the petrochemical industry.

The BP Easington terminal was built in 1967 and was the first terminal to receive and process gas from the North Sea. It has a capacity of 300 MMscfd and processes gas from the West Sole, Hoton, Hyde and Newsham fields. The gas is compressed and routed to the Dimlington site for further processing. The hydrocarbon liquid separated from the gas is also routed to the adjacent Dimlington site for further processing.

The Dimlington site was first operated in 1988 and has a capacity of 950 MMscfd. In addition to further processing the gas from the adjacent BP Easington terminal, it receives and processes gas from the Easington Catchment Area (ECA) and Ravenspurn North and South (Villages Complex).

The Centrica-operated Easington terminal was first operated in 1975 to process gas from the Rough field. In 1985, the field was converted to a storage facility, enabling gas to be stored within the reservoir. The Rough facility no longer supplies gas directly to the end-users but acts as a storage facility for customers (gas shippers/suppliers), allowing gas to be fed into the NTS at times of peak demand or withdrawn from the NTS and re-injected into the reservoir at times of low demand. The movement of gas either into or out of the reservoir is based on 'nominations' made by gas shippers and withdrawn at short notice to meet peaks in demand.

Today, the main functions of the terminal are to receive and condition gas from the Rough and the BP-operated Amethyst offshore facilities, receive treated gas from BP's Dimlington terminal and transfer it into the NTS and to withdraw gas from the NTS during periods of low gas demand and re-inject it into the Rough field for storage.

A new terminal adjacent to the Centrica site commenced production in 2006 to receive sales-quality gas from Norwegian Troll and Sleipner fields via the Langeled pipeline system. Gas from Ormen Lange will begin flowing through the pipeline from October 2007, once the northern leg of Langeled is completed. It is expected that the Langeled system will have a capacity of approximately 2,600 MMscfd and supply a fifth of Britain's gas requirements.

The Langeled Receiving Facilities (LRF) at the terminal are limited to heating, pressure reduction and metering facilities.

Point of Ayr gas terminal

The Point of Ayr terminal processes gas extracted by a number of platforms situated in Liverpool Bay.

Gas from the Liverpool Bay fields is piped to Point of Ayr from the Douglas Complex via a 20" 33.5 km subsea pipeline. At the terminal it is treated by removing hydrogen sulphide, hydrocarbon liquids and water to produce 'sweet' gas, and sent to Connah's Quay via a 24" 7 km underground pipeline at a rate of up to 300 MMscfd.

The gas is then supplied to a reception facility at the combined cycle gas turbine (CCGT) power station at Connah's Quay, where it is 'polished' to remove any dust and fed into the plant's four gas turbines. The terminal is designed to provide the power station with all the gas it needs to generate 1,400 MW of electricity. Surplus gas is sold into the NTS.

Barrow-in-Furness

The gas produced from the various facilities in the Irish Sea is processed at South and North Morecambe terminals located near Barrow-in Furness (operated by Hydrocarbon Resources Ltd (NRL) which is a subsidiary of Centrica Energy.

The South Morecambe terminal commenced production in 1985 with an original capacity of 1,200 MMscfd of gas from the South Morecambe gas field. This capacity was increased to 1,800 MMscfd in the early 1990s. Treated gas is routed to the NTS and stabilised condensate (at up to 4,655 bpd) is stored onsite before export through fiscal meters to a tank farm at Barrow docks.

The North Morecambe terminal commenced production in 1994 from the North Morecambe gas field. The terminal capacity is approximately 530 MMscfd and 2,100 bpd of condensate. In 1999, the North Morecambe Terminal also received gas from the ConocoPhillips-operated Millom and Dalton fields. The North Morecambe terminal is arguably one of the most complex gas terminals in the UK, with carbon dioxide (CO_2) and cryogenic nitrogen removal facilities being required as well as water and hydrocarbon dew pointing facilities in order to meet the sale gas specification. Both the sales gas and condensate are exported via the South Morecambe terminal.

Adjacent to the North Morecambe terminal is the ConocoPhillips-owned but Hydrocarbon Resources Ltd-operated Rivers terminal. This terminal was first operated in 2006 and removes hydrogen sulphide (H_2S) from up to 120 MMscfd of sour gas produced from the Calder field. Sweetened gas, condensate and water/methanol are routed to the adjacent North Morecambe site for further processing.

Theddlethorpe

The ConocoPhillips-operated gas terminal at Theddlethorpe on the Lincolnshire coast receives gas from the Lincoln Offshore Gas Gathering System (LOGGS), Caister Murdoch System (CMS) and Viking Transportation System (VTS). The terminal has a capacity to process 1,600 MMscfd of gas.

The terminal provides gas and condensate processing facilities. Any liquids processed at the Theddlethorpe gas terminal are transported by onshore pipeline to the Humber Oil Refinery. Gas processed at the Theddlethorpe gas terminal is redelivered to the NTS or to the Killingholme Pipeline System (KIPS) operated by E.ON UK.

Teesside – Seal Sands

The Central Area Transmission System (CATS) is operated by BP and transports gas from Everest, Lomond J-Block, Banff, Armada, Seymour, Andrew, ETAP (Eastern Trough Area Project) fields and Erskine fields/areas to two terminals which are located adjacent to each other at Seal Sands, Teesside. The terminals are operated by BP and px Ltd.

The pipeline has a capacity of 1700 MMscfd and the BP terminal has a capacity of 1200 MMscfd. Production first started in 1993. The treated gas is redelivered to the NTS. The gas that is not processed in the BP-operated site is routed for processing to the adjacent px Ltd-operated plant which started operation in 1999. The px Ltd plant is a two-train deepcut expander process with up to 90% of propane recovery. Both trains have 400 MMscfd capacity. One train feeds the gas to the 1875-MW station at Wilton; the second feeds the NTS.

Unlike the other gas terminals that only produce condensate as a liquid by-product, the terminals produce propane, butane and condensate in addition to sales-quality gas. The liquid products are routed to offsite storage or directly to the nearby ConocoPhillips-operated refinery.

Isle of Grain

The Isle of Grain LNG terminal located in the south-east of England was originally a peak shaving LNG storage facility built between 1979 and 1981 and operated by British Gas.

With gas demand rising and domestic production set to decline, the UK is required to import a significant proportion of its gas. The import of liquefied natural gas (LNG) is set to fill part of the supply gap.

Grain LNG Ltd, a wholly owned subsidiary of National Grid, has constructed a liquefied natural gas import and regasification terminal at the Isle of Grain. The terminal commenced operation in July 2005 and has a capacity to receive and process up to 3.3 million tonnes of LNG per annum, equivalent to 420 MMscfd.

An expansion project is currently ongoing, with completion by late 2008 to increase the capacity to 9.8 million tonnes of LNG per annum. The additional capacity is expected to be available late in 2008.

A further two LNG import terminals are under construction near Milford Haven – owned and operated by Dragon LNG and South Hook LNG. Vessels with onboard LNG re-gasification capability have, since February 2007, also been able to deliver gas through the Teesside Gas Port LNG terminal, operated by Excelerate Energy.

20.3 Main pipeline feeds

The feed gas from the offshore facilities is routed to the gas terminals via a number of pipeline systems each of which will have a rated capacity and an entry specification. The entry specification depends on the nature of the pipeline operation (multiphase or single phase operation) and the processing configuration of the host terminal. The entry specification will typically limit entry pressure and temperature, gas composition (including hydrocarbon liquid content), the amount of inerts (carbon dioxide and nitrogen), water content and the level of contaminants such as hydrogen sulphide and mercury.

Appendix 1 summarises the main pipelines. In the case of multiphase flow from the offshore platforms, a mixture of gas and liquid is delivered to the terminal. At high flow rates this arrives as a two-phase mixture. At low flow rates the liquid settles into 'slugs' in the pipeline that have to be swept out periodically by 'pigs' (large spheres). To receive these liquids, a slug catcher is usually installed at the reception point in the terminal. A slug catcher is essentially a vessel with a large liquid hold-up capacity. It can be either a pressure vessel or a network of pipes.

20.4 Terminal management and product allocation

Each terminal is operated by a single company on behalf of its users. The operating company may be the company (or its successor) which first established the terminal and associated pipelines. Alternatively, the operating company may be a third party service provider that operates the terminal on behalf of its owners. In this case, the terminal will operate in a purely tolling arrangement where the offshore producers or shippers will be charged a processing fee for the use of the terminal.

The amount of flow from the offshore facilities is usually under the control of the terminal operator who will have real time information on the status and flow of gas, detection of leaks and the quality of the gas in terms of entry specification from each of the offshore platforms. The terminal operator can curtail production if the offshore shipper fails to meet the pipeline entry specification.

The objectives of terminal management are to ensure that:

- the terminal is operated safely and all the facilities appropriately maintained;
- the terminal is operated in accordance with the relevant Health Safety and Environmental (HS&E) legislation and company HS&E goals;
- the gas and liquid products are allocated to each shipper in an equitable manner;

- the costs of the terminal operation is allocated to each shipper in an equitable manner; and
- the contractual obligations to each shipper and to the terminal operator are met.

As with oil terminals, the terminal management is largely dependent on the contractual rights of the shippers and the obligations of the terminal owners.

In one form, the terminal may be operated as a joint venture between all or some of the shippers. The terminal operator (typically the shipper with the largest equity share) undertakes the operation of the terminal in accordance with a remit agreed between the shippers' representatives, following an agreed contractual structure. Operating costs are shared using a predetermined formula.

Alternatively, the shipper will pay a tariff for the use of the terminal facilities in accordance with an agreed contractual arrangement, ie the terminal operator would act as a third party. This arrangement may involve the terminal operator having some or no equity in the terminal and sets out the level of services to be performed by the terminal operators and the level of tariff. These contractual agreements may have some degree of pro rata operating cost share.

As the pipeline and terminals systems are never identical, no two allocation systems are exactly the same. Product allocation is a complex procedure (particularly if there are a number of shippers entering the pipeline system) and is typically based on accurate metering of the entrant flow rates including gas composition into and from the pipeline system to determine the respective shipper's share of sales gas and liquid products. Such allocation agreements will be underpinned by contractual agreements and rules covering gas substitution with other shippers. Examples are measurement requirements, changes to gas nominations and the timing of such changes, third party/future entrants, capacities including maximum and minimum energy levels in the pipeline system and cutbacks. A number of allocation agreements may also be in place, for example:

- Transportation Allocation Agreement which assesses stock changes in the pipeline, the impact of such stock changes (traceable losses or gains) on product allocation and untraceable losses due to the finite accuracy of the metering methods used.
- Process Allocation Agreement which is a process model of the gas terminal facilities to determine the shippers' share of gas and liquids redelivered to the sales points. These allocation agreements are usually based on the shipper's percentage energy share into the terminal and take account of background fuel gas deduction, contaminant component deductions

(such as hydrogen sulphide (H_2S) and carbon dioxide (CO_2) and flare losses, etc.

- Downstream Allocation Agreements which allocate produced gas to Shippers at the NTS entry point.

On a day-to-day basis, the amount of gas into the pipeline is determined in conjunction with the nomination gas administrator who (via the terminal operator) will inform the offshore producers/shippers the amount of gas (usually in terms of energy content) that they can send into the pipeline system. These restrictions will depend on the various contractual arrangements that are in place, the level of processing capacity in the terminal and the level of stock in the pipeline.

The contractual arrangements may be based on a fixed reservation fee, reserve capacity basis or a mixture of both. A fixed reservation fee is where the pipeline operator pays for a fixed level of capacity in the pipeline and terminal regardless of whether it is used. A reserve capacity basis is where capacity is offered on a reasonable endeavours basis only, ie capacity is not guaranteed. The contractual arrangements may differ from shipper to shipper and will depend on their contractual obligations to meet their sales nominations.

The level of stock in the pipeline can be controlled by 'packing' and 'unpacking' the pipeline. In the case of packing, the inlet flow to the pipeline exceeds that removed at the terminal and the line is 'packed' with gas and the pipeline pressure will rise to a maximum predetermined level. 'Packing' may occur where there is a short-term processing capacity restriction at the terminal or where a shipper packs the line to take advantage of market conditions or to pre-empt short term capacity restrictions on their platform (ie planned maintenance). The line is 'unpacked' where the flow to the terminal exceeds the inlet flow to the pipeline and the pressure will fall again to a predetermined level. This occurs usually where the offshore shippers have a capacity restriction. The level of line pack available to each shipper is determined by the nomination gas administrator and may not always be available depending on the prevailing operating conditions and contractual arrangements.

Additional economic discoveries are connected to the pipelines feeding the terminals using spare capacity or in some cases by expanding, capacity. This is accomplished under contractual provisions appropriate to the individual pipeline and terminal system involved and via industry codes of practice which were designed to maximise the use of infrastructure, thus enhancing the economic development of smaller fields.

Appendix 2 is a summary of approximate and indicative maximum capacities and phase processing involved for each of the UK terminals.

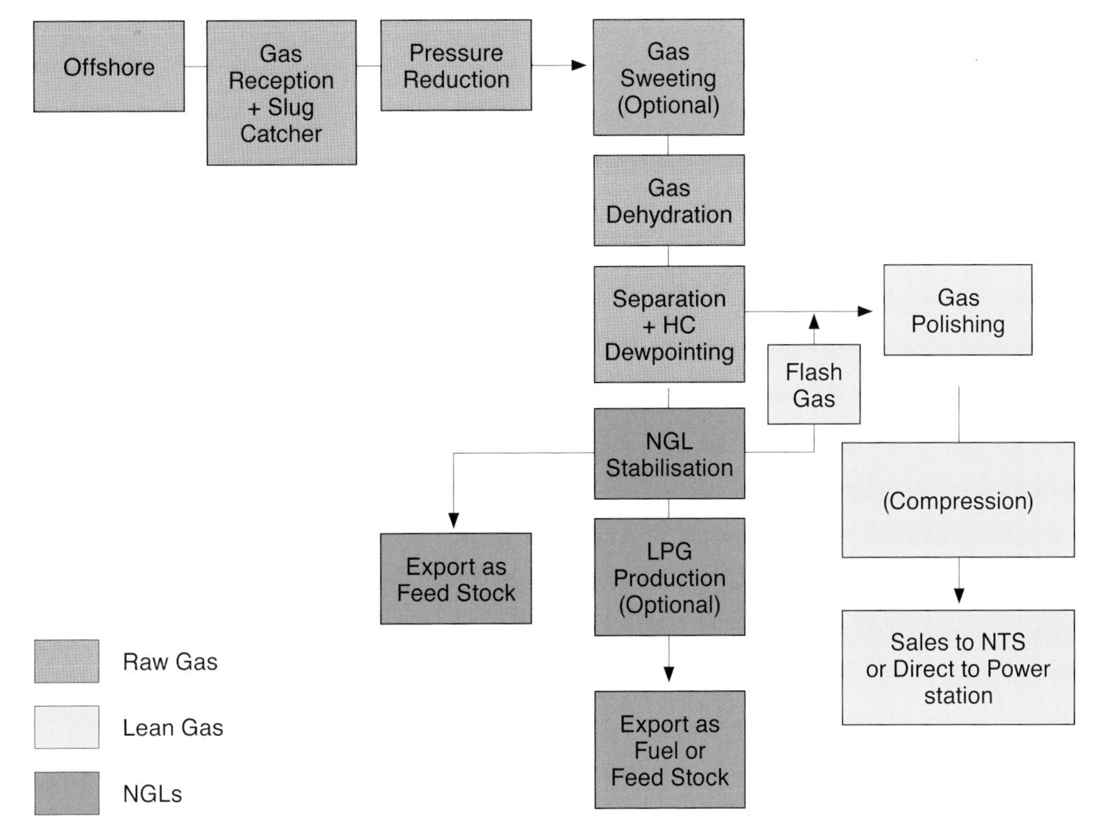

Figure 20–3 Typical gas terminal block diagram overview

20.5 Terminal gas processing and liquid disposal

The natural gas sold to the end-users is very different to the gas that is produced from the reservoir. The processed natural gas consumed by industrial and domestic users is composed almost entirely of methane. However, natural gas produced from the reservoir, although still containing a high proportion of methane, is a mixture of other hydrocarbons such as ethane, propane, butane, and pentanes. In addition, this raw feed stream will contain all or some of the following compounds; water, hydrogen sulphide (H_2S), carbon dioxide, helium, nitrogen, and others. Therefore processing is required (Fig. 20–3).

As the gas enters the terminal, it is fed through a dedicated slug catcher where any free water or liquid hydrocarbons are separated off before the gas enters the main process system. These processing facilities consists of separating all of the various hydrocarbons, contaminants and fluids from the pure natural gas, to produce what is known as 'pipeline-quality' dry natural gas or sales gas. Major transportation pipelines usually impose restrictions on the make-up of the natural gas that is allowed into the pipeline. In the UK, the gas is processed to

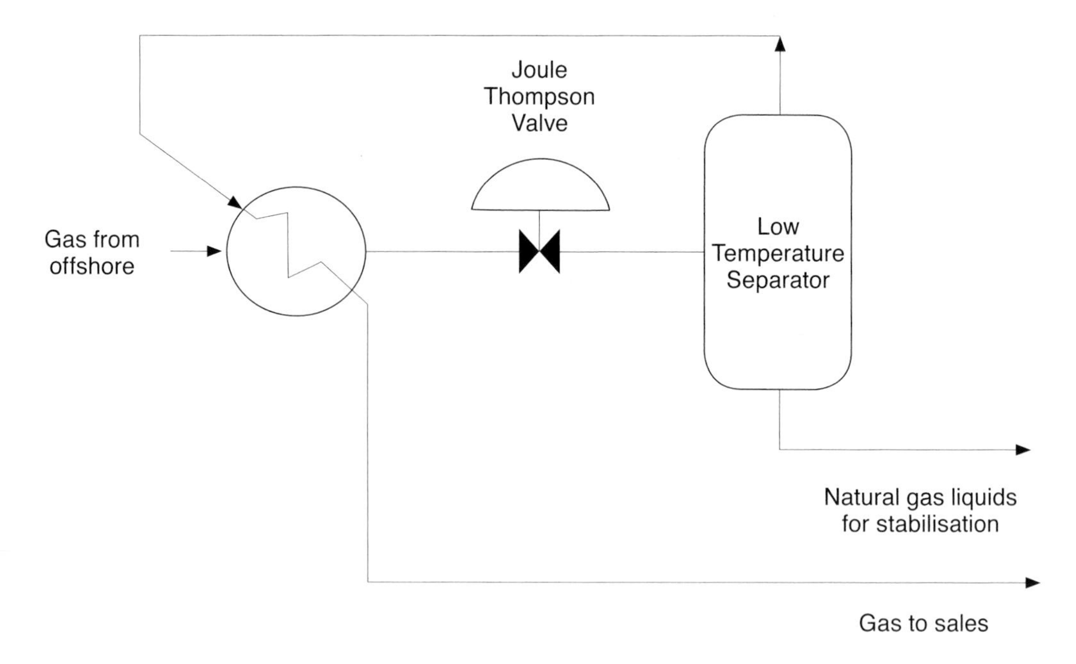

Figure 20–4 Gas refrigeration process

the NGG specification (which itself is designed to enable NGG to meet statutory obligations, principally contained in the Gas Safety (Management) Regulations 1996) as shown in Appendix 3.

During the treatment process, hydrocarbons such as ethane, propane, butane, and pentanes are removed from natural gas in a process called 'hydrocarbon dew pointing'. This can be done by a variety of methods and the methods used in the UK terminals are summarised in Appendix 2.

Hydrocarbon Dewpointing

JT Cooling uses the Joule Thompson (JT) effect that when the pressure of a gas stream is reduced across a control valve, the temperature drops. This auto-refrigeration process is the simplest process but the least efficient as the pressure energy is wasted. The feed gas enters a heat exchanger where it is cooled by interchange of heat with the cold sales gas. The pressure of the gas is reduced across a control valve where the temperature is further reduced, causing hydrocarbon liquids to condense. The liquids are separated from the gas in a low-temperature separator (LTS) for further processing. The cold sales gas is heated up by interchange of heat with the feed gas.

The refrigeration process is an alternative to JT Cooling process where an external refrigerant and gas chiller is used to cool the gas instead of achieving low temperatures by pressure reduction (Fig. 20–4).

As the gas is cooled, any water present in the gas will also condense along with the hydrocarbon liquids. Typically, with refrigeration and JT Cooling processes, the temperature reduction of the gas is such that it is possible to enable these processes to achieve the sales gas water dew point as well as the hydrocarbon dew point specification. This is achieved by injecting methanol or glycol into the gas as it is cooled to prevent the formation of hydrates. The low-temperature separator (LTS) is then operated as a three-phase vessel where the aqueous methanol or glycol is separated from the condensate and the gas. The water-rich methanol or glycol is recovered by routing it to a regeneration system where the water is removed by heating and distillation. The methanol or glycol is returned back to the process. Injecting methanol or glycol into the gas prevents the formation of hydrates and can also dissolve any existing deposits. This ice-like structure can form blockages which can choke filters, valves, pipelines, heat exchangers, etc.

The turbo expander process uses a turbo expander (Fig. 20–5) instead of the control valve to cool the gas. This process is more efficient than JT Cooling, as energy is removed from the gas as it is expanded. This results in a much colder gas temperature for the same reduction in pressure as compared with JT Cooling. Furthermore, a high proportion of the energy removed from the gas is recovered as the turbo expander is connected to a gas compressor which compresses the treated sales gas.

Deep Cut Propane Recovery is a cryogenic process that extracts very high proportions of ethane and propane from the gas. There are a number of licensed processes but most are based around the use of external refrigerants and turbo

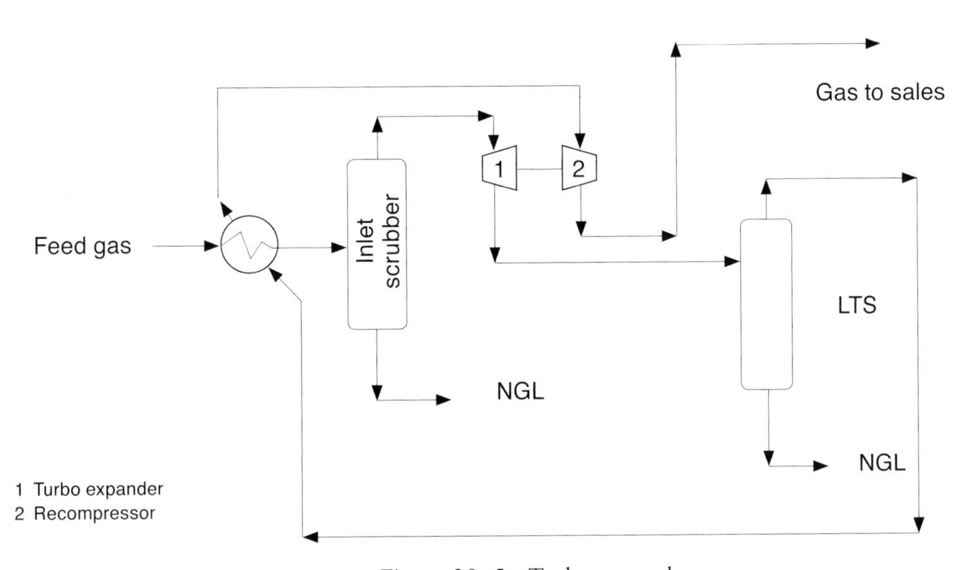

Figure 20–5 Turbo expander

expander technology to obtain very low temperatures (< –100°C) The refrigerants cool the feed gas stream and the turbo expander expands the chilled gases, which causes the temperature to drop significantly. The ethane and heavier hydrocarbon components in the gas stream condense, leaving predominantly methane in gaseous form. The methane is separated from the liquids by a distillation column called a demethaniser and routed to sales. The condensed liquids are recovered for further processing.

With the turbo expansion and propane recovery processes, the gas temperatures are so low that it is not possible for these processes to prevent hydrate formation by injecting methanol or glycol. The feed gas must therefore be dried prior to processing to avoid water condensation and hydrate formation. This is achieved by absorption using glycols, or by adsorption using solid desiccants.

Liquid recovery

The valuable hydrocarbon liquid components are not wasted and are refined to produce useful products such as fuel gas for the terminal's use, Liquefied Natural Gas (LPG) and Natural Gas Liquids (NGLs). These liquid products are sold separately and have a variety of different uses including feedstocks for oil refineries or petrochemical plants. In the UK, the majority of the terminals produce NGLs. The exception are the terminals at Seal Sands which produce LPG in addition to NGL.

Water removal

In addition to separating hydrocarbon liquids from the feed stream, it is necessary to remove most of the associated water. Most of the liquid, free water associated with extracted natural gas, is removed by simple separation methods as the feed arrives at the terminal. However, the removal of the water vapour that exists in solution in natural gas requires a more complex treatment and is done by three methods. These can be either a part of the hydrocarbon dew pointing process where methanol or glycol is injected to remove the water, by absorption using glycols, or by adsorption using solid desiccants.

Sour and acid gas removal

A further step in gas processing involves the removal of sulphur and carbon dioxide if these contaminants are present in sufficient quantities in the feed gas. Gas that contains high quantities of sulphur is termed 'sour gas' and is undesirable because the sulphur compounds it contains can be extremely harmful, even lethal, to breathe as well as being corrosive.

Gas that contains high quantities of carbon dioxide is termed 'acid gas'. Carbon dioxide is removed to below transportation specifications as it is corrosive in the presence of water and will reduce the energy content of the gas. The term applied to removing sulphur and carbon dioxide is called 'sweetening'.

A common process for sweetening natural gas is by absorption with amine solutions. The gas is run through a tower, which contains the amine solution. This solution has an affinity for sulphur and carbon dioxide, and absorbs these contaminants.

The effluent gas is virtually free of sulphur compounds and has carbon dioxide content within the NGG gas specification. The amine is regenerated and the rejected sulphur and carbon dioxide is incinerated or, in the case of Point of Ayr, elemental sulphur is produced for sale. For the case where there is only a small amount of sulphur to be removed (usually in the form of hydrogen sulphide (H_2S) zinc oxide is commonly used to remove the hydrogen sulphide (H_2S) from the gas.

In some cases nitrogen is added to the gas or removed to meet the Wobbe Index specification. (See Appendix 3.) Nitrogen removal as used at the North Morecambe terminal is achieved using cryogenic distillation.

Secondary support systems

Gas terminals have a number of secondary systems in support of the gas processing requirements. These are typically as follows:

Heating medium

Process equipment requirements may require heating of a number of streams. Heat is usually provided via a closed-loop heating medium system. The heating media is usually a synthetic oil or a mixture of glycol and water. The heat is provided via a fired heater or via heat recovered from the exhaust gases of the power generation plant.

Methanol and glycol

Problems offshore may result in higher than normal water levels in the gas reaching the terminal. Under certain temperature and pressure conditions that are usually encountered in the terminal or in the pipeline, natural gas can combine with water to form solid hydrates.

Fuel gas

Fuel gas is required for power generation and/or fired process heater. Fuel gas is also used for blanket and purge purposes.

The fuel gas is conditioned at the correct temperature and pressure to meet the requirements of the users. Sources of fuel gas may be as a result of condensate stabilisation or a side stream taken from the sales gas prior to final metering and export. Backup raw feed gas supplies may also be present.

Cooling medium

The cooling water system provides treated water to meet all the cooling requirements of the site with the exception of refrigeration plant, which will rely on external refrigerants. The system is a closed-loop glycol/water with pumps supplying cooled water to the 'users'. It is then returned via the return header to the cooling towers. Cooling duties may also be provided by fan-driven air coolers.

Refrigeration systems

Refrigeration systems are used, as the processing requirements may result in sub-zero temperatures. The refrigeration system comprises a closed-loop system (similar to that used in a domestic refrigerator) where the refrigerant is vaporised at low pressure by heat exchange with the process fluid in a gas chiller. The vapour refrigerant is then compressed, condensed and returned to the gas chiller. Typical refrigerants commonly used are propane and HCFCs (Hydrochloroflurocarbons). HCFCs are being replaced with non-ozone-depleting HFCs (Hydroflurocarbons) refrigerants.

Relief, vent and flare system

The relief and vent system provides a safe means of collection and disposal for gas vented in the course of planned or emergency operations. In addition, this system collects and disposes of small quantities of gas used to purge the system and from gas-sampling equipment. The gas is collected in a series of pipe networks throughout the site and is disposed of either by a cold vent or a flare.

Waste water treatment

Waste water treatment is an important function of the terminal, to minimise environmental impact. Waste water may contain harmful chemicals and oil that would cause significant environmental damage if discharged directly to the local water course. Effluent waste is usually collected by three separate systems:

- closed drainage system to handle mainly process effluents;
- open drainage system to handle surface water (chiefly rain water) from non- process areas – this system may be further segregated into hazardous and non-hazardous open drains; and
- foul drainage system that is discharged to the sewer.

The effluent from the closed drains system is usually recovered into the process via the slops system or removed by a specialist waste disposal contractor. The open drains system is usually discharged under stringent quality checks via an oil interceptor to the local water course.

Metering

Metering of gas and liquid products is required to ensure that the correct quantities of products have been sold to the customers. The metering is performed to a high accuracy and is termed as fiscal or custody transfer metering. Guidelines for fiscal metering requirements including accuracy, acceptable configurations, maintenance and proving (meter checking) and equipment is set by the Department of Trade and Industry (DTI) in the UK. Metering requirements may also be set by the various commercial and contractual arrangements in place.

20.6 Utilities

The processes on the terminal site are supported by utility systems. These are essential systems without which the terminal would not be able to function. The following utilities are typical of a gas terminal and may be standalone to the terminal or shared with adjacent sites.

Power generation and distribution

Power at the terminal is usually provided by gas turbine power generators that use on-site fuel gas to generate and feed power to the distribution system. The distribution system typically comprises an 11 Kv supply, a 3.3 Kv supply and a 415 v supply to service the various electric demand sizes at site.

A standby generator may also be provided, as well as a backup supply from the local grid. In some cases the local grid may be the primary source of power.

Safety/operational critical power supplies are also backed by a battery-supplied Uninterrupted Power Supply System (UPS). Such a system will also provide power to allow maintenance of instrument monitoring and control systems.

Diesel

Diesel storage facilities are usually provided to support diesel-motor-driven fire pumps and site vehicles.

Instrument and plant air

Compressed air is used to operate the principal control valves, emergency shutdown valves (ESD) and blowdown (BDV) valves, as well as other plant systems. The air is first dried then compressed to feed a high-pressure reservoir system, from where it is distributed. It is critical to the continuity of the site operations that a supply of clean, dry, compressed air at a constant pressure is available at all times.

Nitrogen

Nitrogen is used for vessel and tank blanketing and intermittently for purging operations. It is also available as a back-up supply for the instrument air system should the compressors fail.

Nitrogen is either generated on-site or provided in storage which is periodically topped up by tanker.

Water

Water is required for:

- firewater where the water is fed to the firewater pond and to the firewater reservoir;
- service water for all site buildings domestic use, HVAC systems, safety showers, utility stations located through the site; and
- make-up water to cooling medium systems.

Firewater and fire-fighting systems

Firewater systems are provided to deliver firewater at sufficient pressure anywhere on the terminal to enable trained site personnel to initiate 'first aid' fire-fighting measures by the use of hydrants and hoses, fixed monitors or the fixed foam and deluge systems.

Waste handling

Waste handling and minimisation is a key parameter in meeting the Terminal's environmental goals

Waste is segregated into hazardous (oil and oil contaminated materials, chemicals, sludge) and non-hazardous (eg general, scrap metal, paper, wood) categories and stored in specified containers on-site for off-site disposal

Chemicals

The production of natural gas may require the injection of chemicals. A chemical storage and injection package is typically found on site. The chemicals may typically be corrosion inhibitor, scale inhibitor, surfactants for water treatment, etc.

Field laboratory

There may be a small on-site field laboratory on site to monitor gas and liquid quality.

Appendix 1: Main pipeline feeds to UK gas terminals

Site	Pipeline	Dimension	Commissioned
St Fergus	FLAGS	36-inch, 452 km	1982
	Fulmar	20-inch, 290 km	1986
	SAGE	30-inch, 325 km	1992
	Britannia	26-inch, 185 km	1998
	Atlantic Cromarty	16-inch, 80 km	2006
	Goldeneye	20-inch, 102 km	2003
	Vesterled	32-inch, 360 km	1977
	Frigg	32-inch, 360 km	1978
	Miller	30-inch, 240 km	1992
Bacton	SEAL	34-inch, 474 km	2000
	Sean	30-inch, 106 km	1986
	Leman Bank – Bacton	30-inch, 56 km	1968
	Leman Bank – Bacton	30-inch, 62 km	1969
	Leman Bank – Bacton	30-inch, 65 km	1970
	Leman Bank – Bacton	30-inch 58 km	1971
	Clipper	24-inch, 72.6 km	1990
	Tullow Hewitt Pipeline System	2 x 30-inch, 28 & 33 km	1969
	Thames	24-inch, 89 km	1986
	Lancelot – Bacton (LAPS)	20-inch, 62 km	1993
	Perenco ETS	24-inch, 165 km	
	Interconnector	40-inch, 157 km	1998
	BBL	36-inch, 230 km	2007

Site	Pipeline	Dimension	Commissioned
Easington	BP West Sole	16-inch, 68 km	1967
	BP West Sole	24-inch, 70 km	1982
	Rough	16-inch & 36-inch, 30 km	1975 & 1984
	Amethyst	30-inch, 48 km	1990
	Langeled	42/44-inch, 1200 km	2006
Dimlington	Cleeton	36-inch, 58 km	1988
Theddlethorpe	LOGGS	36-inch, 119 km	1988
	VTS	28-inch, 139 km	1971
	CMS	26-inch, 180 km	1993
	Pickerill	24-inch, 63 km	1992
Barrow-in-Furness	South Morecambe	36-inch, 38 km	1984
	North Morecambe	36-inch, 31 km	1994
	Rivers	24-inch, 43 km	2006
Point of Ayr	Douglas	20-inch, 32 km	1995
Seal Sands	CATS	36-inch, 416 km	1993

(Source: Department of Trade and Industry)

Appendix 2: Summary of UK indicative gas terminal capacities and processing facilities

Terminal	Approx Capacity MMscfd	Type of Water/HC Dewpointing	Other processing	Liquid Products
St Fergus Total	1440	Refrigeration		Condensate
St Fergus Shell	1200	Turbo Expander	Fulmar H_2S Removal	Condensate
Goldeneye	300			Condensate
St Fergus Miller		n/a	n/a	None
St Fergus Exxon Mobil	1710	Turbo Expander	CO_2/H_2S removal	Condensate
Bacton Tullow	800	Refrigeration	H_2S removal (Hewett)	Condensate
Bacton Perenco	1200	Refrigeration		Condensate
Bacton Shell	1700	Refrigeration		Condensate
Bacton SEAL	1100	n/a	n/a	n/a
BP Easington	275	n/a		Condensate via Dimlington
BP Dimlington	770	Refrigeration and Silica Gel		Condensate
Centrica Easington	215	Refrigeration		Condensate
Easington–BG Rough	1920	Refrigeration and Silica gel		Condensate
Point of Ayr	300			
Barrow South Morecambe	1800	Refrigeration	H_2S removal	Condensate
Barrow North Morecambe	560	Silica Gel	CO_2 removal, N_2 removal	Condensate
Barrow Rivers	120	n/a	H_2S Removal	n/a
Theddlethorpe	2330	Refrigeration		Condensate
Seal Sands BP	1200	TEG dehydration, Turbo Expander, JT Cooling	Mercury removal, H_2S removal	Propane Butane Condensate
Seal Sands px	900	TEG and Deep cut Propane Recovery		Propane Butane Condensate

Appendix 3: NGG gas transmission specification

1. Hydrogen sulphide not more than 3.3 ppm.
2. Total sulphur not more than 15 ppm.
3. Hydrogen not more than 0.1 mol %.
4. Oxygen not more than 10 ppm.
5. Hydrocarbon Dewpoint not more than –2°C at any pressure up to 75 bar g.
6. Water Dewpoint not more than -10°C at any pressure up to 75 bar g.
7. Wobbe Number (real gross dry) within 48.14 to 51.41 MJ/m^3 range, and in compliance with Incomplete Combustion Factor (ICF) not more than 0.48 Soot Index (SI) not more than 0.60.
8. Gross Calorific Value (real gross dry) – a value will be set within the band 36.9 to 42.3 MJ/m^3, in compliance with the Wobbe Number, ICF and SI limits described above, subject to a 1MJ/m^3 variation.
9. Not more than 7.0 mol % inerts of which carbon dioxide: not more than 2.0 mol % and nitrogen: not more than 5.0 mol %.
10. The gas shall not contain solid or liquid material which may interfere with the integrity or operation of pipes or any gas appliance (within the meaning of regulation 2(1) of the Gas Safety (Installation and Use) Regulations 1998) which a consumer could reasonably be expected to operate.
11. The gas shall be delivered between 1°C and 38°C.
12. The gas delivered shall have no odour which might contravene the statutory obligation not to transmit or distribute any gas at a pressure below 7 bar g which does not possess a distinctive and characteristic odour.
13. The delivery pressure shall be the pressure required to deliver natural gas at the Delivery Point into the Transco Entry Facility at any time taking into account the Transco System back pressure at the Delivery Point as the same shall vary from time to time. The entry pressure shall not exceed 75 bar g.

GAS TERMINALS AND SALES AGREEMENTS

LEGAL

20.7 Introduction

The first part of this chapter considered transportation generally. This part considers, in some detail, the arrangements for the offtake and disposal of gas.

20.8 The Joint Operating Agreement (JOA)

The JOA will normally provide that each co-venturer has the right (and in fact an obligation) to take its percentage share of oil and gas produced as a result of joint operations. There are major differences between the offtake and disposal of oil and the offtake and disposal of gas.

Whilst the JOA may have reasonably full provisions on oil liftings, it may simply state that in the event of production of NGLs or natural gas 'it may or will become desirable for [the parties] to enter into special arrangements for the disposal of the same' and provide that the representatives of the co-venturers will meet to consider arrangements to deal with any NGL or natural gas if and when it is discovered.

This simple statement might make it seem as if the export and disposal of gas is a reasonably simple process but the fact it is so open is because gas export and disposal is potentially very complex and varies from development to development. The JOA is not normally the place where one finds detailed gas lifting provisions – there are usually detailed and complex transportation, processing and co-mingling agreements involved.

20.9 The Unitisation and Unit Operating Agreement (UOA)

The position is somewhat more complex in the case of unitised areas. In a 'unit' oil and/or gas is found in a structure which underlies more than one block and the blocks are not in the ownership of the same parties. Rather than have both groups drill the same structure from their respective blocks (racing to get as much out as they can and running up double the costs) it can be sensible for both groups to join together to exploit the structure. There are famous examples of the inefficiencies involved in drilling the same structure – many people will have seen pictures of onshore areas in the US in days gone by where large numbers of derricks are in close proximity drilling the same structure in an effort to get as big a share out of the structure as possible.

The parties with an interest in the blocks may agree (perhaps with the encouragement of the DTI) to unitise their interests in the common structure and agree that they will each have a defined percentage interest in the whole of the unit. The key document in the case of unit areas is the 'Unitisation and Unit Operating Agreement' (the UOA or Unit Agreement). The usual way to establish the interest (commonly known as the 'unit interest') of a party to the unit agreement is to establish the interests of each of the blocks (their 'tracts') by working out the percentage of oil or gas thought to be attributable to their tract and then working out the unit interest of each party by multiplying the tract percentage by their interest in the relevant block. For example:

- gas is found in Block 123 and Block 456;
- it is determined that 30% of the gas relates to Block 123 and 70% to 456;
- company A and company B each have a 50% interest in Block 123 – giving them each a 15% unit interest (ie 50% of 30% each); and
- the unit interests of the companies holding Block 456 will similarly be calculated by reference to their holdings in Block 456.

A problem with working out the percentage interests at the stage of entering into the UOA is that the reserves estimates may change as more information becomes available and as the structure becomes better understood. It might be inequitable if the percentages of the parties to the UOA (the 'unit participants') were to be fixed and it were later to be discovered that these were based on inaccurate information. For this reason UOAs usually provide for 'redeterminations' at certain points throughout the life of the UOA in terms of which the unit interests of the unit participants can be adjusted.

This causes a problem from the perspective of lifting gas. A unit participant can be quite happily lifting its unit interest share of gas only to find that due to a redetermination its unit interest has reduced and, accordingly, it has overlifted gas. In such a scenario, it is likely that all of the parties in one tract will have overlifted and all the participants in the other will have underlifted. There may be a 'gas imbalance' in that one tract has lifted more than its entitlement. How can this be addressed?

There are various approaches to this issue. Some involve the overlifting group being required to cut back on liftings in order to address the imbalance. There may be provisions to the effect that when it is established that the remaining reserves have fallen to a certain level that the overlifting group will have no right to lift gas at all until the imbalance has been addressed. In some cases, there may be a recognition of the possibility that the imbalance will not be addressed by the end of field life and in such cases there may be a provision to the effect that at the end of field life an underlifter is to be compensated by the overlifters.

Obviously, when deciding whether to purchase an asset it is essential to establish in the case of a company acquiring an asset where there may be further redeterminations (where the percentage held by that company could change) and whether such a company is inheriting any underlift or overlift positions. This will directly affect the value which an acquiring company will be able to extract from the asset and could have a fundamental impact on the economic model for the investment.

20.10 Transportation – co-mingling and common stream

Transportation from the wellhead to the delivery point under a gas sales contract has been dealt with already. The issues which will be considered in this section are the questions of co-mingling and allocation.

Co-mingling and allocation

Nowadays, it is unusual for gas to be transported from the wellhead to the delivery point without being mixed (or 'co-mingled') with gas from other sources at some point along the way. Usually, reservoir sizes mean that it is uneconomic to construct an export pipeline solely for the gas produced from a particular field. It may be that a gas field can be developed by tying into a nearby system and paying a tariff to the owner of that system for transporting the gas. The owner becomes the 'Shipper' of gas and the pipeline owner is the 'Transporter'. There may be many fields transporting gas through the same pipeline system. Gas enters the pipeline at different points and becomes one co-mingled stream of gas made up of gas from various sources.

The problem then arises as to the quantity of gas which the Shipper should get at the delivery point. Obviously, he cannot get back the same gas as he put into the system – the gas has been co-mingled and he cannot extract the same gas as he put into the stream. It is not as simple as saying that company X put a certain volume of gas into the pipeline at the entry point and so should get the same volume out at the other end. Gas quality can vary. The gas from field A might be quite different in its composition from the gas from field B. The Transportation Agreements with the various Shippers will indicate the quality requirements for system entry – usually by setting minimum entry requirements. Even if all of the gas entering the system falls within the quality requirements there will still be differences – the gas from some fields may be at the top end of the specification whilst the gas from others might be at the lower end of the specification. The legal agreements have to be clear as to who has a right to what at the delivery point.

The amount of gas which the Shipper gets at the delivery point is determined by a complex process known as 'allocation'. The allocation procedure will be set out in the relevant Transportation And Processing Agreements. Different gas processing facilities may have different allocation procedures, eg Theddlethorpe Allocation and Co-mingling Agreement or 'TACA'. These commonly allocate gas on the basis of energy value. X put in gas containing a certain amount of energy and so should get out a quantity of co-mingled gas which would yield the same amount of energy.

Suballocation is also possible. It may be that field Y is a source for the purposes of the allocation arrangements in respect of a transportation and processing agreement. It may be that field Y has agreed with a nearby field group that it will allow gas from that field (field X) to be transported via field Y. For the purposes of the system transportation and processing agreements only Y is a source (X is not). The X and Y groups would need to agree provisions in terms of which the gas allocated to X in terms of the transportation and processing agreements will be allocated (or suballocated) between X any Y.

Substitution borrowing

It may be that the Transportation and Processing Agreements will contain provisions allowing Shippers to 'borrow' gas from other users of the transportation and processing system for the purpose of making the deliveries required to be made to a buyer of a Shipper. The borrower delivers the borrowed gas in 'substitution' for its own gas. These arrangements often set out limits to the amount of gas which can be borrowed both on a day and in aggregate (effectively borrowing limits). They usually provide that gas borrowed is to be repaid within a set time so that the borrowing and lending balances can be brought back into line as soon as possible. Often there are obligations on producers to lend available gas (up to their lending limit) to borrowers to allow the borrower to meet its contractual obligations.

Say, for example, that company X has contracted to sell 10 mmcfd to buyer B on a certain day. On the day, company X introduces gas to the system and is allocated 8 mmcfd at the delivery point. It may be that the system allows X to borrow 2 MMscfd from other users of the system on that day to allow it to meet its contractual commitment to the buyer B (and to avoid the need to make shortfall payments, etc.). 8 MMscfd is allocated to X but 10 MMscfd is attributed to X's gas buyer. X has borrowed 2 MMscfd and will have an obligation to repay that gas at a later stage.

It is important when acquiring an asset to establish what (if any) borrowing or lending positions exist in respect of the asset and what the arrangements will be for bringing the position into balance. Is the potential buyer walking into a situation where the seller of the asset has borrowed gas from other producers, received payment from its gas buyer for the gas and where the potential buyer will have an obligation to 'repay' the borrowed gas? This question should be asked as part of the due diligence process if buying an asset and it obviously impacts directly on the financial projections of the potential buyer.

20.11 Gas sales contracts

There are a number of ways in which gas can be sold. This section considers some of the methods of sale which are used.

Dedication/depletion contracts

In the not so distant past most UK gas was contracted to be sold to British Gas (BG) under long-term contracts. These contracts were *depletion contracts* in terms of which the owners of a gas field would contract to sell all of the gas from that field to BG. Gas from the field was *dedicated* in the sense that the owner of the field undertook that it would not sell gas from that field to anyone other than BG. The key benefit for the seller was that the seller knew that it would have a market for its gas and the purchaser knew that it had a source of supply. Knowledge that there was a market for the gas gave the seller the comfort to make the large investment required to bring the field on stream.

There are still many long-term depletion contracts in existence as some fields are still producing many years after the depletion contract was put in place. There can, however, be various drawbacks with such dedicated/depletion contracts.

For example:

(a) although the price payable for the gas under these contracts will have increased over the years in terms of price adjustment mechanisms contained in the contract, the price is still likely to be considerably less than the price which could now be achieved for gas on the open market ('the Spot Market').

(b) depletion contracts are usually buyer nomination contracts. This means that the buyer tells the seller how much gas it wants to buy at a particular time by giving a nomination to the seller.

The contracts usually give the buyer the right to make a 'zero nomination' – to state that for certain periods it does not wish to buy any gas under the contract. Under depletion contracts it is common for the buyer to buy the maximum daily quantity (MDQ) possible under the contract during the winter months as during those months it should be cooler than in the summer months, the price of gas on the open market will be higher because of increased demand due to the temperature and therefore buying the gas under the depletion contract is likely to be cheaper than buying it on the open market. Normally, the buyer will buy nothing (or as little as possible) under the depletion contract during the summer months as demand for gas on the spot markets should be much less and, therefore, the buyer can buy any gas it needs on the open market at a lower cost than under the depletion contract. The buyer normally looks for the maximum flexibility (or '*swing*') in respect of the volume of gas which it can buy on any day.

The seller then has to supply gas up to the limits set out in the contract. The seller cannot decide that it would like to sell more gas to increase its income as in a buyer nomination contract. The seller can only sell the volume of gas which the buyer wishes to purchase.

This is not ideal, for a variety of reasons. The most obvious one is that the seller cannot control the level of its revenues from gas sales by increasing the volume sold. There may be little or no revenue in the summer months – its revenues will be seasonal. Another implication is that having a depletion contract in place might reduce the likelihood of the owner of the field carrying out work on the infrastructure on the field to increase production rates. If a company is producing a sufficient quantity of gas per day to meet its contractual commitments then there is little incentive to spend money on additional infrastructure to increase its flow rates if it will not be able to sell the gas any more quickly as a result of carrying out the work.

As a result of this, many companies have, or are currently trying to, negotiate their way out of such depletion contracts.

Spot Markets

Another way to sell gas is on the open market or 'Spot Markets'. Spot Markets are basically markets for gas which is not already contracted to be sold ('uncontracted gas'). Various gas marketing companies and gas trading companies have entered the market place and this has led to the creation of a Spot Market. In the spot market the buyer is not interested in the source of the gas which it is buying. It wants a deal where the producer simply contracts to supply gas to the buyer for a period of time (whether it be a day, a weekend, a month or a year).

The price is linked to prices quoted in various indices. Examples of such indices are Spectron Screen, IPE and Energy Argus. These give prices for next day or for periods of days, for weekends, for quarters, for holiday periods, etc.

Price

The contract needs to say what the price will be. In a short-term spot contract the price will probably be ascertained by reference to one of the published price indices although it could be simply a fixed price agreed at the outset. In longer-term contracts (such as depletion contracts) there needs to be some mechanism for price variation over the life of the contract.

The interests of the buyer and seller diverge. The seller will want the price to increase so that it is getting paid something which reflects or at least which changes in line with the market value of the gas. Developing and operating a gas field is costly and the price paid for the gas needs to be enough to make it worthwhile for the seller. The buyer will also want to make sure that the price is such that it can make a profit from on-sale.

For longer contracts the price is usually recalculated throughout the life of the contract at regular intervals using a detailed price formula. The different elements of the equation are there to spread the risk between the buyer and the producer.

There are numerous indices and factors which could be used. To a certain extent this is one part of the contract which probably needs less legal input notwithstanding its significance. The seller and purchaser themselves will probably see this as one of the most important commercial points in the contract and will be willing to negotiate provisions at great length. Pricing provisions will usually include detailed provisions as to what is to happen if an index which is being used ceases to be published or is temporarily unavailable. It will also contain provisions as to what is to happen if there are errors in the published indices.

Quantity

The contract has to deal with how much gas is to be sold. Obviously under a depletion contract the total quantity of gas to be sold under the contract is all gas produced from the field. That is the total amount of gas which is to be sold under the contract but the contract needs to go further to say how much gas will be sold on each day throughout the contract life. This is usually dealt with by setting a DCQ and a '*delivery capacity*'. The Delivery Capacity is the maximum daily amount which the buyer can nominate for delivery and which the seller is obliged to deliver under the contract. It is usually expressed as a percentage of the DCQ – the daily contract quantity which is the average daily flow of gas during a year. The Delivery Capacity might be, for example, 130% of the DCQ. As indicated previously the buyer normally retains the right to make a zero nomination on a day. This means that the seller can be faced with a nomination of between 0% and 130% of the DCQ. The buyer would be said to have a high degree of 'swing' – it could buy nothing on a day or it could buy up to 130% of the DCQ.

Normally, the contract will provide that the seller will use reasonable endeavours to deliver gas nominated by the buyer even where this is in excess of the Delivery Capacity. However, failure to deliver volumes in excess of the Delivery Capacity would not normally lead to any penalty for the seller.

In a supply type contract there is a stated quantity of gas which has to be delivered. There are often penalties/compensation provisions in the event that the seller fails to deliver the contracted/guaranteed quantities.

Shortfall

The buyer will be very keen to ensure that the seller delivers the quantity of gas which is contracted on a day. This is very important as the buyer is not usually the end user of the gas but will be selling the gas on. The buyer may well have entered into contracts to supply gas at a certain price on the assumption that the seller will meet its contractual commitments to supply the right quantity. The buyer may also have booked capacity for the gas in the network. The buyer might suffer a loss if the seller does not deliver the right quantity on the right day.

The quantity of gas which the seller fails to deliver is often termed 'Shortfall'. The contract will ordinarily contain provisions as to what is to happen if there is a shortfall. There are a number of variations.

- One common example is where the contract states that if the seller does not deliver enough in one period (day or month) then in the next period a quantity of gas equal to the amount of the shortfall in the preceding period will be sold to the buyer at a discount to the contract price – for example at 80% of the contract price.
- Another example which is becoming more common is where, if there is a quantity of Shortfall gas, the seller will make a payment to the buyer in respect of that quantity of gas. Normally this is expressed as an amount per unit of Shortfall gas. It might also be expressed as the difference between the cost to the buyer in buying a quantity of gas equal to the shortfall quantity on the Spot Market *less* the amount it would have paid for that quantity of gas had it been delivered under the contract.

Excess Gas

It is possible that the seller might deliver too much gas in a period. This can be problematic for the buyer. The buyer will not want a situation where notwithstanding what has been agreed in terms of quantities the seller can just decide that it will deliver extra gas. Without some protection there would be nothing to stop a seller turning up production when prices are high and getting paid by the buyer. If the seller delivers too much gas the buyer might not have a use for it and it is possible that it will not have secured enough capacity in the network to handle it.

The contract will therefore deal with what is to happen when the seller delivers too much gas ('Excess Gas'). It is difficult to deliver exactly the right amount of gas. There will always be operational and technical reasons why it will be impossible to deliver exactly the right amount of gas. There are numerous ways to deal with this. One of the most common is to provide that the buyer will accept a quantity of Excess Gas (say a percent or two above the nominated amount) but that the Excess Gas will be paid for at a price which is set at a discount to the contract price. One sometimes sees examples where if the seller delivers gas above a certain quantity then that Excess Gas will be the buyer's free of charge.

Take or pay

In a buyer nomination contract the seller is, to a certain extent, in the hands of the buyer. This is especially the case where the contract contains the right for the buyer to make a zero nomination, ie to say that it does not want to buy any gas for a period. This is particularly problematic in the case of long-term depletion contracts.

To give the seller a degree of protection contracts often contain 'take or pay' provisions which state that the buyer is to pay for a minimum quantity of gas in each period whether or not it actually physically takes that gas. It has to take the gas or pay for it. Such a provision means that the seller is guaranteed a least some income under the contract. The take or pay level is normally set as a percentage of the ACQ or 'Annual Contract Quantity'. The ACQ is basically the sum of all the DCQs in a year. A take or pay provision might say that if the buyer buys less than 75% of the ACQ in a year then it has to make a payment to the seller representing the difference between 75% of the ACQ and the amount which it actually took multiplied by the contract price.

For example, assume that the ACQ for a year is 500 units. The take or pay level is 75% of the ACQ (ie 375). The contract price is £1 per unit. In the year the buyer takes 250 units. The buyer would have to make a payment to the seller equal to:

$$(375 - 250) \times £1 = £125$$

The payment under the take or pay provisions would therefore be £125.

In contracts adjustments are normally made to the ACQ figure to take account of quantities of gas which the buyer could not take as a result of force majeure, to take account of under-deliveries by the seller and to take account of any accumulated carry forward.

Make up gas and carry forward gas

Buyers think that it is harsh to have to make payment for gas which they have not taken under 'take or pay' provisions in a contract. As a result, most medium to long-term gas sales contracts contain 'make up' and 'carry forward' provisions. These are tools which allow the take or pay obligation to be averaged out over the contract.

Make up

When a buyer makes a take or pay payment to the seller the contract creates a notional bank which is credited with the volume of gas in respect of which the buyer made a 'take or pay' payment ('make up'). If in the next year the buyer buys more than the take or pay volume for that year he can then get a quantity of gas free of charge up to the volume of make up which he paid for in the preceding year.

Basically, 'I paid you for gas last year which I did not take. I have bought my contractual commitment this year so I want you to give me gas free to "make up" for last year's payment'.

Carry forward

This is quite like make up. This deals with a situation where the buyer buys more than the 'take or pay' level in a year. The amount by which the volume of gas taken exceeds the take or pay level is treated as 'carry forward gas'. This is added to the volume of accrued 'carry forward' from previous years. If, in the next year, the buyer takes less than the 'take or pay' volume then no 'take or pay' payment will be due until the carry forward balance has been removed.

For example:

Contract with ACQ set at 100 units. 'Take or pay' level is 80% of ACQ.

Year 1: Buyer buys 70 units. Take or pay was 80 so buyer makes a 'take or pay' payment in respect of 10 units. The buyer has 10 units of make up gas which he has paid for but has not taken.

Year 2: Buyer buys 90 units. Take or pay is 80. Buyer gets the last 10 units free as this is make up from Year 1.

Year 3: Buyer buys 200 units. Take or pay is 80. Buyer now has 120 units of Carry Forward.

Year 4: Buyer buys 50 units. Take or pay is 80. Buyer should pay 'take or pay' in respect of 30 units. Buyer does not have to do this as he has 120 units of carry forward. 30 are used in this year and the carry forward balance going forward to year 5 is 90 units.

Quality

The contract will state the minimum quality or specification of the gas to be sold under the contract. The buyer will not want to buy poor quality gas or 'sour' gas containing impurities. Some of the impurities in gas can be harmful and can corrode pipelines and other infrastructure. The buyer will not want to have harmful gas delivered to its facilities or into the network. The buyer's customers will have certain minimum criteria for gas which they are willing to purchase. For that reason, contracts contain a minimum specification for the gas under the contract. The buyer will not be obliged to buy the gas delivered by the seller unless it meets the quality criteria under the contract.

Nomination procedure

As indicated previously, contracts are either buyer or seller nomination (although hybrids are a possibility). Either way there needs to a clear procedure in the contract which states who notifies who under the contract of the quantities of gas which are to be delivered and the timeframes for giving the notifications.

It is common to find provision in contracts for some non-binding and some binding nominations. For example, it is common to see a provision in the contract to the effect that the seller will give the buyer a non-binding estimate of its anticipated production on a regular basis – say, annually – with details of what it expects to produce for each month during the next period of 18 months or so (but this can be as long as three to five years). It is common to find provisions to the effect that the buyer will give the seller a non-binding estimate of how much gas it anticipates it will buy over a period of time (maybe 18 months or so). These estimates are really just to give the buyer and seller some idea of the volumes which they may be dealing with so that they can plan accordingly.

At some point, however, there needs to be a binding nomination given by the buyer or the seller. It is common for the binding nomination to be given a month before the delivery date. The buyer or seller will nominate a quantity of gas for delivery in a month (Month M) by a certain day and time in the month preceding Month M (Month M-1). Such a nomination regime is often called 'Month Ahead'.

Sometimes the binding nomination is just made by a certain time on the day preceding the delivery date ('Day Ahead').

Force majeure

Sometimes, for reasons outside the control of the buyer or the seller, it is impossible for either or both of them to comply with their obligations under the contract. In the case of gas sales contracts the most likely scenario is that something has occurred which means that either the seller is unable to supply gas or the buyer is unable to accept delivery of gas. Gas sales contracts contained detailed (and usually greatly negotiated) provisions dealing with force majeure.

In gas sales contracts it is common to have general provisions stating that anything that is outwith the control of the affected party will be force majeure and then to make exceptions to that by stating that certain things will not constitute force majeure. For example, in depletion contracts the following are often excluded as force majeure:

- failure of the seller to procure satisfaction of its obligations under the contract by a third party unless the force majeure event was beyond the control of that third party and that third party acted as a reasonable and prudent operator;
- circumstances affecting the quality of gas which is co-mingled with gas from other sources, or the transportation of gas unless the event was beyond the reasonable control of the owners or operators of the other reservoir or transportation facilities.

In supply-type contracts the buyer often argues that since the seller is not contracting to deliver gas from a certain field or fields and is simply contracting to deliver a certain quantity of gas that there should be no force majeure relief given to the seller at all.

Duration

In a supply contract the contract will last for the supply period contained in the contract subject to the occurrence of usual termination events such as insolvency. In a depletion contract there is also a fixed contract period but there will usually also be provisions which allow the seller to terminate the contract in the event that continued production from the contracted field becomes uneconomic. As the gas in the field depletes there will reach a stage where the seller will not be able to make money selling the gas on the terms set out in the contract. Depletion contracts usually provide that if the seller thinks that it has reached a stage where it would be uneconomic to sell gas under the contract that the contract terms be revised or the contract is terminated. There is usually provision for referral of the matter for determination by an expert in the event of a dispute. There is normally a very long and detailed definition of the term 'uneconomic'.

Delivery point

The contract will state the point at which the seller is to deliver the gas to the buyer. The seller has to be careful here as it can only deliver gas to a point if it owns the infrastructure up to that point or has appropriate transportation arrangements in place in terms of which a third party will allow it to use their infrastructure to transport its product to the Delivery Point. This is an example of one of the areas where it is essential to ensure that the provisions of the sales agreements and the provisions of the transportation arrangements tie-up.

— 21 —

HEALTH AND SAFETY

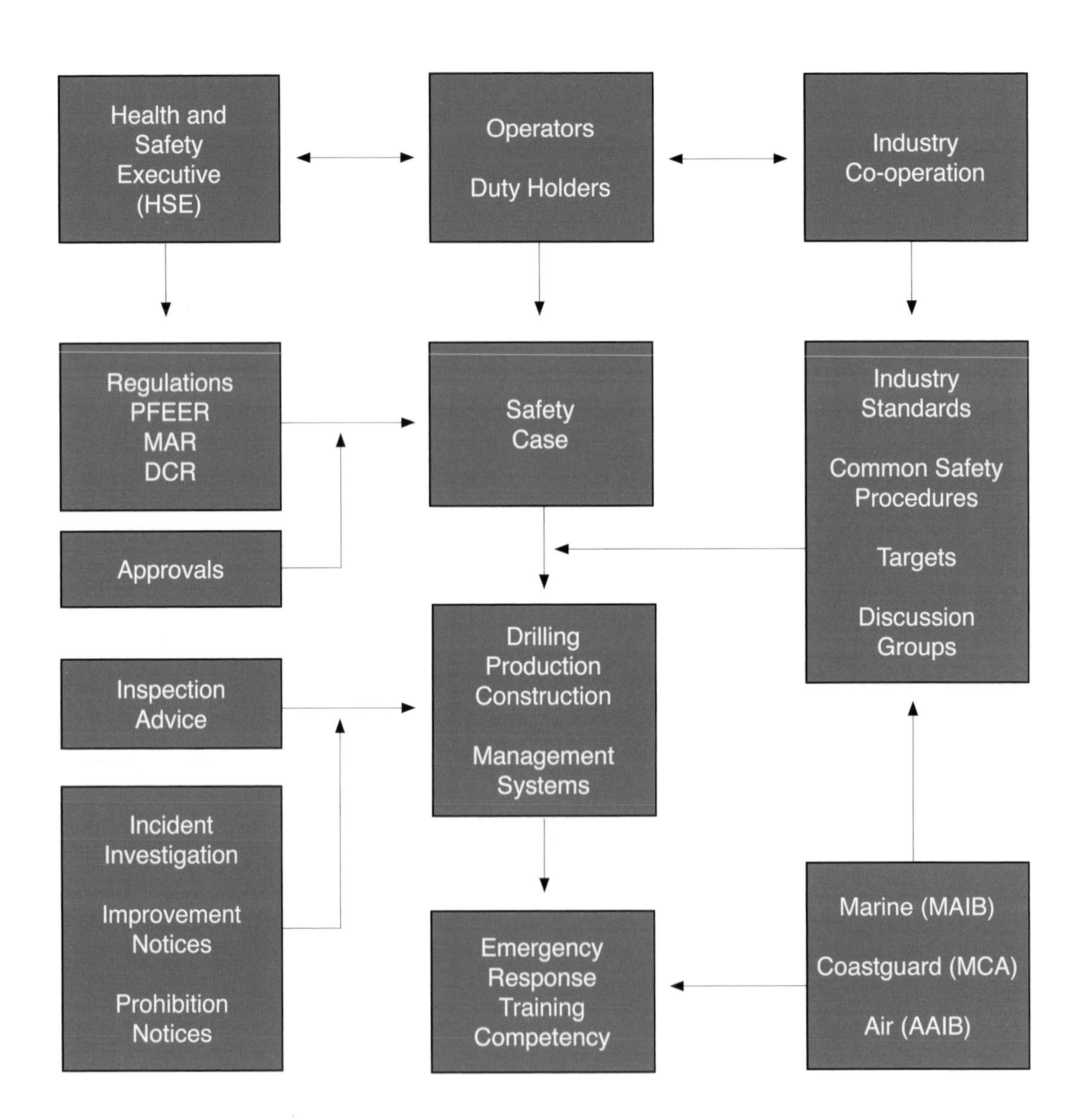
Health and Safety Executive (HSE)
Operators
Duty Holders
Industry Co-operation
Regulations
PFEER
MAR
DCR
Safety Case
Industry Standards
Common Safety Procedures
Targets
Discussion Groups
Approvals
Inspection Advice
Drilling
Production
Construction
Management Systems
Incident Investigation
Improvement Notices
Prohibition Notices
Emergency
Response
Training
Competency
Marine (MAIB)
Coastguard (MCA)
Air (AAIB)

HEALTH AND SAFETY

TECHNICAL

21.1 Introduction

In the early days of UK offshore drilling and production operations, the management of the safety of day-to-day operations on offshore installations were very different from the way that operations are conducted today.

During the early development drilling in the Southern North Sea gas fields, the most senior person on board the installation during concurrent drilling and production operations was the oil company drilling toolpusher. This person was also responsible for the safety of all activities on the installation including the day-to-day safety of the platform production teams. This naturally resulted in a division of priorities between the various departmental groups on board the installation and was further magnified by onshore departmental priorities. Both onshore and offshore, safety officers were employed, but in practice their roles carried minimal authority.

The first offshore legislation to focus on health and safety was the Mineral Workings (Offshore Installations) Act 1971. This Act, and a number of prescriptive Regulations made under it, was enforced by the Department of Energy. The Health and Safety at Work Act 1974 (HSWA) was not applied offshore until 1977; at that time those sections of HSWA and various Regulations made under it were administered by the Department of Energy under an agency agreement granted by the Health and Safety Executive (HSE). It should be remembered that in addition to this responsibility for health and safety regulation, the Department of Energy also had responsibility for field development licensing.

However, regulations relating to stand-by vessels were administered by the Department of Transport. Certifying Authorities (appointed by the Department of Energy) had a quasi-regulatory role to check, test and certify that installations themselves, fire-fighting equipment and life-saving appliances, were 'fit-for-purpose'.

There was, therefore, some scope for confusion as a number of different authorities administered different regulatory requirements. In addition to the scope for administrative confusion, many of the regulations in place relating to issues such as facility construction, fire-fighting equipment and emergency procedures were highly prescriptive and took a 'one-size-fits-all' approach to safety management. In reality, most installations had unique risk profiles requiring site-specific approaches to health and safety management.

It therefore followed that within the oil companies and government departments responsible for development of the offshore industry, tensions existed which were not conducive to the development of a clear safety culture.

As the larger Northern platforms emerged, the need for a Platform Manager to ensure better offshore safety co-ordination of concurrent operations became clear. The position of Offshore Installation Manager (OIM) was introduced on most offshore fixed installations, similar to the role of captain of a ship. In practice, the culture of the industry, together with a reluctance to change departmental authorities both onshore and offshore, gave the position significant responsibility but little authority.

The aftermath of Piper Alpha, the world's worst offshore oil industry disaster, resulted in a radical change in offshore safety management. In addition to applying a new common regulatory framework for all UK offshore installations, the business of the development and enforcement of safety regulation was allocated to the Health and Safety Executive (HSE). This therefore separated industry safety issues from any potential conflict with field developments, and also presented the real possibilities of prosecution for any infringement of safety regulations.

As a result of the pan-industry safety management systems that were put in place following the Piper Alpha Inquiry, and co-operative initiatives across all oil companies, contractors and service companies, the UK North Sea has now become a benchmark model in offshore safety for other similar oil and gas producing areas.

21.2 Piper Alpha disaster

Piper Alpha was a large North Sea oil platform located 180 km north east of Aberdeen. At about 10pm on 6 July 1988 an explosion occurred in the platform's gas compression module. This explosion put the main control room and main power supplies out of action and caused extensive damage to hydrocarbon processing equipment. It is believed that this explosion caused a large oil fire in the oil separation module, which gave rise to a massive plume of black smoke that engulfed much of the platform.

At about 10.20pm there was a second major explosion which caused a massive fireball. This is believed to have been due to rupture of the gas pipeline riser that connected the platform to an adjacent installation.

There were 229 men on the platform at the time. Sixty or so were on nightshift duty, with the remainder in the accommodation. Smoke and flames outside the accommodation made evacuation by helicopter or lifeboat impossible. Some personnel escaped to the sea by the use of ropes and hoses or by jumping off the platform; in the event, only 62 people survived.

The UK Government immediately instituted a two-part Public Inquiry to be led by Lord Cullen. The objective of the first part of the Inquiry was to determine the cause of the disaster. The second part of the Inquiry was to determine how such disasters could be avoided in future.

The first part of the Inquiry concluded that the initial explosion probably resulted from a leak in pipework connected to a condensate pump. A safety valve had been removed from this pipework for maintenance and, with the valve still removed, gas was inadvertently introduced into this section of pipework.

21.3 Lord Cullen Public Inquiry key recommendations

Lord Cullen commenced the Public Inquiry in November 1988 and his Report was published in November 1990. The Report contained three key findings:

- The administration of offshore safety should be transferred to a single agency separate from the industry-sector administrator. This function was transferred to the Health and Safety Executive (HSE).
- The existing array of detailed prescriptive regulations should be revoked and replaced by goal-setting regulations.
- The operator should be required by the regulator to submit a detailed, site-specific technical document justifying the case for safe design and operation of the installation – a so-called 'Safety Case'.

The Cullen Report made 106 detailed recommendations in support of these findings. Responsibilities for implementing them were spread across both the regulator and the industry. Fifty-seven recommendations were to be overseen by the HSE, and progressively implemented through regulatory reform. Offshore operators collectively were responsible for 48, and one was allocated to the Standby Ship Owners Association.

By 1993 all industry recommendations had been substantially implemented. The Offshore Installations (Safety Case) Regulations came into force in 1992. By November 1993 a safety case for every installation had been submitted to the HSE and by November 1995 all had had their safety case accepted by the HSE.

21.4 The Health and Safety Executive

The Health and Safety at Work Act 1974 brought together a fragmented collection of policy makers and inspectorates, and in doing so created two new bodies: the Health and Safety Commission (HSC), and the Health and Safety Executive (HSE). The aims of the Commission are to protect the health, safety and welfare of people at work, and to safeguard others, mainly members of the public, who may be exposed to risks from the way work is carried out. HSC's statutory functions include proposing new or updated laws and standards, conducting research, and providing information and advice. HSC is advised and assisted by HSE, which has statutory responsibilities to make adequate arrangements for the enforcement of health and safety law in relation to specified work activities.

Now the sole UK regulator in relation to offshore health and safety, the HSE also has a pivotal role in encouraging safe operations. HSE is organised into a number of Directorates. The Hazardous Installations Directorate (HID) is the operational arm responsible for major hazards. A dedicated Offshore Division within HID is responsible for the enforcement of regulations in the upstream oil and gas industry. The work of the Offshore Division includes:

- assessment of offshore safety cases;
- inspection of installations for compliance with the law and verifying conformity with the accepted safety case;
- investigation of incidents and complaints;
- formal enforcement where necessary; and
- providing technical information and statistical intelligence.

As well as the operational arm, HSE has staff who work together in HSE's strategy, policy and support divisions to advise HSC on its policy concerns, including major hazards at work through the formulation of policy and new regulations.

21.5 The Safety Case regime

The Offshore Installations (Safety Case) Regulations 2005 (SCR05) require that all installations operating, or to be operated, on the UKCS have a current safety case that has been accepted by HSE. SCR05 applies different requirements to installations used for producing oil and gas to those used for other purposes, such as drilling, or providing accommodation. The duty to submit a safety case (and the various notifications required by SCR05) is generally placed on a single duty-holder in respect of each type of installation, namely the operator of a production installation and the owner of a non-production installation.

For a new production installation to be established offshore an operator must send a notification to HSE at the early design stage. This design notification must be followed by submission of a safety case, for acceptance by HSE, before the installation can be operated. Notifications are also required for relocation of a production installation, combined operations and well operations. None of these notifications require HSE acceptance.

A Safety Case is intended to be a living document, kept up to date and revised as necessary throughout the operational life of the installation so that the case remains current. Any change that makes a material change to the case for safety must be resubmitted to HSE for acceptance. In addition, the duty-holder must carry out a thorough review of the whole safety case at least once every five years (or as directed by HSE). A revision to the safety case must be submitted to HSE and accepted before a fixed installation is dismantled.

A Safety Case is a document that gives confidence to both the duty-holder and HSE that the duty-holder has the ability and means to control major accident risks effectively. The safety case must demonstrate that the duty-holder has systematically identified all hazards with the potential to cause a major accident, evaluated the risks from these (likelihood and consequences), and taken measures to control those risks to ensure compliance with the relevant statutory provisions. Relevant statutory provisions mean those Regulations that apply to an installation or an activity on it or in connection with it (including, for example, PFEER, MAR and DCR detailed below). Major accident hazards are those that could give rise to multiple serious injury or loss of life. The evaluation of major accident risk requires the systematic use of appropriate techniques; these may be qualitative, semi-quantitative or quantitative. If a measure appears practicable, and the cost is not grossly disproportionate to the benefit gained, then the measure is reasonably practicable and should be implemented.

SCR05 is the cornerstone of the offshore health and safety regime. These Regulations require duty-holders to demonstrate their ability to comply with the objectives set by the supporting regulatory framework as it applies to the control of major accidents risks offshore. In particular, they must demonstrate their ability to comply with the relevant parts of the:

- Offshore Installations (Prevention of Fire and Explosion, and Emergency Response) Regulations 1995 (PFEER);
- Offshore Installations and Pipeline Works (Management and Administration) Regulations 1995 (MAR); and
- Offshore Installations and Wells (Design and Construction, etc.) Regulations 1996 (DCR).

PFEER requires measures to prevent fires and explosions on offshore installations, to protect people from the effects of any that do occur, and to secure effective emergency response. The organisation and arrangements to meet the PFEER requirements form part of the management system for the purposes of the safety case demonstration. It is PFEER that required provision of a temporary refuge on an installation (a description of which has to be provided in the safety case); this is a specially designated area, which is designed to ensure that personnel can muster in safety for a period of protection while an incident is being assessed and a decision taken on whether or not to abandon the installation.

DCR includes requirements for safeguarding the integrity of the installation throughout its lifecycle, from design and construction through operation and maintenance, to decommissioning and dismantling. DCR also implements various requirements relating to the workplace environment offshore.

MAR covers such matters as the appointment of installation managers, the use of Permit-to-Work (PTW) systems, communications arrangements, helideck operations, etc.

SCR05 also requires the establishment of independent and competent scrutiny of safety-critical elements throughout the life of the installation, to obtain assurance that these vital systems are 'fit-for-purpose' and are maintained in good repair and condition. The outputs from this 'verification' scheme provide evidence of a duty-holder's compliance with legal obligations such as those arising from PFEER and DCR.

The important difference between SCR05 and PFEER, DCR, etc. is that the former merely requires a written demonstration of compliance, whereas the latter require specific actions to be taken.

21.6 Safety Management System

Safety Management Systems (SMS), like other formal management systems (Quality Management Systems, etc.) are structured processes aimed at achieving a stated policy objective. As with other management systems, the policy aims (which should set a clear direction for the organisation to follow) are achieved by the following:

- setting up an appropriate organisational structures with defined roles, responsibilities and associated training frameworks, with the aim of delivering the policy objectives;
- planning for the establishment of systematic hazard identification, risk assessment and control and the implementation measures and procedures to deliver the policy;
- measuring performance against agreed standards to reveal when and where improvement is needed, both via active systems which monitor the achievement of defined plans and via reactive systems which monitor accidents and incidents; and
- auditing and carrying out performance reviews to ensure that the organisation learns from all relevant experience and applies the lessons.

Although many components of an SMS are very similar to other management system frameworks, some are relatively unique to the safety field; for example PTW systems are an essential component of an effective SMS. A PTW system is appropriate where the nature and scale of the risk arising from the work to be carried out demand a stringent system of control. Examples of work likely to require a permit include entry into confined spaces, hot work, or for controlling all work on live plant and equipment.

21.7 Industry initiatives post-Cullen

The 1992 Safety Case Regulations stood the test of time quite well. Their development, however, which took place before that of the supporting regulatory framework (PFEER, DCR, etc.), did lead to unnecessary legal complexity and several other difficulties. The Safety Case Regulations were completely revised in 2005, in consultation with the offshore industry. Further substantive changes at this time are unlikely.

The Cullen Report recommended that industry should specify the standards used to comply with goal-setting regulations. UKOOA has published guidelines in accordance with this recommendation; these were developed with other stakeholders, including HSE and other trade associations. The guidelines are designed to identify and assess key areas of risk and provide guidance on the measures and procedures most suitable for controlling those risks.

Developments have also taken place in other areas. For example, regulator and industry have worked together to improve 'safe behaviours'. Such initiatives are seen as underpinning the technical/management system approach of the safety case regime.

21.8 Engaging the workforce

Regulations were introduced as early as 1989 in order to provide a voice for the offshore workforce in relation to health and safety management on their installation. Members of the offshore workforce have the right to elect, by secret ballot, a safety representative to represent them in dealings with the installation management on health and safety and to establish safety committees on each platform. There are well over 1000 elected safety representatives working offshore in the North Sea.

The workforce is also involved in developing, reviewing or revising the current safety case for an installation. Regulations require the operator both to consult with the workforce when preparing, revising or reviewing the safety case and to make copies of the accepted safety case available to them.

21.9 Step change in safety

Following a fall in the frequency of injuries between 1989 and 1995, the offshore industry's safety performance appeared to deteriorate in the latter half of the decade. With this in mind, industry leaders and representatives from the three main trade associations (UKOOA, IADC (International Association of Drilling Contractors) and the OCA (Offshore Contractors Association)) decided that enhanced co-operation between the companies operating in the UKCS was necessary in order to achieve continuing health and safety improvements. As a result, the 'Step Change in Safety' initiative was launched in September 1997.

Since its launch, Step Change in Safety has become arguably the oil and gas sector's foremost industry-led health and safety forum, drawing together representatives from across the industry and from a range of backgrounds and levels of seniority. Its activities include:

- the harmonisation of certain safety-related processes (eg, induction processes, man riding hand signals, PTW, etc.);
- the introduction of safety leadership training;
- an online safety site which, amongst other things, hosts discussion forums on safety topics and downloadable publications;

- the creation of SADIE – the Safety Alert Database and Information Exchange, which allows companies to share information on safety incidents and near misses;
- establishment of a number of safety networks and forums (safety reps, OIM's, safety professionals, leadership team, etc.); and
- strengthening of ties and the sharing of good practice between UK operators and those organisations working in other North Sea jurisdictions (Norway, Holland, etc.).

21.10 Government and industry targets

In June 2000, the Health and Safety Commission (HSC) and the Department of the Environment, Transport and the Regions[1] issued a 10-year health and safety improvement strategy statement entitled 'Revitalising Health and Safety'. The document aimed to inject new impetus into the health and safety agenda. At the heart of the document were the following national targets for health and safety:

- to reduce the number of working days lost per 100,000 workers from work-related injury and ill-health by 30% by 2010;
- to reduce the incidence rate of fatal and major injury accidents by 10% by 2010; and
- to reduce the incidence rate of cases of work-related ill-health by 20% by 2010.

In response to this, the UK offshore industry set itself higher targets for improvement:

- a continuous year on year improvement in safety in the offshore industry is targeted to achieve a 50% reduction in the fatal and major injury rate by 2010;
- the rate of working days lost (number of working days lost per 100,000 workers) from work-related injury and ill-health, to reduce by 30% by 2010.

In the light of these targets, recent industry performance in relation to combined fatal and major industry rates is shown in Fig. 21–1.

The following conclusions can be drawn in relation to these fatal and major injury rates:

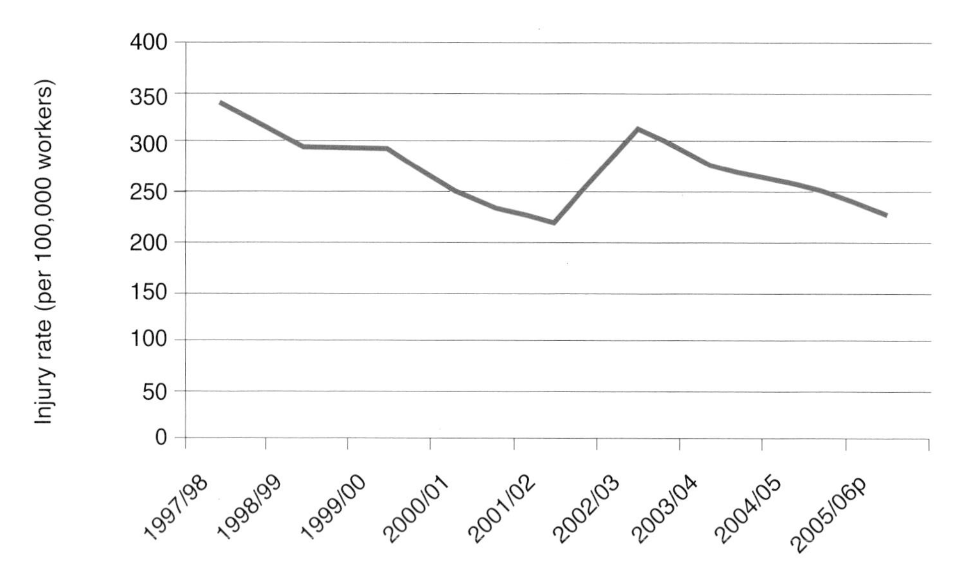

Figure 21–1 Combined fatal and major injury rate 1997/1998 – 2005/06 (provisional)

- there were an estimated 23,072 offshore workers in 2005/06, an increase of 21.8% on the 2004/05 estimate of 18,940 workers (these figures were obtained from an industry-based data source[2]);
- the combined fatal and major injury rate decreased to 225.4 per 100,000 workers in 2005/06 compared to 253.4 in 2004/2005; and
- the decreasing trend in the combined fatal and major injury rate has thus been maintained for a third consecutive year.

Even when taking into account less serious injuries (as demonstrated by 'Over-3-day injury rates') the data also show a broadly improving trend (Fig. 21–2).

The adoption of these strategic objectives has served to broaden UKCS health and safety initiatives to include occupational injury and health alongside the management of major accident hazards. In addition, HSE has developed best practice intervention programmes in the areas of reducing accidents in drilling and deck operations (Key Programme 2): This three-year programme of targeted inspections responded to an unacceptable level of fatal accidents associated with drilling and deck operations mainly during the handling of heavy loads.

As the average age of UKCS installations continues to increase, new strategies are being pursued in relation to the management of major accident hazards. Installation integrity is one of the three key themes of a new strategy for safety (the others are 'Understanding Hazards' and 'Personal Ownership for Safety').

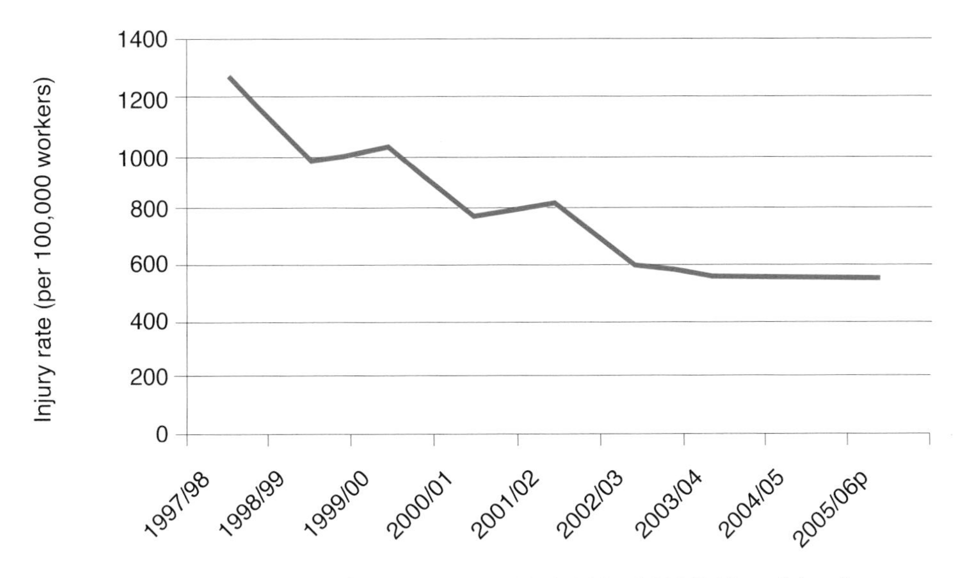

Figure 21–2 Over-3-day injury rate 1997/1998 – 2005/06 (provisional)

Oil & Gas UK is leading the cross-industry effort in this area, in conjunction with the Health and Safety Executive (HSE), which launched a four-year programme on maintenance management in 2004 (known as the KP3 Installation Integrity). This major HSE inspection programme has been aimed at ensuring duty-holders effectively manage the risk of any failure of structure, plant, equipment or systems (key barriers for the prevention of major accidents).

The next phase, as both KP2 and KP3 draw to a conclusion, is for HSE to test, through inspection, the effectiveness of duty-holder arrangements for monitoring, audit and review of those systems relevant to

- major accident initiation/escalation barriers; and
- drilling and deck operations.

Notes

[1] HSC/E is now part of the Department of Work and Pensions (DWP).
[2] Provisional data extracted from Vantage system via Step Change in Safety.

HEALTH AND SAFETY

LEGAL

21.11 Introduction

The first part of this chapter reviewed the history behind the health and safety regime in the UKCS and the practical steps required to build a safe corporate regime in an oil and gas company.

This part looks at the regulators, the regulations, investigations, enforcement powers and sanctions that apply in the oil and gas industry both onshore and offshore.

21.12 The regulators/investigators

There are three principal agencies that are broadly responsible for enforcement of health and safety legislation both offshore and onshore in the oil and gas industry. The Health and Safety Executive (HSE) is the primary agency in relation to both offshore and onshore oil and gas activities. The HSE carries out programmes of inspection, assessment, investigation and, ultimately, enforcement primarily under the Health and Safety at Work Act 1974 (HSWA) but also under the various sector specific and general regulations that apply to the upstream industry.

The Maritime and Coastguard Agency (MCA) and the Marine Accident Investigation Branch (MAIB) also bear some responsibility in respect of offshore health and safety. The MCA is responsible for health and safety on UK ships and there is jurisdiction of maritime health and safety law wherever these ships operate. This can overlap with the HSE's duties in force on health and safety law relative to offshore installations and activities where these activities take place on a ship. It should be noted that the terms 'ship' and 'installation' are not mutually exclusive.

The MCA is responsible for enforcing all merchant-shipping regulations. This includes search and rescue operations and checking ship safety and the safety of their crews by carrying out inspections where necessary on UK ships and foreign vessels in UK water. They also investigate incidents involving ships where there is an accident on board to determine whether there has been a breach of regulations which requires them to recommend enforcement action under those regulations.

The Civil Aviation Authority regulates aviation legislation (CAA). Helicopter operators must satisfy CAA that they continue to meet the requirements for safe public transport operations. They demonstrate this by holding an Air Operators Certificate which requires operators to publish detailed operational procedures in the company's operations manual. They are also responsible for the safety briefing of passengers and, in conjunction with offshore duty-holders, for providing certain personal safety equipment aboard the aircraft.

Helicopter operators have a duty under the Air Navigation Order to permit flights only to suitable landing areas. The Helideck Certification Agency (HCA) acts on behalf of operators for the inspection of helidecks operating in the UKCS and together with them, ensures the application of operational limitations and/or restrictions where appropriate. CAA has no duty to licence offshore helidecks. However, to assist helicopter operators and HCA to discharge their duties, CAA provides 'good practice' guidance (known as CAP 437). This includes criteria that helidecks should meet, and other information enabling operators to comply with their legal obligations. HSE accepts that conformity with CAP 437 demonstrates compliance with their applicable offshore regulations.

21.13 Investigation of accidents

The MAIB investigates accidents involving all UK vessels and other vessels where they have an accident within UK territorial seas. In contrast to the HSE and MCA, the MAIB are not involved in enforcement. They investigate the circumstances of marine accidents in order to determine a cause and, where suitable, to recommend action which might prevent a repetition. The role of the Air Accident Investigation Branch (AAIB) in respect of the investigation of air accidents is similar to that of MAIB.

The MAIB and the MCA investigate accidents that are specifically related to ships and their crew. The HSE generally investigate work-related incidents, including those that take place on, or in connection with, an offshore installation. A memorandum of understanding exists between these agencies dealing with co-operation and co-ordination in respect of their duties. This ensures that where there is an overlap there is an agreement as to who should have primary responsibility for investigating the circumstances of the incident.

The health and safety regime was significantly influenced by the 1990 Cullen Report into the Piper Alpha disaster which claimed the lives of 167 men. Since the implementation of the Piper Alpha Inquiry recommendations, the responsibility for administration and enforcement of HSWA and the other offshore legislation moved from the Department of Energy to the Health and Safety Executive.

HSWA is applied to specified activities outside Great Britain through an Order in Council – currently the Health and Safety at Work, etc. Act 1974 (Application outside Great Britain) Order 2001. The 2001 Order applies HSWA to specified activities within the territorial sea or a designated area including any offshore installation, to any activity on it and to any activity in connection with an offshore installation, and to activities in connection with a well, a pipeline or a diving activity.

HSWA set up two specific bodies: the Health and Safety Commission (HSC) and the Health and Safety Executive (HSE). The Commission is a body of 10 people, appointed by the Secretary of State for Work and Pensions after consultation with organisations representing employers, employees, local authorities and others, as appropriate. The HSC's primary function is to make arrangements to secure the health, safety and welfare of people at work, and it has a general duty to carry out such activities as are considered appropriate to advance the general purposes of the HSWA. This may include carrying out research, proposing new or updating legislation and setting up advisory committees (eg, Offshore Industry Advisory Committee) and generally to assist the Health and Safety Executive to provide advice and information to all levels of industry and commerce both general and specific.

21.14 Powers; inspectors; administrative and criminal sanctions

Powers; investigations

The HSC has a wide range of powers allowing liaison and agreement with Government Departments or public authorities to carry out functions exercisable by that Department or public authority which could reasonably or appropriately be performed by the HSC.

The HSE carries out the day-to-day work of the regulation of health and safety in the workplace. The HSE helps HSC to ensure that risk to people's health and safety from work activities is properly controlled. The HSE has a role in providing recommendations and advice to the Government and, as well as inspectors, has a number of expert advisors and experts to enable it to discharge its function adequately.

The ultimate purpose of the HSE is to ensure that duty-holders manage and control risks effectively, thus preventing harm. The main objective of inspection is to stimulate compliance with health and safety legislation and ensure that a good standard of protection is maintained. Inspectors have, and make use of, important statutory powers. They can enter any premises where work is being carried on, without giving notice. They can talk to employees and safety representatives, take photographs and samples, and impound dangerous equipment and substances. Inspectors can also investigate accidents, dangerous occurrences and complaints. If they are not satisfied with the level of health and safety standards being achieved, they have several means of obtaining improvements:

- advice or warnings;
- improvement notices;
- prohibition notice; or
- prosecution in the criminal courts.

Exceptionally, the HSC may use the powers conferred by HSWA, s 14 whereby it can order investigations and inquiries. This may be in relation to any accident, occurrence or other matter that the HSC finds fit to investigate with a view to making regulations. Under this power the HSC can direct the HSE or any other person to investigate and produce a special report on any particular matter. If the HSE considers that an inquiry is appropriate then it may be carried out with consent of the Secretary of State. The Health and Safety Inquiries (Procedures) Regulations govern the procedure for such inquiries and these must be held in public except in certain specified circumstances (such as that it would be against the interest of national security). The procedure at such inquiries is discretionary at the instance of the body or person appointed to hold the inquiry subject to certain compulsory requirements whereby provision requires to be made for notification of the inquiry, appearances, representation, attendance of witnesses, production of documents and site inspections. The appointed person is required at the end of the inquiry to produce a report to be delivered to the HSE to include findings of fact and any recommendations arising from the circumstances of the inquiry.

For the purposes of an inquiry the appointed person is entitled to enter onto and inspect any premises related to the inquiry and to inspect anything contained on those premises. There are duties of non-disclosure that apply in respect of 'trade secrets', although information may be passed to employees where that information will have some bearing on their health, safety and welfare at the workplace.

As regards witnesses, the appointed person may unilaterally, or at the request of any person entitled or permitted under the Act to appear, give notice on an individual requiring them to appear at the inquiry or to produce a document which is material to the subject of the inquiry. The person subject to such notice may apply to have the notice set aside or varied although to contravene the notice is a summary offence.

Administrative and criminal sanctions

HSWA, and the regulations made under it, are enforced by means of both administrative and criminal sanctions; HSE has a duty to enforce these provisions. HSE has three defined inspectorates being the Field Operations Directorate, the Hazardous Installations Directorate and the Nuclear Safety Directorate. The Hazardous Installations Directorate is responsible for offshore installations and chemical installations (among other matters). The Field Operations Directorate, the largest grouping of inspectors, is responsible for most onshore workplaces.

Inspectors are relevantly qualified individuals who are employed by the HSE to carry into effect the relevant statutory provisions, and to undertake inspections, investigations and enforcement. Inspectors are entitled to exercise the statutory powers conferred under HSWA, s 20 to enforce the relevant statutory provisions within their particular sphere of appointment. Note that OSD inspectors have additional powers under the Offshore Installations (Inspectors and Casualties) Regulations 1973. The limits of any particular inspector's powers are set out in the document appointing him. The inspectors have wide-ranging powers including entry and inspection of premises and equipment or materials in those premises. They are entitled, as part of their investigation to take measurements and photographs, take samples of articles or substances and to cause any article or substance which is a danger to health or safety to be sample tested, removed or rendered harmless where it is thought to be dangerous. The inspector is also entitled to require production of, and to take copies of, books, documents or entries therein for the purposes of his examination or investigation. Inspectors can also take statements.

There are various safeguards laid down in exercise of the inspector's powers. In particular, he is required to allow, where practicable, any responsible person present on the premises to remain present when carrying out his powers in terms of the Act. Otherwise, he is required to advise them in advance of what he intends to do. Where he is required to remove any article or substance he must not do so before leaving a notice with a responsible person or by leaving a notice in a conspicuous position.

The HSC Enforcement Policy Statement indicates that the purpose of enforcement is to:

- ensure that duty-holders take action to deal immediately with serious risks;
- promote and achieve sustained compliance with the law; and
- ensure that duty-holders who breach health and safety requirements, and directors and managers who fail in their responsibilities, may be held to account, which may include bringing alleged offenders before the courts.

Sanctions – improvement notices/prohibition notices

The sanctions most widely used by HSE inspectors are administrative. Where a person is contravening a relevant statutory provision or has previously contravened such a provision or where there is a likelihood that this will recur, then the inspector may serve an improvement notice requiring the person to remedy the contravention. The notice will specify the particular provision being contravened and the reasons why the inspector believes that to be the case. An inspector may serve a prohibition notice; a prohibition notice would be issued if there is, or is likely to be, a risk of serious personal injury, requiring an activity to be stopped immediately, or after a specified time, unless remedial action is taken. The notice is required to specify the statutory provisions being contravened and direct that these activities are no longer to be carried on by, or under the control of, the person. Again, as well as stating that he is of that opinion, the inspector must specify in which respects the person is in breach of the relevant statutory provisions.

Appeals

Appeals against improvement or prohibition notices may be made within 21 days from the date of service. The appeal is made to the Employment Tribunal by means of Notice of Appeal. The Tribunal may cancel or affirm the notice. The Tribunal may allow a late appeal where satisfied that it was not reasonably practicable for an appeal to be made within the 21 days. Where an appeal is brought in respect of an improvement notice then the notice is suspended until the appeal is dealt with. A prohibition notice will be suspended if the applicant applies for suspension pending the hearing of the appeal and this is granted by the Tribunal. Further application for review of a Tribunal decision lies within 14 days of the Tribunal's decision, made by application to the Secretary of the Tribunals on limited specific grounds.

Criminal offences

HSWA, in s 33, also outlines all of the matters which constitute a criminal offence making them subject to prosecution under summary procedure or indictment. The offences are for someone:

(A) to fail to discharge a duty to which they are subject by virtue of sections 2 to 7 [general duties owed by Employers and others under the Act];
(B) to contravene section 8 or 9 [to interfere with or misuse safety equipment or to levy an employee for safety provision];
(C) to contravene any health and safety regulations or agricultural health and safety regulations or any requirement or prohibition imposed under any such regulations (including any requirement or prohibition to which he is subject by virtue of the terms of or any condition or restriction attached to any licence, approval, exemption or other authority issued, given or granted under the regulations);
(D) to contravene any requirement imposed by or under regulations under section 14 or intentionally to obstruct any person in the exercise of his powers under that section;
(E) to contravene any requirement imposed by an inspector under section 20 or 25;
(F) to prevent or attempt to prevent any other person from appearing before an Inspector or from answering any question to which an inspector may by virtue of section 20(2) require an answer;
(G) to contravene any requirement or prohibition imposed by an improvement notice or a prohibition notice (including any such notice as modified on appeal);
(H) intentionally to obstruct an inspector in the exercise or performance of his powers or duties;
(I) to contravene any requirement imposed by a notice under section 27(1) [provision of information];
(J) to use or disclose any information in contravention of section 27(4) or 28;
(K) to make a statement which he knows to be false or recklessly to make a statement which is false where the statement is made
    (ii) in purported compliance with a requirement to furnish any information imposed by or under any of the relevant statutory provisions; or
    (ii) for the purpose of obtaining the issue of a document under any of the relevant statutory provisions to himself or another person;
(L) intentionally to make a false entry in any register, book, notice or other document required by or under any of the relevant statutory provisions

to be kept, served or given or, with intent to deceive, to make use of any such entry which he knows to be false;

(M) with intent to deceive, to forge or use a document issued or authorised to be issued under any of the relevant statutory provisions or required for any purpose thereunder or to make or have in his possession a document so closely resembling any such document as to be calculated to deceive;

(N) falsely to pretend to be an inspector;

(O) to fail to comply with an order made by a court under section 42 [order by Court to take remedial steps].

21.15 Operator's Safety Case

Again following recommendations of the Cullen Report into the Piper Alpha disaster the Offshore Installations (Safety Case) Regulations came into effect in 1992. Following extensive consultation with sector interests, these regulations were replaced in April 2006 by the Offshore Installations (Safety Case) Regulations 2005 (SCR05). The key requirement is for operators to prepare a Safety Case for their installation and to send it to the HSE. No offshore installation can be operated until such a case has been prepared, sent to and accepted by the HSE. The duty-holder who prepares a safety case must include sufficient particulars to *demonstrate* that:

(a) his management system is adequate to ensure –
   (i) that the relevant statutory provisions will, in respect of matters within his control, be complied with: and
   (ii) the satisfactory management of arrangements with contractors and subcontractors;

(b) he has established adequate arrangements for audit and for the making of reports thereof;

(c) all hazards with the potential to cause a major accident hazard have been identified; and

(d) all major accident risks have been evaluated and measures have been, or will be, taken to control those risks to ensure that the relevant statutory provisions will be complied with.

A Safety Case should be revised by the duty-holder as often as is appropriate and there are obligations on the duty-holder to ensure that the procedures and arrangements as laid out in the Safety Case are actually followed. There are new duties under SCR05 for a thorough review of the whole case at least once every five years – or when directed to do so by HSE.

However, to be effective the offshore safety regime requires the support of detailed sector specific regulations. Some of these supporting Regulations also serve to implement EU Directives – such as the Extractive Industries Directive. Of particular note are:

- Offshore Installations (Prevention of Fire and Explosion, and Emergency Response) Regulations 1995 (PFEER). PFEER requires measures to prevent fires and explosions on offshore installations, to protect people from the effects of any that do occur, and to secure effective emergency response.
- Offshore Installations and Pipeline Works (Management and Administration) Regulations 1995 (MAR). MAR covers such matters as the appointment of installation managers, the use of permit-to-work systems, communications arrangements, helideck operations, etc.
- Offshore Installations and Wells (Design and Construction, etc.) Regulations 1996 (DCR). DCR includes requirements for safeguarding the integrity of the installation throughout its lifecycle, from design and construction through operation and maintenance, to decommissioning and dismantling. DCR also implements various requirements relating to the workplace environment offshore.

However, other offshore-sector Regulations should not be overlooked including:

- Offshore Installations (Safety Representatives and Safety Committees) Regulations 1989;
- Offshore Installations and Pipeline Works (First Aid) Regulations 1989; and
- Pipelines Safety Regulations 1996.

21.16 General duties relating to health and safety at work

HSWA imposes certain general duties on various persons in relation to health, safety and welfare at work. The duties extend to the following:

(a) **Employers**

First, it imposes a duty on every risk creator (generally the employer) to ensure, so far as is reasonably practicable, the health, safety and welfare at work of all their employees (and to persons other than their employees who may be affected by the employer's undertaking). Sections 2 and 3 impose an absolute obligation subject only to the defence of reasonable practicability.

Where the employer is a corporate body, the defence can only be made out if all reasonable precautions were taken both by the company and by its employees and agents on its behalf. The duty also extends beyond employees to self-employed contractors and to persons other than employees who may be affected. The Act then goes on from that generality to provide examples of the duty.

1. The provision and maintenance of plant and systems of work that are safe and without risks to health.
2. The provision of such information, instruction, training and supervision as is necessary to ensure the health and safety at work of their employees.
3. As regards any place of work under the employer's control, the maintenance of it in a condition that is safe and without risks to health, and the provision and maintenance of means of access to and egress from it that are safe and without such risks.
4. The provision and maintenance of a working environment for their employees that is, safe, without risks to health, and adequate as regards facilities and arrangements for their welfare at work.

(b) Persons in control of premises

The 1974 Act also imposes a duty on any person who has control of any non-domestic premises such as a factory or offshore installation to take such measures as is reasonable for a person in their position to take to ensure, so far as is reasonably practicable, that the premises, all means of access to or egress therefrom and any plant or substance in the premises are safe and without risks to health.

(c) Equipment suppliers

A further duty is imposed on anyone who designs, manufactures, imports or supplies any article for use at work to ensure, so far as it is reasonably practicable, that the article is so designed and constructed that it will be safe and without risks to health at all times when it is being used at work.

(d) Employees

The duties under the Act also extend to employees themselves. It is the duty of every employee while at work (1) to take reasonable care for the health and safety of themselves and of other persons who may be affected by their acts or omissions at work and (2) as regards any duty or requirement imposed on their employer to co-operate with them as far as is necessary to enable the employer to comply with the duties or requirements of the Act. There are further requirements in HSWA, s 37 where an offence is proved to have been committed with the consent of, connivance of, or has been attributable to any neglect on the part of, any director, manager, secretary or other similar officer of a corporate body.

The Act also empowers the making of Regulations dealing with more specific rules governing health and safety issues in particular situations, industries or types of work. The development of these detailed Regulations has also been influenced by European law. The UK Government has implemented several European Directives dealing with health and safety issues by the means of Regulations made under the 1974 Act. The following regulations have arisen through the implementation of European Directives:

1. **The Management of Health and Safety at Work Regulations 1999**[1]

   These enshrine in statutory form the principles of risk assessment. Every employer must make a suitable and sufficient assessment of the risks to health and safety to which their employees are exposed whilst at work and the risks to which non-employees are exposed arising out of the employer's undertaking.

2. **The Provision and Use of Work Equipment Regulations 1998**[2]

   Work equipment refers to any machinery, appliances, apparatus, tools or installations for use at work. Such equipment must be maintained in an efficient state, in efficient working order and in good repair and where the use of such equipment is likely to involve a specific risk to health and safety employers must restrict its use to specific persons. Employers must provide all necessary health and safety information for the use of equipment. They must ensure that access to any dangerous part of machinery is prevented. All guards and protection devices must be suitable, properly maintained and not easily by-passed or disabled.

3. **The Lifting Operations and Lifting Equipment Regulations 1998**[3]

   It is the duty of every employer to ensure that lifting equipment is of adequate strength and stability for each load and positioned in such a way as to reduce to as low as reasonably practicable the risk of the equipment or load striking a person or drifting or falling. There are detailed rules for the regular inspection of such equipment.

4. **The Personal Protective Equipment at Work Regulations 1992**[4]

   The basic obligation placed on employers by these regulations is to ensure that suitable personal protective equipment is provided to their employees who may be exposed to a risk to their health or safety while at work. This would include items such as protective gloves, goggles, etc. The equipment supplied must be suitable and employers must take all reasonable steps to ensure that the equipment provided to employees is properly used by them. This includes the provision of adequate and appropriate information, instruction and training which enables employees to know the risks which the equipment will avoid or limit.

5. **The Manual Handling Operations Regulations 1992**[5]

   The main object of these regulations is to prevent employees having to undertake any lifting operation which involves a risk of back injury, although the regulations apply to the risk of any type of injury. The primary obligation on the employer is, so far as it is reasonably practicable, to avoid the need for employees to undertake any manual handling operations at work which involve the risk of their being injured.

6. **The Health and Safety (Display Screen Equipment) Regulations 1992**[6]

   These provide detailed rules in relation to the use of computer and visual display units by employees.

7. **The Control of Substances Hazardous to Health (Amendment) Regulations 1999**[7]

   The principal purpose of these regulations is to protect persons against risks to their health, whether immediate or delayed, arising from exposure to substances hazardous to health. Such risks must be assessed and regularly reviewed and appropriate measures taken to prevent any such risks.

21.17 Training and certification

One of the guiding principles of health and safety policy is that prevention is better than cure and that one of the most important factors in reducing risk is to ensure that employees at all levels are given proper training to understand the risks that affect them and what steps are necessary to avoid them. Health and safety training is therefore given a high priority in the oil and gas industry. As well as in-house training by employers there are a number of independent training organisations which provide relevant training courses for the industry. Standards are set and training providers accredited by the Offshore Petroleum Industry Training Organisation (OPITO), an organisation set up by the industry with board members drawn from the UK Offshore Operators Association, the Inter-Union Offshore Oil Committee, the Offshore Contractors Association, the International Association of Drilling Contractors, the Well Service Contractor Association, Offshore Industry

Liaison Committee, the Health and Safety Executive and Department for Education and Employment advisors. Accredited companies provide training and accreditation in many specialised disciplines and areas of work. Before being allowed to work offshore, operators require all personnel to have undertaken an offshore survival course. For UK waters this is known as the Basic Offshore Safety Induction and Emergency Training (BOSIET) course. It provides training in safety, fire prevention and fire fighting, first aid and hypothermia, helicopter safety and escape, and survival at sea. BOSIET certificates remain valid for four years. The certificate is valid for working only in the UKCS and further training and certificates may be required for working in other waters worldwide including the Norwegian sector of the North Sea.

Notes

[1] (SI 1999 No 3242).
[2] (SI 1998 No 2306).
[3] (SI 1998 No 2307).
[4] (SI 1992 No 2966).
[5] (SI 1992 No 2793).
[6] (SI 1992 No 2792).
[7] (SI 1992 No 2382).

— 22 —

WORKING IN THE OIL AND GAS INDUSTRY

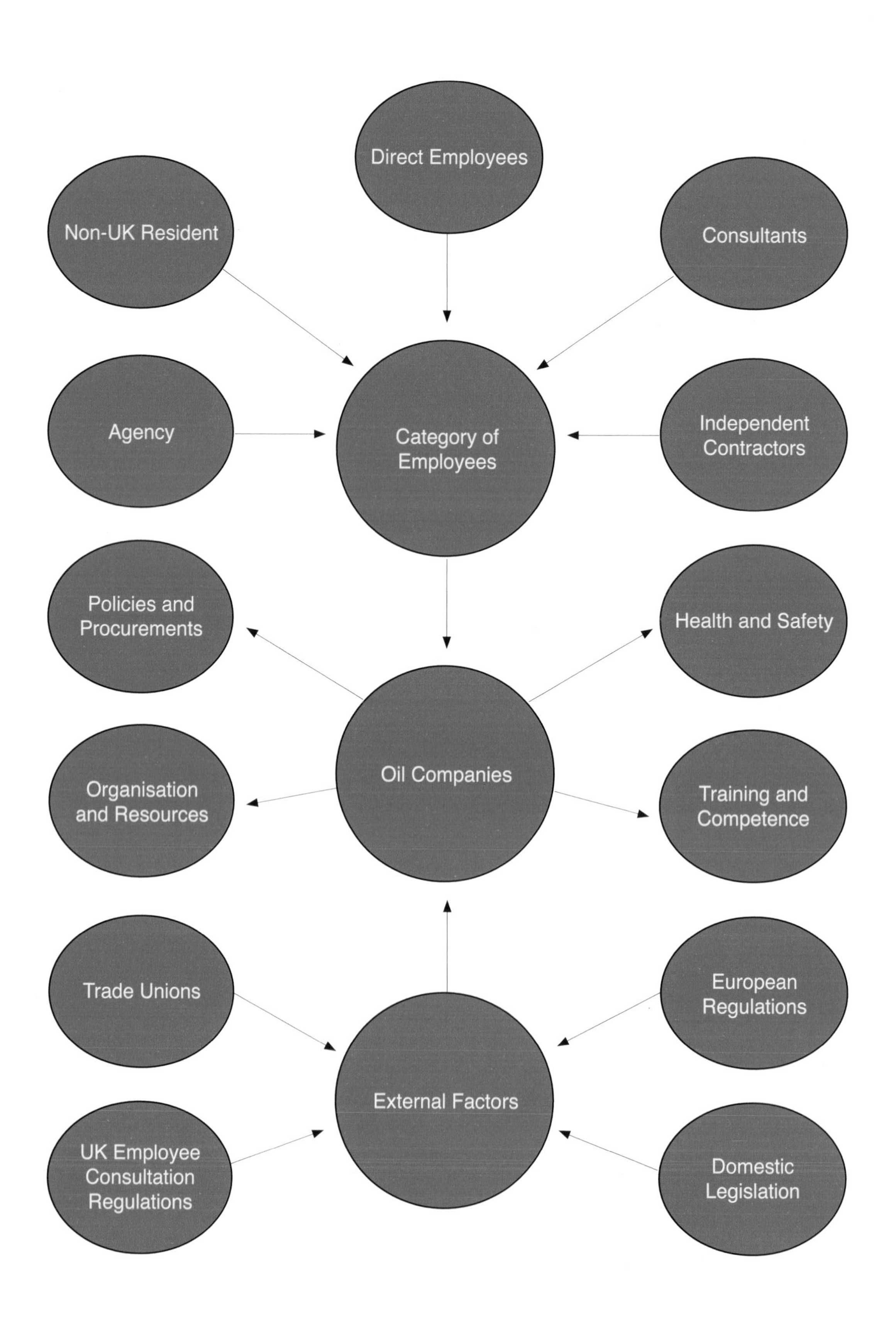
Direct Employees
Non-UK Resident
Consultants
Agency
Category of Employees
Independent Contractors
Policies and Procurements
Health and Safety
Oil Companies
Organisation and Resources
Training and Competence
Trade Unions
European Regulations
External Factors
UK Employee Consultation Regulations
Domestic Legislation

WORKING IN THE OIL AND GAS INDUSTRY

TECHNICAL

22.1 Introduction

The oil and gas industry operates within a framework of employment law which is essentially the same as any other industry in the UK. There are, however, certain characteristics of the industry that distinguish it from most others. This chapter will discuss the issues which make the oil and gas industry unique in its approach to people management and the resultant impact on workers in the industry.

The key distinguishing features of the industry are its complexity, the requirements for shared accountability and team-working, the hazardous nature of the industry, the culture and social institutions, the cyclical demand for labour, and the structure of the industry.

Complexity

The industry is extraordinarily complex, not just technically but also in terms of the organisation required, the number of field partners, the spread of companies involved in any single project, and the range of skills needed, even during 'steady-state' operations.

Shared accountability and team-working

Apart from ad hoc specialists, people who work offshore do so on a regular cycle (such as 14 days on followed by 14 days off), and have a 'back-to-back' who fills the same job during the other half of the cycle. Unlike most onshore industries, this means that even senior managers share their authority, responsibilities and accountability with a colleague. This increases the need for good communication, role clarity and effective team-working.

Hazardous industry

The industry is one of only a small number that needs to be able to manage major hazards which have the potential to cause serious harm to people and the environment. Risk management is central to the industry's business, and impacts on the required competencies, attitudes, and work control systems.

Culture and social institutions

Offshore facilities are often social institutions in their own right because people live where they work and need to socialise with their colleagues.

Cyclical demand for labour

The main drivers of industry activity are outside the industry's control, such as world oil prices, exchange rates, fiscal changes, and political instability elsewhere. These factors affect industry activity and, consequently, the demand for labour. Seasonal factors such as the summer maintenance shutdown season also influence the demand for labour. When demand for labour is high, the industry can experience skills shortages. This increases pressure on existing personnel and drives up costs as companies struggle to secure competent employees to maintain production. In contrast, when demand is low this can result in redundancies. Also, partly due to the cyclical nature of the industry, there is heavy reliance on contract staff, consultants and agency personnel.

Industry structure

Although the oil operating companies take the big investment decisions, they have always been relatively small employers. This is especially true of the small independents, who often outsource most labour-intensive activity. Most people in the industry are employed by the major contractors, their subcontractors, or vendors in the supply chain.

22.2 Employment issues

Resource planning

The combination of factors identified above means that 'people planning' is very important in the industry. In addition to the cyclical nature of the industry, the technical nature means that the industry can suffer from skills shortages. Attraction and retention of technical talent is therefore an important issue and will become more critical as the industry declines in size and profile. Given the specific technical requirements of many roles, a substantial amount of training is required before a worker can be given a managerial position. There is increasing competition for technical talent from other industries with a more 'glamorous' image. The oil and gas industry has had to work hard over the last 10 years to define those areas where collaborative industry effort can attract and retain the technical talent that the industry needs to succeed in a global market. This is evidenced by the fact that every year more than 5000 people move between employers, re-enter the industry, or enter the industry for the first time and a further 3000 professional and technical personnel are employed via agencies or one-man limited companies.

Under the guidance of PILOT's Workforce Capacity and Capability Group, the industry has invested significant resources in programmes at four levels:

- sponsoring targeted programmes aimed at encouraging interest in science and technology among children at key influencing stages in their full-time education;
- addressing 'image and reputation' issues among key groups such as young people, women graduates, and ethnic minorities, by offering consistent careers information;
- providing industry-wide apprenticeship schemes to train young technicians in core disciplines; and
- introducing 'accelerate' programmes to make it easier for capable people with existing skills to find their way into the industry and retrain if necessary.

Pay and benefits

The oil and gas industry has had a reputation for very high rates of pay. To an extent, this remains true, although the long period of low oil prices and cost-cutting eroded many of the differentials with other sectors.

This also has to be seen in the context of the offshore environment. Offshore workers will find that a large proportion of their total remuneration is made up of conditions payments for the social disturbance and inconvenience of working 12-hour shifts and living offshore in a hazardous environment for 14 days at a time. Typical figures in 2007 show that a skilled worker can expect to earn around £40,000 a year offshore in the northern sector – although rates can be much lower in the southern gas fields due to a less hostile working environment.

For onshore staff, rates are still attractive among engineering positions, but struggle to compete with, for example, the financial services or consultancy sectors. A 2005 survey of chemical engineers found the highest median pay rates (£48,000 p.a.) in the oil sector – about 20% more than similarly qualified personnel in chemicals, pharmaceuticals, or food and drink. New graduates joining oil and gas earned a median £25,800 – at least 12% above other comparable industries.

Oil and gas pay rates also need to be seen in the context of the flexible employment market and the cyclical nature of labour demand. Core-crew employment is reasonably stable (among both contractors and operators' own staff), but rates for ad hoc personnel can fluctuate dramatically in response to supply and demand.

This may also be reflected in the overall benefits package. Large employers will offer senior staff a comprehensive benefits package including pension, health and accident insurance, car allowance, and subsidised sports and social facilities – but for most people in the industry remuneration comprises basic pay, offshore and overtime allowances, and accident insurance.

Flexible employment

The UK oil and gas industry benefits from one of the most flexible labour markets in the developed world. There are several different features of this.

The offshore cycle makes it feasible for people to commute long distances to work. People routinely travel to work in the North Sea from every UK region, from Norway, and from all across the European Single Market. Improved transport connections to the main industry centres mean that specialists can fly in from much further afield.

The workforce itself is highly mobile. There is little history of 'job-for-life' attitudes, and there is widespread acceptance that (outside the supermajors) a normal career development pattern will involve several changes of employer.

But there is another side to flexible employment. Large numbers of technical and professional personnel are subcontracted as one-man limited companies or 'consultants' on short-term contracts. Most of the personal tax loopholes were closed years ago, and basic employment rights can still be construed in a 'contract-staff' relationship. This is considered in more detail in the next part of this chapter. Pay rates are often higher for contractors than for permanent staff, and the format remains attractive to individuals. In some ways it is an extension of the enterprise culture. It needs to be seen in the context of rapid changes in definitions of working life and career paths, and the emphasis on 'flexibility' and individually-negotiated employment contracts.

Overall, the flexible employment arrangements in the industry are extremely useful to companies who are growing fast and need to respond quickly in a turbulent business environment.

Organisation design

The way in which work is organised in the industry varies greatly with the phase of field development, the complexity of the project (and individual facilities), and the human resource strategy of the field operator. In all cases, however, the challenge is to create an organisation where priorities, authorities and accountabilities are clear. This is particularly so when there are concurrent operations on a single facility (such as production and drilling, or production and modifications). All organisation structures, however, need to balance competing demands – between production and safety, between production and maintenance (whether topsides or down-hole), between operations and marine activities on FPSOs and semi-submersibles, or between the needs of the operation and the needs of the workforce.

Add in to the mix the competition for scarce and costly resources such as offshore bed-space, helicopter seats, supply-boat availability, and crane operations, and it becomes even more essential to have effective decision-making processes across functions.

In the complex world of oil and gas, where no single person can be an expert in all the technical aspects of all activities, it is essential to develop organisational structures where overall priorities are clear, and decision-makers have access to competent specialists who have known technical authority. This applies at all levels – even where there is a developed concept of asset ownership and area accountability. During workover activity in a well, for example, technical authority may transfer almost imperceptibly among a production supervisor who 'owns' the well, a geoscientist who 'owns' the reservoir, a driller who 'owns' the wireline and work area, and a completions engineer who 'owns' the specialised tool at the end of the wireline. Not all of them will be based permanently at the worksite, and all of them may work for different employers. The individuals involved may also have to change over at different stages in the course of a lengthy operation.

22.3 Development and training

Performance management

Performance management is about clarifying and prioritising corporate goals, and aligning individual goals and achievement with them. The aims are usually that:

- people in the business pursue goals that contribute positively to corporate goals;
- people know what they need to do, and the standards to which they are expected to perform;
- measures of success are clear, balanced, and reflect both individual and corporate performance;
- long-term KPIs (key performance indicators) are not confused with short-term targets.

An ideal system energises managers and workforce to focus on improving areas that are of significance. It gives people the information and freedom they need to realise their potential within their own roles and aligns their contribution with the business success. Appraisal processes are usually a key part of performance management. The aim is to produce continuous improvement in individual performance, so that people exceed standards or progress towards higher-level jobs.

Over the last decade, leading oil and gas employers have radically improved their performance management systems, to clarify the balance between competing priorities, to recognise shared accountability, and to align individual performance with changing business goals. Most have some sort of 'balanced scorecard' approach, to ensure that the focus is not just on financial or production measures.

A recent study of innovative SMEs (small or medium-sized enterprises) found that of the highest performing companies almost all operated with a few simple, but key, business performance measures that were also striking in clarity. The KPIs included individual productivity measures that related directly to key business goals. What was also interesting was that their productivity and business performance were not strongly influenced by 'skills' or 'HR' issues in the conventional sense. The key links were about knowledge – in the sense of knowledge creation, capture, transfer and exploitation.

Across the industry as a whole there has been growing awareness of the need to measure and track intangible assets such as knowledge and organisational learning capability.

Training

In the 20 years since the Piper Alpha disaster, the UK oil and gas industry has become a world leader in competence-based training for emergency response, basic safety, safe systems of work, core technical skills, and behavioural safety.

Trainers accredited by OPITO (an industry-owned training body) now work in 18 countries around the world, and accreditations have grown by 500% in the last five years.

Competence-based approaches provide the key. Analysis of critical activities mean that key roles and competencies can be defined in very precise terms and training can then be targeted towards real needs.

Although still complex, decision-making on training initiatives has been streamlined dramatically by the development of the Industry Leadership Team, the closer relationship with government through PILOT, the new role for OPITO, and the rationalisation of Sector Skills Councils such as COGENT.

The industry Technician Training Scheme is a useful indicator of the success of this collective approach. Launched in 2001, the industry has invested over £44 million to date, and has trained over 600 young people to nationally-recognised standards.

Competence assurance

In the aftermath of the Piper Alpha disaster, the oil and gas industry pioneered the use of standards-based competence assessment, developing techniques that have been adopted in many other oil and gas provinces around the world, and in many onshore industries.

Under the 'Safety Case' regime, duty holders are required to identify key human factors risks, and set out how the risk has been reduced to 'as low as reasonably practicable'. Regulators look closely at competence assurance systems to check how they affect risk.

A competence assurance system is a framework by which an employer manages all the competencies needed in the business. Its core purpose is to ensure that controls are in place to satisfy stakeholders that personnel are competent to carry out their jobs and to prevent loss or injury. It includes:

- defining critical competencies within a risk-based framework;
- analysing job profiles and setting standards of competence;
- planning assessment methods;
- recruiting, selecting, and training people against the standards;
- assessing (and reassessing) people's competence;
- checking and recording assessment results; and
- auditing compliance and reviewing system performance.

Most successful systems focus on critical competencies – where incompetent actions could lead to major hazard effects such as multiple fatalities, extensive damage to assets, uncontrolled emissions to the environment, commercial loss, or loss of reputation.

22.4 Occupational issues

Working time and work cycles

There are variations, but many contractors who work offshore on a regular pattern:

- work 12-hour shifts (with 1½ hours of breaks) followed by 12-hour rest periods;
- spend their 12-hour rest period on the offshore installation;
- work offshore for 14 days per cycle, followed by 14 days' rest onshore.

Compared with an onshore norm of five-day weeks with four weeks' holiday plus bank holidays, that is roughly equivalent to a 41-hour week – above the statutory maximum in many western European and Scandinavian countries.

There is no evidence that 12-hour shifts or even-time cycles present a significant risk to health and safety. New technology has enabled employers to introduce new controls on offshore travel and working time, which prevented the few isolated instances of abuse – such as ad hoc specialists spending excessive days offshore, and workers doing a second shift for another employer on their 'rest' break. However, working time has become a contested issue in the industry – not as a health or safety matter but as a debate on employment rights and practicality. The legal reasons and implications of this are considered in the next part of this chapter but the episode illustrates the dangers of broad-brush employment law which does not address atypical situations.

Social relations and health

Offshore installations are industrial towns at sea. They vary in size, but typically house a core crew of 50–100 men and women. Living quarters are compact but comfortable. Food is good and plentiful, but there is strictly no alcohol. Off-shift workers can work-out in the gym, watch TV, play snooker, read or use a PC. Living with work colleagues, however, means that an offshore worker has to be able to socialise and co-operate in a group.

Offshore installations may be classed as total institutions – places of residence and work, cut off from wider society. As such they are quite different from conventional onshore plants or offices.

Regular visitors offshore often remark that each installation has its own distinctive character and culture. In some cases, these traits have changed little over the years, regardless of redesign and rebuilding, continuous organisational change, and transfers or turnover of personnel.

Occupational health

One aspect of 'living over the factory' is that on offshore installations, lifestyle and workplace can impact on health matters. Occupational health tends to have a lower profile than workplace safety, but is still taken very seriously indeed by the industry. The offshore working environment is one in which the health of the workforce could potentially be harmed by:

- noise and vibration (from compressors, engine rooms, ventilation systems, etc.);
- hazardous substances (dusts from drilling mud preparation, chemicals, etc.);

- musculo-skeletal problems from manual handling activities;
- food and water hygiene (contamination);
- radiation from isotopes;
- accommodation;
- stress.

All oil company operators have professional medical advisors. Collectively they have a Medical Advisory Committee and an Occupational Health Work Group and have published a number of medical guidelines describing good practice. There are strict and effective controls in place on drugs and alcohol misuse offshore.

The industry's record is good. For example, there is no history of ill-health caused by asbestos, lead, ionising radiation, vibrating white finger or cancers. There is a very low incidence rate for health problems resulting from exposure to noise or chemicals. There has been significant investment in training in manual handling techniques to reduce the already low incidence of musculoskeletal problems. There has been considerable effort in recent years to prevent complacency setting in, and to focus on health promotion, dietary considerations and lifestyle change for an ageing offshore population.

Impact on family life

The work pattern of offshore oil and gas workers imposes significant demands on the families concerned. The effects of 'intermittent husband syndrome' were recognised in the 1980s. Key areas of interest were the repeated partings and reunions involved in offshore work, the impact on children of intermittent parent absences, communications with the absent partner, the impact on domestic decision-making, and partners' employment.

Handover of authority, control and accountability is recognised as a key safety issue throughout the oil and gas industry – especially at crew-change time. It may be less apparent, but exactly the same issues apply in the domestic environment every two weeks, but with added emotional pressures. Research studies consistently reported peaks in family-related tensions (for both workers and their partners) in the days immediately around the partings and reunions. One early study noted that the problem was less acute the further couples lived from the heliport. Long-distance commuters had more time to unwind before being plunged back into the family environment, and spouses often had a better social support network if they had not relocated from their home area. Mood disturbance was also reported as common in the final few days of a leave period, with partners becoming 'grumpy', 'tense' or 'over-sensitive' just before returning offshore.

A repeatedly fractured home life and emotional issues were not the only concerns raised by onshore spouses. More practical problems were also of concern, including travel times, inconvenient crew change times, and communications while the worker was offshore. Job security and safety (particularly helicopter safety) were also recurring worries.

More recent research findings present a more favourable impression. It is unclear why the picture now appears to be more positive than 10 or 20 years ago, but possible contributory factors include:

- societal changes, with more widespread acceptance of one-parent relationships;
- partners' absences allowed spouses to develop greater independence, personal confidence, and coping ability;
- coping strategies within individual families have developed over time;
- improvements in offshore telecommunications, and access for personal calls.

Although psychological, emotional and practical problems persist, many offshore families have been remarkably successful in adapting. In a recent survey, one spouse described it as 'a brilliant lifestyle' – and most appeared to have adapted relatively favourably to the demands and challenges of having a partner working offshore.

22.5 Trade Unions

Over the last 40 years there have been very few examples of industrial action by trade unions in the UK oil and gas industry. Relations between employers and trade unions are for the most part positive and constructive.

Following the Employment Relations Act 1999, the large contractor employers and 'official' unions developed a new partnership approach, encouraging union membership in return for no-strike agreements. The partnership approach extended into other areas such as Step Change in Safety and training bodies such as Cogent SSC, OPITO and the Offshore Training Foundation.

Working time is still a major bone of contention. Arguments continue about the legal status of work-time restrictions offshore, and their real potential effects on flexibility, scarce skills, and health and safety.

Despite this, the underlying trend in mainstream UK oil and gas industrial relations has been a shift away from confrontation and towards effective social partnership.

WORKING IN THE OIL AND GAS INDUSTRY

LEGAL

22.6 Introduction

The North-East of Scotland is the epicentre of the United Kingdom Continental Shelf (UKCS), and a base for companies ranging from small independent bodies to major contractors to worldwide operators. As discussed in the technical part of this chapter a strong skills base has developed in the workers servicing this area. The United Kingdom Offshore Oil and Gas Industry Association (Oil & Gas UK) reports that the oil and gas industry provided total employment for approximately 380,000 people in the UK during 2006. Of this total, it is estimated that 290,000 will be directly employed by oil and gas companies or within the supply chain, and the remaining 90,000 jobs will be supported by their economic activity. This employment is spread across the UK with over 100,000 highly skilled oil and gas jobs located in Scotland. Therefore, it is vital for all businesses in the industry to ensure compliance with the frequent developments of the employment legislation. This chapter will provide an overview of some of the employment issues of particular concern in the oil and gas industry.

22.7 Categories of workers

Within any industry it will be found that the legal interpretation of who is an 'employee' is not as straightforward as may initially be thought and a variety of tests have been developed for determining whether a worker is, in fact, an employee. These tests have included: the control that the business has over the worker; whether a mutuality of obligation can be established; whether the work carried out for a business is integrated to the business or is accessory to it; the reality of the business relationship, such as who provides equipment or necessary tools; the duration of the relationship; and who is 'the boss'.

In the oil and gas industry, this can be even more complicated. The cyclical nature of the industry mirrors the requirement to 'hire and fire' workers. When the price of oil is high there is greater demand for skilled staff and, accordingly, salaries and benefit packages require to be structured in such a way as to attract and retain workers. However, when the price of oil is low, the requirement for workers is less, and employers may then have to reduce their workforce. The holder of the exploration and production licence and operator of the rig tends to outsource the requirement to man the rig to service providers. In turn, service providers frequently engage workers provided by employment agencies or use the services of independent contractors rather than employees.

Employees

The contract of employment

An employee is a person who works for the employer under a contact of employment. The contract of employment can be written, oral or implied. The Employment Rights Act 1996 (the ERA) requires that an employee is provided with a written statement detailing the particulars of the employment, no later than two months after the beginning of the employment. This document should detail the express terms and conditions that will regulate the relationship between employee and employer. In addition to the express terms it may be possible, depending on the facts and circumstances, to argue that certain terms are implied into the employment contract, such as terms that are too obvious to detail; terms necessary to make the contract workable; or terms that are the custom and practice of the industry. Some terms may also be incorporated by way of policies and procedures detailed in a staff handbook or collective agreement with a trade union (see below).

Executive directors of limited companies are also classed as employees of the company and have the same rights under the employment legislation as employees. Therefore, executive directors must also be provided with a written statement of the particulars of their employment, although this will usually take the format of a service agreement and is likely to contain more onerous requirements than those in the standard employment contract.

The standard terms that an employer must include in the written statement of particulars are set out at sections 1–6 of the ERA. Other employment legislation may set out minimum requirements in respect of these terms, such as the National Minimum Wage legislation which sets the hourly rates below which salary payments must not fall and the Working Time Regulations 1998 which sets out a worker's minimum entitlement to annual leave. It is also likely that the employer will choose to include in the employment contract other contractual terms, which are not required by the legislation, but are necessary to manage the employment relationship. These will include terms to protect the business, products and processes in respect of confidentiality, intellectual property rights and post-termination restrictions on key employees.

While there is an implied contractual term of confidentiality for the duration of the contract of employment, the extent to which this applies post-termination is not entirely clear and it is likely to cover only information which is a trade secret or is otherwise highly confidential and will not apply to the employee's own subjective knowledge.[1] Employers should therefore ensure that the written statement of particulars contains an express confidentiality term that clarifies what information will be classed as confidential and what obligations are on the employee both during and after the employment contract.

Post-termination restrictions, as the name suggests, cover situations where an employee leaves their employment and intends to work for a competitor or set up in direct competition with the former employer. In this situation, the employer's concern will be that the ex-employee will use trade secrets, client lists, pricings or other confidential information to which they have had access in the course of their employment. Whilst employers must accept that we live in a free market economy and competition is to be expected, employers are entitled to endeavour to protect their reasonable business interests and, therefore, it is common to ask key employees to agree to restrictive covenants in their employment contracts. These clauses can be enforceable, provided that they are confined within reasonable limits and are no more onerous than necessary in the circumstances. In practice, enforcing these clauses can be difficult from the employer's point of view. When asked to enforce a restrictive covenant, the courts will consider several factors including the duration of the covenant, the geographical area specified in the covenant, the clients or employees specified in the covenant, the business to which the covenant relates, the seniority of the employee bound by the covenant and what the parties had in mind at the time of drafting the restriction. Each case will turn on its own facts, and the wider the covenant (ie the longer the duration, the wider the geographical area, etc.), the more difficult it will be to show that the covenant is no wider than necessary to protect the employer's legitimate business interests. The courts have often been reluctant to enforce restrictive covenants that are for more than six-month periods, however a few recent cases have determined that there may be circumstances in which a longer period of restriction of 12 months is reasonable.[2]

Should an employer wish to change the terms of the written statement of particulars, the agreement of both parties is required. This should be achieved by consultation with individual employees or their representatives. The consultation should include an explanation and discussion of the business reasons for the proposed amendments. Where an employer fails to achieve agreement but subsequently implements new terms this may amount to a breach of the contract and provide grounds for the employee to claim breach of contract or to resign and claim that they were constructively dismissed, should they have the necessary length of service to do so.

Terminating the contract of employment

Termination of the employment contract is achieved either by mutual agreement, or by either party giving the required period of notice to terminate the agreement. If the employer fails to give the employee the required notice period, the employee may claim for breach of contract and/or wrongful dismissal. Where an employee has a continuity of employment with the employer of one year or more, the employer may fairly terminate the employment contract only by reason of the employee's capability, conduct, contravention of a statutory duty or retirement, by reason of redundancy or for some other substantial reason (discussed further below). To ensure that the termination of the employment relationship is fair in these circumstances, a procedure must be followed, or the employee will be entitled to claim that the dismissal was unfair.

The statutory procedure that requires to be followed when dismissing an employee was introduced in October 2004 by the Employment Act 2002 (Dispute Resolution) Regulations 2004 (SI 2004 No 752). Essentially, these Regulations set out the minimum procedure an employer requires to follow when dismissing an employee. First, the employer must write to the employee both setting out the conduct, characteristics or circumstances that have led to their contemplating taking this action and inviting the employee to attend a meeting, accompanied by either a fellow colleague or trade union representative, should the employee so wish, to discuss this. The second step requires that a meeting with the employee takes place. The employee must be given a reasonable opportunity to consider the step one letter before the meeting takes place. After the meeting, the employee should be informed of the decision and of the third stage which is a right of appeal. If the employee does appeal the decision a further meeting must be arranged which should ideally be heard by a different, more senior, person from the initial hearing. The dismissal can take place before the appeal meeting. The Regulations also detail a modified procedure but there has not yet been judicial guidance as to when this will be fair and it is believed that the circumstances where this is appropriate will be very limited.

The situations that are potentially fair reason for terminating the employment contract will now be considered.

Where termination is by reason of capability, this relates to the employee's performance, health or qualifications to perform the work of the kind for which he was employed to do. Where the employer wishes to dismiss an employee for incompetence they must have a genuine belief that the employee is incompetent and should have evidence to support that belief. The employee should be made aware of the problems with his performance, and a written warning should be issued (after disciplinary procedure has been followed). The employee should be given a reasonable time in which to improve their performance before a decision is made to dismiss them, during which time his performance should be monitored. Where the employee's mistake was particularly serious it may not be necessary to give time to improve[3] as some jobs require such a high standard of professional skill that a departure from this by the employee may justify a dismissal. Where the employee has shown some improvement in the period given, it may be appropriate to give him more time to improve and for the employer to continue to monitor performance. If the employee has not improved sufficiently in a reasonable period of time, however, the employer should consider if there are alternative positions in the business that the employee could be offered, failing which the employee's dismissal is likely to be justifiable and fair.

Dismissals in respect of lack of qualifications can be hard to justify as an Employment Tribunal is likely to take the view that an employer is aware of, and has accepted at the commencement of the employment relationship, the employee's qualifications. The two situations where a dismissal may be justified are (i) where the required qualifications change and the employee refuses or is unable to attain them, and (ii) where it is discovered that the employee has misled the employer about their qualifications.

Where dismissal is contemplated due to absence arising from illness or injury, the employer should discuss the reason for the absence with the employee. The employer should then consider whether the employee's attendance is likely to improve and may also need to obtain an independent medical report. The employer will then have to consider if it is necessary and reasonable to dismiss the employee, taking into account the length or frequency of absences, the impact on other employees of those absences and the impact on the business. The employer will also need to consider whether the employee's illness could be regarded as a disability under the Disability Discrimination Act 1995, placing them under a duty to consider any reasonable adjustments. Employers should also bear in mind the possibility of giving an employee the opportunity to improve.

Where a termination is by reason of conduct, the misconduct of the employee must either be extremely serious or have been repeated on more than one occasion. In the latter case, evidence that an employee has previously been given disciplinary warnings will help to justify dismissal, particularly if the warning(s) are for a similar offence. The conduct must have taken place during working hours or be likely to have an affect on the performance of the employee's contract or be likely to have an adverse affect on the business if that person continues to be employed by the business. If it is believed that an employee is guilty of misconduct the employer should carry out a fair investigation, during which the employee is given the opportunity to explain and/or defend himself. A dismissal will only be fair if it is a reasonable sanction for the misconduct and therefore the employer should consider other possible penalties and take into account the length of the employee's service and whether a dismissal is consistent with past disciplinary action against other employees for similar misconduct.

When dealing with issues relating to employees' conduct it may, occasionally, become necessary to involve the police. The police have jurisdiction to investigate any offences committed on, under or above, or within 500 metres of an offshore installation in the territorial sea adjacent to the UK or the UKCS in exactly the same way as they would investigate any offence committed in the UK. In respect of the North Sea oil and gas industry, Grampian Police exercise this jurisdiction over all installations in Scottish waters of the North Sea above 55° 50' North, and Scots law will govern any offences committed within that area. It has been agreed that operators will arrange transport for police officers, at no cost to the police, when it is necessary for them to visit an installation.

Redundancy is most commonly the reason given to the employee for the decision to end the employment relationship. However, it is one of the most difficult ways for an employer to justify dismissing an employee. In the first instance, the employer must ensure that there is a genuine redundancy situation, and this is frequently misinterpreted. 'Redundancy' is defined in section 139 of the ERA as being where either (1) the employer has ceased or is planning to cease carrying on business or part of a business in which the employee was employed or (2) that the requirements of the business for employees to carry out work of a particular kind have ceased or diminished. The second hurdle for the employer is to then ensure that the correct procedure is followed which encompasses a period of consultation, selection and consideration of alternative employment. This is discussed in more detail below. Where there is more than one employee in the 'pool' for redundancy the employer will require to prepare a selection criteria to ensure fair selection for redundancy is carried out. Potentially, this can include a consideration of the employees experience, disciplinary record and skill and knowledge. The employees must then be scored in accordance with the criteria and the lowest scoring employees selected for redundancy. The employer must then ensure that any suitable alternative employment or other alternative employment is offered to the employees. The employer should always ensure that ways of avoiding the redundancy are discussed with the employees during the period of consultation.

An employer may also dismiss an employee where continuing to employ the employee in their current position would place either the employee or the employer in breach of a statutory duty or restriction. Before the employer dismisses an employee for this reason he should first consider the possibility of alternative employment or making adjustments to the duties so that the employee can continue in employment.

Since the implementation of the Employment Equality (Age) Regulations 2006 (SI 2006 No 1031), dismissing an employee by reason of retirement also requires that a procedure is followed to ensure that this form of dismissal is fair. This is, essentially, a two-stage process whereby the retirement requires to be at a planned retirement date and the employee requires to be given between six months' and one year's notice that he has a right to request that the employer considers permitting him to work beyond the planned retirement date. Failure to follow the procedure will render the dismissal unfair.

Even if a dismissal is not for one of the five preceding reasons, it may nonetheless be considered fair if the employer can show it was for some other substantial reason of a kind such as to justify the dismissal of an employee holding the position which that employee held. An example of this is so-called 'personality dismissals' where there are personality clashes between the employee and other employees or where it can be shown that the employee's personality leads to difficulties in his behaviour, such as to justify dismissal.[4] Another example would be where a significant customer refuses to work with the employee and flexes their commercial muscle to have him dismissed.[5] If the employee is in prison and therefore unable to perform his duties this may also qualify as some other substantial reason.[6] It may also be fair to dismiss an employee where he has refused to sign new terms and conditions.[7] Essentially, each case will turn on its individual facts and it is important to remember that the employer will still have to show that he followed a fair procedure and acted reasonably in all the circumstances.

Where the employer does not comply with the above and a tribunal finds that a complaint of unfair dismissal is well founded, it may make an order for reinstatement or re-engagement of the employee or an order for compensation. Orders for reinstatement or re-engagement are rarely sought and more often a successful employee will seek compensation only. If compensation is awarded to the employee this will consist of a basic award (calculated in a similar way to a statutory redundancy payment) and may also include an additional compensatory award. As at 1 February 2007, the cap for a compensatory award in a successful claim for unfair dismissal is set at £60,600.

In recent years, the Government has placed much more emphasis on the need for amicable resolution of disputes in the workplace rather than at a Tribunal. This has been particularly evidenced by the statutory Discipline, Dismissal and Grievance Procedures which endeavour to put an obligation on the employer and employee to resolve their disputes without the need for Tribunal action. However, on 21 March 2007, the Government published the outcome of an independent review of the employment dispute resolution system, and also a consultation document in respect of resolution of workplace disputes, which includes repealing the current statutory dispute resolution procedures. It appears, therefore, that there will be further legislation in this regard.

Given the complicated procedures currently necessary to fairly terminate the employment relationship, it is not uncommon for enhanced termination payments to be offered to employees by the employer, provided that the employee agrees to sign a Compromise Agreement. This is an agreement which states that the employee is unable to raise any Court or Tribunal action against the employer in respect of their employment. To be enforceable, the agreement requires to comply with the terms of section 203 of the ERA and in particular the employee will require to obtain independent legal advice on its terms.

Consultants

One alternative to the employment relationship is a Consultancy Agreement. These agreements tend to be entered into where the individual wishes the benefit of working for a variety of employers as a consultant, where the individual wishes to enter into an 'ad hoc' relationship with the company or where the company wishes to retain the benefit of the skills and goodwill of an individual following the sale of a business.

In recent years, Employment Tribunals have looked more closely at whether an individual who, in title, is a consultant is, in fact, an employee and whether there is in place a contract of service or a contract for services. Therefore, in drafting the terms of a Consultancy Agreement it is important to omit, so far as practicable, the usual terms of the employment contract that would point to the control that can be exercised over an employee. It is also common for the individual to provide the services to the business through his own limited company or partnership. The company will pay a flat fee for the services provided and will not be required to make deductions for tax or National Insurance contributions.

The Consultancy Agreement is likely to include terms that detail the services required of the consultant including the standard of services that the consultant is required to carry out for the business; that the consultant will arrange for payment of his or her own taxes and that payment will be issued to the consultant on receipt of an invoice from the consultant detailing days worked in a particular month.

The principal disadvantage to a Consultancy Agreement is that the consultant is not bound by the usual intellectual property, confidentiality and restrictive covenants of the employment contract. With this in mind it is common that consultants are asked to sign a separate Trust and Confidence Agreement in respect of these matters as an additional protection to the business.

Independent contractors

A further type of worker is an independent contractor. Within the oil and gas industry, many workers elect to become contractors as opposed to employees. Generally, this is achieved by the individual setting up a limited company and entering into a formal agreement that he will provide a service to the business engaging him, with the focus being on the completion of the required job as opposed to the manner in which the job is to be carried out. The independent contractor is technically not entitled to rely on the benefits of employee status, such as holiday pay or sickness benefits, but on the other hand the contractor may benefit from a potentially more favourable tax position.

However, even in the situation that both parties agree the status of the worker is that of independent contractor, this is open to challenge as was seen in the case of *Young and Woods Ltd v West* [1980] IRLR 201, where Mr West elected to be classed as 'self-employed', which was agreed to by the appellant company, Young and Woods Ltd. During the time Mr West carried out work for the appellants, they did not make any deductions from payments made to Mr West for tax and National Insurance contributions and did not provide holiday pay or sickness benefits. The Inland Revenue (now known as H M Revenue & Customs) had also agreed to treat Mr West as self-employed. However, when Mr West's work was terminated by the appellants, Mr West claimed that he had been unfairly dismissed. The Court of Appeal confirmed the decision of the Tribunal and Employment Appeal Tribunal and found that Mr West had been an employee employed under a contract of service, regardless of his request that he be treated as self-employed. The Court of Appeal confirmed that the label the parties use to define the working relationship does not change what the relationship is and the courts can, and will, look beyond this label to determine that. Unsurprisingly, the Court of Appeal also stated that as Mr West was an employee, the Inland Revenue had a statutory duty to reclaim the tax deductions granted to him as a self-employed person.

Agency workers

A further type of worker is an agency worker. It is very common for offshore workers to be supplied by employment agencies. The terms of the supply of the worker between the agency and the end-user will be regulated by a contract between the two. There will also be an agreement between the employment agency and the worker. Employment agencies in England, Scotland and Wales must comply with the Employment Agencies Act 1973 and regulations which set out the minimum standards of conduct. The Employment Agency Standards Inspectorate is part of the Department of Trade and Industry. The Inspectorate carries out routine inspection of agencies and investigates complaints on agency conduct. The Department of Trade and Industry issued a consultation paper on 20 February 2007 on measures to protect vulnerable agency workers and it appears there will be new legislation to follow.

Theoretically the worker provided to the end-user by the employment agency is not an employee of either the employment agency or the end-user and, accordingly, the worker is not entitled to the majority of the benefits of the employment protection legislation. However, there has been a raft of case law in which the Tribunals have considered the circumstances in which the worker is in fact an employee of the agency or the end-user. The Court of Appeal first considered this question in *Dacas v Brook Street Bureau (UK) Ltd* [2004] EWCA Civ 217 and determined that while on the facts of this case the employment agency were under no obligation to provide Mrs Dacas with work and did not exercise any day-to-day control over the work that she carried out, there was a possibility that a contract of service between the worker and the end-user could be implied. In that case the worker had not pursued her claim against the end-user to the Court of Appeal and this was not considered in that case. However, the Court of Appeal in *Cable & Wireless Plc v Muscat* [2006] EWCA Civ 220 did consider that relationship and held that a contract for services existed between the worker and end-user and accordingly the worker was entitled to raise an unfair dismissal claim against the end-user. The Employment Appeals Tribunal has most recently considered this situation in the case of *James v London Borough of Greenwich* [2007] IRLR 168 and have readdressed the balance a little in holding that a contract will only be implied where it can be shown to be necessary to do so. The Employment Appeals Tribunal stated that where the arrangements are genuine and implemented accurately, it would be rare for there to be evidence entitling the Tribunal to imply a contract between the worker and the end-user. Further it confirmed that it is not appropriate to imply a contract where the end-user cannot insist on the agency supplying a particular worker.

Foreign workers

The global nature of the oil and gas industry means both that UK employees may be required to work overseas and that foreign employees may be required to work in the UK. It is not always clear what employment protections such workers are entitled to under UK employment law. It is therefore necessary to give particular consideration to the terms of their contract. Employees working in the UK will benefit from many UK employment rights, even where their employer is a foreign business. Employees working overseas may also still benefit from UK employment protection. In addition, employers should be aware that an employee working in another country may also benefit from employment rights in that country – even if the contract of employment states the employment is to be governed by Scots law.

In particular, the Posting of Workers Directive 96/71 applies to all EEA states and provides that certain minimum terms and conditions of national law, regulations or collective agreements should apply to workers posted temporarily by their employer to work in another EEA state. The terms and conditions covered by the Directive are detailed in Article 3 of the Directive and include maximum work periods, minimum rest periods, minimum paid holidays and minimum rates of pay. The Directive provides that workers may benefit from the rights covered by the Directive in the state to which they have been posted, without prejudice to their rights in a country where they are normally employed. With this in mind, employers should consider stating in the contract of employment which courts will have jurisdiction to hear any claims. For example, a Scottish employer sending an employee to work in Norway may want to stipulate that the Scottish courts will have exclusive jurisdiction.

Most UK employment legislation applies to all workers in the UK, whether they are employed in a temporary or permanent basis in the UK – for example, the Working Time Regulations 1998 (SI 1998 No 1833), the National Minimum Wage Act 1998 and health and safety legislation. The House of Lords has recently given particular consideration to the right to claim unfair dismissal under section 94 of the ERA in the joined cases of *Lawson v Serco Ltd, Botham v Ministry of Defence and Crofts & others v Veta Ltd* [2006] IRLR 289 and laid down the following principals:

(a) whether or not a particular claim falls within the territorial scope of the unfair dismissal provision contained in the Employment Rights Act 1996 will depend on the nature of the particular employment arrangement and the issues in the case;
(b) in 'standard cases' where the employee works in Great Britain the employee will be able to pursue a claim of unfair dismissal if they were working in Great Britain at the time of the dismissal;
(c) in cases involving peripatetic employees the employee will be able to pursue the claim of unfair dismissal if they were based in Great Britain during the employment;
(d) in cases involving ex-patriot employees the employee will not be able to pursue their claim of unfair dismissal in the absence of exceptional circumstances. Those exceptional circumstances could include, for example, where the employee was posted abroad by British-based employer to work on behalf of or as a representative of that employer or where the employees are working abroad but within a political or social enclave such as a British military base.

The House of Lords declined to consider whether these principals would apply equally to other rights afforded under the ERA and, therefore, there continues to be uncertainty here.

The rules on when an employee can claim discrimination under the discrimination legislation are slightly different. Although the wording of the legislation differs, generally those employed at an establishment in the United Kingdom are protected while those working wholly outside the UK will not be unless certain conditions are met.

The UK oil and gas industry also attracts many workers from overseas. When employing an individual who is not a UK national, consideration must be given as to whether it is lawful for that individual to work in the UK. To work lawfully in the UK, individuals who are not nationals of an EEA Member State or Switzerland normally require a valid work permit. Swiss nationals and nationals of EEA Member States do not require a work permit, although under the Accession (Immigration and Worker Registration) Regulations 2004 (SI 2004 No 1219) (as amended) nationals of recently acceded Member States who want to work for more than one month are required to register with the Home Office as soon as they find work. Non-EEA nationals (who are subject to immigration control) must obtain work permits. There are certain limited exceptions to the requirement to hold a work permit (such as business visitors, Gibraltarians, students studying in UK institutions and persons engaged in certain occupations, such as ministers of religion) although they may still require immigration clearance. Subject to those exceptions, if an employer wishes to employ a non-EEA national he must first apply for a work permit on his behalf.

22.8 Policies and procedures

Most businesses will wish to set out for their workforce the core policies and procedures that they expect the workforce to comply with. These tend to be non-contractual, set out in the form of a staff handbook or an office manual and apply to both workers and employees. It is clearly beneficial for a business to set out in writing the expectations that they have in respect of how the worker will carry out certain activities and the rules that they expect the workers to comply with. This transparency is also a good way for a business to demonstrate that they have a consistent approach in their treatment of all workers, and hopefully reduce the need for disciplinary action. Generally, policies are not contractually binding. However, where they give a specific benefit to the worker, they may be enforceable. This was discussed in the case of *Keeley v Fosroc International Ltd* [2006] EWCA Civ 1277 in which the Court of Appeal acknowledged that where an employment contract expressly incorporates a staff handbook by reference, it does not necessarily follow that the handbook as a whole will be incorporated, but the fact that a document is presented as a collection of policies does not preclude those terms having contractual effect if by their nature and language they are apt to be contractual terms.

While it is not a legal requirement to have a staff handbook, there are core legal minimum benefits that employees are entitled to and it is beneficial for the business to have policies that confirm to the employee what these are, such as maternity, paternity and adoption rights and disciplinary and grievance procedures. Some employers will offer enhancements to the minimum requirements, and the level of these enhancements may assist in recruiting and retaining workers.

There are also legal minimum requirements on staff and again it is useful for the business to have a policy confirming what these requirements are and that they expect staff to behave in accordance with these procedures. An example of this would be an equal opportunities policy. All workers are protected by the legislation from both direct and indirect discrimination on the grounds of sex, marital status, pregnancy, race, ethnic origin, disability, age, religious beliefs, gender reassignment and sexual orientation. Discrimination and harassment is prohibited not only during an individual's employment, but in advertising vacancies, taking on employees, in some instances to former employees, on occasion to the self-employed and to contract workers and partners and candidates for partnership. Employers may also be vicariously liable for unlawful discrimination by their employees in the course of their employment, whether or not they knew or approved of the employees behaviour. A potential defence to such liability is if the employer can show he took such steps as were reasonably practicable to prevent the employee from acting in that way during the course of his employment. Therefore, a policy in respect of equal opportunities and bullying and harassment is a useful tool for a business to set out the business's intentions in respect of monitoring and managing these requirements, promoting workplace relationships and ensuring that all staff are treated equally and fairly.

Other policies will not be reflecting minimum legal requirements, but are useful to set out to ensure that workers are clear on the business's expectations. For example, it is useful to set out expectations that the business has in respect of matters such as dress code, how to speak to clients, both business and personal use of the telephone, IT and email policy and whether the business has the right to search the worker.

Within the oil and gas industry it is particularly recommended that businesses give consideration to policies on health and safety, medical assessments and drugs and alcohol. These are considered in more detail below.

Health and Safety

The Health and Safety at Work, etc. Act 1974 requires that it is the duty of every employer to ensure, so far as is reasonably practicable, the health, safety and welfare at work of all of their employees. Further, there is a requirement that employers with five or more employees have in place a health and safety policy. The employer is required to ensure that their workplace, whether this is an office or an offshore installation, meets minimum health and safety standards. This will include carrying out risk assessments, providing toilet and sanitisation facilities, meeting fire safety standards and reporting accidents or dangerous incidents within the workplace to the relevant authorities. In the offshore environment, the potential risks such as fire, explosion, release of gas and structural failure, are greater and require to be addressed and there is a wealth of specific regulations that require to be complied with. Health and safety offshore is discussed in greater detail elsewhere in this book.

An employment policy on health and safety should ensure that it contains a statement of the business's policy to provide control of the health and safety risks arising from the working activities, to consult with employees on matters of health and safety, to provide and maintain safe plant and equipment, to ensure safe handling of substances, to provide information and supervision for employees, to ensure that all employees are competent to do their tasks and that they will be provided with adequate training, to prevent accidents and cases of work related ill-health, to maintain a safe and healthy working environment and to revise the policy as necessary. The policy should clearly state who is primarily responsible for ensuring the health and safety of the employees. It should also confirm that the employees will have their own responsibilities to comply with including co-operating with supervisors and managers on health and safety matters; not interfering with anything provided to safeguard their health and safety, to take reasonable care of their own health and safety and to report any concerns to an appointed health and safety representative in the business. There should also be clear instructions on what an employee should do in an emergency situation.

Following the Piper Alpha disaster, the Cullen Inquiry found that some workers were aware of health and safety problems prior to the incident, but did not want to raise them for fear of jeopardising their continued employment. Therefore, businesses are well advised to have a clear reporting system and policy confirming to whom any such concerns should be addressed and that, in accordance with the Public Interest Disclosure Act 1998, no worker will suffer any detriment as a result of making a protected disclosure in respect of such concerns.

Medical assessments

The employer must also ensure that appropriate procedures are in place in respect of considering when an employee is fit to travel offshore. Oil & Gas UK has laid down industry approved standards that apply to all workers going offshore which includes the requirement that every offshore worker holds a valid medical certificate. This is obtained by passing a medical examination, carried out by an Oil & Gas UK Health Advisory Committee approved physician that confirms that the worker is fit to work offshore. Previously, the frequency of these assessments was dependent on age. However, a standard medical examination is now carried out every two years, unless the medical examination determines a more frequent assessment is required. Offshore workers must also hold a valid offshore survival certificate. This will be awarded only after satisfactory completion of an offshore survival course. For working offshore in UK waters the Basic Offshore Safety Induction and Emergency Training course is the appropriate survival course. The offshore survival certificate is valid for four years. As a step to improving health and safety offshore, a 'passport' system has developed in the industry. The Vantage Personnel On Board System is an internet enabled personnel tracking system which holds up-to-date information in respect of offshore workers, including details of the expiry date of an offshore worker's survival training, medical certificates, trip history and emergency contact information. Individuals working offshore will be provided with a Vantage ID which they must take with them when travelling offshore.

Drugs and alcohol

In the offshore environment it is particularly important for employers to have an alcohol and drugs policy in place. A common problem for employers in this industry is dealing with alcohol and drugs issues. Failure to ensure that an employee is fit to work and is not impaired by the effects of alcohol or drugs could render the employer liable for prosecution by the Health and Safety Executive. A lot of rigs therefore operate a zero-tolerance policy and at present the North Sea oil and gas industry enforces a policy preventing offshore workers from travelling offshore while over the legal alcohol limit for driving. As a result, it is not uncommon for employees to be refused transport offshore and be subject to disciplinary action as a result of having alcohol in their system. Dealing with employees in this situation can be difficult and, increasingly, employers are implementing random testing. While employees have the right to respect for their private and family life under the Human Rights Act 1998 this is a qualified right which can be overridden in certain circumstances such as in the interests of public safety or for the prevention of crime which may at times permit random testing. Dismissal following a positive drugs test during random screening, carried out in accordance with the employers policy, has been found to be fair where a key factor was public safety,[8] but employers must be careful in carrying out random testing and ensure that they have an adequate policy in place.

22.9 Communicating with the workforce

The Advisory, Conciliation and Arbitration Service (ACAS) states that 'Employee communications and consultations are the lifeblood of any business'. To a large extent, it will be for an employer to decide what, when and how it wishes to communicate or consult with the workforce. However, there are some statutory provisions for employee participation which employers must comply with and some examples of these are detailed below.

Trade Unions

Perhaps the most established example of workforce participation is through trade unions. There have been statutory provisions obliging employers to consult with recognised trade unions in respect of certain matters, such as health and safety and redundancies, since the 1970s. The law governing trade unions was consolidated in 1992 into the Trade Union and Labour Relations (Consolidation) Act 1992 (TULRCA) which itself has been amended by the Trade Union Reform and Employment Rights Act 1993 and the Employment Relations Act 1999.

A trade union is defined as an organisation which consists wholly or mainly of workers with the principal purpose of the regulation of relations between workers and their employer. Both workers and employees are entitled to be members of a trade union, although certain rights in respect of trade unions, by their nature, relate exclusively to employees, such as the right not to be dismissed for being a member of a trade union.

An employer's obligation to carry out consultation with a trade union only applies to a trade union recognised by that employer. A trade union can be recognised by an employer as a bargaining unit either voluntarily if the employer agrees or through the statutory recognition provisions contained in TULRCA. A trade union can seek statutory recognition where the trade union has made a request for recognition and the employer has either refused the request or no agreement has been reached. An application can then be made to the Central Arbitration Committee (the CAC) who will then consider whether the proposed bargaining unit is appropriate, whether some other bargaining unit would be appropriate, and whether the trade union has the support of a majority of the workers constituting the appropriate bargaining unit. The procedures cannot be used against a small employer who employs fewer than 21 workers.

Where a trade union is recognised, the employer is obliged under statutory provisions to consult with representatives of that trade union in respect of planned collective redundancies, transfers of undertakings, health and safety and training. In addition, the employer and trade union may agree to enter into a recognition agreement which can agree other areas that the employer will consult with the trade union and procedures for such consultation.

A recognised trade union is also entitled to enter into negotiations with an employer on behalf of its workers. This is commonly known as 'collective bargaining'. The purpose of the negotiation is to achieve a collective agreement, which is a written contract between the trade union and the employer setting out the terms and conditions of employment for the union's members. Collective agreements are rarely legally binding in themselves, but their terms are often incorporated into individual contracts of employment either expressly or by implication.

It is possible for a trade union to be 'derecognised'. If the trade union has been voluntarily recognised by the employer, there is nothing in law to prevent the employer from deciding they no longer wish to recognise the trade union and the employer can therefore withdraw the voluntary recognition at any time. By comparison, where a trade union has statutory recognition there is a statutory process for derecognition, and derecognition is not possible during the three years following the date of recognition. After three years, the employer may under TULRCA make a written request to the trade union to ask the trade union to agree to end the collective bargaining arrangements, or may apply for a declaration of derecognition from the CAC. A declaration of derecognition will be awarded if the CAC believes that the application complies with the conditions laid down in paragraph 99(3) of Schedule A1 to TULRCA. Similarly, any worker within the bargaining unit may apply to the CAC to end collective bargaining arrangements within three years of the initial declaration of recognition. To agree to derecognition, the CAC have to be satisfied that at least 10% of the workers within the bargaining unit are in favour of ending collective bargaining, and that the majority of workers would be likely to be in favour, or that the employer employs fewer than 21 workers.

Historically, there have been low rates of trade union membership and recognition in the UKCS due to a variety of factors, including the difficulties of gaining access to members offshore, the geography of the industry, the differing skill levels in the workforce, the nature of shift working and the high rate of movement of the workforce between different installations and employers. Steps have been taken to address this in the past through co-operation between the industry, through Oil & Gas UK, and the interested trade unions entering into agreements in respect of allowing union officials access offshore and consultation with trade unions as 'social partners'. More recently, the implementation of section 2 of the Employment Relations (Offshore Employment) Order 2000 (SI 2000 No 1828) has resulted in offshore workers' unions now being recognised in the same way as any other trade union. The Order enacts certain provisions of TULRCA and the ERA that relate to trade union recognition and the right to take industrial action by those in employment within the territorial waters of the UK, the UKCS and the Frigg gas field. The main effect of the Order is to make provision for collective bargaining offshore.

Information and Consultation of Employees Regulations 2004

More recently, the Government has introduced the Information and Consultation of Employees (ICE) Regulations 2004 (SI 2004 No 3426) which give employees and their representatives the right to be informed and consulted on a regular basis by their employers in respect of a number of workplace issues. Such issues include recent and probable developments of the undertaking's activities and economic situation; the structure and probable development of employment within the undertaking; any possible threats to employment within the undertaking; and any decisions likely to lead to substantial changes in work organisation or in contractual relations within the business through collective redundancies or transfer of employment to another employer.

The Regulations apply to public and private undertakings situated in the UK that carry out economic activities regardless of whether they operate for gain or not. The Regulations have a phased implementation date and initially they applied only to undertakings with at least 150 employees. This was extended on 6 April 2007 to undertakings with at least 100 employees, and from 6 April 2008 this will be further extended to undertakings with at least 50 employees. The Regulations will not apply to undertakings with less than 50 employees. The Regulations only apply to UK nationals based in the UK, which would presumably include employees working in the UKCS (although this is not expressly stated in the Regulations). The total number of employees is based on actual 'employees' and excludes other kinds of workers such as temporary workers or independent contractors.

The requirement to inform and consult employees does not operate automatically. It is triggered either by a formal request from employees for an Information and Consultation (I&C) Agreement, or by employers choosing to initiate the process themselves. An employee request to negotiate an I&C Agreement must be made by at least 10% of the employees in the undertaking. The agreement must set out how the employer will inform and consult employees or their representatives on an ongoing basis. While the Regulations are designed to encourage employers, employees and their representatives to agree information and consultation arrangements that suit their particular circumstances, they do not specify the subjects, method, timing or frequency of the arrangements that are allowed. It is possible for employers to enter into voluntary agreements with employees that fall largely outside the scope of the Regulations. These voluntary agreements will be valid if they are approved by employees in writing, cover all the undertakings' employees and set out how the employer will provide information and how the employees will be able to give their views.

Redundancy

If an employer is considering dismissing an employee or employees by reason of redundancy, they must go through a consultation process. The purpose of such consultation is to discuss ways in which redundancy can be avoided. The procedure for the consultation will depend on the number of redundancies proposed. Failure to comply with the statutory requirements will result in the dismissal being unfair.

If the employer is likely to be making more than 20 employees redundant at one establishment within a 90-day period or less, the employer must consult with the appropriate representatives of the employees affected by the redundancies. Where a trade union is recognised, the appropriate representatives are the trade union representatives. If no trade union is recognised it is necessary to elect employee representatives for this purpose. This must begin in 'good time' and, where there are more than 100 employees likely to be made redundant at one establishment within a 90-day period, consultation must begin at least 90 days before the first of the dismissals takes place. Otherwise, the consultation must take place at least 30 days before the first dismissal takes place.

Even where the proposed redundancies are for a smaller number of employees, the employer remains under a duty to consult with the employees and should ensure that they carry this out over a sufficiently long period to show that the consultation process is genuine. Consultation should be carried out with all employees affected and should be done on an individual basis. The consultation should ensure that the employees are aware of the reasons for the redundancies, understand and have an opportunity to discuss the selection criteria for choosing the employees to be made redundant, have the opportunity to suggest alternatives to the redundancy and consider any alternative employment that may be available within the company.

22.10 The impact of European legislation

The European Union has influenced much of the employment legislation in the UK. This influence is achieved both by way of legislation and by case law in the form of guidance provided by the European Court of Justice (ECJ) on the interpretation of the legislation. Two particular examples of this and their effect on the oil and gas industry are discussed below.

The Working Time Regulations 1998

The Working Time Regulations 1998 (SI 1998 No 1833) were introduced to implement the provisions of the EC Working Time Directive (No 93/104) and part of the EC Young Workers Directive (No 94/33). These Regulations set out the minimum conditions for workers in respect of working hours, daily rest, rest breaks, night work, weekly rest and paid annual leave. The Regulations have been amended to now reflect the consolidated terms of the EC Working Time Directive (No 2003/88).

The territorial application of these Regulations has been under much scrutiny and until recently the Regulations stated that they extended to Great Britain only, and did not specify that the Regulations also extended to the UKCS. This omission has now been addressed by Parliament and the Working Time (Amendment) (No 2) Regulations clarified that the Working Time Regulations do apply to the UKCS from 1 October 2006. However, while this clarification confirms that the Working Time Regulations do apply to the UKCS, there remains the question of whether compliance with the Regulations is achievable in the current offshore employment environment.

The Working Time Regulations currently provide that a worker is entitled to receive four weeks' annual leave in each leave year, although the Government is proposing to increase this to 4.8 weeks from 1 October 2007 and then to 5.6 weeks from 1 October 2008.

The subject matter of annual leave for offshore workers is the basis of 300 test cases which challenge whether the entitlement to paid annual leave is discharged during the normal field break arrangements. At present it is generally believed by employers of offshore workers that workers engaged in a rota of two or three weeks working offshore followed by working two or three weeks onshore, sufficiently addresses the entitlement to take paid annual leave as the workers are able to take their four weeks' paid leave during their time onshore. Employees with trade union backing have challenged this position and argue that they are entitled to paid annual leave in addition to this arrangement. A decision on the substantive issues has been delayed pending consideration of the preliminary point raised by the employers that the Regulations do not apply to the UKCS, however the Employment Appeals Tribunal has confirmed that the Regulations did apply to the UKCS prior to the Working Time (Amendment) (No 2) Regulations. The case has now been remitted to the Employment Tribunal to consider the substantive issues. Further claims will continue to be lodged with the Employment Tribunals in this regard until a decision has been given clarifying this point.

A further concern for the offshore working environment is the potential impact of two recent decisions of the European Court of Justice: *Case C-303/98 Sindicatio de Medicos de Asisgencia Publica (SiMAP) v Conselleria de Sanidad y Consumno de la Generelidad Valenciana* [2002] ECR I-7963 and *Case C-151/02 Landeshaupstadt Kiel v Norbert Jaeger* October 2003. These cases clarified that the definition of 'working time' is to include time where the worker must be present and available at the work place with a view to providing their services. This specifically includes time spent by doctors sleeping on call, provided they are at the place of their work. This approach has been been followed by the Employment Appeals Tribunal.[9] If this decision is to apply to offshore work also, all time spent offshore would qualify as working time, including when workers are asleep or off-shift. Clearly the impact of such interpretation of these Regulations would demand drastic changes in the current work pattern of offshore workers which would obviously prove to be highly impractical and costly. Consequentially, workers would be entitled to work around eight days per month, with 20 days required for compensatory leave.

In addition, an EU review of the Working Time Directive has been ongoing since January 2004. However, progress has been delayed due to disputes between Member States, which particularly concern the proposals to amend the current entitlement to opt-out of some of the working time requirements of the Directive. The European Commission published a Communication to re-examine Directive 93/104 in respect of certain aspects of the organisation of working time. The Commission issued open consultation on the subject matter of the length of the reference period, the definition of working time, the conditions of the application of the opt-out, measures to improve the balance between work and family life and how to find the best balance of these measures. To date, however, there has been no agreement on these proposals.

Transfer of Undertakings (Protection of Employment) Regulations 2006

The Transfer of Undertakings (Protection of Employment) Regulations (SI 2006 No 246) (TUPE) derive from the European Community Acquired Rights Directive (ARD). TUPE 1981 was introduced into the UK legislation pursuant to the European Communities Act 1972, s2(2)(a) to implement the ARD 1977. The ARD was then amended in 1998 during the UK Presidency of the EU, and then latterly consolidated in 2001. Member States were then required to implement the changes and the UK eventually did so in TUPE 2006, pursuant to both the Employment Relations Act 1999, s 38 and the European Communities Act (above) to enable the introduction of wider provisions than the ARD requires, providing greater protection for employees.

The application of the TUPE Regulations.

Regulation 3 of TUPE provides that the Regulations will apply where there is a 'relevant transfer', which is defined in Regulation 3 as either a transfer of an undertaking, which is defined as 'a transfer of an undertaking, business or part of an undertaking or business situated immediately before the transfer in the United Kingdom to another person where there is a transfer of an economic entity which retains its identity' or a service provision change, being outsourcing, a change of contractor or insourcing.

In determining whether there has been a transfer of undertaking, it is necessary to consider whether there is an economic entity that will transfer, whether the business will retain its identity on transfer and whether there is an identifiable group of employees within this context. The ECJ has stated that the 'criteria for establishing whether there is a transfer for the purposes of the Directive is whether the business in question retained its identity'.[10] Accordingly, the question of whether TUPE applies does not simply concern whether the assets of a business have been disposed of, but whether the business is disposed of as a going concern. This can be indicated by the fact that the operation has continued or has been resumed by the transferee after the transfer date and similar activities are being carried out. The ECJ also listed some of the factors that should be taken into account, although it has stressed that these circumstances should be looked at overall and not considered in isolation. These factors include the type of undertaking or business concern; whether the intangible assets to the business, such as know how and good will, are acquired by the transferee; whether the majority of the business employees are taken over by the new employer; whether the business clients or customers are transferred; the degree of similarity between activities carried on before and after the putative transfer and the period, if any, for which those activities were suspended.

The application of TUPE on a service provision change is a recent requirement implemented in 2006, being outsourcing, a change of contractor or insourcing. Outsourcing is defined as a situation where activities are no longer carried out by a person (the 'client') on their own behalf and are carried out by another person (the 'contractor') on the client's behalf. A change of contractor occurs where the activities carried out by the contractor are carried out by a subsequent contractor. Insourcing is defined as when the activities being carried out are no longer to be carried out by a contractor or a subsequent contractor, but are to be carried out by the client. However, the Regulations do not apply on service provision changes where there is no identifiable grouping of employees, if the service is from a contractor on a one-off basis and where the arrangement between the client and contractor is wholly and mainly for the supply of goods for the client's use. As stated in the first section of this chapter, the oil and gas industry has a variety of employment relationships, which include operating companies outsourcing the requirements for manning the rig to drilling companies and contractors. Therefore, this extension to the TUPE Regulations will impact heavily on the industry, given the requirements of the Regulations as discussed below.

TUPE does not apply where there is a share sale takeover or where a contract has been won by an in-house team after competitive tendering where the employer remains the same. Further, the Regulations do not tend to apply where there is a transfer of assets where no employees are involved. Technically, therefore, the sale of equipment alone would not be covered, however this is not a hard and fast rule.[11] TUPE also will not apply to a transfer of undertaking situation outside the UK, although there will be similar provisions in other EU Countries.

It will be evident from the above that there will be many situations in the oil and gas industry where the TUPE Regulations will require to be followed. The question of whether TUPE applies offshore has not been specifically addressed by TUPE 2006. Guidance, therefore, must be taken from the case of *Addison v Denholm Ship Management (UK) Ltd* [1997] ICR 770. In this case, the applicants worked on flotels situated outside the UK territorial waters in the Scottish sector of the continental shelf of the North Sea. The applicants claimed that they were unfairly dismissed and that their employment ought to have been continued under the TUPE 1981 Regulations. The Employment Appeals Tribunal held that the Regulations did not apply to the flotels as they were not situated within the UK for the purpose of the Regulations. However, the Employment Appeals Tribunal also stated that the flotels could not be regarded as the crews' place of work, as 'the location of the undertaking transferred is not necessarily the physical location but where the employer's organisational or operation base is'. While TUPE 2006 does not address this, comment was made in the 2005 Consultation paper that the Government believed that *Addison* was wrongly decided and that TUPE does apply to the UKCS. However, failure to make specific provision on this in the TUPE Regulations means that the legal position remains as stated in *Addison*. It is recommended that in situations involving the UKCS, consideration should be given to where the functions of employment are carried out from, such as where the employee is paid from and where a disciplinary or grievance matter would be held. As it is likely that these functions will be carried out at a base within the UK, rather than offshore, it is safest to assume that TUPE will apply.

Effect of the TUPE Regulations

Essentially, the Regulations provide that employees of the transferor company automatically become employees of the transferee company when the undertaking changes hands, with the employees' existing terms and conditions of employment including continuity of service remaining unchanged.

Regulation 4(4) provides that any changes to the terms and conditions of transferring employees are void where the reason for the change is for a reason connected with the transfer itself or where the changes are not for an economic, technical or organisational reason. Unfortunately, the Regulations do not define what an economic, technical or organisational reason is. The Department of Trade and Industry's Guidance on TUPE 2006 states that a simple harmonisation of terms of employment between transferring employees and existing employees of the transferee is clearly for the reason of the transfer and therefore is not possible to be viewed as an economic, technical or organisational reason. The transferee must therefore take care in these situations to ensure that other employment legislation is complied with.

Regulation 7 retains the provision that an employee will be treated as unfairly dismissed if the sole or principal reason for the dismissal is the transfer or a reason connected with the transfer that is not for an economic, technical or organisational reason entailing changes in the workforce. Therefore, where a dismissal occurs for which the sole or principal reason is the transfer itself, or a reason connected with the transfer that is not an economic, technical or organisational reason entailing changes in the workforce, the dismissal will be automatically unfair under the unfair dismissal legislation. Where a dismissal occurs and the sole or principal reason for the dismissal is not the transfer itself, but a reason connected with it that is an economic, technical or organisation reason, it can potentially be fair under the unfair dismissal legislation, subject to the normal test of reasonableness. It is common for problems to arise here where a purchaser wishes to acquire a business but not all of its employees. If the transferor carries out dismissals pre-transfer then it is likely to be left with substantial claims from the dismissed employees. Practically it is common for the transferee to agree to transfer the employees and after a period of time commence redundancy proceedings with the transferee requiring that the transferor bears the employment costs of the surplus employees up to the point of redundancy by way of a reduction in the price for the business.

Employee liability information

TUPE 2006 now places a duty on the transferor to provide the transferee with employee liability information in respect of any person employed by him assigned to the organisation of resources or employees that is the subject for the relevant transfer. This information should be provided either in writing or in a readily accessible form at a specified date no more than 14 days before the date on which the relevant transfer is due to take place. The Regulations do provide that a lesser time period can be justified in special circumstances where it is not reasonably practicable to provide this information earlier. It remains to be seen how the courts will interpret this provision. Employment liability information means the identity and age of the employee; details of the written statement of terms and conditions of employment; information of any disciplinary procedure taken against an employee or grievance procedure taken by an employee within the previous two years in the circumstances where the Employment Act 2002 (Dispute Resolution) Regulations 2004 (SI 2004 No 752) apply; information of any Court or Tribunal case, claim or action which was either brought by an employee against the transferor within the previous two years or that the transferor has reasonable grounds to believe that an employee may bring against the transferee arising out of the employee's employment with the transferor; and information of any collective agreement which will have effect after the transfer in its application in relation to the employee. Should the transferor fail to provide the transferee with the employee liability information, the transferee has three months within which to lodge a claim, and a Tribunal may award compensation to the transferee of £500 per employee unless the Tribunal considers it just and equitable to award a lesser amount.

Problems are foreseen in respect of the application of these Regulations in accordance with the Data Protection Act 1998 given that passing such information will be 'processing' and accordingly covered by the Data Protection Act. An employee's consent is, therefore, technically required for this information to be passed on. However, it is unusual for an employee to be aware during the early stage of negotiations that a transfer may take place and employers are likely to be reluctant to share this information with their staff.

Information and consultation

Regulation 13 of TUPE 2006 states that all employees of either the transferor or transferee who may be affected by measures taken in connection with the transfer are to be provided with information sufficiently in advance of the transfer to allow them to be consulted upon if necessary. The information that the employer is required to provide is the fact that the transfer is to take place; when the transfer is to take place; the reasons for it; the legal economic and social implications of the transfer; the measures that the employer envisages he will take in relation to any affected employees in connection with the transfer or the fact that no such measures will be taken; and the measures that are envisaged that the transferee will take in relation to any affected employees who are to become employees of the transferee by virtue of the transfer. This information is to be provided to appropriate representatives of the affected employees. Appropriate representatives are either trade union representatives, where an independent trade union is recognised by the employer, or employee representatives appropriately elected by the affected employees. It is also necessary for the employer to consult with these representatives to seek agreement on the measures that are envisaged will be taken. Failure to carry out the requirement entitles employees to seek a Tribunal order for compensation of up to 13 weeks salary, not capped at the statutory rate.

The Employment Appeal Tribunal has confirmed that when assessing compensation for failure to consult, a Tribunal should award the maximum 13 weeks pay as compensation unless there are mitigating circumstances justifying a departure from the maximum award.[13] Accordingly, it is very important that advice is taken to ensure compliance with the information and consultation requirements.

Insolvent businesses

The new Regulations have implemented a possibility for assistance in the rescue of failing businesses. Where the transferor is subject to relevant insolvency proceedings the Regulations provide that some of the transferor's pre-existing debts to employees will not transfer to the transferee. In addition, there is a greater scope for varying the existing terms and conditions of employment of the transferring employees, provided that agreement is reached with employee representatives, that the changes comply with statutory entitlements and that they are made with the intention of safeguarding employment opportunities.

Pensions and TUPE

The Pensions Act 2004, ss 257 and 258 and the Transfer of Employment (Pension Protection) Regulations 2005 (SI 2005 No 649) provide that where a transferor has contributed to a pension scheme, being a final salary scheme, money purchase scheme or stakeholder scheme, the transferee employer is required to contribute to a money purchase or stakeholder pension scheme to match the employee's level of contributions up to a maximum of 6% of salary. While occupational pension schemes themselves do not transfer, the cases of *Beckmann v Dynamo Whichelow MacFarlane* [2005] 364 PBLR and *Martin & Others v South Bank University* [2004] IRLR 74 held that provisions within such pensions schemes relating to benefits for old age, invalidity or survivors should not be treated as part of the scheme itself and, therefore, will transfer.

Notes

1. *Faccenda Chicken Ltd v Fowler* [1986] ICR 297.
2. *Allan Janes LLP v Johal* [2006] EWHC 286 and *Thomas v Farr PLC* [2007] EWCA Civ 118.
3. *Alidair v Taylor* [1978] IRLR 82.
4. *Perkin v St George's Healthcare Trust* [2005] IRLR 934.
5. *Scott Packing v Patterson* [1978] IRLR 166.
6. *Kingston v British Railways Board* [1984] IRLR 146.

[7] *Willow Oaks Developments Ltd t/a Windsor Recruitment v Silverwood and others* [2006] IRLR 28.
[8] *O'Flynn v Airlinks the Airport Coach Company Ltd* [2002] EAT/0269/01.
[9] *Anderson v Jarvis Hotels* [2006] UKEAT/0062/05.
[10] *Spijkers v Gebroders* [1986] 3 ECR 119.
[11] Cases such as *RCO Support Service v Unison* [2002] EWCA Civ 464 and *ECM v Cox* 1999 IRLR 559 should also be considered.
[12] *Sweetin v Coral Racing* [2006] IRLR 252.

— 23 —

TECHNOLOGY APPLICATION

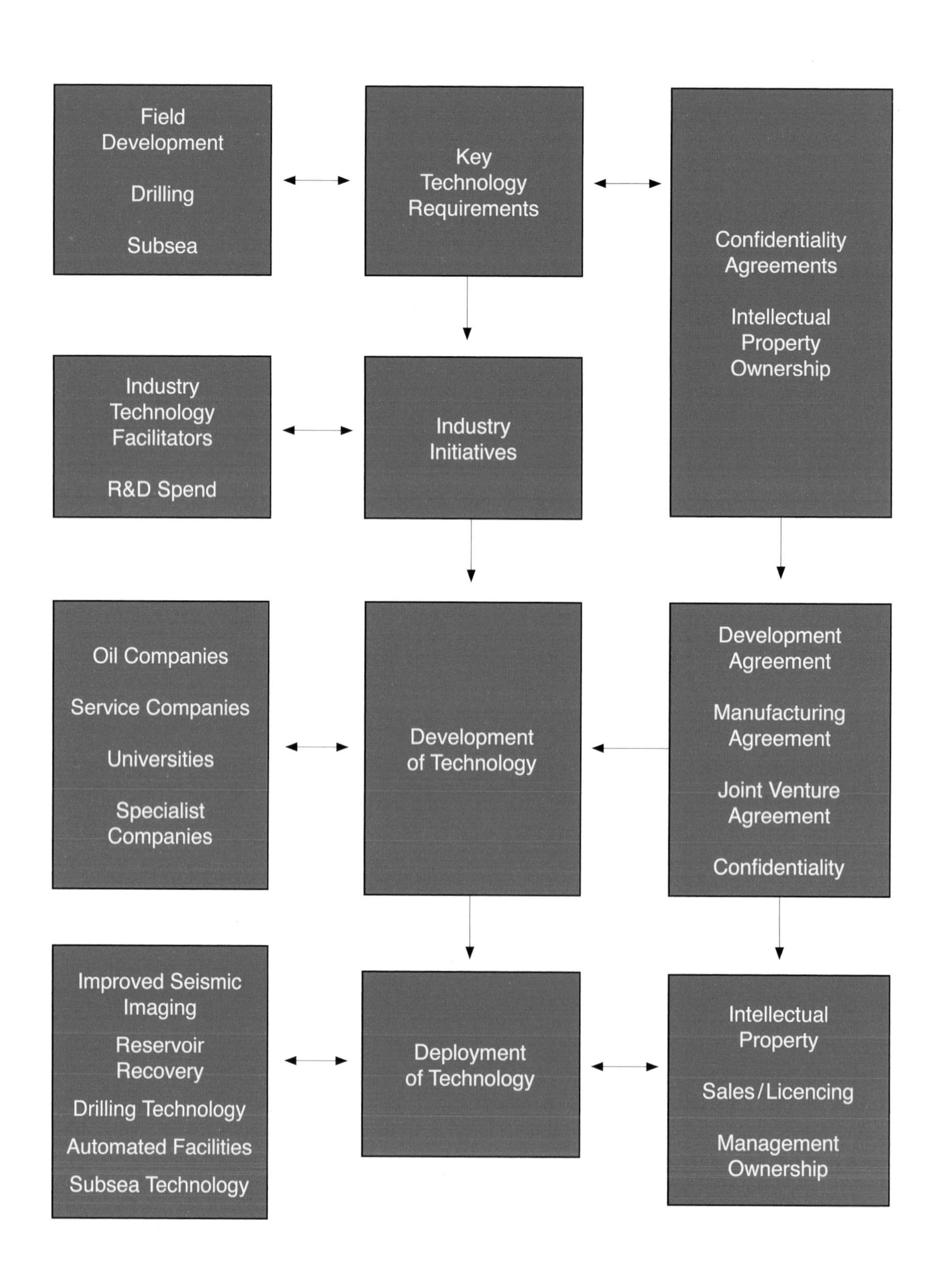
Field
Development
Drilling
Subsea
Key
Technology
Requirements
Confidentiality
Agreements
Intellectual
Property
Ownership
Industry
Technology
Facilitators
R&D Spend
Industry
Initiatives
Oil Companies
Service Companies
Universities
Specialist
Companies
Development
of Technology
Development
Agreement
Manufacturing
Agreement
Joint Venture
Agreement
Confidentiality
Improved Seismic
Imaging
Reservoir
Recovery
Drilling Technology
Automated Facilities
Subsea Technology
Deployment
of Technology
Intellectual
Property
Sales/Licencing
Management
Ownership

TECHNOLOGY APPLICATION

TECHNICAL

23.1 Introduction

The start of oil and gas discoveries and development in the UK North Sea saw the introduction of a completely new industry with equipment and technology imported to meet the needs of large field developments. The learning curve was steep for those persons recruited to operate and manage the business both onshore and offshore. The oil price was high and little attention was paid to technology developments to improve efficiency or recovery.

The first real wake-up call came when the price of oil dropped from $40 to $18 per barrel in the mid-1980s, questioning the UK's competitive position for investment by the international oil companies. Some serious cost reducing innovation became the driver to re-establishing commerciality of many new undeveloped fields. This, in turn, lead to the greater understanding that technology would continue to be the driver as reserves and field sizes decline.

There is always a balance to be considered in using the North Sea as a test ground for new technology. The oil companies have always taken a cautious approach to new technology due to the high cost of failure against a more traditional proven technology. This is further exasperated by much of the new technology being developed within the service industry. In many cases small innovative technology companies are being bought out by the major service companies to gain a competitive edge. There is clearly the need for much greater communication and co-operation between the oil companies and the technology providers.

The demand for oil and gas is expected to rise significantly and technology will continue to play a vital role in the finding and commercial production of reserves globally. In the mature hydrocarbon province of the North Sea, production is declining and new reserves will be more difficult to find, access and produce. The challenges to be faced in stemming the decline will be both technical and commercial but, as is the case with all challenges, there is a window of opportunity for innovative and astute operators and suppliers to better manage and apply new technology to their undoubted competitive advantage.

This chapter explores the business drivers for new technology, and how this has impacted on North Sea production to date. It also considers the possible requirements during the mature phase and how industry initiatives can improve technology application.

23.2 Business drivers for the application of new technology

The current driving force for innovation and the application of new technology in Exploration and Production (E&P) is to meet a forecasted significant increase in oil and gas demand over the next 25 years or so in which the world is expected to consume as much oil again as it has used in the past 150 years. The global demand for oil is expected to grow at 1.6% a year and that for gas at 2.3% a year according to the International Energy Agency's (IEA's) World Energy Outlook (2004 and 2005a) (Fig. 23–1).

The contribution that technology makes to the industry is generally expressed as the volumes of hydrocarbons discovered, increases in the rate at which hydrocarbons might be produced, increases in the volumes of hydrocarbons that will ultimately be produced and reductions in capital and operating expenditure. However, most of the easily accessible oil and gas fields have been developed and the majority of the still-to-be-developed reserves are to be found in smaller accumulations, in more complex reservoirs, in more challenging temperature and pressure regimes and in many cases in more hostile environments such as ultra-deep water or the Arctic (IEA, 2005b).

For an operator to be seen to be associated with successful technology application is a strong recommendation in the intensely competitive world of E&P. Individual oil and gas companies compete in the application of technology to provide value to shareholders, and even oil and gas producing nations compete for business at the international level on the basis of their technological capabilities and achievements. With over half the world's oil reserves completely restricted to national oil companies or offering only limited access to international business, competition between operators for the privilege of being entrusted with the extraction of those reserves is intense. Amongst the super-majors ExxonMobil and Royal Dutch Shell have both stated openly that they make their case to host

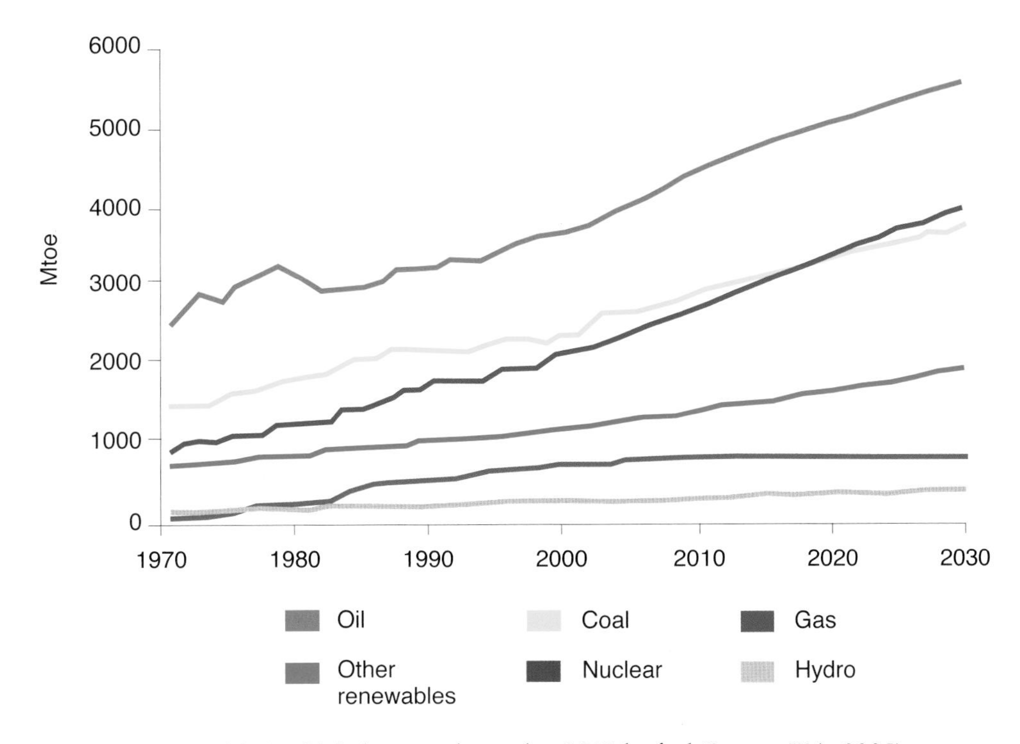

Figure 23–1 Global energy demand to 2030 by fuel (Source: IEA, 2005)

governments largely on the basis of their technological capabilities and their know-how relating to very large and complex projects.

Technology is also central to the industry's efforts to minimise the environmental impact of its operations. In certain North Sea situations, floating production storage and offloading facilities and subsea production systems have been used in place of massive platform-based production facilities. The number of drilling and production locations required to develop fields has also been reduced by the introduction of extended-reach drilling and high angle/horizontal wells that allow reservoirs to be accessed several kilometres from the drilling/production site.

Shell and Statoil signed an agreement in 2006 to work towards developing the world's largest project using carbon dioxide (CO_2) for enhanced oil recovery (EOR) offshore. The project – which could cost up to $1.5 bn and potentially be operational by 2012 – involves capturing CO_2 from a power station in mid-Norway, and pumping it into the Draugen and Heidrun fields for storage and to enhance oil recovery. Power from the plant will also be provided to the offshore fields, enabling near zero CO_2 and nitrogen oxide emissions from these installations.

Concurrent with the technical challenges, the industry is also facing a severe shortage of skilled personnel. Keeping skilled staff is a major issue and a recent study of 1300 employees in 40 E&P companies, service firms and drilling contractors report that there is a strong correlation between a company's reputation and hence retention rates and its role as a technology and innovation leader (Gulf Research, 2006). Forward-looking companies are indeed setting-up technology-enabled global knowledge sharing networks or knowledge communities to help retain and spread hard-earned knowledge throughout their organisations (Conway et al., 2006).

For all the value that new technology has brought to the E&P sector, it is still an enigma that innovation is perhaps the core business process that is managed with the least discipline (Jaruzelski et al., 2005). Exploiting the technology opportunity requires understanding the needs and motivations of operators, alignment with corporate strategy, demonstration of value, streamlined processes for technology deployment and collaboration with partners. In the North Sea area there would appear to be a significant opportunity within the E&P sector to build competitiveness by improving the way in which each of the above activities is planned and managed.

23.3 Impact of new technology on 40 years of North Sea production

Huge investment, immensely skilled people and constant technology innovation and application are the three primary forces that have made the UK sector of the North Sea one of the world's most prolific oil and gas producing provinces. The first phase of oil production in the UK North Sea peaked at 2.63 MMbpd in 1985 and then declined sharply to 1.8 MMbpd by 1991, 25 years after the first exploration well was drilled in the province. A second phase of production growth during the 1990s led to an even higher peak of 3.1 MMbpd in 1999.

Cost-reducing technological innovation was a driver behind this new production and one study claims that at least 17 fields produced after 1985 would not have been commercial without technological advances being applied to their development (Martin, 1997). It also claims that 2.7 billion barrels of reserves were added (between 1985 and 1997) because of technology-induced reserves revisions and that exploration technology resulted in more discoveries or permitted a more accurate appraisal of fields on which the decision to develop was based.

It has been estimated that by 1985 some 400,000 bopd (barrels of oil per day) production from the North Sea were attributable to new technology and this grew to more than 550,000 bopd by 2000 (Fig. 23–2, IEA, 2005b).

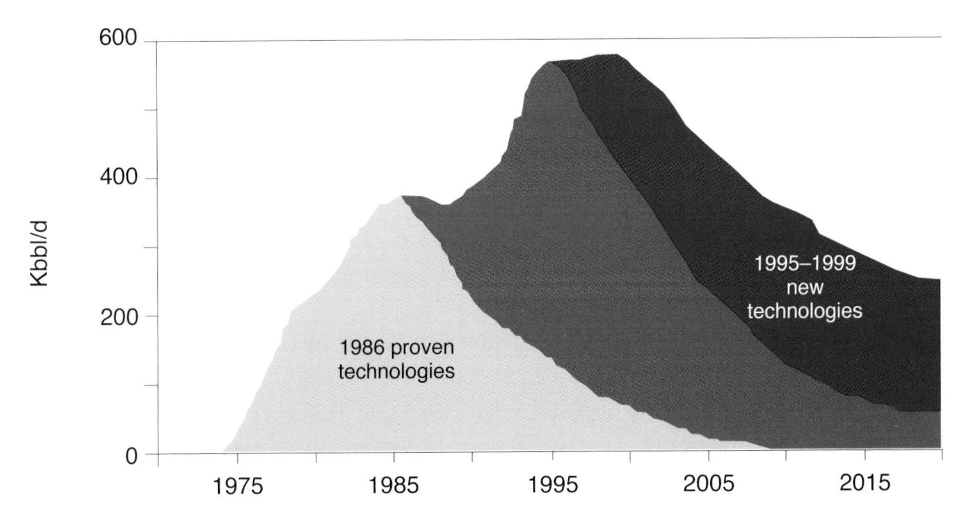

Figure 23–2 Impact of new technology on North Sea oil production (Source: IEA 2005b after Shell)

Industry observers have identified a number of trends that underpinned the production revival after 1991 (Abbots, 2003). The fields developed in the first 25 years of the North Sea's development history had an average reserve size in excess of 300 million barrels. In the next decade at least 40 fields were developed with an average reserve size of 100 million barrels. The first technically challenging developments of heavy oil and HP–HT gas condensate fields were also carried out at that time and considerable progress was made in developing very small fields with reserves of 2–4 million boe (barrels of oil equivalent).

The technologies used in this transformation included:

- improved seismic imaging including 3D and 4D (time-lapse) seismic;
- under-balanced drilling in tight gas reservoirs;
- hydraulic fracture stimulation of low permeability reservoirs;
- horizontal wells;
- high angle extended reach wells;
- minimum facility platforms;
- floating production storage and offloading (FPSO) facilities; and
- subsea completions.

Field Development Planning: 3D Visualisation

Some of the most visible and important applications of new technology in the oil and gas sector have been at the very front end of the field development planning process. The development of faster computers has allowed the analysis of seismic and geological data to evolve from the desktop to full 3D immersive environments (Fig. 23–3). Engineers can perform well planning, seismic interpretation, geological modelling, reservoir modelling and simulations all from within a virtual representation of the geological anatomy of a field. Many major companies use visionariums with 8–10 ft tall screens that curve horizontally through approximately 160°, onto which data are projected to give users the impression of being surrounded by data.

The most impressive systems are immersive visualisation rooms that are based on the virtual reality interface CAVE. In these environments, the data not only surrounds the interpreters but actually appears to fill the room. Members of the asset team literally can walk through the data and discuss the reservoir with one another. Using a 3D pointer, a new production well can be planned from inside the reservoir making full use of the 3D spatial representation of other wells, reservoir variations and structural features such as faults.

Figure 23–3 3D Visualisation (Source: Norsk Hydro)

Useful as visionariums are, the next step is the true 3D desktop display. Operating as either a normal 2D monitor or in 3D mode, these new displays potentially allow any geologist or well engineer the ability to have 3D visualisation at their desks.

Drilling and completions: Horizontal and extended reach wells

A challenge facing all operators is how best to access the reserves in their fields. In the first 25 years of North Sea production activity most fields were developed with a combination of sub-vertical and low to medium angled slanted or deviated wells. A review of some 50 North Sea fields developed between 1965 and 2000 showed, however, that extended reach and high angle/horizontal wells made their mark from 1997 onwards and of 12 fields brought on stream between 1997 and 2000, eight used these technologies (Gluyas and Hitchens, 2003).

The Foinaven field, in water depths of 1500–2000 ft, 190 km west of the Shetlands, was brought on stream through a floating production vessel in 1997. Though it was 21 months late due to problems with new subsea technologies it is a fine example of new technology application (Carruth, 2003). The development consists of subsea wells producing via a seabed manifold, connected by rigid flowlines and flexible risers to the permanently stationed FPSO (Fig. 23–4). Horizontal production wells were chosen with the expectation of getting good production rates and reserves recovery and 22 have been drilled.

BG's Armada development in the Central North Sea consists of three fields Fleming, Drake and Hawkins. Fleming is a large field that lies above the smaller

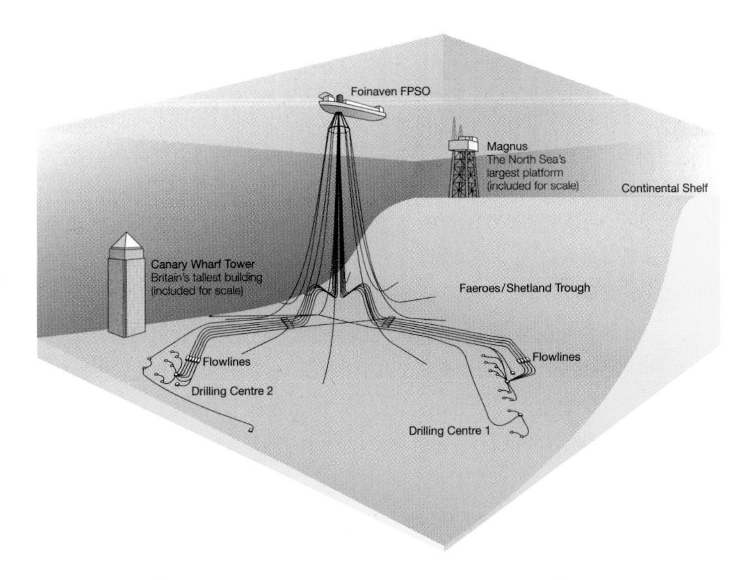

Figure 23–4 The Foinaven field, west of Shetland (Courtesy: BP)

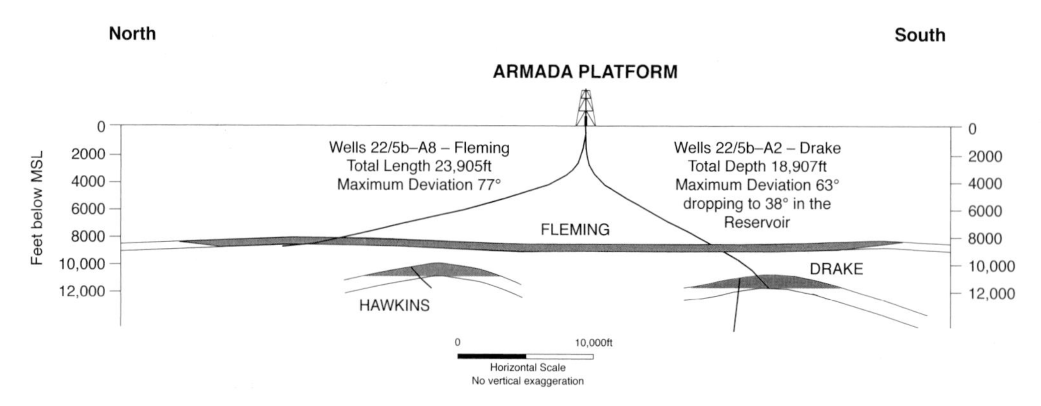

Figure 23–5 True-scale cross-section of extended reach development wells through the Armada fields (Source: Stuart, 2003)

Drake and Hawkins fields and the three fields have been developed from a single 21-slot platform located midway between Drake and Hawkins. This was made possible by very high angle extended reach wells and eight of these were drilled (Stuart, 2003). The longest was drilled at 77° to a total depth of 23,905 ft (Fig. 23–5).

The industry has developed the ability to drill and complete more than one branch radiating from the main borehole and these are described as multilateral wells (Schlumberger Oilfield glossary). They take on many configurations and allow reservoirs to be more effectively and efficiently drained (Fig. 23–6). They are often used to access pockets of by-passed oil left behind in watered-out reservoirs.

One classic multilateral profile is easily visualised as the 'fish-bone' structure where a number of short laterals branch out on both sides of a horizontal well. Production from these laterals is then taken to the surface through the main drainhole using specialised 'junctions' that allow each of the laterals to be produced and, in the most complex systems, to be controlled separately.

Production: Remote working

The first offshore fields were located in shallow water, where all the tasks of field facilities installation and maintenance could be performed by divers. As water depths have increased beyond those in which divers can operate safely, remotely operated vehicles (ROVs), controlled by pilots at the surface via an umbilical, were developed to perform tasks on the seabed and to monitor equipment in the water column such as risers. Whilst these ROVs can perform all the tasks needed to manage and maintain an offshore field, the fact that an umbilical is needed to send power and commands to the vehicles limits their use to fields

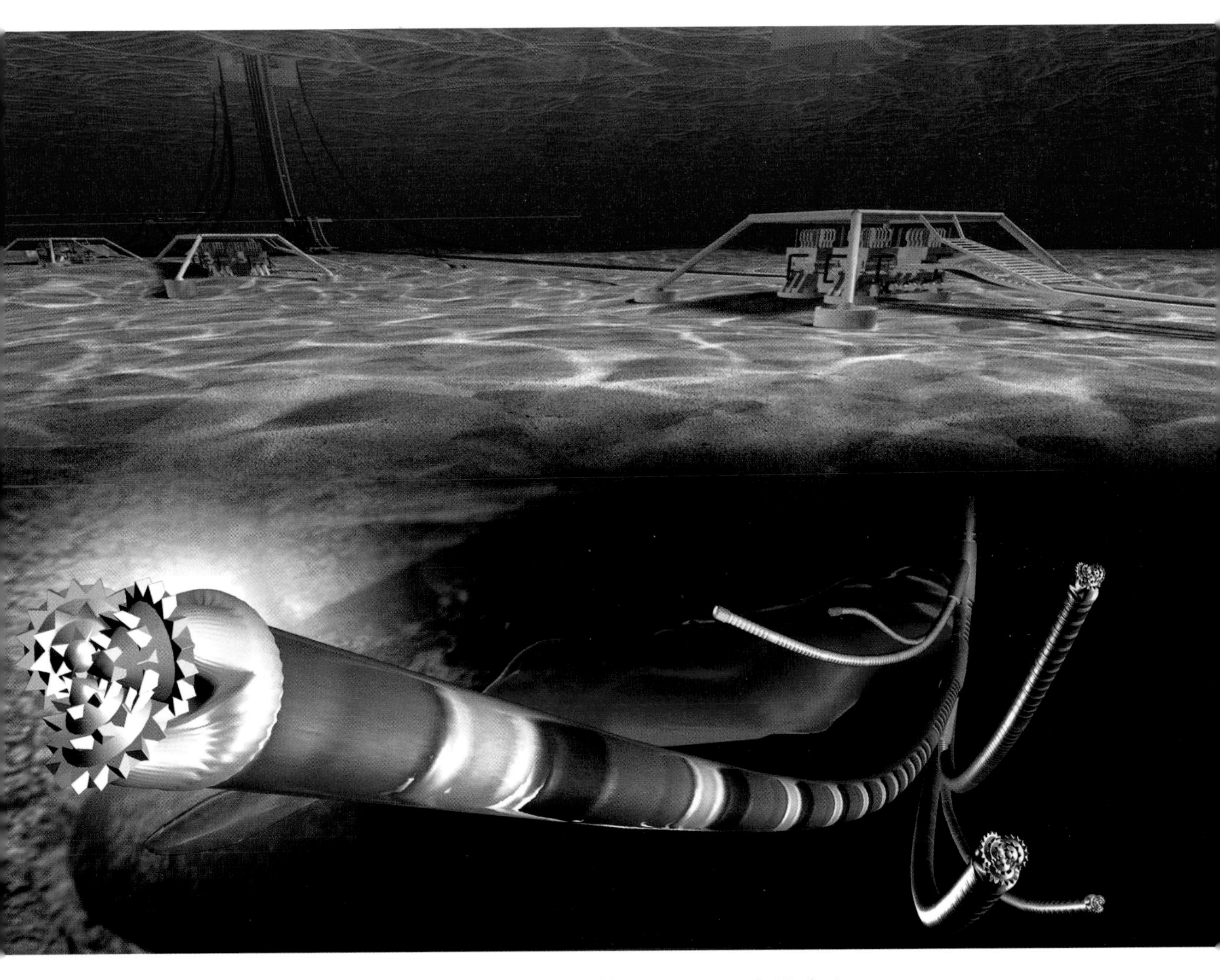

Figure 23–6 Multilateral wells (Source: Norsk Hydro)

with few subsea obstructions (eg mooring lines) or to tasks where the cost of a support vessel can be justified.

To overcome this, the industry is developing autonomous underwater vehicles (AUVs) (Fig. 23–7). The first generation of AUVs are able to perform many of the survey tasks which ROVs performed in the past, but without the need for direct human intervention; pipelines can now be surveyed without needing to mobilise a vessel. The next generation of AUVs will soon be in service and will be able to perform many of the 'manual' tasks such as opening or closing a valve that were previously performed by ROVs with umbilical control.

Figure 23–7 AUV (Source: Subsea 7)

Reservoir production monitoring: 4D Time-lapse seismic

Monitoring of the distribution and movement of fluids in a reservoir during production can contribute markedly to the reduction of operating costs and the improvement of recovery of hydrocarbons. Time-lapse seismic, or repeat 3D seismic surveys over time, is increasingly being used to detect changes in the acoustic properties of reservoir rocks as production takes place. Differences between successive surveys are interpreted in terms of changes in reservoir properties such as fluid saturation, pressure and temperature (Fig. 23–8). These can then be fed into reservoir simulation models which might result in modifications to a reservoir's depletion strategy. The technique is being used to identify undrained reservoir compartments and areas of by-passed hydrocarbons thereby facilitating the optimisation of development well locations and the placement of injection wells for improved oil recovery schemes. Further advances in 4D are expected with the use of permanent sensing arrays such as ocean bottom cables (OBC), downhole seismic acquisition, full-wave field recording devices, passive microseismic listening and 'intelligent field' developments.

The Foinaven field can be mentioned again as a leading exponent of the technology. It was the first North Sea field to have permanently installed seabed cables for repeat seismic monitoring in support of production management. A pre-production baseline survey was shot over part of the field in 1995 and was repeated in 1998 after 10 months of production. Based on the success of these surveys in recognising fluid changes in the reservoir the whole field has been repeat surveyed four times in 1999, 2000, 2002 and 2004 (Ribiero and Macbeth, 2006).

23.4 Technology requirements for the North Sea's mature phase

After almost 40 years of exploration and production activity the UK sector of the North Sea is a mature province with reserves estimated at 21–27 Bboe (billions of barrels of oil equivalent). It is now a prime candidate for the deployment of new technology in seeking to extend its producing life (DTI, 2006). The

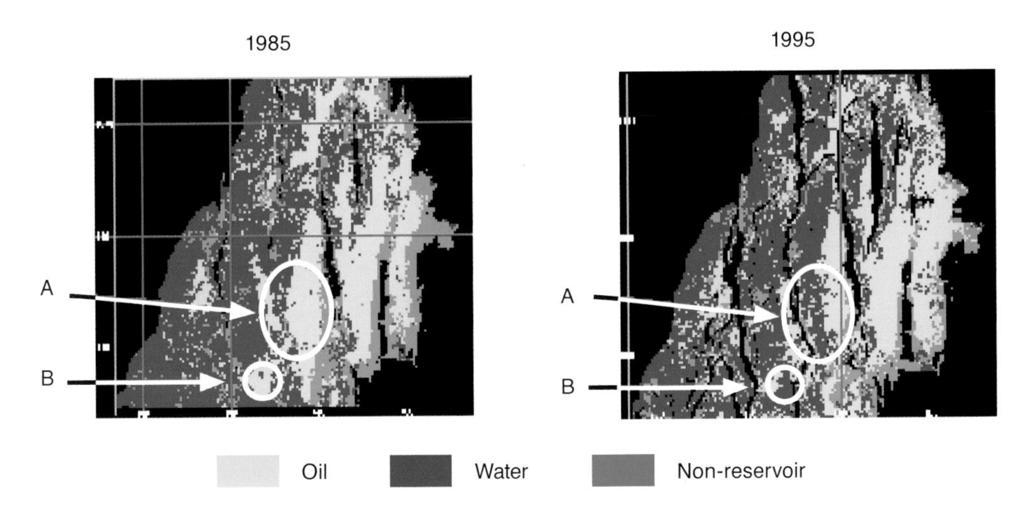

Figure 23–8 Time-lapse seismic maps showing changes in fluid saturation with time (Source: Schlumberger Oilfield Glossary)

Government's target is to reduce the production decline rate from 9% to 4% a year thereby delivering an extra million boe a day by 2020 and resulting in extra production of almost 7 Bboe by 2030 (Fig. 23–9). Three main strategies are being followed, each of which has a technology component. The first involves maximising investment in producing fields by focusing on increasing production from the poorer performing fields. This would require closer co-operation between operators and some imaginative technological solutions to linking small discoveries to existing platforms and pipelines. The second initiative involves unlocking the West of Shetland potential and the third involves making better use of the expertise developed over 40 years in the North Sea to speed up the flow of deals and approvals to enable fallow assets to be developed more quickly.

Target areas for new technology will span the whole E&P lifecycle from exploration to decommissioning. Amongst these will be improved seismic and non-seismic reservoir imaging and pre-drill direct hydrocarbon indicators, improved reservoir characterisation and enhanced recovery, cost-effective drilling and interventions, integrated operations and real time reservoir management, tail-end production and field rejuvenation, and subsea processing and transport. Joint industry improvements in commercial practices will ensure that the technical advances are efficiently put into practice. Figure 23–10 shows

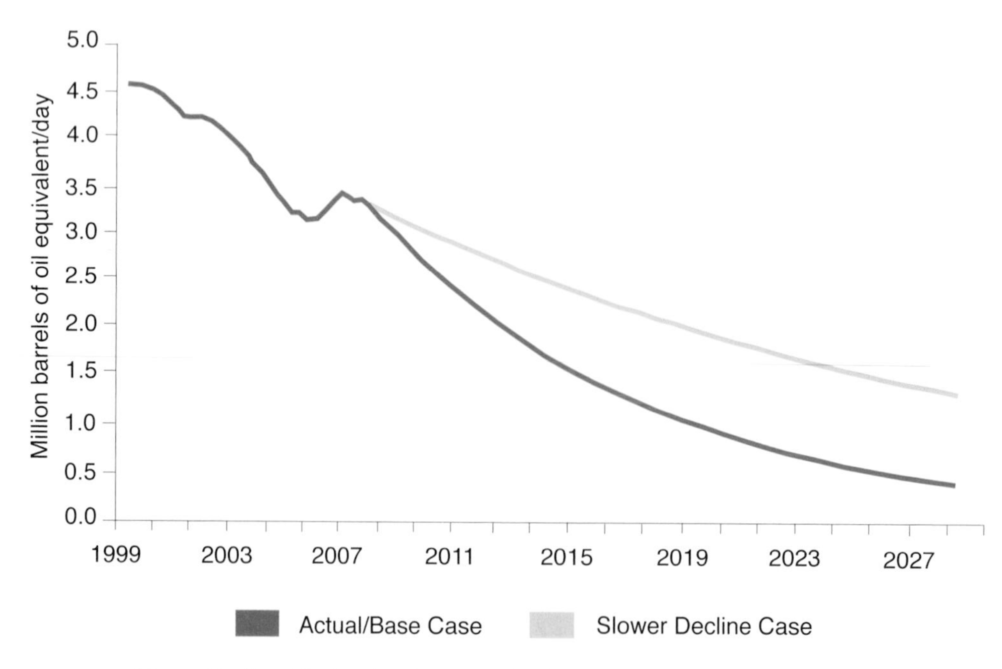

Figure 23–9 UKCS oil and gas production forecast (Source: DTI, 2006)

the relative stage of maturity of a number of technologies and the relative potential value that they might bring to the industry.

Within the overall challenge of finding economically producible hydrocarbons, optimising production rates and maximising recovery, the challenges for improved reservoir imaging are immense. At the exploration stage our ability to better see and image the key elements of source and reservoir rock distribution, trap configuration and integrity and hydrocarbon presence and distribution is an ever-present challenge and one that increases as a province matures. Electromagnetic techniques that complement seismic and offer the ability to distinguish between water and hydrocarbons in those traps prior to them being drilled are just entering the market.

For development planning the emphasis is on reservoir complexity and compartmentalisation which will impact the number and placement of wells required to produce the volumes present. During the production phase the monitoring of reservoir fluid movement is essential for production optimisation. An improved ability to identify the distribution of hydrocarbons in the subsurface and monitor their movement over time is a key component in the extraction of

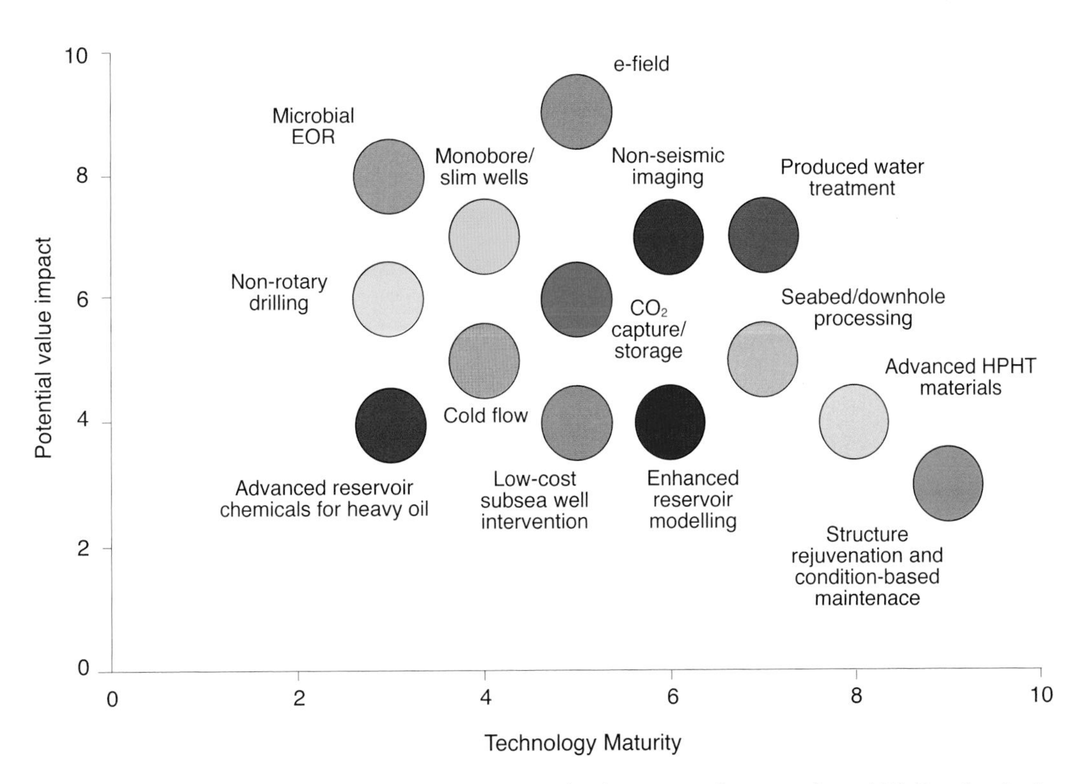

Figure 23–10 Technology maturity versus potential value impact for a number of E&P technologies (Source: OTM research)

added value from a province's hydrocarbon resources. It has a direct impact on well numbers, well costs, well productivities and the ultimate volumes of hydrocarbons produced.

Integrating the need to reduce operating costs with sustained operational integrity will require a balance to be struck between offshore manning numbers and remote operation and monitoring. Real-time drilling, intelligent completions, 3D visualisation and modelling, remote sensing, and monitoring and control are the five key technologies that if used together (sometimes referred to as 'digital oilfield' or 'e-field') will bring about tremendous rewards (CERA, 2003). In practice permanent down-hole monitoring coupled with adjustable flow control could interface with the reservoir to optimise production rates and ultimate recovery. Intelligent completions and real time operations are still in their infancy but if successful they should make a huge difference to both mature production and to production from new fields. The CERA (2003) study claims that application of digital oilfield technologies to ongoing onshore oil operations could add as much as 23% value, and application to deepwater exploration operations could add up to 14% value.

Another key area for technology development will be in the handling of problematic reservoir fluids and the by-products of such fluids. High pressure/high temperature wells are now in production and the improved ability to handle and dispose of corrosive reservoir by-products such as hydrogen sulphide and carbon dioxide will become increasingly important. Re-injection of by-products for disposal or for secondary recovery will require continual improvement both in the processing of the injection fluids and in the monitoring and management of the effects on the reservoir.

The main focus for subsea systems today surrounds reliability. Systems are controlled in real time and are expected to respond to ever-changing situations over the production lifetime (eg dropping reservoir pressure where increased water re-injection may be required, making 25-year lifetime design parameters important). Future demands are likely to include better flexibility, modular design for improved maintainability and increased standardisation on hardware interfaces and software protocols. Furthermore, industry collaborative efforts are driving towards the concept of subsea processing where separation, pumping and compression of the produced fluids takes place on the seabed.

Smaller field developments mean that it will be unlikely that many more large fixed platforms will be built and surface processing of new production will be reliant on the existing infrastructure. This means that a window of opportunity will be available for such fields to be tied back to existing platforms whilst such platforms remain economical to keep in production. Many of the 200 plus fixed structures in the North Sea have been on location for over 20 years so there will be a continual focus on their structural and operational integrity.

23.5 Industry initiatives to improve new technology application

New technology has and will continue to be central to sustaining exploration and development activities in the UK North Sea. The source of the ideas and funding that will promote that new technology is by no means certain as over the last decade the relative roles of the oil majors and the service companies have been brought into question. It might reasonably be assumed that the major oil companies have the human and financial resources to put sustained effort into the promotion and adoption of new technology whereas the smaller independents might, similarly, reasonably be assumed to run with the technologies that are put on to the market by the major service providers. In other words the majors can afford to be innovative whereas the independents need to make the best of what the market makes available to them.

Cyclicity in oil price takes its toll on investment in R&D and the collapse of the oil price at the end of the last decade saw oil companies reducing dramatically their spending on R&D and seemingly being willing to hand over the R&D role to the service companies. This situation was, however, short-lived and it appears that the majors are now gradually increasing their spending again (Fig. 23–11, DTI, 2005). The overall ratio of operating company to service company R&D spend shows a general trough from 1998 to 2001 but by 2005 'big oil' as represented by six majors had re-established its earlier dominant position. It is also noteworthy that major R&D investments are now being made by a relatively new but powerful group of companies, the International National Oil Companies (INOCs) such as Petrobras, PetroChina, China Petroleum & Chemicals Corp. (Sinopec) and Statoil. Among them globally, these four companies invested more than £700 million in R&D in 2005.

The role of intellectual property (IP) amongst operators in the North Sea is also changing. As the province becomes more mature, the focus for technology is increasingly to improve performance of existing business, as opposed to entering new provinces or developing 'unconventional' oil and gas. In this performance improvement climate, operators have fewer opportunities for genuine differentiation and competitive advantage from owning proprietary technology, and can better utilise IP to accelerate technology commercialisation or enhance working relationships with service companies. On a global basis, oil companies are showing a steady decrease in patents held, whereas the major service companies are showing a steady increase (Rao and Rodriguez, 2005). A key issue relating to technology application is therefore how to manage this IP 'asymmetry' between operators and service companies, such that operator needs are clearly understood, and effective knowledge-sharing and collaboration take place to enable appropriate risk analysis and optimum technology specification and implementation.

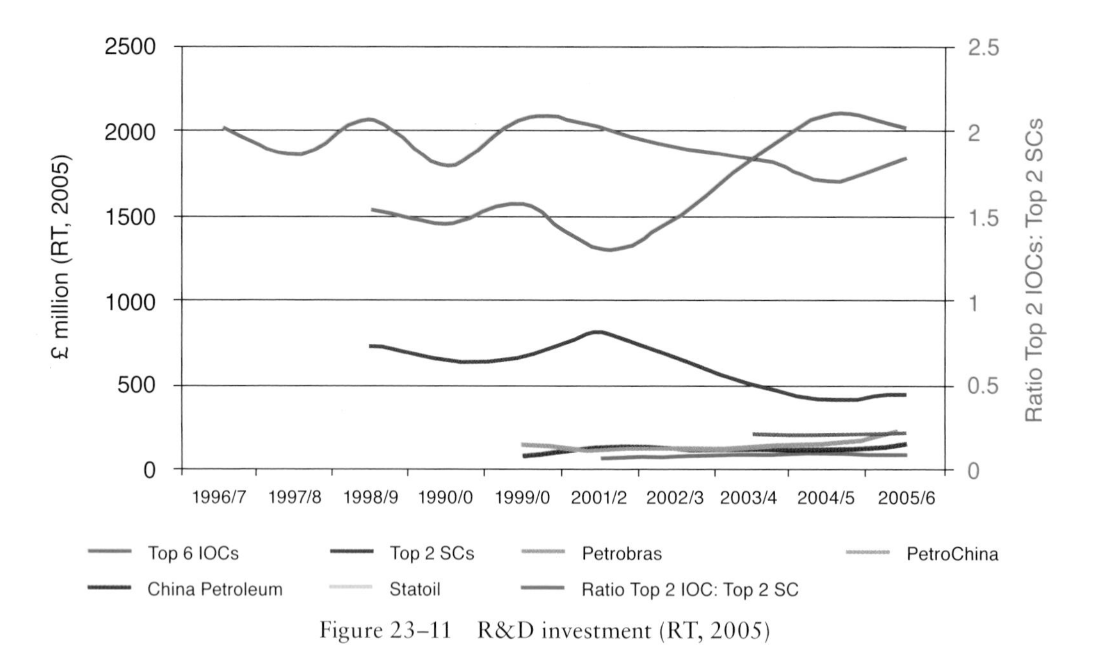

Figure 23–11 R&D investment (RT, 2005)

Competitive though the industry is, there are those who believe that partnerships between international oil companies, national oil companies, service companies and academia for the development of technology are the way forward (Donnelly, 2006). Such co-operation should lower costs and lead times and encourage standardisation around the technologies. Companies could then compete on how well they deployed and used the technologies.

The oil and gas industry, though, has always taken a cautious and conservative approach to new technology due to the real and perceived high cost of failure that can be associated with delays to project schedules and loss of production should a new technology fail. Incremental advances in technology have been preferred to radical solutions. The authority and autonomy of asset-driven organisations with their short-term performance driven targets has no doubt supported a culture of adopting known and reliable technologies and an aversion to risk-taking with new technology. As a result, a number of innovative technologies may well have found themselves on the shelf – expandable tubulars, casing/liner drilling, managed pressure and under-balanced drilling may be amongst them.

To overcome the apparently widening gap in communication between the operators and the smaller innovative technology providers as opposed to the major service providers, a new approach to the management of technology in the North Sea has been emerging. Forward-thinking independent technology management organisations are acting as facilitators to bridge the gap between user and supplier. Such companies are able to bring their independent knowledge to bear on longer term R&D strategy and planning issues that are of interest to the technology user whilst also guiding the provider to where their innovative ideas can be of maximum value.

These organisations can also provide valuable links between users by creating and managing databases and knowledge sharing networks, and can share experiences of new technology through state-of-the-art reviews of applications. On the other side of the supply chain, technology management companies can help to develop customer–supplier relationships, promote their clients' technology and help source R&D funding. They can also work with government and industry bodies to strengthen supply chain relationships and create export opportunities for proven new technology that was specifically developed for the North Sea.

One such example of a structured process for creating business value from the deployment of new E&P technologies is OTM's Technology Management Cycle (Fig. 23–12 – www.otmnet.com). It brings together several areas of upstream oil and gas technology management. Initially, it means identifying technology needs, carrying out market intelligence on available and emerging

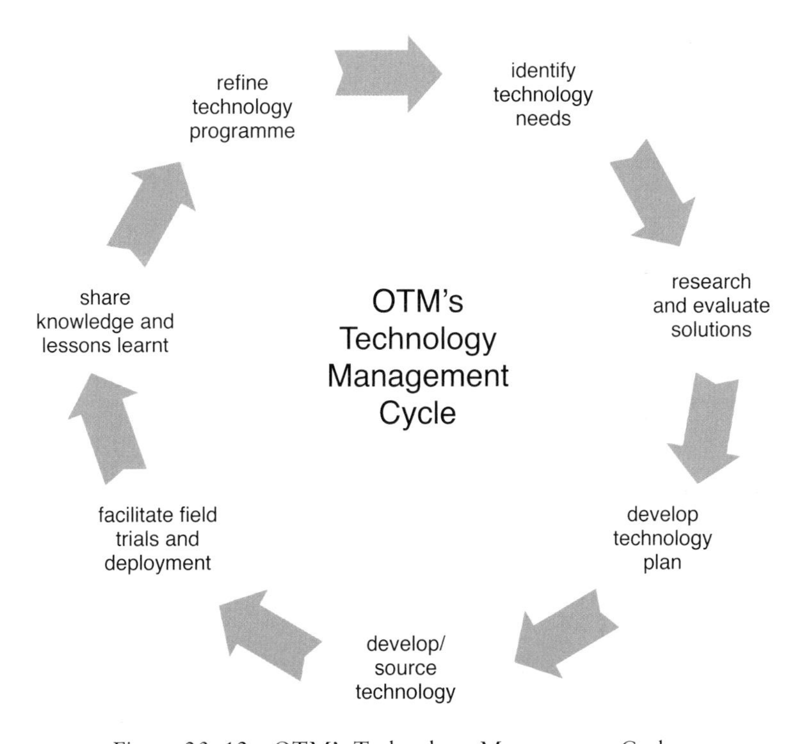

Figure 23–12 OTM's Technology Management Cycle

technologies and the preparation of an overall technology plan or 'roadmap'. The implementation phase covers sourcing of the technology components, and business case development for field trialing and deployment of the chosen solutions. The final phases include sharing knowledge and lessons learned from the completed technology deployments, assessing the value that the technology has brought to the business and eventually closing the loop by re-looking at a company's technology strategy and programme and refining it where at all possible.

TECHNOLOGY APPLICATION

LEGAL

23.6 Introduction

The development of new technology will now be one of the key factors in estimating and re-evaluating reservoir potential including net present value of a reservoir and also in developing the exploration, appraisal, development and production of that reservoir. The pace of technology adoption in the oil and gas industry has tended to be slow by comparison to other industries. However, the requirement to find new reserves and better ways of recovering oil and gas have now increased demand for new technology and its development.

One of the key differentials in the oil and gas industry is the ownership and deployment of technology. The ownership of technology largely rests on the ownership of the underlying rights to intellectual property in that technology.

The value and worldwide market penetration of many large and small oil and gas service providers, some of whom may be much bigger than some of the oil and gas upstream companies, depends on the ownership of certain patents, copyright and trademarks.

The competitive advantage on winning a licence in a Licence Round, for instance, may be the deployment and interpretation of new seismic data derived from new seismic technology. It could be, as another example, that the winning of a tender for the development of a well depends on the deployment of a world-beating patented process for a new Christmas tree. World-beating technology will often be deployed by its owner only into areas where it knows it can properly protect the rights in intellectual property to it.

In order to understand the key to ownership of technology it is a prerequisite to know and understand the legal rights to intellectual property.

To give an example of the importance of intellectual property ownership, if an upstream oil and gas company contracted with a contractor to deploy and install a new type of subsea production unit but the contractor had inadvertently contracted to purchase the unit from a subcontractor who had infringed a third party's patent rights, then that third party could apply for an injunction (England) or interdict (Scotland) to prevent the unit from being sold, deployed or used by the contractor, subcontractor and oil and gas company without its permission.

The oil and gas company and contractor may be caught as secondary infringers and the whole field operation could be shut down until a substitute has been installed or a deal has been agreed with the third party.

This chapter deals largely with the development of new technology in the oil and gas industry as opposed to its deployment on projects. The key to both development and deployment is in the ownership of intellectual property rights. The ownership of intellectual property rights is a substantial and complex subject but it is important for any company, which proposes to sell goods and/or services to another company, to establish whether it has the property rights to deal in, use, sell and market those rights or if it requires the permission, consent or licence from a third party. As a result, there is a substantial risk of a contracting party buying in goods and services from another party being involved as a 'secondary infringer'. Therefore, operators, co-venturers and contractors, in every part of the industry, are very careful to deal with persons who own their intellectual property rights and to avoid those who purport to own those rights but do not, or whose rights are being contested.

23.7 Intellectual property

There is no legal definition of 'intellectual property rights' as such, but the term may be broadly defined as meaning those rights in intangible property owned by a party. They may include patents as well as the unpatented right of 'know-how', trademarks, copyright, database right, registered and unregistered design rights, topography right, and the common law right to protect confidential information. The most important rights encountered in the oil and gas industry are often patent rights, trademarks, copyright, and the right to keep information (including trade secrets) confidential. A list and description of those rights, together with a summary, are set out in the Appendix to this chapter.

Patents

For a company to establish a patent right in respect of an invention, it must create the invention or work as well as establish a proper root of title to the ownership of the intellectual property right in that work. An employee of a company may, for instance, invent a new process. There is potential for that new invention to form part of an application for the grant of a patent whether in the UK, in the European Patents Office, or in another country. In order to make that application, the employer will have to establish whether the employee created the invention in the course of his normal duties as an employee, or in the course of specifically assigned duties falling outside his normal duties. Alternatively, the invention may have been made in the course of the duties of the employee but because of the nature of the employee's duties, and his particular responsibilities arising from them, the employee had a special obligation to promote the interests of his employer.

The following questions should, therefore, be asked. Is it the employee who owns the invention or is it the employer? Is it an invention which is capable of being granted a patent? To answer the latter question, there are certain requirements that must be satisfied. For example, the invention needs to be new, it should involve an inventive step, it must be capable of industrial application and it must not be specifically excluded from protection as a patent.

Novelty requirement

The most important test to satisfy is the novelty test. In order for the invention to be treated as new or novel it must not form part of the state of the art. In other words, it must not have been published or made available to the public by some form of disclosure before the priority date of the invention, ie before the date on which the patent application has been filed.

In order for the application to be successful, the examiner in the relevant patents office must have carried out searches which do not reveal that there has been any public disclosure of that invention before the first patent application has been filed. If an employee, as inventor, has inadvertently published his invention, informed another company of the invention without having that company enter into a confidentiality agreement or disclosed the invention to a third party by another means, then the invention will not satisfy one of the main tests for a grant of a patent. The importance of a grant of a patent is that it gives monopoly rights from the date of first publication to use that invention to the exclusion of third parties in the territory to which the patent has been granted.

To continue with this example of the hypothetical employer/employee, the employer will also have to establish who actually made the invention. Did that employee invent the process himself? Were there a number of employees involved from the same office? Or was there a combination of employees of that employer and external consultants?

If, for instance, one employee was the first to claim that invention, but in fact he had collaborated with other employees in the same office, then those other employees must be named as co-inventors on the application form for the patent. However, if the employee had collaborated with an external consultant, then the rule is that the consultant will own the intellectual property it creates unless there is a prior agreement between the employer commissioning that consultant to assign all created intellectual property under that commission.

Inventive step requirement

Having gone through that process, it will be necessary to establish whether there is a sufficient inventive step and to meet that requirement the invention must not be obvious to a person skilled in the art otherwise known as 'notional uninventive skilled man'. Before a company spends a substantial amount of money pursuing a patent application in a number of jurisdictions, it must be sure that the inventive step test has been met as this is the most likely area for an attack by a third party as to the validity of the patent after it is granted. One half of all patents granted are revoked and the process is, therefore, a risky one.

Copyright

Intellectual property rights cover a wide spectrum and it may be that an employee has made a number of detailed drawings in which copyright could be claimed by virtue of it being an artistic work. Copyright can be claimed for information set out in research notebooks, specifications, logarithms, data flow diagrams and working diagrams as long as it is being expressed in some tangible form, mainly for evidential purposes. It may be a literary work having been written down or some type of artistic work having been drawn. Copyright attempts to protect the form of the *expression* of ideas, not ideas as such. However, copyright is not a monopoly; it is a right to prevent the unauthorised copying of a work.

For a literary or artistic work to claim copyright it must be original, so that the employee (keeping with this example) must have created the work through his own skill, judgement and individual effort and it must not have been copied from other works. If the employee has created copyright in the work in the course of his employment, then the employer will be the first owner of the copyright in the work.

Design right

That employee may have created a design right capable of registration by, for instance, designing a panel for a lifting system on a rig. The registered design right affords protection to the 'attractiveness' of a design and must therefore satisfy the requirement of 'eye appeal'. In addition, the design should be new and of individual character. There is also an unregisterable design right which automatically protects the function of a design and therefore protects the shape or configuration of an article.

Confidentiality

The employer may require the employees to enter into employment contracts and Trust and Confidence Agreements to ensure that a duty of good faith is expressly stated between the employees and employer to hold secret information as confidential, and to prevent publication of that information. In this way, the employer would have protected its 'know-how' which might include the way in which certain systems are integrated or a technique for controlling loss of pressure in a reservoir.

Ownership

In order for a company to establish what it owns, it needs to review what has been created, whether it is capable of protection through an intellectual property right, the type or right which could protect it and whether, in fact, third parties own those rights. In the latter case, it would need to seek licences from those third parties to use those intellectual property rights which might prevent it from commissioning certain goods or it might need to devise new ways round those intellectual property rights to avoid paying royalties or simply not being granted a licence to use those rights.

23.8 Reservoir data

The operator and its co-venturers will have entered into duties of confidentiality in a Joint Operating Agreement (JOA) or Unitisation Agreement (UOA). The data relating to a reservoir will be regarded by the operator and its co-venturers as being secret in its nature and the operator will take steps to safeguard that data. While an operator will seek to have absolute ownership in the data in the reservoir and in a project, it may not usually expect to have any intellectual property ownership in technology created by a contractor which it wishes to hire in on the project at an early stage for, for instance, developing a Field Development Programme. However, it might expect to own all intellectual property rights created by the project team including the contractor on that particular project to bring a prospect into field development. Therefore, there will be detailed negotiations on the definitions on a project contract awarded to a contractor over the definitions of rights in intellectual property and improvements to that intellectual property.

23.9 Development of technology

The development of new technology may first be made by a design engineering company or it may be an operator which has created a concept and wishes to commission a contractor to further develop a concept into a new technology.

At the very outset, parties will need to decide who is owning the intellectual property rights and how they will be owned.

Development Agreement

In many cases, in the oil and gas industry partnering is seen as a way forward. This may be achieved by two project parties entering into a Development Agreement for the specific purpose of working on a defined project to create new technology. It may be the case that neither party wants to enter into a formal joint venture and wants to retain rights in its own background intellectual property. The parties will seek to agree how the new technology is to be owned and then to be commercialised.

Manufacturing Agreement

Alternatively, a design engineering company may have filed patents over an invention and wish to commission a third party to manufacture a prototype which it has designed. The manufacturer and the commissioning party will both enter into a Manufacturing Agreement in which there will be a specification given by the commissioning party, and the manufacturer will produce drawings and designs to turn the specification into a fully worked-up prototype. It will often be the case that the commissioning party requires the manufacturer to assign all intellectual property rights created in any designs or processes which it has invented while manufacturing the prototype.

Joint venture/limited partnership

It may be the case that two parties have complimentary skills, for example, one may be involved in chemical engineering, and the other in process engineering. They may decide to establish a project through a Project Development Agreement and then, if that is successful, to form a formal joint venture by creating a joint venture company or limited partnership to hold all the intellectual property rights developed in the project, and for the project company to commercialise in its own right, by marketing or selling the developed product.

The creation of a formal joint venture may require an Investment Agreement, detailed Articles of Association, assignation of intellectual property rights from each of the parties required by the joint venture company and the transfer in or employees or secondment of employees to the joint venture company. This process will be a very complex one and may require months of negotiation.

Research and Development Agreement

A party wishing to develop new technology may also commission research to be carried out by a university under a Research and Development Agreement. These agreements are likely to require careful negotiation as there is often a strong

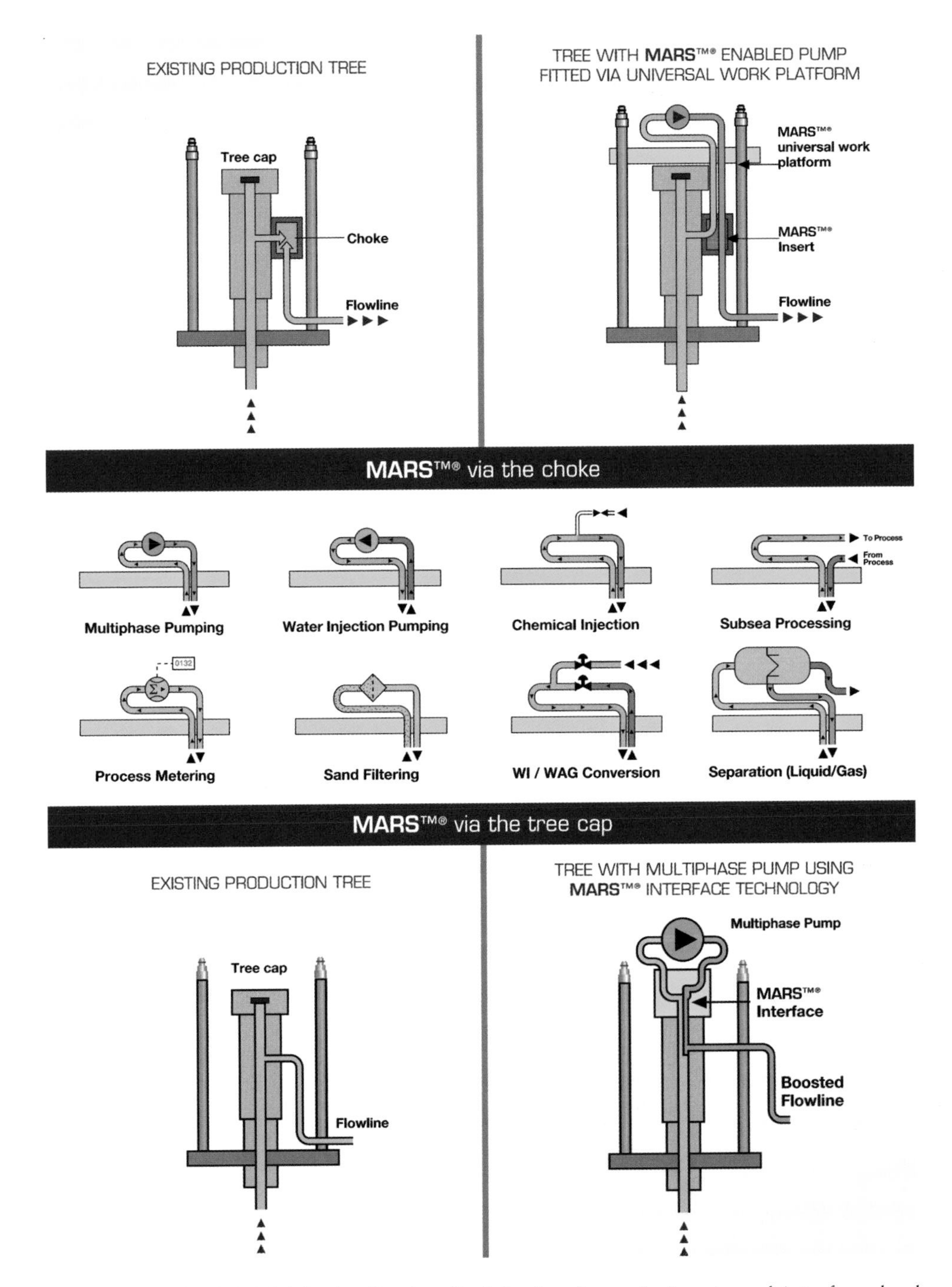

Figure 23–13 MARS (Multiple Application Re-injection System). A universal interface developed by DES Operations which enables any process equipment (eg pumps, meters, separators, etc.) to be retrofitted onto any wellhead

desire by the company to keep all research confidential until commercialisation, whereas the researchers in the university may wish to publish the results of the research as early as possible. Research funding may come from a charitable trust which could require the intellectual property rights to be owned by the trust. The company may wish the researchers to enter into Trust and Confidence Agreements and restrict them from carrying out other research projects or publishing data on them; however, this may be in breach of other contracts those researchers may have already entered into.

Accelerated Development of Technology

The deployment of new technology in a field may be the catalyst for a field development becoming economically and commercially viable. The new technology may have solved some problem in, for instance, the reservoir.

Oil and gas companies may accelerate early and unproven technology into a field at a time of higher oil and gas prices. The acceleration process may start by engaging a company holding key technology to design and integrate the new technology at a front engineering and design stage of field development. A technology company may therefore be contracted under a design and engineering contract to develop a part of the field architecture using the new technology. If the technological solution is developed this may lead to the award by the oil and gas company to a contract to manufacture the technology and install it into the field subject to successful factory testing and system integration testing.

The ownership of the intellectual property rights in the new technology may be a contentious issue. The technology company will insist in retaining ownership to all background intellectual property (ie technology owned by the party bringing it into the field development). It will also try and retain all rights to the foreground intellectual property relating to the new technology (ie that technology which is created during the field development); it might argue that all inventions within a defined area of technology will be owned by the technology company. The technology company will do this to deploy the same technology into other fields owned by other oil and gas companies. The oil and gas company commissioning the work may argue that it should own jointly the foreground intellectual property to the technology or have a worldwide licence to it for its fields; this argument, however, may impede the deployment of new technology across the industry and is likely to be contested.

23.10 The process

In developing new technology, it will often be the case that the party developing the technology will start with an idea which is then developed into an invention and committed to writing through some tangible form. The designs may be

Figure 23–14 MARS RE-EN Tree system. A modular derivative of the MARS (Multiple Application Re-injection System) which enables multiple simultaneous processing modules to be re-used on multiple wellheads, while maintaining full wellbore access

worked up through a process which will then form part of a specification, which is to be developed into a prototype. The party developing the technology may be constrained by its own lack of capital and may be required to raise venture capital to further develop the project or rely on some partnering agreement.

Once a prototype has been made it will be tested and, if the test results show a degree of success, it may lead the funders of the project to take it to the next stage. This will involve either entering into a commercial relationship under a Project Development Agreement with the party wishing to deploy it into a specific field, or to build the new technology on spec in the hope that end-users will purchase the product and repay the investment in the project. Before purchasing the product, an end-user will normally fully test the equipment and if satisfied with the test, contract the purchase of equipment on its own purchase order with its standard terms and conditions. Under those terms and conditions a party may attempt to take some ownership in the intellectual property rights over the technology and may also seek substantial warranty and indemnity cover in case of faulty design or workmanship which a new technology company may not have the capability to meet.

The process of developing a technology through to commercialisation is, therefore, often risky and hazardous with the result that many new technologies despite their technical success may never become a *commercial* success.

As an example of new developed technology being accelerated into field development relatively early on is the Cameron DES MARS: a multiple application, re-injection system for enhancing reservoir recovery. Pictures of the system are set out in Figs. 23–13 and 23–14. The system was designed in the UK, manufactured out in different locations in Europe and is being deployed into various fields worldwide.

23.11 Competition rules and anti-competitive behaviour

Both EC and UK legislation tends to promote co-operative or partnering arrangements to further innovation rather than new product development. As explained above, a lot of research and development is now either carried out by large service companies or partnering arrangements between small, medium and large-sized companies.

Arrangements between small and medium-sized companies, that is those enterprises with an annual turnover of €14 million or below, a total balance sheet value of below €27 million and employing no more than 250 people, are generally not caught by any of the rules and legislation either in the UK or EC which prevent anti-competitive behaviour.

Even large companies which carry out partnering arrangements are, in most cases, not in the ambit of the legislation because their product development does not lead to the relevant combined market share held by the undertakings which are parties to it. They will usually not exceed 15% of the relevant market share in the case of agreements between non-competitors and 10% in the case of agreements between actual or potential competitors. 'Actual or potential competitors' are defined in the Commission's Guidelines on the application of Article 81 of the EC Treaty to horizontal co-operation agreements (2001/C 3/02). Those thresholds are reduced to 5% of the relevant market if the effect of the parallel networks or similar agreements established by several manufacturers are traders.

The competition regime

In terms of EC legislation the main prohibitions on anti-competitive behaviour are found in Article 81 and Article 82 of the EC Treaty. Article 81(1) of that Treaty prohibits agreements within the Common Market which may affect trade between Member States and which have the object or effect of restricting competition within the Common Market. Article 82 prohibits any abuse by one or more undertakings with a dominant position within the Common Market, or a substantial part of it, if the abuse may affect trade between Member States.

Competition law in the UK has no specific regime dealing with research and development agreements, as this is largely dealt with at an EC level in terms of the research and development block exemption regulation (Commission Regulation (EC) No 2659/2000 of 29 November 2000 on the application of Article 81(3) of the Treaty to categories of Research and Development Agreements).

There are two provisions of the Competition Act 1998 in the UK which are, however, relevant to co-operation and partnering arrangement for research and development technology. The first is Chapter 1, which prohibits agreements between undertakings which may affect trade in the UK and which have the object of restricting competition within the UK or a part of the UK. The second is Chapter 2, which prohibits any abuse by one or more undertakings of the dominant position within the UK or any part of it, which may affect trade in the UK.

There are, within EC legislation, individual and block exemptions from the prohibition, *de minimis* levels which are not deemed to be anti-competitive and procedures for notification. There is a similar regime in the UK, which to an extent matches that in the EC. The effect of breaching both the EC legislation and UK legislation has significant consequences, as the agreements or arrangements will be void and unenforceable in respect of the provisions which restrict competition. Furthermore, the European Commission has the ability to impose fines on parties to such agreements of up to 10% of their worldwide group turnover and in the UK, and the breach could potentially lead to disqualification of directors under the Company Directors Disqualification Act 1986 (as amended by the Enterprise

Act 2002). However, very few research and development projects for partnering arrangements will breach such legislation.

In terms of EC legislation under Article 81, there is the option to apply for individual applications for exemption from the prohibition and also the Commission has issued a block exemption in Regulation 2659/2000 to categories of research and development agreements. There are also Guidelines[1] in the application of Article 81 to horizontal agreements. In accordance with Regulation 2659/2000, notice can be given of agreements of minor importance that they do not have an appreciative effect on competition, therefore, fall outside the prohibition in Article 81(1). Where there are fully functioning joint ventures, these are assisted under the EC Merger Regulation (Regulation 4064/89 on a control of concentrations between undertakings); a full joint venture is one which forms on the lasting basis all the functions of an autonomous economic entity.

In terms of vertical agreements, they are assessed under the Vertical Agreement Block Exemption (Regulation 2790/1999) and its accompanying guidelines. Whether particular co-operative arrangements for research and development breach EC legislation, will depend whether the 'object' or 'effect' restricts, distorts or prevents competition in the Common Market. It is helpful that the Commission has stated that most Research and Development Agreements do not fall under Article 81(1) and it should be noted that the Commission has block exempted these agreements where the parties have a combined market share not exceeding 25%. It is possible to apply for negative clearance where the Commission may certify that 'on the basis of the facts in its possession, there are no grounds under Article 81(1) or Article 82 of the Treaty for action on its part in respect of agreement, decision or practice'. Or it may be possible for the Commission to provide a 'comfort letter' whereby it informally states that in the Commission's view the agreement either does not fall within Article 81(1) or merits exemption and that it is closing its file. In terms of Article 82, if it appears that a company has less than 40% in a given defined market, there would be a presumption that there was no evidence of a dominant position.

Under the Competition Act 1998, an agreement will only infringe Chapter 1 prohibition if its effect on competition and trade in the UK is likely to be appreciable. In terms of Chapter 2 prohibition, there would only be a breach where one of the parties to an Research and Development Agreement holds the dominant position in the UK, or a part of it, and by virtue of the provisions of the agreement could be said to be abusing that dominant position which has an adverse effect on trade within the UK.

23.12 Litigation

It is very important for the creator of intellectual property rights to demonstrate a good and marketable title to those intellectual property rights as it is common for such rights to be challenged by competitors or other third parties. Litigation on intellectual property rights tends to be very expensive and within the UK will end up either in the High Courts in England or in the Court of Session in Scotland.

A third party claiming infringement of its intellectual property rights may seek an interim or full injunction in England together with damages, or an interim interdict or interdict together with damages in Scotland. It may also seek orders against other parties (for instance, an operator or co-venturer in the field who are using the technology and products) to prevent them using it and if granted, such orders could have a catastrophic effect on the operations of a field.

The fear of an infringement action leads operators and co-venturers to require full indemnities from contractors it is purchasing technology or products from. The reputational risk of a primary or secondary action against an end-user is such that operators and co-venturers would prefer not to deploy new technology where they believe that there is any risk or any infringement action against them.

The second reason why it is so important to provide a good route of title to intellectual property rights, is that the end-users will not pay premiums for technology which can be easily accessed from another source.

23.13 The sale and licensing of technology

For small and medium-sized enterprises (SMEs), it may be the case that they have accessed costly development capital which needs to be paid back together with a substantial premium to their funders.

Sale and Purchase Agreements

In these circumstances, the SME might wish to sell the technology at a point where it could get a reasonable return. The point of sale may be prior to the first commercial sale of the technology or the deployment of technology in the field. Alternatively, it may be that the seller wants to hold on until it can be proved that a number of the products have been sold and successfully deployed. Sale and Purchase Agreements of technology are often dependant on the seller demonstrating to the purchaser, a good and marketable title to the intellectual property rights and data surrounding the technology. For the right technology, it has been known for the large service companies to pay very substantial premiums.

Licensing

An alternative way of small or medium companies returning capital to funders would be by licensing. Licensing may also be used whereby an operator or large service company may have no wish to own exclusive rights in the technology and may be prepared to licence it out on a non-exclusive basis.

The licensing of technology can take different forms. Generally, a licence may be on an exclusive basis within a given number of territories. This means that the licensor grants exclusive rights to the licensee for that technology in those given territories, and that no other party apart from the licensee can use that technology. It could be that the licensor grants a licence for sole rights to the technology, which would mean that the licensor would retain the right to continue to use the technology within the given territories, but other than that the licensee had all the rights to the technology as against third parties. The third form of licensing arrangement can be on a non-exclusive basis whereby the licensor would licence technology to the licensee, but retain the right to licence to any other party.

The licence may be restricted in a number of ways in that it might be restricted to a number of territories in the world, to a term that was shorter than the life of the intellectual property rights, or there may not be a broad range of uses granted under the licence. For instance a licence to use, sell, market, distribute, prepare and otherwise use. In terms of licensing arrangements, parties to the licence will need to ensure that the licence terms are not breaching EC or UK legislation in terms of anti-competitive behaviour.

There is, under EC legislation, a technology transfer block exemption as set out in, the Technology Transfer Block Exemption Regulation 772/2004 EC,[2] which covers, for instance, pure patent licences, know-how licences and mixed patent and know-how licences. The block exemption does not cover trademarks, copyright or other intellectual property unless such rights are ancillary to the patents and/or know-how. Within the block exemption, there is a grey list that sets out a series of restrictions which are generally territorial in nature but are permitted, a white list in which certain clauses are not regarded to be restrictive in competition and also a black list which if such a clause is included in an agreement, it would mean that the agreement cannot benefit from the block exemption. There is also an opposition procedure whereby a party can provide accelerated notification for an agreement as long as that agreement does not include any black lists of restrictions.

If a party does sell or licence patents, trademarks, copyright, or registered or unregistered designs, there are different formal procedures which must be followed to assign such intellectual property rights and to notify the relevant patents office, all of which will need to be adhered to if the transfer or licence is to become effective.

Project Development Agreement

As an example of a co-operation agreement between two different parties, they may enter into a Project Development Agreement. In such an agreement, both parties would acknowledge that the other party may have valuable background intellectual property which it is licensing to the project for use in the project only. The agreement would then go on to state how the foreground intellectual property is to be owned and held. Each party would indemnify the other from infringement action of their own background intellectual property and in the agreement it would set out the milestones and objectives for the project. It would nominate project leaders from both sides and a project process in order to achieve a Final Report. It may also set out the objectives to commercialise a product and future commercial arrangements for such commercialisation. There would be confidentiality provisions, warranties and a provision dealing on how long the term of the project should last. There may also be restrictions on soliciting or inducing another party, employees or officers to leave.

Joint Industry Project Agreement

There have been a number of Joint Industry Project Agreements entered into between operators and SMEs. Under such an agreement, an operator and its co-venturers may fund a project to be carried out by a small or medium-sized business and a university. There would be project objectives to be achieved and progress reports to be provided to funders of the project. A steering committee would monitor progress of the project and approve amendments to the projects and a plan for commercialisation of the technology. There would be provisions on ownership of intellectual property and an acknowledgement by co-venturers that the SME would own its own background intellectual property, however, the foreground intellectual property may be owned on a share basis. Alternatively, the foreground intellectual property may be owned by the SME who grants to each participant and its co-venturers, an irrevocable worldwide non-exclusive royalty free licence to use the foreground intellectual property.

23.14 Field technology

In some cases, the operator and co-venturers may have designed and invented new field technology for deployment on a particular project. In those circumstances, they may enter into a Technology Agreement in which the parties can have an interest free, worldwide licence to use that technology on other fields in which they are co-venturers. This may, for instance, apply to the design of a platform or a Floating Production Storage and Offloading vessel (FPSO). Such agreements normally recite background intellectual property being licensed in, and available to, all the parties and the joint development of the new foreground intellectual property which is then capable of licence to all co-venturers in that field.

Appendix

A summary of intellectual property rights

The law on intellectual property (IP) in the UK offers protection to the creators of works in a number of areas. The four main types of IP are patents, trademarks, copyright and designs. Protection is also afforded to a number of related rights.

1. Patents

Legislation

The law which regulates this area in the UK is the Patents Act 1977 (the 1977 Act).

What is a patent?

A patent is granted to inventions. There is no statutory definition of an 'invention' but there are certain exclusions listed in the 1977 Act which gives an indication of what does *not* constitute an invention. (See section on exclusions below.) Patents offer protection by providing the inventor with a legal right to prevent others from manufacturing, using, selling or importing the patented invention. There are two authorities that grant patents in the UK – the UK Patent Office and the European Patent Office (based in Munich).

Registration

Protection only arises upon registration.

Ownership

Reference is made throughout the 1977 Act to the 'Proprietor' of a patent, yet the Act does not define 'proprietor'. However, there is a rebuttable presumption in section 7(4) which states that the person who makes the application for the patent shall be taken to be the person who is entitled to the grant of the patent.

Duration

The maximum term of patent protection is 20 years, after which the patent may be used by others to produce or use the invention. However, from the fourth anniversary of the date of filing the patent, renewal fees have to be paid annually to maintain the patent. If unpaid, the patent will cease to have effect.

Exclusions

The following are expressly stated in section 1(2) of the 1977 Act to not be inventions – (a) a discovery, scientific theory or mathematical method; (b) a literary, dramatic, musical or artistic work or any other aesthetic creation whatsoever; (c) a scheme, rule or method for performing a mental act, playing a game or doing business, or a program for a computer; or (d) the presentation of information.

Section 1(3) of the 1977 Act, indicates that a patent shall not be granted for an invention, where the commercial exploitation of that invention would be contrary to morality or public policy. There are also, in accordance with Schedule A2 of the 1977 Act, certain types of biological subject matter which are not patentable (for example, the process for cloning human beings and any variety of animal or plant).

Application

Section 14 indicates that UK patent applications must 'be made in the prescribed form' and contain the following:

- A *request* for the grant of a patent.
- A specification containing the *description* of the invention.
  The description will give an explanation about the invention which has been created by identifying certain features of the invention which distinguish it from existing inventions. It will also give a brief history of the invention. The description should be as detailed as possible and no additional information may be added at a later stage.
- One or more *claims*.
  The claim sets out the legal protection which is to be conferred by the patent. It will define the matter for which the applicant seeks protection, it must be clear and concise and it must be supported by the description.
- Any *drawing* referred to in the description or any claim.
  Drawings provide a visual representation of the invention. They will show technical and constructional features of the invention and may be used to show different views of the invention. There are very precise rules given by the Patent Office as to the nature of drawings.
- An *abstract*.
  This will give the name of the invention along with a brief summary of its technical features.

- *Know-how.*

  When applying to obtain a patent the applicant may feel that it is beneficial for them to with hold certain information which may be of advantage to their competitors to know, for example, if a particular type of material is used or a specific technique. Applicants will therefore try to disclose as little information as possible so as to protect their 'know-how'. At the very least, however, an applicant should provide all necessary information to enable a person who is skilled in that particular field to make the invention and the amount of information required and deemed to be satisfactory will ultimately lie with the Patent Office.

Patentability

In order for an invention to be patentable, there are certain conditions which must first be satisfied.

- The invention must be '*new*' (section 2 of the 1977 Act).

  An invention is said to be new if it does not form part of the 'state of the art', ie having been made available to the public (whether in the UK or elsewhere) at any time before the priority date of that invention. In other words, the invention must never have been made public, anywhere in the world, before the date on which a patent application has been filed.

- It must involve an '*inventive step*' (section 3 of the 1977 Act).

  An invention is said to have an inventive step where it is not obvious to a person skilled in the art.

- It must be capable of *industrial application* (section 4 of the 1977 Act).

  If the invention can be made or used in any kind of industry, including agriculture, then it will be considered to be capable of industrial application.

- Contrary to *morality* or public policy.

  A patent shall not be granted if it is contrary to morality or public morality (section 1 (3) of the 1977 Act).

Infringement

Section 60(1) of the 1977 Act sets out the instances in which a person will infringe a patent if he does any of the following without the consent of the proprietor:

(a) where the invention is a product, he makes, disposes of, offers to dispose of, uses or imports the product or keeps it whether for disposal or otherwise;

(b) where the invention is a process, he uses the process or he offers it for use in the United Kingdom when he knows, or it is obvious to a reasonable person in the circumstances, that its use there without the consent of the proprietor would be an infringement of the patent;

(c) where the invention is a process, he disposes of, offers to dispose of, uses or imports any product obtained directly by means of that process or keeps any such product whether for disposal or otherwise.

Section 60(5) of the 1977 Act sets out the circumstances where infringement will *not* occur, including, for example, the following: if an act is done privately and for purposes which are not commercial or for experimental purposes relating to the subject-matter of the invention.

2. Trademarks

Registered Protection

Statutory protection is given to trademarks via the Trade Marks Act 1994 (the 1994 Act).

What is a trademark?

A 'trademark' for the purposes of the Act is defined in section 1 of the 1994 Act as being 'any sign capable of being represented graphically which is capable of distinguishing goods or services of one undertaking from those of other undertakings'. A trademark consists of words (including personal names), designs, letters, numerals or the shape of goods or their packaging.

Registration Procedure

Sections 37–41 of the 1994 Act deal with the registration procedure. There are four stages leading to full registration of trademarks in UK law and they are as follows:

The application

The application for a trademark must contain the following: (a) a request for registration of a trademark, (b) the name and address of the applicant, (c) a statement of the goods or services in relation to which it is sought to register the trademark, and (d) a representation of the trademark (section 32 of the 1994 Act).

Examination

After the application has been filed the Registrar will examine the application to ascertain whether or not it satisfies the requirements of the Act. In doing so, the Registrar will conduct a search of earlier marks. If the application does not appear to satisfy the Acts requirements, the applicant will be given a time period within which to rectify the application.

Publication, observation and opposition

Once the application has been accepted by the Registrar, the Registrar shall cause the application to be published in the 'prescribed manner', meaning publication in the Trade Marks Journal. Once in the journal, third parties will then be given the opportunity to comment on the application in the form of observations or make oppositions. An applicant will be able to withdraw their application at any time or restrict the goods or services covered by the application. If the application has already been published then the withdrawal or restriction should also be published.

Registration

When the application has been accepted, and there has been no opposition made against it, the Registrar will then register the application subject to the fact that registration fees have been paid.

Duration of registration (section 42 of the 1994 Act)

Registration of a trademark lasts for a period of ten years from the date of registration. It may be renewed for further periods of ten years subject to the payment of a renewal fee. The duration of trademark application differs from other forms of IP protection in that the length of protection on offer is unlimited – there is no maximum period and it is open to renewal every ten years indefinitely.

Absolute grounds for refusal

Section 3(1) (a) of the 1994 Act provides that a sign which does not satisfy the requirements of the 1994 Act will not be registerable. Section 3(2) places further limitation on the type of signs that may be registered by providing that sign shall not be registered as a trademark if it consists exclusively of (a) the shape which results from the nature of the goods themselves, (b) the shape of goods which is necessary to obtain a technical result, or (c) the shape which gives substantial value to the goods.

In addition, there are a number of other reasons whereby a trademark will not be registerable, including the following – if the trademark is 'devoid of any distinctive character', if the mark consists of signs which are customary in the current language. In addition, a trademark will not be registerable if it is contrary to morality, or if the mark can be said to deceive the public in any way regarding the nature, quality or geographical origin of the goods or service. There are also specially protected emblems which will not be registerable such as the national flag of the UK or the flag of Scotland, England, Wales, Northern Ireland or Isle of Man if it appears to the Registrar that use of the mark would be misleading or grossly offensive, representations of the Royal Crown or any of the Royal flags or a trademark which consists of or contains words, letters or devices which might lead people to think that the applicant has Royal patronage.

Relative grounds for refusal

Section 5 of the 1994 Act lays down the relative grounds for refusal to register a trademark application. A trademark may not be registered if in comparison to an earlier registered mark where: (1) the marks are *identical* and the goods and services are *identical*, (2) the marks are *identical* and the goods and services are *similar*, if there is likelihood of confusion on the part of the public (which includes the likelihood of association with the earlier trademark), (3) the marks are *similar* and the goods and services are *identical or similar*, if there is likelihood of confusion on the part of the public, which includes the likelihood of association with the earlier trademark or (4) the marks are *identical or similar*, the goods or services are *not similar* and the earlier trademark has a reputation in the UK and the use of the applicant's mark would take unfair advantage of the distinctive character or the repute of the earlier trademark.

Infringement

For infringement to occur, the defendant must have used the mark 'in the course of a trade' and comparison with the infringing sign will be necessary. For the purpose of this section a person will 'use' a sign if he (a) affixes it to goods or the packaging thereof, (b) offers or exposes goods for sale, puts them on the market or stocks them for those purposes under the sign, or offers or supplies services under the sign, (c) imports or exports goods under the sign or (d) uses the sign on business papers or in advertising.

Section 10 of the 1994 Act sets out four circumstances in which a trademark can be infringed, which correspond with the four relative grounds for refusal in section 5 as listed above. Where infringement is found to have occurred, the court can make an order to have the offending sign to be erased, removed or obliterated from any infringing goods, material or articles in the infringer's possession, custody or control. Or, where this is not practicable, it may alternatively make an order to secure the destruction of the infringing goods, material or articles in question (section 15 of the 1994 Act).

In addition, the proprietor of a registered trademark may apply to the court for an order for the delivery up to him or articles which a person has in his possession, custody or control in the course of a business (section 16 of the 1994 Act).

Assignment

Trademarks are capable of being assigned (section 24 of the 1994 Act).

Licensing

The owner of a trademark may grant a licence to enable a licensee to use the trademark under the circumstances set out within the terms of the licence itself. This Act allows a person other than the owner to make use of the mark without infringement occurring. Licences may be general or limited (section 28(1)).

Unregistered Protection

Unregistered trademarks are protected by the common law principle of '*passing off*'. There are three elements which a claimant must satisfy in a claim for passing off.

- *Goodwill.* Goodwill can arise in the name or symbol which is associated with a business;
- A person has made a *misrepresentation* that is likely to deceive the public. A misrepresentation will occur where the defendant does or says something which would imply that his goods are connected in some way with the claimants. The state of mind of the defendant is not relevant. All that matters is that the misrepresentation causes some confusion to the public.
- The misrepresentation must *damage* the goodwill of the claimant. A common form of damage is loss of profit of the claimant's business.

3. Copyright

Registered right

The law on UK copyright can be found in the Copyright, Designs and Patents Act 1988 (1988 Act).

Definition of copyright

Section 1(1) of the 1998 Act defines copyright as a 'property right which subsists ... in the following descriptions of work: (a) original literary, dramatic, musical or artistic works; (b) sound recordings, films, broadcasts or cable programmes; and (c) the typographical arrangement of published editions'.

Duration of copyright

The time length of protection given by copyright is dependent upon the type of work in question and can be summarised as follows (sections 12–15A of the 1988 Act):

- for literary, dramatic, musical and artistic works the general duration of protection is *70 years* from the year in which the author of the work dies (subject to certain exceptions including works of unknown authorship and computer-generated works);
- for sound recordings the duration of protection is *50 years* from the end of the year in which it was made or published;
- for films copyright protection expires *70 years* from the year in which the death occurs of the last to die of the following persons – the principal director, the author of the screen play, the author of the dialogue or the composer of the music specially created for and used in the film;
- for broadcasts and cable programmes the duration of protection is *50 years* from the end of he year of the broadcast;
- for typographical arrangement or published editions the duration of protection is *25 years* from the end of the year in which the edition was first published.

Works

Copyright law offers protection to the creation and use of certain 'works'. In order to qualify for protection the work must fall under one of the following nine categories as specified in section 1 of the 1988 Act – (1) original literary works, (2) dramatic works, (3) musical works (4) artistic works, (5) sound recordings, (6) films, (7) broadcasts, (8) cable programmes and (9) typographical arrangement of published editions.

In addition, there are four other requirements that the work must satisfy before protection is afforded to it:

- the work must be *recorded in material form* (only applicable to literary, dramatic and musical works) mainly for evidential purposes;
- the work should be *original* (again only applicable to literary, dramatic and musical works);
- the work must be *sufficiently connected* to the UK; and
- the work must *not be excluded* from protection on grounds of public policy (ie works which could be said to be immoral or blasphemous could be excluded from protection).

Rights
Certain rights are conferred on the copyright owner, which if performed by a party other than the owner will amount to primary infringement. The rights conferred on the copyright owner are as follows:

- the right to copy the work;
- the right to issue copies of the work to the public;
- the right to rent or lend the work to the public;
- the right to perform, show or play the work in public;
- the right to broadcast the work or include it in a cable programme service;
- the right to make an adaptation of the work or do any of the above in relation to the adaptation; and
- the right to authorise another to do any of the (above) acts restricted by the copyright.

Primary infringement
Infringement is dealt with in sections 17–21 of the 1988 Act. Any transgression of the above rights by a person other than the copyright owner (and without the copyright owner's permission) will constitute primary infringement. In order for primary infringement to occur there must be direct involvement by a defendant in the act of infringement and at least a substantial part of the claimant's work must have been taken by the defendant and used in the act of infringement.

Secondary Infringement
The law affords further protection for those persons who assist the primary infringer. This is knows as secondary infringement and is dealt with in sections 22–26 of the 1988 Act. It will occur where someone deals with infringing copies for commercial purposes. This covers, for example, importing infringing copies into the UK otherwise for private/domestic use and selling or hiring out infringing copies.

Secondary infringement will also occur where a person facilitates copying of the work. The 1988 Act states that infringement will occur when a person supplies an 'article' specifically designed or adapted for making copies of the copyright work. As the article must be *specifically designed* it is not enough that the piece of equipment is capable of copying like a photocopier. Instead, this is intended to cover articles such as moulds and templates. In order for secondary infringement to occur actual constructive knowledge is required on the part of the infringer.

Exceptions
There are, in fact, a number of exemptions and defences in UK copyright law. These can be found in Part I, Chapter III of the 1988 Act and will become relevant only once infringement has been established. Some examples of the exceptions are:

- fair dealing (for the purposes of private study, criticism or review and for the reporting of current events);
- incidental inclusion of copyright material (this would cover for example the inclusion of a painting in a film);
- disclosure in the public interest;
- library uses, educational uses, public administration, cultural preservation, exceptions for artistic works, exceptions for computer programs, exceptions for databases, defences for film and sound protection, broadcast and cable programmes and various other miscellaneous defences also exist.

Unregistered right

In the UK the right arises automatically therefore there is no requirement that a work is registered for copyright protection to arise.

4. Moral rights

While Part I Chapter IV of the 1988 Act grants various rights to the owner of copyright works indicated above, the 1988 Act also confers *moral rights* on authors of the works. Moral rights are non-economic interests and are more concerned with the personality and reputation of authors. Infringement of any of the moral rights of an author is a breach of their statutory duty and will result in a reward of damages.

The 1988 Act recognises the following moral rights:

(i) The right to be identified as author or director of the works

Scope of the right
The right, as set out in section 77 of the 1998 Act, is granted to authors of literary, dramatic, musical, artistic works, and in films. The author of a literary work or dramatic work has the right to be identified whenever (a) the work is published commercially, performed in public, broadcast, included in a cable programme service or (b) copies of a film or sound recording including the work are issued to the public. The author also has a right, in the case of commercial publication or issue to the public of copies of a film or sound recording, to be identified in

or on *each copy* of the work, or if appropriate in some other manner likely to bring his identity to the notice of a person acquiring a copy (section 77(7)(a) of the 1988 Act).

Assertion

The right can only arise if it has been asserted (section 81 of the 1988 Act). The right may generally be asserted in two ways: (1) where the copyright in the work is assigned, the right may be asserted by including a statement that the author/director of the works asserts their right to be identified; or (2) by an instrument in writing signed by the author/director.

Duration

This right lasts the same length of time as copyright subsists in the work (section 86(1) of the 1988 Act).

Infringement

Infringement of the right will occur when the author has not been properly identified on the work. Identification must be in a 'clear and reasonably prominent manner' and should appear in or on each copy of the work. Where this is not possible, it must at the very least appear in a manner which is likely to bring the identity of the author to the attention of a person acquiring a copy of the work

Exceptions

There are various exceptions to this right which are set out in section 79 of the 1988 Act. For example, the right is expressly stated to not apply to computer programs, typefaces, computer-generated works, the reporting of current events and to publications in a newspaper, magazine, periodical, magazine or dictionary. The right will not apply in respect of work made for the purpose of reporting current events.

(ii) The right to object to derogatory treatment of the work – Section 80

Scope of the right

This right protects the reputation of the author of the works. It applies to the authors of literary, dramatic, musical or artistic works and also to the director of films.

Duration

This right lasts the same length of time as copyright subsists in the work.

Infringement

In order for this right to be infringed there must be a 'derogatory treatment' of the work in question. 'Treatment' of a work means any addition, deletion, alteration or adaptation of the work, other than a translation of a literary or dramatic work or an arrangement or transcription of a musical work involving no more than a change of key or register. A treatment will be 'derogatory' if it amounts to a distortion or mutilation of the work or is otherwise prejudicial to the honour or reputation of the author or director.

In relation to literary, dramatic or musical works the right will be infringed where a derogatory treatment of the work is published commercially, performed in public, broadcast or included in a cable programme service or when copies of a film or sound recording (containing the derogatory work) is issued to the public.

In the case of artistic work, infringement will occur where a derogatory treatment of the work is published commercially or when a visual image of the derogatory treatment of the work is exhibited in public, broadcast or included in a cable programme service (section 80 (4)).

Secondary infringement

Secondary Infringement (section 83 of the 1988 Act) will occur when a person (a) possesses in the course of business, (b) sells, lets for hire, offers, exposes for sale or hire, (c) in the course of business exhibits in public or distributes or (d) distributes otherwise than in the course of business so as to affect prejudicially the honour or reputation of the author, an article which he knows or has reason to believe is an infringing article.

Exceptions

There are various exceptions and qualifications to this right which are set out in sections 81–82 of the 1988 Act. For example, it does not apply to a computer program or to any computer-generated works, it does not apply in relation to any work made for the purpose of reporting current events, and it will not apply in relation to publication in a newspaper, magazine, periodical, encyclopaedia or dictionary.

The right will not be infringed by anything done for the purpose of avoiding the commission of an offence, complying with a duty imposed by or under an enactment or in the case of the British Broadcasting Corporation, avoiding the inclusion in a programme broadcast by them of anything which offends against good taste or decency, or which is likely to encourage or incite to crime, or to lead to disorder or to be offensive to public feeling.

Further, the right does not apply to anything done in relation to any work by or with the authority of a copyright owner unless the author or director (a) is identified at the time of the relevant act or (b) has previously been identified in or on published copies of the work (section 82 of the 1988 Act).

(iii) The right to object against false attribution (ie the right *not* to be identified as author of the works)

Scope of the right

The right is set out in section 84 of the 1988 Act and applies to a 'person' rather than specifically the author or director, and therefore encompasses situations where *any* person has been wrongly named as an author.

Duration

This right will subsist until 20 years after the death of the author/director and in that regard is less extensive than the other moral rights (section 86 of the 1988 Act).

Infringement

The right will be infringed by a person who issues copies of a work to the public or exhibits in public an artistic work on which there is false attribution. Thus, a person who merely issues copies of the falsely attributed work will have infringed the right rather than the person who makes the false attribution.

Infringement will also occur, in the case of literary, dramatic or musical works, by a person who performs the work in public, broadcasts it or includes it in a cable programme service where that person knows (or has reason to believe) that the attribution is false (section 84(3)).

5. Database right

The database right is a right which is related to copyright. A 'database' is a collection of data or other materials that is arranged in such a way so that the information is easily accessible by electronic or other means. In terms of protection of databases there are two levels – copyright protection and the database right.

Copyright protection

The database may be protected by the Copyright, Designs and Patents Act 1988 (the 1988 Act). In order to receive such protection the usual requirement for copyright must be satisfied (as discussed above) and, in particular, the database must have originality in the arrangement or selection of the contents.

The Database right

This is a relatively new right and was established through the Copyright and Rights in Databases Regulations 1997 (SI 1997 No 3032). This right is distinct from, and in addition to, any copyright protection that may exist. It does not require registration.

Substantial investment requirement

The database right will only arise if there has been a substantial investment in obtaining and presenting the information contained on the database (Regulation 13(1)).

Duration

Basic protection lasts for 15 years from the date on which the database was completed (Regulation 17(1)). However, if the database was published at some point during that 15-year period then the term will be 15 years from the date of first publication.

Owner/maker

The person who created the database is considered to be the first owner of it. The maker must take the initiative in obtaining, verifying or presenting the content of the database and also assumes the risk of investment. An exception to this general rule of ownership is where the data is made by an employee during the course of his employment, in which case, the employer will be regarded as the owner. In order to qualify for the database right protection, the maker must be a national of an EEA state or habitually resident within the EEA, a body incorporate under the law of an EEA state (and either has its central administration or place of business within the EEA or has its registered office in the EEA and its operations are linked in an ongoing basis with the economy of an EEA state), or a partnership formed under the law of an EEA state.

Infringement

Infringement will occur when another person, without the consent of the owner, 'extracts or re-utilises all or a substantial part of the contents of the database' (Regulation 16(1)). Extraction is taken to mean the 'permanent or temporary transfer' of the contents of the database to 'another medium by any means or in any form', and 're-utilisation' means taking the contents of the database and making them available to the public. The repeated and systematic extraction or re-utilisation of *insubstantial* parts of the contents of the database can also amount to infringement.

Exceptions

There are various exceptions to the database right, whereby infringement cannot be said to have occurred when the database is made available to the public. For example, a *lawful user* of a database which has been made available to the public in any manner shall be entitled to extract or re-utilise insubstantial parts of the contents of the database for any purpose. A database that has been made available to the public in any manner is not infringed by *fair dealing* if (1) that part is extracted from the database by a person who is a lawful user of the database, (2) if it is extracted for the purpose of illustration for teaching or and (3) the source is indicated (Regulation 20(1)).

6. Design rights

The protection which the law affords to the creation of designs can be split into two fields – the registered design right and the unregistered design right.

Registered design right

The Registered Designs Act 1949, as amended by the Copyright, Designs and Patents Act 1988 (RDA 1949) gives statutory protection to registered designs. Protection is given to a 'design' for a 'product'. This right covers two-dimensional and three-dimensional designs.

Registration

Applications should be sent to the Design Registry in the Patent Office for registration.

Eye appeal

The registered design right is more concerned with the 'attractiveness' a design, hence the need to satisfy the requirement of 'eye appeal'. A 'design' in this context means the appearance of the whole or part of a product resulting from the features of, in particular, the lines, contours, colours, shape, texture or materials of the product or its ornamentation (RDA 1949, s 1(2)). 'Product' means any industrial or handicraft item other than a computer program: and in particular includes packaging, get-up, graphic symbols, typographic typefaces and parts intended to be assembled into a complex product.

No design right will apply in relation to features of appearance of a product which are solely dictated by the product's technical function or in relation to designs which are contrary to public policy or morality.

Novelty and individual character

In order for a design to qualify for protection under the registered right, it must be new, ie it must not be the same as any other design. A design is said to be new if no identical design or no design whose features differ only in material details, has been made available to the public. A design will have individual character if a user of the design's overall impression differs from the impression of the user of a different design which has already been made available to the public. Whether a design can be said to be 'new' or to have 'individual character' will ultimately be a question of fact.

Proprietorship

The person which creates the design is treated as the proprietor of the design, except if the design was created in pursuance of a commission for money or money's worth, then the person commissioning the design shall be treated as the original proprietor of the design. Similarly, if the design is created by an employee in the course of his employment, his employer shall be treated as the original proprietor of the design.

Duration

The registered design right lasts for a period of five years from the date of registration of the design. However, this right may be extended by applying to the registrar for an extension for a second, third, forth and fifth period. Thus, in whole, the right can potentially last for a period of 25 years (RDA 1949, s 8).

Copyright protection for designs

Protection is also given to designs in the Copyright, Designs and Patents Act 1988, ss 51, 52 and 53. Section 51 of the 1998 Act states that copyright is not infringed by making an article from a design document or model recording or embodying a design for anything other than an artistic work or a typeface. A design document means a 'record of a design whether in the form of a drawing, a written description, a photograph, data stored in a computer or otherwise' (section 51(3)).

Unregistered design right

Scope of the right

The unregistered design right is established under Part III of the Copyright, Designs and Patents Act 1988 and, as its name suggests, there is no need for registration – the right arises automatically on the creation of the design.

Unlike the registered design right, the unregistered right does not relate to 'appearances' but is instead concerned with the 'function' of a design. A 'design' means the design of any aspect of the shape or configuration (whether internal or external) of the whole or part of an article (section 213(2) of the 1988 Act). The owner of the unregistered design right has the exclusive right to *reproduce* the design for commercial purpose by (a) making articles to that design or (b) making a design document recording the design for the purpose of enabling such articles to be made (section 216 of the 1988 Act). Reproduction is taken to mean 'copying the design so as to produce articles exactly or substantially to that design'.

Exclusions

In order for a design to be protected it must not fall within the exclusions in section 213(3). Namely, a design right is stated not to subsist in (1) a method or principle of construction or (2) features of a shape or configuration of an article which (a) enable the article to be connected to or placed in, around or against another article so that either article may perform its function ('must-fit'), (b) are dependant upon the appearance of another article of which the article is intended by the designer to form an integral part ('must-match') or (c) in features that are a surface decoration (beading or engraving would, therefore, not be protected).

Ownership

In general, the designer will be the first owner of any design right (section 215(1)). A 'designer' means the person who created the design. However, there are certain exceptions to this – (1) where the design right is created in pursuance of a commission, the person commissioning the design will be the first owner of the design right (section 214(2)) and (2) if the design is created by an employee in the course of his employment then his employer will be the first owner (section 214(3)).

Originality

Protection will arise only in respect of 'original' designs. A design will not be original if it is common place in the design field at the time of its creation (section 213(4)). It is difficult to ascertain precisely what 'common place' in fact means and there is little guidance to be found. To determine whether a design is common place, it will be useful to consider similar designs in the particular field and compare the design in question to see just how many similarities there are between them.

Duration

The period of protection afforded is two-fold and is set out in section 216(1) of the 1988 Act. Protection will last either *15 years* from the end of the calendar year in which the design was first recorded in a design document or an article was first made to the design (which ever occurs first). However, if articles made to the design are made available for sale or hire within five years from the end of that calendar year, *10 years* from the end of the calendar year in which that first occurred.

Infringement

Primary infringement of the design right will occur if a person, without the license of the design right owner, does or authorises another, to do anything which is the exclusive right of the design right owner, ie reproducing the design for commercial purposes. It will be necessary to show that there is some sort of 'connection' between the original design and the infringing article. Reproduction will have occurred if it can be seen that the original design has been copied 'so as to produce articles exactly or substantially to that design'.

Secondary infringement will occur if a person (without the license of the design right holder) (a) imports into the UK for commercial purposes, (b) has in his possession for commercial purposes, or (c) sells, lets for hire, or offers or exposes for sale or hire, in the course of a business an article which is, and which he knows or has reason to believe is, an infringing article.

7. Confidential information

What is confidential information?

This common law right prevents persons from using or disclosing ideas (in the case of trade secrets) or previously undisclosed information of others. In order for information to be considered confidential information and therefore be protected under the common law right all that is required is that the idea/information must be secret (ie not commonly available to public knowledge). The information does not need to be recorded in a material form, nor be novel or inventive. A wide range of subject-matter can be considered information.

Action for breach of confidence

If a person feels that there has been an unauthorised disclosure of their confidential information they may decide to bring an action for breach of confidence. There are there elements that must be satisfied in order to succeed in such an action each of which will be dealt with in turn.

The information must be 'protectable'

In order to be protected the information must be identified in sufficient detail. There are few restrictions on subject-matter which may be considered to be information but there are limitations on the types of information that will receive protection. The following types of information will not receive any protection by this common law right: (a) trivial information (this will have more of an impact in the area of trade secrets than in confidential information as ideas are expected to have some form of economic value or worth; (b) immoral information; (c) vague information (a certain level of detail will be required before protection arises); and (d) information in the public domain (if information is considered to be the common knowledge of the general public then it will not be protected. It follows that the information must contain a degree of secrecy).

There must be an obligation of confidentiality

A duty of confidence will usually arise where a relationship is established between parties. In the case where there is a direct relationship between the parties, the obligation may arise by contractual conditions, both express or implied. Equally, a third party may be bound by a duty of confidentiality if the third party is *aware* that the information it receives is confidential or after having received the information in good faith the third party subsequently becomes aware that the information is confidential.

It is further possible for persons who have no connection whatsoever to any of the parties (ie 'a stranger') to come under a duty of confidentiality. In such circumstances the factors in determining whether or not there has been a breach of confidentiality include whether the stranger was acting 'illegally' in obtaining the information and whether the stranger knew that the information was confidential.

A duty of confidentiality further exists between employers and employees during the course of employment. The employment contract will usually deal with the precise scope of the duty involved. Upon the termination of a contract of employment the employer will want to ensure that any confidential information the employee obtained during the course of his employment will not be passed onto any future employer. However, it would not be fair if an employer could prevent entirely an employee from making use of the skill or knowledge which the employee has obtained during the course of employment. The law therefore recognises that an employee is entitled to use such normal skills and knowledge in any future employment so long as the employee does not reveal any special knowledge and secrets of his former employer. To protect himself, an employer will usually include in the employment contract restrictive covenants to prevent the employee from working in that same trade for a specified period and within a specific geographical zone.

There must be a breach of confidence
In determining whether the obligation has been breached there must be an unauthorised use or disclosure of the confidential information. Once the information has been communicated in circumstances which bring about a duty of confidentiality then that person, the 'confidant', is under an obligation not to disclose that information without the consent of the 'confider'. Proof of illegitimate use will be required. State of mind is irrelevant therefore it will not be a defence to say that disclosure was made unconsciously, without malice or without a view to financial gain. Proof of the disclosure is all that will be required.

Defences to a claim

There are several defences to a claim of breach of confidential information. *Consent* will be a defence if the defendant can show that he had the consent of the claimant. There is also the *Public interest defence*. The disclosure of information will be justified as being in the interests if the public if it relates to a criminal offence, if the information reveals a danger to the health and safety of the public or if it evidences a miscarriage of justice, for example. A third potential defence is the rule *de minimis non curat lex*, meaning the law is not concerned with trivialities.

Remedies

The principal remedy to a breach of confidentiality claim is an *injunction* in England or *interdict* in Scotland to restrain the use and disclosure of confidential information. Where the obligation of confidentiality is contractual, *damages* may be awarded and in certain circumstances the claimant may be entitled to an *Account of Profits* for wrongful use or disclosure.

Notes

1. Guidelines on the application of Article 81 to horizontal co-operation agreements (2001/C 3/02).
2. Commission Regulation (EC) No 772/2004 of 27 April 2004 on the application of Article 81(3) of the Treaty to categories of technology transfer agreements.

— 24 —

TOWARDS 2020 – AND BEYOND

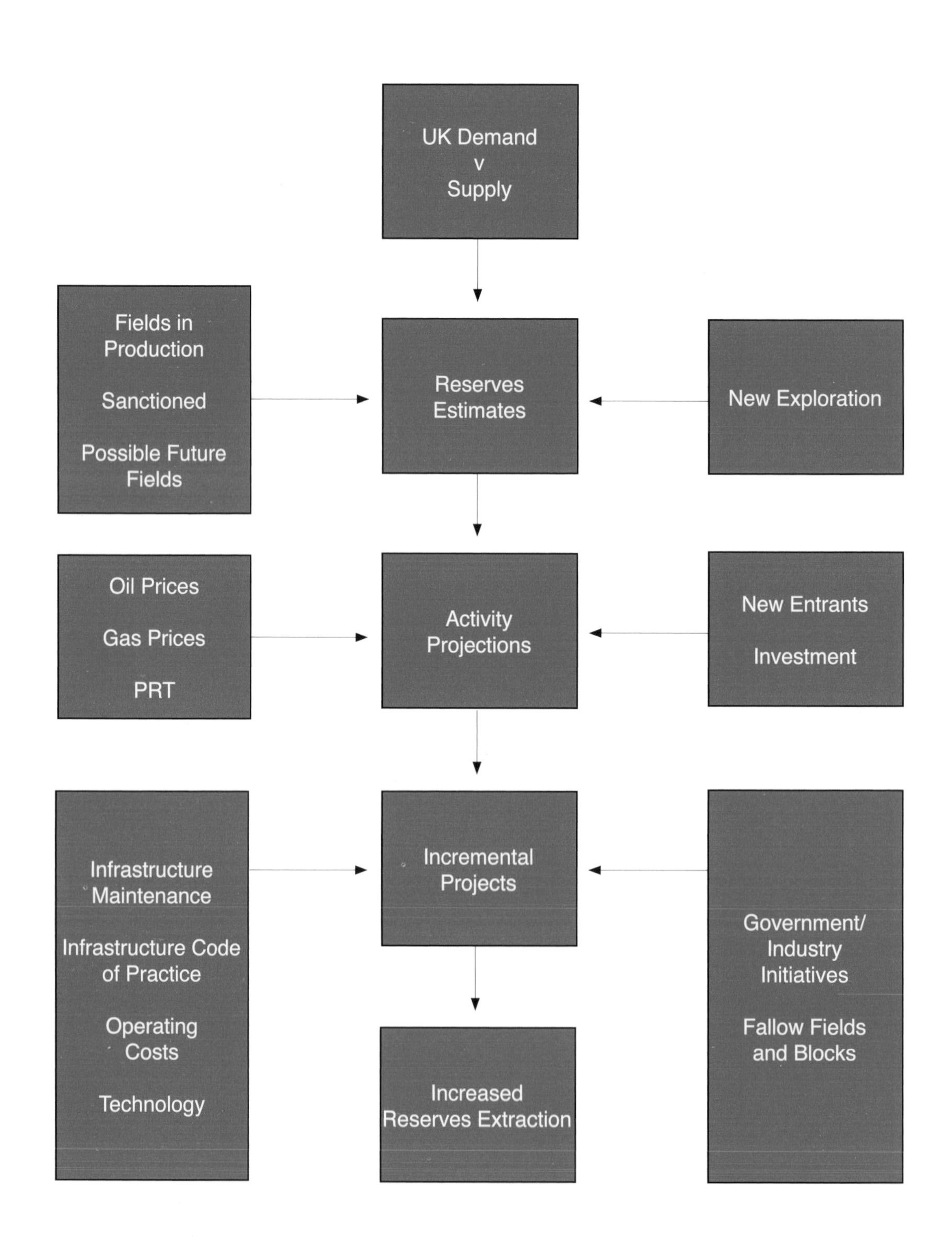

UK Demand
v
Supply
Fields in Production
Sanctioned
Possible Future Fields
Reserves Estimates
New Exploration
Oil Prices
Gas Prices
PRT
Activity Projections
New Entrants
Investment
Infrastructure Maintenance
Infrastructure Code of Practice
Operating Costs
Technology
Incremental Projects
Government/ Industry Initiatives
Fallow Fields and Blocks
Increased Reserves Extraction

TOWARDS 2020 – AND BEYOND

TECHNICAL

24.1 The UK Continental Shelf in its world context

Production from the UKCS peaked in 1999 and has been declining steadily since then, but remains very important in a UK context and significant in world terms. Thus, in 2005 oil production (including NGLs) was 1.8 mmb/d which constituted 2.2% of the world total (BP, 2006). In the same year, total gas production was 8.94 mmcf/d which constituted 3.2% of the world total. The UK is also a major consumer of both products, with oil demand of 1.79 mmb/d and gas consumption of 9.6 mmcf/d in 2005 (BP, 2006). The UK became a net gas importer in 2004, and should soon become a consistent net oil importer as well.

Given the highly international character of the oil market and, increasingly, the gas market as well, world trends in both demand and supply will have a major impact on UK production and consumption through the resulting effect on prices. Long-term world trends are notoriously difficult to predict. There are many factors which determine energy and oil demand through time including population growth, the rate of economic growth, the (changing) industrial and commercial structure, and the extent of energy-saving technological progress. For oil and gas, the extent to which substitute fuels are available in a competitive form determine their share of the energy mix. In recent years, the growing concern over CO_2 and other emissions has led to the setting of ambitious targets for reductions in emissions which entail substantial moderation in the growth of oil demand. Currently there are many uncertainties regarding how vigorously Governments around the world will implement CO_2 reduction policies which add to the difficulties of predicting energy, oil and gas demand.

Given these difficulties, the construction of scenarios is a resort which is often made to model the outcomes of a set of logical, consistent assumptions. The International Energy Agency (IEA) conducts a large such exercise every year and much attention is given to the findings. In their recent publication (IEA, 2006) the IEA have two scenarios, termed Reference and Alternative. Under the former, conventional assumptions were made about determining factors such as population and economic growth, but no new government policies were introduced in the period up to 2030. The Alternative scenario incorporated the effects of further policy measures to deal with both climate change and energy security problems. In the Reference case world population growth was postulated to be 1% per year (considerably lower than in the period 1980–2004), and world economic growth at 3.4% per year (the same as in the period 1990–2004). The world oil price was assumed to decline to $47.80 per barrel by 2015 and subsequently increase to $55 by 2030 (all at 2005 prices).

Within this framework world primary energy demand was projected to grow at 1.6% per year to 2030, with oil growing at 1.3% per year (from 83.6 mmb/d in 2005 to 116.3 mmb/d in 2030), and natural gas at the substantially higher pace of 2% per year. Both energy and oil demand are projected to grow at much higher rates in the developing countries (especially in Asia) compared to OECD countries. In OECD Europe total energy demand is projected to grow at 0.6% per year, with oil at only 0.2% per year and gas at a much higher rate of 1.4% per year. In developing countries total energy demand could grow at 2.6% per year, oil at 2.5%, and gas at 3.7% per year.

Under the IEA Alternative policy scenario the world average growth rate in total primary energy demand to 2030 is 1.2% per year, with oil growing at 0.9% per year (reaching 111 mmb/d in 2030), and natural gas at 1.5%, with the corresponding annual rates for OECD Europe being 0.3% for total primary energy, 0.1% for oil, and 0.9% for natural gas. In the developing countries primary energy demand grows at 2.1% annually, oil at 1.9% and gas at 3.1%.

To meet the prospective growth in world oil demand under the Reference case the IEA projects non-OPEC crude production to grow at an average rate of 0.7% per year to 2030 to 57.6 mmb/d, with non-conventional oil making a contribution of 7.4 mmb/d by 2030. OPEC production grows at an average rate of 2.1% per year, which entails output growing from 33.6 mmb/d in 2005 to 56.3 mmb/d by 2030 when it accounts for 49% of the world's needs. Under the Alternative policy scenario, with oil demand in 2030 being over 11% less than in the reference case (and gas nearly 13% less), OPEC's share of total oil production becomes less than 44%.[1]

Of course, reflecting the major uncertainties, all such long-term projections are subject to considerable margins of error, but, particularly on the energy/

oil/gas demand side, the IEA are extremely well informed. Their findings are broadly consistent with those of other studies on long-term energy/oil demand. Thus, Shell has produced interesting long-term scenarios for many years. In their most recent study (Shell, 2005) there are three detailed scenarios. Under the first, termed Low Trust Globalisation, world oil demand grows at 1.5% per year, reaching around 110 mmb/d in 2025. This scenario is consistent with relatively high oil prices as OPEC acts in a relatively cohesive manner, and does not increase production very substantially. The second scenario, termed Open Doors is one where oil demand grows at nearly 2% per year, attaining around 120 mmb/d in 2025. OPEC production increases very substantially. The third scenario termed Forces of Global Integration and Fragmentation, reflects relatively low economic growth and strong conservation measures. The consequence is that world oil demand grows at less than 1% per year and by 2025 it could be around 96 mmb/d. Given the multiple uncertainties there is a broad consistency between the results of these studies.

The longer-term supply side uncertainties are probably greater than those relating to demand. The studies noted above take what may be described as middle-of-the road views on potential world oil production. For some years there has been a keen debate on the prospects for longer-term world oil production, with some arguing that the peak is imminent and others taking the view that it will not occur for a considerable number of years, especially if non-conventional oil is included. The differences in the results of the studies are quite staggering, with some showing world production of conventional oil in 2020 or around 118 mmb/d and others as low as 65 mmb/d. By 2030 the range becomes even greater. When non-conventional oil is included the range by 2030 is from 120 to 65 mmb/d.[2]

These enormously wide ranges reflect different views regarding total remaining resources in place, recovery factors, technological progress, and other factors determining economic production. The willingness of the protagonists in the debate to make strong, confident predictions in the absence of full key information has not contributed to a very scientific debate, and has not been very helpful to policy-makers. It is clear that prospective production and oil prices in the medium term will depend to a marked degree on the willingness of OPEC member countries to undertake the large investments necessary to exploit their correspondingly large resource base. This is a key unknown, and in particular it is unclear to what extent the international oil companies can obtain access to these reserves. In at least some of the countries where the industry is controlled by national oil companies there are both capital and technological constraints which may well prevent the expeditious and full exploitation of the reserves.

The current verdict of market makers reflected in forward price curves, is that relatively high oil prices will prevail over the next few years. But these forward market indicators have not proved noticeably accurate predictors of oil prices in the past. Oil companies tend to take cautious views on oil and gas prices in screening long-term investments. Those employed below to model future UK production reflect these sentiments.[3]

24.2 Prospective UK oil and gas demand

In the case of the UK the world prospects as discussed above impact on consumers and producers through their effects on oil and gas prices. As in other countries, UK oil and gas demand depend on the pace of economic growth, the (changing) structure of industry and commerce, and technological changes favouring less polluting forms of energy. Much also depends on government policies over a wide range of issues. Thus, transportation policy (including road pricing) will affect the demand for motor gasoline and diesel. Decisions to encourage the building of new nuclear power stations and/or extend the life of old ones will affect the demand for gas for power generation. The vigour with which policies to reduce CO_2 emissions are pursued will affect the demand for oil and gas products in all using-sectors of the economy.

There is much agreement that the demand for oil in the UK will grow quite slowly. The only significant area of growth is transportation. There has been a long-term decline in UK oil consumption from its peak in 1973. The power generation sector is a notable example. The run-down of much heavy, energy-intensive industries in the 1980s such as steel and ship-building, have also contributed to the long-term decline in oil consumption. In the future, very modest increases are foreseen. The DTI's recent forecasts[4] indicate annual average growth rates to 2020 in the range 0.045%–0.48%. These produce consumption in 2020 in the range 1.8–1.92 mmb/d. For gas, the expected growth rates are higher, but the uncertainty is greater, and a range of 0.33%–1.76% annual average increase to 2020 is predicted, producing consumption between 9.9 mmcf/d–12/26 mmcf/d in 2020. These figures can be related to the projections of production in Section 24.5 below to indicate the prospective extent of UK import dependence.

24.3 UK remaining reserves and potential

Prospective production and related activity in the UKCS depends on many factors, but a key element is the likely remaining reserves. Reflecting the growing maturity of the province these have been falling for some years but they remain substantial. While various estimates of the remaining potential are made, those made by the DTI are worthy of special attention because of the comprehensive and well-informed databases to which they have access. In all such exercises there are considerable uncertainties and the estimates have to be regularly updated in the light of fresh information on matters such as reservoir performance, new discoveries (or lack of them), and technological progress.

In their most recent update[5] the DTI indicate the remaining potential under several different headings. Thus, reserves are split into three main categories, namely proven, probable, and possible. Proven reserves indicate those which have a probability of 90% or more of being produced with today's technology. Probable reserves are not yet in the proven category but have a probability exceeding 50% of being technically and economically producible. Possible reserves are in neither of the above categories but have a significant though less than 50% chance of being technically and commercially producible. On this basis remaining proven oil reserves at January, 2006 were estimated at 3.87 billion barrels, probable reserves at 2.25 billion, and possible at 3.38, billion producing a maximum of 9.5 billion barrels.

In the DTI's classification system, account is taken of what are termed possible additional reserves in existing discoveries. Currently these are not technically nor commercially producible but, of course, technological progress may convert them to become economically viable. The oil reserves in this category are in the range 510–3,170 million barrels with a central estimate of 1,525 million barrels. The DTI also makes estimates of what are termed undiscovered resources. These are based on a statistical analysis of mapped leads involving risk analysis, including the use of the Monte Carlo technique. Clearly there is much greater uncertainty attached to the results of this modelling and a substantial range is presented. In the West of Scotland area (other than West of Shetland) detailed information is in any case not available. The most recent estimates of undiscovered oil resources are in the range 2.6–11.9 billion barrels with a central estimate of 5.6 billion barrels. In the latter 2.76 billion barrels are in the Central North Sea and 2.1 billion barrels in West of Shetland/West of Scotland.

When all the above categories are added together the total remaining oil potential from the UKCS is in the range 7–24.5 billion barrels with a central estimate of 13.2 billion barrels. With total depletion to date of 23.17 billion barrels it can be concluded that, while there is a substantial amount left in the glass it is less than half full on central estimates, but, taking an optimistic view, what can eventually be drained from it could approach what has been already extracted.

With respect to natural gas the same classification is employed. Thus, remaining proven reserves are estimated at 17 tcf, probable reserves at 8.7 tcf, and possible at 9.8 tcf. Possible additional resources are estimated to be in the range 2.4 tcf–10 tcf with a central estimate of 5 tcf. Undiscovered resources are estimated to be in the range 8 – 36.5 tcf with a central estimate of 14.9 tcf. When all categories are added together the total remaining potential is in the range 27.4–82.0 tcf with a central estimate of 45.5 tcf. Depletion to date has been 70.9 tcf, and so concluding comments similar to those applying to oil are appropriate for the gas potential in its historic context.

The remaining total potential of oil plus gas is conveniently amalgamated and expressed in terms of billions of barrels of oil equivalent (bn boe). Thus, remaining proven plus probable plus possible reserves are in the range 6.8–15.6 bn boe, with the central estimate being 10.5 bn boe. Possible additional reserves are in the range 0.9–4.9 bn boe with the central estimate being 2.4 bn boe. Undiscovered resources are in the range 4.0–18.2 bn boe with the central estimate being 8.2 bn boe. Thus, the total remaining potential is in the range 11.7–38.7 bn boe with the central estimate being 21.1 bn boe. To put this in perspective, aggregate depletion to date has been 35.4 bn boe.

24.4 Methodology, data and assumptions for making activity projections

The projections of production and expenditures from the UKCS have been made through the use of financial modelling, including the use of the Monte Carlo technique, informed by a large, recently updated, field database validated by the relevant operators. The field database incorporates key, best estimate information on production, and investment, operating and decommissioning expenditures. These refer to 316 sanctioned fields, 112 incremental projects (76 probable and 23 possible) relating to these fields, 19 probable fields, and 23 possible fields. All these are unsanctioned but are currently being examined for development. An additional database contains 215 fields defined as being in the category of technical reserves. Summary data on reserves (oil/gas) and block location are available for these. They are not currently being examined for development by licensees.

Monte Carlo modelling was employed to estimate the possible numbers of new discoveries in the period to 2030. The modelling incorporated assumptions based on recent trends relating to exploration effort, success rates, sizes, and types (oil, gas, condensate) of discovery. A moving average of the behaviour of these variables over the past 10 years was calculated separately for six areas of the UKCS (Southern North Sea, (SNS), Central North Sea (CNS), Moray Firth (MF), Northern North Sea (NNS), West of Scotland (WOS), and Irish Sea (IS)), and the results employed for use in the Monte Carlo analysis. Because of the very limited data for WOS and IS over the period judgmental assumptions on success rates and average sizes of discoveries were made for the modelling.

It is postulated that the exploration effort depends substantially on a combination of (a) the expected success rate, (b) the likely size of discovery, and (c) oil/gas prices. In the present study, three future oil/gas price scenarios were employed as follows:

Future oil and gas price scenarios		
	Oil Price (real) $/bbl	Gas Price (real) Pence/therm
High	40	36
Medium	30	28
Low	25	24

Figure 24–1

These values are below current market levels but are used to reflect values generally used by investors when assessing long-term investments.

The postulated numbers of annual exploration wells for the whole of the UKCS are as follows:

Exploration wells		
	2006	2030
High	50	38
Medium	38	27
Low	31	20

Figure 24–2

The annual numbers are modelled to decline in a linear fashion over the period.

It is postulated that success rates depend substantially on a combination of (a) recent experience, and (b) size of the effort. It is further suggested that higher effort is associated with more discoveries but with lower success rates compared to reduced levels of effort. This reflects the view that low levels of effort will be concentrated on the lowest risk prospects, and thus higher effort involves the acceptance of higher risk. For the UKCS as a whole, three success rates were postulated as follows:

Success rates
Medium effort/Medium success rate = 23%
High effort/Low success rate = 19%
Low effort/High success rate = 24%

Figure 24–3

It is assumed that technological progress will maintain these success rates over the time period.

The mean sizes of discoveries made in the last few years for each of the six regions were calculated. It was further assumed that the mean size of discovery would decrease in line with historic experience. Such decline rates are quite modest. For purposes of the Monte Carlo modelling of new discoveries the Standard Deviation (SD) was set at 50% of the mean value. In line with historic experience the size distribution of discoveries was taken to be lognormal.

Using the above information the Monte Carlo technique was employed to project discoveries in the six regions to 2030. For the whole period the total numbers of discoveries for the UKCS were are follows:

Total number of discoveries to 2030	
High effort/Low success rate	221
Medium effort/Medium success rate	179
Low effort/High success rate	146

Figure 24–4

For each region the average development costs (per boe) of fields in the probable and possible categories were calculated. These reflect substantial cost inflation over the last two years. Using these as the mean values the Monte Carlo technique was employed to calculate the development costs of new discoveries. A normal distribution with a SD = 20% of the mean value was employed. For the whole of the UKCS the average development costs on this basis were $9.45/boe. Annual operating costs were modelled as a percentage of accumulated development costs. This percentage varied according to field size. It was taken to increase as the size of the field was reduced reflecting the presence of economies of scale in the exploitation costs of fields.

With regard to fields in the category of technical reserves it was recognised that many have remained undeveloped for a long time, but it was assumed that, reflecting the high current costs and prospective technological progress, their development costs would be aligned with those for new discoveries for each of the regions. For purposes of Monte Carlo modelling a normal distribution of the recoverable reserves for each field with a SD = 50% of the mean was assumed. With respect to development costs the distribution was assumed to be normal with a SD = 20% of the mean value.

The annual numbers of new field developments were assumed to be constrained by the physical and financial capacity of the industry. This subject is currently very pertinent in the UKCS. The ceilings were assumed to be linked to the oil/gas scenarios with maxima of 22, 20 and 17 respectively under the High, Medium, and Low Cases. These constraints do *not* apply to incremental projects which are additional to new field developments. To put these assumptions in perspective, 13 new fields received development approval in 2005.

A noteworthy feature of the 112 incremental projects in the database is the expectation that the great majority will be executed over the three years from 2006. It is virtually certain that in the medium and longer-term many further incremental projects will be designed and executed. They are just not yet at the serious planning stage. Such projects can be expected not only on currently sanctioned fields but also on those presently classified as in the field categories of probable, possible, technical reserves and future discoveries.

Accordingly, estimates were made of the potential extra incremental projects from all these sources. Examination of the numbers of such projects and their key characteristics (reserves and costs) being assessed by operators over the past five years indicated a decline rate in the volumes. On the basis of this it was felt that, with a decline rate reflecting historic experience, further portfolios of incremental projects could reasonably be expected. As noted above such future projects would be spread over *all* categories of host fields. Their sizes and costs reflect recent trends.

The financial modelling incorporated a discount rate, field economic cut-off, and the full details of the current petroleum tax system including the changes in the 2006 Budget. The base case has a post-tax discount rate of 10% in real terms. An important assumption is that adequate infrastructure will be available to facilitate the development of the future projects. It is also important to note that it is assumed that investment decisions are made on the basis of the oil/gas prices indicated. When the prospective investments in probable and possible fields and incremental projects were subjected to economic analysis it was found that most were quite small and the returns in terms of NPVs were correspondingly often small. It was felt that, to reflect the relationship between the risks and rewards involved, a minimum expected NPV at the discount rates employed would be necessary before the project/field was sanctioned. For purposes of this study minimum NPVs of £10 million were employed as thresholds.

24.5 Results of modelling

(a) Characteristics of new fields/projects

To highlight the current and prospective position of the industry some key features of the fields/projects were examined. A striking feature of the probable/possible fields is their relatively small size with the average being under 15 mmboe and the 68% range being 2.3–22.1 mmboe. The unit development costs are relatively high reflecting both recent cost escalation and the lack of economy of scale. Thus, the average is $9.45/boe (real terms). The total lifetime average cost is $15.3/boe. This excludes the costs of capital.

Less surprising are the results for the probable incremental projects where the average size is 8.4 mmboe. The range at the 68% level is 1.9–13.5 mmboe. The average development cost is $7.7/boe and the average lifetime cost $10.9/boe. The average size of possible incremental project is 19.9 mmboe, but this finding is greatly affected by one very large project. Thus, the 68% range is 3–19 mmboe. The average development cost is $9.75/boe and the average total cost $13.2/boe.

The average size of fields in the technical reserves category is 23.4 mmboe with the 68% range being 3.1–32.2 mmboe. The Monte Carlo modelling produced an average development cost of $10.1/boe with the total costs being as much as $20/boe.

The Monte Carlo modelling produced an average size of new discovery of just under 27 mmboe with the 68% range being 11.9–44.8 mmboe. The modelling produced average development costs of $8.9/boe and average total costs of $19.5/boe.

(b) Potential number of new fields in production

A basic indicator of the changing activity levels is the number of fields in production. These are shown in Figs 24–5, 24–6 and 24–7 by the different categories of fields under the three price scenarios. Incremental projects are not shown separately. Under the $30, 28 pence case the numbers rise to a peak of around 280 in 2010. By 2020 the total is around 270. Currently sanctioned fields

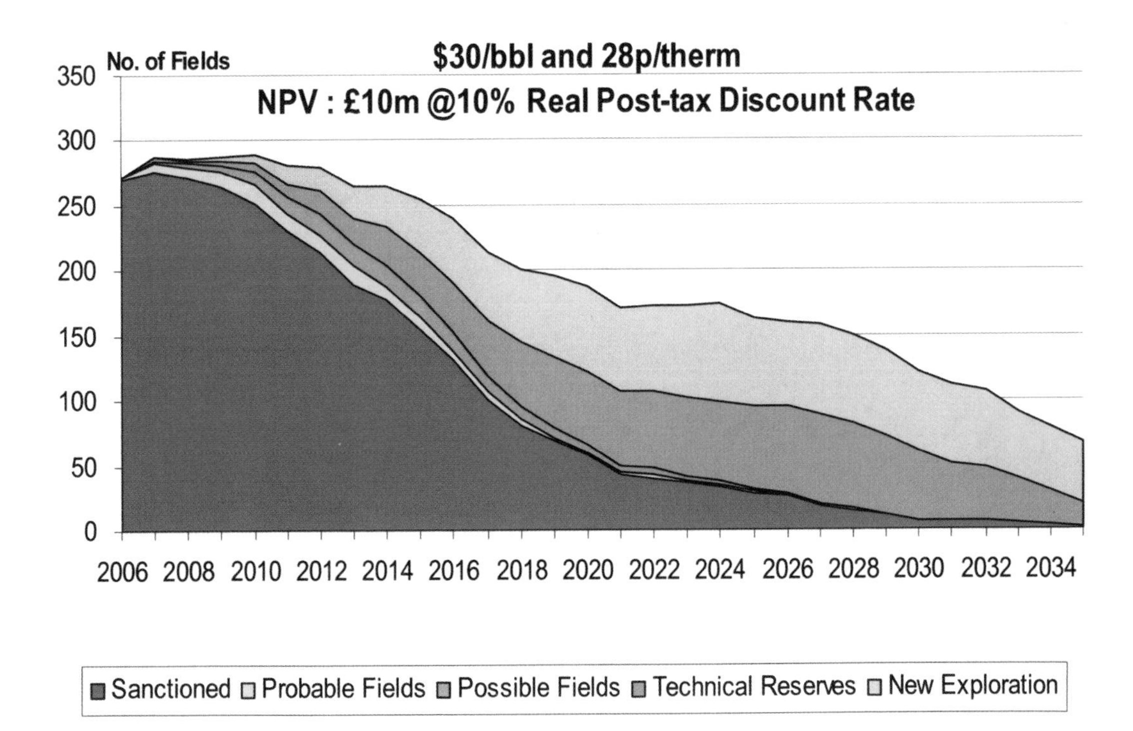

Figure 24–5 Potential number of fields in production

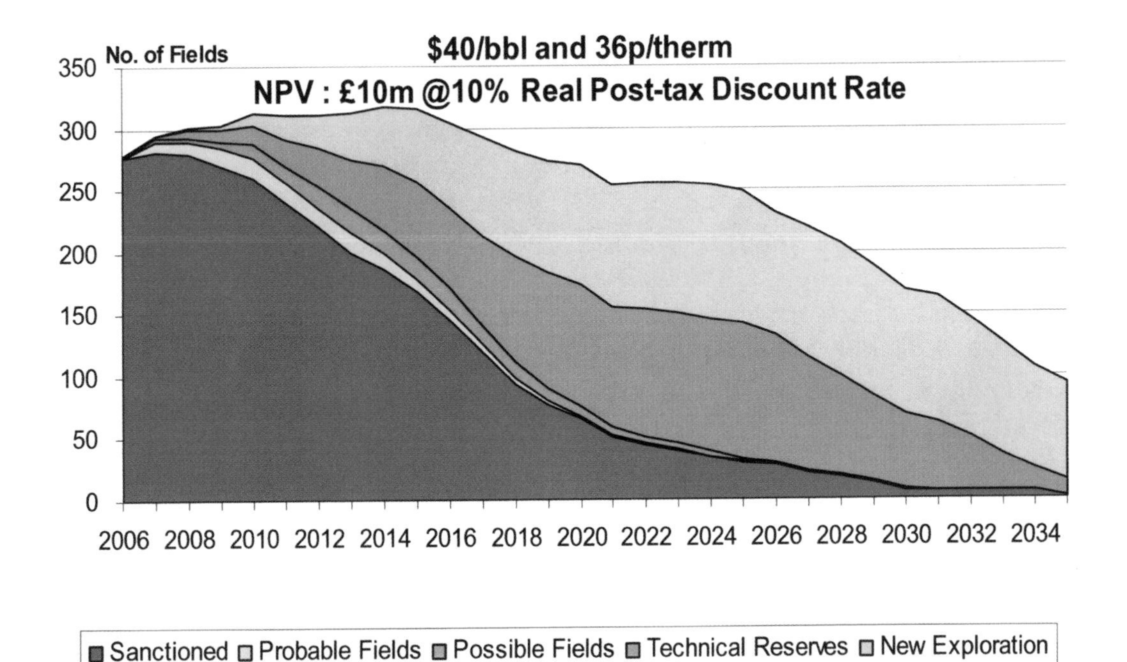

Figure 24–6 Potential number of fields in production

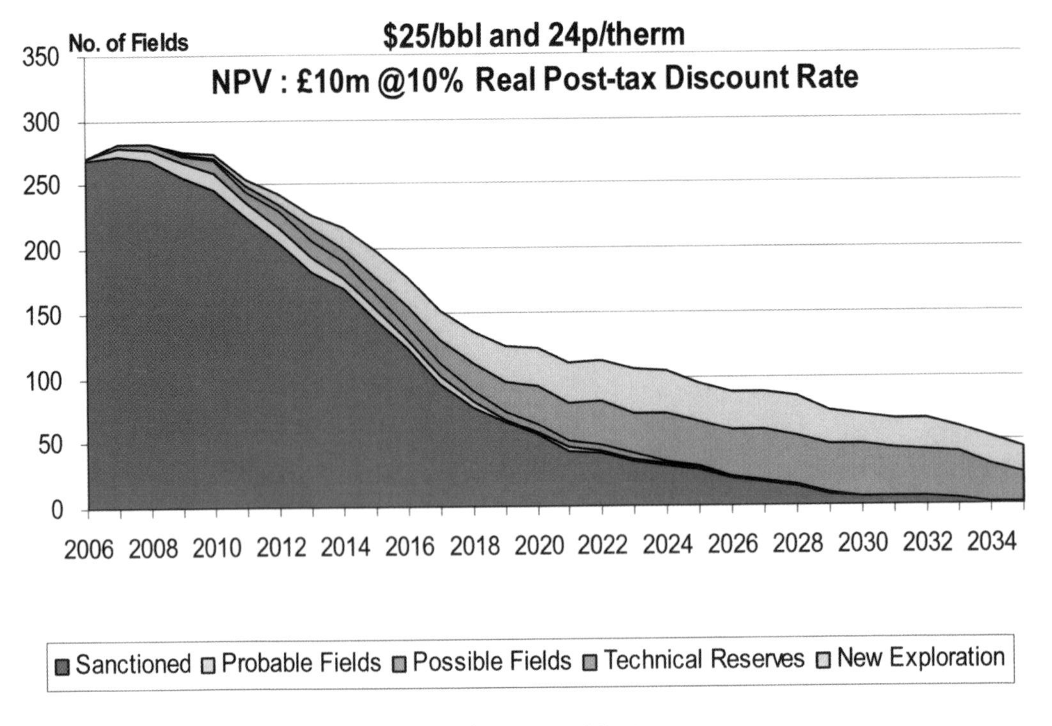

Figure 24–7 Potential number of fields in production

constitute the majority until 2017, but by 2020 new discoveries and fields in the technical reserves categories constitute the great majority of the fields.

Under the $40, 36 pence case the number of fields increases to a peak of 320 in 2014–2015 after which there is a decrease to around 265 in 2020. In that year the great majority of fields are in the technical reserves/new discoveries categories.

Under the $25, 24 pence scenario the number of fields in production increases to around 275 over the next few years but falls off rapidly after 2010. By 2020 there are less than 120 producing fields with a substantial proportion still being from those already sanctioned.

(c) Production

Potential oil production (excluding NGLs) under the $30, 28 pence scenario is shown in Fig. 24–8. After a worthwhile increase in 2007–2008 a key feature is the fairly fast decline from sanctioned fields. In the later part of the period the pace of decline moderates such that in 2020 production from this category of field is around 200,000 b/d. Incremental projects make a major contribution to the moderation of the decline rate over the next few years.

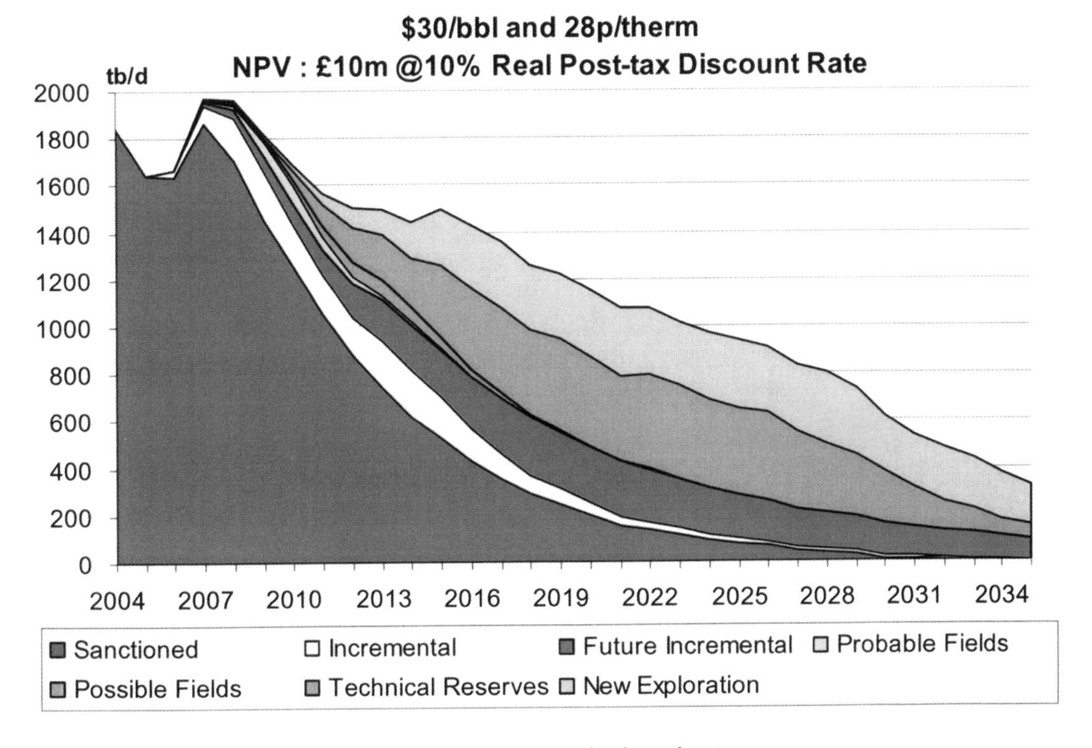

Figure 24–8 Potential oil production

Other features of the results are the major long-term contributions made by fields in the technical reserves category and new discoveries from 2015 onwards. In 2020, total production is around 1.2 mmb/d and in future incremental projects, technical reserves, and new discoveries contribute the great majority of the output.

In Fig. 24–9 prospective production of natural gas (excluding NGLs) is shown. In 2010 6.9 bcf/d is produced and 4 bcf/d in 2020. Production from the sanctioned fields falls at a fairly fast pace after 2007, but by 2013 this category of field still accounts for over 50% of total output. By 2020 technical reserves and new discoveries account for around 60% of total production.

In Fig. 24–10 prospective total hydrocarbon production (including NGLs) is shown under the $30, 28 pence scenario. From 3.35 mmboe/d in 2005 it grows to nearly 3.7 mmboe/d in 2007 but falls to below 3 mmboe/d in 2010. By 2020 it is just below 2 mmboe/d and by 2030 just over 1 mmboe/d. By 2020 the great majority of the production comes from future incremental projects and fields in the technical reserves and new discovery categories.

In Fig. 24–11 oil production prospects under the $40, 36 pence case are shown. Exploration activity and the pace and volume of new field developments

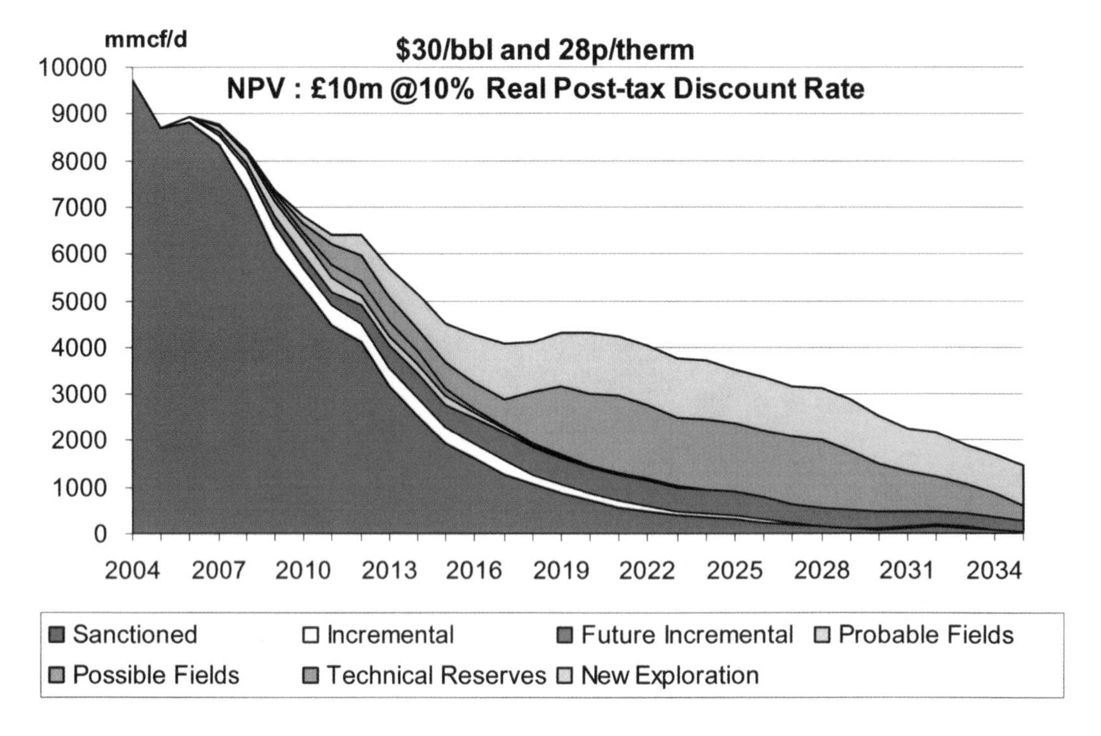

Figure 24–9 Potential gas production

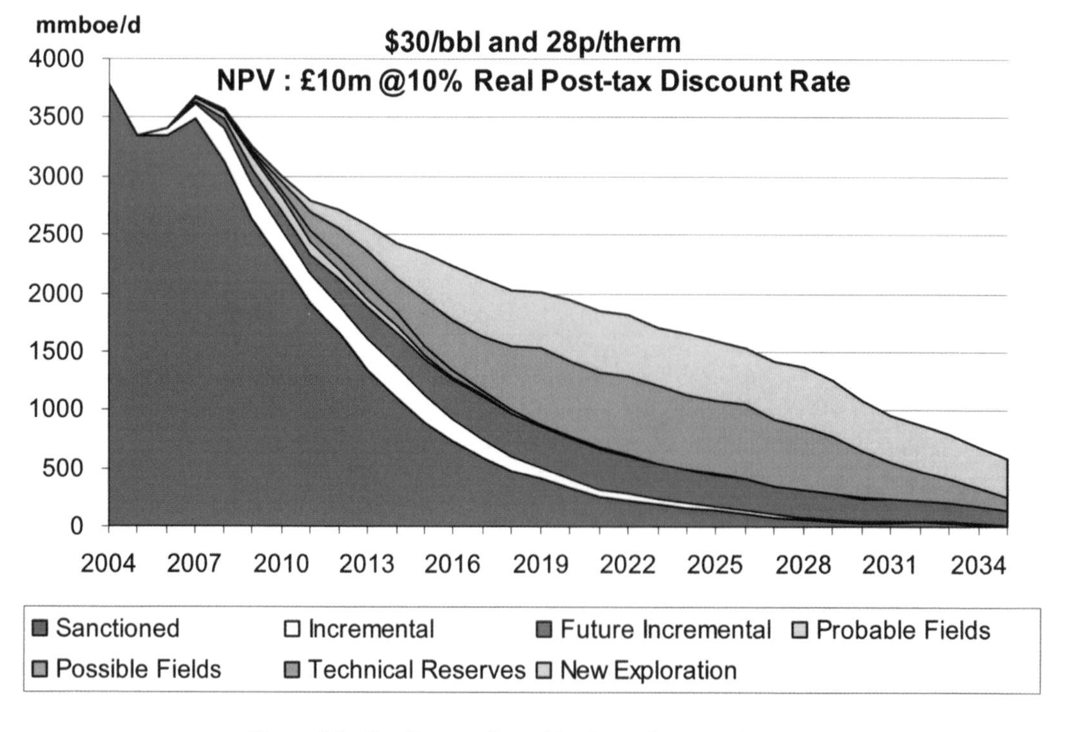

Figure 24–10 Potential total hydrocarbon production

are significantly higher under this scenario. Aggregate production holds up very well in the short-term, but falls to 1.7 mmb/d in 2010. There is only a gentle fall after that due to the development of large numbers of fields in the categories of new discoveries and technical reserves. By 2020 output is 1.35 mmb/d with the great majority coming from technical reserves, new discoveries and future incremental projects.

In Fig. 24–12 gas production under the $40, 36 pence scenario is shown. Output falls to around 7 bcf/d in 2010. Thereafter, the development of large numbers of field in the categories of technical reserves and new discoveries moderates the decline rate. By 2020 output is 5.59 bcf/d.

In Fig. 24–13 total hydrocarbon production (including NGLs) is shown under the $40, 36 pence scenario. In this case the PILOT target of 3 mmboe/d in 2010 is attained. The moderation to the decline rate in the following few years is noteworthy. It depends overwhelmingly on the development of many fields in the technical reserves and new discoveries categories. By 2020 production has fallen to 2.35 mmboe/d.

In Figs. 24–14, 24–15 and 24–16 oil, gas and total hydrocarbon production are shown under the $25, 24p scenario. Oil production falls quickly after 2008

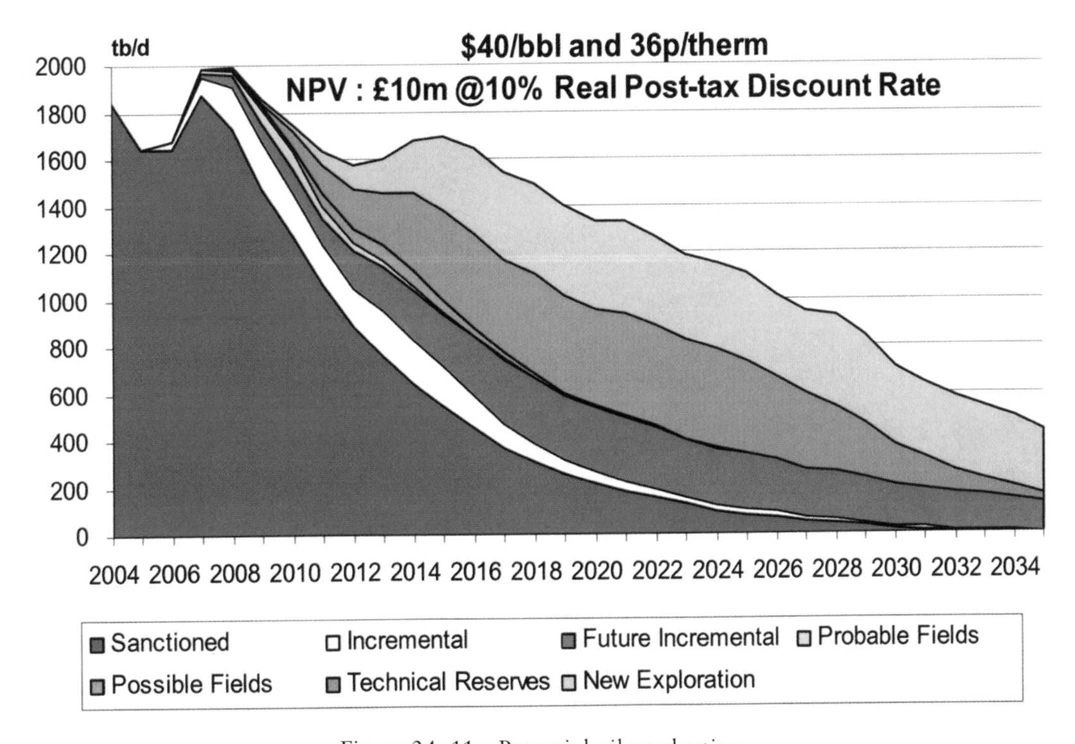

Figure 24–11 Potential oil production

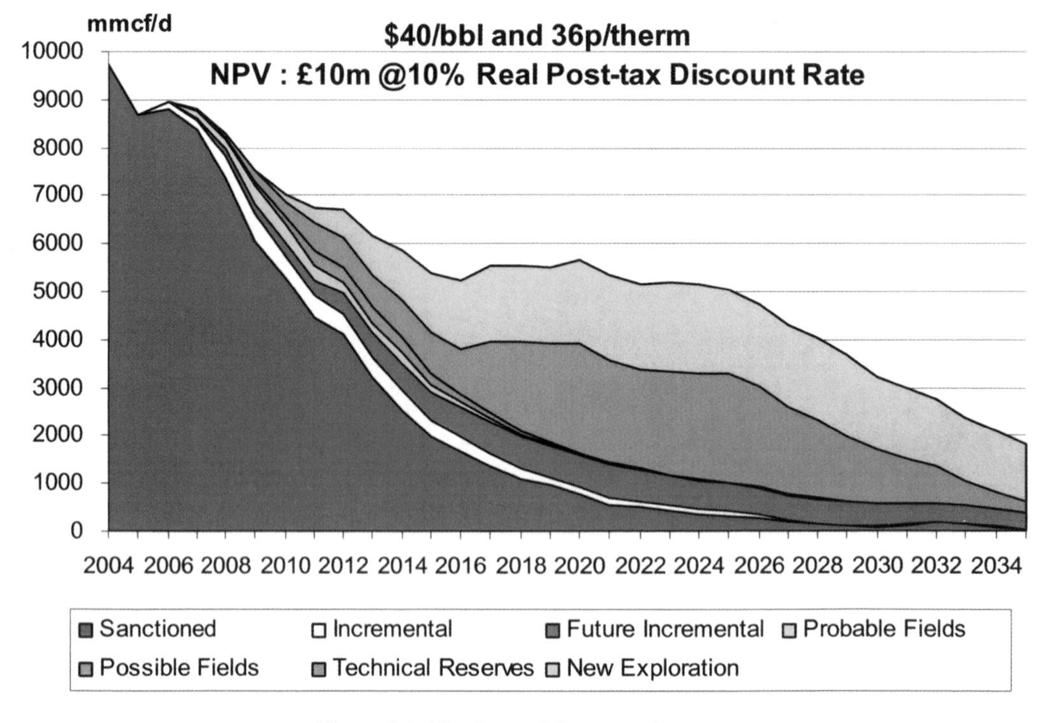

Figure 24–12 Potential gas production

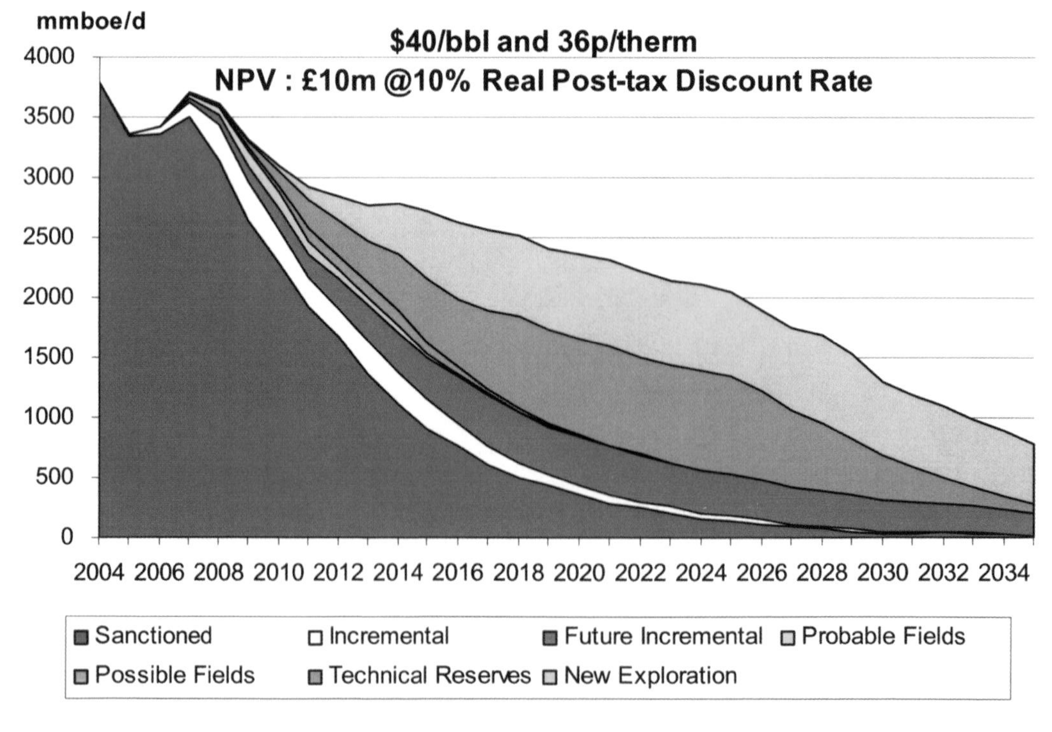

Figure 24–13 Potential total hydrocarbon production

to a level of just over 1.5 mmb/d in 2010. By 2020 it is around 0.75 mmb/d. The longer term contributions from technical reserves and new discoveries are very much less under this scenario.

A similar picture emerges with gas production. It falls sharply from 8.8 bc/f in 2007 to 6.6 mcf/d in 2010. In 2020 it is around 3 bcf/d. Total hydrocarbon production is around 3.68 mmboe/d in 2007 but falls to 2.8 mmboe/d in 2010 and 1.3 mmboe/d in 2020. The long-term price sensitivity of both oil and gas production is highlighted by the results.

(d) Consistency with official estimates of reserves

It was felt appropriate to test for consistency the projections made above against independent estimates of remaining reserves. In Fig. 24–17 cumulative production is shown from 2006 to 2035 under the three scenarios according to category of development. It is seen that in the $25, 24 pence case the grand total is 17.5 bn boe. Under the $30, 28 pence it is 21.6 bn boe, and under the $40, 36 pence case 24.6 bn boe. As noted above total cumulative production to date is around 35.4 bn boe. The central DTI estimate of total potential remaining reserves is 21.1 bn boe with the low estimate being 11.7 bn boe and the high

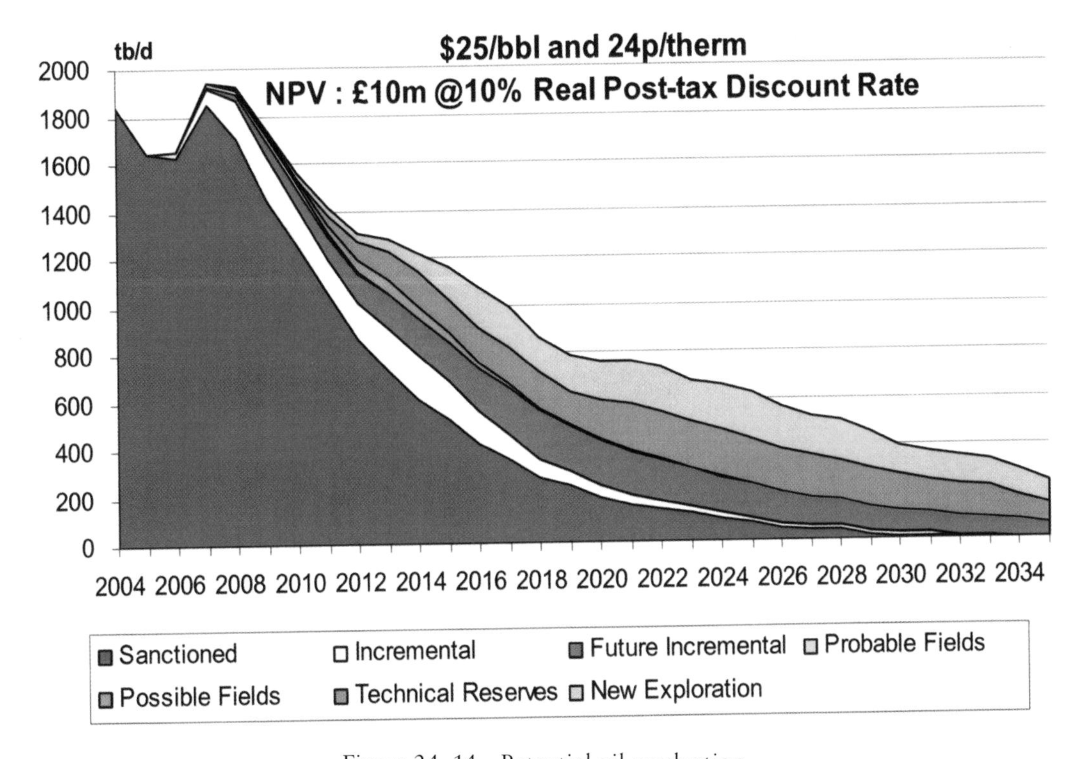

Figure 24–14 Potential oil production

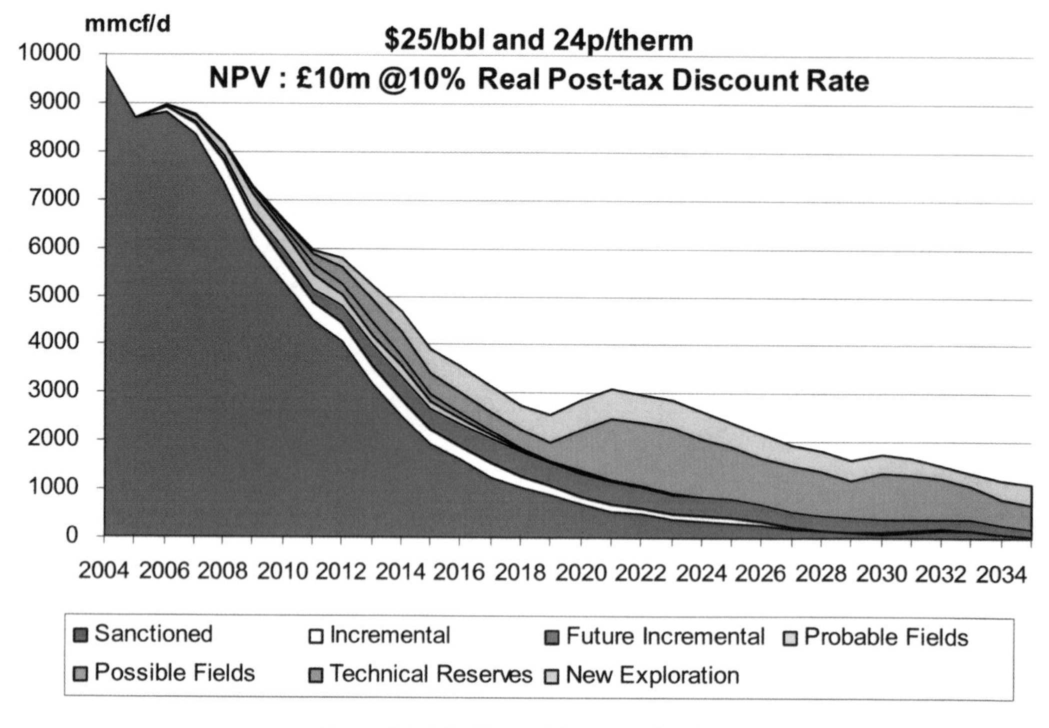

Figure 24–15 Potential gas production

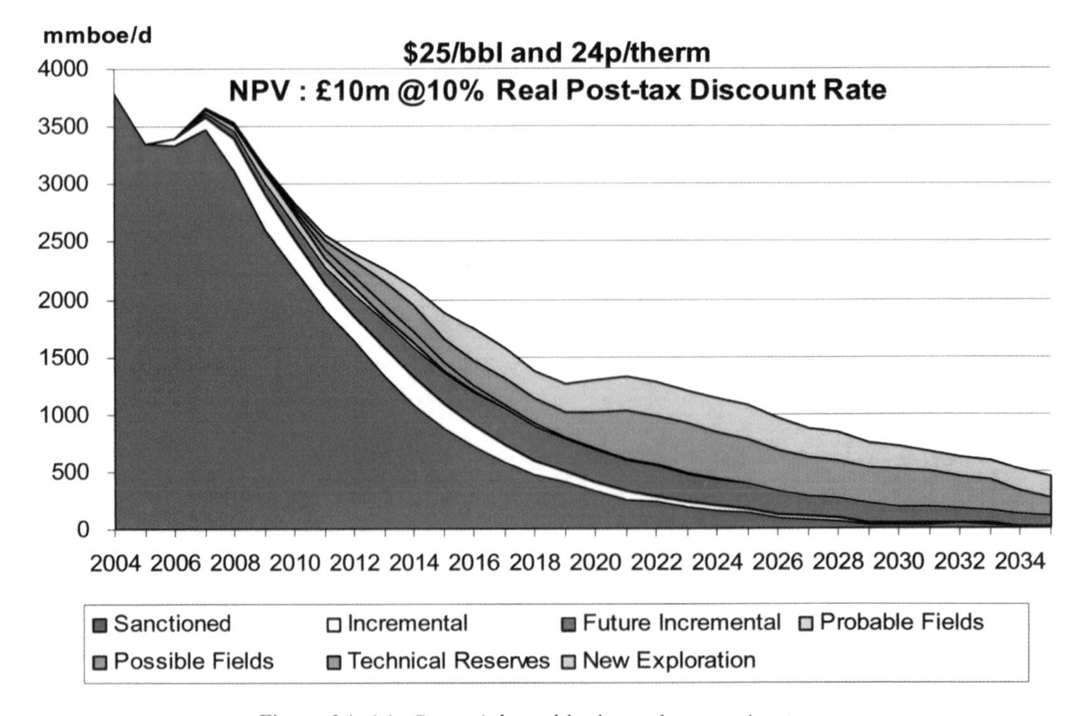

Figure 24–16 Potential total hydrocarbon production

one 38.7 bn boe. The results of this study are felt to be consistent with these estimates of remaining potential.

(e) Total development expenditures

Development expenditures under the $30, 18 pence cases are shown in Figs 24–18, 24–19 and 24–20 (at 2006 prices). In the early part of the period the expenditures are dominated by the requirements for the sanctioned fields, current incremental projects, and probable fields. Thus, the total field investment could be well over £4 billion in 2007. After that there is a significant price sensitivity to the prospective levels. At the $30, 28 pence case field investment falls off but remains on average at well over £3 billion per year to 2016. Under the $40, 36 pence case, while there are annual variations, the average annual level of field investment is in excess of £4 billion to 2016. Under the $25, 24 pence case field investment falls very substantially from 2007 onwards.

(f) Operating expenditures

In Figs. 24–21, 24–22 and 24–23 prospective operating expenditures are shown. Under the $30, 28 pence case they exceed £5 billion in 2006 and 2007 and then fall off at a modest pace but still attain a level of £4.3 billion in 2010.

Sanctioned		Current Incremental	Future Incremental (all fields)	Probable (excluding incremental)	Possible (excluding incremental)	Technical Reserves (excluding incremental)	New Exploration (excluding incremental)	Aggregate (rounded)
$25 24p	9.3	1.2	2.0	0.20	0.25	2.6	2.0	17.5
$30 28p	9.4	1.2	2.5	0.27	0.3	4.1	3.8	21.6
$40 36p	9.5	1.25	3.0	0.28	0.3	4.85	5.4	24.6

Figure 24–17 Cumulative potential production from 2006 to 2035 (bn boe)

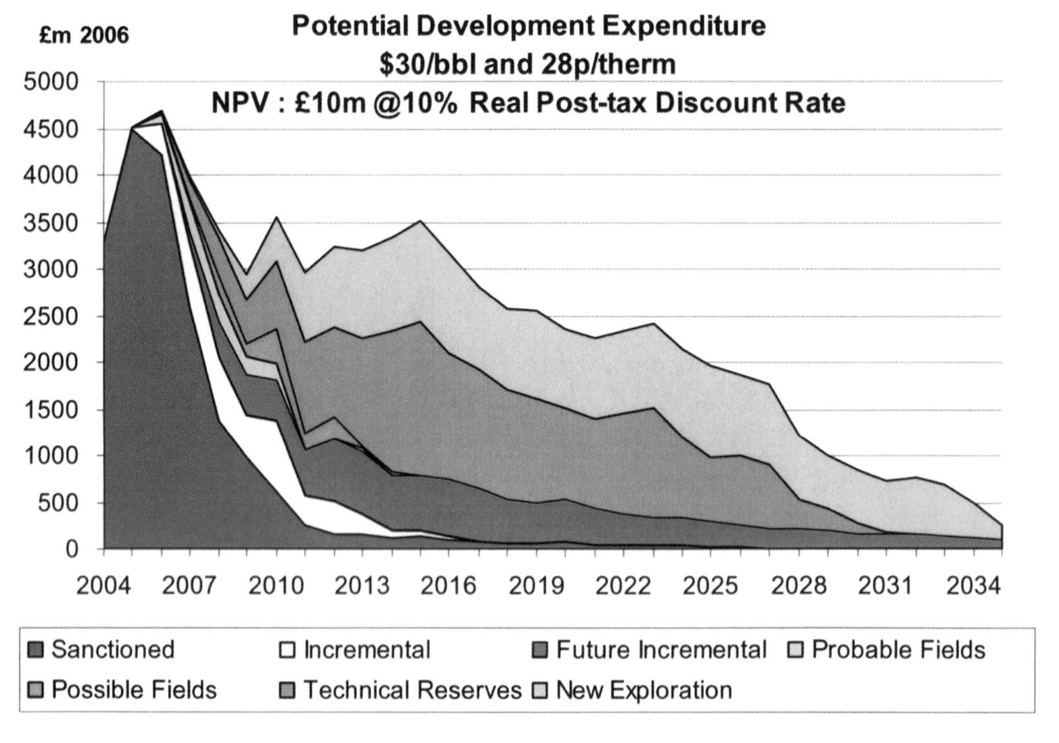

Figure 24–18 Potential development expenditure

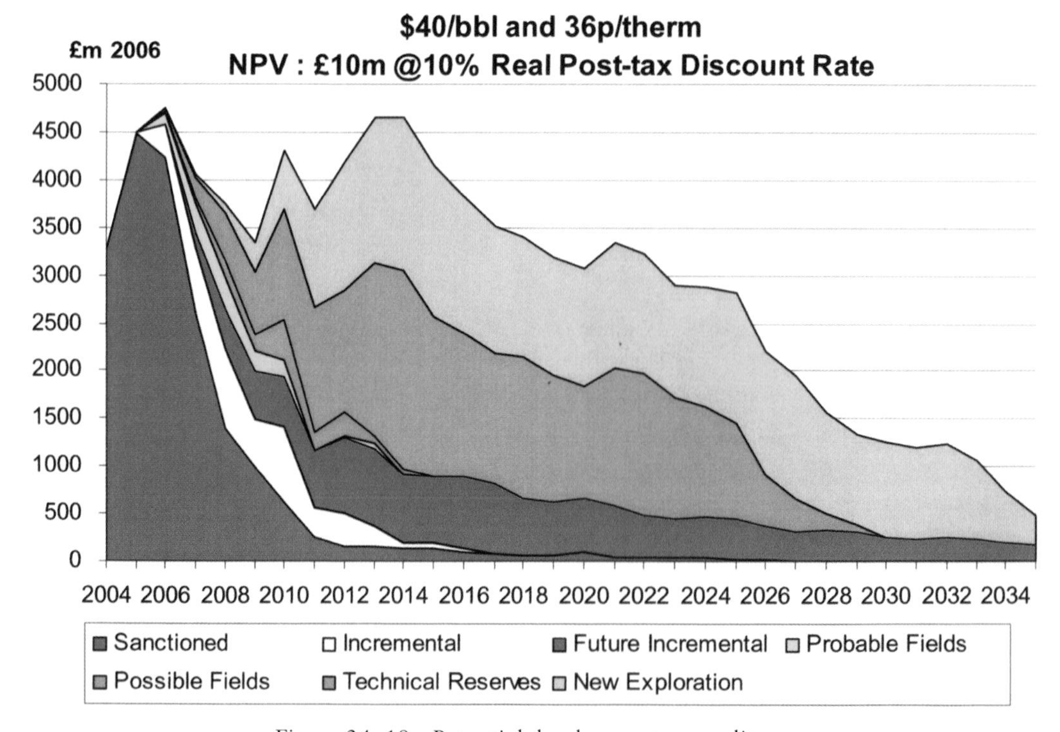

Figure 24–19 Potential development expenditure

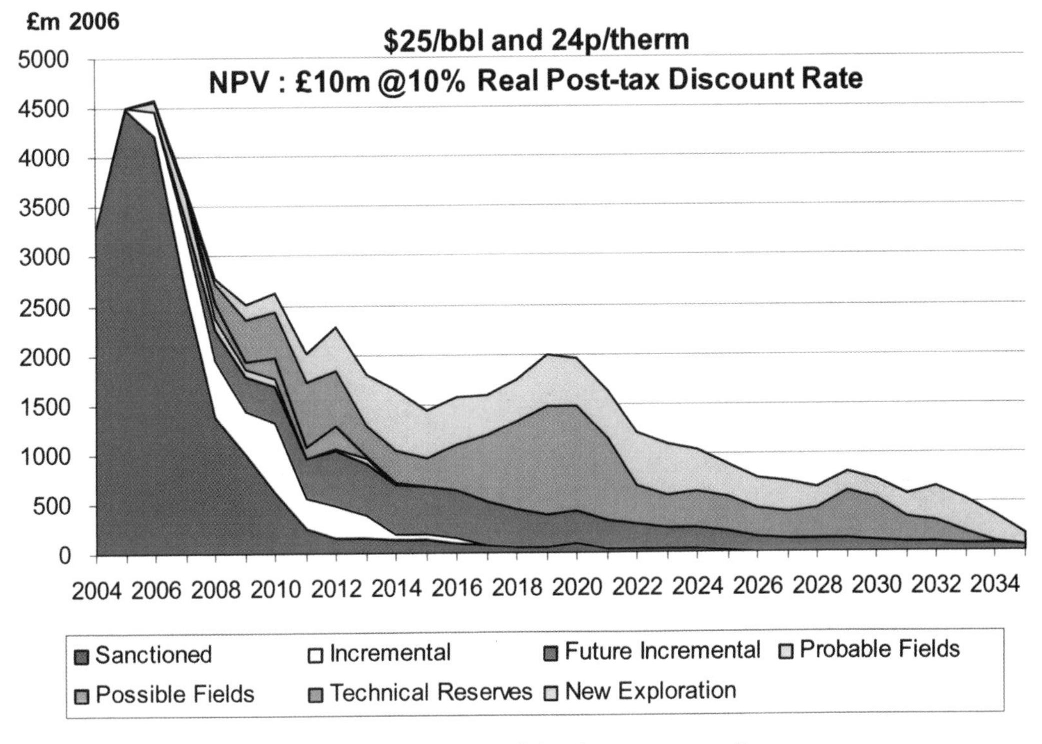

Figure 24–20 Potential development expenditure

The fall-off thereafter is rather faster reflecting the cessation of production of many fields.

Under the $40, 36 pence case the fall-off from the peak in 2006–2007 is very modest and in 2010 the level is still £4.5 billion, which level is also attained as far ahead as 2015. Under the $25, 24 pence case the operating expenditures fall-off at a quite rapid rate.

(g) Decommissioning expenditures

Prospective decommissioning costs to 2035 are shown under the 3 scenarios in Figs. 24–24, 24–25 and 24–26. It should be stressed that the expenditures relate to *field* decommissioning and generally *exclude* main pipelines and terminals which may or may not remain operational by the end of the period. If they were decommissioned within the period the total would be considerably higher. It should be noted that the negative costs show circumstances where the decommissioning of some facilities has been postponed through the presence of incremental projects. The values above the zero line indicate the total costs incurred over the whole period.

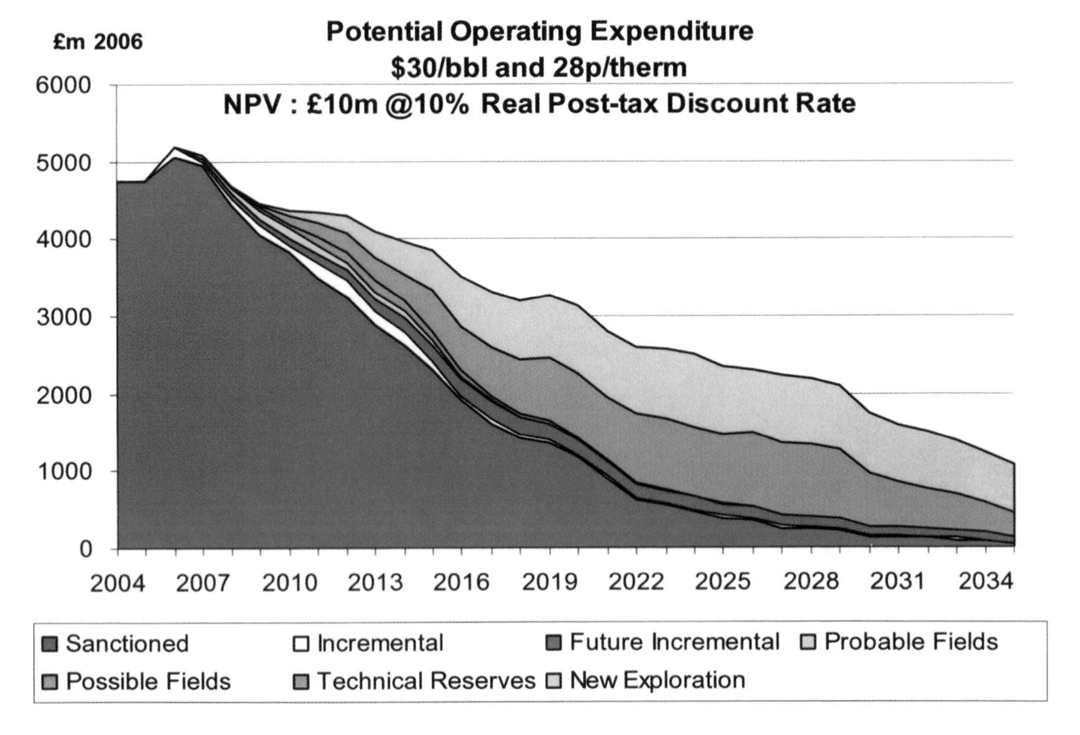

Figure 24–21 Potential operating expenditure

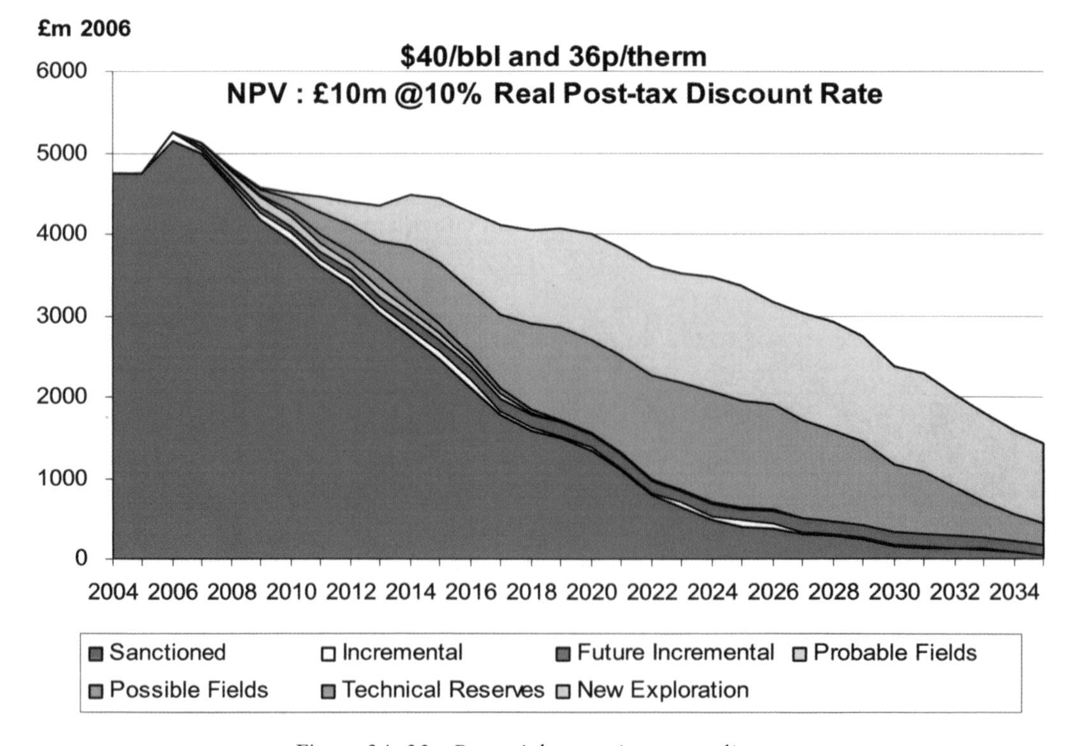

Figure 24–22 Potential operating expenditure

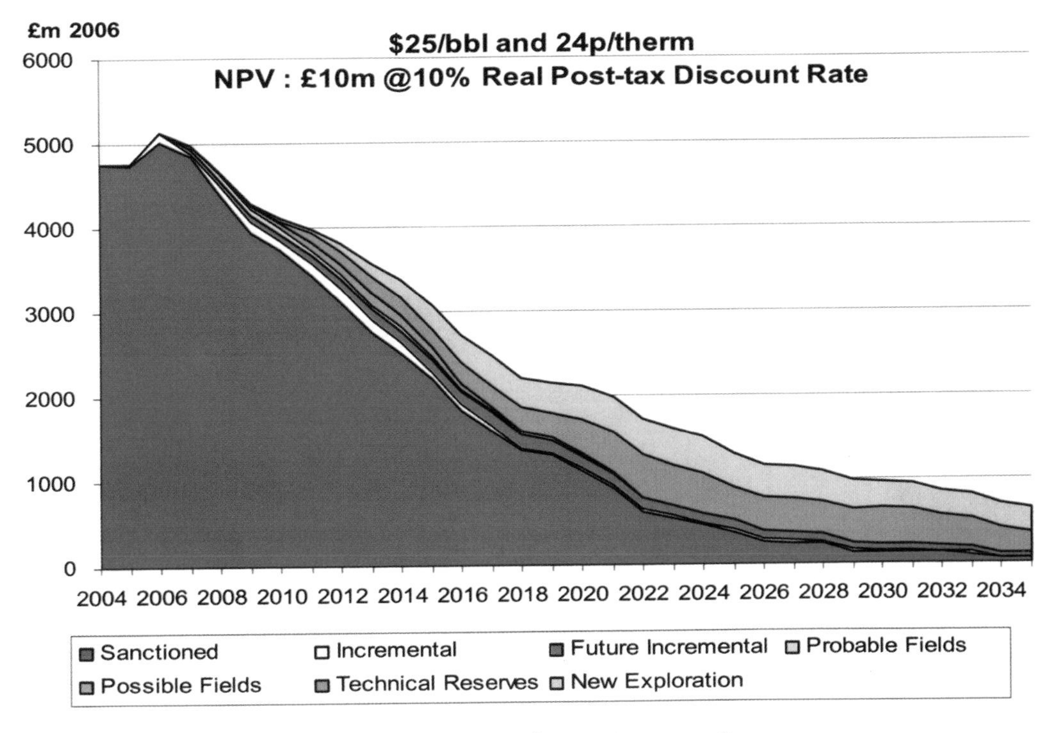

Figure 24–23 Potential operating expenditure

The phasing varies according to the price scenario as higher prices prolong the economic lives of fields. It is also noteworthy that the cumulative total of decommissioning costs in the period to 2035 increases as the oil price increases. This is because the number of new projects/fields being developed increases with price, but, because they are mostly small, many reach cessation of production by 2035. Under the central case total decommissioning costs are over £14 billion by that date.

24.6 Conclusions

In this study the prospects for activity levels in the UKCS to 2035 have been modelled taking into account the up-to-date situation regarding field sizes, development and operating costs, prospectivity of exploration, and the recent tax increase. A striking feature of the prospects (undeveloped fields and incremental projects) is their relatively small size with the average size of the probable and possible fields being under 15 mmboe and that for the incremental investments being around 9 mmboe (ignoring one non-typical very large project). Another feature is the high unit cost with the average lifetime cost of the probable and

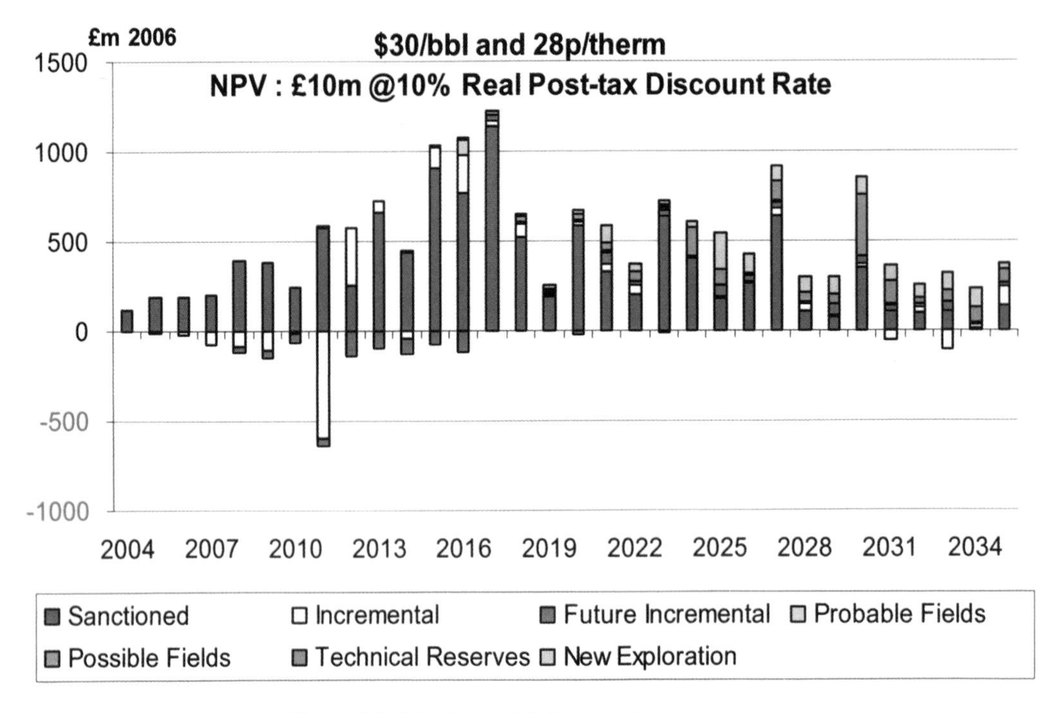

Figure 24–24 Potential decommissioning costs

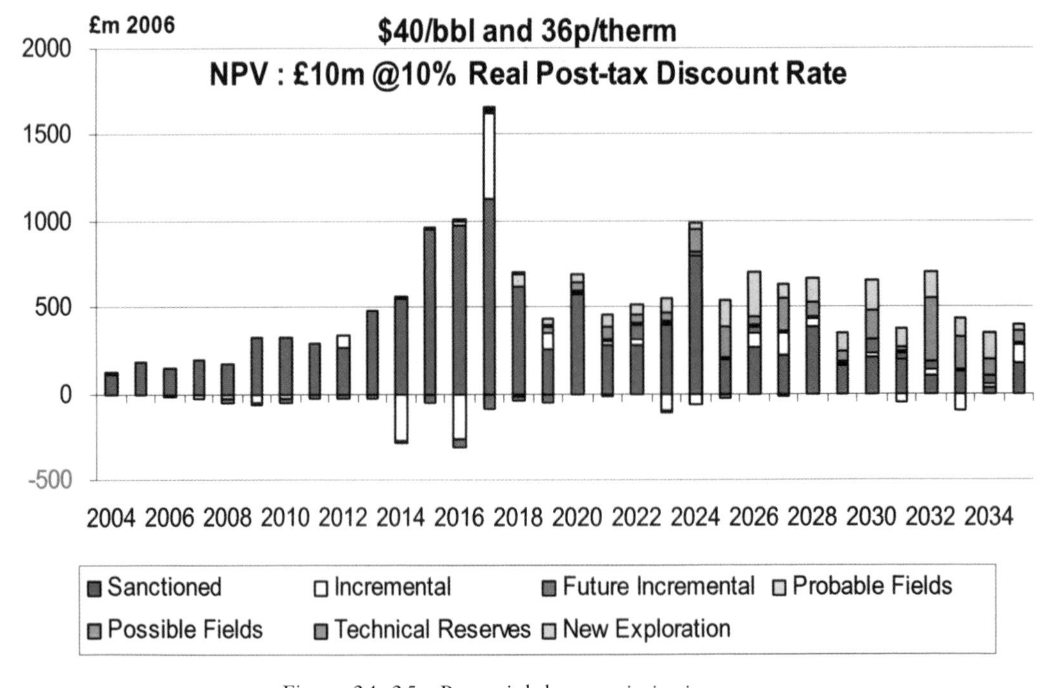

Figure 24–25 Potential decommissioning costs

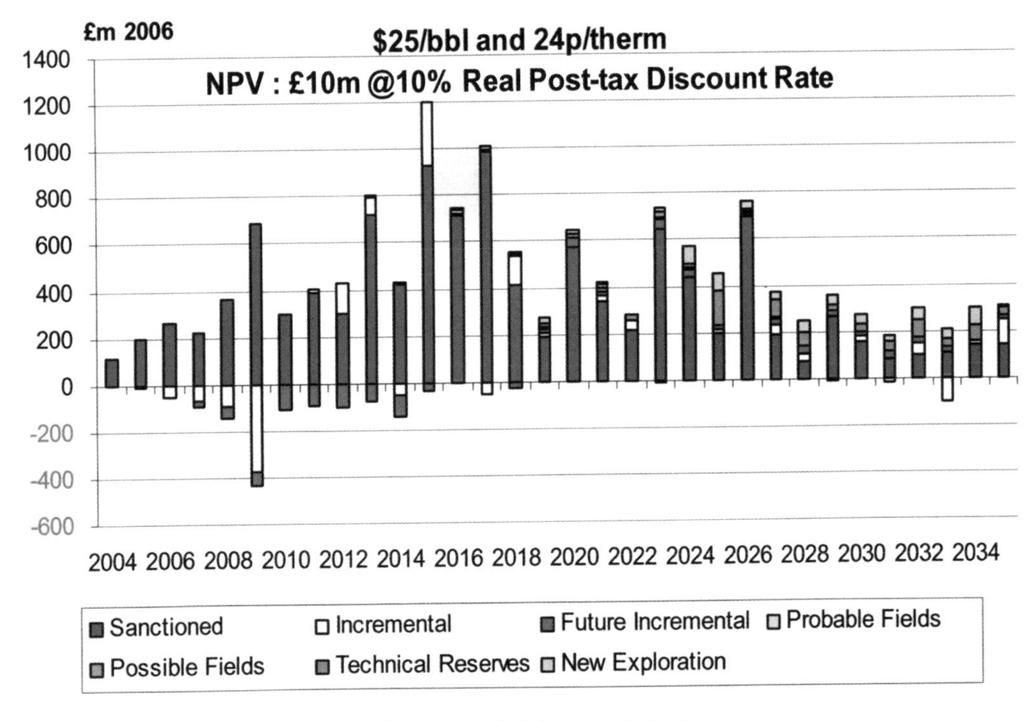

Figure 24–26 Potential decommissioning costs

possible fields exceeding $15 per boe and those for technical reserves and new discoveries averaging around $20/boe.

These features are reflected in the size of the expected returns expressed in NPVs at real post-tax discount rates. Thus, under a price scenario of $30, 28 pence in the period to 2035, 500 fields/projects had positive NPVs at 10% real discount rate but only 365 had NPVs in excess of £10 million. At $40, 36 pence 578 fields/projects had positive returns and 519 had NPVs in excess of £10 million. Under the $25, 24 pence price scenario 390 fields/projects had positive returns but only 221 had NPVs in excess of £10 million.

The consequences are that under the $30, 28 pence case, with a £10 million or better NPV requirement, total hydrocarbon production could be nearly 3 mmboe/d in 2010 and over 1.9 mmboe/d in 2020. By 2035 total cumulative production from 2006 could be 21.6 bn boe. Under the $40, 36 pence case production could be just over 3 mmboe/d in 2010 and 2.4 mmboe/d in 2020 with total recovery of 24.6 bn boe by 2035. Under the $25, 24 pence case total production could be 2.8 mmboe/d in 2010, 1.3 mmboe/d in 2020 with total recovery of 17.5 bn boe. The long-term price sensitivity of production is clearly substantial.

This is reflected in the behaviour of field investment. Under the $40, 36 pence price case it holds up well for many years averaging over £4 billion per year for a considerable number of years. Under the $30, 28 pence scenario field investment falls below current levels but averages more than £3 billion per year for a considerable number of years. Under the $25, 24 pence case field investment falls at a sharp pace.

It should be stressed that the indicated activity levels, particularly those under the $30, 28 pence case and $40, 36 pence price scenarios are conditional on the success of the various PILOT/DTI initiatives currently in progress, including in particular the fallow fields/blocks initiative, the stewardship initiative, and the infrastructure Code of Practice. Further, the development of many small fields in the longer term depends on the prolongation of the life of the infrastructure of pipelines, terminals and processing platforms. To attain the production and activity levels indicated under the $30, 28 pence and $40, 36 pence scenarios requires a cultural change in the industry to increase the number of field developments occurring annually. Currently this is much constrained by the shortage of drilling rigs, other equipment, and personnel. Hopefully, these shortages will be eased in the coming years.[6]

Notes

[1] To put these figures in perspective, OPEC's share of world oil production was 41.7% in 2005 and back in 1973 it was 51.9%.

[2] For a discussion of the early peak production view, see C.J. Campbell, *The Essence of Oil and Gas Depletion* (2003), and R.W. Bentley, 'Global Oil and Gas Depletion: an Overview' in *Energy Policy* 189 (2002). For the opposing view, see P.R. Odell, *Why Carbon Fuels will Dominate the 21st Century's Global Energy Economy* (2004), and M. Lynch, 'Forecasting Oil Supply: Theory and Practice' (2002) 42 *The Quarterly Review of Economics and Finance* 373.

[3] In early 2006 the Royal Bank of Scotland published the results of a survey of investors in the UKCS on this question. The median value for oil was $33 per barrel and for gas 23 pence per therm.

[4] For both oil and gas the DTI UK demand projections are based on the High and Low cases in UK Energy and CO_2 Emissions Projections (UEP26), DTI, July, 2006 – www.dti.gov.uk/files/file31861.pdf

[5] See DTI, http://www.og.dti.gov.uk/information/bb_updates/chapters/reserves_index.htm

[6] Since the above study was undertaken it has become clear that there has been further cost escalation, project completion delays, and some reserves downgrading. The result is that the short-term production projections shown in the charts will require downward revisions.

TOWARDS 2020 – AND BEYOND

LEGAL

24.7 Introduction

This part of the chapter examines some of the factors which are driving the change in UK energy policies generally and some of the legal considerations which derive from it. It is, of course, not possible to know what the future holds for the North Sea oil and gas industry. At best, mathematical models and other tools may be utilised to predict trends. However, future production will be affected by factors and policies, be they political, economic or social, which are often outwith the control of the industry. What is clear is that the situation will not remain static. Some of the drivers, arising from legal obligations (both national and international), will be summarised and the way in which these factors are shaping the industry of the future will be considered.

24.8 What is driving the change in UK energy policies?

The last five years have seen an intensive period of activity in the formulation and application of an energy policy for the UK. The Government's Energy White Paper[1] which was published in February 2003, clearly recognised the need for a long-term policy on the production and use of energy within the UK and, for the first time, gave environmental issues a central role in policy decisions. Legislation has been enacted to support the policy aims[2] and annual reports are published detailing the progress which has been made in implementing policies.[3] The recent Stern Report,[4] which was commissioned and published by the Government, focused on the potential economic cost of climate change. The report was highly publicised and will most likely result in environmental issues being given an even higher profile in future energy policies.

Any change in the UK's energy policies will have, in addition to other external factors, a knock-on effect on the UK oil and gas industry.

There are four main factors which appear to be driving the changing face of energy policy, namely: availability; security of supply; climate change; and economics. These four factors do not, of course, stand alone but are often closely interrelated.

Availability

The fact that North Sea oil and gas production has peaked and is now on the decline is widely reported in the public arena. News reports in the past two years have made much of the fact that the UK is now a net importer of gas and will probably move to being a net importer of oil by 2010. This has to be viewed against the background of sharply increasing global demand for energy. The need to maximise the recovery of the remaining reserves in the North Sea and, at the same time, find alternative sources of energy (whether by importing fossil fuels or by the use of alternative sources of energy) is clear.

Security of supply

Closely allied to the topic of availability is that of security. Our modern society depends on a secure and reliable supply of affordable energy. The California energy crisis of 2001, and to a lesser extent the fuel blockades of September 2000 in the UK, vividly illustrate how much of our daily lives depend directly on a reliable supply of transport fuel, electricity and gas. At a local level, threatened fuel supplies leads to civil disruption whereas on a global level the acquisition of rights to oil and gas is fraught with difficulty. Add in the factor that much of the world's fossil fuel supply is found in countries which may be politically unstable and the overall picture is of increasing global demand on a dwindling resource resulting in those countries with a reserve of oil and gas having a global political influence which is much larger than it would be otherwise.

The UK Government, being conscious of the changes in the UK energy market supplies, has established the Joint Energy Security of Supply Group to review the situation and make recommendations. A recent DTI report[5] recognised that North Sea oil and gas will continue to play a key role in the UK's energy supplies for many decades to come and that it is necessary, therefore, to maximise production from those assets. The import of fossils fuels, however, will increase and to this end the UK Government is promoting treaties and agreements at an international level in order to secure future supplies from areas other than the UKCS. In addition to maximising access to fossil fuel supplies, consideration is also being given to the need to have a diverse base of energy sources.

Climate change

It appears to be widely accepted now that the global climate is changing and that the level of carbon dioxide (CO_2) in the atmosphere is one of the main causes. From a peripheral consideration in previous decades, climate change has now become a major factor in energy policy. The Government's Energy White Paper[6] makes the reduction of carbon emissions one of the central aims of the UK's energy policy. The Royal Commission on Environmental Pollution's recommendation that the UK should aim to reduce carbon dioxide emissions by 60% by 2050 has been accepted by the Government. This ambitious target is well in excess of the UK's current commitments under international obligations. The UK is a signatory to, and has ratified, the United Nations Framework Convention on Climate Change (UNFCCC). The UNFCCC is an international framework which was established in 1992 with the objective of achieving stabilisation of greenhouse gases in the atmosphere at a level which would prevent dangerous interference with the climate system. A Protocol to the UNFCCC was agreed in 1997 (the Kyoto Protocol) whereby developed nations were required to cut greenhouse gas emissions by an average of 5.2% below 1990 levels over the period 2008–2012. The protocol came into force on 16 February 2005 and the parties which have ratified the protocol are now legally bound to implement policies to effect the reduction in greenhouse gas emissions. The USA and Australia are the only major developed countries which have not ratified the Kyoto Protocol. The legally binding reduction targets which are set under the Kyoto Protocol are currently binding only on certain developed countries. Countries such as China, are not 'Annex I' countries (such countries being subject to binding reduction targets), may already be, or may become, significant contributors to global emissions. Details of the UK's specific obligations under the Kyoto Protocol are dealt with later in this chapter.

Although a large proportion of the required carbon dioxide emission reduction may be achievable by energy efficiency measures, focus is increasingly turning to alternative sources of energy. Such sources may be low carbon (such as biomass power) or renewable sources (such as wind power, hydro generation, solar power, tidal power, etc.). Nuclear power, which for a period seemed to have been dropped from the political agenda, may have to be reconsidered since one of its strongest advantages is zero carbon emissions (at least with respect to the fission process itself).

Economics

Economics, although listed as a separate heading here, impacts on all of the areas discussed above. As the price of oil and gas substantially increases ever higher, marginal prospects and reworking of mature areas become more attractive. It is estimated that approximately half of the UK's oil and gas reserves in the North

Sea remain in situ. The decline in production is a result of the readily available resources decreasing. Already, extraction of reserves, which a few decades ago would have been considered unobtainable, is taking place. Improvements in technology and the utilisation of the existing infrastructure have made previously inaccessible reserves available. There will always be an economic calculation to be made as to whether extraction of stranded reserves or sidetracking is economically, as well as technically, feasible and the result will change as factors such as the price of oil and gas and the availability of technology change.

The Stern Report[7] was the first major report to address the economic consequences of climate change. The report accepted that climate change is real and is accelerating and went on to examine the possible economic cost of dealing with the impact of climate change and the economic cost of taking action to reduce greenhouse gas emissions. The report concluded that ignoring climate change will eventually damage economic growth, whereas the benefits of strong, early action will considerably outweigh the costs of such action.

The need to reduce greenhouse gas emissions, and in particular carbon dioxide emissions, has been accepted by the Government for some time and has already led to the creation of several emission trading schemes. The UK launched a voluntary emissions trading scheme in March 2002 but this has since been overtaken by the EU Emissions Trading Scheme. In addition, the Kyoto Protocol envisages three mechanisms by which countries may reduce their emissions. One of the mechanisms is emission trading which it is anticipated will be a strong economic tool for implementing energy policies. Progress towards setting up an international emissions trading scheme took a step forward when the delegates at the United Nations Climate Change Conference in Montreal (November 2005) approved the terms of such a trading scheme. Further details of emissions trading are given below.

24.9 National and international legal obligations

Currently, in the UK, there are numerous schemes in place to promote energy policies. Some schemes are voluntary or advisory and others give rise to contractual obligations. Although it is beyond the scope of this chapter to examine all of the schemes, some of the main schemes and the obligations arising from them are considered below. UK energy policy is shaped not only at a domestic level but also by obligations which the UK has undertaken as a result of obligations under international treaties. Legislation is usually enacted at a national level to ensure that these obligations are complied with. The international obligations which have the greatest effect on current energy policies are those arising under the UNFCCC and those which arise as a result of the UK being a member of the European Union.

Emissions trading

Both the EU and the bodies set up under the terms of the UNFCCC have opted to utilise emission trading schemes as a means of implementing their stated policies.

(i) UK Emissions Trading Scheme

The UK Government set up a voluntary emissions trading scheme in March 2002[8] and although this scheme has now ceased to operate, it is worth mentioning briefly since it sets out the background to recent governmental thinking on emissions trading. Under the UK scheme, 33 direct participants voluntarily agreed to reduce their emissions of carbon dioxide (or carbon dioxide equivalent). In addition to the direct participants, other companies which had entered into Climate Change Agreements with the Government (in order to benefit from a reduction in their Climate Change Levy discussed below at p 859) were permitted to use the trading scheme to purchase or sell allowances. The scheme ran from 2002 to 2006 and as such overlapped with the EU Emissions Trading Scheme ('EU ETS') which commenced on 1 January 2005.

(ii) EU Emissions Trading Scheme

The EU, in addition to formulating policies and proposals under the European Climate Change Programme, recognises that all of its Member States are parties to the Kyoto Protocol and recent European decisions and European legislation relating to climate change have been made against this background. The European Union Council, on behalf of the European Community, approved the Kyoto Protocol and the joint fulfilment of the commitments under the Protocol. This led to the Emissions Trading Directive[9] which established a scheme for greenhouse emission allowance trading within the Community. Later legislation[10] amended the Emissions Trading Directive in order to take account of the flexible mechanisms envisaged by the Kyoto Protocol (discussed below). The UK Government is obliged to pass national legislation in order to give effect to these and other associated European Directives. The UK legislation[11] (the Regulations), replaces and consolidates earlier UK legislation on this subject and sets out the rules of the EU ETS.

The EU ETS commenced on 1 January 2005, with the first phase running from 2005 to 2007. The second phase will run from 2008 to 2012 to coincide with the first Kyoto Commitment Period. The EU ETS runs on a similar basis to the UK Scheme ie on a cap and trade basis. Member States are responsible for ensuring that each installation covered by the scheme holds a greenhouse gas emissions trading permit. Activities which are listed in Schedule 1 to the Regulations may only emit specified emissions under (and to the extent stated in) a greenhouse gas emissions permit. Offshore installations may, depending on the size and type of installation, be considered as a combustion installation of the type listed in Schedule 1, and as such come under the ambit of the Regulations. Activities at mineral oil refineries are also covered by the Regulations.

Under the National Allocation Plan (which must be produced by each Member State government) the installations are allocated a number of allowances. The greenhouse gas emissions permit will contain a requirement that, on an annual basis, the operator of each installation must surrender a number of allowances equal to the emissions made by that installation in the previous year.

The year 2005 was the first year during which emissions were verified and recorded and operators were required to surrender sufficient allowances in respect of emissions made during 2005 no later than 30 April 2006. Allowances may be traded on the electronically linked national registers (the UK register is operated by the Environment Agency). Companies which have emissions less than their allowances may trade their excess allowances or retain the allowances for use in the following year. Companies which have insufficient allowances to surrender have various options open to them. These include purchasing allowances (either on the spot market or on forward contracts), cutting output or investing in cleaner technology. Should the latter option be chosen it may be possible to buy some time for the new technology to come on stream by using some of the following year's allowances (which are allocated before the surrender date for the previous year).

Companies which are unable to obtain sufficient allowances to surrender for the emissions which they have produced will be subject to financial penalties and in addition their allocation of allowances for the following year will be descreased by the number of allowances which they failed to surrender.

The EU ETS is set up to run in phases. The initial phase is three years long (1 January 2005 to 31 December 2007) and the subsequent phases will last for five years. The emissions allowances and penalties will be set in respect of each phase (and then allocated in detail by Member State governments between the affected installations) and will be subject to review in respect of future cycles. The possibility of expanding the EU ETS to cover other types of installations and gases other than carbon dioxide is being considered.

The appointed regulator for offshore installations is the DTI. The regulator has the power to enforce conditions attached to greenhouse gas emissions permits, to serve enforcement notices and, if deemed necessary, to enter installations in order to carry out duties under the Regulations. The Regulations set out various actions/omissions which are offences in terms of the Regulations, eg making emissions without the relevant permit, breaching the terms of the permit (which would include failing to surrender sufficient allowances), making misleading statements and failing to comply with an enforcement notice. These offences are punishable by a fine or by imprisonment (maximum two years). If the offence is committed by a company the directors or managers of the company may be charged with the offence (in addition to any finding in respect of the company itself). The civil penalty in respect of excess emissions is, in the first phase, €40 for each tonne of CO_2 equivalent for which no allowances have been surrendered. This penalty will rise to €100 per tonne from 1 January 2008.

The EU ETS has to operate against the background of the Kyoto Protocol. As mentioned above, recent changes to the Regulations have been passed in order to facilitate links to the mechanisms agreed under the Kyoto Protocol. The following part of this chapter looks at the obligations under UNFCCC and the Kyoto Protocol.

(iii) UNFCCC and the Kyoto Protocol

The UNFCCC was adopted and signed by 162 countries at the Rio Earth Summit in 1992. The objective of the Convention was to stabilise greenhouse gas concentrations at a level that would prevent dangerous interference with the climate system. The UK ratified the Convention in 1993. At the Rio Summit it was agreed that the nations would meet regularly to review progress and it was at the 1997 meeting in Kyoto that the participating nations agreed to reduce greenhouse gas emissions by 5% from 2008 to 2012. The Kyoto Protocol became legally binding in 1995. The global cut in emissions of 5.2% is to be achieved by different reductions for different countries. The European Union must deliver a reduction of 8% and following the allocation between the EU Member States the UK has agreed to reductions of 12.5% for the UK. The parties to the Protocol met again in Montreal in November 2005 during which time more detailed rules as to how the Kyoto Protocol is to operate in practice were agreed.

The Kyoto Protocol sets reduction targets for certain developed countries. These reduction targets are legally binding on those countries which have ratified the protocol. The targets apply to a combination of six different greenhouse gases (expressed in terms of carbon dioxide equivalent emissions) (of which CO_2 is only one). In addition to setting reduction targets, the Kyoto Protocol establishes three different mechanisms which are designed to allow the parties to achieve their emission targets by the least expensive route. The mechanisms which have been adopted are: clean development, joint implementation and emissions trading.

The Clean Development Mechanism provides a means for companies to undertake projects in countries without a Kyoto target which will reduce those countries emissions of greenhouse gases. The projects may be credited with Certified Emissions Reductions (CERs) which can be used either by governments (to retire the CERs to meet Kyoto targets) or by companies (to surrender the CERs to meet obligations under the EU ETS). In the UK, the Department for Environment, Food and Rural Affairs (DEFRA) is responsible for dealing with approval of prospective projects which wish to benefit from the Clean Development Mechanism.

The Joint Implementation Mechanism (JI) operates in a similar way but applies to projects which are undertaken in countries with a Kyoto target. Projects which meet the criteria have the ability to earn Emissions Reduction Units (ERUs) which can then be used in a similar way as CERs. DEFRA will issue letters of approval to UK companies wishing to participate in JI projects abroad but is not at present approving JI projects in the UK.

Emissions Trading under the Kyoto Protocol allows parties with a Kyoto target to trade units (equal to one tonne of emissions) with other parties with targets. The units which may be traded are CERs, ERUs, AAUs (Assigned Amount Units, being the units assigned to each party under the Kyoto Protocol) or RMUs (Removal Units, being units issued to parties as a result of land use (and in particular forestry) which results in greenhouse gas sinks being created). Each party must establish a national registry to facilitate and record the trading of units. In addition, an international transaction log is to be established to verify and record transactions.

The credits obtained under the Kyoto mechanisms may be used either for compliance with the Kyoto targets or to satisfy obligations under the EU ETS. Enforcement of obligations under the Kyoto Protocol is the responsibility of the Enforcement Branch of the Compliance Committee. The Enforcement Branch is responsible for determining whether or not a party is complying with its emissions target or its reporting requirements, or has lost its eligibility to participate in the Kyoto mechanisms. If a party has failed to meet its emissions target the party will be granted 100 days within which it must make up any shortfall in compliance by acquiring further units (eg by trading or through projects, etc.). If at the end of the 100-day period the party has not made up the shortfall, the difference is transferred to the second commitment period along with a 30% penalty and the party must fulfil that obligation then in addition to the party's original obligations under the second commitment period. As a further deterrent, the defaulting party will also be barred from selling allowances under the trading scheme and will be required to develop a compliance action plan. There are no financial penalties, however, the Enforcement Branch may make a public declaration of non-compliance.

A recent DTI forecast[12] indicates that although the UK is on track to meet its obligations under the Kyoto Protocol the higher domestic target set by the UK Government is unlikely to be achieved. The DTI predicts that if current policies are continued the UK will achieve a reduction in carbon dioxide emission of 14% below 1990 levels by 2010.

The Climate Change Programme

The UK Government introduced its Climate Change Programme in 2000, with a stated aim of reducing carbon dioxide emissions. International obligations, in addition to domestic policy, have resulted in the emissions trading schemes which are discussed above. The UK Government has utilised further domestic economic instruments in an attempt to limit CO_2 emissions, including the Climate Change Levy and the Renewables Obligation.

(i) The Climate Change Levy

The Climate Change Levy[13] is a tax which the UK Government applies to the use of energy in industry, commerce and the public sector. The levy was introduced on 1 April 2001 and there are different rates for gas, electricity, coal and LPG. The levy does not apply to oil which is already the subject of excise duty. The levy does not apply to certain sectors (eg domestic, transport, energy production) and where the levy does apply there are certain exemptions which may be claimed (eg in respect of electricity which is generated from new renewable energy, fuel used by certain combined heat and power schemes, fuel used in electrolysis.) For those sectors which are affected by the levy a cut in employers' National Insurance Contributions, enhanced capital allowances and other measures are designed to encourage businesses to become more energy efficient by using the measures available to negate the effects of the levy.

Certain energy intensive sectors may be able to access the Climate Change Agreement scheme. Under the terms of this scheme companies which agree to stringent energy efficiency and/or carbon emission reduction targets are eligible for an 80% levy discount. Targets must be attained in order to retain the discount.

(ii) The Renewables Obligation

As part of the Government's Climate Change Programme, the Secretary of State was given the power[14] to require licensed electricity suppliers to source a specific percentage of the electricity which they supply from renewable sources. The Renewables Obligation Scheme is described in Chapter 25 above.

24.10 How are these changes and obligations shaping the future of the North Sea Oil and Gas Industry?

As with all other industries, the North Sea oil and gas industry does not remain static. Although some changes are being forced on it by government policies and the current economic climate, the industry itself is driving forward change in recognition of the province's increasing maturity.[15] There is recognition also that the industry will have to adapt if it is to continue to attract essential investment against the growing competition for investment from other regions such as the Gulf of Mexico and West Africa. As part of these changes the major players are to some extent refocusing their exploration programmes towards newer provinces and are divesting some North Sea assets to smaller independent companies which may be more flexible and have the incentive to focus on marginal efficiency gains.

Response by the DTI and UKOOA

Both the United Kingdom Offshore Operators Association (UKOOA) and the DTI have formulated policies to ensure that the resources in the North Sea are utilised as efficiently as possible. For example, the DTI has introduced changes to the licensing system. The fallow fields initiative means those licences on which there is no meaningful activity risk being forfeited and new variations on the traditional Production Licence now mean that it is possible for new entrants to prove technical, environmental and financial capability in respect of a proposed work programme after the award of a licence rather than prior to the award. UKOOA has been active in promoting resource stewardship to increase the size of available resources, ensure that resources are extracted as efficiently as possible and to extend the life of existing infrastructure. As regards the latter point it is recognised that the ability to tie-in smaller discoveries and stranded reserves into the existing infrastructure will be paramount in determining the financial viability of such projects.

Use of new technology

The Government recognises that fossil fuels will continue to be a major source of energy for decades to come.[16] In light of this, it is anticipated that developments in new technology will continue to enable better recovery of the resources which are available and more environmentally responsible use of the resources which are currently being produced.

Improvements in seismic survey quality have already enabled more accurate evaluation of geological formations and new engineering methods have enabled much higher recovery rates than would have been envisaged a decade ago. The Stafjord Field Late-Life Project gives a good illustration of the changing recovery prospects. The Statfjord Field, which lies partly in the Norwegian sector and partly in the UK sector came on stream in 1979. At that time recovery rates for oilfields were usually less than 25% of in-place reserves. Following the implementation of the Stafjord Late-Life Project Statoil predict that the recovery rate should reach nearly 70%.

New technology is also being used to reduce carbon dioxide emissions produced by fossil fuel combustion. The main Carbon Abatements Technology

(CAT) options involve increasing the efficiency of current combustion processes using new technology, altering the make up of the raw material (eg so-called co-firing using a mix of fossil fuel and biomass) and carbon dioxide capture and storage (CCS). CCS (sometimes referred to as carbon sequestration), is the least developed of the alternative technologies but it is one which the North Sea oil and gas industry is watching with interest. CCS involves the removal or capture of carbon dioxide (from flue or fuel gas streams) and its transportation and subsequent storage in underground geological formations. Various different methods are being developed for carbon dioxide capture but the process most commonly used currently involves the use of amine-based solvents. The carbon dioxide is then transported (on a large scale project this is usually by pipeline) and injected into underground geological formations such as depleted oil fields and saline aquifers. The use of depleted oil or gas fields has the advantage of a readily available infrastructure which may be utilised for transport and a vast body of knowledge in respect of the geological structure to be used. On the other hand, the distance over which the carbon dioxide may have to be transported will often be a distinct disadvantage. Saline aquifers may be easier to access and have much larger capacities but little is usually known of their geological structure. Although CCS technology is currently being used on several industrial-scale projects, there are still some areas of concern. Chief amongst these is the possibility of leakage from the storage structure and much research is being directed at the detection and prevention of carbon dioxide leaks. The oldest CCS project currently in operation is Statoil's Sleipner Project in the Norwegian North Sea which commenced in 1996. Carbon dioxide from the Sleipner natural gas production facility is injected into a saline aquifer beneath the North Sea. To date there has been no evidence of the gas leaking from the saline aquifer.

Redeployment of skills

In addition to physical resources, the North Sea oil and gas industry has a highly skilled workforce both in the industry itself and in the resulting service industries. These skills, along with the technology developed for the industry, are valuable assets which may be redeployed. Redeployment may take the form of providing technology and expertise for oil and gas exploration in other geographical areas or, more importantly for the UK industry base, the skills and technology may be used to research and develop other forms of energy. UK service companies in particular may need to look to international markets in order to survive the changing face of North Sea production.

New uses for existing infrastructure

The availability of, and the need to maintain, the existing infrastructure is being given increased attention. As mentioned above, access to existing infrastructure may be the only economically feasible way of accessing some reserves. In addition, existing structures may be required for access to CCS or other new technologies. Offshore wind farms, although in early stages in the UK are on the increase and it is possible that some of the existing offshore structures may be utilised for such projects. Talisman's Beatrice wind farm project will produce an interesting alliance between fossil fuels and renewable energy when the electricity produced by the offshore turbines will be used to power production from the Beatrice field.

In summary, whilst it is accepted that the North Sea is regarded as a mature area and that production will inevitably decline, many forecasters take an optimistic view in that there are still opportunities for the industry which has grown up around North Sea oil and gas. New technology is increasing the availability of the remaining reserves and is opening up new avenues for alternative energy production. Further discoveries, although not on the scale of previous discoveries, are still being made and the existing production units still need to be maintained, serviced and, in due course, abandoned. The demise of the North Sea oil and gas industry may yet be some time off but when it does happen the industry will leave behind a pool of skills and technology which, if exploited fully, could be a valuable legacy for the UK to carry into the future.

Notes

1. Energy White Paper: *Our Energy Future – creating a low carbon economy*, Cm 5761 (2003).
2. The Sustainable Energy Act 2003; the Energy Act 2004.
3. Third Annual Report on The Implementation of the Energy White Paper, DTI, July 2006.
4. *The Stern Review on the Economics of Climate Change*, Sir Nicholas Stern (October 2006).
5. The Secretary of State's first report to Parliament on Security of Gas and Electricity Supply in Great Britain, DTI, July 2005.
6. Energy White Paper: *Our Energy Future – creating a low carbon economy*, Cm 5761 (2003).
7. *The Stern Review on the Economics of Climate Change*, Sir Nicholas Stern (October 2006).
8. The UK Greenhouse Gas Emissions Trading Scheme 2002, Department of Environment, Food and Rural Affairs.
9. Directive 2003/87/EC of the European Parliament and Council.
10. Directive 2004/101/EC of the European Parliament and Council.
11. The Greenhouse Gas Emissions Trading Scheme Regulations 2005 (SI 2005 No 925), as amended by The Greenhouse Gas Emissions Trading Scheme (Amendment) and National Emission Inventory Regulations 2005 (SI 2005 No 2903).

[12] House of Commons Environment, Food and Rurual Affairs Committee, 9th Report of Session 2004–2005, 'Climate Change: Looking Forward', HC 130.
[13] As implemented by the Finance Act 2000.
[14] The Electricity Act 1989, as amended by the Utilities Act 2000 and the Energy Act 2004.
[15] Striking a balance 2005: The sustainability strategy update and progress report of the UK Offshore Oil and Gas Industry, UKOOA, 2005.
[16] The DTI's Second Annual Report on the Implementation of the Energy White Paper. DTI, July 2005.

— 25 —

RENEWABLES

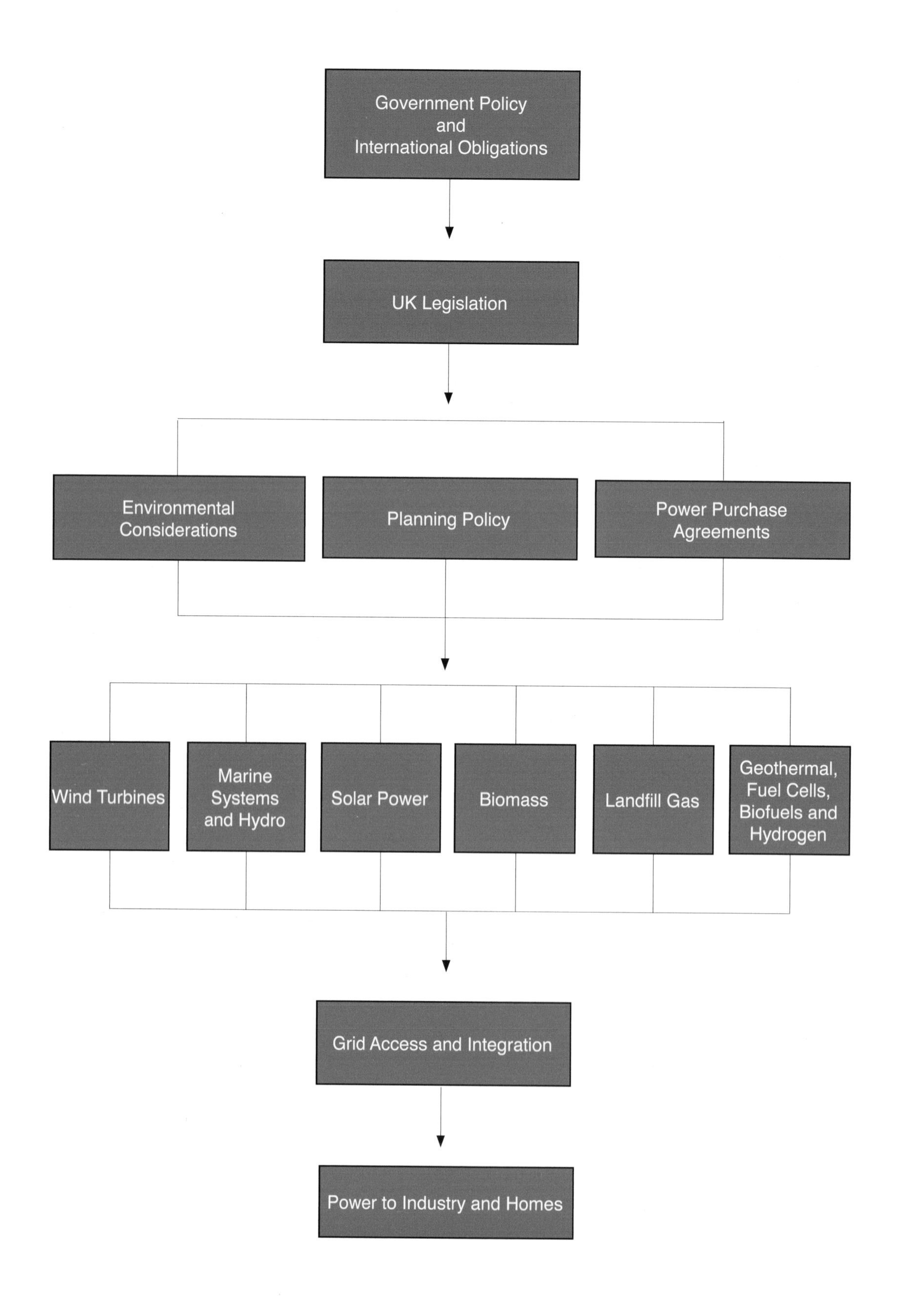

Government Policy
and
International Obligations
UK Legislation
Environmental Considerations
Planning Policy
Power Purchase Agreements
Wind Turbines
Marine Systems and Hydro
Solar Power
Biomass
Landfill Gas
Geothermal, Fuel Cells, Biofuels and Hydrogen
Grid Access and Integration
Power to Industry and Homes

RENEWABLES

25.1 Introduction

It is now generally accepted that renewable energy must form part of the UK's energy policy both in terms of diversity of supply and as a response to climate change commitments (DEFRA, 2001). The original impetus for developing renewable energy was triggered by the oil crisis in 1973. However, development was hampered by the fact that the price of energy from renewable sources remained higher than that for energy derived from fossil fuels. Intensive work in the intervening period has not changed the relative economics significantly, therefore, the factors currently driving development of renewable energy technology focus on climate change and security of supply.

Climate change, which many scientists think is the result of increased emissions of carbon dioxide and other greenhouse gases, is now an issue of global concern. The use of renewable energy sources as opposed to fossil fuels has the potential to reduce the amount of emissions and hence reduce the impact of climate change. The UK's stated ambition is for the world's developed economies to cut emissions of greenhouse gases by 60% by around 2050. The Energy White Paper of 2003[1] builds on that ambition with respect to the UK and seeks to ensure that UK energy policy attempts to sustainably integrate energy, the environment and economic growth. The use of renewable energy is therefore seen as an important element in addressing the climate change issue.

Security and diversity of supply

Fossil fuels are a finite resource and as the amount of fossil fuel diminishes (both in terms of the UK's fossil fuel resources and global resources generally) the availability of other energy sources will become increasingly important. Within a few years, the UK will have become a net importer of both oil and gas. In order to reduce the UK's reliance on fossil fuels from other countries, the development of other energy sources, (and in particular renewable energy), is being pursued.

In the UK, and elsewhere in the developed world, future energy concerns are generally linked to electricity generation. Currently, renewable energy sources account for some 6% of electricity generated, whereas gas accounts for 40%, coal 32% and nuclear 22%. Whereas in the past, energy supply has been dominated by relatively few sources, in the future there will be a far more diversified energy mix which will be more complex to control, manage and integrate into the distribution system.

Although much of the recent research and development on renewable energy has been targeted at generating electricity, the potential applications for renewable energy are much wider. There is an increasing interest in heat production either by stand alone combustion systems, (often in conjunction with district heating schemes as in Sweden), or through combined heat and power (CHP) installations. The use of renewable energy in the transport sector (eg in the form of biodiesel) is also being pursued.

As a result of the concerns regarding climate change and diversity of supply, the UK Government (in common with many other governments around the world) has introduced various policy and fiscal measures to encourage and support the development of renewable energy technology and to create a favourable market for energy derived from renewable sources. It is anticipated that, in the long run, the cost of providing energy from renewable sources will fall as the efficiency of the technology improves and the economies of scale associated with larger projects begin to feed through. At present, however, renewable energy developments continue to rely on governmental policy measures to ensure their viability.

25.2 Renewable energy technologies

The term 'renewable energy' does not have a definitive meaning but is merely a convenient way of describing energy derived from resources which are self-replenishing. The Scottish Executive's National Planning Policy Guideline No 6[2] describes renewable energy as those energy flows that occur naturally and repeatedly in the environment. Although the term renewable energy may be generic rather than specific, there is a fair degree of consensus as to the different sources of energy which come under the umbrella term 'renewable energy'. Of the wide range of technologies that come under the umbrella of renewable energy many (for example, wind, wave, photovoltaic and tidal current based technologies) only generate electricity whereas others (for example, biomass fuels) can be used to generate electricity, produce heat or be used as liquid transport fuels. The following part of this chapter looks briefly at the main sources of renewable energy.

Wind

Wind has been used for centuries as a means of powering machinery and, more recently, the focus has moved to the use of wind to produce electricity. Technology has developed rapidly in the last two decades with wind turbines becoming larger and more efficient. Wind turbines probably represent the most commercially advanced and fastest growing of the renewable energy technologies. There is 34,000 MW of wind energy capacity currently installed in Europe. The European Wind Energy Association has set targets of 45,000 MW by 2010 and 180,000 MW by 2050.[3]

Modern wind turbines usually consist of blades mounted on a horizontal axis, however, there are alternative vertical axis turbines such as Darrieus or Gorlov turbines. At present the design most favoured in the UK appears to be the three-blade horizontal axis mounted on a steel tower. All turbines work on the same principle, ie wind passing over the blades causes the blades to turn. The turning blades rotate a shaft leading into a gear box which increases the rotational speed sufficiently to power an electrical generator. The electricity produced then passes through a transformer to produce the correct voltage before either being used directly (off-line systems) or entering the distribution network (grid-connected systems). An anemometer and wind vane on the wind turbine constantly measure wind speed and direction and machinery at the top of the tower and enables the blades to be turned to face the wind and to be tilted for maximum efficiency. Recent developments in turbine technology have enabled the production of larger turbines with rotor diameters up to 90 metres and power output up to 5 MW. The towers on which the turbines are mounted are fixed to relatively small concrete bases permitting, at least in theory, the use of the land for agriculture right up to the base of the towers. Wind turbines are usually deployed in wind farms – ie a cluster of wind turbines that acts and is connected to the power system as a single electricity producing unit (Petersen and Madsen, 2004). The grouping of turbines within a wind farm is important as the pattern in which the turbines are arranged will affect wind capture. A minimum separation distance between turbines of 5–10 rotor diameters is required to prevent 'wind-shadowing'. Wind farms are controlled by a central monitoring system which does not necessarily need to be onsite.

The amount of power produced by a wind turbine depends on the density of the air, the area swept by the blades and, most crucially, the wind speed. Wind turbines generally start generating electricity at a wind speed of around 8 miles per hour, generate maximum rated power at 30 miles per hour and shut down to prevent damage at wind speeds in excess of 50 miles per hour.[4] The intermittent and variable nature of wind is one of the major disadvantages of wind power.

Despite the recent rapid increase in the use of wind turbines there are some concerns regarding the technology. Although modern turbines operate at a relatively low noise level the mechanical parts of the turbine do produce a certain level of noise. Aerodynamic noise may also be produced as the blades sweep the air. Another area of concern is the visual impact of wind farms. By the very nature of the geographical and physical requirements for a wind turbine to operate efficiently, wind turbines are highly visible. The overall impact will depend on various factors including landscape characteristics, number of turbines, design and size of turbines and the use of access tracks, power lines and substations.

Concerns have also been raised regarding the impact on bird populations and on safety generally. With regard to the former, bird populations may be disrupted during the construction of wind farms, however, the main concern is the possibility of bird strike caused by birds flying into the path of blades. When assessing the potential of bird strike, consideration must be given to the species which may be affected (particularly relevant if the proposed site is the habitat of a species protected under UK or EU legislation), density of birds, flight paths and seasonal patterns. General safety concerns arise in several areas. The most obvious is the loss of a turbine blade or ice splatter.

Most turbines have vibration sensors which will prevent the blades turning if an imbalance is detected. Another area of concern is the production of shadow flicker which occurs when the sun passes behind the blades. The shadow which is cast may appear to flicker when the blades rotate. Shadow flicker only occurs when a particular combination of time of day, season and geography occurs and therefore it is possible to calculate the degree to which shadow flicker will occur. The most effective solution to a potential problem of shadow flicker is to ensure that the turbines are not sited too closely to buildings.

Finally, wind turbines also produce electro-magnetic radiation which can interfere with communication signals. This may constitute a nuisance factor in respect of radio and television reception but will be more serious if the interference would affect air traffic control or emergency services. The main restraints on further wind farm developments at present remain (i) public perception as to the visual impact and (ii) access to the national grid.

Weighing against the concerns/problems with wind farms is the fact that once construction is complete, operating and maintenance costs are small. There is no need for a wind farm to be permanently manned and the technology is useful for rural locations or mobile use, eg on boats.

Figure 25–1 Offshore wind development

Offshore wind farms are a relatively new phenomenon in UK waters. The first UK offshore wind farm was commissioned in 2000 off the coast of Northumberland (Fig. 25–1). The technology used offshore is based on onshore technology, but there are additional factors to take into consideration such as construction and transportation costs, the requirement for the towers, blades and turbine machinery to be protected from corrosion and of course the cabling necessary to transport the electricity to shore. Although most of the current offshore developments are in relatively shallow water, the Beatrice offshore demonstration wind project (to be tied in to the Beatrice platform in the Moray Firth) will be the world's deepest offshore wind farm and may well open the way for future deep water projects.

Marine energy

The UK has access to predictable and reliable tidal currents and wave patterns. Although researchers are currently exploring the potential of using temperature differences in water as an energy source, at present marine energy devices either harness wave energy or tidal energy. From a Scottish perspective, by 2020, there is the potential for 10% of Scotland's electricity production to come from marine resources, ie 1300 MW of marine energy capacity installed in Scottish waters, increasing at a rate of 100 MW per year.[5]

(i) Wave

The kinetic energy contained in wave movement can be captured by a variety of devices and then utilised to power a turbine. The potential global wave energy contribution to the electricity market is estimated at some 2000 TWh/yr, approximately 10% of the world electricity consumption. Over 1000 wave energy devices have been patented worldwide, classified into five basic types (Lemonis, 2004):

Oscillating water column	Limpet, Scotland; Energetech Oscillating Water Column, Australia
Overtopping devices	Floating Wave Power Vessel, Sweden; Wave Dragon, Denmark
Heaving devices	Archimedes Wave Swing, The Netherlands; Point Absorber Wave Energy Converter, Denmark
Pitching devices	Pelamis, UK
Surging devices	Pendulator, Japan

The most common device for capturing wave energy is some form of Oscillating Water Column (OWC) which generally comprises a partially submerged structure with a chamber enclosing a column of air on top of a column of water. As the water level rises and drops the air is forced up the chamber and then pulled back down the chamber. The moving air flows through a turbine which, in turn, powers a generator.

(ii) Tidal

Tidal power devices consist of either those devices which place turbines to capture the energy in the tidal range (ie barrage type devices) or those that harvest the energy in tidal currents. The global tidal range energy potential is estimated at 3000 GW with some 1000 GW (3,800 TWh/yr) being available in relatively shallow water). Tidal current energy conversion technologies are predicted to supply up to 48 TWh/yr from sites around Europe (Lemonis, 2004).

Tidal systems traditionally involve the construction of a barrage (dam) across a tidal basin. As the tide comes in, a sluice is opened allowing the water to flow into the basin. The sluice is then closed trapping the water in a reservoir behind the dam as the tide retreats. The water behind the dam can then be released to produce power using traditional hydroelectric technology. Turbines which permit electricity to be generated both by the incoming and the outgoing tides greatly increase the generating potential of such barrage systems. However, in order for barrage systems to be viable there needs to be a large tidal range.

The first large-scale commercial tidal range energy plant was built on the La Rance estuary in France and generates 240 MW. It is the only industrial-sized tidal power station in the world and because of high capital costs and potentially significant environmental impacts it is unlikely that another will be built on this scale.

In addition to devices which utilise the tidal range, there are tidal systems which utilise tidal current. These systems use either technology similar to that used for wind energy conversion (ie turbines with a horizontal or vertical axis) or the oscillating hydrofoil technique (Lemonis, 2004). The following systems are currently being developed:

- horizontal axis – Seaflow, UK
- vertical axis – ENERMAR, Italy
- oscillating – Stingray, UK

When the turbine system is used, the turbines are usually mounted on an underwater fence which is deployed in channels between two land masses. The density of water is some 850 times higher than that of air and therefore the power intensity in water currents is significantly higher than in airflows. This

Figure 25–2 Rotech Holdings Ltd's underwater turbines (© Rotech Holdings Ltd)

enables a water current turbine to be built on a considerably smaller scale than an equivalent-powered wind turbine.

The fence system has the advantage of having less impact on the environment than the barrage system and, as it can be deployed in channels between two land masses, the availability of suitable locations is greater. Recent developments, particularly in Norway, have involved small tidal power plants situated in narrow fjords, which utilise underwater turbines (Fig. 25–2).

In addition to the restrictions placed on marine energy by specific geographical requirements the other main drawback of marine energy (particularly tidal energy) is the intermittent and variable nature of electricity production due to the tidal cycle and seasonal variations. There are also environmental factors to consider, (particularly with reference to tidal energy systems), such as the effect on aquatic life, increase in turbidity and salinity and disruption of sediments.

Hydro

Hydroelectric power has been providing Scotland with a considerable amount of electricity for several decades. At present, the large hydro schemes produce over 10% of the country's electricity. The existing developments usually consist of a large reservoir and dam. Such developments have high initial capital costs but, following construction, generally have low running costs and a long lifetime.

The principle behind hydro power is the use of flowing water to drive a wheel or turbine which may then be used to generate electricity. The power output depends on the volume of water available and the vertical distance through which the water falls. In order to maintain constancy of flow the water used must either have low variation in flow and come from a deep source (to permit draw off) or a suitable reservoir must be constructed to provide such conditions. Most large hydro plants have large water storage capacity to ensure constant water flow throughout the year. Smaller schemes and run-of-river schemes may have very little or no storage capacity and as such are subject to weather and seasonal fluctuations with the resulting fluctuations in power output. Such specific requirements define the location and size of hydro schemes. The construction of large reservoirs and dams is controversial and, in the UK at least, new schemes tend to concentrate on smaller scale development with low visual impact. Many developing countries, however, are turning to large-scale hydro projects to provide a reliable source of electricity notwithstanding the environmental and population relocation factors.

Hydro power is considered a 'green' source of energy in that it does not produce particulates or harmful gases. It is somewhat ironic, therefore, that in certain parts of the world the changing weather patterns, (which many accept as evidence of global warming caused by greenhouse gases), have resulted in large hydro schemes being compromised by low reservoir levels.

Eligibility of hydro power under the Renewable Obligations provision (discussed later) depends on the size of the hydro generating station. The most important exclusion relates to large hydro generating stations (being stations with a capacity of greater than 20 MW) which were commissioned before 1 April 2002.

In addition to visual impact and population relocation (more relevant with larger schemes) an additional environmental concern with hydro schemes is the impact on fish and freshwater animals. In particular, migratory fish such as salmon are at particular risk and hydro schemes may be required to incorporate fish passes and ladders in order to alleviate the impact on such fish.

Fuel cells

A fuel cell is a device for directly converting the chemical energy of a fuel into electrical energy in a constant temperature process. Fuel cells operate on a wide range of fuels, including hydrogen. The principle of operation of a fuel cell is similar to electrolysis but in reverse – gases such as hydrogen or oxygen are pumped in and DC electricity is the output. The only by-products are water and there are essentially no pollutants. The voltage produced from one cell is low (typically 0.7–0.8 volts) and so multiple cells are deployed to generate a useful voltage.

The low-temperature fuel cells (AFC, PEMFC, PAFC (Fig. 25–3)) require a relatively pure supply of hydrogen whereas the high temperature ones (MCFC, SOFC (Fig. 25–3)) can operate on a range of hydrocarbons. A particularly interesting application is the use of biofuels or solid carbon in SOFCs (Irvine et al., 2005).

Potential applications for fuel cells range from battery replacement in consumer products through residential scale combined heat and power to distributed energy generation, where commercial application is limited by cost (Brandon, 2004).

Fuel cells may also be used to power vehicles. Depending on the type of fuel used, the amount of carbon dioxide produced can range from essentially zero, to a level on par with conventional fossil fuel combustion.

There are five main types of fuel cell:

Type	Abbreviation	Operating temperature
Alkaline	AFC	60–250°C
Polymer	PEMFC	80–120°C
Phosphoric acid	PAFC	150–220°C
Molten carbonate	MCFC	600–700°C
Solid oxide	SOFC	600–1000°C

Figure 25–3 Types of fuel cell (Source: Brandon, 2004)

Solar power

Solar power systems may conveniently be divided into solar thermal power devices and photovoltaic power devices.

(i) Photovoltaics

Photovoltaic energy conversion involves the direct conversion of sunlight to electricity via semi-conductor devices known as solar cells. Such cells commonly have a potential conversion efficiency of 10%. The basic element is the photovoltaic cell which consists of semi-conductor materials which have both negative and positive charge carriers, the n and p layers. When photons from ultraviolet, visible, and near-infrared light enter the cell, electrons in the semi-conductor material are freed, and an electric current is generated. Single photovoltaic cells are usually connected together and then packaged into weather resistant modules which can then be further connected and arranged to form panels of the required size.

Although technological development is increasing the efficiency of cells, the large area of panel required to collect a useful amount of solar energy is still one of the main drawbacks of photovoltaic systems, eg a 1000 MW plant operating at 10% conversion efficiency would cover an area of 10 km^2. The largest scale commercial photovoltaic plant operates in Germany (the Bavaria Solarpark) and covers 63 acres. In addition to the size of the panel, the other limiting factor is obviously sunlight. Location, season and weather conditions all affect the amount of solar energy captured by photovoltaic cells.

Photovoltaic panels may be either grid connected or stand alone. Stand alone systems are particularly useful for areas where access to the electricity grid is restricted. Grid connected systems, on the other hand, permit excess electricity to be sold to an electricity supplier and for electricity to be purchased when the panels are not generating, eg in the evening.

The environmental impact of photovoltaics is probably lower than that of any other renewable or non-renewable electricity generating system. Very small quantities of toxic substances are used in their manufacture with only a slight risk that they might be released into the environment. There is a visual impact but for small scale systems roof top arrays are being developed to merge into the roof tiles and, therefore, reduce the level of visual impact.

(ii) Solar thermal systems

Solar thermal systems differ from photovoltaic systems in that the solar energy captured does not directly produce electricity. The energy collected may be used to heat water and/or space for domestic or industrial use or it may be used to heat some type of fluid which will be used to drive a turbine (either directly or by first producing steam). The turbine then powers a conventional electricity generator.

The simplest form of solar thermal system (other than passive space heating systems) comprises a covered absorber plate behind which is a system of tubes containing a liquid which removes the captured heat from the collector (the absorber plate) to the point of use. More complex systems, and systems which power electricity generation, use concentrators to provide higher temperatures in the heat exchange system. Concentrators use various shapes of reflectors to focus the sun onto a receiver. In order to maximise exposure to the sun, collectors such as dish or parabolic trough systems may rotate in order to track the sun throughout the day. As with the photovoltaic systems, however, a relatively large area is required for collection (particularly with non-concentrating systems) and the conversion rate is poor. One of the largest solar thermal power plants is the 1,000-acre plant in the Mojave Desert (Fig. 25–4).

Geothermal

Geothermal energy is simply the natural heat of the earth. Although the resource is enormous there are considerable challenges in extracting the heat. The most powerful sources are contained in geopressure brines, hot dry rock, magma and hydrothermal reservoirs. Of these sources the hydrothermal reservoirs are the most easily accessible and technology exists whereby these reservoirs of heated water, or in some cases steam, can be used to drive turbines to generate electricity. The technology to recover heat from hot rocks and other structures is still in the experimental stage.

Figure 25–4 Solar power plant, Mojave Desert (© AP/PA Photos)

An alternative method of recovering geothermal energy is by using geothermal heat pumps to circulate fluid through a series of subterranean pipes. In the winter, the liquid absorbs heat from the ground which is then concentrated and used to heat buildings. In the summer, the system can be used to cool buildings by transferring heat from the buildings back to the ground. This system depends on the fact that the top 15 metres of the earth's surface remain at a fairly consistent temperature. In locations where geothermal heat is found near the surface of the earth, a similar system of heat pumps can be used to directly transfer the heat to provide hot water in addition to space heating.

Exploitation of geothermal energy is dependent, to a large extent, on the accessibility of the resource. Hydrothermal reservoirs and other deep heat structures are usually located in specific geographical areas. To a lesser extent, the use of heat pumps is also location driven since it is dependent on the amount of sun. From an environmental perspective geothermal energy is reasonably clean with very few emissions and minimal visual effect, however, concerns have been raised about subsidence and disposal of solids from hydrothermal reservoirs. One of the main advantages of geothermal energy is that it is available 24 hours a day.

Biomass

Biomass, particularly wood, has been a fuel since time immemorial and even now accounts for around 50% of energy use in the world. Much of that use is in developed countries, where the forest products industries utilise their waste wood for producing process heat and potentially electricity. The major source of biomass energy worldwide is wood – whether as fuel wood for open fires in developing countries or sophisticated large-scale conversion systems in developed countries. The wood may be from natural or plantation forests and is increasingly being harvested as a further product in an integrated harvesting system. In these systems, trees are harvested and products flow to the conventional forest products industries (sawmills, pulp and board mills), with the forestry by-products being utilised for energy production. There is increasing interest in securing the biomass resource from fast-growing energy plantations of shrub-like varieties of willow and poplar. Growing, harvesting and processing these crops presents particular problems, not least of which is that the cost of the raw material is significantly higher than that obtained from conventional forest operations. Other biomass resources which can be used for fuel are cereal straw, sugarcane bagasse, rice husks, and purpose grown energy crops such as the giant grasses (eg *Miscanthus* spp).

As with other renewable energy sources eligibility under the Renewables Obligation scheme[6] is crucial. Until recently, the requirement for individual components in a biomass fuel source to be tested separately inhibited the use of pre-blended materials and co-firing (where a power plant uses more than one raw material). Recent changes to the rules of the Renewable Obligations scheme, however, have decreased the purity of biomass required for eligibility from 98 to 90% (being the percentage of the energy content which is derived from plant or animal matter) and have also made it easier to use biomass in co-firing. Co-firing biomass in an existing fossil fuel power plant (for which the Renewable Obligations Scheme contains detailed rules) may be attractive as there will be existing transport links and grid connections.

It is worth noting that in terms of the Renewables Obligation Orders 'energy crop' is defined as a plant crop planted after 31 December 1989 and grown primarily for the purpose of being used as fuel. This definition excludes some of the biomass sources mentioned above (eg slow-grown wood, timber industry by-products, etc.). It is also possible (although perhaps not in terms of the Renewable Obligations Scheme) to utilise waste from industrial processes in a biomass plant. Such sources however may come under the terms of the European Waste Incineration Directive[7] and as such their use will be subject to regulations which may affect the financial viability of projects using such resources.

In addition to the benefit of being a renewable resource, biomass also has the advantage of being a low carbon fuel. Although biomass does release carbon dioxide on combustion, the theory behind the use of biomass is that the carbon dioxide released into the atmosphere on combustion of biomass is absorbed, by photosynthesis, by the next generation of crops planted to replace the crops used. Even with constant replenishment of crops, however, biomass is not carbon neutral because energy will be extended harvesting the crops and transporting them to the power plant.

Biomass is an attractive source of renewable energy in that through the different conversion processes (Fig. 25–5) which are available, heat, electricity, liquid fuels and gases can be obtained. Utilising combined heat and power systems (CHP) means that both heat and power can be produced. The liquid fuels can be used in the transport sector or in static applications to produce heat and/or electricity.

Conversion Process	Energy carrier	Application
Combustion	Heat	Heat
	Steam	Process heat/electricity
Gasification	Gas/liquid	Electricity
Pyrolysis	Liquid	Electricity, transport
Biological (anaerobic digestion)	Biogas	Heat/electricity
Biological(fermentation)	Liquid (ethanol)	Transport

Figure 25–5 Biomass conversion processes

The Scottish Executive's Forum for Renewable Energy Development in Scotland (FREDS) considered that Scottish biomass is uniquely placed with the UK to contribute to both Scottish and UK renewable targets by 2010 rather than the 2015 indicated by the DTI for England and Wales.[8]

Biofuels

Biofuels are derived from vegetable oils which occur naturally and are extracted by crushing the seeds. The oils (triglycerides) are treated by adding methanol or ethanol in a process called transesterfication to produce biodiesel. The biodiesel can be used in an internal combustion engine without having to modify the engine. In Europe and Canada rape methyl ester (RME) from oil seed rape is attracting most interest, whereas in the USA most production is based on soya oil and recycled cooking oil. Their wide-scale use should have a significant impact on greenhouse gas emissions.

Landfill gas, biogas and sewage treatment plant gas

Fermentation of organic matter results in the production of gases such as methane. The fermentation may take place in plants specifically constructed for that purpose (ie for the production of biogas) or may occur naturally in landfill sites where biodegradable waste will produce carbon dioxide and methane (both of which are greenhouse gases). The production of methane from landfill sites is particularly problematic because its global warming potential is far greater than that of carbon dioxide and, in addition, the gas can migrate underground causing an explosive hazard. The collection and use of such gases therefore has additional benefits.

The utility of gas produced in fermentation processes will depend on the amount of gas produced and the quality of the gas produced. Processes using specifically constructed anaerobic digesters can control the process to some extent and, if the biogas is being produced for a specific purpose (eg as a fuel source for vehicles), the gas can then be cleaned so that it is of the required quality. Alternatively, gas which does not meet the required quality can be co-fired with natural gas to improve combustion. Although landfill gas is more difficult to regulate in terms of production and quality it is possible to collect landfill gas by using a series of wells to divert it to a collection point where it can then be treated.

Hydrogen

Hydrogen is considered by many to be the fuel of the future as it has many advantages (Boyle, 2004) including acting as a store for intermittent renewable energy systems. Hydrogen is not an energy source in its own right. It can be burned in place of conventional fuels and also be electrochemically oxidized more readily than most hydrocarbons which means that it can be used in fuel cells. Fuel cells are the most attractive for renewable energy applications due to the high efficiency that is possible over a wide range of application scales.[9]

The hydrogen economy is thought by many to have the potential to deliver a low carbon future over the next 50 years. The use of hydrogen as a transport fuel offers significant opportunities for cost competitive CO_2 reduction by 2030.

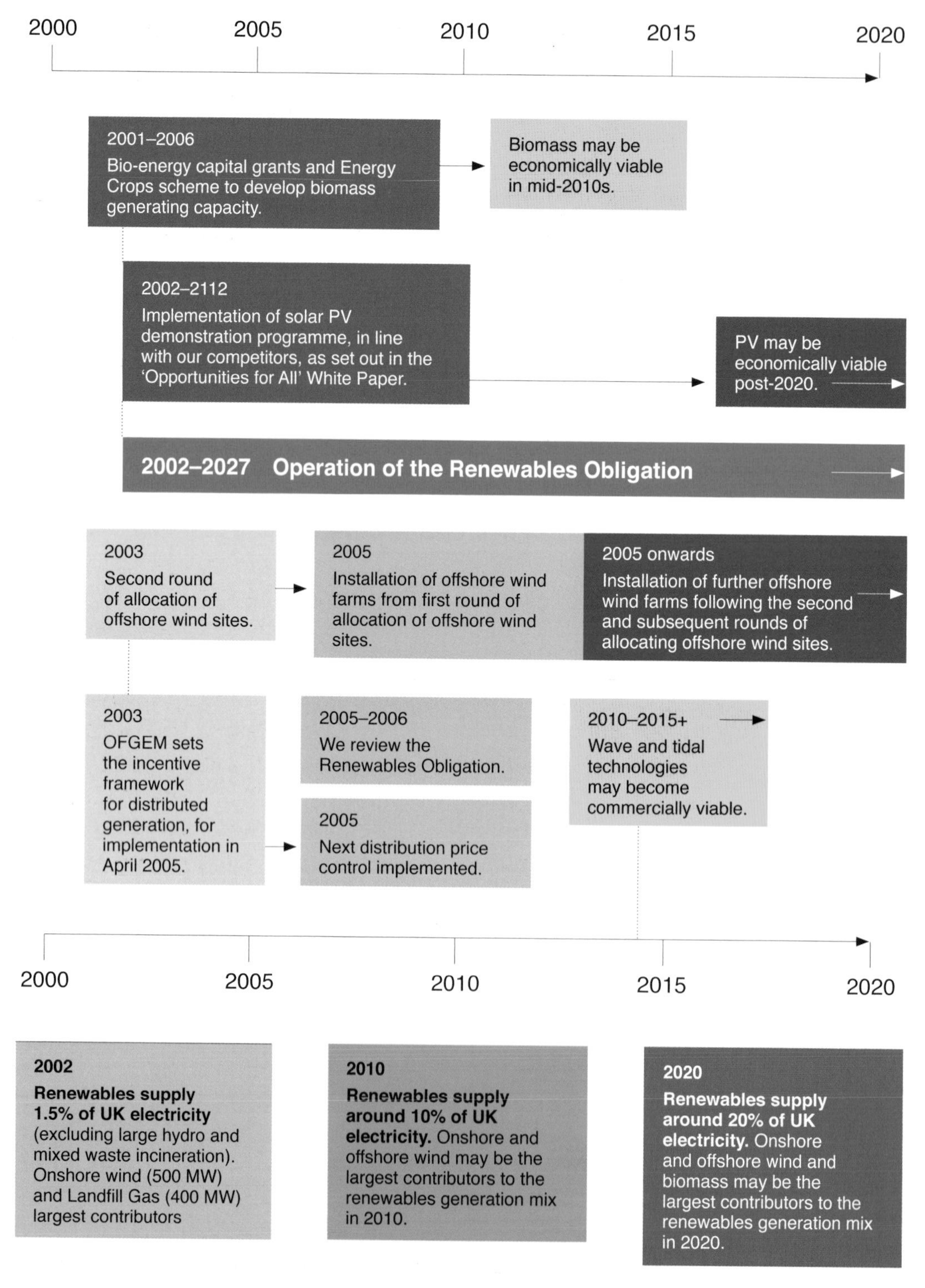

Figure 25–6 Creating a low carbon economy
(Source: UK Energy White Paper, 2003, p 59. Crown copyright).

25.3 Timescale for deployment of renewable technologies

In the UK Energy White Paper (2003, Fig. 25–6)[10] a renewable energy timeline was produced which indicated the key dates on a critical path to achieve 10% of electricity from renewable energy sources by 2010 and doubling the renewable share in the following decade. This timeline, whilst drawn up for the UK and its policies, is a reasonable scenario of how renewable energy technologies will enter the energy mix elsewhere over the next 15 years. This foresees biomass becoming economically viable by the mid-2010s, photovoltaics may be economically viable post 2020, from 2010 to 2015 wave and tidal technologies may become commercially viable, and offshore wind farms will have been coming online from 2005 onwards. Clearly, significant shifts upwards in the price of fossil fuels and technology breakthroughs may well accelerate the overall process. However, all this presupposes that the problems of distributed generation and integration into the national grid (discussed below) are resolved.

25.4 The market for renewable energy

Overview

As mentioned previously, the price of energy derived from renewable sources is higher than that derived from fossil fuels. In order to create a favourable market for renewable energy, the UK Government has put in place various policy measures to encourage and support the development of a renewable energy industry. In this part of the chapter we consider the legal obligations arising from those policy measures and certain other legal and/or policy considerations which should be taken into account when considering renewable energy developments. While the sources which are commonly considered to be renewable have been described above, it is worth noting that policy measures may not apply evenly to all types of renewable energy.

The Renewables Obligation

The approach taken by the Government to encourage the use and development of renewable energy technology has so far been a combination of 'carrot and stick'. The stick part of the approach is provided by a legal obligation on electricity providers to supply a percentage of electricity sourced from a renewable supply and the carrot part of the approach involves financial incentives and a guaranteed market for renewable energy (at least until 2027). The central plank of the current policy in relation to renewable energy is the Renewable Energy Obligation (the 'Obligation'). Under the Obligation, licensed electricity suppliers are required to source a specific percentage of the electricity which they supply from renewable sources. The obligations are detailed in two separate Orders (one for England and Wales[11] and the other for Scotland)[12] however, the provisions in the two different orders are almost identical.

Under the terms of The Renewables Obligation (Scotland) Order 2006 (ROS) electricity suppliers are obliged to source an increasing percentage of their supply from qualifying renewable energy sources. The Scottish Executive has recently increased its aspirational target for electricity generated from renewable sources (a term which is wider than those sources which qualify in terms of the ROS) to 40% by 2020.[13] The Obligation as set out in the ROS is 6.7% for the period 2006/2007 rising in incremental stages to a level of 15.4% for the period 2015/2016 and remaining at that level until 2027.

In practice, the Obligation scheme is operated by the Office of Gas and Electricity Markets (Ofgem). In brief, if a qualifying renewable energy generator is accredited by Ofgem, that generator can then receive renewables obligation certificates (ROCs) in respect of the electricity which it generates from renewable sources. The obligation which the electricity suppliers have to meet can be discharged either by the purchase of ROCs from the accredited generators or by paying a buyout price. It is possible for ROCs to be traded separately from the electricity which was generated from the renewable source.

(i) Qualifying sources

Only electricity generated from 'eligible renewable sources' may be taken into account by a supplier in meeting the Obligation. The ROS does not define in any great detail exactly what constitutes a renewable source but instead provides that electricity generated from renewable sources, other than that generated by certain excluded types of generating station, will be eligible in terms of the Obligation. It is worth noting, however, that the Utilities Act 2000 (from which the power to make the renewables obligations is derived) gives a wide interpretation to the term renewables namely 'sources of energy other than fossil fuel or nuclear fuel'.[14]

The main types of generating stations which are excluded are those large hydro stations which were commissioned before 2002. Given the scale of hydro power in Scotland and the number of older stations this does exclude a sizeable proportion of renewable energy from the Obligation. One assumes that the reasoning behind this is that the Obligation's purpose is to encourage development of renewable energy sources to a point where they become economically attractive and not to rely merely on existing renewable energy sources.

(ii) Discharging the obligation

The ROS and the corresponding English Order are administered and enforced by Ofgem. There are several methods by which an electricity supplier burdened by the Obligation may discharge the Obligation. The main method is for the supplier to produce to Ofgem, evidence indicating that either it, or another supplier has on its behalf, supplied the specified percentage of electricity from renewable sources to customers in the UK. The evidence to be produced is a ROC.

Alternatively, the supplier can meet its obligation by making a buyout payment (or by a combination of both the payment and ROCs). A ROC certifies that a generating station has generated from renewable sources and that the resultant electricity has been supplied to customers in Britain. One ROC is issued for each MWh of electricity generated. Suppliers are required to produce evidence of compliance with their obligations (or pay a buyout price) by 1 October in each year (in respect of the preceding obligation period which runs from 1 April to 31 March each year). The proceeds from buyout payments are paid back to suppliers according to the ratio of ROCs presented by the supplier against the total number of ROCs for the given period thus giving companies an additional incentive to source supplies from renewable sources rather than relying on making a buyout payment.

As part of its duties in administering the Obligation scheme, Ofgem publishes an annual report giving detailed statistics relating to the operation of the

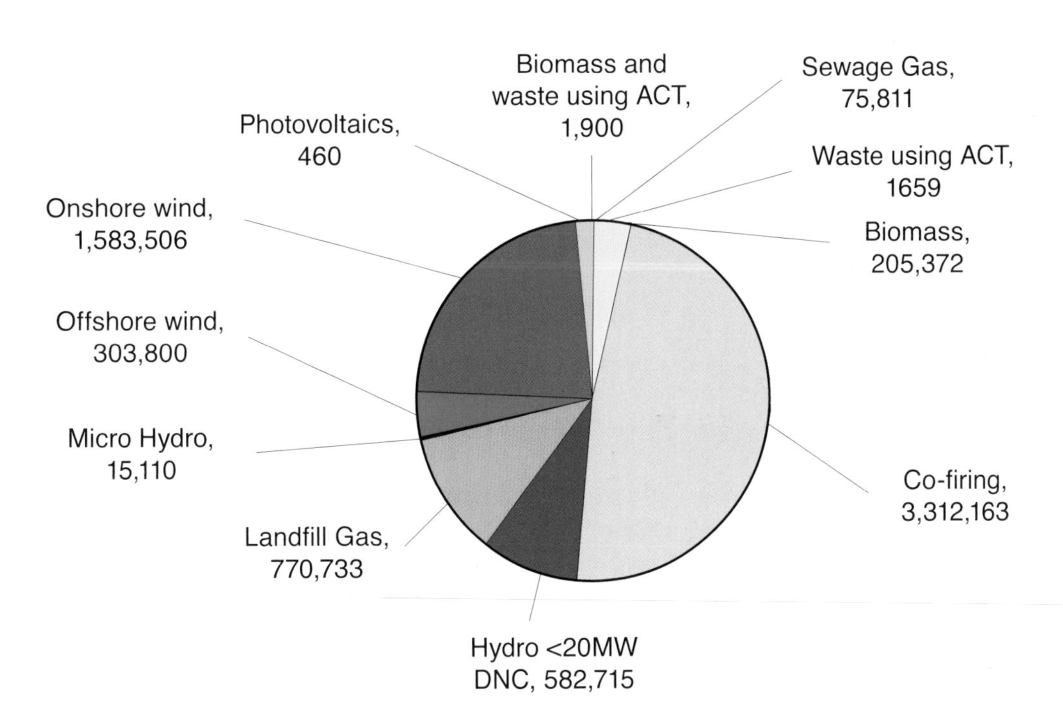

Figure 25–7 Breakdown of the total generating capacity accredited under the Renewable Obligation Schemes in terms of technology type (Ofgem, Renewables Obligation: Annual Report 2005–06, p 31)

scheme.[15] The report gives useful details as to the extent of the Obligation which is satisfied by ROCs (as opposed to buyout) and also the types of renewable energy generators which are being issued with ROCs. In the 2005/2006 period the majority of ROCs issued were issued to landfill gas and co-firing generating stations with onshore wind and biomass generation also being issued with a significant number of ROCs. Figure 25–8 gives a breakdown of ROCs issued in the 2005–2006 period according to technology type. The breakdown shown relates to all ROCs issued in the UK. There are, however, significant differences across the UK. In Scotland, for example, onshore wind and small hydro stations were the main recipients of ROCs (Fig. 25–9). Ofgem has the power to issue Enforcement Notices to licensed suppliers who fail to meet their renewables obligation. Failure to comply with such notices may attract financial penalties.

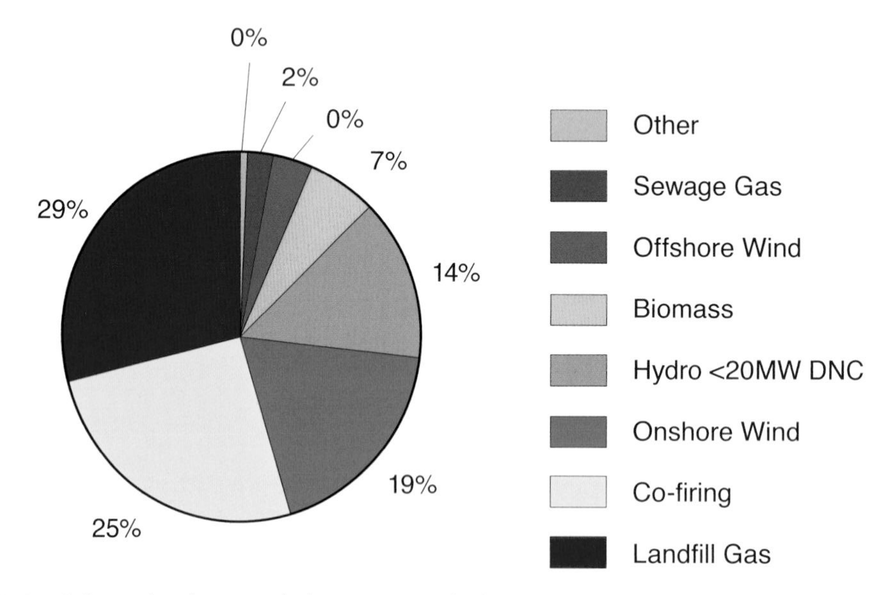

Figure 25–8 Other technologies include ACT, micro hydro, wave power and PV. Percentage breakdown of the total number of Renewables Obligation Certificates issued in the UK in the 2005–2006 obligation period in terms of technology type (Ofgem, Renewables Obligation: Annual Report 2005–06, p 22)

The Climate Change Levy

Since April 2001 the Government has levied a charge on energy consumed by public, commercial and industrial customers in the UK.[16] This charge (known as the Climate Change Levy (CCL)) is currently set at 0.43 p/kWh for electricity, 0.96p/kg LPG for heating, 0.15p/kWh for natural gas and 1.17p/kg for coke and coal. Electricity produced from qualifying renewable sources however

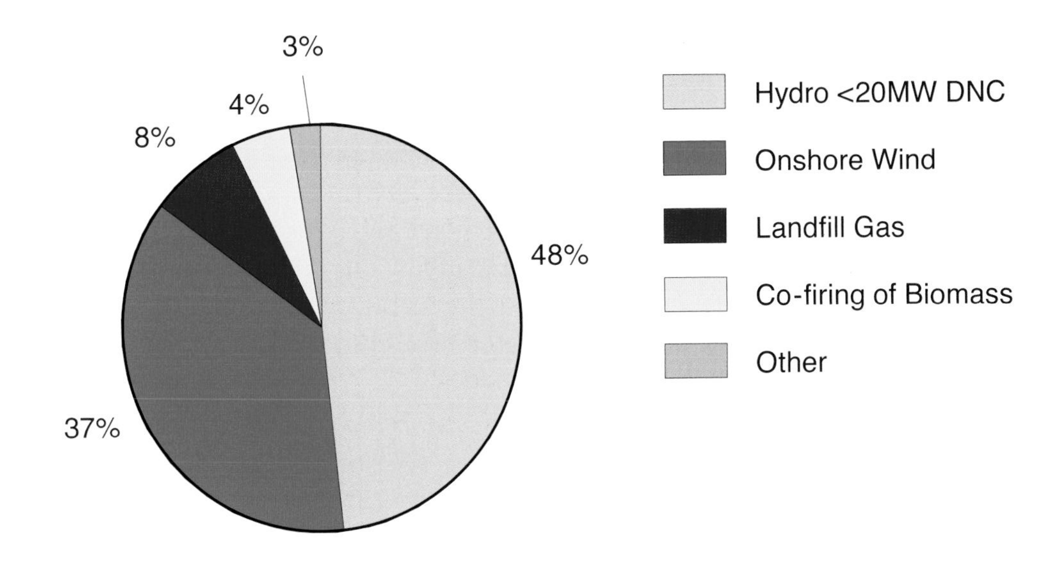

Figure 25–9 Other technologies include biomass, micro hydro, sewage gas and ACT. Percentage breakdown of the number of Renewable Obligation Certificates issued in Scotland in the 2005–2006 obligation period in terms of technology type (Ofgem, Renewables Obligation: Annual Report 2005–2006, p 24)

is exempt from CCL. As with the Renewables Obligation, Ofgem is responsible for accrediting those generators which wish to claim exemption from CCL and for issuing levy exemption certificates (LECs). LECs, therefore, are a further mechanism for adding value to electricity produced from renewable sources. Unlike ROCs, however, which may be split from the electricity which they relate to, LECs must be traded with the electricity for which they were issued.

The CCL is intended to be fiscally neutral in that funds received from the CCL are repaid to industry by a combination of a reduction in employers' NICs and capital tax allowances for energy saving/efficiency schemes.

25.5 Renewable energy developments – other considerations

Planning permission and other consents

(i) The planning/consent regimes

The planning/consent regime applicable to a renewable energy development is governed by the potential size (in production terms) of the development. All generating plants (whether powered by renewable energy or not) over 50 MW and new hydro plants over 1 MW require authorisation by the Scottish Executive (for developments in Scotland) or the Secretary of State for Trade and Industry (if the development is in England). Such developments are governed by specific legislation (the Electricity Act 1989) which, in certain circumstances, enables a Public Inquiry to be held in respect of the planning application. Applications for generating plants below these levels and other renewable energy developments are considered within the general planning system.

The land use policy framework relating to renewable energy installations is set out in the National Planning Policy Guideline (NPPG) 6[17] which in Scotland is supported by Planning Advice Note (PAN) 45.[18] In England equivalent guidance is given under Planning Policy Statement 22.[19] With regard to renewable

Technology	Issues which may be relevant
Wind	Visual impact (particularly in National Scenic Areas or national parks) Impact on bird population (particularly if proposed site is near nesting or feeding areas or migratory routes) Proximity to airfields (height of turbines and electromagnetic fields) Shadow flicker Noise
Hydro	Impact on local landscape Impact on other water users (eg recreational use) Effect on aquatic habitats, fish and other aquatic species
Biomass	Noise Pollution Control (By-products and emissions) Transport
Landfill Gas	Safety Emissions
Wave/Tidal (shoreline only)	Impact on coast Impact on coastal birds

Figure 25–10 Issues which may be relevant in the consideration of planning applications for renewable energy developments

developments offshore, different considerations and legislation apply and the regime applicable will depend on whether or not the proposed development lies within the Offshore Renewable Energy Zone which was created by the Energy Act 2004.[20]

(ii) General planning policy

The general principle behind planning policy relating to renewable energy developments is that such developments should be accommodated where the technology can operate efficiently and environmental impacts can be addressed satisfactorily.[21] Location is an important factor and if the proposed development site contains priority habitats or species, or the site has significant historic, scientific or environmental features, the importance of such features will carry considerable weight when considering the environmental impact.

All renewable energy developments are constrained in their choice of location by factors such as the availability of the energy resource and access to the electricity transmission system. However, there are often additional issues which are relevant to the individual technologies. A brief summary of some of the main issues which may be considered when a planning application is determined is given in Fig. 25–10.

Planning consent may be granted with conditions relating to decommissioning attached. With regard to wind turbines, for example, the structures may have to be dismantled and removed and the area (including access roads) restored.

(iii) Environmental considerations

An important aspect in obtaining planning permission for a renewable energy development is the consideration of the environmental impact of the proposed project. The applicable regulations and the extent to which public consultation and/or a full environmental impact assessment (EIA) will be required will depend on the nature of the proposed development. Developments that require consent under the Electricity Act 1989 (large-scale generators) will fall to be considered under different environmental regulations[22] from those developments which are considered under the general planning system.[23] The requirements of the different environmental regulations are, however, broadly similar. Whether or not an Environmental Statement must be submitted along with an application for consent or planning permission will depend on the type of development. Schedule 1 developments (eg large generating stations, waste incinerators, etc.) will always require an Environmental Statement. Schedule 2 developments (eg smaller generating stations, certain wind farms, etc.) will require an Environmental Statement if the development is likely to have a significant effect on the environment by virtue of factors such as its size, nature or location.

25.6 Grid integration/access to electricity transmission system

Any source of renewable energy has to fit into the existing pattern of energy distribution. The existing electricity infrastructure in the UK was designed for the requirements of traditional (usually large-scale) electricity generation. This, allied with the current restraints on connection and access to the system means that access to the system is a factor which parties considering a renewable energy project must consider at a very early stage.

In recent years, the electricity transmission and distribution system in the UK has undergone substantial changes. Most of the changes have been as a result of the British Electricity Trading and Transmission Arrangements (BETTA) which came in to full force on 1 April 2005. The main aim of BETTA arrangements was the creation of a single, competitive market for the trading of wholesale electricity in the UK which would be operated by one independent entity which would also have responsibility for a single set of arrangements governing access to and use of the UK transmission system. The National Grid Company plc (NGC) has been appointed as the single system operator and as part of the introduction of BETTA, NGC introduced a new system of charging for transmission.

Prior to the implementation of BETTA, access to the transmission system was provided by the relevant transmission licensee. In Scotland this was Scottish Hydro Electric Limited (SHETL) in the north of the country and Scottish Power Transmission Limited (SPTL) in the south. Under the old arrangements, generators in Scotland could only access the English market by first obtaining a contract with SHETL or SPTL for access to the England–Scotland Interconnector and then obtaining a separate contract for access to the England and Wales Transmission System. Now that BETTA is in place generators contract with NGC for connection to and use of the transmission system in the UK as a whole.

Although the process of applying for access to the transmission system has been simplified, access is still constrained by the lack of available capacity. Under the new BETTA rules an electricity generator which applied for grid connection (with one of the old transmission licensees) on or before 31 December 2004 will be connected to the national system dependent only on transmission upgrades within Scotland having been undertaken (and not upgrades in England and Wales or to the Interconnector). Generators which apply for grid connection after 31 December 2004 can only be connected subject to all necessary grid reinforcements (including upgrades to the Interconnector and, in respect of Scottish based generators, upgrades to the English system) having been completed.

Substantial upgrades will be required to the electricity transmission system to enable renewable energy developments to be accommodated. Certain transmission upgrades have already been approved by Ofgem but these have not been without difficulties. Construction of new high-voltage pylon lines has attracted considerable protest from local inhabitants and environmentalists.

In addition to the capacity constraints, initial access to the grid may be problematic. Many of the sites suitable for renewable energy developments (eg wind farms, tidal and wave power stations) are situated in remote locations. In contrast, the current grid reflects the locations of power stations and major population centres. The locations in Scotland, for example, which offer the greatest potential for renewable energy development are in the North and West of the country, often some distance from the existing major grid connections. Connection to the grid may well turn out to be prohibitively expensive. It is worth noting, however, that the UK Government does have a power under the Energy Act 2004 to limit transmission charges for renewable generators in specific areas if the government thinks that the transmissions charges would deter renewable development in that area. This may be particularly relevant for renewable generators in the Western Isles, Orkney and Shetland.

As well as access to the grid, integration must be considered. This is particularly important where the supply is intermittent. For example, biomass-fuelled power plants are likely to have outputs in the 5–50 MWe range, run almost continuously and can be directed directly to the grid. Wind and wave power plants are likely to be configured in groups of generators (eg windfarms) with a number of units working but with only one point of connection to the grid generating 50–100 MWe or more. These may be connected directly to the grid. In contrast to the biomass plants, however, wind and wave plants only generate electricity intermittently and relatively unpredictably and so intermediary storage may be required to balance the system. Tidal power systems are intermittent but highly predictable, particularly those coming from tidal barrages.

A partial and potential way to overcome the potential problems of grid access is through the use of embedded generation. This use of large numbers of small-scale systems would obviate the need for large-scale electricity grids but it would need to entail society taking a different view of its access to electricity, or more particularly heat, light and power.

25.7 Power Purchase Agreements

A Power Purchase Agreement (PPA) is a contract regulating the generation and sale of electricity. It is a crucial agreement for all power plant operators and is normally drawn between the owner of the plant (the generator) and the buyer of the electricity (usually an electricity supplier). PPAs may cover periods from one up to 12 years and during this term the buyer usually agrees to take all of the output from the generator. An obligation to provide a specified volume, although preferred by the buyer, will be resisted by the generator. In addition to the sale and purchase of energy the PPA will generally cover the operation and financing of the development/generating plant and may also seek guarantees relating to performance.

The actual value of a PPA is comprised of different elements: the market value of power (often called the Base Electricity Unit (BEU)), the ROC value, the ROC recycle payment and the Levy Exemption Certificate (LEC). The ROC is the most valuable component thus underlying the importance of the Renewables Obligation.

Government commitment to the Renewables Obligation until at least 2027 has enabled long-term power purchase contracts to be negotiated with renewable energy suppliers. In addition to increasing investor confidence in the renewable energy sector, long-term PPAs which guarantee the sale of the electricity (and possibly the ROCs) are usually required if the developer of a renewable energy project wishes to raise debt-finance. In such circumstances the PPA will typically have to be for at least the same period as the debt finance and may require a minimum price to be fixed for the output from the project. Recent concerns over the stability of ROC prices (as a result of predictions that the supply of ROCs will soon exceed demand for ROCs) mean that it is becoming more difficult to secure long term PPAs which, in turn, has a knock-on effect on the availability of project finance.

25.8 Conclusion

Renewable energy technologies can make a significant contribution to the future energy mix of the UK and in so doing will have the effect of reducing greenhouse gas emissions. Those developments which are currently viable, are dependant to some extent on the Renewables Obligation scheme and other governmental policies. Support for the Renewables Obligation scheme and the cost of alternative fuels (fossil or nuclear) are, therefore, crucial factors in determining the growth of the renewable energy sector in the near future. In addition, current capacity constraints within the transmission system may well have the potential over the next two decades to prevent the full exploitation of renewable energy resources.

Notes

1 DTI, Energy White Paper: *Our Energy Future – creating a low carbon economy*, Cm 5761 (2003).

2 NPPG (revised 2000) No 6: *Renewable Energy Developments.*

3 Todd, 'Renewables in Europe – partnership and innovation' in Imabi and Mitchell (eds), *Proceedings World Renewable Energy Congress* (2005).

[4] Wind Turbine Technology, BWEA Briefing Sheet, The British Wind Energy Association, September 2005.
[5] Scottish Executive, *Harnessing Scotland's Marine Energy Potential – Marine Energy Group* (MEG) Report (2004).
[6] Refer to page 865 – Renewables Obligation discussion.
[7] Waste Incineration Directive, 2000/76/EC as applied by the Waste Incineration (England and Wales) (Regulations 2002 (SI No 2980) and the Waste Incineration (Scotland) Regulations 2003 (SI 2003 No 170).
[8] Scottish Executive, Promoting and accelerating the market penetration of Biomass Technology in Scotland – Biomass Group (BEG) Report (2005).
[9] Scottish Executive, *Hydrogen and Fuel Cell Opportunities for Scotland – The Hydrogen Energy Group Report* (2006).
[10] DTI, Energy White Paper: *Our Energy Future – creating a low carbon economy* (2003).
[11] Renewables Obligation Order 2006 (SI 2006 No 1004).
[12] Renewables Obligation (Scotland) Order 2006 (SSI 2006 No 173).
[13] Executive Note to the Renewables Obligation (Scotland) Order 2006.
[14] Utilities Act 2000, s 62.
[15] Renewables Obligation: Third Annual Report, Ofgem, 27 February 2005.
[16] Finance Act 2000 (s 30), and the Climate Change Levy (General) Regulations 2001 (SI 2001 No 838).
[17] Scottish Executive National Planning Policy Guideline NPPG 6: Renewable Energy Developments, November 2000.
[18] Planning Advice Note PAN 45: Renewable Energy Technologies, Scottish Executive Development Department, January 2002.
[19] Planning Policy Statement 22: Renewable Energy, Office of the Deputy Prime Minister (2004).
[20] See the Energy Act 2004 and the Electricity Act 1989. There are also numerous relevant statutory instruments and the reader is referred to the DTI Guidance Note on the Offshore Windfarm Consents Process as a starting point for further information.
[21] NPPG 6: see n 17 above.
[22] The Electricity Works (Environmental Impact Assessment) 'Scotland) Regulations 2000 (SSI 2000 No 320) and the Electricity Works (Environmental Impact Assessment) (England and Wales) Regulations (SI 2000 No 320).
[23] Environmental Impact Assessment (Scotland) Regulations 1999 (SSI 1999 No 1) and the Town and Country Planning (Environmental Impact Assessment) (England and Wales) Regulations 1999 (SI 1999 No 293).

REFERENCES AND FURTHER READING

Abbots, I., 2003 'Foreword' in J.G. Gluyas and H.M. Hitchens (eds), *United Kingdom Oil and Gas fields, Commemorative Millenniuum Volume, Geological Society Memoir* 20

Boyle, G. (ed), 2004 *Renewable Energy – Power for a sustainable future* (2nd edn)

BP, 2006 *Statistical Review of World Energy* (June)

Brandon, N.P., 2004 'Fuel cells' in C.J. Cleveland (ed) *Encyclopedia of Energy* **2**, 749

Brennard, T.P., Van Hoorn, B., James, K.H. and Glennie, K.W., 1998 'Historical Review of North Sea Exploration' in K.W. Glennie (ed), *Petroleum Geology of the North Sea* (4th edn) 1–29

Brooks, J. and Glennie, G.W. (eds), 1987 *Petroleum Geology of Northwest Europe: Proceedings of the 3rd Conference* (Geological Society)

Carruth, A.G., 2003 'The Foinaven Field, Blocks 204/19, 204/24a, UK North Sea' in J.G. Gluyas and H.M. Hitchens (eds), *United Kingdom Oil and Gas Fields, Commemorative Millennium Volume, Geological Society Memoir,* **20**, 121–130

CERA, 2003 'The Digital Oil Field of the Future: Enabling Next Generation Reservoir Performance'

Conway, M., Bedford, D. and Oehler, M., 2006 'Knowledge Management Enhances Technical Training Program, The Way Ahead', SPE **12**(3)

Daker, L.P., 2001 *The Practice of Reservoir Engineering*

Dandekar, A.Y., 2006 *Petroleum Reservoir Rock and Fluid Properties*

Danesh, A., 1998 *PVT and Phase Behaviour of Petroleum Reservoir Fluids*

Darling, T., 2005 'Well Logging and Formation Evaluation', *Gulf Drilling Guides*

DEFRA, 2001 'The UK's Third National Communication under the United Nations Framework Convention on Climate Change'

Donnelly, J., 2006 'Cazalot, Jr.' *Journal of Petroleum Technology* 24

DTI, 2005 'R&D Scoreboard' (and other yearbooks)

DTI, 2006 'The Energy Challenge', *Energy Review Report*

Earlougher, R.C., 1977 *Advances in Well Test Analysis*, SPE

Fleet, A.J. and Boldy, S.A.R. (eds), 1999 *Petroleum Geology of Northwest Europe: Proceedings of the 5th Conference* (Geological Society)

Glennie, K.W. (ed), 1990 *Introduction to the Petroleum Geology of the North Sea* (3rd edn)

Glennie, K.W. 1998 (ed), *Petroleum Geology of the North Sea* (4th edn)

Gluyas, J.G. and Hitchens, H.M. (eds), 2003 'Appendix 1', *United Kingdom Oil and Gas Fields, Commemmorative Millennium Volume, Geological Society Memoir*, 20

Gluyas, J.G. and Hitchens, H.M. (eds), 2003 *United Kingdom Oil and Gas Fields Commemorative Millennium Volume* (Geological Society)

Gluyas, J.G. and Swarbrick, R., 2004 *Petroleum Geoscience*

Gulf Research, 2006 'Attracting and retaining employees in the Oilfield: A survey of employer reputation and job satisfaction among oil and gas industry personnel', *World Oil*

Hill, G., 2006 'Tackling Climate Change', **197** *SPE Review*

IEA, 2004 *World Energy Outlook*

IEA, 2005a *World Energy Outlook*

IEA, 2005b *Resources to Reserves, Oil & Gas Technologies for the Energy Markets of the Future*

IEA, 2006 *World Energy Outlook* (2006)

Illing, L.V. and Hobson, G.D. (eds), 1981 *Petroleum Geology of Northwest Europe: Proceedings of the 2nd Conference* (Geological Society)

Irvine, J., Tao, Z., Jain, S., Bradley, J., Lakeman, B. and Pointon, K., 2005 'Fuel cells in the renewable energy economy' in M.S. Imabi and C.P. Mitchell (eds), *Proceedings World Renewable Energy Congress*

Jaruzelski, B., Dehoff, K. and Bordia, R., 2005 'The Global Innovation 1000: Money Isn't Everything', *Strategy and Business* **41**, 54

Kearey, P., Brooks, M. and Hill, I., 2002 *An Introduction to Geophysical Exploration* (3rd edn) 77

Lee, J., 1982 *Well Testing*, SPE

Lemonis, G., 2004 'Wave and Tidal Energy Conversion' *Encyclopedia of Energy* **6**, 449

Martin, S., 1997 'Tax of Technology? The Revivial of North Sea Oil Production', *Oxford Institute for Energy Studies*

McCain, W.D., 1990 *Properties of Petroleum Fluids*

Parker, R.J. (ed), 1993 *Petroleum Geology of Northwest Europe: Proceedings of the 4th Conference* (Geological Society)

Petersen, E. and Madsen, P.H., 2004 'Wind Farms', *Encyclopedia of Energy* **6**, 449

Rao, V. and Rodriguez, R., 2005 'Accelerating Technology Acceptance: Hypotheses and remedies for risk-averse behaviour in technology acceptance', SPE paper 98511

Ribiero, C. and Macbeth, C., 2006 'Time-lapse seismic inversion for pressure and saturation in Foinaven Field, West of Shetland', *First Break* **24**, 63–72

Rider, M., 2002 *The Geological Interpretation of Well Logs* (2nd edn)

Schlumberger Oilfield Glossary

Selly, R.C., 1998 *Elements of Petroleum Geology* (2nd edn)

Shell International Limited, 2005 *Shell Global Scenarios to 2025*

Stuart, I.A., 2003 'The Armada development, UK Central North Sea: The Fleming, Drake and Hawkins Gas-Condensate Fields' in J.G. Gluyas and H.M. Hitchens (eds), *United Kingdom Oil and Gas Fields, Commemorative Millennium Volume, Geological Society Memoir* **20**, 139–151

UKOOA and NHM, *1997 Britain's offshore and oil and gas handbook*

Woodward, A.W. (ed), 1975 *Petroleum and the Continental Shelf of Northwest Europe*, Vol 1

GLOSSARY

20th Round JOA form of JOA agreed upon on the 20th Licensing Round.

Abandon to cease work on a well which is non-productive, to plug off the well with cement plugs and salvage all recoverable equipment. Also used in the context of field abandonment.

Annulus the space between the drillstring and the well wall, or between casing strings, or between the casing and the production tubing.

Appraisal well a well drilled as part of an appraisal drilling programme which is carried out to determine the physical extent, reserves and likely production rate of a field.

Archie Equation a formula for calculating the amount of water in a reservoir (Sw = water saturation). $Sw = \sqrt{[(0.62\ Rw)/\Phi^{2.15}\ Rt)]}$ where Rw = formation water resistivity, Φ = porosity and Rt = true formation resistivity. All of these values can be obtained from well logs.

Asphaltene components of bitumen in oil.

Associated Gas natural gas associated with oil accumulations, which may be dissolved in the oil at reservoir conditions or may form a cap of free gas above the oil.

Barite ($BaSO_4$) a mineral added to drilling mud to increase the density.

Barrel a unit of volume measurement used for petroleum and its products (1 barrel = 35 Imperial gallons (approx.), or 159 litres (approx.): 7.3 barrels = 1 ton: 6.29 barrels = 1 cubic metre).

bbl one barrel of oil.

bcf billion cubic feet (1 bcf = 0.83 million tonnes of oil equivalent).

bcm billion cubic metres (1 cubic metre = 35.31 cubic feet).

Bearer Bill class of Bill of Lading which is made out to bearer when the oil is delivered.

Bill of Lading a document issued by or on behalf of a carrier of goods by sea to the person (ie the Shipper) whom he has contracted for the carriage of goods.

Block an areal subdivision of the UKCS of 10 minutes of latitude by 12 minutes of longitude measuring approximately 10 × 20 kms, forming part of a quadrant. Each quadrant is divided into a grid, five Blocks wide and six deep, and numbered 1 to 30 from NW to SE, eg Block 9/13 is the 13th block in Quadrant 9.

Blow-out preventers (BOPs) hydraulically operated valves installed on the wellhead during well operations, designed to immediately shut off an uncontrolled flow of hydrocarbons.

C and F Sale sale contract under which the buyer arranges insurance and the seller is liable for the cost and freight.

Call option right to purchase an asset (typically shares) for an agreed fee (the option price).

Cap rock an impermeable rock which overlies the reservoir and prevents the escape of hydrocarbons from the trap.

Capex capital expenditure.

Carbonate reservoir rock a reservoir rock that is composed predominantly of limestone or dolomite.

Carried interest an arrangement where a co-venturer pays all or part of another co-venturer's costs of exploration, drilling, testing and completion in a field usually in exchange for equity in the joint venture or repayment out of production revenues.

Carrier bed a porous and permeable rock through which the hydrocarbons migrate prior to being trapped in a reservoir.

Carry forward quantity of gas in excess of the take or pay level which can be carried forward into future years and offset against any amount taken by the buyer which is less than the take or pay level (and would otherwise incur a payment by the buyer).

Casing string the steel tubing that lines a well after it has been drilled. It is formed from sections of steel tube screwed together.

Charter contract for the hire of a vessel.

Christmas tree (Xmas tree) The assembly of fittings and valves on the top of the wellhead which control the production rate of oil or gas.

Clastic reservoir rock a reservoir rock that is composed predominantly of transported detrital material (eg sandstones).

CNS Central North Sea.

CO carbon monoxide.

CO_2 carbon dioxide.

Co-mingle where gas is mixed with gas from other sources.

Completion the installation of permanent wellhead and subsurface equipment for the production of oil and gas.

Condensate hydrocarbons which are in the gaseous state under reservoir conditions and which become liquid when temperature or pressure is reduced. A mixture of pentanes and higher hydrocarbons.

Contract for difference contract where the buyer pays the difference between the current value and the value at contract time to the seller.

Coring taking rock samples from a well by means of a special tool – a 'core barrel'.

Co-venturers the parties to an agreement (typically a JOA or UOA) who hold a working interest.

Credit derivative an arrangement for the separate trading of credit risk; for example, it may be a credit default swap or credit default option.

Crude oil an unrefined fluid composed predominantly of compounds made up of carbon and hydrogen (hydrocarbons). Varies in viscosity and colour from black to golden.

Cubic foot a standard unit used to measure quantity of gas (at atmospheric pressure) (1 cubic foot = 0.0283 cubic metres).

Cuttings rock chippings cut by the drill bit, and brought to the surface with the mud. Used by geologists to obtain lithology data.

Data the data and information which relate to reserves.

Decommissioning preferred term (rather than Abandonment) for the reuse, recycling or disposal of redundant oil and gas facilities.

Delivered Ex Ship delivery where risk passes when the ship arrives at its destination and the goods are made available to the buyer.

Demise charter party an agreement whereby the charterer takes possession of the vessel as if he is the owner of it.

Demurrage a fee paid by the Charterer as a result of a delay beyond the reasonable or agreed time for loading or unloading.

Derivatives the collective term used to describe certain types of financial instruments such as futures, options and swaps.

Development phase the phase in which a proven oil or gas field is brought into production by the drilling of production (development) wells.

Dew point is the temperature to which a parcel of air must be cooled, at constant barometric pressure, for water vapour to condense into water.

Dewpointing separation of ethane, propane, butane and pentane from natural gas using the dew point.

Diagenesis changes that transform a sediment into a sedimentary rock.

Discovery an exploration well which has encountered hydrocarbons.

Downstream transportation, refining and marketing of petroleum.

Dry gas natural gas composed mainly of methane with only minor amounts of ethane, propane and butane and little or no heavier hydrocarbons in the gasoline range.

Dry hole a well which has proved to contain no hydrocarbons.

Dynamic positioning the use of computer controlled directional thruster propellers to enable a floating rig or drill ship to maintain position without using anchors.

Earn in mechanism by which the farminee acquires a transferred interest upon fulfilling specified earn-in obligations.

Enhanced oil recovery a process whereby oil is recovered other than by the natural pressure in a reservoir.

Environmental Impact Assessment (EIA) an assessment on the likely effect a project may have on the environment (taking into account biophysical, social and other relevant effects).

Equity that part of the share capital of the company which is entitled to all the net profits after all creditors have been paid; it can also mean, in a JOA or UOA, a co-venturers right to net profits on its working interest after all costs have been paid.

Execution Deed document annexed to the Master Deed containing the operative wording of the transfer/novation arrangements.

Exploration well a well in an unproven area or prospect. May also be known as a 'wildcat well'.

Farm-in when a company acquires an interest in a block by taking over all or part of the financial commitment for drilling an exploration well.

Farminee the party who acquires an interest in a block as a result of a farm-in.

Farmor a co-venturing party holding a percentage interest who transfers part of that interest to a third party as a result of a farm-in.

Farm-out when a company sells a working interest in a block.

Field a geographical area under which an oil or gas reservoir lies.

Field Development Plan/Programme plan for production of the field by drilling of production wells.

Forward contract agreement to buy or sell an asset on a specified date which is typically used by a mechanism to hedge risk.

Futures contract a contract for the purchase or sale of a commodity in which it is sold for future delivery.

Gas field a field containing gas but no crude oil.

Gas Formation Volume the volume of natural gas when it arises from the subsurface reservoir and expands to 1 cubic foot at surface conditions; it is measured in rcf/scf.

Gas Imbalance the situation where a unit participant has overlifted quantities of gas due to it holding a reduced unit interest subsequent to a termination.

Gas in Place an estimate of the total amount of gas contained in a reservoir.

Hedging strategy designed to control or limit exposure to risk during investment activity.

Hook-up the period during which all connections and services are made operable for full production testing. It is also a term used for the offshore connection of module piping and facilities during the offshore construction phase.

Horizontal well a well which is drilled up to 90° from vertical, horizontal to the geological strata.

Hydrocarbon a compound containing only the elements hydrogen and carbon. May exist as a solid, a liquid or a gas. The term is mainly used in a catch-all sense for oil, gas and condensate.

In Situ 'in its place'.

Injection well a well used for pumping water or gas into the reservoir.

Jacket the lower steel section, or 'legs', of an offshore platform.

Joint Operating Committee the committee established under a Joint Operating Agreement by the co-venturers in a block to manage their working interests.

Knock-out facilities tanks or filters used to separate oil and water.

Laydays time allowed for loading or unloading before demurrage becomes payable.

Letter of credit a document from one bank on behalf of its customer to another bank evidencing that a credit line has been opened on behalf of the first bank's customer guaranteeing payment if certain conditions are met. A letter of credit may be irrevocable or revocable.

Licence a right to explore for and/or produce hydrocarbons granted by the government or its agency; in the UK a licence is awarded by the Secretary of State for the DTI.

Licensing round the annual issue of licences by the Secretary of State.

Lifting procedures the arrangement for a co-venturer to lift oil under a contract and includes the nomination of lifting of that co-venturer's substance entitlement percentage of production and which is then adjusted in accordance with allocation procedures.

Lithology a specific rock type.

Littoral of, or pertaining to, a shore or coastal region.

LNG (liquefied natural gas) oilfield or naturally occurring gas, mainly methane, liquefied for transportation.

LPG (liquefied petroleum gas) light hydrocarbon material, gaseous at atmospheric temperature and pressure, held in the liquid state by pressure to facilitate storage, transport and handling. Commercial liquefied gas consists essentially of either propane or butane, or mixtures thereof.

Make-up quantity of gas in excess of the take or pay level which can be used to make up for any volume taken by the buyer for which a take or pay payment was made in a previous year.

Master Deed document which standardises the documentation process for UKCS transfers of licence interests and/or documents. It was developed by UKOOA's Progressing Partnership Working Group, the DTI and a number of other interested organisations. It greatly expedites the transfer of UKCS offshore licence interests and other agreements relating to associated assets and infrastructure.

Mercaptans organic compounds of carbon, hydrogen and sulphur which gives gasoline an offensive odour.

Metamorphic rocks rocks generated during deep burial in the Earth's crust by high temperatures and pressures.

Miscible fluids which can mix without the existence of an interface.

Model Clauses clauses for the operation and maintenance of the licence which are incorporated in a licence.

Mud a mixture of base substance and additives used to lubricate the drill bit and to counteract the natural pressure of the formation.

Napthas a range of distilled fractions from heavy gasolines to some of the lighter kerosene distillates. The major refinery feedstock for gasoline manufacture.

Natural drive the flow of hydrocarbons from the reservoir under natural pressure.

Natural gas Gas, occurring naturally, and often found in association with light crude petroleum.

Net profit interest where a co-venturer grants a third party a share of net profit of production revenues after deduction of all costs (which may include interest) and in return that third party may pay a cash consideration or pay part or the whole of the costs of the co-venturer.

NGLs natural gas liquids. Liquid hydrocarbons found in association with natural gas.

NNS Northern North Sea.

NOx nitrous oxides.

Nomination procedure contractual provision by which either the buyer or seller of gas states the quantities of gas to be delivered and the timeframes for providing the notifications.

Off-Specification Petroleum petroleum which does not meet the requirements of the transporter or the terminal operator for transporting or processing petroleum.

Oil a mixture of liquid hydrocarbons of different molecular weights.

Oil field A geographic area under which an oil reservoir lies. May also have a gas cap.

Oil Formation Factor the number of reservoir barrels required to make up one stock tank barrel of oil taking into account shrinkage and is measured in rb/stb.

Oil in place an estimated measure of the total amount of oil contained in a reservoir, and, as such, a higher figure than the estimated recoverable reserves of oil.

Operator the company that has legal authority to explore and drill wells and undertake the production of hydrocarbons. The operator is often part of a consortium and acts on behalf of this consortium.

Opex operating expenditure.

Options a type of security that gives the holder the right but not the obligation to buy or sell a specified amount of security at a specified price, before or at a specified time.

Order Bills class of Bill of Lading made to the order of a person named in a bill.

Ordinary shares shares of common stock in a company.

Overlifting Gas where a unit participant lifts a greater quantity of gas than its entitlement under the UOA.

Overriding royalty payment made based on a percentage of oil or gas produced in return for the transfer of a participating interest in a field.

Pay zone rock in which oil and gas are found in exploitable quantities.

Permeability the property of a formation which quantifies the flow of a fluid through the pore spaces and into the wellbore.

Petroleum a generic name for hydrocarbons, including crude oil, natural gas liquids, natural gas and their products.

Pigs bullet-shaped, cylindrical or spherical capsules which are inserted into the pipeline and travel along it with the fluid to clear deposits that have built-up (eg wax) or liquid accumulations in the case of gas pipelines.

Pore throat the pore space between grains in a sedimentary rock.

Porosity the percentage of empty space within a reservoir rock.

Possible reserves those reserves which at present cannot be regarded as 'probable' but are estimated to have a significant, but less than 50%, chance of being technically and economically producible.

Pour point the lowest temperature at which an oil will pour under given conditions.

Preference shares shares of a company which have a preferential right to income and capital over ordinary shares and may be redeemed; income and redemption payments are dependent on a company having distributable profits.

Primary recovery recovery of oil or gas from a reservoir purely by using the natural pressure in the reservoir to force the oil or gas to surface.

Probable reserves those reserves which are not yet proven but which are estimated to have a better than 50% chance of being technically and economically producible.

Proven reserves those reserves which, on the available evidence, are virtually certain to be technically and economically producible (ie having a better than 90% chance of being produced).

psi pounds per square inch.

Put option an option contract giving the owner the right but not the obligation, to sell a specified amount of an underlying security at a specified price within a specified time.

Quadrant an areal subdivision of the UKCS of 1 degree of longitude by 1 degree of latitude typically around 6600 sq km. On the UKCS each Quadrant is further subdivided into 30 Blocks.

Recoverable reserves that proportion of the oil and/gas in a reservoir that can be removed using currently available techniques.

Recovery factor the ratio of recoverable oil and/or gas reserves to the estimated oil and/or gas in place in the reservoir.

Redetermination mechanism by which the unit interests of unit participants may be adjusted in accordance with information facilitating the better understanding of the structure.

Reservoir the underground rocks where oil and gas have accumulated. It consists of a porous rock to hold the oil or gas, and a cap rock that prevents its escape.

Roughneck drill crew members who work on the derrick floor, assembling or disassembling drillpipe when running or pulling a drillstring.

Roundtripping recovering the drill string from the well for remedial work and returning it to continue drilling.

Roustabout drill crew members who handle the loading and unloading of equipment and assist in general operations around the rig.

Safety Case a report submitted by an operator to demonstrate that all potential hazards on an offshore installation have been reviewed and mitigated as far as reasonably practical.

SCF (Standard Cubic Foot) the volume in cubic feet of natural gas under defined surface conditions (namely 60°F and 1 atmosphere).

Seal an impermeable rock which overlies the reservoir and prevents the escape of hydrocarbons from the trap.

Secondary recovery recovery of oil or gas from a reservoir by artificially maintaining or enhancing the reservoir pressure by injecting gas, water or other substances into the reservoir rock.

Section 29 notice a notice served under section 29(1) of the Petroleum Act 1998 obliging each person on whom it is served to submit an abandonment programme to the Secretary of State.

Send or pay provisions if a shipper fails to transport (or send for transportation) in a given time period a quantity of product then the shipper has to pay a tariff on the difference between the send or pay quantity and the quantity that was actually transported by the shipper in that time period.

Shipper the field owner who is shipping oil or gas.

Shortfall the difference between the quantity of oil or gas actually delivered and the quantity due to be delivered under the agreement.

Shutdown an event during which production ceases automatically due to a process anomaly or, manually for essential work to be undertaken.

SNS Southern North Sea.

Sole risk under a JOA or UOA the co-venturer who bears the sole risk of carrying out a programme of work in a field.

Sour gas oil or gas with a high proportion of sulphur compounds, eg hydrogen sulphide.

SOx sulphurous oxides.

Specific gravity is a measure of the density of a material.

Spot market market for uncontracted gas.

Spud-in the operation of drilling the first part of a new well.

Stabilised crude oil from which volatile gases (at surface temperatures and pressures) have been removed.

Stock Tank Barrel of Oil one barrel of oil at surface conditions after the solution gas has bubbled out of it.

Straight Consigned or Seaway Bills Bill of Lading whose terms are non-negotiable.

Suspended well a well that has been capped off temporarily.

Swap an over-the-counter (OTC) bilateral contract to manage financial risk.

Tankage crude oil storage in a tank.

Tie-back wells that have been connected via a pipeline on the sea-floor to a central production facility.

Time charter charter of a vessel for a particular period or periods of time.

Toolpusher offshore supervisor of drilling operations. Responsible for the day-to-day activities for ensuring the safe and uninterrupted execution of the drilling programme.

Topsides the superstructure of a platform.

Town Gas a generic term referring to manufactured gas produced for sale to consumers and municipalities.

Tract participation an estimate of the percentage of hydrocarbons in each separate block of a unitised reservoir under a UOA.

Transportation Agreement agreement for the transportation of gas, entered into between the field owners and the owners of gas pipeline structures.

Transporter the pipeline owner.

Ullage the space unfilled by hydrocarbons in a pipeline or a storage tank.

Unconformity a plane of erosion or non-deposition between two groups of rocks.

Underlifting Gas where a unit participant lifts a lesser quantity of oil and gas under the JOA.

Unit Operating Agreement (UOA) an agreement entered into where a reservoir straddles more than one block, where the interests in the blocks are owned by different co-venturers.

Unit Operating Committee (UOC) the committee established under a UOA by the co-venturers in a unitised field to manage the working interests.

Unit owners the co-venturers under a UOA owning the working interests in a unitised field.

Unitisation the joint venture arrangements of different owners under different blocks who share the same common reservoir structure.

Upstream the extractive part of the oil and gas industry.

Vapour pressure the pressure required to prevent a liquid from turning into vapour.

Voyage charters a charter of a vessel for a particular voyage or number of voyages.

Warrants a security that entitles the holder to buy stock of the company that issued it at a specified price, which is much higher than the stock price at time of issue.

Water flood the injection of water into a reservoir to create an artificial water drive.

Well log a record of the geological formations penetrated during drilling, including technical details of the operation.

Wild well a well that is flowing oil and gas out of control.

Work programme the work programme set out in a licence to be undertaken by the licence holders.

Workover remedial work to the equipment within a producing well, the well pipework, or relating to attempts to improve productivity.

ABBREVIATIONS

ACV	Authorised Contract Value
ADS	Atmospheric Diving Suits
AFE	Authorisation For Expenditure
AHTS	Anchor Handling, Towing and Supply vessel
API	American Petroleum Institute
AUV	Autonomous Underwater Vehicle
bbopd	billion barrels of oil per day
BfD	Basis for Design
BIMCO	The Baltic and International Maritime Council
boe	barrels of oil equivalent
BOP	Blow Out Preventer
bopd	barrels of oil per day
BOQ	Bills Of Quantities
BS&W	Bottom Solids and Water
CAA	Civil Aviation Authority
CAT	Carbon Abatements Technology
CAVE	Computer Assisted Virtual Environment
CCL	Casing Collar Locator
CCL	Climate Change Levy
CDS	Condensate Disposal System
CFR	Cost and Freight
CIF	Cost Insurance and Freight
CRINE	Cost Reduction Initiative in a New Era
CRISTAL	Contract Regarding a Supplement to Tanker Liability of Oil Pollution
CT	Coiled Tubing
CT	Corporation Tax
DCR	Offshore Installation and Wells (Design and Construction, etc.) Regulations
DP	Dynamically Positioned

DR	Discount Rates
DSA	Decommissioning Security Agreement
DST	Drill Stem Test
DSV	Diving Support Vessel
DTI	Department of Trade and Industry
E&A	Exploration and Appraisal
E&P	Exploration and Production
ECP	Expanding Cement Packer
EIA	Environmental Impact Assessment
EMV	Expected Monetary Value
EPIC	Engineering Procurement, Installation and Construction Contract
ESD	Emergency Shutdown
ESP	Electric Submersible Pump
EU ETS	EU Emissions Trading Scheme
FEED	Front End Engineering and Design
FID	Final Investment Decision
FLAGS	Far North Liquids and Associated Gas System (pipeline)
FOB	Free Onboard
FPAL	First Point Assessment
FPSO	Floating Production Storage and Offtake/Offloading Vessel
FYA	First Year Allowance
GPS	Global Positioning System
GR	Gamma Ray
HMRC	HM Revenue and Customs
HP-HT	High Pressure-High Temperature
HSC	Health and Safety Commission
HSE	Heath and Safety Executive
HSWA	Health and Safety at Work Act
HWU	Hydraulic Workover Units
IEA	International Energy Agency
IFRS	International Financial Reporting Standards
IMHH	Industry Mutual Hold Harmless Agreement
IMO	International Maritime Organisation
IRR	Internal Rate Of Return

ISDA	International Swaps and Derivatives Association
ITOPF	International Tanker Owners Pollution Federation
JNCC	Joint Nature Conservation Committee.
LBSOG	Large Business Service, Oil and Gas (previously Oil Taxation Office)
LIFT	Licence Information for Trading
LOGIC	Leading Oil and Gas Industry Competitiveness
MAIB	Marine Accident Investigation Branch
MARPOL	International Convention for Prevention of Pollution
Mbbls (or MMbbls)	million barrels oil
Mboe (or MMboe)	million barrels oil equivalent
Mbopd (or MMbopd)	million barrels oil per day
MCA	Maritime and Coastguard Agency
Mcfd (or MMcfd)	millions of cubic feet per day (of gas)
MDT	Mean Down Time
MEA	Mineral Extraction Allowances
MHSWR	Management of Health and Safety at Work Regulations (UK)
MOD	Money-of-the-day
MODU	Mobile Offshore Drilling Unit
MWD	Measurement While Drilling
NFFO	National Federation of Fishermans' Organisation
NPD	Norwegian Petroleum Directorate
NPV	Net Present Value
NTS	National Transmission System
OBM	Oil Based Mud
OFGEM	The Office of Gas and Electricity Markets
OIM	Offshore Installation Manager
OPEC	Organisation of the Petroleum Exporting Countries
OPITO	Offshore Petroleum Industry Training Organisation
OPOL	Offshore Pollution Liability Agreement
OSCP	Oil Spill Contingency Plan
OSPAR	Oslo and Paris Convention for the Protection of the Marine Environment of the North East Atlantic
P&M	Plan and Machinery Allowances
PBR	Polished Bore Receptacle

PEP	Project Execution Plan
PFEER	Prevention of Fire, Explosion and Emergency Response Regulations
PI	Productivity Index
PIMS	Pipeline Integrity Management System
PLT	Production Logging Tool
POSA	Platform Operating and Services Agreement
PRT	Petroleum Revenue Tax
PSV	Platform Supply Vessel
PTW	Permit to Work
PUD	Proven Undeveloped Discovery
PV	Present Value
PVT	Pressure-Volume-Temperature
PWA	Permit to Work Application
PWA	Pipeline Works Authorisation
R&DA	Research and Development Allowances
rb	reservoir barrels
rcf	reservoir cubic feet
RFT	Repeat Formation Tester
ROC	Renewables Obligation Certificate
ROV	Remotely Operated Vehicle
RT	Real Terms
SC	Supplementary Charge
SCF	Standard Cubic Foot/Feet
SCO	Stabilised Crude Oil
SEA	Strategic Environmental Assessment
SFF	Scottish Fishermen's Federation
SILK	SEAL (gas export pipeline to Bacton) interconnector pipeline
SNS	Southern North Sea
SOLAS	International Convention for Safety for Life at Sea
SPE	Society of Petroleum Engineers
SPOTS	Sole Pit Offshore Transportation System
SSSV	Subsurface Shutdown Valve
SSV	Surface Shutdown Valve
stb	stock tank barrel
STOOIP	Stock Tank Oil Originally In Place

TAML	Technical Advancement Of Multilaterals
tcf	trillion cubic feet (of gas)
TCP	Tubing Conveyed Perforating
TOC	Total Organic Carbon
TWT	Two Way Time
UHC	Unburned Hydrocarbons
UKCS	United Kingdom Continental Shelf
UKOOA	UK Offshore Operators Association Limited
UNCLOS	United Nations Convention on the Law of the Seas
VoI	Value of Information
WEG	Wireline Entry Guide
WOB	Weight On Bit
WPC	World Petroleum Congress

INDEX

Location references are to page numbers.
Figures are referenced by page number followed by f, eg 52f

C

Index compiled by Christine M. Gane, BA, LLB, Accredited Indexer